Greenland
(Kalatdlit-Nunat)
Alaska
Yukon
N.W.T.
Nunavut
[Labrador]
Nfld.
St.Pierre
and Miquelon
B.C.
Alta.
Sask.
Man.
Ont.
Que.
P.E.I.
N.B.
N.S.
Vt.
Maine
N.H.
Mass.
R.I.
Conn.
N.J.
Del.
Md.
Wash.
Oreg.
Idaho
Mont.
N.Dak.
S.Dak.
Minn.
Wis.
Mich.
N.Y.
Pa.
Wyo.
Nebr.
Iowa
Ill.
Ind.
Ohio
W.Va.
Va.
Nev.
Utah
Colo.
Kans.
Mo.
Ky.
Calif.
Tenn.
N.C.
S.C.
Okla.
Ark.
Ariz.
N.Mex.
Ala.
Ga.
Miss.
Tex.
La.
Fla.
Mexico

Flora of North America

Contributors to Volume 11, Parts 1 and 2

Daniel Adams
Zoya V. Akulova-Barlow
Robert J. Alier
Jenna M. Annis
Peter W. Ball
Julie A. Ballenger
David J. Bogler
Alice Broadhead
Steven L. Broich
Luc Brouillet
Rachel K. Clark
Alfonso Delgado-Salinas
Óscar Dorado
Matthew L. Duley
John E. Ebinger
Ashley N. Egan
Paul R. Fantz
Frank T. Farruggia
Gabriel Flores-Franco
John M. Gillett†
Douglas H. Goldman
Rosaura Grether
Zachary E. Guthrie

Richard R. Halse
Neil A. Harriman†
Héctor M. Hernández
Denis M. Kearns
Brian R. Keener
Alexander Krings
Thomas G. Lammers
Matt Lavin
Carolyn K. Levings
Alan W. Lievens
Melissa A. Luckow
Brigitte Marazzi
Robert H. Mohlenbrock
Guy L. Nesom
Hiroyoshi Ohashi
Matthew A. Parker
Derick B. Poindexter
Jay A. Raveill
James L. Reveal†
María de Lourdes Rico-Arce
Brant W. Riegel
Rhonda Riggins
Erin Thais Riley
Velva E. Rudd†

David S. Seigler
Teresa Sholars
Leila M. Shultz
Beryl B. Simpson
Ernest Small
Solange Sotuyo
Shannon C. K. Straub
Lawrence R. Stritch
James C. Sugar
David M. Sutherland
Ralph L. Thompson
Leticia Torres-Colín
Debra K. Trock
Gordon C. Tucker
Billie L. Turner†
L. J. G. van der Maesen
Michael A. Vincent
Wade Wall
Alan S. Weakley
Stanley L. Welsh
Martin F. Wojciechowski
Michael Woods
Richard P. Wunderlin

Editors for Volume 11, Parts 1 and 2

David E. Boufford
Assisting Taxon Editor for Fabaceae

Tammy M. Charron
Managing Editor

Kanchi Gandhi
Nomenclatural and Etymological Editor

Martha J. Hill
Senior Technical Editor

Robert W. Kiger
Bibliographic Editor

Thomas G. Lammers
Assisting Taxon Editor for Fabaceae

Geoffrey A. Levin
Lead Editor (2019–2021)

Jay A. Raveill
Assisting Taxon Editor for Fabaceae

John L. Strother
Reviewing Editor

Michael A. Vincent
Lead Taxon Editor for Fabaceae

James L. Zarucchi†
Editorial Director and Lead Editor (to 2019)

Volume 11, Parts 1 and 2 Composition

Tanya Harvey
Layout Artist and Editorial Assistant

Kristin Pierce
Compositor and Editorial Assistant

Wisteria frutescens

Flora of North America

North of Mexico

Edited by FLORA OF NORTH AMERICA EDITORIAL COMMITTEE

VOLUME 11

Magnoliophyta: Fabaceae, part 1

SUBFAMILIES CERCIDOIDEAE, DETARIOIDEAE, CAESALPINIOIDEAE, AND FABOIDEAE, TRIBES SOPHOREAE TO LOTEAE

NEW YORK OXFORD • OXFORD UNIVERSITY PRESS • 2023

Oxford University Press is a department of the University of Oxford.
It furthers the University's objective of excellence in research,
scholarship, and education by publishing worldwide.

Oxford New York
Auckland Cape Town Dar es Salaam Hong Kong Karachi Kuala Lumpur
Madrid Melbourne Mexico City Nairobi New Delhi Shanghai Taipei Toronto

With offices in
Argentina Austria Brazil Chile Czech Republic France Greece Guatemala Hungary Italy
Japan Poland Portugal Singapore South Korea Switzerland Thailand Turkey Ukraine Vietnam

Published by Oxford University Press, Inc.
198 Madison Avenue, New York, New York 10016
www.oup.com

Library of Congress Cataloging-in-Publication Data
(Revised for Volume 11)
Flora of North America North of Mexico
edited by Flora of North America Editorial Committee.
Includes bibliographical references and indexes.
Contents: v. 1. Introduction—v. 2. Pteridophytes and gymnosperms—
v. 3. Magnoliophyta: Magnoliidae and Hamamelidae—
v. 22. Magnoliophyta: Alismatidae, Arecidae, Commelinidae (in part), and Zingiberidae—
v. 26. Magnoliophyta: Liliidae: Liliales and Orchidales—
v. 23. Magnoliophyta: Commelinidae (in part): Cyperaceae—
v. 25. Magnoliophyta: Commelinidae (in part): Poaceae, part 2—
v. 4. Magnoliophyta: Caryophyllidae (in part): part 1—
v. 5. Magnoliophyta: Caryophyllidae (in part): part 2—
v. 19, 20, 21. Magnoliophyta: Asteridae (in part): Asteraceae, parts 1-3—
v. 24. Magnoliophyta: Commelinidae (in part): Poaceae, part 1—
v. 27. Bryophyta, part 1—
v. 8. Magnoliophyta: Paeoniaceae to Ericaceae—
v. 7. Magnoliophyta: Salicaceae to Brassicaceae—
v. 28. Bryophyta, part 2—
v. 9. Magnoliophyta: Picramniaceae to Rosaceae—
v. 6. Magnoliophyta: Cucurbitaceae to Droseraceae—
v. 12. Magnoliophyta: Vitaceae to Garryaceae—
v. 17 Magnoliophyta: Tetrachondraceae to Orobanchaceae—
v. 10 Magnoliophyta: Proteaceae to Elaeagnaceae—
v. 11 Magnoliophyta: Fabaceae, parts 1 and 2

ISBN: 9780197619803 (v. 11, set); ISBN: 9780197577974 (v. 11, part 1); ISBN: 9780197577981 (v. 11, part 2)
1. Botany—North America.
2. Botany—United States.
3. Botany—Canada.
I. Flora of North America Editorial Committee.
QK110.F55 2002 581.97 92-30459

1 2 3 4 5 6 7 8 9

Contents

Jim Zarucchi working in the MO herbarium.
Photo courtesy of the Missouri Botanical Garden.

This volume is dedicated to the memory of our friend and esteemed colleague James L. Zarucchi (1952–2019), Editorial Director of the *Flora of North America North of Mexico* (1996–2019) and student of Fabaceae systematics.

Founding Member Institutions

Flora of North America Association

Agriculture and Agri-Food Canada
Ottawa, Ontario

Arnold Arboretum
Jamaica Plain, Massachusetts

Canadian Museum of Nature
Ottawa, Ontario

Carnegie Museum of Natural History
Pittsburgh, Pennsylvania

Field Museum of Natural History
Chicago, Illinois

Fish and Wildlife Service
United States Department of the Interior
Washington, D.C.

Harvard University Herbaria
Cambridge, Massachusetts

Hunt Institute for Botanical Documentation
Carnegie Mellon University
Pittsburgh, Pennsylvania

Jacksonville State University
Jacksonville, Alabama

Jardin Botanique de Montréal
Montréal, Québec

Kansas State University
Manhattan, Kansas

Missouri Botanical Garden
St. Louis, Missouri

New Mexico State University
Las Cruces, New Mexico

The New York Botanical Garden
Bronx, New York

New York State Museum
Albany, New York

Northern Kentucky University
Highland Heights, Kentucky

Université de Montréal
Montréal, Québec

University of Alaska
Fairbanks, Alaska

University of Alberta
Edmonton, Alberta

The University of British Columbia
Vancouver, British Columbia

University of California
Berkeley, California

University of California
Davis, California

University of Idaho
Moscow, Idaho

University of Illinois
Urbana-Champaign, Illinois

University of Iowa
Iowa City, Iowa

The University of Kansas
Lawrence, Kansas

University of Michigan
Ann Arbor, Michigan

University of Oklahoma
Norman, Oklahoma

University of Ottawa
Ottawa, Ontario

University of Louisiana
Lafayette, Louisiana

The University of Texas
Austin, Texas

University of Western Ontario
London, Ontario

University of Wyoming
Laramie, Wyoming

Utah State University
Logan, Utah

For their support of the preparation of this volume,
we gratefully acknowledge and thank:

Fondation Franklinia

The Philecology Foundation

The Andrew W. Mellon Foundation

The David and Lucile Packard Foundation

an anonymous foundation

Chanticleer Foundation

The William and Flora Hewlett Foundation

The Stanley Smith Horticultural Trust

Hall Family Charitable Fund

WEM Foundation

William T. Kemper Foundation

Illustration Sponsorship, Volume 11, Parts 1 and 2

For sponsorship of illustrations included in this volume, we express sincere appreciation to:

Mac H. Alford, Janelle Burke, Lawrence Kelly, Tatyana Livshultz, Fabian Michelangeli, and Cindy Skema
Desmanthus cooleyi—in honor of Melissa A. Luckow, by her graduate students

Brian Anderson, Geoffrey A. Levin, and Angela Wisehard, Prairie Research Institute, Champaign, Illinois
Acacia redolens, *Mariosousa millefolia*, and *Vachellia rigidula*—in honor of John E. Ebinger

Arizona Native Plant Society, Tucson
Clitoria mariana var. *mariana*
Coursetia glandulosa

Errol C. Briggs, Barre, Vermont
Trifolium pratense

Leo P. Bruederle, Denver, Colorado
Aeschynomene virginica—in memory of David E. Fairbrothers

California Native Plant Society, Dorothy King Young Chapter, Gualala
Lupinus polyphyllus var. *burkei*—in honor of Teresa Sholars

Julian P. Donahue, Tucson, Arizona
Coursetia glandulosa
Desmodium arizonicum
Macroptilium gibbosifolium

Kirk Garanflo, Hoffman Estates, Illinois
Senna hebecarpa
Baptisia leucophaea

David Giblin, Seattle, Washington
Cladrastis kentukea

Arthur V. Gilman, Marshfield, Vermont
Astragalus robbinsii var. *minor*

Richard R. Halse, Corvallis, Oregon
Alhagi maurorum
Caragana arborescens
Halimodendron halodendron
Sphaerophysa salsula

Rexford and Martha Hill, Saint Louis, Missouri
Wisteria frutescens, Volume 11, part 1, frontispiece

Idaho Native Plant Society, White Pine Chapter, Moscow
Lupinus lepidus var. *cusickii*

Mississippi Native Plant Society, Jackson
Erythrina herbacea—in honor of Sidney G. McDaniel

Nancy Morin, Point Arena, California
Vicia sativa var. *sativa*—in memory of Frank Bisby

Katy Pye, Mendocino, California
Vicia americana var. *americana*

Kathleen Sayce, Nahcotta, Washington
Lupinus littoralis var. *littoralis*

Stephen Sentoff, Madison, Wisconsin
Dalea purpurea var. *purpurea*

Clemens van Dijk, Eindhoven, The Netherlands
Marina parryi
Vicia caroliniana

Michael and Mary Vincent, Oxford, Ohio
Trifolium macrocephalum, Volume 11, part 2, frontispiece

West Virginia Native Plant Society, Morgantown
Trifolium virginicum

Jennifer Whipple, Yellowstone National Park, Wyoming
Lupinus leucophyllus

Flora of North America Editorial Committee

(as of Oct. 2022)

Project Staff — past and present involved with the preparation of Volume 11

Barbara Alongi, *Illustrator*

Mike Blomberg, *Imaging*

Margaret Bornemann, *Assisting Technical Editor*

Ariel S. Buback, *Assisting Technical Editor*

Trisha K. Distler, *GIS Analyst*

Tanya Harvey, *Layout Artist and Editorial Assistant*

Linny Heagy, *Illustrator*

Rexford L. Hill, *Data Analyst*

Suzanne E. Hirth, *Editorial Assistant*

Cassandra L. Howard, *Senior Technical Editor*

Ruth T. King, *Editorial Assistant*

Marjorie C. Leggitt, *Illustrator*

John Myers, *Illustration Compositor*

Kristin Pierce, *Editorial Assistant and Compositor*

Andrew C. Pryor, *Assisting Technical Editor*

Heidi H. Schmidt, *Managing Editor* (2007–2017)

Mary Ann Schmidt, *Senior Technical Editor*

Yevonn Wilson-Ramsey, *Illustrator*

Contributors to Volume 11, Parts 1 and 2

Daniel Adams
The University of North Carolina at Chapel Hill
Chapel Hill, North Carolina

Zoya V. Akulova-Barlow
El Cerrito, California

Robert J. Alier
Eastern Illinois University
Charleston, Illinois

Jenna M. Annis
Eastern Illinois University
Charleston, Illinois

Peter W. Ball
University of Toronto
Mississauga, Ontario

Julie A. Ballenger
Columbus State University
Columbus, Georgia

David J. Bogler
Missouri Botanical Garden
St. Louis, Missouri

Alice Broadhead
North Carolina State University
Raleigh, North Carolina

Steven L. Broich
Oregon State University
Corvallis, Oregon

Luc Brouillet
Université de Montréal
Montréal, Québec

Rachel K. Clark
North Carolina State University
Raleigh, North Carolina

Alfonso Delgado-Salinas
Universidad Nacional Autónoma de México
Mexico City, Mexico

Óscar Dorado
Centro de Educación Ambiental e Investigación Sierra de Huautla
Universidad Autónoma del Estado de Morelos
Cuernavaca, Mexico

Matthew L. Duley
Miami University
Oxford, Ohio

John E. Ebinger
Eastern Illinois University
Charleston, Illinois

Ashley N. Egan
Utah Valley University
Orem, Utah

Paul R. Fantz
North Carolina State University
Raleigh, North Carolina

Frank T. Farruggia
Smithsonian Institution,
National Museum of Natural History
Washington, DC

Gabriel Flores-Franco
Universidad Autónoma del Estado de Morelos
Cuernavaca, Mexico

John M. Gillett†
Nepean, Ontario

Douglas H. Goldman
United States Department of Agriculture
Greensboro, North Carolina

Rosaura Grether
Universidad Autónoma Metropolitana-Iztapalapa
Mexico City, Mexico

Zachary E. Guthrie
Eastern Illinois University
Charleston, Illinois

Richard R. Halse
Oregon State University
Corvallis, Oregon

Neil A. Harriman†
University of Wisconsin Oshkosh
Oshkosh, Wisconsin

Héctor M. Hernández
Instituto de Biología
Universidad Nacional Autónoma de México
Mexico City, Mexico

Denis M. Kearns
Bakersfield, California

Brian R. Keener
The University of West Alabama
Livingston, Alabama

Alexander Krings
North Carolina State University
Raleigh, North Carolina

Thomas G. Lammers
University of Wisconsin Oshkosh
Oshkosh, Wisconsin

Matt Lavin
Montana State University
Bozeman, Montana

Carolyn K. Levings
Oklahoma Panhandle State University
Goodwell, Oklahoma

Alan W. Lievens
Texas Lutheran University
Seguin, Texas

Melissa A. Luckow
L. H. Bailey Hortorium
Cornell University
Ithaca, New York

Brigitte Marazzi
Natural History Museum of Canton Ticino
Lugano, Switzerland

Robert H. Mohlenbrock
Southern Illinois University
Carbondale, Illinois

Guy L. Nesom
Academy of Natural Sciences of Drexel University
Philadelphia, Pennsylvania

Hiroyoshi Ohashi
Tohoku University
Sendai, Japan

Matthew A. Parker
State University of New York
Binghamton, New York

Derick B. Poindexter
The University of North Carolina at Chapel Hill
Chapel Hill, North Carolina

Jay A. Raveill
Central Missouri State University
Warrensburg, Missouri

James L. Reveal†
Cornell University
Ithaca, New York

María de Lourdes Rico-Arce
Royal Botanic Gardens
Kew, Richmond, Surrey, England

Brant W. Riegel
Eastern Illinois University
Charleston, Illinois

Rhonda Riggins
San Luis Obispo, California

Erin Thais Riley
Montana State University
Bozeman, Montana

Velva E. Rudd†
National Museum of Natural History
Smithsonian Institution
Washington, DC

David S. Seigler
University of Illinois
Urbana, Illinois

Teresa Sholars
Mendocino, California

Leila M. Shultz
Utah State University
Logan, Utah

Beryl B. Simpson
The University of Texas at Austin
Austin, Texas

Ernest Small
Ottawa Research and Development Centre
Agriculture and Agri-Food Canada
Ottawa, Ontario

Solange Sotuyo
Instituto de Biología
Universidad Nacional Autónoma de México
Mexico City, Mexico

Shannon C. K. Straub
Hobart and William Smith Colleges
Geneva, New York

Lawrence R. Stritch
United States Forest Service
Washington, D.C.

James C. Sugar
North Carolina State University
Raleigh, North Carolina

David M. Sutherland
University of Nebraska
Omaha, Nebraska

Ralph L. Thompson
Berea College
Berea, Kentucky

Leticia Torres-Colín
Universidad Nacional Autónoma de México
Mexico City, Mexico

Debra K. Trock
California Academy of Sciences
San Francisco, California

Gordon C. Tucker
Eastern Illinois University
Charleston, Illinois

Billie L. Turner†
The University of Texas at Austin
Austin, Texas

L. J. G. van der Maesen
Wageningen Agricultural University
Wageningen, The Netherlands

Michael A. Vincent
Miami University
Oxford, Ohio

Wade Wall
North Carolina State University
Raleigh, North Carolina

Alan S. Weakley
The University of North Carolina at Chapel Hill
Chapel Hill, North Carolina

Stanley L. Welsh
Brigham Young University
Provo, Utah

Martin F. Wojciechowski
Arizona State University
Tempe, Arizona

Michael Woods
Troy University
Troy, Alabama

Richard P. Wunderlin
University of South Florida
Tampa, Florida

Taxonomic Reviewers for Volume 11, Parts 1 and 2

John Anderson
Bureau of Land Management
Wickenberg, Arizona

David E. Boufford
Harvard University Herbaria
Cambridge, Massachusetts

Glenn Dreyer
Connecticut College
New London, Connecticut

Alina Freire-Fierro
Universidad Técnica de Cotopaxi
Latacunga, Ecuador

Richard R. Halse
Oregon State University
Corvallis, Oregon

C. Barre Hellquist
Massachusetts College of Liberal Arts
North Adams, Massachusetts

Michael J. Huft
Valparaiso, Indiana

Joseph H. Kirkbride Jr.
United States National Arboretum
Washington, DC

Aaron Liston
Oregon State University
Corvallis, Oregon

James B. Phipps
Western University
London, Ontario

Peter H. Raven
Missouri Botanical Garden
St. Louis, Missouri

Yuri Roskov
Illinois Natural History Survey
Champaign, Illinois

Marianne M. le Roux
University of Johannesburg
Johannesburg, South Africa

Richard W. Spellenberg
New Mexico State University
Las Cruces, New Mexico

Livia Wanntorp
Swedish Museum of Natural History
Stockholm, Sweden

Tom Wendt
The University of Texas at Austin
Austin, Texas

Dieter H. Wilken
Santa Barbara Botanic Garden
Santa Barbara, California

Martin F. Wojciechowski
Arizona State University
Tempe, Arizona

Regional Reviewers

ALASKA / YUKON

Bruce Bennett
Yukon Department of Environment
Whitehorse, Yukon

Justin Fulkerson
Alaska Center for Conservation Science
University of Alaska Anchorage
Anchorage, Alaska

Steffi M. Ickert-Bond, Regional Coordinator
University of Alaska, Museum of the North
Fairbanks, Alaska

Robert Lipkin
Alaska Natural Heritage Program
University of Alaska Anchorage
Anchorage, Alaska

David F. Murray
University of Alaska, Museum of the North
Fairbanks, Alaska

Carolyn Parker
University of Alaska, Museum of the North
Fairbanks, Alaska

Mary Stensvold
Sitka, Alaska

PACIFIC NORTHWEST

Edward R. Alverson
Lane County Parks Division
Eugene, Oregon

Curtis R. Björk
University of British Columbia
Vancouver, British Columbia

Mark Darrach
University of Washington
Seattle, Washington

Walter Fertig
Washington Natural Heritage Program
Olympia, Washington

David E. Giblin
University of Washington
Seattle, Washington

Richard R. Halse
Oregon State University
Corvallis, Oregon

Linda Jennings
University of British Columbia
Vancouver, British Columbia

Aaron Liston, Regional Coordinator
Oregon State University
Corvallis, Oregon

Frank Lomer
New Westminster, British Columbia

Kendrick L. Marr
Royal British Columbia Museum
Victoria, British Columbia

Jim Pojar
British Columbia Forest Service
Smithers, British Columbia

Peter F. Zika
University of Washington
Seattle, Washington

SOUTHWESTERN UNITED STATES

Tina J. Ayers
Northern Arizona University
Flagstaff, Arizona

Walter Fertig
Washington Natural Heritage Program
Olympia, Washington

H. David Hammond†
Northern Arizona University
Flagstaff, Arizona

G. F. Hrusa
Lone Mountain Institute
Brookings, Oregon

Max Licher
Northern Arizona University
Flagstaff, Arizona

Elizabeth Makings
Arizona State University
Tempe, Arizona

James D. Morefield
Nevada Natural Heritage Program
Carson City, Nevada

Nancy R. Morin, Regional Coordinator
Point Arena, California

Donald J. Pinkava†
Arizona State University
Tempe, Arizona

Jon P. Rebman
San Diego Natural History Museum
San Diego, California

Glenn Rink
Northern Arizona University
Flagstaff, Arizona

James P. Smith Jr.
Humboldt State University
Arcata, California

Gary D. Wallace†
California Botanic Garden
Claremont, California

WESTERN CANADA

William J. Cody†
Agriculture and Agri-Food Canada
Ottawa, Ontario

Bruce A. Ford, Regional Coordinator
University of Manitoba
Winnipeg, Manitoba

Lynn Gillespie
Canadian Museum of Nature
Ottawa, Ontario

A. Joyce Gould
Alberta Environment and Parks
Edmonton, Alberta

Vernon L. Harms
University of Saskatchewan
Saskatoon, Saskatchewan

Elizabeth Punter
University of Manitoba
Winnipeg, Manitoba

ROCKY MOUNTAINS

Jennifer Ackerfield
Denver Botanic Gardens
Denver, Colorado

Walter Fertig
Washington Natural Heritage Program
Olympia, Washington

Ronald L. Hartman†
University of Wyoming
Laramie, Wyoming

Bonnie Heidel, Regional Coordinator
University of Wyoming
Laramie, Wyoming

Robert Johnson
Brigham Young University
Provo, Utah

Ben Legler
University of Idaho
Moscow, Idaho

Peter C. Lesica
University of Montana
Missoula, Montana

Donald H. Mansfield
The College of Idaho
Caldwell, Idaho

B. E. Nelson
University of Wyoming
Laramie, Wyoming

Leila M. Shultz
Utah State University
Logan, Utah

NORTH CENTRAL UNITED STATES

Anita F. Cholewa
University of Minnesota
St. Paul, Minnesota

Neil A. Harriman†
University of Wisconsin Oshkosh
Oshkosh, Wisconsin

Bruce W. Hoagland
University of Oklahoma
Norman, Oklahoma

Craig C. Freeman, Regional Coordinator
The University of Kansas
Lawrence, Kansas

Robert B. Kaul†
University of Nebraska
Lincoln, Nebraska

Gary E. Larson†
South Dakota State University
Brookings, South Dakota

Deborah Q. Lewis
Iowa State University
Ames, Iowa

Ronald L. McGregor†
The University of Kansas
Lawrence, Kansas

Stephen G. Saupe
College of Saint Benedict/ St. John's University
Collegeville, Minnesota

Lawrence R. Stritch
Martinsburg, West Virginia

George Yatskievych
The Universtiy of Texas at Austin
Austin, Texas

SOUTH CENTRAL UNITED STATES

Jackie M. Poole, Regional Coordinator
Fort Davis, Texas

Robert C. Sivinski
University of New Mexico
Albuquerque, New Mexico

EASTERN CANADA

Sean Blaney
Atlantic Canada Conservation Data Centre
Sackville, New Brunswick

Luc Brouillet,
Regional Coordinator
Institut de recherche en biologie végétale
Université de Montréal
Montréal, Québec

Jacques Cayouette
Agriculture and Agri-Food Canada
Ontario, Ottawa

Frédéric Coursol
Jardin botanique de Montréal
Montréal, Québec

William J. Crins
Ontario Ministry of Natural Resources
Peterborough, Ontario

Marian Munro
Nova Scotia Museum of Natural History
Halifax, Nova Scotia

Michael J. Oldham
Natural Heritage Information Centre
Peterborough, Ontario

NORTHEASTERN UNITED STATES

Ray Angelo
New England Botanical Club
Cambridge, Massachusetts

David E. Boufford,
Regional Coordinator
Harvard University Herbaria
Cambridge, Massachusetts

Tom S. Cooperrider†
Kent State University
Kent, Ohio

Allison Cusick
Carnegie Museum of Natural History
Pittsburgh, Pennsylvania

Arthur Haines
Canton, Maine

Michael A. Homoya
Indiana Department of Natural Resources
Indianapolis, Indiana

Robert F. C. Naczi
The New York Botanical Garden
Bronx, New York

Anton A. Reznicek
University of Michigan
Ann Arbor, Michigan

Edward G. Voss†
University of Michigan
Ann Arbor, Michigan

Kay Yatskievych
Austin, Texas

SOUTHEASTERN UNITED STATES

Mac H. Alford
University of Southern Mississippi
Hattiesburg, Mississippi

J. Richard Carter Jr.
Valdosta State University
Valdosta, Georgia

L. Dwayne Estes
Austin Peay State University
Clarksville, Tennessee

W. John Hayden
University of Richmond
Richmond, Virginia

Wesley Knapp
North Carolina Natural Heritage Program
Asheville, North Carolina

John B. Nelson
University of South Carolina
Columbia, South Carolina

Chris Reid
Louisiana State University
Baton Rouge, Louisiana

Bruce A. Sorrie
University of North Carolina
Chapel Hill, North Carolina

Dan Spaulding
Anniston Museum of Natural History
Anniston, Alabama

R. Dale Thomas†
Seymour, Tennessee

Lowell E. Urbatsch
Louisiana State University
Baton Rouge, Louisiana

Alan S. Weakley,
Regional Coordinator
University of North Carolina
Chapel Hill, North Carolina

Theo Witsell
Arkansas Natural Heritage Commission
Little Rock, Arkansas

B. Eugene Wofford
University of Tennessee
Knoxville, Tennessee

FLORIDA

Loran C. Anderson
Florida State University
Tallahassee, Florida

Bruce F. Hansen
University of South Florida
Tampa, Florida

Richard P. Wunderlin,
Regional Coordinator
University of South Florida
Tampa, Florida

Preface for Volume 11, Parts 1 and 2

Since the publication of *Flora of North America* Volume 10 (the twenty-second volume in the *Flora* series) in 2021, the membership of the Flora of North America Association [FNAA] Board of Directors has changed. John L. Strother and Alan S. Weakley have departed the board. As a result of a reorganization finalized in 2003, the FNAA Board of Directors succeeded the former Editorial Committee; for the sake of continuity of citation, authorship of *Flora* volumes is to be cited as "Flora of North America Editorial Committee, eds."

Most of the editorial process for this volume was done at Miami University in Oxford, Ohio, and at the Missouri Botanical Garden in St. Louis. Final processing and composition took place at the Missouri Botanical Garden; this included pre-press processing, typesetting and layout, plus coordination for all aspects of planning, executing, and scanning the illustrations. Other aspects of production, such as art panel composition plus labeling and occurrence map generation, were carried out elsewhere in North America.

Illustrations published in this volume were executed by four very talented artists: Barbara Alongi, Linny Heagy, John Myers, and Yevonn Wilson-Ramsey. Barbara Alongi illustrated *Abrus, Acacia, Acaciella, Acmispon, Adenanthera, Aeschynomene, Albizia, Andira, Anthyllis, Apios, Arachis, Baptisia, Bauhinia, Brongniartia, Cajanus, Calliandra, Canavalia, Centrosema, Cercis, Chapmannia, Cicer, Cladrastis, Clitoria, Coronilla, Coursetia, Dalbergia, Dermatophyllum, Desmanthus, Dichrostachys, Diphysa, Ebenopsis, Enterolobium, Erythrina, Galactia, Genistidium, Gliricidia, Glycine, Havardia, Hosackia, Indigofera, Lackeya, Leucaena, Lotus, Lysiloma, Maackia, Mariosousa, Millettia, Mimosa, Mucuna, Neptunia, Nissolia, Olneya, Ornithopus, Pachyrhizus, Paraserianthes, Peteria, Phanera, Pickeringia, Piscidia, Pithecellobium, Prosopis, Pueraria, Rhynchosia, Robinia, Samanea, Securigera, Senegalia, Sophora, Sphinctospermum, Stylosanthes, Styphnolobium, Tamarindus, Tephrosia, Thermopsis, Vachellia, Wisteria, Zapoteca,* and *Zornia.* She also created the frontispiece for Part 1 depicting *Wisteria frutescens.* Linny Heagy illustrated *Crotalaria.* John Myers illustrated the following genera: *Alhagi, Astragalus, Caragana, Colutea, Galega, Glycyrrhiza, Halimodendron, Hedysarum, Lathyrus, Lens, Oxytropis, Pisum, Sphaerophysa,* and *Vicia.* Yevonn Wilson-Ramsey prepared illustrations for *Alysicarpus, Amorpha, Amphicarpaea, Ancistrotropis, Aspalthium, Caesalpinia, Cassia, Ceratonia, Chamaecrista, Cologania, Cytisus, Dalea, Delonix, Denisophytum, Desmodium, Dipogon, Errazurizia, Erythrostemon, Eysenhardtia, Genista, Gleditsia, Guilandina, Gymnocladus, Hoffmannseggia, Hoita, Hylodesmum, Kummerowia, Lablab, Laburnum, Ladeania, Leptospron, Lespedeza, Lupinus, Macroptilium, Marina, Medicago, Melilotus, Onobrychis, Ononis, Orbexilum, Oxyrhynchus, Parkinsonia, Parryella, Pediomelum, Peltophorum, Phaseolus, Pomaria, Psorothamnus, Retama, Rupertia, Senna, Sesbania, Sigmoidotropis, Spartium, Strophostyles, Tara, Trifolium, Trigonella, Ulex,* and *Vigna,* and she created the frontispiece for Part 2 depicting *Trifolium macrocephalum.* In addition to preparing various illustrations, John Myers composed and labeled all of the line drawings that appear in Vol. 11, parts 1 and 2.

Starting with Volume 8, published in 2009, the circumscription and ordering of some families within the *Flora* have been modified so that they mostly reflect that of the Angiosperm Phylogeny Group [APG] rather than the previously followed Cronquist organizational structure. The groups of families found in this and future volumes in the series are mostly ordered following E. M. Haston et al. (2007); since APG views of relationships and circumscriptions have evolved, and will change further through time, some discrepancies in organization will occur. For practical publishing purposes, Surianaceae, Polygalaceae, and Elaeagnaceae were moved from Volume 11 to Volume 10. Volume 11 is published in two parts, the first containing subfamilies Cercidoideae, Detarioideae, and Caesalpinioideae, and the first part of Faboideae (tribes Sophoreae to Loteae), and the second containing the rest of subfamily Faboideae (tribes Robinieae to Fabeae). The literature cited and index for the entire volume appear at the end of part 2. Volume 30 of the *Flora of North America* will contain a comprehensive index to the published volumes.

Support from many institutions and by numerous individuals has enabled the *Flora* to be produced. Members of the Flora of North America Association remain deeply thankful to the many people who continue to help create, encourage, and sustain the *Flora*.

Introduction

Scope of the Work

Flora of North America North of Mexico is a synoptic account of the plants of North America north of Mexico: the continental United States of America (including the Florida Keys and Aleutian Islands), Canada, Greenland (Kalâtdlit-Nunât), and St. Pierre and Miquelon. The *Flora* is intended to serve both as a means of identifying plants within the region and as a systematic conspectus of the North American flora.

The *Flora* will be published in 30 volumes. Volume 1 contains background information that is useful for understanding patterns in the flora. Volume 2 contains treatments of ferns and gymnosperms. Families in volumes 3–26, the angiosperms, were first arranged according to the classification system of A. Cronquist (1981) with some modifications, and starting with Volume 8, the circumscriptions and ordering of families generally follow those of the Angiosperm Phylogeny Group [APG] (see E. M. Haston et al. 2007). Bryophytes are being covered in volumes 27–29. Volume 30 will contain the cumulative bibliography and index.

The first two volumes were published in 1993, Volume 3 in 1997, and Volumes 22, 23, and 26, the first three of five volumes covering the monocotyledons, appeared in 2000, 2002, and 2002, respectively. Volume 4, the first part of the Caryophyllales, was published in late 2003. Volume 25, the second part of the Poaceae, was published in mid 2003, and Volume 24, the first part, was published in January 2007. Volume 5, completing the Caryophyllales plus Polygonales and Plumbaginales, was published in early 2005. Volumes 19–21, treating Asteraceae, were published in early 2006. Volume 27, the first of two volumes treating mosses in North America, was published in late 2007. Volume 8, Paeoniaceae to Ericaceae, was published in September 2009, and Volume 7, Salicaceae to Brassicaceae, appeared in 2010. In 2014, Volume 28 was published, completing the treatment of mosses for the flora area, and at the end of 2014, Volume 9, Picramniaceae to Rosaceae was published. Volume 6, which covered Cucurbitaceae to Droseraceae, was published in 2015. Volume 12, Vitaceae to Garryaceae, was published in late 2016. Volume 17, Tetrachondraceae to Orobanchaceae, was published in 2019. Volume 10, Proteaceae to Elaeagnaceae, was published in 2021. The correct bibliographic citation for the *Flora* is: Flora of North America Editorial Committee, eds. 1993+. Flora of North America North of Mexico. 23+ vols. New York and Oxford.

Volume 11, parts 1 and 2 treat 1345 species in 153 genera contained in Fabaceae. For additional statistics please refer to Table 1 on p. xxii.

Contents · General

The *Flora* includes accepted names, selected synonyms, literature citations, identification keys, descriptions, phenological information, summaries of habitats and geographic ranges, and other biological observations. Each volume contains a bibliography and an index to the taxa included in that volume. The treatments, written and reviewed by experts from throughout the systematic botanical community, are based on original observations of herbarium specimens and, whenever possible, on living plants. These observations are supplemented by critical reviews of the literature.

Table 1. *Statistics for Volume 11 of Flora of North America.*

Family	Total Genera	Endemic Genera	Introduced Genera	Total Species	Endemic Species	Introduced Species	Conservation Taxa
Fabaceae	153	3	51	1345	690	247	252
Totals	**153**	**3**	**51**	**1345**	**690**	**247**	**252**

Basic Concepts

Our goal is to make the *Flora* as clear, concise, and informative as practicable so that it can be an important resource for both botanists and nonbotanists. To this end, we are attempting to be consistent in style and content from the first volume to the last. Readers may assume that a term has the same meaning each time it appears and that, within groups, descriptions may be compared directly with one another. Any departures from consistent usage will be explicitly noted in the treatments (see References).

Treatments are intended to reflect current knowledge of taxa throughout their ranges worldwide, and classifications are therefore based on all available evidence. Where notable differences of opinion about the classification of a group occur, appropriate references are mentioned in the discussion of the group.

Documentation and arguments supporting significantly revised classifications are published separately in botanical journals before publication of the pertinent volume of the *Flora*. Similarly, all new names and new combinations are published elsewhere prior to their use in the *Flora*. No nomenclatural innovations will be published intentionally in the *Flora*.

Taxa treated in full include extant and recently extinct or extirpated native species, named hybrids that are well established (or frequent), introduced plants that are naturalized, and cultivated plants that are found frequently outside cultivation. Taxa mentioned only in discussions include waifs known only from isolated old records and some non-native, economically important or extensively cultivated plants, particularly when they are relatives of native species. Excluded names and taxa are listed at the ends of appropriate sections, for example, species at the end of genus, genera at the end of family.

Treatments are intended to be succinct and diagnostic but adequately descriptive. Characters and character states used in the keys are repeated in the descriptions. Descriptions of related taxa at the same rank are directly comparable.

With few exceptions, taxa are presented in taxonomic sequence. If an author is unable to produce a classification, the taxa are arranged alphabetically and the reasons are given in the discussion.

Treatments of hybrids follow that of one of the putative parents. Hybrid complexes are treated at the ends of their genera, after the descriptions of species.

We have attempted to keep terminology as simple as accuracy permits. Common English equivalents usually have been used in place of Latin or Latinized terms or other specialized terminology, whenever the correct meaning could be conveyed in approximately the same space, for example, "pitted" rather than "foveolate," but "striate" rather than "with fine longitudinal lines." See *Categorical Glossary for the Flora of North America Project* (R. W. Kiger and D. M. Porter 2001; also available online at http://huntbot.andrew.cmu.edu) for standard definitions of generally used terms. Very specialized terms are defined, and sometimes illustrated, in the relevant family or generic treatments.

References

Authoritative general reference works used for style are *The Chicago Manual of Style,* ed. 14 (University of Chicago Press 1993); *Webster's New Geographical Dictionary* (Merriam-Webster 1988); and *The Random House Dictionary of the English Language*, ed. 2, unabridged (S. B. Flexner and L. C. Hauck 1987). *B-P-H/S. Botanico-Periodicum-Huntianum/Supplementum* (G. D. R. Bridson and E. R. Smith 1991), *BPH-2: Periodicals with Botanical Content* (Bridson 2004), and *BPH Online* [http://fmhibd.library.cmu.edu/HIBD-DB/bpho/findrecords.php] (Bridson and D. W. Brown) have been used for abbreviations of serial titles, and *Taxonomic Literature*, ed. 2 (F. A. Stafleu and R. S. Cowan 1976–1988) and its supplements by Stafleu et al. (1992–2009) have been used for abbreviations of book titles.

Graphic Elements

All genera and more than 25 percent of the species in this volume are illustrated. The illustrations may show diagnostic traits or complex structures. Most illustrations have been drawn from herbarium specimens selected by the authors. Data on specimens that were used and parts that were illustrated have been recorded. This information, together with the archivally preserved original drawings, is deposited in the Missouri Botanical Garden Library and is available for scholarly study.

Specific Information in Treatments

Keys

Dichotomous keys are included for all ranks below family if two or more taxa are treated. More than one key may be given to facilitate identification of sterile material or for flowering versus fruiting material.

Nomenclatural Information

Basionyms of accepted names, with author and bibliographic citations, are listed first in synonymy, followed by any other synonyms in common recent use, listed in alphabetical order, without bibliographic citations.

The last names of authors of taxonomic names have been spelled out. The conventions of *Authors of Plant Names* (R. K. Brummitt and C. E. Powell 1992) have been used as a guide for including first initials to discriminate individuals who share surnames.

If only one infraspecific taxon within a species occurs in the flora area, nomenclatural information (literature citation, basionym with literature citation, relevant other synonyms) is given for the species, as is information on the number of infraspecific taxa in the species and their distribution worldwide, if known. A description and detailed distributional information are given only for the infraspecific taxon.

Descriptions

Character states common to all taxa are noted in the description of the taxon at the next higher rank. For example, if sexual condition is dioecious for all species treated within a genus, that character state is given in the generic description. Characters used in keys are repeated in the descriptions. Characteristics are given as they occur in plants from the flora area. Characteristics that occur only in plants from outside the flora area may be given within square brackets, or instead may be noted in the discussion following the description. In families with one genus and one or more species, the family description is given as usual, the genus description is condensed, and the species are described as usual. Any special terms that may be used when describing members of a genus are presented and explained in the genus description or discussion.

In reading descriptions, the reader may assume, unless otherwise noted, that: the plants are green, photosynthetic, and reproductively mature; woody plants are perennial; stems are erect; roots are fibrous; leaves are simple and petiolate; flowers are bisexual, radially symmetric, and pediceled; perianth parts are hypogynous, distinct, and free; and ovaries are superior. Because measurements and elevations are almost always approximate, modifiers such as "about," "circa," or "±" are usually omitted.

Unless otherwise noted, dimensions are length × width. If only one dimension is given, it is length or height. All measurements are given in metric units. Measurements usually are based on dried specimens but these should not differ significantly from the measurements actually found in fresh or living material.

Chromosome numbers generally are given only if published and vouchered counts are available from North American material or from an adjacent region. No new counts are published intentionally in the *Flora*. Chromosome counts from nonsporophyte tissue have been converted to the $2n$ form. The base number (x =) is given for each genus. This represents the lowest known haploid count for the genus unless evidence is available that the base number differs.

Flowering time and often fruiting time are given by season, sometimes qualified by early, mid, or late, or by months. Elevations 100 m and under are rounded to the nearest 10 m, between 100 m and 200 m to the nearest 50 m, and over 200 m to the nearest 100 m. Mean sea level is shown as 0 m, with the understanding that this is approximate. Elevation often is omitted from herbarium specimen labels, particularly for collections made where the topography is not remarkable, and therefore precise elevation is sometimes not known for a given taxon.

The term "introduced" is defined broadly to refer to plants that were released deliberately or accidentally into the flora and that now are naturalized, that is, exist as wild plants in areas in which they were not recorded as native in the past. The distribution of introduced taxa are often poorly documented and changing, so the distribution statements for those taxa may not be fully accurate.

If a taxon is globally rare or if its continued existence is threatened in some way, the words "of conservation concern" appear before the statements of elevation and geographic range.

Criteria for taxa of conservation concern are based on NatureServe's (formerly The Nature Conservancy)—see http://www.natureserve.org—designations of global rank (G-rank) G1 and G2:

G1 Critically imperiled globally because of extreme rarity (5 or fewer occurrences or fewer than 1000 individuals or acres) or because of some factor(s) making it especially vulnerable to extinction.

G2 Imperiled globally because of rarity (5–20 occurrences or fewer than 3000 individuals or acres) or because of some factor(s) making it very vulnerable to extinction throughout its range.

The occurrence of species and infraspecific taxa within political subunits of the *Flora* area is depicted by dots placed on the outline map to indicate occurrence in a state or province. The Nunavut boundary on the maps has been provided by the GeoAccess Division, Canada Centre for Remote Sensing, Earth Science. Authors are expected to have seen at least one specimen documenting each geographic unit record (except in rare cases when undoubted literature reports may be used) and have been urged to examine as many specimens as possible from throughout the range of each taxon. Additional information about taxon distribution may be presented in the discussion.

Distributions are stated in the following order: Greenland; St. Pierre and Miquelon; Canada (provinces and territories in alphabetic order); United States (states in alphabetic order); Mexico (11 northern states may be listed specifically, in alphabetic order); West Indies; Bermuda; Central America (Belize, Costa Rica, El Salvador, Guatemala, Honduras, Nicaragua, Panama); South America; Europe, or Eurasia; Asia (including Indonesia); Africa; Atlantic Islands; Indian Ocean Islands; Pacific Islands; Australia; Antarctica.

Discussion

The discussion section may include information on taxonomic problems, distributional and ecological details, interesting biological phenomena, and economic uses.

Selected References

Major references used in preparation of a treatment or containing critical information about a taxon are cited following the discussion. These, and other works that are referred to in discussion or elsewhere, are included in Literature Cited at the end of the volume.

CAUTION

The Flora of North America Editorial Committee **does not encourage, recommend, promote, or endorse** any of the folk remedies, culinary practices, or various utilizations of any plant described within this volume. Information about medicinal practices and/or ingestion of plants, or of any part or preparation thereof, has been included only for historical background and as a matter of interest. Under no circumstances should the information contained in these volumes be used in connection with medical treatment. Readers are strongly cautioned to remember that many plants in the flora are toxic or can cause unpleasant or adverse reactions if used or encountered carelessly.

Key to boxed codes following accepted names:

- [C] of conservation concern
- [E] endemic to the flora area
- [F] illustrated
- [I] introduced to the flora area
- [W] weedy applies to taxa listed as weeds on the State and Federal Composite List of All U.S. Noxious Weeds (https://plants.usda.gov/java/noxComposite) and the Composite List of Weeds from the Weed Science Society of America (https://wssa.net/wssa/weed/composite-list-of-weeds), with input from treatment authors and reviewers.

Flora of North America

FABACEAE Lindley
• Bean Family

Leguminosae Jussieu

Michael A. Vincent[1]

Trees, shrubs, subshrubs, vines, or herbs, annual, biennial, or perennial, sometimes twining, armed or unarmed, usually synoecious, rarely dioecious. **Stems** erect, ascending, decumbent, or prostrate, rarely producing resins. **Leaves** deciduous or persistent, usually alternate, rarely opposite, subopposite, whorled, or clustered on spurs, 1–3-pinnate, rarely palmate or 1–4-foliolate, or phyllodic; stipules usually present, rarely absent, sometimes spinelike, often adnate to petiole; petiole usually present, pulvini usually present; stipels sometimes present; blade margins lobed, dentate, serrate, or entire. **Inflorescences** axillary or terminal, racemes, spikes, cymes, panicles, pseudoracemes, umbels, heads, or simple. **Flowers** bisexual or unisexual, radially or bilaterally symmetric, papilionaceous, caesalpinioid, or mimosoid, rarely pseudopapilionaceous; perianth and androecium hypogynous or perigynous; epicalyx absent; hypanthium sometimes present; sepals 5, rarely 4 or 6, connate into a tube, rarely nearly distinct; petals 5, rarely 4, 6, 1, or 0, distinct or slightly connate proximally; nectary present or absent, in a ring at base of ovary and staminal column; stamens (1–)10(–250+), filaments connate into tube enclosing pistil and monadelphous or diadelphous, or distinct; anthers 2-locular, monomorphic or dimorphic and then alternately basifixed and dorsifixed, dehiscence longitudinal or by pores; pistil 1, 1-carpellate, free from hypanthium, ovary superior, 1-locular or longitudinally septate and 2-locular (in *Astragalus*), sometimes with lateral constrictions or transverse septae; placentation marginal; style 1, apical; stigma 1, terminal; ovules 1–100+, anatropous, hemitropous, or campylotropous. **Fruits** legumes or loments, dehiscent or indehiscent, rarely drupes or samaroid. **Seeds** 1–100+; endosperm scant or copious; embryo large, curved or straight. x = 6, 7, 8, 9, 10, 11, 12, 16.

Genera ca. 770, species ca. 20,900 (153 genera, 1345 species in the flora): nearly worldwide.

Fabaceae are the third-largest angiosperm family after Orchidaceae and Asteraceae (M. J. M. Christenhusz et al. 2017). The closest relatives of Fabaceae appear to be Polygalaceae,

[1] The author wishes to acknowledge co-authorship with David J. Bogler on all family keys to genera.

Quillajaceae D. Don, and Surianaceae (D. E. Soltis et al. 2011). While the family Fabaceae is strongly supported as monophyletic (Angiosperm Phylogeny Group 2016), subfamilial classification has proven to be more complicated. Historically, Fabaceae (often under the alternative name Leguminosae) were considered easily divided into three groups based on morphological features, especially of flowers (A. Cronquist 1981; see morphology discussion below): the caesalpinioids (Caesalpiniaceae R. Brown, or Fabaceae subfam. Caesalpinioideae de Candolle), the mimosoids (Mimosaceae R. Brown, or Fabaceae subfam. Mimosoideae de Candolle), and the papilionoids (Papilionaceae Giseke [Fabaceae in the strict sense], or Fabaceae subfam. Papilionoideae de Candolle [Faboideae Rudd]). Polyphyly of the caesalpinioids has long been suspected, as have affinities to mimosoids, based on morphological data (R. M. Polhill and J. E. Vidal 1981). Phylogenetic studies have confirmed that mimosoids are embedded within a paraphyletic caesalpinioid clade (A. Bruneau et al. 2001, 2008). Most recently, the Legume Phylogeny Working Group (2017) has recognized six subfamilies: Caesalpinioideae (including a monophyletic "mimosoid clade"), Cercidoideae, Detarioideae, Dialioideae LPWG, Duparquetioideae LPWG, and Faboideae [as Papilionoideae]; Dialioideae and Duparquetioideae do not occur in the flora area. Arrangement of genera in this treatment follows the subfamilial classification of Legume Phylogeny Working Group, with the sequence of genera within the subfamilies adapted from G. P. Lewis at al. (2005).

Leaves in Fabaceae are usually compound, often pinnate or twice-pinnate, but also sometimes palmate; leaves with only one blade are likely derived from ancestral compound leaves and are termed unifoliolate (as in *Cercis*; S. A. Owens 2000). In some taxa, the rachis in a pinnate leaf is extremely reduced (as in *Ladeania*), making the leaf superficially appear palmate; these leaves are termed pseudopalmate. A characteristic feature of most legume leaves is the pulvinus (plural pulvini), a jointlike thickening of petioles and petiolules that is involved with leaf movement related to changes in light or moisture availability (nyctinasty; T. M. Rodrigues and S. R. Machado 2007) or touch (thigmonasty; J. Braam 2005). Extrafloral nectary glands may be present on leaves (blades, rachises, or petioles) of some taxa, especially in the Detarioideae and Caesalpinioideae, and these may be stalked or sessile, and of various shapes.

Inflorescences in Fabaceae can consist of a single flower, or flowers may be arranged in spikes or heads, which can be grouped in larger paniculate structures, racemes, pseudoracemes (where each node in the racemelike inflorescence bears several flowers), cymes, panicles, or umbels (umbelliform racemes or pseudoracemes with greatly reduced internodes).

Flowers in Fabaceae are generally five-merous, with more or less distinct petals (which are sometimes differentiated into blade and claw) and often with connate sepals. Floral structure conforms in general to three main types: papilionaceous, caesalpinioid, or mimosoid. **Papilionaceous** flowers (from Latin *papilio*, butterfly) are usually bilateral and somewhat perigynous. Sepals are connate, at least at the base, into a tube that sometimes completely encloses the floral bud, with or without lobes at the distal end. The usually five petals are arranged into a keel formed from the innermost (abaxial) pair, the wings, the lateral pair positioned outside the keel, and a banner (sometimes called the standard), which is positioned outermost in the bud, surrounding the other petals. The keel petals may be completely distinct from each other or may be connate at the distal end, while the wing petals are usually distinct from each other. The banner petal, which is often the largest of the petals, may be straight (as in *Erythrina*), or reflexed at a joint or callous or from its base (as in *Maackia*). The stamens in a papilionaceous flower are usually ten and may be monadelphous (as in *Lupinus*) or diadelphous (in a 9 + 1 arrangement, with nine filaments connate into a closed tube or at least partially open sheath surrounding the pistil and one stamen distinct from the others, as in *Trifolium*) and are not usually long-exserted or the showy part of the flower. The pollen is in monads. **Caesalpinioid** (or pseudopapilionaceous) flowers are often bilateral (zygomorphic) and perigynous (rarely hypogynous). The sepals in caesalpinioid flowers are distinct or nearly so, imbricate or valvate in bud, or connate into a five-lobed cup or even nearly absent. The petals are usually less obviously organized into keel, wings, and banner. The keel and wings may be positioned as in papilionaceous flowers (as in *Cercis*), or they may be more widely open and more similar to each other. The banner petal is situated in the bud to the inside of the wing petals and is sometimes smaller than the other petals (as in *Caesalpinia*). Stamens in caesalpinioid flowers range from one to ten, sometimes more, and are often distinct. They are often shorter than the corolla, though sometimes much longer and showy, and are sometimes heteromorphic, of differing sizes or shapes, sometimes with a mix of fertile and sterile (staminodial) anthers. The pollen is usually in monads. **Mimosoid** flowers are regular (radially symmetric) and hypogynous or slightly perigynous, and the most distinctive of the floral types, usually small and individually inconspicuous. They are not organized as noted above but instead have corollas that are often connate into a tube, rarely distinct, and valvate (rarely imbricate) in the bud. The sepals are usually connate at the base, usually regular, and often lobed distally. The petals may be shorter than or longer than the calyx. Stamens are distinct from one another or proximally connate, range in number from twice as many as the petals to many, and are usually longer or even very much longer than the perianth and thus are the showiest part of the flower. The pollen is usually in tetrads or polyads (Legume Phylogeny Working Group).

Fruits of Fabaceae are generally legumes, usually 1-carpellate and 1-locular, with seeds positioned marginally, and often dehiscent into two valves at maturity. Legumes can vary greatly in morphology (C. R. Gunn 1984, 1991; J. H. Kirkbride et al. 2003), ranging from flattened laterally (as in *Pisum*) to inflated at maturity (as in *Astragalus crassicarpus*), and from a few millimeters to 60 centimeters. They are often dry at maturity but may be fleshy (as in *Styphnolobium japonicum*), with valves (the two halves of the fruit wall) ranging in texture from thin and fragile to thick and woody. Fruits of some *Astragalus* species may be partially or completely bilocular, due to intrusion of tissue (the replum) from the dorsal (abaxial) suture (Kirkbride et al.; S. L. Welsh 2007). Some legumes are indehiscent (as in *Arachis*), while others may open along one or both sutures; some taxa have fruits which are explosively dehiscent (as in *Zapoteca*); valves may remain flat post-dehiscence or may be twisted. A modified form of legume, the loment, is divided into one-seeded indehiscent sections (sometimes called joints) that break apart from each other at maturity (as in *Desmodium*); a craspedium is similar, but the one-seeded segments leave behind the replum as they fall away (as in *Mimosa pudica*). *Andira* is unusual among North American Fabaceae for its drupelike fruit. A few taxa produce samaroid fruits, such as *Dalbergia ecastaphyllum*. In addition, some taxa in the flora area have geocarpic fruits (*Arachis* species; *Trifolium amphianthum* has geocarpic cleistogamous fruits, in addition to the chasmogamous fruits produced on long, erect peduncles).

Seeds of legumes range in number from one to more than 75, and may be positioned in the fruit parallel, obliquely, or transversely to the length of the fruit (C. R. Gunn, 1991; J. H. Kirkbride et al. 2003). They may possess a true aril (as in *Pithecellobium*), an aril-like, enlarged funiculus, or these may be absent. The hilum (scar of attachment to the funiculus) is sometimes used in identification, and may vary in outline from V-shaped, to linear or circular, or other shapes, and can be variable in size or conformation. A pleurogram (U-shaped or elliptic line) is often present in mimosoid legumes but is usually absent in other groups. The embryo radicle is usually curved in subfam. Faboideae, and is usually straight in the rest of the subfamilies.

Roots of many Fabaceae bear nodules containing nitrogen-fixing bacteria (rhizobia, in numerous genera) that have coevolved with their hosts, which allow the plants to occupy marginal, nitrogen-poor habitats (D. P. S. Verma and J. Stanley 1989; J. P. W. Young and K. E. Haukka 1996; M. Andrews and M. E. Andrews 2017). Nitrogen fixation by rhizobial symbionts of Fabaceae is ecologically important in natural systems and in agricultural systems.

The economic importance of legumes to humans is second only to that of grasses (J. A. Duke 1981; P. H. Graham and C. P. Vance 2003). Among important legume food crops are the grain legume (pulse) genera *Arachis*, *Cicer*, *Faba* Miller, *Glycine*, *Glycyrrhiza*, *Lens*, *Phaseolus*, *Pisum*, *Tamarindus*, and *Vigna*, which provide a large portion of the dietary protein requirements and other products to people worldwide. In addition, legume forage crops, including *Medicago*, *Trifolium*, and *Vicia*, are important for production of grazing animals and as nectar sources for bees. Many other genera, such as *Albizia*, *Cassia*, *Cercis*, *Delonix*, *Gleditsia*, *Laburnum*, *Lupinus*, *Robinia*, *Senna*, and *Wisteria* are grown as ornamental plants. In addition, important lumber trees, such as species of *Acacia* and *Dalbergia*, are members of Fabaceae. Natural gums, such as gum Arabic (often from *Acacia* or *Senegalia* species) and guar gum [from *Cyamopsis tetragonoloba* (Linnaeus) Taubert], as well as dyes such as true indigo (from *Indigofera tinctoria*) and haematoxylin (from *Haematoxylum campechianum* Linnaeus), are derived from species of Fabaceae.

In the key to genera of Fabaceae, characters and character states are sometimes used that are included in descriptions of taxa within the relevant genera but not in the generic descriptions themselves. Such characters are not usually found as part of a normal genus description (for example, measurements), but they are included in the key because they are useful for identifying some genera within the family.

The following taxa are excluded from the flora due to lack of documentation, because they are waifs that did not become established, or because they are only known from cultivation in the flora area: *Carmichaelia* R. Brown (D. Isely 1998); *Chesneya nubigena* (D. Don) Ali (Isely); *Cojoba graciliflora* (S. F. Blake) Britton & Rose (as *Pithecellobium graciliflorum* S. F. Blake; R. W. Long and O. Lakela 1971; D. B. Ward 1972; R. P. Wunderlin 1998); *Cullen americanum* (Linnaeus) Rydberg (P. A. Rydberg 1919–1920; J. K. Small 1933); *C. corylifolium* (Linnaeus) Medikus (as *Psoralea corylifolia* Linnaeus; R. R. Tatnall 1946); *Hippocrepis comosa* Linnaeus (E. T. Wherry et al. 1979; A. F. Rhoads and W. M. Klein 1993); *Lotononis bainesii* Baker (Wunderlin); *Otholobium fruticans* (Linnaeus) C. H. Stirton (A. Kellogg 1877; Isely); and *Scorpiurus muricatus* Linnaeus (Tatnall; Rhoads and Klein; M. D. Cullina et al. 2011).

Recent additions to the flora area that are not treated here include: *Callerya reticulata* (Bentham) Schot (Florida; http://florida.plantatlas.usf.edu/Plant.aspx?id=4377); *Dorycnium hirsutum* Seringe (California; E. Dean et al. 2008); *Lonchocarpus punctatus* Kunth (Florida; R. P. Wunderlin 1998); and *Psophocarpus tetragonolobus* (Linnaeus) de Candolle (Florida; http://florida.plantatlas.usf.edu/Plant.aspx?id=4403).

SELECTED REFERENCES Isely, D. 1990. Leguminosae. In: A. E. Radford et al., eds. 1980+. Vascular Flora of the Southeastern United States. 2+ vols. Chapel Hill. Vol. 3, part 2. Isely, D. 1998. Native and Naturalized Leguminosae (Fabaceae) of the United States (Exclusive of Alaska and Hawaii). Provo. Legume Phylogeny Working Group. 2017. A new subfamily classification of the Leguminosae based on a taxonomically comprehensive phylogeny. Taxon 66: 44–77. Lewis, G. P. et al., eds. 2005. Legumes of the World. Kew. Polhill, R. M. and P. H. Raven, eds. 1981. Advances in Legume Systematics. Parts 1 and 2. 2 vols. Kew. Tucker, S. C. 2003. Floral development in legumes. Pl. Physiol. (Lancaster) 131: 911–926. Wojciechowski, M. F. 2003. Reconstructing the phylogeny of legumes (Leguminosae): An early 21st century perspective. In: B. B. Klitgaard and A. Bruneau, eds. 2003. Advances in Legume Systematics. Part 10. Kew. Pp. 5–35. Wojciechowski, M. F., M. Lavin, and M. J. Sanderson. 2004. A phylogeny of legumes (Leguminosae) based on analysis of the plastid *mat*K gene resolves many well-supported subclades within the family. Amer. J. Bot. 91: 1846–1862.

Key to Subfamilies

David J. Bogler
Michael A. Vincent

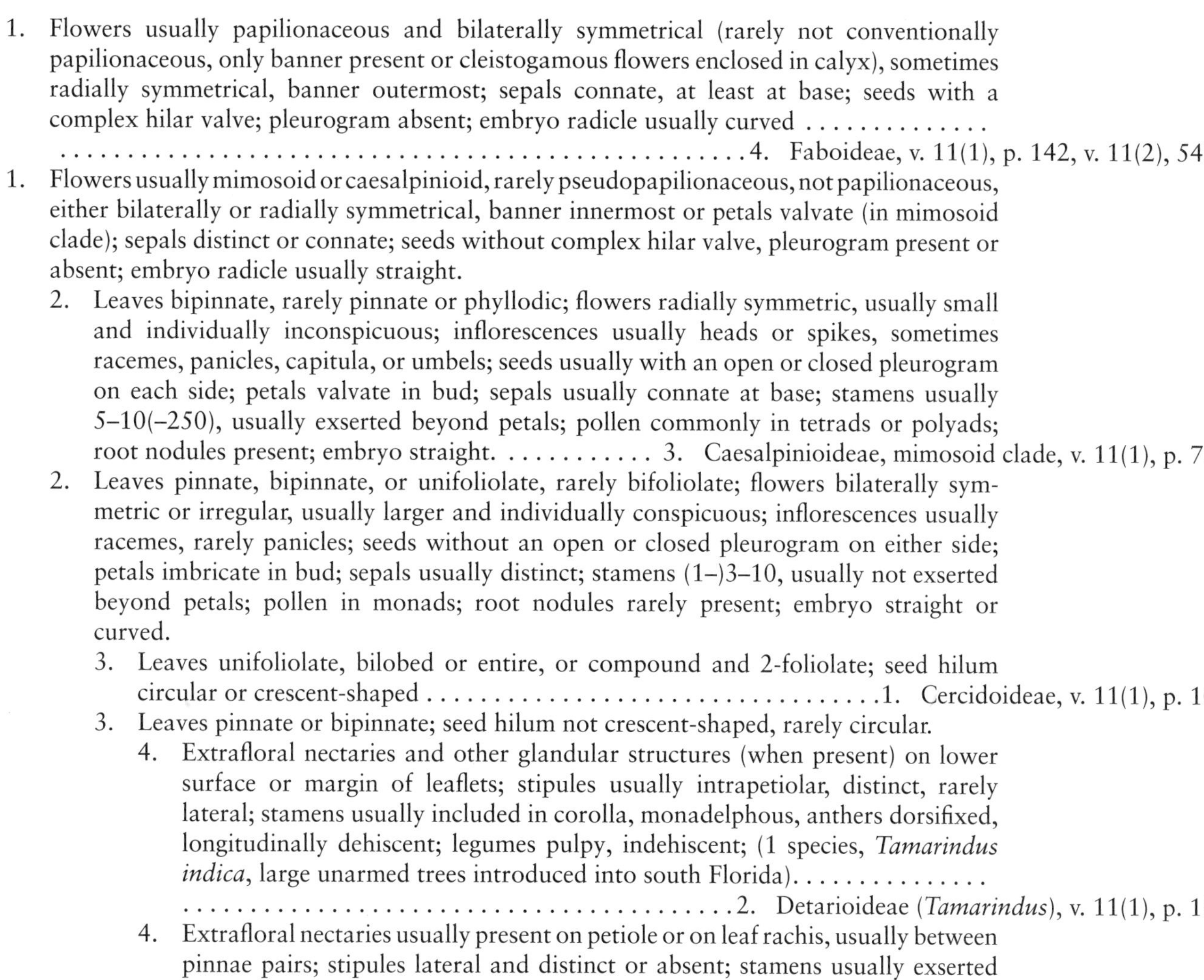

1. Flowers usually papilionaceous and bilaterally symmetrical (rarely not conventionally papilionaceous, only banner present or cleistogamous flowers enclosed in calyx), sometimes radially symmetrical, banner outermost; sepals connate, at least at base; seeds with a complex hilar valve; pleurogram absent; embryo radicle usually curved . . . . 4. Faboideae, v. 11(1), p. 142, v. 11(2), 543
1. Flowers usually mimosoid or caesalpinioid, rarely pseudopapilionaceous, not papilionaceous, either bilaterally or radially symmetrical, banner innermost or petals valvate (in mimosoid clade); sepals distinct or connate; seeds without complex hilar valve, pleurogram present or absent; embryo radicle usually straight.
   2. Leaves bipinnate, rarely pinnate or phyllodic; flowers radially symmetric, usually small and individually inconspicuous; inflorescences usually heads or spikes, sometimes racemes, panicles, capitula, or umbels; seeds usually with an open or closed pleurogram on each side; petals valvate in bud; sepals usually connate at base; stamens usually 5–10(–250), usually exserted beyond petals; pollen commonly in tetrads or polyads; root nodules present; embryo straight. . . . . 3. Caesalpinioideae, mimosoid clade, v. 11(1), p. 73
   2. Leaves pinnate, bipinnate, or unifoliolate, rarely bifoliolate; flowers bilaterally symmetric or irregular, usually larger and individually conspicuous; inflorescences usually racemes, rarely panicles; seeds without an open or closed pleurogram on either side; petals imbricate in bud; sepals usually distinct; stamens (1–)3–10, usually not exserted beyond petals; pollen in monads; root nodules rarely present; embryo straight or curved.
      3. Leaves unifoliolate, bilobed or entire, or compound and 2-foliolate; seed hilum circular or crescent-shaped . . . . 1. Cercidoideae, v. 11(1), p. 10
      3. Leaves pinnate or bipinnate; seed hilum not crescent-shaped, rarely circular.
         4. Extrafloral nectaries and other glandular structures (when present) on lower surface or margin of leaflets; stipules usually intrapetiolar, distinct, rarely lateral; stamens usually included in corolla, monadelphous, anthers dorsifixed, longitudinally dehiscent; legumes pulpy, indehiscent; (1 species, *Tamarindus indica*, large unarmed trees introduced into south Florida). . . . . 2. Detarioideae (*Tamarindus*), v. 11(1), p. 18
         4. Extrafloral nectaries usually present on petiole or on leaf rachis, usually between pinnae pairs; stipules lateral and distinct or absent; stamens usually exserted from corolla, filaments distinct, anthers basifixed or dorsifixed, dehiscing by apical pores or lateral slits; legumes dry, dehiscent on one or both sutures or indehiscent . . . . 3. Caesalpinioideae, excluding mimosoid clade, v. 11(1), p. 19

Fabaceae subfamilies, tribes, and genera. Subfamilial classification follows the Legume Phylogeny Working Group (2017), with the sequence of genera adapted from G. P. Lewis at al. (2005).

Volume 11, Part 1

Volume 11, Part 2

a. Fabaceae Lindley subfam. Cercidoideae Legume Phylogeny Working Group, Taxon 66: 68. 2017

Trees, shrubs, or woody vines, usually unarmed. **Extrafloral nectaries** present or absent, stipular, not on petiole or rachis. **Stipules** lateral, free. **Leaves** unifoliolate or 2-foliolate. **Flowers** caesalpinioid or pseudopapilionaceous, bilateral; sepals connate or distinct, spathaceous or 2–5-lobed; petals distinct, (2–)5(or 6); stamens usually 10, rarely 1, 3, or 5, filaments partly connate or distinct, anthers dorsifixed; pollen in monads, rarely in tetrads. **Fruits** legumes, dehiscent or indehiscent. **Seeds** with apical crescent-shaped or circular hilum, complex hilar valve absent, pleurograms absent; embryo straight. $x = 7$.

Genera 12, species ca. 335 (3 genera, 8 species in the flora): North America, Mexico, West Indies, Central America, South America, e, s Europe, Asia, Africa; introduced widely.

Key to Genera of Subfamily Cercidoideae

1. Vines, twining, tendrils present . . . . 3. *Phanera*, v. 11(1), p. 17
1. Trees or shrubs, tendrils absent.
    2. Leaves unifoliolate, not lobate; inflorescences fascicled from old wood, appearing before leaves; flowers pseudopapilionaceous (banner enclosed by wings which are enclosed by keel petals); fertile stamens 10; legumes narrowly winged; seeds with a circular hilum, funicular aril lobes absent; widespread . . . . 1. *Cercis*, v. 11(1), p. 10
    2. Leaves unifoliolate or 2-foliolate, usually 2-lobate; inflorescences not fascicled from old wood, usually appearing after leaves; flowers caesalpinioid; fertile stamens 1, 3, 5 or 10; legumes not winged; seeds with a crescent-shaped hilum, funicular aril lobes present; Florida, Texas . . . . 2. *Bauhinia*, v. 11(1), p. 14

1. CERCIS Linnaeus, Sp. Pl. 1: 374. 1753; Gen. Pl. ed. 5, 176. 1754 • Redbud [Greek *kerkis*, spatula, probably alluding to shape of pods]

Julie A. Ballenger

Michael A. Vincent

Trees or shrubs, unarmed. **Stems** gray or gray-brown to red-brown, twigs dark red-brown, erect, hairy or glabrous. **Leaves** alternate, 2-ranked, unifoliolate; stipules present, caducous, ovate, membranous; petiolate, petiole glabrous or hairy; pulvinate proximally and distally; blade margins entire, surfaces glabrous or hairy. **Inflorescences** cauliflorous or from short shoots on wood one year or older, fasciculate; bracts present, caducous. **Flowers** pseudopapilionaceous, appearing before leaves, banner enclosed by wings, wings enclosed by keel petals; calyx slightly zygomorphic, enlarged adaxially, persistent, lobes 5, connate, magenta, rounded to broadly triangular; corolla: petals 5, free, clawed, usually pink, rarely white, [magenta], inserted on floral cup; keel locked abaxially by folds in each petal forming a pocket; stamens 10, distinct, enclosed in keel pocket; filaments hairy proximally, inserted on floral cup; anthers versatile, 2-locular, dehiscing by longitudinal slits; ovary laterally compressed, short stalked; style tapering to a narrow tube, stigma triangular, terminal. **Fruits** legumes, sessile or short-stipitate, brown to red-brown or dark magenta, compressed laterally, lanceolate, narrowly winged on prominently veined abaxial suture, dull or glossy, indehiscent or dehiscent, if dehiscent, opening on one or both margins, glabrous or sparsely hairy. **Seeds** 3–7, red-brown, laterally compressed, with circular hilum, funicular aril lobes absent, orbicular. *x* = 7.

Species 10 (3 in the flora): North America, n Mexico, e, s Europe, Asia.

Cercis is found in mesic to arid habitats in North America and Eurasia. North American *Cercis* appears to have diverged from western Eurasian *Cercis* in the middle Miocene (P. A. Fritsch and B. C. Cruz 2012). *Cercis spokanensis* Knowlton is a fossil taxon from the Pacific Northwest.

In spite of the inclusion of *Cercis* in floras of New Mexico (I. Tidestrom and T. Kittell 1941; W. C. Martin and C. R. Hutchins 1980; K. W. Allred and R. D. Ivey 2012), no specimens of *Cercis* outside cultivation in that state could be located.

SELECTED REFERENCES Ballenger, J. A. 1992. A Biosystematic Revision of the Genus *Cercis* L. (Leguminosae) in North America. Ph.D. dissertation. Miami University. Fritsch, P. W. and B. C. Cruz. 2012. Phylogeny of *Cercis* based on DNA sequences of nuclear ITS and four plastid regions: Implications for transatlantic historical biogeography. Molec. Phylogen. Evol. 62: 816–825. Hopkins, M. 1942. *Cercis* in North America. Rhodora 44: 193–211.

1. Leaf blades coriaceous, leaves thickened (0.15–0.3 mm thick), margins distinctly sinuate, surfaces dull to glossy adaxially, glabrous or hairy abaxially and adaxially; arid regions of Oklahoma, Texas. . . . . 1. *Cercis canadensis* (in part)
1. Leaf blades thin, leaves (0.05–0.25 mm thick) to subcoriaceous, margins flat, surfaces usually dull (sometimes slightly reflective but not glossy), glabrous or hairy abaxially, glabrous adaxially; s Canada, c, e, w United States (including Oklahoma and Texas).
   2. Leaf blade apex usually obtuse to acuminate, sometimes retuse; adaxial surface dull, abaxial surface glabrous or hairy, often much lighter in color; calyx 5–6.8 mm wide; s Canada, c, e United States. . . . . 1. *Cercis canadensis* (in part)
   2. Leaf blade apex emarginate to retuse, adaxial surface dull or slightly reflective, abaxial surface glabrous or hairy, both surfaces nearly concolor; calyx 6.4–10 mm wide; w United States.
      3. Calyx 6.4–9.2 mm wide; banner 3.4–5.3 mm wide, wings 4.7–6.5 mm, keel 5.8–7.5 mm wide; California, Oregon . . . . 2. *Cercis occidentalis*
      3. Calyx 8.4–10 mm wide; banner 4.9–6.3 mm wide, wings 7.2–9 mm, keel 7.2–8.9 mm wide; Intermountain region of Arizona, Nevada, Utah . . . . 3. *Cercis orbiculata*

1. Cercis canadensis Linnaeus, Sp. Pl. 1: 374. 1753 • Eastern redbud F

Siliquastrum canadense (Linnaeus) Medikus

Shrubs or trees. **Stems** gray-brown to red-brown, twigs glabrous or tomentose. **Leaves:** petiole 10–50 mm, glabrous or hairy; blade dull to dark green, membranous, subcoriaceous, or coriaceous, thickened (0.15–0.3 mm) or thin (0.05–0.25 mm), blades cordate, suborbiculate, orbiculate, or reniform, 24–110 × 20–116 mm, base nearly truncate to cordate, margins flat or sinuate, veins 5–9, palmate, prominent, apex obtuse to acuminate, sometimes retuse, surfaces glabrous or hairy abaxially, sometimes restricted to veins or vein axils, glabrous adaxially, sometimes glossy. **Pedicels** glabrous or hairy. **Flowers:** calyx 5–7.6 mm wide; petals usually pink, rarely white, nectar guides magenta, banner 4.4–6.5 × 3–5.8 mm, wings 4.5–7.1 × 3.2–4.8 mm, keel 6.5–9.5 × 4.3–7 mm. **Legumes** dull brown, magenta, or red-brown, 48–109 × 7–21 mm, winged on abaxial suture, sometimes glossy, waxy, surfaces glabrous or hairy.

Subspecies 3 (3 in the flora): North America, n Mexico.

1. Leaf blades thin (0.05–0.25 mm) to subcoriaceous, margins flat, apex acuminate or obtuse, surfaces usually dull (sometimes slightly reflective but not glossy), glabrous or hairy abaxially, glabrous adaxially; s Canada, c, e United States . . . . 1a. *Cercis canadensis* subsp. *canadensis*
1. Leaf blades thickened (0.15–0.3 mm), coriaceous, margins distinctly sinuate, apex obtuse to retuse, surfaces dull or glossy adaxially, glabrous or hairy abaxially and adaxially; arid regions of Oklahoma, Texas.

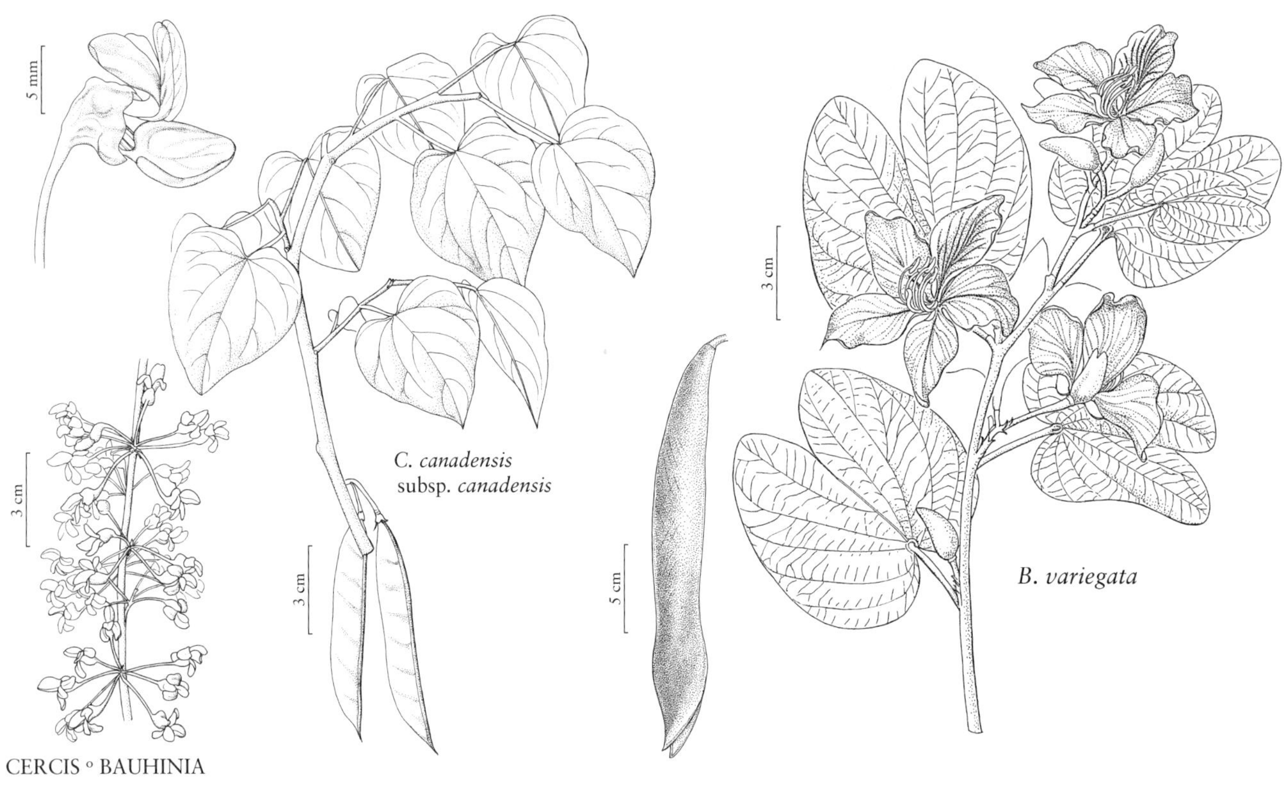

CERCIS ◦ BAUHINIA

[2. Shifted to left margin.—Ed.]

2. Leaf blade abaxial surface, petiole, and twigs tomentose, adaxial surface, flower pedicel, and legumes sparsely hairy, leaf blades averaging 59 × 56 mm; sw Texas in arid environments . . . . 1b. *Cercis canadensis* subsp. *mexicana*
2. Leaf blade abaxial surface, petiole, and twigs glabrous, adaxial surface (glossy), flower pedicel, and legumes glabrous; leaf blades averaging 72 × 75 mm; Oklahoma (Arbuckle Mountains) to w Texas (limestone formations of Edwards Plateau). . . . . .1c. *Cercis canadensis* subsp. *texensis*

1a. Cercis canadensis Linnaeus subsp. **canadensis** [F]

Cercis canadensis var. *pubescens* Pursh; *C. dilatata* Greene; *C. ellipsoidea* Greene; *C. georgiana* Greene

Shrubs or trees. Twigs glabrous. **Leaves:** petiole 19–50 mm, glabrous, or with sparse, pilose hairs distally; blade dull green abaxially, usually darker green adaxially, membranous to subcoriaceous, thin (0.05–0.25 mm), blades suborbiculate to reniform, 47–110 × 56–116 mm, base cordate or nearly truncate, margins flat, apex acuminate or obtuse, surfaces glabrous or hairy abaxially (hairs sometimes restricted to veins or vein axils), glabrous adaxially. **Pedicels** glabrous. **Flowers:** calyx 5–6.8 mm wide; banner 4.7–6.5 × 3.3–5.8 mm, wings 4.5–6.7 × 3.3–4.8 mm, keel 6.5–8.2 × 4.7–7 mm. **Legumes** dull brown, 50–109 × 9–19 mm, mostly glabrous. $2n = 14$.

Flowering Mar–May. Forests, forest edges; 0–1000 m; Ont.; Ala., Ark., Conn., Del., D.C., Fla., Ga., Ill., Ind., Iowa, Kans., Ky., La., Md., Mass., Mich., Miss., Mo., Nebr., N.J., N.C., Ohio, Okla., Pa., S.C., Tenn., Tex., Va., W.Va., Wis.; Mexico (Nuevo León, Tamaulipas).

The only presumed native Canadian record of subsp. *canadensis* is from 1892 on Pelee Island, Ontario, where it was collected by John Macoun and has not been seen since; it occasionally escapes from cultivation in southern Ontario (G. E. Waldron 2003). Reports from Utah are based on casual escapes from cultivation (S. L. Welsh et al. 2008).

Siliquastrum cordatum Moench is an illegitimate, superfluous name that pertains here.

1b. Cercis canadensis Linnaeus subsp. **mexicana** (Rose) A. E. Murray, Kalmia 12: 19. 1982 • Mexican redbud

Cercis mexicana Rose in N. L. Britton et al., N. Amer. Fl. 23: 202. 1930; *C. canadensis* var. *mexicana* (Rose) M. Hopkins

Shrubs or small trees. Twigs tomentose. **Leaves:** petiole 10–34 mm, tomentose, hairs pale brown to rusty brown; blade dull green abaxially, usually darker green adaxially, coriaceous, thickened (0.15–0.3 mm), blades cordate to orbiculate, 24–76 × 39–85 mm (averaging 59 × 56 mm), base nearly truncate to cordate, sinus 4–14 mm deep, margins sinuate, apex obtuse to retuse, surfaces tomentose abaxially, sparsely hairy adaxially. **Pedicels** sparsely hairy. **Flowers:** calyx 5.5–7.6 mm wide; banners 4.4–6.5 × 3–5.3 mm, wings 4.8–7.1 × 3.2–4.3 mm, keel 6.5–9.5 × 4.3–6.2 mm. **Legumes** dull brown, 48–89 × 8–19 mm, sparsely hairy.

Flowering Mar–Apr. Limestone hills, bluffs, forests, forest edges; 300–1500 m; Tex.; Mexico (Coahuila, Nuevo León, San Luis Potosí).

Subspecies *mexicana* is known from the Big Bend region of Texas and is found in Brewster, Crockett, Pecos, Terrell, and Val Verde counties. It is common in xeric environments and is characterized by dull, undulate leaves, and by petioles, leaves, and reproductive structures densely covered with hairs.

1c. Cercis canadensis Linnaeus subsp. **texensis** (S. Watson) A. E. Murray, Kalmia 12: 19. 1982 • Texas redbud [E]

Cercis occidentalis Torrey ex A. Gray var. *texensis* S. Watson, Smithsonian Misc. Collect. 258: 209. 1878; *C. canadensis* var. *texensis* (S. Watson) M. Hopkins; *C. nitida* Greene; *C. texensis* (S. Watson) Sargent

Shrubs. Twigs glabrous. **Leaves:** petiole 17–41 mm, glabrous; blade pale green abaxially, dark green, glossy, and reflective adaxially, coriaceous, thickened (0.15–0.3 mm), blades orbiculate to reniform, 26–97 × 20–104 mm (averaging 72 × 75 mm), base cordate, sinus 5–22.5 mm deep, margins sinuate, apex obtuse to retuse, surfaces glabrous. **Pedicels** glabrous. **Flowers:** calyx 5.6–5.9 mm wide; banner 4.5–6.3 × 3.3–4.4 mm, wings 4.7–6.5 × 3.4–3.6 mm, keel 7–8.5 × 4.4–6.2 mm. **Legumes** magenta to red-brown, 53–95 × 7–21 mm, glabrous, glossy waxy.

Flowering Mar–Apr. Limestone bluffs, canyons; 100–800 m; Okla., Tex.

Subspecies *texensis* ranges from the Arbuckle Mountains of south-central Oklahoma south and west through Texas to Kinney and Val Verde counties. It is found on limestone bluffs and is characterized by coriaceous, glossy, and undulate leaf blades, and glabrous leaves and twigs. The taxon is morphologically distinct, yet it apparently readily hybridizes with subspp. *canadensis* and *mexicana* along contact zones.

Cercis reniformis Engelmann ex A. Gray is an invalid name that pertains here.

2. Cercis occidentalis Torrey ex A. Gray, Boston J. Nat. Hist. 6: 177. 1850 • Western redbud

Cercis californica Torrey ex Bentham; *C. latissima* Greene; *C. nephrophylla* Greene; *Siliquastrum occidentale* (Torrey ex A. Gray) Greene

Shrubs or small trees. Stems gray-brown, twigs glabrous. **Leaves:** petiole 8.5–35 mm, glabrous; blade dull green, subcoriaceous, thin (0.05–0.25 mm), blades orbiculate to reniform, 29–69.5 × 43–93 mm, base cordate, sinus 5–19 mm deep, margins flat, apex emarginate to retuse, surfaces glabrous, sometimes hairy on veins or in vein axils abaxially. **Pedicels** glabrous. **Flowers:** calyx 6.4–9.2 mm wide; petals pink, nectar guides magenta, banner 4.7–7.1 × 3.4–5.3 mm, wings 4.7–6.5 × 3.5–5.4 mm, keel 6.5–10.2 × 5.8–7.5 mm. **Legumes** red-brown to brown, 49–94 × 9–24 mm. $2n = 14$.

Flowering Feb–Apr. Dry, shrubby slopes, canyons, stream banks, chaparral, foothill woodlands, yellow-pine forests; 0–3000 m; Calif., Oreg.; Mexico (Baja California).

Cercis occidentalis ranges widely in California, but in Oregon it is found only in Jackson County.

Morphological trends of reduced leaf size and broader and shorter fruits were recognized in one population of *Cercis occidentalis* found in the Laguna Mountains east of San Diego (J. A. Ballenger 1992). This area warrants further collections and assessment of both flowering and fruiting specimens.

3. Cercis orbiculata Greene, Repert. Spec. Nov. Regni Veg. 11: 111. 1912 • Intermountain redbud [E]

Cercis canadensis Linnaeus var. *orbiculata* (Greene) Barneby; *C. occidentalis* Torrey ex A. Gray var. *orbiculata* (Greene) Tidestrom

Shrubs or small trees. Stems gray, twigs glabrous. **Leaves:** petiole 19–46 mm, glabrous or sparsely hairy; blade dull green, subcoriaceous, thin (0.05–0.25 mm), blades reniform, 29–79 × 43–93 mm, base cordate, sinus 9–23 mm deep, margins flat, apex emarginate to retuse, surfaces glabrous, sometimes hairy in vein axils abaxially. **Pedicels** glabrous. **Flowers:** calyx 8.4–10 mm wide; petals pink, nectar guides magenta, banner 5.9–7 × 4.9–6.3 mm, wings 7.2–9 × 5–6 mm, keel 9–11.5 × 7.2–8.9 mm. **Legumes** red-brown to brown, 60–105 × 13–19 mm, tapering unequally at ends, distal portion often wider than proximal.

Flowering Mar–Apr. Canyons, dry washes; 600–2200 m; Ariz., Nev., Utah.

Cercis orbiculata occurs in the Intermountain area. It can be found in dry, shady canyons (especially in limestone or sandstone) and is also encountered in hanging gardens and along small streams in riparian woodland habitats. *Cercis orbiculata* is common in the canyons along the Colorado River; it also occurs in cool protected, high elevation canyons in the Sierra Ancha Mountains.

Flowers of *Cercis orbiculata* are larger and longer than those of *C. occidentalis.*

Cercis arizonica Patraw and *C. arizonica* Rose ex N. N. Dodge are invalid names that pertain here.

2. BAUHINIA Linnaeus, Sp. Pl. 1: 374. 1753; Gen. Pl. ed. 5, 177. 1754 • Orchid tree [For Caspar Bauhin, 1560–1624, Swiss botanist and physician, and his elder brother, Jean Bauhin, 1541–1612, Swiss botanist; the bilobed leaves symbolizing the brotherly relationship]

Richard P. Wunderlin

Casparia Kunth

Shrubs or trees, usually unarmed (intrastipular spines present in *B. aculeata*). **Stems** ascending [semiscandent], glabrous or young growth pubescent becoming glabrescent. **Leaves** alternate, unifoliolate or bifoliolate; stipules present, caducous [persistent]; petiolate, petiole with basal pulvinus and apical secondary and tertiary pulvini; leaflet(s) 1 or 2, blade 2-lobate [unlobed] when unifoliolate, venation palmate, margins entire, surfaces glabrous, glabrate, or pubescent. **Inflorescences** (1 or)2–10[–15]-flowered, terminal, subterminal, or axillary, racemes [panicles or corymbs], usually appearing after leaves; bract 1; bracteoles 2. **Flowers** caesalpinioid; calyx actinomorphic in bud, closed and becoming spathaceous [splitting to base into 2–5 lobes]; corolla white, pink, pinkish, or purple [green], glabrous or pubescent; fertile stamens 1, 3, 5, or 10, monadelphous or diadelphous [distinct]; anthers dorsifixed, versatile, dehiscing longitudinally [apically or porate]; staminodes 0–9; style filiform or stout. **Fruits** legumes, stipitate, compressed, linear or narrowly ellipsoid, elongate [subreniform], dehiscent [indehiscent], pubescent, glabrate, or glabrous. **Seeds** [1–]5–25[–30], oblong to subglobose [reniform], dull; hilum crescentic, with funicular aril lobes. $x = 14$.

Species 150–160 (4 in the flora): s United States, Mexico, West Indies, Central America, South America, Asia (Malesia), Africa; tropical and temperate areas.

Bauhinia has been treated historically as a diverse, pantropical genus of about 350 species and divided into subgenera, sections, subsections, or series (R. P. Wunderlin et al. 1987). Currently, botanists (for example, G. P. Lewis and F. Forest 2005; Wunderlin 2010) recognize it as consisting of 150–160 species. Following these workers, *Phanera* is treated here as distinct from *Bauhinia.* In the flora area, the former is easily distinguished as consisting of woody vines with axillary tendrils and the calyces split into two distinct segments, in contrast to *Bauhinia*, which are trees or shrubs without tendrils and with spathaceous calyces (rarely 3–5-lobed).

More than 30 species of *Bauhinia* are cultivated in subtropical regions from southern California to Florida (R. B. Ledin and E. A. Menninger 1956); only the four treated here are known to be naturalized in the flora area. Other commonly cultivated species include: *B. acuminata* Linnaeus, *B. divaricata* Linnaeus, *B. forficata* Link, *B. galpinii* N. E. Brown, *B. monandra* Kurz, and *B. tomentosa* Linnaeus. The Hong Kong orchid tree, a sterile hybrid of *B. purpurea* and *B. variegata*, *B.* ×*blakeana* Dunn (*B. purpurea* ×*variegata* 'Blakeana' cv, C. P. Y. Lau et al. 2005), with intermediate flowers, is also commonly cultivated.

Bauhinia species are most commonly planted as ornamentals; the young leaves, flowers, and fruits of some species have been used for food and fodder. Folk medicinal uses of leaves, bark, flowers, and fruits have been described for various species including treatments for respiratory problems, skin diseases, hemorrhoids, malaria, worms, and diabetes. A complex of chemicals (alkaloids, flavonoids, glycosides, lectins, and sesquiterpenes) is produced, some of which have been shown in modern studies to have medicinal potential. The bark is sometimes removed and used for cordage. The wood of some species is useful; the trees are generally too small to be of importance for timber.

SELECTED REFERENCES Ledin, R. B. and E. A. Menninger. 1956. *Bauhinia*—The so-called orchid trees. Natl. Hort. Mag. 35: 183–200. Sinou, C. et al. 2009. The genus *Bauhinia* s.l. (Leguminosae): A phylogeny based on the plastid *trn*L-*trn*F region. Botany (Ottawa) 87: 947–960.

1. Branches with intrastipular spines; fertile stamens 10 . . . . 1. *Bauhinia aculeata*
1. Branches without intrastipular spines; fertile stamens 1, 3, or 5.
    2. Leaves bifoliolate, or unifoliolate and blades 2-lobate ¾+ length; fertile stamen 1 . . . . 2. *Bauhinia lunarioides*
    2. Leaves unifoliolate and blades 2-lobate ¼–½ length; fertile stamens 3 or 5.
        3. Flower buds clavate, 4- or 5-angled toward apex; fertile stamens 3 . . . . 3. *Bauhinia purpurea*
        3. Flower buds fusiform, not angled; fertile stamens 5 . . . . 4. *Bauhinia variegata*

1. Bauhinia aculeata Linnaeus, Sp. Pl. 1: 374. 1753 • White orchid tree [I]

Subspecies 2 (1 in the flora): introduced, Florida; Mexico, West Indies, Central America, South America.

Bauhinia aculeata consists of two subspecies. The typical subspecies, to which our material is referred, naturally occurs 0–1700 m in open, tropical deciduous forests. Subspecies *grandiflora* (Jussieu) Wunderlin, which occurs in Bolivia, Ecuador, and Peru, is distinguished by larger leaves (to 120 mm) and by flowers with a conspicuously elongated hypanthium (10–)20–50(–80) mm.

1a. Bauhinia aculeata Linnaeus subsp. **aculeata** [I]

Bauhinia albiflora Britton & Rose

Shrubs or trees, to 8 m. **Branches** tomentose when young, soon glabrate, with 1 or 2 slightly curved intrastipular spines to 1 cm. **Leaves** unifoliolate; stipules linear, 4 mm; petiole 0.5–3 cm, tomentose, strigose, or glabrate; blade suborbiculate to broadly lanceolate, 30–60 × 25–50 mm, emarginate or 2-lobate to ⅓(–½) length, base cordate to rounded, 7–9-veined, apex of each lobe rounded to acute, surfaces tomentose, strigose, or glabrate. **Racemes** (1–)3–10-flowered; subterminal and axillary; bract linear, 2–5 mm; bracteoles similar to bract. **Pedicels** 0.5–1 cm. **Flowers:** buds linear-lanceolate, 30–40 mm; hypanthium tubular, 3–10 mm; petals white, narrowly elliptic to obovate, subequal, 30–80(–100) mm; fertile stamens 10, 5 alternate ones shorter; filaments shortly connate basally, 20–60(–75) mm; anthers 4–7 mm;

staminodes 0; gynoecium arcuate, nearly equaling stamens; ovary and gynophore pilose, style glabrate; stigma capitate. **Legumes:** stipe 10–20 mm; linear to narrowly ellipsoid, 70–150 × 15–25 mm. **Seeds** 5–10, brown, oblong to subglobose, 6–11 × 5–8 mm; funicular aril lobes equal, 2–2.5 mm.

Flowering summer. Disturbed sites; 0–50 m; introduced; Fla.; Mexico; West Indies (Lesser Antilles); Central America (El Salvador, Panama); South America (Colombia, Venezuela).

Subspecies *aculeata* is locally escaped in Miami-Dade County.

2. **Bauhinia lunarioides** A. Gray ex S. Watson, Smithsonian Misc. Collect. 258: 205. 1878 • Texas plume, Anacacho orchid tree

Bauhinia congesta (Britton & Rose) Lundell; *B. jermyana* (Britton) Lundell; *Casparia congesta* Britton & Rose; *C. jermyana* Britton

Shrubs, to 4 m. **Branches** loosely strigose when young, soon glabrate. **Leaves** uni- or bifoliolate; stipules broadly lanceolate, 1 mm; petiole 0.5–1(–1.5) cm, loosely strigose; blade broadly ovate to suborbiculate, (10–)15–25(–30) × (15–)20–25(–30) mm, 2-lobate ¾+ length or bifoliolate, base cordate or, rarely, truncate, (5–)11-veined, apex of each lobe rounded, surfaces strigose to glabrate abaxially, glabrous adaxially. **Racemes** 2–6(–10)-flowered; terminal or subterminal; bract lanceolate, 1 mm; bracteoles similar to bract, smaller. **Pedicels** 0.5–1 cm. **Flowers:** buds sometimes purplish tinged, narrowly lanceolate, 10–20 mm; hypanthium cyathiform, 1–2 mm; petals white or pale pink, elliptic-lanceolate to ovate, subequal, 15–25 mm; fertile stamen 1, subequaling petals; filament shortly connate basally with staminodes, 15–25 mm; anther 5–7 mm; staminodes 9, 5–7 mm; gynoecium slightly arcuate, subequaling stamens; ovary and gynophore pilose, style glabrate; stigma capitate. **Legumes:** gynophore 5 mm; linear, 50–80 × 10–20 mm. **Seeds** 5–10, dark brown, oblong, 7–10 × 6–8 mm; funicular aril lobes unequal, 1.5 mm and 0.5 mm.

Flowering spring(–early summer). Desert scrub, on calcareous soils; 400–600 m; Tex.; Mexico (Coahuila, Nuevo León).

In the flora area, *Bauhinia lunarioides* is known from Kinney, Maverick, and Val Verde counties along the lower Rio Grande River.

Bauhinia lunarioides is cultivated in tropical areas, as well as the southern United States.

3. **Bauhinia purpurea** Linnaeus, Sp. Pl. 1: 375. 1753 • Purple orchid or butterfly tree [I]

Trees, to 10 m. **Branches** glabrescent when young. **Leaves** unifoliolate; stipules broadly lanceolate, 1–2 mm; petiole to 2 cm, sparsely strigose; blade suborbiculate, 60–120 × 60–120 mm, 2-lobate ⅓–½ length, base rounded to cordate, 9–13-veined, apex of each lobe rounded to acute, surfaces sparsely hairy abaxially, glabrous adaxially. **Racemes** 6–10-flowered; terminal or subterminal; bract ovate, 1–2 mm; bracteoles similar to bract. **Pedicels** 1–1.5 cm. **Flowers:** buds, clavate, 30–40 mm, 4 or 5-angled mainly toward somewhat twisted apex, velvety; hypanthium tubular, 7–12 mm; petals pink to dark purple, narrowly lanceolate, posterior broader, oblanceolate, subequal, 30–50 mm; fertile stamens 3; filaments shortly connate basally with staminodes, 30–40 mm; anthers 5–7 mm; staminodes 5 or 6, 6–10 mm; gynoecium arcuate, nearly equaling stamens; ovary velvety, style and gynophore glabrous; stigma oblique. **Legumes:** stipe 10 mm; linear, 200–250 × 25–25 mm. **Seeds** 10, brown, subglobose, 15 × 15 mm; funicular aril lobes subequal, 2 mm.

Flowering fall. Disturbed sites; 0–50 m; introduced; Fla.; Asia; introduced also in tropical areas nearly worldwide.

Bauhinia purpurea is widely cultivated and is often naturalized, as in southern Florida.

4. **Bauhinia variegata** Linnaeus, Sp. Pl. 1: 375. 1753 • Mountain ebony [F] [I]

Bauhinia candida Aiton; *B. variegata* var. *alboflava* de Wit; *B. variegata* var. *candida* Voigt; *Phanera variegata* (Linnaeus) Bentham

Trees, to 15 m. **Branches** pubescent or glabrescent. **Leaves** unifoliolate; stipules broadly lanceolate, 1–2 mm; petiole 3–4 cm, glabrous; blade broadly ovate to suborbiculate, 60–160 × 60–160 mm, 2-lobate ¼–⅓ length, base cordate, 11–13-veined, apex of each lobe rounded, surfaces sparsely puberulous abaxially, glaucous, glabrous adaxially. **Racemes** 3–8-flowered; mostly subterminal; bract and bracteoles triangular, minute. **Pedicels** 0.5 cm. **Flowers:** buds fusiform, 3–4 mm; hypanthium tubular, 15 mm; petals white or purple, obovate, subequal, 40–55 mm; fertile stamens 5; filaments shortly connate basally with staminodes, 20–40 mm; anthers 7 mm;

staminodes 1–5, 2–3 mm; gynoecium arcuate, nearly equaling stamens; ovary pubescent (mainly on sutures), style and gynophore glabrous; stigma capitate. **Legumes:** stipe 15 mm; linear, 200–300 × 20–25 mm. **Seeds** 10–25, brown, subglobose, 1–15 × 15 mm; funicular aril lobes subequal, 1 mm.

Flowering fall. Disturbed sites; 0–50 m; introduced; Fla.; Asia; introduced also in tropical areas worldwide.

Bauhinia variegata is widely cultivated worldwide and is often naturalized, as in southern Florida. It is listed as a Category I invasive species by the Florida Exotic Pest Plant Council.

3. PHANERA Loureiro, Fl. Cochinch. 1: 37. 1790 • [Greek *phaneros*, manifest, visible, alluding to well-spread calyx and corolla] [I]

Richard P. Wunderlin

Vines, perennial, woody, unarmed, glabrous throughout [pubescent]. **Stems** twining, with [rarely without] axillary tendrils. **Leaves** alternate, bifoliolate [unifoliolate]; stipules present, caducous [persistent]; petiolate, petiole with basal pulvinus and apical secondary and tertiary pulvini; leaflets 2, blade [2-lobate when unifoliolate], venation palmate, margins entire, surfaces glabrous. **Inflorescences** [1 or 2–]15-flowered, axillary [terminal or subterminal], racemes [panicles or corymbs], usually appearing after leaves; bract 1, subpersistent or caducous; bracteoles 2. **Flowers** caesalpinioid; calyx actinomorphic in bud, splitting into 2[or 3–5] lobes [cup-shaped]; corolla white to pinkish, [purple, yellow, orange, or green]; fertile stamens 3, monadelphous [distinct]; anthers dorsifixed, versatile, dehiscing longitudinally, [apically or porate]; staminodes 7[or 8]; style filiform [stout]. **Fruits** legumes, stipitate, compressed, linear, elongate, [narrowly ellipsoid or subreniform], dehiscent [indehiscent], glabrous. **Seeds** [1–]5–10[–20], subglobose [oblong or reniform], dull; hilum crescentic, with funicular aril lobes. $x = 14$.

Species 90–100 (1 in the flora): introduced, Florida; Asia (Malesia); introduced widely.

Phanera was previously treated as part of *Bauhinia* (R. P. Wunderlin et al. 1987), which recently has been divided into nine genera (G. P. Lewis and F. Forest 2005; Wunderlin 2010). The single *Phanera* species treated here can readily be distinguished from the four species of 2. *Bauhinia* in the flora area on the basis of habit, as discussed under that genus.

SELECTED REFERENCE Hao, G. et al. 2003. Phylogenetics of *Bauhinia* subgenus *Phanera* (Leguminosae: Caesalpinioideae) based on ITS sequences of nuclear ribosomal DNA. Bot. Bull. Acad. Sin. 44: 223–228.

1. Phanera yunnanensis (Franchet) Wunderlin, Phytoneuron 2011-19: 1. 2011 • Yunnan bauhinia [F] [I]

Bauhinia yunnanensis Franchet, Pl. Delavay., 190. 1890

Vines to 15 m. **Stems** slender. **Leaves:** stipules lanceolate, 3 mm; petiole slender, to 3 cm; blade obliquely ovate, 60 × 30 mm, base cordate, apex rounded. **Racemes** lax, elongated; bract subulate, 2 mm; bracteoles similar to bract, smaller, near middle of pedicel. **Pedicels** 2 cm. **Flowers:** buds oblong, 8 mm; hypanthium tubular, 8 mm; calyx splitting into 2 distinct segments; petals narrowly obovate, subequal, 20 mm, claw 5 mm; filaments 25 mm, shortly connate basally with staminodes; anthers 3 mm; staminodes 6–7 mm; gynoecium arcuate, nearly equaling stamens; stigma oblique. **Legumes:** stipe 5 mm; often slightly falcate, 60–150 × 15 mm, acute at both ends, rugulose. **Seeds** dark brown, 6 × 6 mm; funicular aril lobes subequal, 1 mm.

Flowering spring–fall. Disturbed sites; 0–50 m; introduced; Fla.; Asia; introduced also in tropical areas nearly worldwide.

Phanera yunnanensis is frequently cultivated in tropical and subtropical areas and is naturalized in the flora area in Miami-Dade County.

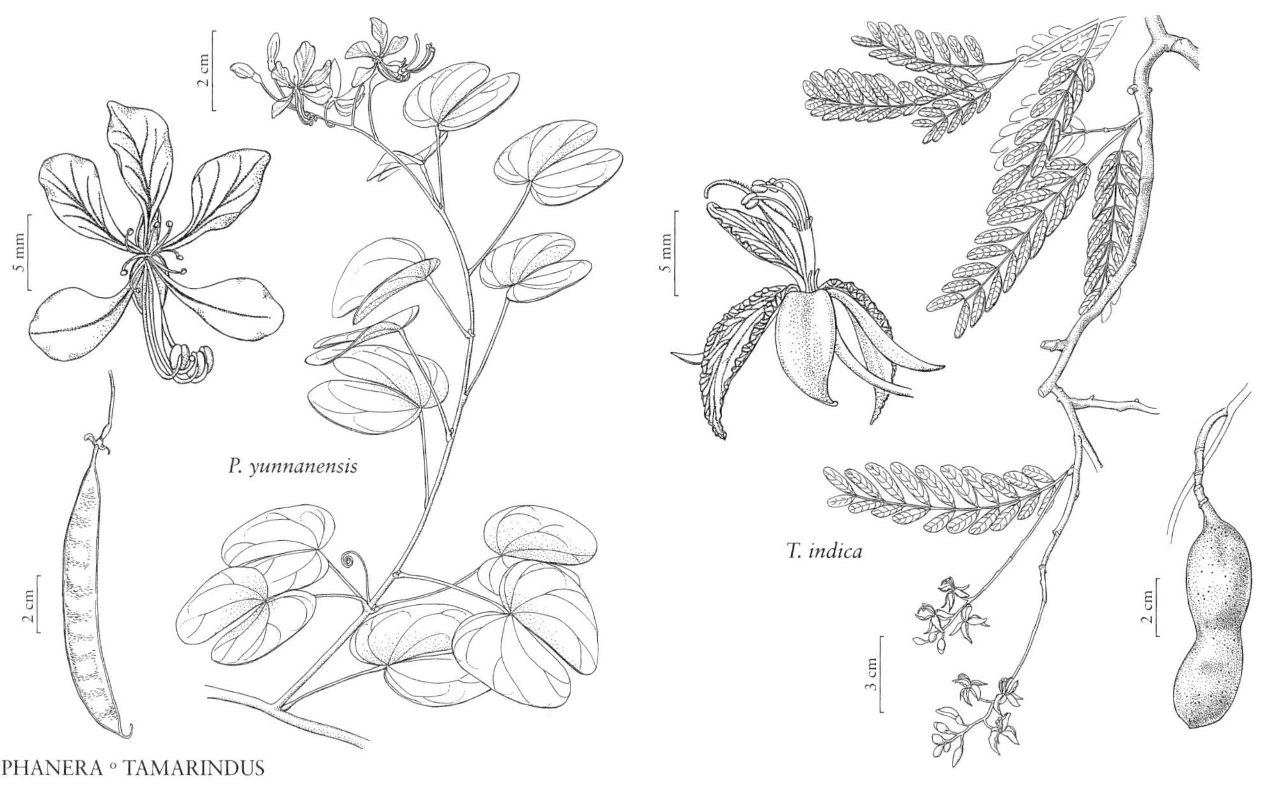

PHANERA ◦ TAMARINDUS

b. FABACEAE Lindley subfam. DETARIOIDEAE Burmeister, Hand. der Naturgesch. 319. 1837 (as Detarieae)

Trees, unarmed. **Extrafloral nectaries** often present abaxially or on leaflet margins. **Stipules** intrapetiolar (between petiole and axillary bud) or lateral, free. **Leaves** pinnate. **Flowers** caesalpinioid, bilateral; sepals connate, lobes 4; petals 5, 2 reduced to scales; stamens 10, filaments connate, anthers dorsifixed; pollen in monads. **Fruits** legumes, indehiscent. **Seeds** with lateral punctiform hilum, complex hilar valve absent, pseudopleurogram present; embryo straight. $x = 12$.

Genera 84, species ca. 760 (1 genus, 1 species in the flora): introduced, Florida; Asia; introduced also in Mexico, West Indies, Central America, South America, Africa; tropical to warm temperate regions.

4. TAMARINDUS Linnaeus, Sp. Pl. 1: 34. 1753; Gen. Pl. ed. 5., 20. 1754 • Tamarind [Arabic *tamar*, date, and *indus*, of India] [I]

Gordon C. Tucker

Brant W. Riegel

Trees, unarmed. **Branches** spreading to ascending. **Stems** densely strigose or villous, glabrescent. **Leaves** ± persistent, alternate, even-pinnate; stipules present, caducous; petiolate; leaflets (8–)10–20(–32), opposite, stipels absent, blade margins entire, surfaces glabrous. **Inflorescences** 5–10(–15)-flowered, terminal, racemes; bracts and bracteoles present. **Flowers** caesalpinioid;

calyx narrowly turbinate, lobes 4; corolla creamy white to yellowish, streaked with red, abaxial 2 petals scalelike, adaxial 3 developed; stamens 10, monadelphous; anthers dorsifixed. **Fruits** legumes, stipitate, compressed, broadly elliptic to oblong, indehiscent, glabrous; mesocarp thick, pulpy. **Seeds** (1–)3–6[–14], obovoid to orbicular; hilum lateral, embryo erect. $x = 12$.

Species 1: introduced, Florida; Asia; introduced also in Mexico, West Indies, Central America, South America, Africa; tropical to warm temperate regions.

1. Tamarindus indica Linnaeus, Sp. Pl. 1: 34. 1753 [F] [I]

Trees 5–10[–25] m; bark brownish gray, shaggy. **Leaves** 3.5–15 cm; stipules linear, 4 × 1 mm, apex acuminate; petiole (3–)5–8(–11) mm, glabrous; rachis straight, (2–)5–10.5 cm; petiolules absent; leaflet blades oblong-elliptic, (8–)12–18(–21) × (3–)4–7(–9) mm, base round to oblique, apex truncate, emarginate, surfaces lustrous. **Inflorescences** lax; axis glabrous; bracts caducous, red-tinged, 2 × 0.5–1 mm, apex truncate or obtuse; bracteoles caducous, paired proximal to calyx, red-tinged, 2 × 1 mm, apex subacute. **Pedicels** (5–)8–12 mm. **Flowers:** calyx 10–12 mm, puberulent; lobes lanceolate, abaxial-most lobe 2 mm longer than 2 lateral lobes, 2 adaxial lobes rounded, connate nearly to apex; petals: abaxial 2 scalelike, adaxial 3 well developed, 10–15 mm; stamens: 3 fertile, 7 sterile and bristlelike; filaments connate ⅔ their length; anthers dehiscing laterally, 2.5 mm; ovary stipitate, stalk adnate to calyx tube, 8 mm, puberulent; style glabrous; stigma terminal, truncate or capitate. **Legumes** (5–)7.5–12[–20] × 2–2.5 cm, base broadly rounded, apex rounded, surfaces rough, leathery in age. **Seeds** dark brown to black, 10–15 mm, glossy, smooth. $2n = 24$ (26, 28).

Flowering spring–summer. Thickets, pinelands; 0–50 m; introduced; Fla.; Asia; introduced also in Mexico, Central America, South America, Africa; worldwide in tropical regions.

Tamarindus indica is planted as an ornamental in southern Florida. Fruits from plants in the West Indies, and those planted or naturalized in North America, are generally shorter and have fewer seeds than those from the Old World. Tamarind is an important tree in most tropical countries. The pulpy mesocarp of the fruits has a pleasant, acidic flavor; it is an essential ingredient in Worcestershire sauce and Caribbean-style jerk sauces.

c. FABACEAE Lindley subfam. CAESALPINIOIDEAE de Candolle, Prodr. 2: 473. 1825

Mimosoideae de Candolle

Trees, shrubs, or herbs, rarely vines, unarmed or armed. **Extrafloral nectaries** often present on petiole or rachis, sometimes stipular or bracteal. **Stipules** lateral, free, or absent. **Leaves** bipinnate, sometimes pinnate or tripinnate, 2-foliolate, or phyllodic. **Flowers** caesalpinioid (noncaesalpinioid in *Ceratonia*) or mimosoid, bilateral or radial; sepals distinct or connate; petals (0 or)5(or 6), distinct or connate; stamens (2–)5–250+, filaments distinct or connate, heteromorphic or some or all sometimes modified or staminodial, anthers basifixed or dorsifixed; pollen in monads, tetrads, or polyads. **Fruits** legumes, dehiscent or indehiscent, or loments (in *Prosopis*). **Seeds** usually with an apical hilum, complex hilar valve absent, pleurogram on each face, open or closed; embryo straight. $x = 7, 8, 9, 11, 12, 13, 26, 28$.

Genera 148, species ca. 4400 (38 genera, 174 species in the flora): nearly worldwide.

SELECTED REFERENCES Barneby, R. C. and J. W. Grimes. 1996. Silk tree, guanacaste, monkey's earring: A generic system for the synandrous Mimosaceae of the Americas. Part 1. *Abarema*, *Albizia*, and allies. Mem. New York Bot. Gard. 74(1): 1–292. Bruneau, A. et al. 2001. Phylogenetic relationships in the Caesalpinioideae (Leguminosae) as inferred from chloroplast *trn*L intron sequences. Syst. Bot. 26: 487–514. Bruneau, A. et al. 2008. Phylogenetic patterns and diversification in the caesalpinioid legumes. Botany (Ottawa) 86: 697–718. Irwin, H. S. and R. C. Barneby. 1981. Cassieae. In: R. M. Pohlhill and P. H. Raven, eds. 1981. Advances in Legume Systematics. Parts 1 and 2. 2 vols. Kew. Vol. 1, pp. 97–106. Irwin, H. S. and R. C. Barneby. 1982. The American Cassiinae. Mem. New York Bot. Gard. 35: 1–918. Polhill, R. M. and J. E. Vidal. 1981. Caesalpinieae.

In: R. M. Polhill and P. H. Raven, eds. 1981. Advances in Legume Systematics. Parts 1 and 2. 2 vols. Kew. Pp. 81–96. Tucker, S. C. 1996. Trends in evolution of floral ontogeny in *Cassia* sensu stricto, *Senna*, and *Chamaecrista* (Leguminosae: Caesalpiniodeae: Cassieae: Cassiinae); a study in convergence. Amer. J. Bot. 83: 687–711. Wunderlin, R. P. 2010. Reorganization of the Cercideae (Fabaceae: Caesalpinioideae). Phytoneuron 2010-48: 1–5. Wunderlin, R. P., K. Larsen, and S. S. Larsen. 1987. Reorganization of the Cercideae (Fabaceae: Caesalpinioideae). Biol. Skr. 28: 1–40.

Key to Genera of Subfamily Caesalpinioideae, Excluding Mimosoid Clade

1. Leaves mostly pinnate (sometimes also bipinnate and unifoliolate).
    2. Corollas absent; inflorescences often on older branches and trunk; leaves even-pinnate; legumes flat with thickened margins . . . . 10. *Ceratonia*, v. 11(1), p. 50
    2. Corollas present; inflorescences not usually on older stems or trunk; leaves even- or odd-pinnate, often bipinnate; legumes flat or cylindric, without thickened margins.
        3. Trees, often armed (with straight or branching thorns); inflorescences spicate clusters; flowers polygamous or dioecious; corollas not obvious; leaves clustered from spurs . . . . 9. *Gleditsia* (in part), v. 11(1), p. 47
        3. Trees, shrubs, or herbs, armed or unarmed; inflorescences not spicate clusters; flowers bisexual; corollas obvious; leaves clustered on spurs or not clustered.
            4. Stamen filaments proximally villous, much longer than anthers; stems photosynthetic, yellowish green; leaves clustered, alternate from spurs, bipinnate but sometimes appearing pinnate; legumes constricted between seeds. . . . . 19. *Parkinsonia* (in part), v. 11(1), p. 68
            4. Stamen filaments glabrous, usually nearly same length as anthers; stems not photosynthetic, brownish (except *Senna armata*); leaves not clustered on spurs, pinnate.
                5. Trees; leaf petiole and rachis without glands; stamens 10, filaments of 3 abaxial stamens sigmoidally incurved, usually longer than anthers; legumes indehiscent, not corrugated over seeds; inflorescences usually terminal . . . . 7. *Cassia*, v. 11(1), p. 45
                5. Herbs, shrubs, or trees; leaf petiole and rachis with or without glands; stamens (2 or)3–10, all filaments straight; legumes dehiscent or indehiscent, often corrugated over seeds; inflorescences terminal or axillary.
                    6. Bracteoles absent; petals subequal; stamens 6–10, usually dwindling from one side to the other; legumes either indehiscent or tardily dehiscent through 1 or both sutures, if the latter then not coiling, or valves breaking into 1-seeded joints; stipules inconspicuous; flowers in axillary racemes, sometimes aggregated into compound racemes; root nodules absent. . . . . 6. *Senna*, v. 11(1), p. 30
                    6. Bracteoles present; petals unequal; stamens (2 or)3–10, radially symmetric or bilateral, equal or irregularly unequal; legumes elastically dehiscent, valves coiling; stipules conspicuous, striate, often persistent; flowers in reduced few-flowered axillary racemes; root nodules present . . . . 5. *Chamaecrista*, v. 11(1), p. 22

1. Leaves bipinnate (sometimes also pinnate, rarely unifoliolate).
    7. Trees; flowers usually unisexual, appearing apetalous, polygamous or dioecious; petals and sepals small and similar, greenish yellow; legumes usually pulpy between seeds.
        8. Trees unarmed; leaves bipinnate, leaflet blade margins entire; inflorescences terminal, racemes or panicles; legumes thick, turgid, woody; seeds 2–5, subglobose . . . . 8. *Gymnocladus*, v. 11(1), p. 46
        8. Trees often armed with simple or branched thorns (cultivars sometimes unarmed); leaves bipinnate in terminal growth, pinnate from spur shoots, leaflet blade margins often crenulate; inflorescences axillary, spicate racemes; legumes usually thin, flat, flexible; seeds 1–25(–30), compressed to subterete . . . . 9. *Gleditsia* (in part), v. 11(1), p. 47

[7. Shifted to left margin.—Ed.]

7. Trees, shrubs, herbs, or vines; flowers bisexual, obviously petalous; petals and sepals easily differentiated; legumes not pulpy between seeds.
 9. Trees, 8–35 m, unarmed.
  10. Corollas yellow, less than 25 mm diam., petals not clawed; calyx imbricate; stigma peltate, broad; stipules 1 mm, triangular, entire; legumes 4–12 cm, margins winged, indehiscent; seeds 1–4 . . . . 18. *Peltophorum*, v. 11(1), p. 67
  10. Corollas scarlet and yellow, 80–100 mm diam., petals clawed; calyx valvate; stigma capitate; stipules 5–15 mm, pinnate; legumes 30–60 cm, margins not winged, dehiscent; seeds 20–40 . . . . 20. *Delonix*, v. 11(1), p. 71
 9. Herbs, shrubs, subshrubs, or small trees to 6 m, armed or unarmed.
  11. Leaves odd-bipinnate.
   12. Leaflet blades not glandular-punctate (inflorescences often conspicuously glandular-pubescent); calyx persistent in fruit . . . . 17. *Hoffmannseggia*, v. 11(1), p. 63
   12. Leaflet blades glandular-punctate; calyx deciduous or persistent in fruit.
    13. Shrubs, trees, or perennial herbs; stipules ovate, lanceolate-ovate to deltate or suborbiculate, usually early deciduous, persistent, or subpersistent; sepals ovate-lanceolate to orbiculate, persistent in fruit; androecium and gynoecium free, not cupped in lower sepal; legumes lanceolate-oblong; leaflet blades eglandular or with conspicuous black, sessile glands along margin, these sometimes sunken in sinuses of crenulated margin . . . . 15. *Erythrostemon*, v. 11(1), p. 56
    13. Shrubs, subshrubs, or perennial herbs; stipules filiform or linear to lanceolate, persistent or tardily deciduous; sepals linear, deciduous in fruit; androecium and gynoecium cupped in the lower sepal; legumes oblong, oblong-lanceoloid, lunate, or ovate; leaflet blades with multiple orange, glandular dots on abaxial surfaces (drying black) . . . . 16. *Pomaria*, v. 11(1), p. 59
  11. Leaves even-bipinnate.
   14. Legumes covered with prickles on faces; seeds ovoid or globose to subglobose, 15–25 mm wide; flowers functionally unisexual, segregated on separate male and female racemes . . . . 14. *Guilandina*, v. 11(1), p. 54
   14. Legumes not covered with prickles; seeds ovoid or ellipsoid, 4–10 mm wide; flowers bisexual.
    15. Legumes indehiscent, compressed or subterete, valves not twisting.
     16. Branches brown or gray-brown; legumes oblong, compressed, ± fleshy, leathery; calyx irregular, abaxialmost sepal covering others in bud; petals yellow, banner with red medial markings . . . . 13. *Tara*, v. 11(1), p. 53
     16. Branches green or yellowish green; legumes oblong to linear, compressed or subterete, sometimes torulose; calyx nearly radially symmetric, valvate, sepal lobes nearly distinct; petals all yellow, banner without red markings . . . . 19. *Parkinsonia* (in part), v. 11(1), p. 68
    15. Legumes dehiscent, valves twisting, laterally-compressed.
     17. Corollas yellow to orange or red; petals glabrous . . . . 11. *Caesalpinia*, v. 11(1), p. 51
     17. Corollas consistently yellow, banner sometimes with red marks; petals pubescent . . . . 12. *Denisophytum*, v. 11(1), p. 52

5. CHAMAECRISTA (Linnaeus) Moench, Methodus, 272. 1794 • Sensitive pea [Greek *chamai*, dwarf, small, and Latin *crista*, crest or tuft, alluding to far-exserted stamens]

Brigitte Marazzi

Cassia [unranked] *Chamaecrista* Linnaeus, Sp. Pl. 1: 379. 1753 (as Chamaecristae); *Cassia* Linnaeus subg. *Absus* (de Candolle) Symon

Herbs, annual or perennial, shrubs, or trees, unarmed; roots with bacterial nodules, rarely from woody rootstock. **Stems** erect, procumbent, or prostrate, branches usually straight, sometimes zigzag, glabrous or pubescent. **Leaves** alternate, even-pinnate; stipules present; petiolate; extrafloral nectaries or glandular hairs present or absent, extrafloral nectaries on petiole, sessile, subsessile, or stipitate, usually cup-shaped; leaflets 1–28(–32)[–40] pairs, blade margins usually entire, surfaces glabrous or pubescent. **Inflorescences** 1–10(–20)-flowered, axillary, racemes, erect; bracts present, inconspicuous; bracteoles 2, caducous or persistent at anthesis. **Flowers** caesalpinioid, asymmetric, enantiostylous; calyx bilateral, lobes 5, persistent; corolla yellow, petals unequal, blades narrowed to claw, claw sometimes red-spotted or orange reddish; stamens (2 or)3–10, equal or irregularly unequal; filaments glabrous, usually nearly equal to anthers; anthers basifixed, dehiscing by apical pores or short slits, lateral sutures ciliolate; ovary shortly stipitate, incurved, linear, often hairy, sometimes glabrous; style usually terminating in minute, stigmatic cavity. **Fruits** legumes, stipitate, flat, straight or curved, linear or linear-oblong, elastically dehiscent, coiling at dehiscence, glabrous or pubescent, often corrugated over seeds. **Seeds** 1–25+, obovoid-ellipsoid to rhomboid or trapezoid. x = 7, 8.

Species ca. 330 (12 in the flora): North America, Mexico, West Indies, Central America, South America, Asia, Indian Ocean Islands (Madagascar, Seychelles), Australia.

Chamaecrista was segregated from the large genus *Cassia* and placed in subtribe Cassiinae, together with *Cassia* in the strict sense and *Senna* (H. S. Irwin and R. C. Barneby 1981, 1982). In recent molecular phylogenetic studies *Cassia* and *Senna* appear as sister taxa (B. Marazzi et al. 2006; A. Bruneau et al. 2008; Marazzi and M. J. Sanderson 2010), whereas *Chamaecrista* appears more distantly related and sister of the monospecific *Batesia* Spruce ex Bentham (Bruneau et al.). Among traditional caesalpinioids, *Chamaecrista* seems to be the only genus possessing rhizobial root nodules (H. D. L. Corby 1988; J. I. Sprent 2001). Flowers of *Chamaecrista* are asymmetric and specialized in relation to buzz pollination (pollen-collecting bees vibrate the flowers to release pollen from the anthers; G. Gottsberger and I. Silberbauer-Gottsberger 1988).

Of the six sections recognized in the current classification of *Chamaecrista* (H. S. Irwin and R. C. Barneby 1982), only sects. *Apoucouita* (H. S. Irwin & Barneby) H. S. Irwin & Barneby and *Xerocalyx* (Bentham) H. S. Irwin & Barneby appear as monophyletic, whereas the monospecific sect. *Grimaldia* (Schrank) H. S. Irwin & Barneby is embedded within sect. *Absus* (de Candolle ex Colladon) H. S. Irwin & Barneby, and sects. *Caliciopsis* H. S. Irwin & Barneby and *Xerocalyx* are nested within sect. *Chamaecrista* (A. Conceição et al. 2009). These molecular phylogenetic analyses suggest that a shift from a relatively species-poor group of rainforest trees to a more diverse and species-rich clade of savannah shrubs occurred early in the diversification history of *Chamaecrista*. The latter clade is composed of two ecologically and morphologically distinct main subclades (Conceição et al.). Almost 81% of *Chamaecrista* species occur in the Americas (G. P. Lewis et al. 2005).

In North America, *Chamaecrista* is represented by species of sects. *Caliciopsis*, *Chamaecrista*, and *Grimaldia*. All but *C. greggii*, a microphyllous shrub or small tree, are annual or perennial herbaceous plants. The United States represents the northern limit of the geographic distribution of *Chamaecrista* in the Americas.

SELECTED REFERENCE Conceição, A. et al. 2009. Phylogeny of *Chamaecrista* Moench (Leguminosae-Caesalpinioideae) based on nuclear and chloroplast DNA regions. Taxon 58: 1168–1180.

1. Leaflets 1 or 2 pairs.
   2. Leaflets 2 pairs; racemes terminal . . . . 1. *Chamaecrista absus*
   2. Leaflets 1 pair; racemes axillary . . . . 11. *Chamaecrista rotundifolia*
1. Leaflets 2–28(–32)[–40] pairs.
   3. Shrubs or trees, xerophytic, microphyllous; leaflets (2 or)3–5(or 6) pairs . . . . 7. *Chamaecrista greggii*
   3. Herbs, mesophytic, not microphyllous; leaflets 2–28(–32)[–40] pairs.
      4. Leaflets 2–9 or (4 or)5–12 pairs.
         5. Stems usually erect, rarely procumbent, regularly branched . . . . 12. *Chamaecrista serpens*
         5. Stems procumbent or prostrate, long and weakly or not branched.
            6. Sepal venation parallel; leaflets (4 or)5–12 pairs; petals 5–14 mm; Texas . . . . 2. *Chamaecrista calycioides*
            6. Sepal venation reticulate; leaflets 2–5 or (5 or)6–9 pairs; petals 3.5–6.5(–7) or 11–15 mm; peninsular Florida and Florida Keys.
               7. Leaflets (5 or)6–9 pairs; petals to 11–15 mm; Florida Keys . . . . . 8. *Chamaecrista lineata*
               7. Leaflets 2–5 pairs; petals 3.5–6.5(–7) mm; peninsular Florida . . . 10. *Chamaecrista pilosa*
      4. Leaflets (6–)8–28(–32)[–40] pairs.
         8. Stems procumbent or prostate or mat-forming, branches straight or in zigzag pattern; on sandy plains and sand dunes of coastal Texas.
            9. Pedicels 5–15 mm; stipules pale green becoming brownish or yellowish, 3+ times as long as wide; stems rarely from woody rootstock, branches usually straight . . . . 3. *Chamaecrista chamaecristoides*
            9. Pedicels 20–42 mm; stipules green, to 2 times as long as wide; stems often from horizontal, woody rootstock, branches often in zigzag pattern . . . . 6. *Chamaecrista flexuosa*
         8. Stems erect, branches usually straight; wide range of habitats.
            10. Racemes usually 1(or 2)-flowered; pedicels 0.5–4[–16] mm; petals to 3.5–8(–9)[–16] mm . . . . 9. *Chamaecrista nictitans*
            10. Racemes 1–4(or 6)-flowered; pedicels (6–)8–22(–26) mm; petals to (6–)8–23(–26) mm.
               11. Roots horizontal and rhizomelike . . . . 4. *Chamaecrista deeringiana*
               11. Roots not rhizomelike . . . . 5. *Chamaecrista fasciculata*

1. Chamaecrista absus (Linnaeus) H. S. Irwin & Barneby, Mem. New York Bot. Gard. 35: 664. 1982 • Tropical sensitive pea [I]

Cassia absus Linnaeus, Sp. Pl. 1: 376. 1753

Varieties 2 (1 in the flora): introduced, Arizona; s Asia (India); introduced also in w Mexico, Central America; nearly pantropical.

Chamaecrista absus appears to be known since 1640 from a plant in Egypt (probably cultivated), called the Absus of Prosper Alpinus. The origin of the species is unclear, as some authors consider it likely to be native in the Old World and introduced in the New World, where it occurs in scattered and discontinuous populations (H. S. Irwin and R. C. Barneby 1977, 1982); others argue that the status depends from the variety considered (R. McVaugh 1987).

1a. Chamaecrista absus (Linnaeus) H. S. Irwin & Barneby var. **meonandra** (H. S. Irwin & Barneby) H. S. Irwin & Barneby, Mem. New York Bot. Gard. 35: 664. 1982 [I]

Cassia absus Linnaeus var. *meonandra* H. S. Irwin & Barneby, Mem. New York Bot. Gard. 30: 282. 1978

Herbs or shrubs, perennial, to 1–2 m. **Stems** erect. **Leaves** (1.5–)2–9(–11.5) cm; petiole (7–)10–15 mm; extrafloral nectary 0, sticky glandular hairs present; leaflets 2 pairs, blades obovate and apices obtuse to rhombic-elliptic or -ovate and apices acute, 8–46 × 5–28 mm. **Racemes** usually 8–20-flowered, terminal. **Pedicels** 1.5–4 mm; bracteoles persistent or late caducous, proximal to calyx. **Flowers:** calyx pale green, sometimes red-tinged, sepal venation reticulate; corolla yellow, fading orange brownish or orange reddish, petals to 4.3–7.2 mm; stamens (2 or)3 or 4, staminodes sometimes 1 or 2; anthers yellow, 1.1–2.8 mm; ovary usually hairy. **Legumes** straight or slightly curved, linear, 22–50 × 5–8 mm. **Seeds** 3.4–5.1 mm. **2*n*** = 28.

Flowering late summer–early spring. Grasslands, disturbed savannas, open places in deciduous forests, stony or sandy arid to semiarid vegetation; 0–1500 m; introduced; Ariz.; Mexico (Baja California Sur, Jalisco, Nayarit, Sinaloa, Sonora); Central America (Costa Rica, Guatemala, Honduras).

Variety *meonandra* may be native to the Americas (R. McVaugh 1987), but it may be that its ancestor colonized North America through long-distance dispersal from Africa, where var. *absus* is considered to be native. Variety *absus* is characterized by a 5-merous androecium, in which 1–3 (fertile) stamens are often smaller in size (H. S. Irwin and R. C. Barneby 1977, 1982).

2. Chamaecrista calycioides (de Candolle ex Colladon) Greene, Pittonia 4: 32. 1899 • Woodland sensitive pea

Cassia calycioides de Candolle ex Colladon, Hist. Nat. Méd. Casses, 125, plate 20, fig. B. 1816

Varieties 2 (1 in the flora): Texas, Mexico, South America.

Variety *lentiformis* H. S. Irwin & Barneby occurs locally in Oaxaca, Mexico, and has minute flowers (the sepals and petals 2.5–3 mm) with 3–5 stamens.

2a. Chamaecrista calycioides (de Candolle ex Colladon) Greene var. **calycioides**

Herbs, perennial, to 0.9 m. **Stems** prostrate, long and weakly branched. **Leaves** 1–4 (–6) cm; stipules persistent; petiole 2–4.5 mm; extrafloral nectary 1(–3), stipitate; leaflets (4 or)5–12 pairs, blades oblong-elliptic, 5–13 × 0.7–2.3 mm. **Racemes** 1–3(or 10)-flowered, axillary. **Pedicels** 1–10(–25) mm; bracteoles persistent, proximal to calyx. **Flowers:** calyx green, sepals lanceolate-acuminate, venation parallel; corolla yellow fading orange, petals to 5–14 mm; stamens 8–10; anthers yellow, to 3.3–6(–7.2) mm; ovary hairy. **Legumes** straight, linear, 25–45 × 3–7 mm. **Seeds** 2.4–3.1 mm. **2*n*** = 16.

Flowering mid spring–early fall. Grasslands, sandy soils; 0–600 m; N.Mex., Tex.; Mexico; South America.

Variety *calycioides* is known to occur in southern Texas.

3. Chamaecrista chamaecristoides (Colladon) Greene, Pittonia 4: 29. 1899 • Beach sensitive pea

Cassia chamaecristoides Colladon, Hist. Nat. Méd. Casses, 134. 1816, based on *Cassia chamaecrista* Miller, Gard. Dict. ed. 8, Cassia no. 17. 1768, not Linnaeus 1753

Varieties 3 (1 in the flora): Texas, Mexico.

Chamaecrista chamaecristoides appears to be one of the first flowering plants to colonize coastal sand dunes (especially in the Gulf of Mexico), where it contributes to decreased sand movement, ultimately stabilizing the dunes (M. L. Martinez and P. Moreno-Casasola 1998). Three varieties are recognized in *C. chamaecristoides*. While var. *cruziana* is an annual herb that sometimes survives the winter, the other two varieties, var. *brandegeei* (Britton & Rose) H. S. Irwin & Barneby and var. *chamaecristoides*, are perennials that occur only in Mexico and differ from each other and var. *cruziana* in the width of their pods, 3–4 mm and 5–6 mm, respectively.

3a. Chamaecrista chamaecristoides (Colladon) Greene var. **cruziana** (Britton & Rose) H. S. Irwin & Barneby, Mem. New York Bot. Gard. 35: 773. 1982

Chamaecrista cruziana Britton & Rose in N. L. Britton et al., N. Amer. Fl. 23: 288. 1930

Herbs, annual, forming low mats or low thickets, to 0.5–1.8 m diam. **Stems** straight, rarely from woody rootstock. **Leaves** 1.5–5 cm; stipules pale green becoming brownish or yellowish, 3+ times as long as wide; petiole (2–)2.5–5 (–6.5) mm; extrafloral nectary 1(–3), subsessile or shortly stipitate, very small; leaflets 8–17(or 19) pairs, blades semi-oblong or -obovate, 3–12 × 0.5–2.8 mm. **Racemes** 1–3-flowered, axillary. **Pedicels** 5–15 mm; bracteoles distal to mid pedicel. **Flowers:** calyx brownish or yellowish, sepal venation reticulate; corolla yellow, petals usually very unequal, to 9–17(–19) mm; stamens 10; anthers red, (5.5–)6.5–9(–11) mm; ovary hairy, hairy along sutures, or glabrous. **Legumes** straight, usually linear, (25–)30–65 × 4–5 mm. **Seeds** 3.4–4.3 mm.

Flowering summer–early fall. Dunes, beaches, associated sandy flats; 0–10 m; Tex.; Mexico (Tamaulipas).

Variety *cruziana* has been found along the Texas Gulf coast from Aransas County southward along the coast into Mexico to the Tamaulipas/Veracruz border (H. S. Irwin and R. C. Barneby 1982).

4. Chamaecrista deeringiana Small & Pennell, Bull. Torrey Bot. Club 44: 345. 1917 • Florida Keys sensitive pea [E]

Cassia deeringiana (Small & Pennell) J. F. Macbride

Herbs, perennial, to 0.9 m; roots horizontal, rhizomelike. **Stems** erect, not or weakly branched. **Leaves** 3–8.5 cm; petiole 3–7 mm; extrafloral nectary 1, subsessile or shortly stipitate; leaflets 8–18(–20) pairs, blades lanceolate- or linear-oblong, 9–20 × 2–3.3 mm. **Racemes** 1–4-flowered, supra-axillary. **Pedicels** (6–)8–22(–26) mm; bracteoles distal to mid pedicel. **Flowers:** calyx greenish, sepal venation reticulate; corolla rich yellow, petals all or some reddish spotted at claw, to (6–)8–22(–26) mm; stamens 10; anthers all or some yellow, dull reddish, or both, to 8–10.5 mm; ovary often hairy, sometimes glabrous. **Legumes** straight or slightly curved, linear, 35–75(–85) × 4.5–6 mm. **Seeds** (2.8–)3.2–4.8 mm.

Flowering spring–mid summer. Pine and pine-oak forests; 0–200 m; Ala., Fla., Ga., Miss.

The horizontal root system of *Chamaecrista deeringiana*, the only feature distinguishing this species from sympatric specimens of *C. fasciculata*, is interpreted as an adaptation to its fire-prone habitat.

Chamaecrista deeringiana is locally abundant in central and southern peninsular Florida, and in western Florida northward into Baldwin County, Alabama; it has also been documented from Peach and Taylor counties, Georgia, and Harrison County, Mississippi.

5. Chamaecrista fasciculata (Michaux) Greene, Pittonia 3: 242. 1897 (as fascicularis) • Partridge pea [E] [W]

Cassia fasciculata Michaux, Fl. Bor.-Amer. 1: 262. 1803; *C. brachiata* (Pollard) J. F. Macbride; *C. chamaecrista* Linnaeus var. *robusta* Pollard; *C. depressa* Pollard; *C. fasciculata* var. *depressa* (Pollard) J. F. Macbride; *C. fasciculata* var. *ferrisiae* (Britton) B. L. Turner; *C. fasciculata* var. *macrosperma* Fernald; *C. fasciculata* var. *puberula* (Greene) J. F. Macbride; *C. fasciculata* var. *robusta* (Pollard) J. F. Macbride; *C. fasciculata* var. *rostrata* (Wooton & Standley) B. L. Turner; *C. mississippiensis* Pollard; *C. triflora* Jacquin; *C. venosa* Castiglione ex Zuccagni; *Chamaecrista bellula* Pollard; *C. brachiata* Pollard; *C. camporum* Greene; *C. depressa* (Pollard) Greene; *C. fasciculata* var. *macrosperma* (Fernald) C. F. Reed; *C. ferrisiae* Britton; *C. littoralis* Pollard; *C. mississippiensis* (Pollard) Pollard ex A. Heller; *C. puberula* Greene; *C. robusta* (Pollard) Pollard ex A. Heller; *C. rostrata* Wooton & Standley; *C. tracyi* Pollard

Herbs, annual, rarely overwintering, to 1.4 m; roots not rhizomelike. **Stems** erect. **Leaves** 2.5–11 cm; petiole (2–)2.5–9 mm; extrafloral nectary 1(–3), sessile or shortly stipitate; leaflets (7 or)8–22(–26) pairs, blades linear-oblong, oblong, oblong-oblanceolate, or -elliptic, apex mucronulate to subacute, (5.5–)7–20(–23) × (1.3–)1.5–5(–6) mm. **Racemes** 1–4(or 6)-flowered, supra-axillary. **Pedicels** (6–)8–22(–26) mm; bracteoles distal to mid pedicel. **Flowers:** calyx greenish, sepal venation reticulate; corolla yellow, fading brown or orange, rarely whitish, 2–4 petals with reddish maculate at claw, to 10–23 mm; stamens 10; anthers all or some yellow, yellow and red-tipped, red, red-brown, or red-violet, to (5.5–)6–10.5 mm; ovary often hairy, sometimes glabrous. **Legumes** straight or curved, linear-oblong, (3–)3.5–6.5(–10) × (25–)30–75(–85) mm. **Seeds** (2.8–)3.2–4.8(–6.3) mm. $2n = 16$.

Flowering mid spring–early fall(–winter). Open woods, fields, roadsides, inland and coastal dunes, coastal prairies, disturbed hardwood prairies, tallgrass prairies, sandy patches in shortgrass prairies, pine-savannas, usually in dry, sandy soils; 0–1400 m; Ont.; Ala., Ark., Conn., Del., D.C., Fla., Ga., Ill., Ind., Iowa, Kans., Ky., La., Md., Mass., Mich., Minn., Miss., Mo., Nebr., N.J., N.Mex., N.Y., N.C., Ohio, Okla., Pa., R.I., S.C., S.Dak., Tenn., Tex., Vt., Va., W.Va., Wis.

Due to its high morphological variation, *Chamaecrista fasciculata* has been characterized by a history of shifting species and infraspecific taxonomic boundaries. Even its current definition is not satisfactory (H. S. Irwin and R. C. Barneby 1982), especially considering the high similarity (and probably very close relationship) with other partially sympatric species of *Chamaecrista*, such as *C. chamaecristoides*, which occurs in Texas, and *C. deeringiana* in the southeastern United States. *Chamaecrista fasciculata* also closely resembles *C. nictitans* but can be distinguished by its ovoid-acuminate floral buds, which are globose-ovoid in *C. nictitans*. *Chamaecrista fasciculata* is the first non-papilionoid legume to become a model species in genomics (S. R. Singer et al. 2009). It has been used to address research questions ranging from climate change (J. R. Etterson 2004) to specialized pollination biology (C. B. Fenster 1995) and ant-plant interactions (M. T. Rutter and M. D. Rauser 2004; R. S. Rios et al. 2008).

Cassia chamaecrista Linnaeus is a rejected name that pertains here.

6. Chamaecrista flexuosa (Linnaeus) Greene, Pittonia 4: 27. 1899 [F]

Cassia flexuosa Linnaeus, Sp. Pl. 1: 379. 1753

Varieties 2 (1 in the flora): Texas, Mexico, West Indies, Central America, South America.

Variety *flexuosa* tends to have larger leaves (4–14 cm) with more leaflet pairs (usually 25–65, rarely as few as 20).

6a. Chamaecrista flexuosa (Linnaeus) Greene var. **texana** (Buckley) H. S. Irwin & Barneby, Mem. New York Bot. Gard. 35: 700. 1982 • Texas sensitive pea [F]

Cassia texana Buckley, Proc. Acad. Nat. Sci. Philadelphia 13: 452. 1862; *C. itzana* Lundell; *Chamaecrista texana* (Buckley) Pennell

Herbs, perennial, to 0.5 m; often with horizontal, woody rootstock. **Stems** procumbent or prostrate, branches often zigzag. **Leaves** 1.5–4.5 cm; stipules to 2 times as long as wide; petiole (1–)1.5–5.5(–10) mm; extrafloral nectary 1 or 2, sessile and concealed in petiolar sulcus or shortly stipitate; leaflets 9–21(–25) pairs, blades linear-oblong, -oblanceolate, or oblong-elliptic, 1–8.5 × 0.4–2.1(–2.5) mm. **Racemes** 1 or 2(or 3)-flowered, axillary. **Pedicels** 20–42 mm; bracteoles shortly proximal to calyx. **Flowers:** calyx red-brown, sepal venation reticulate; corolla bright yellow, petals to 10.5–16 mm; stamens 10; anthers yellow, to 4.5–8.5(–9) mm; ovary gray-hairy. **Legumes** straight or slightly curved, linear-oblong, 25–70 × 3.5–5 mm. **Seeds** 3–3.9 mm. $2n = 16$.

Flowering year-round. Dunes, sandy plains, sandy flats behind barrier beaches, roadsides, old fields; 0–500 m; Tex.; Mexico.

Variety *texana* occupies the northern part of the range of the species distributed throughout the Americas to northern Argentina. In the flora area, it is known from Bastrop, Karnes, and Maverick counties.

7. Chamaecrista greggii (A. Gray) Pollard ex A. Heller, Cat. N. Amer. Pl. ed. 2, 5. 1900 • Gregg's sensitive pea

Cassia greggii A. Gray, Smithsonian Contr. Knowl. 3(5): 59. 1852

Varieties 3 (1 in the flora): Texas, n Mexico.

Two exclusively Mexican varieties, var. *macdougaliana* (Rose) H. S. Irwin & Barneby and var. *potosina* (Britton & Rose) H. S. Irwin & Barneby, are distinguished from var. *greggii* by leaflet venation and number of pairs and length of leaflets. While vars. *greggii* and *macdougaliana* commonly have three or more pairs of leaflets, and the leaflets are to 11 mm, var. *potosina* usually has exactly two pairs which are to 11–17 mm. Compared to var. *greggii*, the inner primary leaflet vein on the proximal side of midrib is longer in var. *macdougaliana*, that is, to or beyond the middle of the leaflet blade, and the tertiary venation is absent.

7a. Chamaecrista greggii (A. Gray) Pollard ex A. Heller var. **greggii**

Shrubs or trees, to 3.5 m, microphyllous. **Stems** erect. **Leaves** 0.7–3 cm; petiole (1.5–)2–5.5(–7) mm; extrafloral nectary 1, on petiole or next to first pair of leaflets, shortly stipitate; leaflets (2 or)3–5(or 6) pairs, blades oblong or oblanceolate to oblong-elliptic or obovate, 5–11(–14) × 2–4.2 mm. **Racemes** 1(or 2)-flowered, axillary. **Pedicels** (9–)12–30(–35) mm; bracteoles nearly mid pedicel. **Flowers:** calyx yellowish, petaloid, sepal venation reticulate or apparently absent; corolla yellow, petal to (8–)9–14.5(–16) mm; stamens 10; anthers yellow, 3.4–5.3 mm, similar in size; ovary hairy, at least along sutures. **Legumes** straight or weakly curved, linear-oblong, (25–)30–46(–50) × (5–)6–7.5 mm. **Seeds** 4–5 mm.

Flowering (late winter–)spring–mid fall. Open or shrubby hillsides and thickets, limestone or caliche soils; 20–150 m; Tex.; Mexico (Coahuila, Nuevo León, Tamaulipas).

In the flora area, var. *greggii* is known from Jim Wells and Live Oak counties.

8. Chamaecrista lineata (Swartz) Greene, Pittonia 4: 31. 1899 [F]

Cassia lineata Swartz, Prodr., 66. 1788

Varieties 6 (1 in the flora): Florida, s Mexico, West Indies, n South America (Colombia).

Three of the six varieties of *Chamaecrista lineata* have a narrow geographic distribution: var. *keyensis* is known only from the Florida Keys; var. *pinoi* (Britton & Rose) H. S. Irwin & Barneby is known exclusively in southern Mexico (Chiapas and Oaxaca); and var. *brevipila* (Urban) H. S. Irwin & Barneby is endemic to southeastern Cuba. The remaining three varieties, var. *brachyloba* (Grisebach) H. S. Irwin & Barneby, var. *jamaicensis* (Britton) H. S. Irwin & Barneby, and var. *lineata*, are more widespread in the West Indies and Colombia (H. S. Irwin and R. C. Barneby 1982). In contrast to var. *keyensis*, vars. *brachyloba* and *jamaicensis* possess a stipitate extrafloral nectary with the stalk at least as long as the diameter of the nectary head, and vars. *brevipila*, *lineata*, and *pinoi* are fruticose.

8a. Chamaecrista lineata (Swartz) Greene var. **keyensis** (Pennell) H. S. Irwin & Barneby, Mem. New York Bot. Gard. 35: 756. 1982 • Narrowpod sensitive pea [E] [F]

Chamaecrista keyensis Pennell, Bull. Torrey Bot. Club 44: 344. 1917; *Cassia keyensis* (Pennell) J. F. Macbride

Herbs, perennial, to 0.7(–0.8) m. **Stems** procumbent or prostate, weakly or not branched. **Leaves** 1.7–3.5(–4) cm; petiole 1–5.5 (–6.5) mm; extrafloral nectary 1, sessile subsessile, not sunken in petiole; leaflets (5 or)6–9 pairs, blades oblong-oblanceolate, 7–12 × 2–4.5(–5) mm. **Racemes** 1–3(or 4)-flowered, nearly axillary. **Pedicels** (8–)9–26(–32) mm; bracteoles mid or distal on pedicel. **Flowers:** calyx yellowish, sepal venation reticulate; corolla yellow, petals to 11–15 mm; stamens 10; anthers 7(or 8), smaller ones yellow or sometimes red-dotted, (2 or)3 longer ones red, to 5.5–9 mm; ovary densely hairy. **Legumes** straight or weakly curved, linear, 33–45 × 4.5–5 mm. **Seeds** 2.5–3.8(–4.3) mm.

Flowering spring–early summer(–late summer). Pinelands, limestone soils; 0–10 m; Fla.

Variety *keyensis* is known from Miami-Dade and Monroe counties.

9. Chamaecrista nictitans (Linnaeus) Moench, Methodus, 272. 1794 • Sensitive partridge or wild sensitive pea [W]

Cassia nictitans Linnaeus, Sp. Pl. 1: 380. 1753

Herbs, annual, rarely overwintering, to 0.8(–1)[–1.2] m. **Stems** erect, incurved ascending. **Leaves** (1.5–)2–8(–9) [15–21] cm; petiole (1.5–)2–7 mm; extrafloral nectary 1(or 2), near mid petiole, stipitate; leaflets (6–)8–28(–32)[–40] pairs, blades usually straight, sometimes falcate, linear, narrowly oblong, or oblong-elliptic, (3–)4–26 × 1–3 mm. **Racemes** 1 (or 2)-flowered, axillary. **Pedicels** 0.5–4[–16] mm; bracteoles mid pedicel. **Flowers:** calyx greenish, sepal venation reticulate; corolla yellow, sometimes fading pinkish, petals to 3.5–8(–9)[–16] mm; stamens [2–]4–8 [or 9]; anthers yellow-orange or red, to (1.4–)1.6–3 [–9.5] mm, different sizes; ovary usually hairy throughout, rarely glabrate. **Legumes** straight, linear-oblong, [14–](15–)18–48(–56)[–78] × [2.4–]2.5–5.5 (–5.8) mm. **Seeds** [1.9–](2.2–)2.4–3.4[–3.7] mm.

Varieties 13 (3 in the flora): United States, Mexico, West Indies, Central America, South America (Argentina, Brazil, Paraguay, Peru).

Chamaecrista nictitans is distinguished from the closely similar *C. fasciculata* (and *C. deeringiana*) by its globose-ovoid floral buds, which are ovoid-acuminate in the latter two species. All three varieties in the flora area belong to subsp. *nictitans* and are characterized by two to nine fertile stamens, while all other varieties have ten fertile stamens (they belong to the other subspecies): subsp. *brachypoda* (Bentham) H. S. Irwin & Barneby, subsp. *disadena* (Steudel) H. S. Irwin & Barneby, and subsp. *patellaria* (Colladon) H. S. Irwin & Barneby (H. S. Irwin and R. C. Barneby 1982). The key to varieties in the flora is adapted from Irwin and Barneby.

1. Leaflet blade margins ciliolate, some hairs 0.4+ mm; ovules 8–19. . . . . 9c. *Chamaecrista nictitans* var. *leptadenia*
1. Leaflet blade margins glabrous or hairs to 0.4 mm; ovules 5–10.
   2. Stems and petioles glabrous or hairs whitish, to 0.7 mm . . . . 9a. *Chamaecrista nictitans* var. *nictitans*
   2. Stems and petioles covered with hairs yellow or orange reddish, 1–2.5 mm. . . . . .9b. *Chamaecrista nictitans* var. *aspera*

9a. Chamaecrista nictitans (Linnaeus) Moench var. **nictitans** [E]

Cassia aspera Muhlenberg ex Elliott var. *mohrii* Pollard; *C. multipinnata* Pollard; *C. multipinnata* var. *nashii* Pollard; *C. nictitans* Linnaeus var. *hebecarpa* Fernald; *C. nictitans* var. *leiocarpa* Fernald; *C. procumbens* Linnaeus; *Chamaecrista mohrii* (Pollard) Small ex Britton & Rose; *C. nictitans* var. *commixta* Pollard & Maxon; *C. procumbens* (Linnaeus) Greene

Herbs to 0.7 m. **Stems** glabrous or hairs whitish, to 0.7 mm. **Leaves** 2–7 cm; stipules usually persistent; petiole 2–7 mm; leaflets (6–)8–23(–26) pairs, blades (4–)6–26 × 1–3 mm, margins glabrous or hairs to 0.4 mm. **Pedicels** 0.5–2 mm. **Flowers:** petals to 3.5–6.5(–7) mm; stamens 4 or 5, staminodia 0–2(or 3); anthers to (1.4–)1.7–2.8 mm; ovary usually slightly hairy, rarely glabrate; ovules 5–10. **Legumes** 18–43 × (2.8–)3.2–5.5(–5.8) mm. **Seeds** 2.7–3.4 mm.

Flowering mid summer–winter. Open woods, thickets, sandy fields and pastures, shores, waste places, old fields, cleared land, roadsides; 10–1000 m; Ala., Ark., Del., D.C., Fla., Ga., Ill., Ind., Kans., Ky., La., Md., Mass., Mich., Miss., Mo., N.H., N.J., N.Y., N.C., Ohio, Okla., Pa., R.I., S.C., Tenn., Tex., Vt., Va., W.Va., Wis.

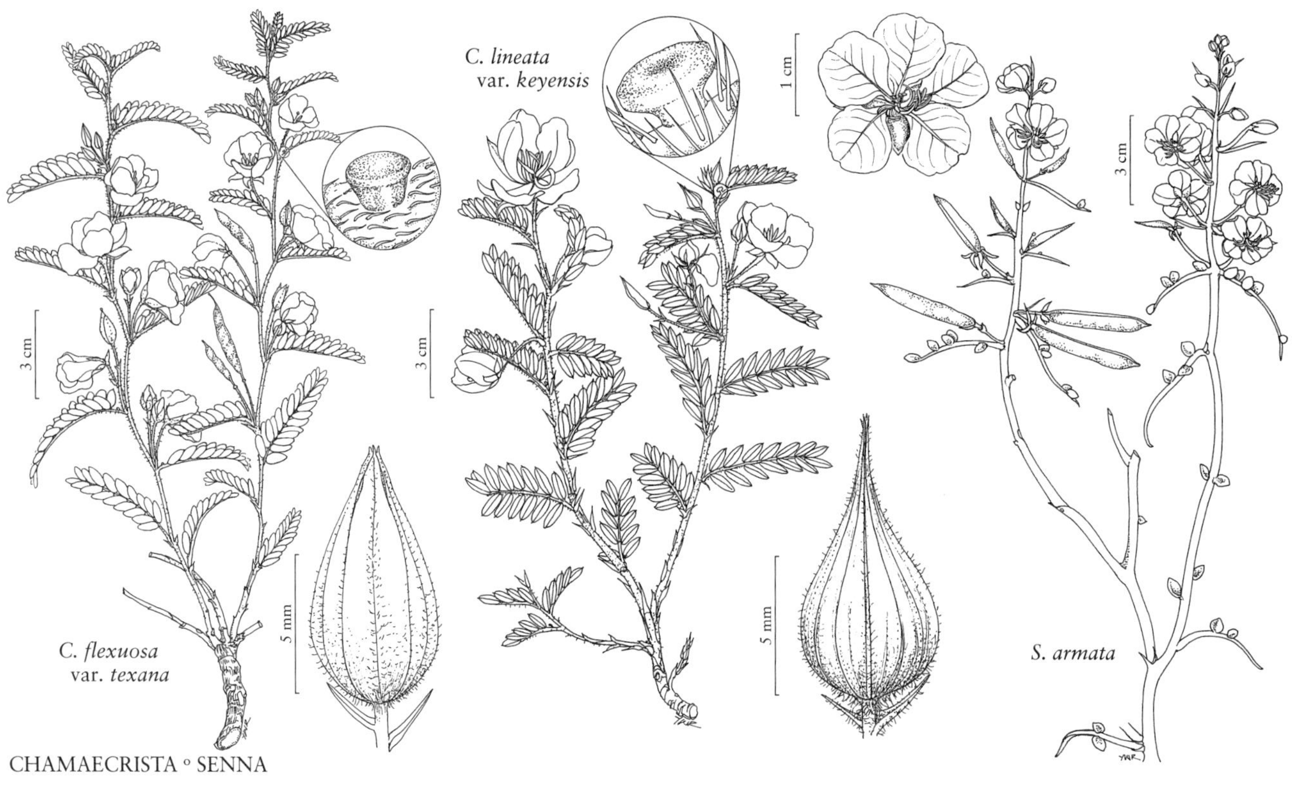

CHAMAECRISTA ∘ SENNA

9b. Chamaecrista nictitans (Linnaeus) Moench var. **aspera** (Muhlenberg ex Elliott) Torrey & A. Gray ex H. S. Irwin & Barneby, Mem. New York Bot. Gard. 35: 838. 1982

Cassia aspera Muhlenberg ex Elliott, Sketch Bot. S. Carolina 1: 474. 1817; *C. nictitans* Linnaeus var. *aspera* (Muhlenberg ex Elliott) Torrey & A. Gray

Herbs to 0.8(–1) m. **Stems** pubescent, hairs yellow or orange reddish, 1–2.5 mm. **Leaves** (1.5–)2–7.5(–9) cm; stipules persistent; petiole (1.5–)2–7 mm, pubescent, hairs yellow or orange reddish, 1–2.5 mm; leaflets (12–) 16–28(–32) pairs, blades 4–14 × 1–2.3 mm, margins glabrous or hairs to 0.4 mm. **Pedicels** 1–2.5 mm. **Flowers:** petals to 5–8(–9) mm; stamens 5–8, staminodia 0–2 (or 3); anthers to 1.6–2.8 mm; ovary slightly hairy throughout; ovules 5–10. **Legumes** (15–)18–32(–36) × (3.5–)4–5.5 mm. **Seeds** (2.2–)2.4–3.3 mm.

Flowering mid summer–mid winter. Sandy pinelands, beaches, dunes, limestone or coral detritus, old fields, along roadsides, ditches, and railways; 0–50 m; Fla., Ga., S.C.; West Indies (Bahamas, Cuba, Grand Cayman, Jamaica); Central America (Honduras).

Variety *aspera* is widespread in Florida, and ranges north along the coastal plain to scattered populations in Georgia and South Carolina.

9c. Chamaecrista nictitans (Linnaeus) Moench var. **leptadenia** (Greenman) Gandhi & S. L. Hatch, Sida 13: 123. 1988

Cassia leptadenia Greenman, Proc. Amer. Acad. Arts 41: 238. 1905; *C. leptadenia* var. *mensalis* Greenman; *Chamaecrista leptadenia* (Greenman) Cockerell; *C. nictitans* var. *mensalis* (Greenman) H. S. Irwin & Barneby

Herbs to 0.6(–0.8) m. **Stems** glabrous or hairs whitish, to 0.7 mm. **Leaves** (2–)2.5–8(–9) cm; stipules usually persistent; petiole (1.5–)2–5(–6) mm, usually glabrous; leaflets (7–)10–22(–25) pairs, blades (3–)4–14 × 1–3 mm, margins ciliolate, some hairs 0.4+ mm. **Pedicels** 0.5–4 mm. **Flowers:** corolla often fading pinkish, petals to 3.5–7(–7.5) mm; stamens (4 or)5–8, staminodia 0; anthers to 2–3 mm; ovary hairy throughout; ovules 8–19. **Legumes** (17–)20–48(–56) × 2.5–3.8(–4) mm. **Seeds** 2.5–3.2 mm.

Flowering mid summer–mid fall. Arid grasslands, desert slopes and washes, thorn-forests, open spaces in pine and oak forests; 10–2000 m; Ariz., N.Mex., Tex.; Mexico (Baja California, Chihuahua, Durango, Guerrero, Jalisco, Nayarit, Oaxaca, Sinaloa, Sonora).

Variety *leptadenia* is known from Cochise, Gila, Graham, Greenlee, Pima, Pinal, and Santa Cruz counties in Arizona, Doña Ana, Grant, Hidalgo, and Luna counties in New Mexico, and Brewster, Jeff Davis, and Presidio counties in Texas.

10. Chamaecrista pilosa (Linnaeus) Greene, Pittonia 4: 28. 1899 • Hairy sensitive pea [I]

Cassia pilosa Linnaeus, Syst. Nat. ed. 10, 2: 1017. 1759; *Disterepta pilosa* (Linnaeus) Rafinesque

Varieties 2 (1 in the flora): introduced, Florida; West Indies, Central America, South America (Brazil).

Variety *luxurians* (Bentham) H. S. Irwin & Barneby is distributed in northeastern Brazil; the leaves usually have 6–11 pairs of leaflets and the extrafloral nectary is conspicuously stipitate.

10a. Chamaecrista pilosa (Linnaeus) Greene var. **pilosa** [I]

Cassia macropoda (Standley) Standley; *Chamaecrista macropoda* Standley

Herbs, perennial, to 1.3 m. **Stems** procumbent, not or weakly branched. **Leaves** 1.5–4.5(–5) cm; petiole 2–6 mm; extrafloral nectary 0 or 1, proximally on petiole, shortly stipitate; leaflets 2–5 pairs, blades oblong-oblanceolate or semi-obovate, 10–24 × 3.5–9(–9.5) mm. **Racemes** 1 or 2(3–6)-flowered, axillary. **Pedicels** (20–)25–50 mm; bracteoles distal to mid pedicel. **Flowers:** calyx greenish yellow or reddish, sepal venation reticulate; corolla yellow, early fading pinkish reddish, petals to 3.5–6.5(–7) mm; stamens 5, staminodes 0–3; anthers yellow or reddish, 3.2–4.5 mm; ovary gray-hairy. **Legumes** straight or slightly curved, linear, (17–)23–47 × 3–4 mm. **Seeds** 2–3 mm. $2n = 16$.

Flowering summer. Savannas, dunes, waste places, roadsides; 0–100 m; introduced; Fla.; West Indies; Central America.

Cassia emarginata Miller is a later homonym that pertains here.

In the flora area, var. *pilosa* is known from Highland, Martin, Palm Beach, and St. Lucie counties.

11. Chamaecrista rotundifolia (Persoon) Greene, Pittonia 4: 31. 1899 • Roundleaf sensitive pea

Cassia rotundifolia Persoon, Syn. Pl. 1: 456. 1805

Varieties 2 (1 in the flora): Florida, Mexico, West Indies, Central America, South America.

Variety *grandiflora* (Bentham) H. S. Irwin & Barneby, which occurs in South America, is distinguished by its relatively larger flowers; the longest petal is 7–17 mm and the longest anther is 5–11.5 mm.

11a. Chamaecrista rotundifolia (Persoon) Greene var. **rotundifolia**

Cassia bifoliolata de Candolle ex Colladon; *C. fabaginifolia* Kunth; *C. monophylla* Vellozo; *C. pentandra* Raddi; *C. pentandria* Larrañaga; *Chamaecrista bifoliolata* (de Candolle ex Colladon) Greene

Herbs, perennial, to 0.1–0.7 m. **Stems** procumbent. **Leaves** (0.3–)0.7–4.5(–5) cm; petiole 2–8(–10) mm; extrafloral nectary 0; leaflets 1 pair, blades obliquely obovate to broadly oblanceolate, 0.5–4(–4.5) × 0.5–1.5(–2) mm. **Racemes** 1–3-flowered, axillary. **Pedicels** (12–)15–45(–60) mm; bracteoles distal to mid pedicel. **Flowers:** calyx greenish, yellowish and partly reddish, or reddish brown, sepal venation reticulate; corolla yellow, drying pinkish brown or orange-brown, petals to 3–6.5(–7) mm; stamens (4 or) 5, staminodes (0 or)1–3; anthers yellow, (1.7–)2–4.4 mm, similar in size; ovary gray-hairy or yellowish hairy. **Legumes** straight or slightly curved, linear-oblong, (15–)20–55(–60) × 3–5(–6) mm. **Seeds** 2.2–3.2(–2.4) mm. $2n = 16$.

Flowering mid summer–late winter. Openings in woods, waste places, roadsides, disturbed forests, lawns, pastures; 0–100 m; Fla.; Mexico (Colima, Jalisco, Michoacán, Nayarit, Oaxaca, Sinaloa); West Indies; Central America; South America.

Variety *rotundifolia* is found in weedy areas in central peninsular Florida.

12. Chamaecrista serpens (Linnaeus) Greene, Pittonia 4: 29. 1899

Cassia serpens Linnaeus, Syst. Nat. ed. 10, 2: 1018. 1759

Herbs, perennial, to 0.4 m. **Stems** usually erect, rarely procumbent, regularly branched. **Leaves** 1–3.5(–4) cm; petiole 2–4 mm; extrafloral nectary 1(or 2), near mid petiole, rarely a second gland on rachis, sessile; leaflets (4 or)5–10(–12) pairs, blades oblong to oblong-oblanceolate, narrowly obovate, or obliquely obovate, apex obtuse or deltate-acute, 3–12 × 1.5–0.4–6.3 mm. **Racemes** 1(or 2)-flowered, axillary. **Pedicels** 12–40(–45) mm; bracteoles distal to mid pedicel. **Flowers:** calyx yellowish, sometimes also partly reddish, sepal venation reticulate; corolla yellow, petals to 5–19(–20) mm; stamens 10; anthers yellow, to 2.5–9.5 mm; ovary loosely hairy. **Legumes** straight, linear-oblong, 14–40(–45) × 2.5–5 mm. **Seeds** 2.3–3(–3.3) mm.

Varieties 7 (2 in the flora): s United States, Mexico, West Indies, Central America, South America.

Of the seven described varieties, var. *wrightii* is the only one native to the flora area. Variety *serpens* is introduced in Florida and is the only small-flowered variety, with the longest petal to 7(–8) mm. Among the large-flowered varieties, var. *delicata* (Britton & Rose) H. S. Irwin & Barneby occurs locally sympatric with var. *wrightii* in Mexico and is distinguished from the latter by its slightly smaller flowers (the longest petal to 12 mm and the longest anther to 5.5 mm). In contrast to vars. *delicata* and *wrightii*, in the remaining large-flowered varieties, the leaves of var. *grandiflora* (Bentham) H. S. Irwin & Barneby, var. *isthmogenes* H. S. Irwin & Barneby, var. *mensarum* (Molina) H. S. Irwin & Barneby, and var. *oaxacana* H. S. Irwin & Barneby usually have only three to seven leaflets pairs.

1. Petals to 5–7 mm; leaflets (4 or)5–7(or 8) pairs; Florida . . . . .12a. *Chamaecrista serpens* var. *serpens*
1. Petals to 13–19(–20) mm; leaflets 7–9(–12) pairs; Arizona, New Mexico. . . . . 12b. *Chamaecrista serpens* var. *wrightii*

12a. Chamaecrista serpens (Linnaeus) Greene var. **serpens** [I]

Leaves 1–3 cm; leaflets (4 or) 5–7(or 8) pairs. **Flowers:** petals to 5–7 mm; anthers to 2.5–4 mm; ovary loosely hairy. **Legumes** 14–32 × 3–5 mm.

Flowering year-round. Savannas, campos, roadsides, waste places; 10–1600 m; introduced; Fla.; West Indies; Central America; South America.

Variety *serpens*, an uncommon plant, is found in central peninsular Florida in Highland, Hillsborough, Lake, and Polk counties.

12b. Chamaecrista serpens (Linnaeus) Greene var. **wrightii** (A. Gray) H. S. Irwin & Barneby, Mem. New York Bot. Gard. 35: 714. 1982 • Wright's sensitive pea

Cassia wrightii A. Gray, Smithsonian Contr. Knowl. 5(6): 50. 1853; *C. palmeri* S. Watson; *Chamaecrista alamosensis* Britton & Rose; *C. chiapensis* Britton & Rose; *C. mazatlensis* Rose; *C. mexiae* Britton; *C. ortegae* Britton; *C. palmeri* (S. Watson) Greene; *C. wrightii* (A. Gray) Wooton & Standley

Leaves 2–3.5(–4) cm; leaflets (6 or)7–10(–12) pairs. **Flowers:** petals to 13–19(–20) mm; anthers to 2.5–9.5 mm. **Legumes** 14–40(–45) × 2.5–3.5(–4) mm.

Flowering late spring–early winter. Dry hillsides and grassy places, coastal plains, desert habitats, pine-oak forests; 0–2100 m; Ariz., N.Mex.; Mexico (Chiapas, Chihuahua, Durango, Guerrero, Jalisco, Sonora).

Variety *wrightii* is known in the flora area from Santa Cruz County in Arizona, and Grant and Luna counties in New Mexico.

6. SENNA Miller, Gard. Dict. Abr. ed. 4, vol. 3. 1754 • [Arabic *sana* or *sena*, splendor, probably alluding either to bright yellow flowers or to use of leaves and pods of *Senna alexandrina* as a gentle laxative]

Brigitte Marazzi

Michael A. Vincent

Cassia Linnaeus sect. *Senna* (Miller) de Candolle ex Colladon; *Cassia* subg. *Senna* (Miller) Bentham

Herbs, annual, biennial, or perennial, shrubs, or trees, unarmed; roots without bacterial nodules. **Stems** erect, glabrous or pubescent. **Leaves** alternate, even-pinnate, mesophyllous to sclerophyllous, rarely phyllodic; stipules present, caducous or persistent; petiolate; extrafloral nectaries 0 or 1–8, on petioles, on rachis between proximal pair of leaflets only, or between proximal and subsequent pairs of leaflets, sessile or stipitate, glandlike and concave; leaflets (or phyllodes) 2–28, blade margins usually entire, surfaces glabrous or pubescent. **Inflorescences** 1–40+-flowered, axillary, racemes, sometimes aggregated into compound racemes, erect; bracts present, usually early or late caducous, rarely persistent at anthesis; bracteoles absent. **Flowers** caesalpinioid, monosymmetric or asymmetric, enantiostylous; calyx usually early or late caducous, rarely persistent after anthesis, bowl- or vase-shaped, lobes 5, greenish to yellowish; corolla yellow to yellow-orange, petals subequal, blades narrowed to claw; stamens 6–10, often heterantherous, with 1 adaxial set of 3 staminodes, 1 middle set of 4 short stamens and 1 abaxial set of 2 or 3 long stamens, or not heterantherous and stamens similar in shape and only slightly different in size; filaments stiff, or arcuate, glabrous, nearly same length as anthers; anthers stiff, basifixed, dehiscing by 1 or 2 apical pores or short slits; ovary shortly stipitate, incurved, linear, usually hairy, rarely glabrous; style linear or incurved, usually terminating in minute stigmatic tip. **Fruits** legumes, stipitate, flat to cylindrical, straight or curved [spiral], often corrugated over seeds, indehiscent or partly dehiscent, glabrous or pubescent. **Seeds** 10–20, ovoid, obovoid, ellipsoid to rhomboid, or pyriform, usually areolate. x = 12, 13, 14.

Species 300–350 (25 in the flora): North America, Mexico, West Indies, Bermuda, Central America, South America, Australia; introduced in Asia, Africa, Atlantic Islands, Indian Ocean Islands, Pacific Islands.

Senna was segregated from the large *Cassia* and placed in subtribe Cassiinae, together with *Cassia* in the narrow sense and *Chamaecrista* (H. S. Irwin and R. C. Barneby 1981, 1982). A number of *Senna* species have been used as purgatives or laxatives, several other species have been cultivated as ornamentals (L. T. F. Colladon 1816; M. A. Luckow 1996), and some have become invasive weeds (Irwin and Barneby 1982). *Senna* is a remarkable example of floral specialization in relation to buzz pollination (that is, pollen-collecting bees vibrate flowers; S. L. Buchmann 1974). The nectarless flowers of *Senna* display a wide range of traits typical of buzz-pollinated flowers: poricidal anthers, heteranthery, point-tipped stigma, and enantiostyly (deflection of the carpel to the left or right) often accompanied by asymmetric corolla and androecium (B. Marazzi et al. 2007; Marazzi and P. K. Endress 2008). Another characteristic feature of *Senna* is the conspicuous glandlike extrafloral nectaries (EFNs) on leaves and, sometimes, also at the base of pedicels in 80% of the species (Irwin and Barneby 1982; Marazzi and M. J. Sanderson 2010). Less well known are recently reported cryptic EFNs embedded within stipules, bracts, and sepals in species previously thought to lack extrafloral nectaries (Marazzi et al. 2013). Extrafloral nectaries offer nectar to ants in return for their protection from insect herbivores (R. R. Fleet and B. L. Young 2000). *Senna* is a relatively old genus with several fossil fruits described from the Eocene (P. S. Herendeen 1992; L. Calvillo Canadell and S. R. S. Cevallos-Ferriz 2005), and probably diverged from its sister *Cassia* in the narrow sense about 50 million years ago (Marazzi and Sanderson). The current classification of *Senna* (Irwin and Barneby 1982), recognizing 35 series in six sections [*Astroites* H. S. Irwin & Barneby, *Chamaefistula* (de Candolle ex Colladon) H. S. Irwin & Barneby, *Paradictyon* H. S. Irwin & Barneby, *Peiranisia* (Rafinesque) H. S. Irwin & Barneby, *Psilorhegma* (Vogel) H. S. Irwin & Barneby, and *Senna*], has been adopted worldwide but received little support in molecular phylogenetic studies, as only sect. *Psilorhegma* is monophyletic (Marazzi et al. 2006).

In North America, all of the sections are represented except for the monospecific *Astroites* and *Paradictyon* from central Mexico and South America, respectively. Several ornamental species are cultivated in warmer areas of North America and may escape, especially in Arizona, California, and Florida, including *Senna bacillaris* (Linnaeus f.) H. S. Irwin & Barneby,

S. corymbosa, *S. didymobotrya* (Fresenius) H. S. Irwin & Barneby, *S. multijuga* (Richard) H. S. Irwin & Barneby, *S. spectabilis* (de Candolle) H. S. Irwin & Barneby, and *S. surattensis*. Currently, *S. corymbosa* and *S. surattensis* are considered naturalized in North America, along with at least another six introduced species. A few of the introductions have regionally been recognized as problematic invasive plants (*S. multiglandulosa* in California and *S. pendula* in Florida), and two other species (*S. obtusifolia and S. occidentalis*) are considered noxious weeds in many countries worldwide.

Two species, *Senna bicapsularis* (Linnaeus) Roxburgh and *S. italica* Miller, have been excluded since all specimens examined were misidentified. Specimens known in North America as *S. bicapsularis* have been confirmed to represent misidentifications or misapplications of *S. pendula* var. *glabrata* (naturalized in North America), as noted by others (D. Isely 1998; R. P. Wunderlin et al., http://florida.plantatlas.usf.edu/; S. M. Landry and K. N. Campbell, unpubl.). The African native *S. italica* was reported as naturalized on chrome ore piles in Maryland (C. F. Reed 1964), but its occurrence in North America is restricted to that single, and rather old, collection report. *Senna italica* lacks glandlike extrafloral nectaries on leaves. The other species in North America without extrafloral nectaries (see key below) are shrubs or small trees with straight fruits, whereas *S. italica* is herbaceous with curved, kidney-shaped fruits.

SELECTED REFERENCES Marazzi, B. et al. 2006. Phylogenetic relationships within *Senna* (Leguminosae, Cassiinae) based on three chloroplast regions: Patterns in the evolution of floral symmetry and extrafloral nectaries. Amer. J. Bot. 93: 288–303. Marazzi, B. et al. 2007. Diversity of anthers and stigmas in the buzz-pollinated genus *Senna* (Leguminosae, Cassiinae). Int. J. Pl. Sci. 168: 371–391. Marazzi, B. and P. K. Endress. 2008. Patterns and development of floral asymmetry in *Senna* (Leguminosae, Cassiinae). Amer. J. Bot. 95: 22–40. Marazzi, B. and M. J. Sanderson. 2010. Large-scale patterns of diversification in the widespread legume genus *Senna* and the evolutionary role of extrafloral nectaries. Evolution 64: 3570–3592.

1. Extrafloral nectaries absent from leaves.
    2. Stipules persistent; inflorescences spikelike racemes, often apparently terminal, bearing flowers in conelike head; bracts conspicuous, covering buds and caducous as pedicel elongates, 10+ mm; corollas monosymmetric, lower and upper petals similar in shape; shrubs, rarely arborescent shrubs . . . . . 1. *Senna alata*
    2. Stipules caducous or persistent; inflorescences not spikelike racemes; bracts early caducous, to 5 mm; corollas highly asymmetric, shape of 1 or both lower petals highly modified, flag-shaped; shrubs or trees.
        3. Leaves 8.5–28.5 cm, leaflet pairs 2–5 . . . . . 4. *Senna atomaria*
        3. Leaves 1.2–3.7 cm, leaflet pairs 3 or 4 . . . . . 25. *Senna wislizeni*
1. Extrafloral nectaries present on leaves at petiole base, or between 1 or more leaflet pairs, or along dorsal (upper) margin of phyllodes, where putative leaflets should be inserted.
    4. Leaves sclerophyllous or xerophytic, usually modified as phyllodes, rarely absent; shrubs.
        5. Stamens 7; staminodes 3; flowers monosymmetric; leaves often irregularly present or absent on same plant; branch tips often acuminate. . . . . 2. *Senna armata*
        5. Stamens 10; staminodes 0; flowers slightly asymmetric, enantiostylous; leaves always present; branch tips not acuminate . . . . . 3. *Senna artemisioides*
    4. Leaves mesophyllous or slightly sclerophyllous, not modified as phyllodes; herbs, shrubs, or trees.
        6. Extrafloral nectaries usually at base of or along petiole or both, rarely also with nectary between leaflet pairs; leaves mesophyllous, leaflet pairs (2–)4–10.
            7. Anthers of abaxial stamens elongated beyond pores, apical appendage conspicuous and linguiform, thickened; extrafloral nectaries usually at base of petiole only (sometimes along petiole or leaflet pairs in *S. ligustrina*).
                8. Bracts longer than bud, often blackish green; leaflets pairs 4 or 5(or 6); branches dark green and blackish . . . . . 17. *Senna occidentalis*
                8. Bracts equal to or shorter than bud, green; leaflet pairs 4–8; branches green.

9. Legumes 120–230 × 2–5 mm; extrafloral nectaries globose egg-shaped; Arizona, New Mexico . . . . 10. *Senna hirsuta*
9. Legumes 70–140 × 5–9 mm; extrafloral nectaries globose-flattened; Florida . . . . 11. *Senna ligustrina*

7. Anthers of abaxial stamens truncate, apical appendage inconspicuous or absent; extrafloral nectaries at base of or along petiole, sometimes between first leaflet pair.
10. Styles apically dilated; extrafloral nectaries usually between first leaflet pair, sometimes on petiole near first pair . . . . 14. *Senna mexicana*
10. Styles not apically dilated; extrafloral nectaries at base of or along petiole.
11. Ovaries densely hairy; ovules 10–16; racemes to 25–37-flowered; legumes 5.5–8 mm wide, each seed compartment nearly as wide as long . . . . .9. *Senna hebecarpa*
11. Ovaries glabrous or slightly hairy; ovules 20–28; racemes usually 5–15-flowered; legumes 7.5–11 mm wide, each seed compartment wider than long . . . . 13. *Senna marilandica*

[6. Shifted to left margin.—Ed.]

6. Extrafloral nectaries not at base or along petiole, usually between leaflet pair; leaves mesophyllous or slightly sclerophyllous, leaflet pairs 1–10.
12. Stamens 10, staminodes 0; androecium heterantherous . . . . 24. *Senna surattensis*
12. Stamens 7, staminodes 3; androecium heterantherous or not.
13. Stamens heterantherous, middle stamens ½ as long as abaxial or smaller; legumes indehiscent, usually pendulous (erect or curved downward in *S. obtusifolia*); herbs, shrubs, or trees, to 1.2–5(–6) m; leaves usually glabrous or slightly hairy, rarely densely hairy.
14. Leaflet pairs 3.
15. Shrubs or trees, to 3.5 m; leaflet blades more than 3 times as long as wide; racemes 4–18-flowered; petals same shape and size, monosymmetric . . . 6. *Senna corymbosa*
15. Herbs, to 1.5(–2.4) m; leaflet blades usually less than 3 times as long as wide; racemes 1 or 2(or 3)-flowered; petals: 1 lower petal conspicuously larger, asymmetric . . . . 16. *Senna obtusifolia*
14. Leaflet pairs 4–9.
16. Leaflet pairs 5–9; extrafloral nectaries between many or all leaflet airs . . . . 15. *Senna multiglandulosa*
16. Leaflet pairs 4 or 5(–7); extrafloral nectaries between first leaflet pair, rarely also second pair . . . . 19. *Senna pendula*
13. Stamens usually not heterantherous, lengths about equal, 3 abaxial ones slightly longer (except heterantherous in *S. lindheimeriana* and *S. orcuttii*); legumes usually dehiscent, erect; herbs, usually perennial (biennial in *S. durangensis*), to 1.5 m; leaves hairy, often densely.
17. Leaflet pairs 2–8.
18. Leaflet pairs 2–4; stipules to 1 mm wide; racemes (2–)4–8-flowered . . . . 7. *Senna covesii*
18. Leaflet pairs (3 or)4–8; stipules 1–3 mm wide; racemes usually 5–25-flowered.
19. Leaflets pallid green; petals to 10.5–16 mm; legumes 5–9 mm wide . . . . 12. *Senna lindheimeriana*
19. Leaflets dull glaucescent; petals to 8–10.5 mm; legumes 3.5–6.5 mm wide . . . . .18. *Senna orcuttii*
17. Leaflet pairs 1.
20. Leaflet blades broadly obovate or oblong-obovate, length usually to 1.8 times width.
21. Calyces caducous; ovules 38–44; legumes with 2 series of seeds . . . 8. *Senna durangensis*
21. Calyces persistent into developing fruit; ovules 16–26; legumes with 1 series of seeds . . . . .20. *Senna pilosior*
20. Leaflet blades lanceolate, oblanceolate, oblong, oblong-elliptic, obovate-elliptic or ovate-oblong, length often more than 2 times width.

[22. Shifted to left margin.—Ed.]

22. Calyces often persistent into developing fruit; ovules 6–12; leaflet blades 2–5 mm wide; herbs to 0.2 m . . . . 21. *Senna pumilio*
22. Calyces caducous; ovules 18–40; leaflet blades (3–)4–16 mm wide; herbs to 0.2–0.7 m.
    23. Leaflet blades lanceolate or lanceolate-oblong, length usually more than 4 times width . . . . .23. *Senna roemeriana*
    23. Leaflet blades oblong, ovate-oblong, oblong-elliptic, or obovate-elliptic, length usually less than 4 times width.
        24. Styles to 1.5 mm, distally dilated; racemes 1–3-flowered. . . . . .5. *Senna bauhinioides*
        24. Styles 3–3.5 mm, linear; racemes 1(or 2)-flowered . . . . 22. *Senna ripleyana*

1. **Senna alata** (Linnaeus) Roxburgh, Fl. Ind. ed. 1832, 2: 349. 1832 • Candlestick senna, emperor's candlesticks [I]

Cassia alata Linnaeus, Sp. Pl. 1: 378. 1753

Shrubs, rarely arborescent, to 4 m. **Leaves** mesophyllous, first leaflet pair often caducous, 20–75 cm, ± glabrous; stipules persistent; extrafloral nectaries 0; leaflet pairs 6–14, blades oblong to obovate, 70–210 × 30–135 mm. **Racemes** 40+-flowered, spikelike, bearing flowers in conelike head, often apparently terminal; bracts conspicuous, covering buds, caducous as pedicel elongates, firm, yellow to light orange, 10+ mm. **Pedicels** 4–11 mm. **Flowers** asymmetric (enantiostylous); calyx yellow; corolla bright yellow to yellow-orange, bowl-shaped, petals monosymmetric, lower and upper petals similar in shape, firm, strongly concave, longest petal 15–24 mm; androecium heterantherous, stamens 7, staminodes 3; anthers of middle stamens 2.6–4 mm, of abaxial stamens 9.5–13 mm, dehiscing by 1 or 2 short slits, apical appendage 0; gynoecium incurved, ovules 44–58; ovary densely hairy; style incurved. **Legumes** ascending, flat, straight or slightly curved, tetragonal, 110–190 × 9–12 mm, carinate by sutures and winged along middle of each valve, tardily dehiscent. **Seeds** dark brown, rhomboid. 2*n* = 24.

Flowering spring–summer. Riverbanks, lakeshores, seasonally wet savannas, disturbed habitats, pastures, plantations, roadsides, waste places; 0–500(–2000) m; introduced; Ala., Fla., La., Miss., Okla., Tex.; n South America; introduced also in Mexico, West Indies, Bermuda, Central America, Asia, Africa, Atlantic Islands, Indian Ocean Islands, Pacific Islands (Hawaii), Australia.

Due to its attractive candlelike yellow inflorescences, *Senna alata* has been cultivated worldwide. In addition to its laxative properties, *S. alata*, sometimes called ringworm senna or ringworm bush, may be useful as a treatment for ringworm and other fungal infections (S. Palanichamy and S. Nagarajan 1990; H. Martin and M'P. Bindanda 2008). Likely native to tropical northern South America (H. S. Irwin and R. C. Barneby 1981), *S. alata* is now naturalized and listed as weedy in many countries outside the flora area (W. T. Parsons and E. G. Cuthbertson 2001; Pacific Island Ecosystems at Risk (PIER) 2006, http://www.hear.org/pier/species/senna_alata.htm).

2. **Senna armata** (S. Watson) H. S. Irwin & Barneby, Mem. New York Bot. Gard. 35: 292. 1982 • Desert or spiny senna [F]

Cassia armata S. Watson, Proc. Amer. Acad. Arts 11: 136. 1876

Shrubs, to 2 m, branches green, often attenuate. **Leaves** sclerophyllous, modified as phyllodes, 2–9 cm, thinly pubescent or glabrate; stipules caducous; extrafloral nectaries (0 or)1 or 2, highly reduced, on rachis, ± sessile; leaflet pairs (0 or)2–8(–10), often irregularly inserted or absent, blades ovate, apex obtuse or subacute, 2–9 × 1–6 mm. **Racemes** 1 or 2-flowered; bracts caducous. **Pedicels** 8–21 mm. **Flowers** monosymmetric; calyx yellow; corolla yellow, longest petal 7.5–13 mm; androecium not heterantherous, stamens 7, staminodes 3; anthers 3–4.3 mm, dehiscing by 1 apical pore, apical appendage 0; gynoecium linear, ovules 6–12; ovary hairy; style incurved. **Legumes** erect, flat or turgid, straight, linear, 20–45 × 5–6.5 mm, not or faintly corrugated over seeds, tardily dehiscent. **Seeds** dark brown, ovoid.

Flowering early spring–summer. Sandy to gravelly desert washes, alluvial fans, flood plains; 150–1800 m; Ariz., Calif., Nev.; Mexico (Baja California).

Representative of the Mohave and Sonoran Deserts, *Senna armata* is the only North American senna displaying a highly xerophytic habit with green, nearly leafless stems (described as rushlike in the desert floras; R. M. Turner et al. 1995). Otherwise, this habit characterizes the unrelated group of a dozen species of *Senna* ser.

Aphyllae (Bentham) H. S. Irwin & Barneby from aridlands in southern South America (H. S. Irwin and R. C. Barneby 1982). Owing to its highly xerophytic habit, *S. armata* was considered taxonomically isolated due to its xerophytic morphology (Irwin and Barneby), but, according to molecular phylogenetic analyses (B. Marazzi et al. 2006; Marazzi and M. J. Sanderson 2010), it is, in fact, included in the same clade as species of ser. *Brachycarpae* (Bentham) H. S. Irwin & Barneby (*S. bauhinioides*, *S. covesii*, *S. lindheimeriana*, and *S. roemeriana*, which also occur in North America).

3. Senna artemisioides (Gaudichaud-Beaupré ex de Candolle) Randell, J. Adelaide Bot. Gard. 12: 220. 1989 • Silver senna [I]

Cassia artemisioides Gaudichaud-Beaupré ex de Candolle in A. P. de Candolle and A. L. P. P. de Candolle, Prodr. 2: 495. 1825

Shrubs, to 3 m. **Leaves** slightly to highly xerophytic as phyllodes, 0.8–5 cm, finely hairy; stipules caducous; extrafloral nectaries 1–8, between first leaflet pair, sometimes also 1 or all subsequent pairs, sessile; leaflet pairs 0–8, blades linear to narrowly elliptic, 20–70 × 1–8 mm. **Racemes** 2–10-flowered; bracts early caducous. **Pedicels** 4–15 mm. **Flowers** slightly asymmetric, enantiostylous; calyx yellowish to greenish; corolla yellow, longest petal 6–10 mm; androecium not heterantherous, stamens 10, staminodes 0; anthers 1.5–5 mm, dehiscing by 2 pores, apical appendage 0; gynoecium incurved, ovules unknown; ovary slightly hairy; style slightly incurved. **Legumes** pendulous, flat, straight or slightly curved, 20–80 × 6–12 mm, corrugated over seeds, indehiscent. **Seeds** dark brown or dull, obovoid. $2n$ = 28, 56.

Flowering late fall–early spring. Rocky and desert sand and soils; 0–700 m; introduced; Ariz., Calif.; Australia.

Due to its remarkable morphological and genetic variation (especially in leaflet number and form), *Senna artemisioides* has a shifting taxonomic history. The species, as circumscribed by Randell, was divided into several morphological forms by B. R. Randell and B. A. Barlow (1998). *Senna artemisioides*, as presented here, encompasses four common morphological forms found in North America: subsp. *filifolia* Randell, subsp. *petiolaris* Randell, nothosubsp. *sturtii* (R. Brown) Randell, and subsp. *zygophylla* Randell. D. E. Symon (1998) considered individuals of subsp. *petiolaris* characterized by arcuate phyllodes to be a separate species, *S. phyllodinea* (R. Brown) Symon, mainly because of the absence of individuals with an intermediate leaf morphology transitioning to the phyllode shape. Although this argument is reasonable, *S. phyllodinea* has not been accepted and adopted in other floristic studies. It must be noted that phyllodes consist of the lateral compression of both the petiole and the rachis, and not only of the petiole, as reported by Randell and Barlow. Along the adaxial margin of the phyllode, there is, in fact, a reduced extrafloral nectary at each insertion place of the suppressed leaflets.

4. Senna atomaria (Linnaeus) H. S. Irwin & Barneby, Mem. New York Bot. Gard. 35: 588. 1982 • Flor de San José [I]

Cassia atomaria Linnaeus, Mant. Pl. 1: 68. 1767; *C. emarginata* Linnaeus

Shrubs or trees, to 20 m. **Leaves** mesophyllous to slightly sclerophyllous, 8.5–28.5 cm, hairy, sometimes densely; stipules caducous; extrafloral nectaries 0; leaflet pairs 2–5, blades bicolored, usually obovate to elliptic, sometimes ovate, 20–130 × 10–60 mm. **Racemes** 5–55-flowered, not spikelike; bracts early caducous, to 5 mm. **Pedicels** 13–28 mm. **Flowers** asymmetric, enantiostylous; calyx greenish to yellow; corolla yellow-orange, slightly dark-veined, longest petal 12–23 mm, highly asymmetric, 1 or both lower petals highly modified, strongly concave and folded over stamens (flag-shaped); androecium slightly heterantherous, stamens 7 (similar in shape and size, abaxial ones slightly longer), staminodes 3; anthers 2.8–5 mm, dehiscing by 2 short slits, apical appendage 0; gynoecium incurved, ovules 46–70; ovary glabrate, sometimes becoming hairy after fertilization; style stout. **Legumes** pendulous, flat, straight, 220–370 × 80–140 mm, woody, indehiscent or splitting transversely into woody segments. **Seeds** reddish brown, obovoid to oblong-obovoid.

Flowering late winter–late spring. Disturbed habitats; 0–20 m; introduced; Fla.; Mexico (Baja California Sur, Campeche, Chiapas, Colima, Guerrero, Jalisco, México, Michoacán, Nayarit, Oaxaca, Quintana Roo, San Luis Potosí, Sinaloa, Sonora, Tabasco, Tamaulipas, Veracruz, Yucatán); Central America (including Caribbean Islands); South America (Colombia, Ecuador, Venezuela).

As with other trees from deciduous and semi-deciduous vegetation, *Senna atomaria* is covered with flowers before developing the foliage (H. S. Irwin and R. C. Barneby 1982). In the flora area, it occurs naturalized only very locally in Collier County (R. P. Wunderlin et al., http://florida.plantatlas.usf.edu/).

5. Senna bauhinioides (A. Gray) H. S. Irwin & Barneby, Phytologia 44: 499. 1979 • Twinleaf senna

Cassia bauhinioides A. Gray, Boston J. Nat. Hist. 6: 180. 1850; *Earleocassia bauhinioides* (A. Gray) Britton

Herbs, perennial, to 0.4 m. **Leaves** slightly sclerophyllous, 1.5–5.5 cm, hairy; stipules caducous; extrafloral nectary 1, between leaflet pair, stipitate or subsessile; leaflet pairs 1, blades obliquely oblong or ovate-oblong, 8–46 × 5–16 mm. **Racemes** 1–3-flowered; bracts caducous. **Pedicels** 3–11 mm. **Flowers** monosymmetric; calyx caducous, yellowish to pale green; corolla yellow, longest petal 5–10 mm; androecium not heterantherous, stamens 7, staminodes 3; anthers to 1.8–2.8 mm, dehiscing by 1 apical pore, apical appendage 0; gynoecium nearly linear, ovules 22–36; ovary densely hairy; style incurved, to 1.5 mm, distally dilated. **Legumes** erect, cylindrical, curved, 17–30(–50) × 4.5–6.5 mm, slightly corrugated over seeds, dehiscing apically downward. **Seeds** brownish olive green becoming gray, paddle-shaped to pyriform.

Flowering mid spring–mid fall. Stony hillsides, plains, bajadas, dry washes; 100–1800 m; Ariz., N.Mex., Tex.; Mexico (Chihuahua, Coahuila, Nuevo León, Sonora).

Senna bauhinioides is one of three sennas in North America that can form and sprout from a woody taproot (along with *S. pumilio* and *S. ripleyana*; H. S. Irwin and R. C. Barneby 1982).

6. Senna corymbosa (Lamarck) H. S. Irwin & Barneby, Mem. New York Bot. Gard. 35: 397. 1982 • Argentine senna [I]

Cassia corymbosa Lamarck in J. Lamarck et al., Encycl. 1: 644. 1785; *Adipera corymbosa* (Lamarck) Britton & Rose

Shrubs or trees, to 3.5 m. **Leaves** mesophyllous, 5.5–9.5 cm, glabrous or glabrate; stipules caducous; extrafloral nectary 1, between first leaflet pair, sessile or short-stipitate; leaflet pairs 3, blades oblong-lanceolate, 25–60 × 5–14 mm. **Racemes** 4–18-flowered; bracts caducous. **Pedicels** 13–23 mm. **Flowers** monosymmetric; calyx brownish to greenish yellow; corolla golden yellow, longest petal 8–16 mm; androecium heterantherous, stamens 7, middle stamens ½ as long as abaxial or smaller, staminodes 3; anthers of middle stamens to 3.6–4.8 mm, of abaxial stamens 5.2–6.5 mm, dehiscing by nearly U-shaped pore, apical appendage inconspicuous; gynoecium incurved, ovules 34–50; ovary hairy; style slightly incurved. **Legumes** somewhat pendulous, cylindrical, straight, 40–120 × 6–10 mm, corrugated over seeds, indehiscent. **Seeds** dull brown or dark reddish brown, obliquely obovoid or oblong-ellipsoid. $2n = 28$.

Flowering early winter–mid spring. Thickets, brushy stream and river banks, waste places; 0–500 m; introduced; Fla., Ga., La., Miss., S.C., Tex.; s South America.

Senna corymbosa has been cultivated for over two centuries and is a common ornamental in many botanical gardens worldwide; it has become naturalized in warmer western Europe and South Africa (H. S. Irwin and R. C. Barneby 1982).

7. Senna covesii (A. Gray) H. S. Irwin & Barneby, Phytologia 44: 499. 1979 • Desert senna, Coues's cassia [W]

Cassia covesii A. Gray, Proc. Amer. Acad. Arts 7: 399. 1868; *Earleocassia covesii* (A. Gray) Britton

Herbs, perennial, to 0.7 m. **Leaves** slightly sclerophyllous, 2–10 cm, hairy; stipules persistent, to 1 mm wide; extrafloral nectaries between all leaflet pairs, stipitate; leaflet pairs 2–4, blades obovate to elliptic-obovate or oblong-elliptic, 10–38 × 5–19 mm. **Racemes** (2–)4–8-flowered; bracts caducous. **Pedicels** 8–17 mm. **Flowers** monosymmetric; calyx pale green, pinkish, or yellowish; corolla golden yellow, longest petal 9–15 mm; androecium not heterantherous, stamens 7, staminodes 3; anthers 2.5–4.2 mm, dehiscing by 1 apical pore, apical appendage 0; gynoecium linear, slightly incurved, ovules 28–42; ovary hairy; style filiform, incurved. **Legumes** erect, cylindrical, slightly curved, 180–350 × 50–80 mm, shallowly corrugated over seeds, dehiscing apically downward. **Seeds** brown, rhomboid.

Flowering late winter–early fall. Sandy and gravelly desert washes, slopes, and stony hills, disturbed desert roadsides; 0–1200 m; Ariz., Calif., Nev., N.Mex.; Mexico (Baja California, Sinaloa, Sonora).

8. Senna durangensis (Rose) H. S. Irwin & Barneby, Phytologia 44: 499. 1979

Cassia durangensis Rose, Contr. U.S. Natl. Herb. 10: 98. 1906

Varieties 2 (1 in the flora): Texas, n Mexico.

Senna durangensis has often been confused with *S. pilosior*, which is characterized by a persistent calyx (H. S. Irwin and R. C. Barneby 1982); see discussion under 20. *S. pilosior* for differences.

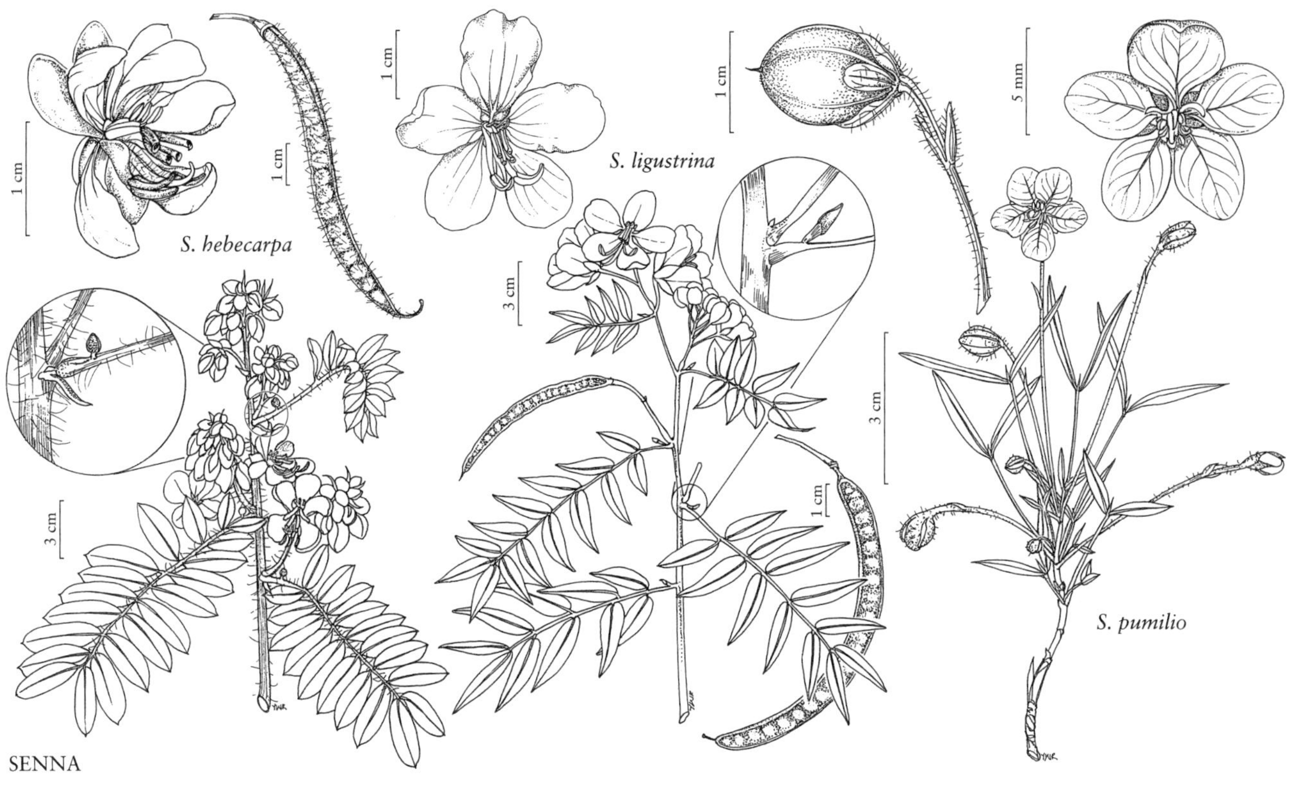

SENNA

8a. **Senna durangensis** (Rose) H. S. Irwin & Barneby var. **iselyi** (H. S. Irwin & Barneby) H. S. Irwin & Barneby, Phytologia 44: 499. 1979 • Isely's senna

Cassia durangensis Rose var. *iselyi* H. S. Irwin & Barneby, Sida 6: 11. 1975

Herbs, biennial, to 0.4 m. **Leaves** slightly sclerophyllous, 1.5–7.5 cm, hairy; stipules tardily deciduous; extrafloral nectary 1, between leaflet pair, subsessile; leaflet pairs 1, blades broadly, obliquely obovate, 20–40 × 14–23 mm. **Racemes** 1 or 2-flowered; bracts caducous. **Pedicels** 6–15 mm. **Flowers** monosymmetric; calyx caducous, pale green; corolla yellow, longest petal 7–12 mm; androecium not heterantherous, stamens 7, staminodes 3; anthers 2.2–3 mm, dehiscing by 1 apical pore, apical appendage 0; gynoecium nearly linear, ovules 38–44; ovary densely hairy; style linear. **Legumes** erect, flat to cylindrical, straight, 20–40 × 5 mm, corrugated over seeds, dehiscing apically downward, with 2 series of seeds. **Seeds** brown or olive brown, paddle-shaped or pyriform.

Flowering mid spring–mid fall. Mesquite thickets, sandy banks, sandy loam soils, alluvial valleys, roadsides; 0–150 m; Tex.; Mexico (San Luis Potosí, Tamaulipas).

Variety *durangensis*, known from northern Mexico, is distinguished from var. *iselyi* by its 2–5-flowered inflorescences and the longest petals 11–13 mm. Variety *iselyi* has been reported from the trans-Pecos region of southern Brewster County, but the identification of materials from that region is tentative (A. M. Powell and R. D. Worthington 2018).

9. **Senna hebecarpa** (Fernald) H. S. Irwin & Barneby, Mem. New York Bot. Gard. 35: 446. 1982 • American senna [E] [F]

Cassia hebecarpa Fernald, Rhodora 39: 413, plate 481. 1937; *C. hebecarpa* var. *longipila* C. F. Reed; *Senna hebecarpa* var. *longipila* (E. L. Braun) C. F. Reed

Herbs, perennial, to 0.8–2.2 m. **Leaves** mesophyllous, 13–23 cm, finely hairy; stipules caducous; extrafloral nectary 1, base of or along petiole, sessile or shortly stipitate; leaflet pairs 6–10, blades elliptic, oblong-elliptic, or lanceolate-elliptic, 30–60 × 10–20 mm. **Racemes** 25–37-flowered; bracts caducous. **Pedicels** 11–22 mm. **Flowers** monosymmetric; calyx pinkish brown; corolla yellow, longest petal 8–12 mm; androecium heterantherous, stamens 7, staminodes 3; anthers of middle stamens 2.6–3.5 mm, of abaxial stamens 4–5 mm, truncate, dehiscing by 2 pores, apical appendage 0; gynoecium incurved, ovules 10–16; ovary densely hairy; style incurved, not dilated.

Legumes ascending, flat, curved downward, 60–115 × 5.5–8 mm, corrugated over seeds, tardily dehiscent, each seed compartment nearly as wide as long. **Seeds** ochre, yellowish brown, or dark reddish brown, ovoid or rhomboid.

Flowering mid summer–early fall. Open woodlands, valley floors, creek banks, swamps, thickets, pastures; 0–500 m; Ont.; Conn., Del., Ill., Ind., Ky., Md., Mass., Mich., Mo., N.H., N.J., N.Y., N.C., Ohio, Pa., Tenn., Vt., Va., W.Va.

10. Senna hirsuta (Linnaeus) H. S. Irwin & Barneby, Phytologia 44: 499. 1979

Cassia hirsuta Linnaeus, Sp. Pl. 1: 378. 1753; *Ditremexa hirsuta* (Linnaeus) Britton & Rose

Varieties 7 (1 in the flora): sw United States, Mexico, South America, Asia, Africa, Pacific Islands, Australia; worldwide in tropical and subtropical regions.

Recent molecular phylogenetic analyses of *Senna hirsuta* (B. Marazzi et al. 2006; Marazzi and M. J. Sanderson 2010) suggest that this species is paraphyletic and may actually represent more than one species.

10a. Senna hirsuta (Linnaeus) H. S. Irwin & Barneby var. **glaberrima** (M. E. Jones) H. S. Irwin & Barneby, Phytologia 44: 499. 1979 • Woolly senna [W]

Cassia leptocarpa Bentham var. *glaberrima* M. E. Jones, Contr. W. Bot. 12: 7. 1908; *Ditremexa glaberrima* (M. E. Jones) Britton & Rose

Herbs, perennial, to 2 m; branches green. **Leaves** mesophyllous, 5.5–18 cm, very finely hairy to glabrate; stipules caducous; extrafloral nectary 1, base of petiole, sessile, globose egg-shaped; leaflet pairs 4–8, blades ovate- or lanceolate-acuminate, 30–80 × 8–32 mm. **Racemes** usually 4–10-flowered; bracts caducous, green, equal to or shorter than bud. **Pedicels** 9–25 mm. **Flowers** monosymmetric; calyx greenish or yellowish; corolla yellow, longest petal 10–15 mm; androecium heteranthcrous, stamens 7, staminodes 3; anthers of middle stamens 3.8–5.4 mm, of abaxial stamens 5–7 mm, elongated beyond pores, dehiscing by 2 pores, apical appendage short, linguiform, thickened; gynoecium incurved, ovules 60–78; ovary hairy; style incurved. **Legumes** ascending, flat, curved, 120–230 × 2.5–4.5 mm, shallowly corrugated over seeds, indehiscent. **Seeds** brown to brownish olive green, obovoid.

Flowering mid summer–mid fall. Washes, riverbeds, thickets, secondary woodlands, grasslands, disturbed pastures, roadsides; 700–2100 m; Ariz., N.Mex.; Mexico (Aguascalientes, Chihuahua, Guanajuato, Jalisco, Michoacán, Morelos, Oaxaca, Sonora, Tamaulipas, Zacatecas).

Varieties *glaberrima* and *leptocarpa* (Bentham) H. S. Irwin & Barneby are the only two varieties in which the adaxial surfaces of leaflets are glabrous or glabrate (H. S. Irwin and R. C. Barneby 1982). However, these two varieties have disjunct distributions, with var. *leptocarpa* occurring locally in northeast Argentina and adjoining regions of Brazil (Irwin and Barneby) and Paraguay (B. Marazzi et al. 2006b).

11. Senna ligustrina (Linnaeus) H. S. Irwin & Barneby, Mem. New York Bot. Gard. 35: 409. 1982 • Privet senna [F]

Cassia ligustrina Linnaeus, Sp. Pl. 1: 378. 1753; *C. bahamensis* Miller; *C. turquinae* (Britton) León; *Ditremexa confusa* Britton; *D. ligustrina* (Linnaeus) B. D. Jackson; *Peiranisia turquinae* Britton

Herbs, perennial, bushy, to 2 m; branches green. **Leaves** mesophyllous, 10–27 cm, glabrous or glabrate; stipules caducous; extrafloral nectaries 1(or 2), base of petiole or, in some leaves, along petiole, sometimes also between first, and rarely subsequent, pair of leaflets, subsessile or shortly stipitate, globose-flattened; leaflet pairs 4–8, blades obliquely lanceolate, 30–70 × 6–22 mm. **Racemes** usually 5–40-flowered; bracts caducous, green, equal to or shorter than bud. **Pedicels** 10–26 mm. **Flowers** monosymmetric; calyx greenish or yellowish; corolla yellow, longest petal 12–25 mm; androecium heterantherous, stamens 7, staminodes 3; anthers of middle stamens to 3.6–5 mm, of abaxial stamens 4–5.8 mm, elongated beyond pores, dehiscing by U-shaped pore, apical appendage short, linguiform, thickened; gynoecium incurved, ovules 36–56; ovary finely hairy; style slightly incurved. **Legumes** ascending, subcylindrical, slightly curved, 70–140 × 5–8.5 mm, corrugated over seeds, indehiscent. **Seeds** olive green or smoke-gray, obovoid to oblong-ellipsoid.

Flowering mid summer–early spring (year-round). Open woodlands, thickets, hammocks, pastures, roadsides; 0–40 m; Fla.; West Indies; Central America (Panama).

12. Senna lindheimeriana (Scheele) H. S. Irwin & Barneby, Phytologia 44: 500. 1979 • Velvetleaf senna

Cassia lindheimeriana Scheele, Linnaea 21: 457. 1848; *Earleocassia lindeheimeriana* (Scheele) Britton

Herbs, perennial, to 1.5 m. **Leaves** slightly sclerophyllous, 6–16 cm, densely hairy; stipules caducous, 1–3 mm wide; extrafloral nectaries between all leaflet pairs, stipitate; leaflet pairs 4–8, blades oblong-elliptic or ovate- to obovate-elliptic, 20–50 × 8–20 mm. **Racemes** usually 5–25-flowered; bracts caducous. **Pedicels** 6–22 mm. **Flowers** monosymmetric; calyx usually pale green or pinkish, rarely yellow; corolla yellow, longest petal 10.5–16 mm; androecium heterantherous, stamens 7, staminodes 3; anthers 3–5.1 mm, dehiscing by 1 apical pore, apical appendage 0; gynoecium linear, ovules 20–28; ovary densely hairy; style incurved. **Legumes** erect, flat, straight, 30–65 × 5–9 mm, shallowly corrugated over seeds, dehiscent. **Seeds** brown, obovoid or oblong-obovoid. **2*n*** = 28.

Flowering spring–fall. Stony hillsides, desert washes, *Larrea* scrub, mesquite grasslands, chaparral; 0–1900 (–2100) m; Ariz., N.Mex., Tex.; Mexico (Chihuahua, Coahuila, Nuevo León, Sonora, Tamaulipas).

13. Senna marilandica (Linnaeus) Link, Handbuch 2: 140. 1829 (as marylandica) • Maryland senna [E] [W]

Cassia marilandica Linnaeus, Sp. Pl. 1: 378. 1753; *C. reflexa* Salisbury; *Ditremexa marilandica* (Linnaeus) Britton & Rose; *D. medsgeri* (Shafer) Britton & Rose; *D. nashii* Britton & Rose; *Senna riparia* Rafinesque

Herbs, perennial, to 0.6–2 m. **Leaves** mesophyllous, 12–27 cm, finely hairy; stipules caducous; extrafloral nectary 1, base of or along petiole, sessile or shortly stipitate; leaflet pairs 5–9, blades elliptic, oblong-elliptic, or lanceolate, 30–60 × 9–24 mm. **Racemes** usually 5–15-flowered; bracts caducous. **Pedicels** 9–17 mm. **Flowers** monosymmetric; calyx pinkish brown; corolla yellow, longest petal 8–14 mm; androecium heterantherous, stamens 7, staminodes 3; anthers of middle stamens 2.6–3.5 mm, of abaxial stamens 4–5 mm, truncate, dehiscing by 2 pores, apical appendage 0; gynoecium incurved, ovules 20–28; ovary glabrous or slightly hairy; style incurved, not dilated. **Legumes** ascending, flat, curved downward, 65–110 × 7.5–11 mm, corrugated over seeds, tardily dehiscent, each seed compartment wider than long. **Seeds** dark reddish brown, obovoid or oblong-obovoid. **2*n*** = 28.

Flowering mid summer–early fall. Open woodlands, valley floors, creek banks, swamps, thickets, pastures; 0–500 m; Ala., Ark., Calif., Conn., D.C., Fla., Ga., Ill., Ind., Iowa, Kans., Ky., La., Md., Mass., Miss., Mo., Nebr., N.J., N.Y., N.C., Ohio, Okla., Pa., S.C., Tenn., Tex., Va., W.Va., Wis.

Senna marilandica is introduced in southern California.

14. Senna mexicana (Jacquin) H. S. Irwin & Barneby, Mem. New York Bot. Gard. 35: 414. 1982

Cassia mexicana Jacquin, Pl. Hort. Schoenbr. 2: 41, plate 203. 1797; *Adipera mexicana* (Jacquin) Britton & Rose

Varieties 5 (1 in the flora): Florida, Mexico, West Indies.

14a. Senna mexicana (Jacquin) H. S. Irwin & Barneby var. **chapmanii** (Isely) H. S. Irwin & Barneby, Mem. New York Bot. Gard. 35: 417. 1982 • Chapman's senna

Cassia chapmanii Isely, Mem. New York Bot. Gard. 25(2): 199. 1975

Herbs, perennial, bushy, to 2.5 m. **Leaves** mesophyllous, 5–14 cm, glabrate; stipules caducous; extrafloral nectary 1, usually between first leaflet pair, sometimes on petiole near first leaflet pair, subsessile or shortly stipitate; leaflet pairs (2–)4 or 5(or 6), blades obliquely lanceolate or lanceolate-elliptic, 24–54 × 6.5–16 mm. **Racemes** usually 3–16-flowered; bracts caducous. **Pedicels** 7–26 mm. **Flowers** monosymmetric; calyx greenish or brownish; corolla yellow, longest petal 9–14 mm; androecium heterantherous, stamens 6, staminodes 3 + 1; anthers of middle stamens to 3.3–5.2 mm, of abaxial stamens 4.6–6.5 mm, truncate, dehiscing by 2 pores, apical appendage inconspicuous; gynoecium incurved, ovules unknown; ovary usually finely hairy, rarely glabrous; style incurved, apically dilated. **Legumes** ascending, sometimes erratically pendulous, compressed subcylindrical, straight, linear, 50–120 × 5–9 mm, slightly corrugated over seeds, tardily dehiscent. **Seeds** brownish olive green, obovoid to oblong-ellipsoid.

Flowering late summer–early spring. Pine savannas, sandy or rocky coastal areas; 0–20 m; Fla.; West Indies (Bahamas, Cuba).

Variety *chapmanii* has fewer pairs of leaflets than var. *berteriana* (Balbis ex de Candolle) H. S. Irwin & Barneby (with 7–16 pairs), non-thickened leaflet margins compared to the thickened margins in var. *shaferi* (Britton & P. Wilson) H. S. Irwin & Barneby, fewer pairs with larger leaflets than var. *mexicana* (with 5–8 pairs, leaflets 13–28 × 4–10 mm), and narrower leaflets (3–4.5 times longer than wide) than var. *latifolia* (Bentham) H. S. Irwin & Barneby (leaflets 1.2–2.4 times longer than wide). While var. *chapmanii* is geographically isolated from vars. *berteriana* and *mexicana*, it co-occurs in the Bahamas with var. *latifolia* and in Cuba with var. *shaferi* (H. S. Irwin and R. C. Barneby 1982).

15. Senna multiglandulosa (Jacquin) H. S. Irwin & Barneby, Mem. New York Bot. Gard. 35: 357. 1982 • Glandular senna [I]

Cassia multiglandulosa Jacquin, Icon. Pl. Rar. 1(3): 8, plate 72. 1783; *C. tomentosa* Linnaeus f.

Shrubs or trees, to 5(–6) m. **Leaves** mesophyllous, 6–17.5 cm, finely and densely hairy; stipules caducous; extrafloral nectaries 1, between many or all leaflet pairs, sessile; leaflet pairs 5–9, blades oblong-elliptic or lanceolate- to oblanceolate-elliptic, 23–47 × 6–17 mm. **Racemes** usually 3–15-flowered; bracts caducous. **Pedicels** 12–26 mm. **Flowers** monosymmetric; calyx yellow; corolla deep yellow, longest petal 12–19 mm; androecium heterantherous, stamens 7, middle stamens ½ as long as abaxial or smaller, staminodes 3; anthers of middle stamens 3.7–5 mm, of abaxial stamens 6–7.5 mm, dehiscing by 2 pores, apical appendage inconspicuous; gynoecium incurved, ovules 30–50; ovary densely hairy; style slightly incurved. **Legumes** somewhat pendulous, cylindrical, 70–135 × 7–10 mm, slightly corrugated over seeds, indehiscent. **Seeds** brown or dark reddish brown, obovoid. $2n$ = 24.

Flowering late spring–mid winter. Open places in disturbed forests or scrub-woodlands, lava-flows, rocky riverbanks and outcrops, waste places; 0–500[2000–3100] m; introduced; Calif.; Mexico (Chiapas, Guanajuato, México, Michoacán, Oaxaca, Puebla, San Luis Potosí); Central America (Guatemala); w South America; introduced also in Asia (India, Malaysia), s Africa, Atlantic Islands (Macaronesia), Pacific Islands (Hawaii, New Caledonia, New Zealand), Australia.

Senna multiglandulosa is listed as naturalized in countries where it has been introduced as an ornamental; for example, New Zealand (C. J. Webb et al. 1988); Australia (B. R. Randell and B. A. Barlow 1998).

16. Senna obtusifolia (Linnaeus) H. S. Irwin & Barneby, Mem. New York Bot. Gard. 35: 252. 1982 • Java-bean, sicklepod [W]

Cassia obtusifolia Linnaeus, Sp. Pl. 1: 377. 1753; *C. tora* var. *humilis* Persoon; *C. tora* var. *obtusifolia* (Linnaeus) Haines; *C. toroides* Rafinesque

Herbs, annual or biennial, to 1.2(–2.4) m. **Leaves** mesophyllous, 3.5–17 cm, pallid green, slightly and finely hairy or glabrous; stipules caducous; extrafloral nectary 1, usually between first leaflet pair, rarely also between second, sessile or shortly stipitate; leaflet pairs 3, blades obovate to cuneate-obovate or broadly cuneate-oblanceolate, 17–65 × 10–40 mm. **Racemes** usually 1 or 2(or 3)-flowered; bracts caducous. **Pedicels** 7–28 mm. **Flowers** asymmetric, enantiostylous; calyx pale green; corolla pale yellow, longest petal 9–15 mm, 1 lower petal conspicuously larger; androecium heterantherous, stamens 7, middle stamens ½ as long as abaxial or smaller, staminodes 3; anthers of middle stamens 1–2.8 mm, of abaxial stamens 2–5 mm, dehiscing by U-shaped slit, apical appendage inconspicuous, cupped; gynoecium incurved, ovules 16–38; ovary hairy; style incurved. **Legumes** erect or curved downward, flat, straight, 60–180 × 2.5–6 mm, faintly corrugated over seeds, indehiscent. **Seeds** dark reddish brown, rhomboid or subcylindroid-oblong. $2n$ = 24, 26, 28.

Flowering late spring–mid winter. Lakeshores, riverbanks, river beds, disturbed habitats, pastures, plantations, orchards, roadsides, waste places; 0–1700 m; Ala., Ark., Calif., Fla., Ga., Ill., Ind., Kans., Ky., La., Md., Mass., Miss., Mo., N.J., N.Y., N.C., Okla., Pa., S.C., Tenn., Tex., Va., W.Va.; introduced in Asia, Africa, Atlantic Islands, Indian Ocean Islands, Pacific Islands, Australia.

Senna obtusifolia is one of the most widespread weedy sennas native to the Americas (H. S. Irwin and R. C. Barneby 1982) and is probably naturalized circumtropically. The species is considered a noxious weed in many countries, posing problems especially for agriculture; it is able to completely invade pastures by dominating grass species, it strongly competes with crops, affecting yields negatively, and, although generally unpalatable to stock, if eaten, it is toxic to cattle. For these reasons, in Australia *S. obtusifolia* is designated as potentially of national concern, and authorities estimate that this invader can lead properties to become unproductive (Weeds of Australia, www.environment.gov.au/cgi-bin/biodiversity/invasive/weeds/weedsearch.pl; Land Protection, www.nrw.qld.gov.au/factsheets/pdf/pest/pp18.pdf). In the flora area, its range of distribution appears to have expanded from five southern and southeastern states in the early 1980s (Florida, Kentucky, Missouri, Texas, and Virginia; Irwin and Barneby) to currently almost half of the states. Although a few specimens were collected as far north as Nebraska and Wisconsin, it is not known to be established in those states.

Senna tora (Linnaeus) Roxburgh (*Cassia tora* Linnaeus) is sometimes considered synonymous with *S. obtusifolia*. However, due to differences in length and curvature of the fruit and in length of the petiole and pedicel, B. R. Randell and B. A. Barlow (1998) considered it distinct. H. S. Irwin and R. C. Barneby (1982) observed a range rather than distinct categories in the measures and shapes of these traits, and only molecular phylogenetic and biogeographic studies accompanied by morphometric analyses may definitively solve this taxonomic dilemma.

17. Senna occidentalis (Linnaeus) Link, Handbuch 2: 140. 1829 • Coffee senna, septic weed [I] [W]

Cassia occidentalis Linnaeus, Sp. Pl. 1: 377. 1753; *Ditremexa occidentalis* (Linnaeus) Britton & Rose

Herbs, perennial, bushy, to 2.2 m; branches dark green and blackish. **Leaves** mesophyllous, 11–26 cm, glabrous or glabrate; stipules caducous; extrafloral nectary 1, base of petiole, sessile or subsessile; leaflet pairs 4 or 5(or 6), blades lanceolate- or ovate-acuminate, 45–100 × 12–38 mm. **Racemes** usually (1 or)2–5-flowered; bracts caducous, longer than bud, often blackish green. **Pedicels** 8–21 mm. **Flowers** monosymmetric; calyx pinkish or fuscous; corolla yellow, longest petal 12–17 mm; androecium heterantherous, stamens 6, staminodes 3 + 1; anthers of middle stamens 3.2–5.2 mm, of abaxial stamens 4.9–6.6 mm, elongated beyond pores, dehiscing by U-shaped pore, apical appendage linguiform, thickened; gynoecium incurved, ovules 40–60; ovary densely hairy; style slightly incurved. **Legumes** ascending, flat, slightly curved or straight, linear, 80–135 × 6.5–9.5 mm, corrugated over seeds, dehiscent. **Seeds** olive green or brownish, obovoid. $2n$ = 26, 28.

Flowering mid summer–early winter. Disturbed habitats, waste places, roadsides; 0–1200 m; introduced; Ala., Ark., Fla., Ga., Ill., Ind., Iowa, Kans., La., Md., Mass., Miss., Mo., N.Y., N.C., Okla., S.C., Tenn., Tex., Va.; Mexico; West Indies; Central America; South America; introduced also in tropical and subtropical Eurasia, Africa, Australia.

Although *Senna occidentalis* is probably native to the tropical New World, the species is now weedy in so many countries worldwide, including also other parts of the New World, that the exact range of its geographic distribution as a native is a matter of speculation (H. S. Irwin and R. C. Barneby 1982). In the flora area, it is considered as naturalized (R. Kral et al. 2012; R. P. Wunderlin et al., http://florida.plantatlas.usf.edu/). In most countries, *S. occidentalis* is considered a noxious weed able to aggressively invade pastures and crop cultivations, posing very similar problems to cattle and agriculture as *S. obtusifolia* (see discussion in 16. *S. obtusifolia*).

18. Senna orcuttii (Britton & Rose) H. S. Irwin & Barneby, Phytologia 44: 500. 1979 • Orcutt's senna [C]

Peiranisia orcuttii Britton & Rose in N. L. Britton et al., N. Amer. Fl. 23: 267. 1930; *Cassia orcuttii* (Britton & Rose) B. L. Turner

Herbs, perennial, to 0.6 m. **Leaves** slightly sclerophyllous, 5–10 cm, dull glaucescent, sparsely hairy; stipules caducous, 1–3 mm wide; extrafloral nectaries between all leaflet pairs, stipitate; leaflet pairs 3–6, blades oblong- or ovate-elliptic, 15–40 × 7–13 mm. **Racemes** usually 5–25-flowered; bracts caducous. **Pedicels** 0–5 mm. **Flowers** monosymmetric (similar to *S. lindheimeriana* but smaller); calyx usually pale green, rarely yellow; corolla yellow, longest petal 8–10.5 mm; androecium heterantherous, stamens 7, staminodes 3; anthers 3–5 mm, dehiscing by 1 apical pore, apical appendage 0; gynoecium linear, ovules unknown; ovary densely hairy; style incurved. **Legumes** erect, flat, straight or slightly incurved, 40–120 × 3.5–6.5 mm, shallowly corrugated over seeds, dehiscent. **Seeds** brown, obovoid or oblong-obovoid.

Flowering spring–summer. Stony hillsides, canyon floors; of conservation concern; 1300–1800 m; N.Mex., Tex.; Mexico (Chihuahua, Coahuila).

19. Senna pendula (Humboldt & Bonpland ex Willdenow) H. S. Irwin & Barneby, Mem. New York Bot. Gard. 35: 378. 1982 [I]

Cassia pendula Humboldt & Bonpland ex Willdenow, Enum. Pl. 1: 440. 1809; *Chamaefistula pendula* (Humboldt & Bonpland ex Willdenow) G. Don

Varieties 18–20 (1 in the flora): introduced, Florida; Mexico, West Indies, Central America, South America; introduced also in Africa (South Africa), Pacific Islands, Australia.

Senna pendula is often confused with close relative *S. bicapsularis*, which is absent from North America and has shorter pedicels, only to 5 mm (H. S. Irwin and R. C. Barneby 1982; B. Marazzi et al. 2006b).

19a. Senna pendula (Humboldt & Bonpland ex Willdenow) H. S. Irwin & Barneby var. **glabrata** (Vogel) H. S. Irwin & Barneby, Mem. New York Bot. Gard. 35: 382. 1982 • Valamuerto [I]

Cassia indecora Kunth var. *glabrata* Vogel, Gen. Cass. Syn., 19. 1837; *C. coluteoides* Colladon

Shrubs, to 3(–5) m. **Leaves** mesophyllous, 5–13 cm, glabrous or glabrate; stipules caducous; extrafloral nectaries 1(or 2), between first, rarely also subsequent, leaflet pairs, sessile; leaflet pairs 4 or 5(–7), blades obovate or oblanceolate to elliptic-oblanceolate, 25–65 × 9–23 mm. **Racemes** usually 4–35-flowered; bracts caducous. **Pedicels** 8–33 mm. **Flowers** monosymmetric; calyx yellowish; corolla golden yellow, longest petal 16–26 mm; androecium heterantherous, stamens 7, middle stamens ½ as long as abaxial or smaller, staminodes 3; anthers of middle stamens to 5–7 mm, of abaxial stamens 7–10 mm, dehiscing by U-shaped pore, apical appendage inconspicuous; gynoecium incurved, ovules 70–96; ovary hairy; style slightly incurved. **Legumes** somewhat pendulous, subcylindrical, straight, 90–160 × 9–16 mm, corrugated over seeds, indehiscent. **Seeds** obliquely obovoid, brown or dark reddish brown.

Flowering late winter–early summer. Grasslands, disturbed woodlands, roadsides; 0–100 m; introduced; Fla., Tex.; South America (Argentina, Brazil, Paraguay).

Variety *glabrata* is native to South American grasslands. Among southeastern South American varieties, var. *glabrata* belongs with var. *missionum* H. S. Irwin & Barneby (endemic to northeast Argentina) and var. *recondita* H. S. Irwin & Barneby (endemic to coastal southeast Brazil) to a group characterized by a longer style (5–10 mm) compared to that of the other varieties in the region, var. *ambigua* and var. *paludicola* H. S. Irwin & Barneby (1.5–5 mm). The subcylindrical fruits distinguish var. *glabrata* from the other two varieties that have laterally compressed fruits (H. S. Irwin and R. C. Barneby 1982).

The Florida Exotic Pest Plant Council (https://www.fleppc.org/) listed var. *glabrata* as a Category I weedy species, meaning that it is invading and disrupting native plant communities in Florida. According to H. S. Irwin and R. C. Barneby (1982), the Mexican and Central American var. *ovalifolia* H. S. Irwin & Barneby may have escaped from cultivation in Florida, as well as occurring as an adventive in the very south of Texas. However, var. *ovalifolia* is not reported as naturalized in Florida (R. P. Wunderlin et al., http://florida.plantatlas.usf.edu/) or in Texas, although an unspecified *Senna pendula* is listed with no variety in the Texas invasives database (Texas Invasive Plant and Pest Council, https://texasinvasives.org/professionals/tippc.php). The two varieties are distinguished by the length of their styles: 5–8 mm in var. *glabrata* and 2.7–5 mm in var. *ovalifolia* (Irwin and Barneby).

20. Senna pilosior (B. L. Robinson ex J. F. Macbride) H. S. Irwin & Barneby, Phytologia 44: 500. 1979 • Trans-Pecos senna

Cassia bauhinioides A. Gray var. *pilosior* B. L. Robinson ex J. F. Macbride, Contr. Gray Herb. 59: 27. 1919; *C. pilosior* (B. L. Robinson ex J. F. Macbride) H. S. Irwin & Barneby

Herbs, perennial, to 0.7 m. **Leaves** slightly sclerophyllous, 1.5–7.5 cm, hairy; stipules tardily deciduous; extrafloral nectary 1, between leaflet pair, stipitate; leaflet pairs 1, blades broadly, obliquely obovate to oblong-obovate, 15–40 × 10–25 mm. **Racemes** 2–6-flowered; bracts caducous. **Pedicels** 6–15 mm. **Flowers** monosymmetric; calyx persistent into developing fruit, pale green; corolla yellow, longest petal 8.5–10 mm; androecium not heterantherous, stamens 7, staminodes 3; anthers 2.3–3.7 mm, dehiscing by 1 apical pore, apical appendage 0; gynoecium nearly linear, ovules 16–26; ovary densely hairy; style linear. **Legumes** erect, flat, straight, 20–40 × 5.5–7.5 mm, corrugated over seeds, dehiscing apically downward, with 1 series of seeds. **Seeds** dull pinkish or grayish brown, pyriform. 2*n* = 28.

Flowering spring–mid fall. Sandy banks, desert washes; 600–1500 m; Tex.; Mexico (Chihuahua, Coahuila, Durango).

Senna pilosior is the only senna in North America with sepals persisting into fruit development and falling off before fruit matures and dehisces. Persistent sepals are diagnostic to distinguish *S. pilosior* from the close relatives *S. bauhinioides* and *S. durangensis*; the trio is, in fact, characterized by a history of repeated misidentifications (H. S. Irwin and R. C. Barneby 1982).

21. Senna pumilio (A. Gray) H. S. Irwin & Barneby, Phytologia 44: 500. 1979 • Dwarf senna [F]

Cassia pumilio A. Gray, Boston J. Nat. Hist. 6: 180. 1850; *Tharpia pumilio* (A. Gray) Britton & Rose

Herbs, perennial, to 0.2 m. **Leaves** slightly sclerophyllous, 1.5–10 cm, hairy; stipules persistent; extrafloral nectary between leaflet pair, highly reduced; leaflet pairs 1, blades lanceolate-acuminate or oblanceolate, 10–50 × 2–5 mm. **Racemes** 1-flowered;

bracts caducous. **Pedicels** 6–21 mm. **Flowers** monosymmetric; calyx often persistent into developing fruit, pale green; corolla pale yellow, longest petal 5.5–10 mm; androecium not heterantherous, stamens 7, staminodes 3; anthers to 2.9–4 mm, dehiscing by 1 apical pore, apical appendage 0; gynoecium nearly linear, ovules 6–12; ovary hairy; style linear. **Legumes** erect, cylindrical, straight, 8–15 × 6–8 mm, not corrugated over seeds, dehiscing apically downward. **Seeds** brown, paddle-shaped to pyriform. **2*n*** = 28.

Flowering late winter–mid summer. Gravelly clay mounds and flats, sandy soils; 50–2000 m; Tex.; Mexico (Chihuahua, Coahuila, Durango, Nuevo León).

Senna pumilio is one of three sennas in North America forming and sprouting from a woody taproot (along with *S. bauhinioides* and *S. ripleyana*; H. S. Irwin and R. C. Barneby 1982).

22. Senna ripleyana (H. S. Irwin & Barneby) H. S. Irwin & Barneby, Phytologia 44: 500. 1979 (as ripleyi) • Ripley's senna [C]

Cassia ripleyana H. S. Irwin & Barneby, Sida 6: 13, fig. 1. 1975

Herbs, perennial, to 0.2 m. **Leaves** slightly sclerophyllous, 1–5 cm, hairy; stipules persistent; extrafloral nectary 1, between leaflet pair, stipitate; leaflet pairs 1, blades oblong-elliptic or obliquely obovate-elliptic, 6–20 × 3–10 mm. **Racemes** 1(or 2)-flowered; bracts caducous. **Pedicels** 5–10 mm. **Flowers** monosymmetric; calyx caducous, yellowish to pale green; corolla yellow or orange-yellow, longest petal 8.5–9 mm; androecium not heterantherous, stamens 7, staminodes 3; anthers 3–3.5 mm, dehiscing by 1 apical pore, apical appendage 0; gynoecium nearly linear, ovules 18–28; ovary densely hairy; style incurved, linear, 3–3.5 mm. **Legumes** erect, cylindrical, straight or slightly curved, 13–24 × 5–8 mm, slightly corrugated over seeds, dehiscing apically downward. **Seeds** pinkish brown, olive green, or ochre, pyriform.

Flowering mid summer–early fall. Gravelly, desert hilltops and flats; of conservation concern; 1400–1700 m; Tex.; Mexico (Chihuahua, Zacatecas).

Senna ripleyana is one of three sennas in North America forming and sprouting from a woody taproot (the other species are *S. bauhinioides* and *S. pumilio*). The species appears to be rare (recorded from Brewster County), but perhaps it has been overlooked or misidentified as *S. bauhinioides* (H. S. Irwin and R. C. Barneby 1982).

23. Senna roemeriana (Scheele) H. S. Irwin & Barneby, Mem. New York Bot. Gard. 35: 282. 1982 • Twoleaf senna

Cassia roemeriana Scheele, Linnaea 21: 457. 1848; *Earleocassia roemeriana* (Scheele) Britton

Herbs, perennial, to 0.7 m. **Leaves** slightly sclerophyllous, 2.5–9.5 cm, hairy; stipules caducous; extrafloral nectary 1, between leaflet pair, shortly stipitate; leaflet pairs 1, blades lanceolate-oblong or lanceolate, 20–70 × 4–14 mm. **Racemes** 1–5-flowered; bracts caducous. **Pedicels** 9–16 mm. **Flowers** monosymmetric; calyx caducous, pale green; corolla yellow or orange-yellow, longest petal 12–17 mm; androecium not heterantherous, stamens 7, staminodes 3; anthers 2.2–3.3 mm, dehiscing by 1 apical pore, apical appendage 0; gynoecium nearly linear, ovules 22–40; ovary densely hairy; style slightly incurved. **Legumes** erect, subcylindrical, straight or slightly curved, 20–35 × 4.5–6.5 mm, corrugated over seeds, dehiscing apically downward. **Seeds** brown or pinkish brown, paddle-shaped or pyriform. **2*n*** = 28.

Flowering spring–early fall. Mesquite grasslands, chaparral, draws in shortgrass prairies, barren hillsides, desert washes, roadsides; 100–2000 m; N.Mex., Okla., Tex.; Mexico (Chihuahua, Coahuila, Nuevo León).

24. Senna surattensis (Burman f.) H. S. Irwin & Barneby, Mem. New York Bot. Gard. 35: 81. 1982 • Glaucous senna, scrambled egg plant [I]

Cassia surattensis Burman f., Fl. Indica, 97. 1768; *C. fastigiata* Vahl; *C. suffruticosa* J. Koenig ex Roth; *C. surattensis* subsp. *suffruticosa* (J. Koenig ex Roth) K. Larsen & S. S. Larsen; *Psilorhegma suffruticosa* (J. Koenig ex Roth) Britton; *Senna speciosa* Roxburgh

Shrubs or trees, to 4(–6) m. **Leaves** mesophyllous, 8–18 cm, finely, densely hairy; stipules caducous; extrafloral nectaries 1–3, between first only, or also subsequent, leaflet pairs, sessile; leaflet pairs 6–10, blades obovate, obovate-elliptic, oblanceolate-obtuse, 20–50 × 8–20 mm. **Racemes** usually 5–21-flowered; bracts late caducous. **Pedicels** 16–25 mm. **Flowers** slightly asymmetric; calyx greenish; corolla pale yellow, longest petal 16–24 mm; androecium heterantherous, stamens 10, staminodes 0; anthers of 9 short stamens 4–5.2 mm, of 1 long stamen 4.5–6.5 mm, dehiscing by 2 pores, apical appendage 0; gynoecium slightly incurved, ovules 18–30; ovary slightly hairy; style slightly

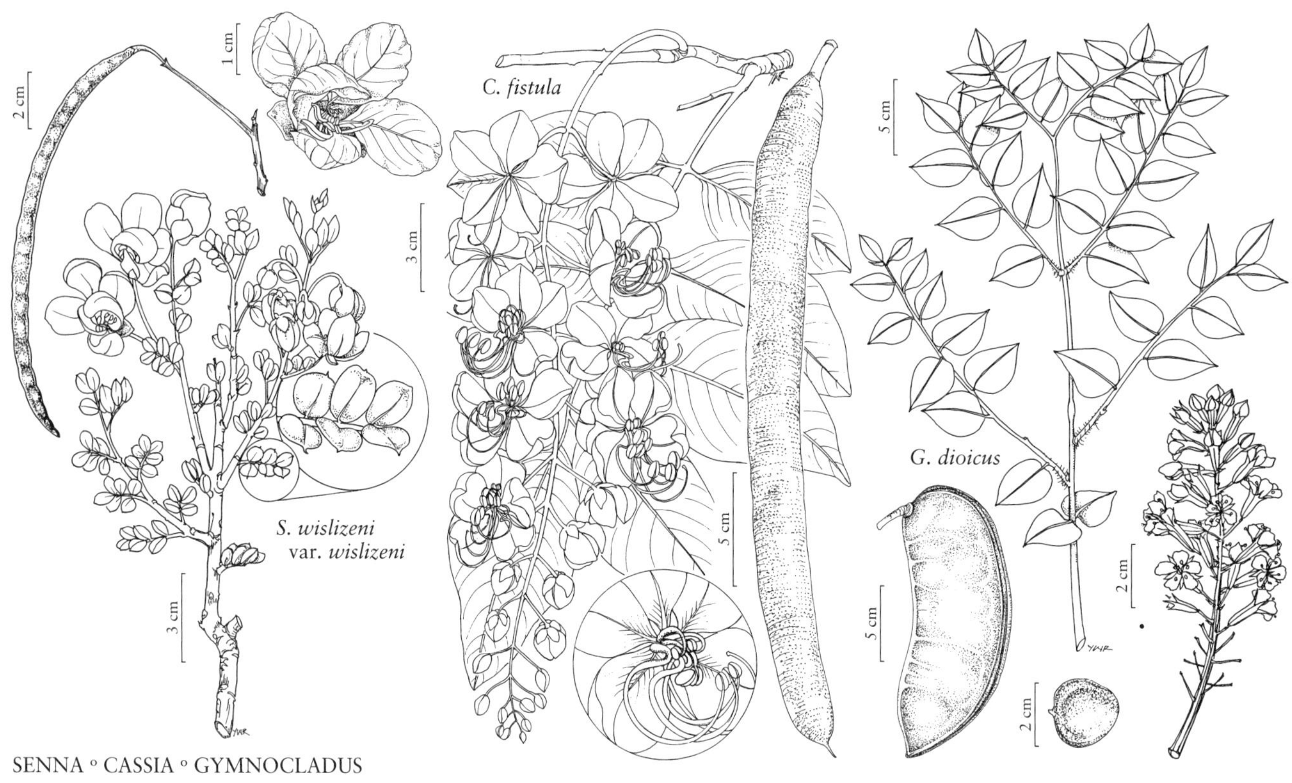

SENNA ◦ CASSIA ◦ GYMNOCLADUS

incurved. **Legumes** somewhat pendulous, flat, slightly curved, 70–100 × 11–15 mm, slightly corrugated over seeds, indehiscent. **Seeds** dark reddish brown, oblong-ellipsoid.

Flowering late winter–late fall. Habitat unknown; 0–10 m; introduced; Fla.; Asia; Africa; Pacific Islands; Australia; introduced also in West Indies (Bahamas, Puerto Rico, Saint Vincent).

Senna surattensis has been cultivated for centuries as an ornamental in tropical regions, making inference about its origin and native range of geographic distribution a matter of speculation (G. Bentham 1863–1878; D. E. Symon 1966; H. S. Irwin and R. C. Barneby 1982). In North America it is cultivated in California and Texas in addition to Florida (D. Isely 1998). *Senna surattensis* is often confused with *S. multiglandulosa*; they are similar in habit and widely cultivated, but *S. surattensis* possesses seven heterantherous stamens and three staminodes. The similar and closely related *S. sulfurea* (Colladon) H. S. Lewis & Barneby (with two long stamens instead of one) was considered a subspecies of *S. surattensis* by B. R. Randell (1989).

25. Senna wislizeni (A. Gray) H. S. Irwin & Barneby, Phytologia 44: 500. 1979 [F]

Cassia wislizeni A. Gray, Smithsonian Contr. Knowl. 3(5): 60. 1852; *Palmerocassia wislizeni* (A. Gray) Britton

Varieties 4 (1 in the flora): sw United States, Mexico.

25a. Senna wislizeni (A. Gray) H. S. Irwin & Barneby var. **wislizeni** • Wislizenus's senna [F]

Shrubs, to 1 m. **Leaves** xerophytic, first pair of leaflets often caducous, 1.2–3.7 cm, strigulose; stipules persistent; extrafloral nectaries 0; leaflet pairs 3 or 4, blades obovate, 4–10 × 2.5–7.5 mm. **Racemes** 2–17-flowered, not spikelike; bracts caducous, to 5 mm. **Pedicels** 12–26 mm. **Flowers** asymmetric, enantiostylous; calyx yellowish, greenish, or purplish brown; corolla bright yellow, highly asymmetric, lower petals strongly concave (flag-shaped), longest petal 16–28 mm; androecium heterantherous, stamens 7, staminodes 3; anthers of middle stamens 4–6.2 mm, of abaxial stamens 4.8–6.2 mm, dehiscing by 2 apical slits, apical appendage 0; gynoecium incurved, ovules 22–25; ovary glabrous; style incurved. **Legumes** ascending, flat, straight or slightly curved, 70–240 × 5.5–8 mm, corrugated over seeds, tardily dehiscent. **Seeds** brown to pinkish brown, rhomboid to paddle-shaped.

Flowering late spring–mid fall. Foothills of desert mountains; 800–1600 m; Ariz., N.Mex., Tex.; Mexico (Chihuahua, Coahuila, Sonora).

Varieties *wislizeni* and *villosa* (Britton) H. S. Irwin & Barneby display persistent stipules and the fruits are corrugated over the seeds, whereas stipules are promptly caducous and fruits are not corrugated in vars. *pringlei* (Rose) H. S. Irwin & Barneby and *painteri* (Britton) H. S. Irwin & Barneby. Variety *villosa* and var. *wislizeni* are distinguished by their vestiture: the former is pilosulous, whereas the latter is strigulose (H. S. Irwin and R. C. Barneby 1982).

7. CASSIA Linnaeus, Sp. Pl. 1: 376. 1753; Gen. Pl. ed. 5, 178. 1754, name conserved • Shower tree [Greek *kasia*, a kind of cinnamon from Asia] I

Brigitte Marazzi

Trees, unarmed. **Stems** spreading, glabrous or silky-hairy when young. **Leaves** alternate, even-pinnate; stipules present, caducous; petiolate; extrafloral nectaries absent; leaflets 6–16 [–50], blade margins entire, surfaces glabrous or slightly hairy. **Inflorescences** 20+-flowered, usually terminal, racemes; bracts present, caducous [persistent]; bracteoles present. **Flowers** caesalpinioid, hypanthium solid; calyx usually caducous, rarely persistent, zygomorphic, turbinate or vase-shaped, lobes 5; corolla yellow [pink, red, or white], blades narrowed to claw; stamens 10, heterantherous, usually 3 staminodes, 4 shorter stamens, length of 3 longer stamens to 2 times shorter; filaments glabrous, nearly same length as anthers, staminodes and short stamens linear, long stamens sigmoidal; anthers dorsifixed, dehiscing by lateral slits and/or basal pores; style terminating in minute stigmatic cavity. **Fruits** legumes, stipitate, usually linear in profile or cylindrical, sometimes rectangular-cuboid, indehiscent, woody, glabrous. **Seeds** 40–100, obovoid-ellipsoid. x = 12, 14.

Species ca. 32 (1 in the flora): introduced, Florida; nearly worldwide in tropical areas.

Cassia in the broad sense first became known to European botanists through the fruits that were used in herbal medicines imported from Asia by way of Egypt and Asia Minor (L. T. F. Colladon 1816; H. S. Irwin and R. C. Barneby 1982). Only three species were known to J. P. de Tournefort (1700) when he first defined the genus. Characterized by a long taxonomic history, *Cassia* was considered to be the twentieth largest flowering plant genus (D. G. Frodin 2004), including approximately 600 species (Irwin and B. L. Turner 1960), before being subdivided into the smaller *Cassia* in the strict sense, and the almost equally large *Chamaecrista* and *Senna* (Irwin and Barneby 1981, 1982). This division has been supported by morphological (S. C. Tucker 1996; T. Boonkerd et al. 2005) and molecular phylogenetic (A. Bruneau et al. 2008) studies. In the latter, *Cassia* and *Senna* are sister genera; *Chamaecrista* appears more distantly related. In contrast to *Chamaecrista* (A. Conceição et al. 2009) and *Senna* (B. Marazzi et al. 2006), phylogenetic relationships within *Cassia* are still unclear.

Flowers of *Cassia* are pollinated by bees, which vibrate the flowers to release pollen from the anthers (G. Gottsberger and I. Silberbauer-Gottsberger 1988).

Cassia trees are appreciated as ornamentals in gardens and parks and along streets throughout the tropics and subtropics, owing to their showy yellow [or pink] flowers. In North America, trees are cultivated especially in California and Florida, and escaped specimens of the most widely cultivated species, *C. fistula*, have become naturalized occasionally in Florida (R. P. Wunderlin and B. F. Hansen, www.florida.plantatlas.usf.edu). Other commonly cultivated species are *C. grandis* Linnaeus f. (coral shower tree; from Central America and South America) and *C. javanica* Linnaeus (pink shower tree, apple blossom cassia, Java cassia; from southeast Asia). *Cassia leptophylla* Vogel (gold medallion tree; from Brazil) is often cultivated in southern California, and *C. roxburghii* de Candolle (red or Ceylon cassia; from India and Sri Lanka) is cultivated in Florida. The presence of a sixth cultivated species, *C. afrofistula* Brenan (Kenyan shower tree; from Africa and Madagascar), in Florida needs confirmation.

SELECTED REFERENCE Irwin, H. S. and B. L. Turner. 1960. Chromosomal relationships and taxonomic considerations in the genus *Cassia*. Amer. J. Bot. 47: 309–318.

1. Cassia fistula Linnaeus, Sp. Pl. 1: 377. 1753
• Golden or rain shower, Indian laburnum, pudding pipe tree, purging cassia [F] [I]

Bactyrilobium fistula (Linnaeus) Willdenow; *Cassia bonplandiana* de Candolle; *C. fistuloides* Colladon; *Cathartocarpus fistula* (Linnaeus) Persoon

Trees to 20 m. **Leaves** bicolored, papery; petiole 40–90 mm; leaflets 10–25 pairs and blades small, or 3–10 pairs and blades larger, subsymmetrically ovate, apex rounded to apiculate or retuse. **Racemes** pendent; bracteoles caducous at anthesis (distal to base). **Pedicels** laterally compressed, 30–75 mm. **Flowers:** calyx reflexed at anthesis, greenish or brownish; petals to 21–32 mm, claw 1–2.5 mm; filaments 5–13 or 26–43 mm; anthers of shorter stamens strongly connate, dehiscing by basal pore, of longer stamens by lateral slits and basal pore; ovary incurved, linear, slightly hairy. **Legumes** pendulous, dark brown-black, 300–600 × 15–25 mm. **Seeds** transverse, biconvex, embedded in glutinous, blackish pulp, 7.5–10 × 6–7 × 2.5–3 mm.

Flowering summer–fall. Open, dry deciduous forests; 0–100 m; introduced; Fla.; se Asia; introduced also in s Mexico, West Indies, Central America, South America, Africa, Indian Ocean Islands (Madagascar), Australia.

Cassia fistula has long been used for ritual adornment and, especially, for the laxative and purgative properties of its fruits. The plant is used locally also as a remedy for anthrax, blood poisoning, dysentery, malaria, and kidney stones, as a vermifuge, and to purify wounds and ulcers (C. H. Bosch 2008).

Of the other species cultivated in North America, only *Cassia leptophylla* has yellow flowers; it differs from *C. fistula* in its erect inflorescences and greater number of leaflet pairs. In contrast, *C. grandis*, *C. javanica*, and *C. roxburghii* have pink flowers (and also pink-whitish in *C. javanica*). Bracts fall off before anthesis in the former species; they are persistent in the latter two. *Cassia roxburghii* differs from the similar *C. javanica* in its much shorter pedicels (1–2 cm) and smaller leaflets (20–40 mm) (H. S. Irwin and R. C. Barneby 1982).

8. GYMNOCLADUS Lamarck in J. Lamarck et al., Encycl. 1: 733. 1785, name conserved • Coffee-tree, chicot [Greek *gymnos*, naked, and *klados*, branch, alluding to appearance of seemingly dead branches in winter]

Derick B. Poindexter

Daniel Adams

Alan S. Weakley

Trees, unarmed, dioecious, pubescent on young growth and reproductive parts. **Stems** erect, stout, glabrescent. **Leaves** alternate, even- or irregularly-bipinnate; stipules present [absent], subulate; petiolate; pinnae 3–10 pairs, proximalmost reduced to single leaflets, opposite, subopposite, or alternate; stipels absent or present, subulate; leaflets 6–14[–30], irregular, blade margins entire, surfaces pubescent abaxially when young, glabrous or glabrescent adaxially. **Inflorescences** 15–50-flowered, terminal, racemes or panicles; bracts and bracteoles usually absent, sometimes present, minute. **Flowers** caesalpinioid, hypanthium elongate; calyx tubular, lobes 5; corolla whitish, appearing apetalous; stamens 10, distinct; anthers dorsifixed. **Fruits** legumes, sessile, compressed, turgid, oblong, curved slightly with abrupt point, tardily dehiscent, woody, pulpy between seeds, glabrous. **Seeds** 2–5, subglobose to somewhat flattened. $x = 14$.

Species ca. 4 (1 in the flora): c, e North America, Asia (China); introduced in South America, Europe, Australia.

Roasted seeds of *Gymnocladus* were formerly used as a coffee substitute (J. P. Spaeth and J. W. Thieret 2004). D. H. Janzen and P. S. Martin (1982) suggested that *Gymnocladus* seeds were once dispersed by now extinct megafauna with which they coevolved. Its wood is durable, has a desirable appearance when polished, and is used for cabinets, fence posts, and construction (T. S. Elias 1980).

SELECTED REFERENCE Spaeth, J. P. and J. W. Thieret. 2004. Notes on "coffee" from the Kentucky coffeetree (*Gymnocladus dioicus*, Fabaceae). Sida 21: 345–356.

1. Gymnocladus dioicus (Linnaeus) K. Koch, Dendrologie 1: 5. 1869 • Kentucky coffee-tree [E] [F]

Guilandina dioica Linnaeus, Sp. Pl. 1: 381. 1753

Trees to 30 m. **Stems** with numerous branches; bark dark brown, to 3 cm diam., deep fissures present forming crusty ridges; twigs somewhat hairy early, pithy, stout, gradually becoming brown and imprinted with leaf scars. **Leaves** 30–90 × 40–60 cm; stipules 1 cm; first, sometimes also second, pinnae consisting of leaflets often 2 times as large as others; pinnae short-petiolulate; leaflets 6–14, terminal often absent; blades ovate to oval, 30–70 mm, base rounded, apex acuminate, woolly and pinkish when unfolding, surfaces abaxially pale green, adaxially shiny, dark green. **Flowers:** calyx 1 cm, hairy, lobes linear-lanceolate; corolla actinomorphic, petals 5, oblong, 1–1.5 cm; stamens shorter than petals, filaments hairy, anthers bright orange; ovary sessile, hairy; style short. **Legumes** borne in clusters of 3–5, dark red-brown, 12–25 × 3–7 cm, glaucous, margins thick, with dark pulp surrounding seeds. **Seeds** dark brown, 2 cm, hard; endosperm thin. $2n = 28$.

Flowering May–Jun. Rich bottomlands, slope forests, disturbed areas; 10–1000 m; Ont.; Ark., Conn., Del., D.C., Ga., Ill., Ind., Iowa, Kans., Ky., Maine, Md., Mass., Mich., Minn., Mo., Nebr., N.J., N.Y., N.C., N.Dak., Ohio, Okla., Pa., S.Dak., Tenn., Tex., Va., W.Va., Wis.; introduced in South America, Europe, Australia.

Some of the more peripheral northern, eastern, and southeastern occurrences of *Gymnocladus dioicus* (Delaware, District of Columbia, Georgia, Maine, Massachusetts, eastern Maryland, New Jersey, North Carolina, North Dakota, eastern Pennsylvania, Quebec, and South Carolina) are presumably escapes from horticultural introductions, but the exact limits of native and introduced distributions are unclear in some areas.

9. GLEDITSIA J. Clayton in C. Linnaeus, Sp. Pl. 2: 1056. 1753; Gen. Pl. ed. 5, 476. 1754 • Honey- or water-locust [For Johann Gottlieb Gleditsch, 1714–1786, German botanist and friend of Linnaeus]

Derick B. Poindexter

Daniel Adams

Alan S. Weakley

Trees [shrubs], armed or unarmed, trunk and branches with simple or compound thorns or thornless. **Stems** erect. **Leaves** alternate, usually even-bipinnate on new growth and main branches or even-pinnate from spur shoots, rarely odd-pinnate or -bipinnate, sometimes abnormally large, unifoliolate; stipules present; petiolate; pinnae 2–6(–8)[–10] pairs, increasing in length distally; leaflets (1–)4–32, blade margins usually crenulate, rarely entire or irregularly crenulate, surfaces glabrous or pubescent. **Inflorescences** 5–100-flowered, axillary, racemes in spicate clusters; bracts present, caducous. **Flowers** caesalpinioid; calyx bell-shaped, lobes 3–5; corolla petals 3–5, not obvious, greenish [white]; stamens 3–7(–10), distinct, inserted with petals on margin of disc; anthers dorsifixed. **Fruits** legumes, stipitate, flat or compressed and plump, straight or falcate, sometimes twisted, short-ovate or oblong, ± indehiscent, papery or woody, glabrous or pilose. **Seeds** 1–25(–30), transverse, compressed to subterete, orbicular or ovoid-elliptic. $x = 14$.

Species ca. 16 (2 in the flora): North America, s South America, e, se, w Asia, w Africa; warm temperate, subtropical, or tropical areas within northern temperate zone; introduced in South America, Europe, Australia.

Gleditsia is of timber importance; the pulp of the pods has been used to make soap. *Gleditsia triacanthos* (honey-locust) is frequently cultivated in gardens and arboreta. In urban plantings thornless forms (= forma *inermis* Zabel) are primarily used. D. C. Michener (1986) argued against the taxonomic recognition of such forms in *G. triacanthos*, citing phenotypic instability that results in a continuum of thorn production, including reversion in mature, previously thornless individuals.

Gleditsia has also received favor as a fodder tree due to its production of large, sweet legumes that are valued by cattle and other livestock. This modern day preference by livestock is a contemporary phenomenon, facilitated by human agricultural practice. D. H. Janzen and P. S. Martin (1982) described the anachronistic nature of large-fruited trees, such as *Gleditsia triacanthos* and *Gymnocladus dioicus*, which quite likely had much larger and more dense distributions when their coevolved megafaunal dispersers existed.

Fruit extract of *Gleditsia sinensis* Lamarck from Asia has demonstrated promise in the treatment of multiple forms of cancer (L. M. C. Chow et al. 2003).

Phylogenetic studies show that *Gleditsia* as monophyletic, in the *Umtiza* clade, and sister to *Gymnocladus*. Both genera show fragmented, relictual distributions (A. Schnabel et al. 2003; G. P. Lewis 2005).

Gleditsia ×*texana* Sargent is a hybrid between *G. aquatica* and *G. triacanthos* that shows a range of morphological intergradation between the two parents even within a single site (C. S. Sargent 1922; B. A. Smith and D. L. Marsh 1993). It is distinguished by: trees to 36 m, 75 cm diam.; leaves pinnate or bipinnate, 15 cm, pinnae 3–7, leaflets 8–15 pairs, blades 1.5–2.5 cm, surfaces pale green abaxially, dark green and shiny adaxially; racemes 8–10 cm; staminate flowers with yellow corollas, stamens exserted, anthers green; legumes straight, 10–15 × 2 cm, usually pulpless, with oblique and rounded base and blunt apex, surfaces puberulent; seeds many, compressed, and elliptic. The hybrid is known from Arkansas, Florida, Indiana, Louisiana, Mississippi, South Carolina, and Texas.

SELECTED REFERENCE Schnabel, A., P. E. McDonel, and J. F. Wendel. 2003. Phylogenetic relationships in *Gleditsia* (Leguminosae) based on ITS sequences. Amer. J. Bot. 90: 310–320.

1. Legumes ovate, 3–5(–8) cm, straight; seeds 1[–3]. . . . . 1. *Gleditsia aquatica*
1. Legumes oblong, 20–40 cm, straight or slightly twisted; seeds 4–25(–30) . . . . 2. *Gleditsia triacanthos*

1. Gleditsia aquatica Marshall, Arbust. Amer., 54. 1785 • Water-locust [E]

Trees to 50 m, trunk to 75 cm diam., armed or unarmed; bark to 4 mm thick, dull gray to red-brown, shallow fissures breaking bark into smooth plates; twigs yellow-brown, becoming gray or red-brown and shiny, smooth; thorns pointed, simple or branched. **Leaves** 10–20 cm, surfaces glabrate or glabrescent; bipinnate: pinnae usually 4 or 5 pairs, sometimes 1+ pinnae replaced by an abnormally large, single leaflet to 6 cm, leaflets 7–9 pairs, blades 1–2.5 cm, length 1.5–2 times width; pinnate: slightly petiolulate, petiolules glabrous, leaflets 7–12 pairs, blades elliptic-oblong, (1.5–)2.5–4 cm, length 1.5–2 times width, surfaces abaxially dull green, adaxially shiny, dark green. **Racemes** 5–15 cm, staminate flowers clustered. **Pedicels** 0–3 mm. **Flowers:** perianth-hypanthium 2.5–3 mm; calyx lobes lanceolate, obtuse, slightly hairy; corolla oblong; stamens 3–7(–10); ovary long-stalked, glabrous. **Legumes** long-stalked, flat, straight, asymmetrically ovate, oblique, 3–5(–8) × (0.5–)1.5–2 cm, indehiscent; valves papery, transversely striate, pulpless. **Seeds** 1[–3], slightly compressed or subterete, orbicular, 1 × 1 cm. **2*n*** = 28.

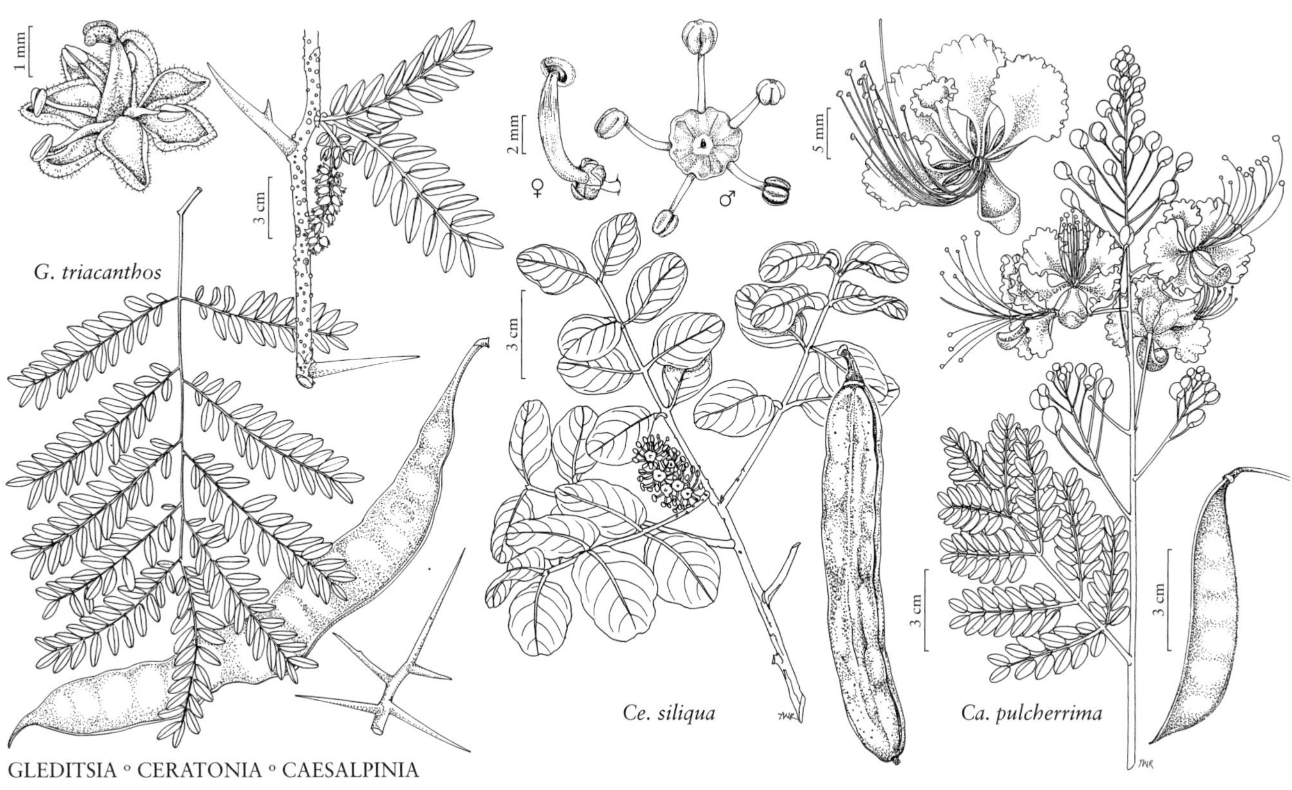

GLEDITSIA ◦ CERATONIA ◦ CAESALPINIA

Flowering Apr–Jun. Swamp forests in Coastal Plain and Mississippi Embayment, areas with long winter flooding, with *Nyssa*, *Taxodium*, bottomland *Quercus* spp., *Carya aquatica*; 0–200 m; Ala., Ark., Fla., Ga., Ill., Ind., Ky., La., Miss., Mo., N.Y., S.C., Tenn., Tex., W.Va.

Gleditsia aquatica is most common in the Mississippi Valley (C. S. Sargent 1922; T. S. Elias 1980). Occurrences away from the southeastern Coastal Plain in southeastern West Virginia, northern Kentucky, and northwestern Illinois are non-native.

2. Gleditsia triacanthos Linnaeus, Sp. Pl. 2: 1056. 1753 • Honey-locust [E] [F] [W]

Trees to 40 m, trunk to 60–90 cm diam., armed (usually unarmed in cultivation); bark to 12–20 mm thick, lengthwise fissures forming narrow, rough plates or ridges; twigs slender, green-red to brown; thorns long, pointed, usually forked, sometimes extensively so, sometimes clustered. **Leaves** 15–20 cm, surfaces glabrate, primary veins puberulent; bipinnate: pinnae 2–6(–8) pairs, sometimes 1+ pinnae replaced by an abnormally large, single leaflet to 6 cm, leaflets (2–)5–8 pairs, blades 1.3–2.5 cm, length 1.5–2 times width; pinnate: slightly petiolulate, petiolules glabrate, leaflets 10–14 pairs, blades ovate-oblong, 1.5–3.5 cm, length 1.5–2 times width, surfaces abaxially pale green, adaxially shiny, dark green. **Racemes** 5–9 cm. **Flowers:** perianth-hypanthium 3–5 mm; calyx lobes unequal, elliptic-lanceolate, acute, hairy; corolla oval to oblong; stamens 5–7(–10); ovary woolly. **Legumes** laterally compressed and plump, oblong, straight or curved and twisted in age, 20–40 × 2–3(–4) cm, ± indehiscent; valves ± woody, pulp prominent. **Seeds** 4–25(–30), compressed, ovoid-elliptic, 0.9 × 0.5 cm. **2*n*** = 28.

Flowering May–Jun. Bottomlands, disturbed areas; 0–2500 m; N.S., Ont.; Ala., Alaska, Ariz., Ark., Calif., Colo., Conn., Del., D.C., Fla., Ga., Idaho, Ill., Ind., Iowa, Kans., Ky., La., Maine, Md., Mass., Mich., Minn., Miss., Mo., Mont., Nebr., Nev., N.H., N.J., N.Mex., N.Y., N.C., N.Dak., Ohio, Okla., Pa., R.I., S.C., S.Dak., Tenn., Tex., Utah, Vt., Va., Wash., W.Va., Wis., Wyo.; introduced in South America, Europe, Asia, Africa, Australia.

Widespread use of *Gleditsia triacanthos* for hundreds of years as a planted tree has greatly expanded the range and also obscured its original native area, which appears to have been the United States west of the Appalachian Mountains and east of the Great Plains (E. L. Little 1971). Its natural habitat was also centered in forested bottomlands, but because of its wide horticultural use it can now be found in a wide range of upland habitats.

10. CERATONIA Linnaeus, Sp. Pl. 2: 1026. 1753; Gen. Pl. ed. 5, 450. 1754 • [Greek *keration*, little horn, probably alluding to fruit shape] [I]

Douglas H. Goldman

Trees or shrubs, evergreen, sometimes dioecious, unarmed. **Stems** erect to spreading, shortly appressed-pubescent. **Leaves** alternate, even-pinnate; stipules present; petiolate; leaflets (2 or)3–10(–12), opposite to alternate, stipels absent, blade margins entire, surfaces sparsely pubescent, hairy on midvein abaxially, glabrous adaxially. **Inflorescences** often on older branches and trunk, (10–)20–50(–70)-flowered, axillary, racemes, spikelike; bracts present. **Flowers** noncaesalpinioid, unisexual, often with unpleasant odor; calyx turbinate, lobes 5; corolla absent; stamens (2–)5(–8), distinct, staminodia absent in pistillate flowers; anthers basifixed; ovary puberulent, rudimentary in staminate flowers, with large, fleshy, green disk at base in both staminate and pistillate flowers. **Fruits** legumes, sessile or subsessile, straight to falcate, flattened, linear to oblong, with thickened margins, indehiscent, sparsely short-pubescent. **Seeds** 1–17, ovoid to oblong. $x = 12$.

Species 2 (1 in the flora): introduced, California; se Europe (e Mediterranean), se Asia (Arabia), n Africa.

Ceratonia may be closely related to *Gleditsia* and *Gymnocladus*, which also bear relatively large legumes (A. Bruneau et al. 2008). *Ceratonia oreothauma* Hillcoat, G. P. Lewis & Verdcourt is native to the Arabian Peninsula and Somalia.

SELECTED REFERENCE Batlle, I. and J. Tous. 1997. Carob Tree, *Ceratonia siliqua* L. Gatersleben and Rome.

1. Ceratonia siliqua Linnaeus, Sp. Pl. 2: 1026. 1753 • Carob, St. John's bread [F] [I]

Trees or shrubs 1–10 m. **Leaves** (1.5–)5–30 cm; leaflet blades ovate to elliptic or obovate, 20–60(–80) × 10–40(–50) mm, leathery, apex blunt or rounded to retuse. **Racemes** often from trunks and older branches, 1.5–10(–25) cm; bracts often deciduous, deltate, 0.5–1 mm. **Flowers** relatively small; calyx not persistent, lobes 0.4–2 mm, larger than rudimentary tube, apex acute to obtuse, puberulent; style relatively short; stigma 2-lobed. **Legumes** usually pendulous, 5–30 cm, with sweet, pulpy substance between seeds. **Seeds** brown, compressed. $2n = 24$.

Flowering summer–fall. Floodplains, stream banks, woodland margins, disturbed areas; 0–500[–1000] m; introduced; Calif.; se Europe (e Mediterranean); se Asia (Arabia); introduced also elsewhere in Mediterranean region, and worldwide in areas with Mediterranean and dry-subtropical climates.

Ceratonia siliqua seeds were apparently the historical source of the carat-standard of jewelers; in biblical times, the fruit was used as a forage for pigs (L. J. Musselman 2007). It has had numerous medicinal (A. Chevallier 1996) and industrial uses, and as a coffee and chocolate substitute (G. P. Lewis 2005).

11. CAESALPINIA Linnaeus, Sp. Pl. 1: 380. 1753; Gen. Pl. ed. 5, 178. 1754 (as Caesalpina) • [For Andrea Caesalpino, 1519–1603, Italian naturalist and physician to Pope Clement VIII] [I]

Solange Sotuyo

Brasilettia (de Candolle) Kuntze

Trees or shrubs, armed, eglandular; bark and branches with prickles. **Stems** ascending, glabrous. **Leaves** alternate, even-bipinnate; stipules present; petiolate; pinnae 4–10 pairs; stipels present, setose; leaflets 3–15, thin to subcoriaceous, blade margins entire, surfaces glabrous. **Inflorescences** 10–30-flowered, terminal or axillary, racemes, often branched; bracts present, caducous. **Pedicels** present. **Flowers** caesalpinioid, monomorphic; calyx persistent, obconic, lobes 5, abaxialmost sepal covering others in bud; corolla yellow to orange or red; stamens 10, distinct, 2–2.5 times as long as corolla; anthers dorsifixed. **Fruits** legumes, stipitate, compressed, oblong-elliptic, explosively dehiscent, valves twisting, tip acuminate. **Seeds** [2–]8–10[–12], flat, ovate to elliptic, 6–7.3 mm wide. x = 12.

Species ca. 9 (1 in the flora): introduced; Mexico, West Indies, Central America, South America, Asia, Africa, Indian Ocean Islands (Madagascar), Australia; introduced also elsewhere in tropical areas.

E. Gagnon et al. (2016) provided compelling evidence for subdivision of *Caesalpinia* in the broad sense into segregate genera, of which *Caesalpinia* (in a narrowed circumscription), *Denisophytum*, *Erythrostemon*, *Guilandina*, and *Tara* occur in the flora area.

1. Caesalpinia pulcherrima (Linnaeus) Swartz, Observ. Bot., 166. 1791 • Pride-of-Barbados [F] [I]

Poinciana pulcherrima Linnaeus, Sp. Pl. 1: 380. 1753

Shrubs or small trees, 1–6 m. **Leaves:** stipules caducous; petiole 3.2–6.5 mm, glabrous; rachis 4.5–20(–25) cm, glabrous; pinnae pairs opposite; leaflets jugate, blades elliptic to ovate, (6–)10–22(–25) × 4–10 (–12) mm, apex rounded, mucronate. **Inflorescences** 12–35 cm; bracts oblong, 4.5–7.7 × 1.3–2.6 mm. **Pedicels** articulate, (2.5–)3–6.2 cm. **Flowers:** calyx red or yellow, 3–4.8 × 2–3.5 mm, glabrous; abaxial lobes (11–)13–17 × 7.2–10 mm, margins denticulate, lateral lobes ovate, (8.2–)10–13.5 × (4.5–)5.5–8 mm, apex rounded, adaxial lobes oblong to elliptic, (7.5–)8–12.5 × (3.3–)4–6.5 mm; banner with a central scarlet blotch, ovate, (3.5–)4–7(–8.5) × (4.5–)6–10.5 mm, cordate, claw conduplicate, 6–16 mm; abaxial lateral lobes obovate, 10–16 × 9–18.5 mm, claw 5.8–11 mm, adaxial lateral lobes obovate (9–)10–16 × (9–)10.7–17.6 mm, margins crenulate, apex rounded, claw 6–11.5 mm; filaments red, exserted, (2.4–)3.8–7 mm, densely pubescent on basal ¼; anthers yellow, 1.3–2.5 × 0.9–1.6 mm; ovary falcate, 2–3 × 4.5–6.3 mm; style 4.5–6.3 mm, stigma terminal, porate; ovules 5–12. **Fruits** red when mature, falcate, (6–)7–9.5 × 1.5–2.1 cm. **Seeds** brown or olive, 7.4–9.6 × 6–7.3 mm. $2n$ = 24.

Flowering year-round. Roadsides, thickets; 0–50 m; introduced; Fla., Tex.; South America; introduced also in Mexico, West Indies, Central America, Asia, Africa, Indian Ocean Islands.

Caesalpinia pulcherrima is widely cultivated as a garden ornamental.

12. DENISOPHYTUM R. Viguier, Notul. Syst. (Paris) 13: 349. 1948 • [Derivation uncertain; probably for Marcel Denis, 1897–1929, French botanist and expert on *Euphorbia* of Madagascar, and Greek *phyton*, plant]

Solange Sotuyo

Shrubs, armed, eglandular; bark and branches with prickles. **Stems** ascending or scrambling, glabrous. **Leaves** alternate, usually even-bipinnate; stipules present, caducous; petiolate; pinnae 2–12, opposite; leaflets 4–14[–22], thin to subcoriaceous, blade margins entire, surfaces glabrous. **Inflorescences** 3–14-flowered, terminal [axillary], racemes; bracts present, caducous. **Pedicels** present, usually relatively long. **Flowers** caesalpinioid, monomorphic; calyx persistent, obconic, lobes 5, abaxialmost sepal covering others in bud; corolla yellow; stamens 10, distinct, 2–2.5 times as long as corolla; anthers dorsifixed. **Fruits** legumes, stipitate, compressed, falcate, oblong-elliptic, elastically dehiscent, valves twisting, tip acuminate, glabrous. **Seeds** 1[–3], laterally compressed, ovoid, 4–5 mm wide. x = 12.

Species 8 (1 in the flora): Florida, Mexico, West Indies (Antilles), South America, Africa, Indian Ocean Islands (Madagascar).

Denisophytum has a highly disjunct trans-continental distribution. *Denisophytum buchii* (Urban) Gagnon & G. P. Lewis is found in Haiti, *D. pauciflorum* in Florida and Cuba, *D. rosei* (Urban) Gagnon & G. P. Lewis in the Dominican Republic, *D. sessilifolium* (S. Watson) Gagnon & G. P. Lewis in Mexico, and *D. stuckertii* (Hassler) Gagnon & G. P. Lewis is endemic to Argentina and Paraguay. The remaining species are found in northern Madagascar, northern Kenya, Somalia, and the Arabian Peninsula (E. Gagnon et al. 2016).

Denisophytum species are difficult to distinguish from *Caesalpinia*, since no consistent diagnostic characters have been found to differentiate the two genera. The corolla of *Denisophytum* species is consistently yellow and the flowers are bee pollinated, whereas corollas of *C. pulcherrima* in the flora area are usually red (rarely yellow) and the flowers are usually butterfly pollinated (R. W. Cruden and S. M. Hermann-Parker 1979).

1. Denisophytum pauciflorum (Grisebach) Gagnon & G. P. Lewis, PhytoKeys 71: 47. 2016 • Few-flowered holdback [C] [F]

Libidibia pauciflora Grisebach, Cat. Pl. Cub., 78. 1866 (as Lebidibia); *Caesalpinia pauciflora* (Grisebach) C. Wright; *Poinciana pauciflora* (Grisebach) Small

Shrubs to 2 m; prickles inevident to conspicuous, mostly nodal and paired, those of leaves usually in stipellate position. **Leaves** 4–10 cm; stipules not seen; leaflet blades elliptic to obovate, 5–14 × 3–10 mm, surfaces finely punctate, only midvein evident. **Inflorescences** relatively small, terminal. **Pedicels** jointed. **Flowers** shortly stipitate distal to hypanthial cup; calyx irregular, abaxial lobe cucullate, 5–6 mm, investing others in bud; petals 6–9 mm, shortly pilose. **Fruits** opening from adaxial suture, 2–4 × 1 cm, obliquely beaked, coriaceous. **Seeds** 4–6 × 4–5 mm. $2n$ = 24.

Flowering Feb–Aug. Pinelands, palmetto-pine woodlands, hammocks, roadsides; of conservation concern; 0–10 m; Fla.; West Indies (Cuba).

Denisophytum pauciflorum is known from Monroe County, where it occurs on Big Pine, Cudjoe, and Summerland keys.

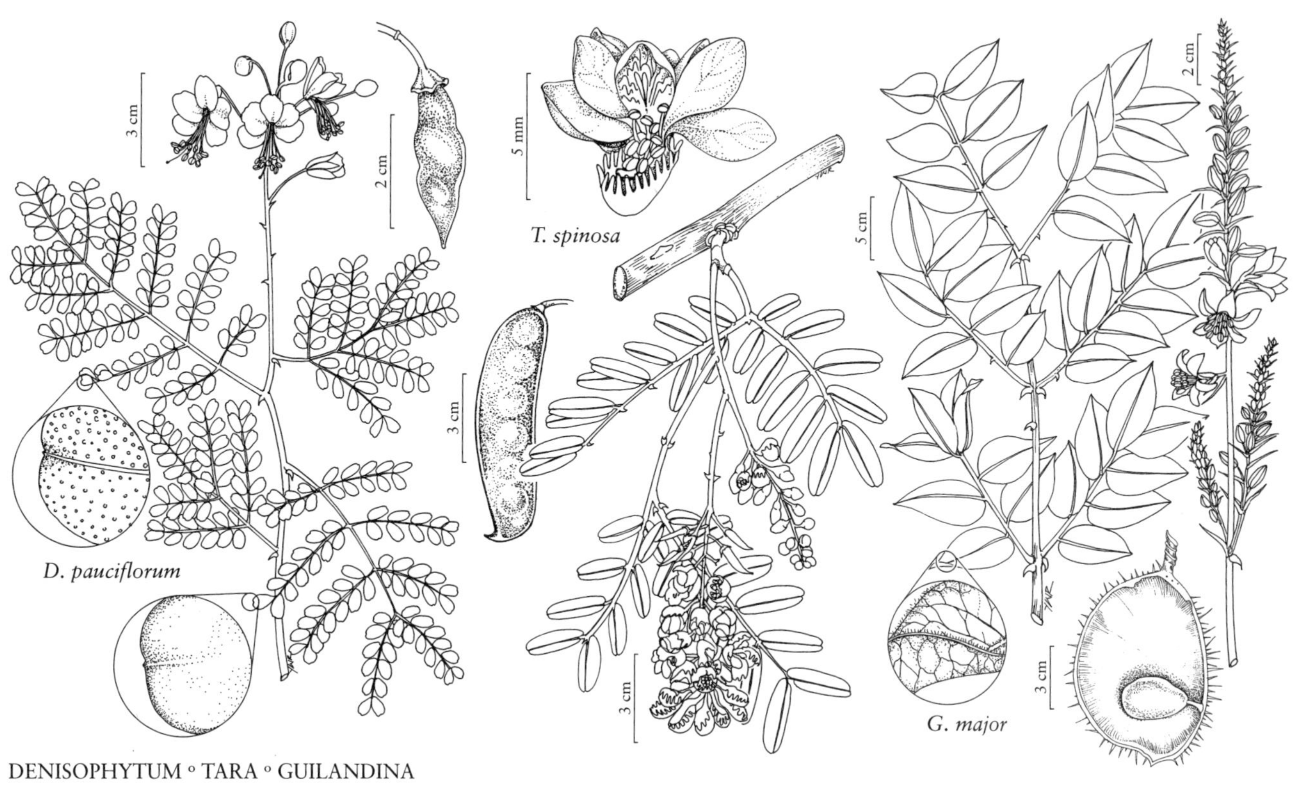

DENISOPHYTUM ◦ TARA ◦ GUILANDINA

13. TARA Molina, Sag. Stor. Nat. Chili ed. 2, 153, 282. 1810 • [Quechua (central Andes Mountains) name for cluster of tubercles, probably alluding to legumes in rows] [I]

Solange Sotuyo

Shrubs or trees, armed, eglandular, with deflexed prickles on bark and branches, branches brown or gray-brown. **Stems** erect, glabrous. **Leaves** alternate, even-bipinnate; stipules present, caducous, minute; petiolate; pinnae 2 or 3(or 5) pairs, opposite; leaflets 2–12(–24), opposite, subcoriaceous; blade margins entire, surfaces puberulent or glabrescent abaxially, glabrous adaxially, eglandular. **Inflorescences** 10-flowered, terminal or axillary, racemes; bracts present, caducous. **Flowers** caesalpinioid, monomorphic; calyx persistent, obconic, abaxialmost sepal covering others in bud, lobes 5; corolla yellow, banner with red medial markings; stamens 10, distinct, shorter than or slightly longer than corolla, filaments pubescent; anthers dorsifixed. **Fruits** legumes, sessile, straight, laterally-compressed to turgid, oblong, indehiscent, tip blunt, ± fleshy, leathery, glabrous or puberulent. **Seeds** 4–8, ellipsoid, 8–10 mm wide. x = 12.

Species 3 (1 in the flora): introduced, California; Mexico, West Indies, Central America, South America, Atlantic Islands (Canary Islands); introduced also in ne Africa.

Of the three *Tara* species, *T. cacalaco* (Bonpland) Molinari & Sánchez Och. occurs in Mexico, *T. spinosa* is found in South America (Chile, Ecuador, and Peru), and *T. vesicaria* (Linnaeus) Molinari, Sánchez Och. & Mayta ranges from Mexico to Guatemala and Nicaragua and extends into the Caribbean. *Tara spinosa* is cultivated across the tropics and subtropics as a source of tannins and as an ornamental (E. Gagnon et al. 2016).

1. **Tara spinosa** (Molina) Britton & Rose in N. L. Britton et al., N. Amer. Fl. 23: 320. 1930 • Spiny holdback [F] [I]

Poinciana spinosa Molina, Sag. Stor. Nat. Chili, 158. 1782; *Caesalpinia pectinata* Cavanilles; *C. spinosa* (Molina) Kuntze; *C. tara* Ruiz & Pavon; *Tara tinctoria* Molina

Shrubs or trees 2–8 m, armed, bark and branches with dispersed, curvate prickles. **Leaves:** stipules not seen; petiole 20–30 mm; rachis 4.5–20(–25) cm; blades oblong to elliptic, 10–40(–45) × 15–20 mm, surfaces glandular-dotted abaxially. **Racemes** pubescent. **Pedicels** jointed, (2.5–)5–10 mm. **Flowers:** calyx lobes red when in bud or greenish yellow, (3–)6(–7) mm; corolla banner with central scarlet blotch, (5.1–)6–7(–8.5) mm; filaments exserted, pale yellow, 6.8–7 mm, pubescent; anthers yellow, 1 × 0.5 mm; ovary pubescent; style 4.5–6.3 mm. **Legumes** (6–)7–10 × (1–)1.5–2.5(–3) cm. **Seeds** 4–8.

Flowering Oct–Nov. Riparian areas, bluffs, sage scrub, road and railroad rights-of-way; 0–400[–2000] m; introduced; Calif.; South America (n Chile, Colombia, Peru, Venezuela); introduced also in ne Africa.

Tara spinosa is cultivated as an ornamental and has escaped locally in southern California as far north as Santa Barbara County.

Tara vesicaria is sometimes cultivated in southern Florida and has been documented as an escape near planted individuals. It differs from *T. spinosa* by leaflets that are in 1–3 pairs and have rounded to emarginate apices and oblique bases.

Coulteria tinctoria Kunth is an illegitimate and superfluous name that pertains here.

14. GUILANDINA Linnaeus, Sp. Pl. 1: 381. 1753; Gen. Pl. ed. 5, 179. 1754 • Nicker beans or nuts, nickels [For Melchior Wieland, ca. 1520–1589, who settled in Italy and Latinized his surname to Guilandinus]

Solange Sotuyo

Shrubs, trees, or perennial vines, armed, prickles on trunk and branches, woody. **Stems** spreading or climbing, pubescent or glabrous. **Leaves** opposite, odd-bipinnate [pinnate]; stipules present, persistent, leafy; petiolate; pinnae 3–11 pairs, opposite or subopposite; leaflets 5–20(–48), membranous to subcoriaceous; blade margins entire, surfaces glabrous or pubescent. **Inflorescences** ca. 20-flowered, axillary, racemes, often branched, flowers in staminate or pistillate racemes, pistillate flowers seemingly bisexual but anthers without pollen; bracts present, caducous. **Flowers** caesalpinioid, monomorphic or dimorphic; calyx persistent, obconic, lobes 5; corolla light white to yellow; stamens 5, distinct; anthers dorsifixed. **Fruits** legumes, stipitate, turgid, broadly elliptic to oblong, dehiscent, faces densely covered by prickles. **Seeds** 1–4, ovoid or globose to subglobose, 15–25 mm diam.; germination hypogeal. $x = 12$.

Species ca. 20 (2 in the flora): sc, se United States, Mexico, West Indies, Central America, South America, Asia, Africa, Indian Ocean Islands, Pacific Islands; pantropical.

Caesalpinia in the broad sense has a complex taxonomy not only because of the lack of detailed morphological studies across its geographical range but also because of the great morphological variation in several species that seems to intergrade among proposed genera. Molecular and morphological studies have demonstrated that the genus is polyphyletic. G. P. Lewis et al. (2005) reinstated the genera *Coulteria* Kunth, *Erythrostemon*, *Guilandina*, *Libidibia* (de Candolle) Schlechtendal, *Mezoneuron* Desfontaines, *Poincianella* Britton & Rose, and *Tara* following the findings of diverse authors.

1. Stipules conspicuous, leafy; bracts linear-lanceolate, recurved; ovules 2; seeds leaden gray . . . . 1. *Guilandina bonduc*
1. Stipules subulate or linear, or absent; bracts subulate, ascending to spreading; ovules 4; seeds yellow . . . . 2. *Guilandina major*

1. Guilandina bonduc Linnaeus, Sp. Pl. 1: 381. 1753 • Gray nicker bean 

Caesalpinia bonduc (Linnaeus) Roxburgh

Shrubs or trees, spreading or semi-climbing, to 15 m. **Stems** pubescent; densely armed with prickles 1–6 mm. **Leaves:** stipules persistent or deciduous, conspicuous, leafy, 3–25 mm, 2 or 3-lobed, lobes unequal, asymmetric, apex mucronate and rounded to emarginate; petiole 5–10 mm; rachis (15–)20–50(–80) cm, armed abaxially with recurved prickles often paired at insertion of pinnae; pinnae 3–11 pairs, 4–20 cm; leaflets (4 or)5–10(–24), opposite to subopposite, blades ovate-oblong to elliptic-oblong, (0.8–)1.3–4.5(–6.5) × (0.5–)0.8–2.2(–2.5) cm, base usually rounded to acute, rarely acuminate, apex acute to obtuse, mucronate, surfaces pubescent or glabrous, midveins and margins pubescent. **Inflorescences** axillary, (10–)20(–60) cm; bracts recurved, linear-lanceolate, 0.8–1.6 cm, longer than buds, pubescent. **Pedicels** 2–6 mm, jointed. **Flowers:** sepals reflexed during anthesis, 6.5–8 × 2–3 mm, shorter than petals, pubescent; corolla yellow or greenish yellow, (10–)12–13 × 3–4 mm; banner claw reflexed, 3 × 1 mm, glabrous abaxially, densely hairy adaxially; claws of other petals spatulate basally, 7 × 2 mm, hairy adaxially, sometimes ciliate; filaments 2–5 mm, hairy basally; anther 1–1.3 mm; ovary 2–3 mm, covered with stiffish hairs, densely set with long prickles; ovules 2; style 3 mm, hairy, stigma ciliate. **Fruits** (3–)4.5–7.6(–9) × (2.5–)3.5–4.5 cm, faces densely spreading-prickly. **Seeds** 1 or 2, leaden gray, ovoid to globose, 15–20 mm diam., smooth, hard, cuticle of testa with parallel concentric lines. $2n = 24$.

Flowering Aug–Jan. Coastal habitats, wet forests, disturbed sites, stream banks, inland in secondary forests; 0–20 m; introduced; Fla., La.; Mexico; West Indies; Central America; South America; Asia; Africa; Indian Ocean Islands; Pacific Islands.

Guilandina bonduc is found in most coastal areas in the tropics. The native range is difficult to determine since its seeds are widely dispersed by ocean currents.

2. Guilandina major (Medikus) Small, Fl. S.E. U.S., 591, 1331. 1903 • Yellow nicker bean F

Bonduc majus Medikus, Theodora, 43. 1786, based on *Guilandina bonduc* Linnaeus, Sp. Pl. ed. 2, 1: 545. 1762, not *G. bonduc*, 1753; *G. bonduc* var. *major* (Medikus) de Candolle; *G. ovalifolia* (Urban) Britton; *Caesalpinia ovalifolia* Urban

Vines, climbing, to 15 m. **Stems:** branchlets glossy to dull, hairy or glabrous; prickles straight or recurved, 0.5–3 mm on a small, orbicular base, sometimes with recurved prickles on an ellipsoid base. **Leaves** to 75 cm; stipules caducous or absent, subulate or linear, 1–3 mm, apex acute; rachis 30–45 cm, armed with recurved prickles at base of pinnae and scattered in between; pinnae 3–8 pairs, 7–35 cm; leaflets 6–14 per pinna, opposite or alternate, blade ovate to oblong (subsymmetrical), (5–)6–7 × (2.7–)3.2 cm, membranous to subcoriaceous, base acute to rounded, oblique, margins curved, apex rounded to acute, mucronate, surfaces hairy or glabrous. **Inflorescences** supra-axillary, 10–50 cm; bracts ascending to spreading, subulate, 1–3 mm. **Pedicels** 6–12 mm. **Flowers:** sepals reflexed during anthesis, 7–9 × 2.5–3 mm, ± equal, petals not exceeding sepals; corolla yellow, 4–7 × 2–3 mm; banner claw reflexed, 3 × 1 mm, densely hairy; claws of other petals 7 × 2 mm, hairy adaxially, sometimes ciliate; filaments 6–7 mm in staminate flowers, 5 mm in pistillate flowers, hairy basally; anther 0.5–1 mm; pistil in pistillate flowers 2.5–7 mm; ovary 4–5 mm, hairy, densely set with long prickles; ovules 4; style 3 mm, hairy, stigma ciliate; pistil rudimentary in staminate flowers, 1 mm, hairy. **Fruits** 8–13 × 4–6 cm, faces densely set with prickles. **Seeds** 2–4, yellow (gray-green when immature), globose to subglobose, 15–25 mm diam., smooth, with parallel concentric lines.

Flowering Nov–Mar. Vine thicket vegetation; 0–20 m; Fla.; West Indies; South America (Guyana); Asia; Indian Ocean Islands (Madagascar); Pacific Islands; Australia.

Guilandina major is known from Martin, Miami-Dade, Monroe, and Palm Beach counties.

Caesalpinia major (Medikus) Dandy & Exell (1938, not A. Braun, 1851) is an illegitimate name that pertains here.

15. ERYTHROSTEMON Klotzsch in J. H. F. Link et al., Icon. Pl. Rar. 2: 97, plate 39. 1844 • [Greek *erythros*, red, and *stemon*, stamen, alluding to purplish red filaments]

Solange Sotuyo

Poincianella Britton & Rose

Herbs, perennial, shrubs, or trees, armed or unarmed. **Stems** spreading, ascending, or erect, glandular or eglandular, glabrous or pubescent. **Leaves** alternate, odd-bipinnate; stipules present, caducous or persistent, ovate-lanceolate to orbiculate; petiolate or short-petiolate; pinnae 2–15 pairs, alternate, opposite, or subopposite; stipels present; leaflets 7–23, opposite, blade margins entire, sometimes revolute, surfaces glabrous or pubescent, often glandular-punctate with conspicuous black, sessile glands along margins, these sometimes sunken in sinuses of crenulated margin. **Inflorescences** 6–40+-flowered, axillary or terminal, racemes; bracts present, persistent or caducous. **Flowers** caesalpinioid, monomorphic, androecium and gynoecium free, not cupped in lower sepal; calyx zygomorphic, persistent, margins fimbriate-glandular, lobes 5; corolla yellow (or orange, red, or white in ornamental plants); stamens 10, distinct; anthers versatile. **Fruits** legumes, sessile, flattened, straight or falcate, lanceolate-oblong, elastically dehiscent, subligneous, leathery, glandular or eglandular, pubescent or glabrous. **Seeds** (1–)3–6, brown, ovate. x = 12.

Species ca. 30 (4 in the flora): w, s United States, Mexico, Central America, South America; introduced in Africa, Australia.

In some species of *Caesalpinia* and allied genera, such as *Erythrostemon*, stalked glands in the shape of wine glasses have been called pixie-cup glands.

1. Leaflets 3–7 pairs on lateral pinnae, 8–20 pairs on terminal pinna. . . . . 1. *Erythrostemon caudatus*
1. Leaflets on lateral and terminal pinnae ± equal in number (2–11 pairs).
    2. Filaments 70–95(–120) mm, much longer than banner; inflorescence axis densely stipitate-glandular; legumes 8–10.8 cm . . . . 2. *Erythrostemon gilliesii*
    2. Filaments 9–13 mm, shorter to longer than banner; inflorescence axis eglandular; legumes 2.5–7.5 cm.
        3. Shrubs or trees, 1–6 m, not clonal; pinnae 2–4(or 5) pairs, leaflets (2 or)3–5 (or 6) pairs, blades obovate-elliptic, 10–35 mm; calyx densely pubescent on inner surface, inflorescence moderately pubescent or glabrous; legumes 4.4–7.5 cm; seeds (1 or)2–5. . . . . 3. *Erythrostemon mexicanus*
        3. Herbs or shrubs, 0.3–0.8 m, clonal; pinnae 3 or 4 pairs; leaflets 2 or 3 pairs, blades obovate to elliptic, 4–11 mm; base of calyx and apex of pedicel stipitate-glandular, inflorescence otherwise eglandular; legumes 2.5 cm; seeds 1 or 2 . . . 4. *Erythrostemon phyllanthoides*

1. Erythrostemon caudatus (A. Gray) Gagnon & G. P. Lewis, PhytoKeys 71: 120. 2016 • Tailed nicker [F]

Hoffmannseggia caudata A. Gray, Boston J. Nat. Hist. 6: 179. 1850 (as Hoffmanseggia); *Caesalpinia caudata* (A. Gray) Fisher; *Schrammia caudata* (A. Gray) Britton & Rose

Herbs, unarmed, to 1 m, base woody, from thick, woody rootstock. **Stems** several, glabrous, sparsely glandular. **Leaves:** stipules persistent, suborbiculate, 3 mm, base auriculate, apex rounded, surfaces pubescent, margins ciliate and fimbriate-glandular, scarious; petiole 1.5–3 cm, glabrous, sparsely glandular; rachis 3–5 cm, glabrous, sparsely glandular; pinnae 2–4 pairs, opposite or subopposite, also with terminal pinna distinctly longer than lateral pinnae; leaflets in 3–7 opposite pairs on lateral pinnae, 8–20 pairs on terminal pinna, blades obliquely ovate, terminal blades 1–6 × 0.5–4 mm, median blades 4.5–9 × 3.5–7 mm, fleshy, margins thickened, apex acute, apiculate, main and secondary veins brochidodromous, surfaces glabrous; blades with dark, punctate glands sparsely scattered over abaxial surface or blades eglandular but gland-tipped at apiculate apex, with gland-tipped appendage at base of each petiolule insertion. **Inflorescences** 6–15-flowered, axillary or terminal; axis glabrous or very sparsely pubescent, also sparsely glandular; bracts ovate, 3–4 mm, apex acute, pubescent and sparsely glandular. **Pedicels** unarticulate, 5–8 mm, crinkled-pubescent with white hairs, sessile- and stipitate-glandular. **Flowers:** calyx lobes 7–7.5 mm, lower lobe cucullate, outer surface crinkled-pubescent and glandular (most glands sessile); petals clawed, blades glabrous with pubescent claw margins, outer surfaces densely glandular with sessile, subglobose, mushroom cap-shaped glands; banner broadly ovate, 8 × 8 mm (including 0.5 mm claw); lower laterals oblanceolate, 10.5–12 × 4.5–5 mm (including 1.5 mm claw); upper laterals broadly elliptic, 9–11 × 5.5–6 mm (including 0.5 mm claw); filaments 10–11 mm, densely pubescent on basal 1/3–1/2, sparsely pubescent on distal 1/2–2/3, hairs mostly reflexed; anthers 1.5 × 0.8 mm; ovary densely lanate and densely sessile-glandular basally, or distal 1/2 and margin densely pubescent, basal 1/2 glandular; style 10–11 mm, glabrous; stigma a terminal, tubular or flared, fringed chamber. **Legumes** 2.4–4.6 × 1–1.6 cm, papery or leathery, sparsely pubescent or glabrescent, sparsely to moderately glandular with short-stalked or sessile glands. **Seeds** (1–)3 or 4.

Flowering nearly year-round. In orange or red sand, sandy gravel in open areas of mesquite; 0–200 m; Tex.; Mexico (Nuevo León, Tamaulipas).

Erythrostemon caudatus is known from southern Texas northward to Dimmit County.

2. **Erythrostemon gilliesii** (Hooker) Klotzsch in J. H. F. Link et al., Icon. Pl. Rar. 2: 98, plate 39. 1844 • Yellow bird-of-paradise [I] [W]

Poinciana gilliesii Hooker, Bot. Misc. 1: 129, plate 34. 1829; *Caesalpinia gilliesii* (Hooker) D. Dietrich

Shrubs, unarmed, to 3 m. **Stems** glabrous when young becoming short-pilose and capitate-glandular. **Leaves:** stipules subpersistent, lanceolate-ovate to deltate or suborbiculate, 3–4 mm, stiff to hard, fringed on margins, apex acuminate to rounded, surfaces pubescent, margins fimbriate-glandular; petiole 1.5–3 cm, with broad pulvinus at base, pulvinus channeled, glabrous or short-hairy; rachis 9.5–21.5 cm, glabrous or sparsely red-glandular; pinnae 8–15 pairs, opposite (proximally) to alternate (distally), also with terminal pinna; leaflets in 7–11 opposite pairs, blades oblong-elliptic to narrowly ovate, 6–11 × 2–3 mm, margins thickened, apex acute, midvein evident abaxially, surfaces glabrous; blades with submarginal row of black, punctate glands, these sometimes sparse or absent. **Inflorescences** 30–40-flowered, terminal; axis spreading-pubescent, densely stipitate-glandular with pixie-cup glands; bracts caducous before anthesis, lanceolate-ovate, 18–23 mm, apex acuminate, pubescent with fimbriate-glandular margins. **Pedicels** unarticulate, 20–30 mm, abscising at base only, spreading-pubescent and densely stipitate-glandular with pixie-cup glands. **Flowers:** calyx lobes 18–25 mm, margins capitate-glandular ciliate, fringed at tip and slightly fringed on outer margin, abaxially short-pilose and capitate-glandular, adaxially glabrous; petals not clawed, blades glabrous and eglandular; banner broadly obovate, 22–32 × 17–20 mm, without appendage; lower laterals broadly obovate, 22–32 × 12–16 mm; upper laterals broadly obovate, 22–32 × 16–18 mm; filaments crimson, 70–95(–120) mm, pubescent on proximal 1/3; anthers 3 × 1.5 mm; ovary densely pubescent and stipitate-glandular; style crimson, 90–100(–120) mm, pubescent on at least proximal 1/3; stigma a terminal, funnel-shaped, unfringed chamber. **Legumes** 8–10.8 × 1.9–2.1 cm, subligneous, finely pubescent, glandular with stipitate, pixie-cup glands, these wearing off as fruit matures. **Seeds** 1–6, 10 × 9 mm. $2n = 24$.

Flowering nearly year-round. Disturbed areas, flood plains, rocky, thorn-scrub forests; 0–1700 m; introduced; Ariz., Calif., Nev., N.Mex., Okla., Tex., Utah; South America (Argentina, Uruguay); introduced also in Mexico, Africa, Australia.

Erythrostemon gilliesii can create dense stands in forests. The species is cultivated as an ornamental nearly worldwide.

3. **Erythrostemon mexicanus** (A. Gray) Gagnon & G. P. Lewis, PhytoKeys 71: 124. 2016 • Mexican bird-of-paradise

Caesalpinia mexicana A. Gray, Proc. Amer. Acad. Arts 5: 157. 1861; *C. robinsoniana* (Britton & Rose) G. P. Lewis; *Poincianella mexicana* (A. Gray) Britton & Rose; *P. robinsoniana* Britton & Rose

Shrubs or trees, unarmed, 1–6 m. **Stems** bark greenish gray, smooth, with raised orange-brown or pale gray lenticels in semaphore lines, inner bark green, glabrous or pubescent. **Leaves:** stipules early caducous, ovate, 15 mm, base cordate-auriculate proximal to point of attachment, apex acute to rounded, surface glabrous, margins ciliate and glandular; petiole 2–8 cm, glabrous or pubescent, eglandular; rachis 4–12 cm, glabrous or pubescent, eglandular; pinnae 2–4(or 5) pairs, opposite, also with terminal pinna; leaflets in (2 or)3–5(or 6) opposite pairs, petiolulate, blades obovate-

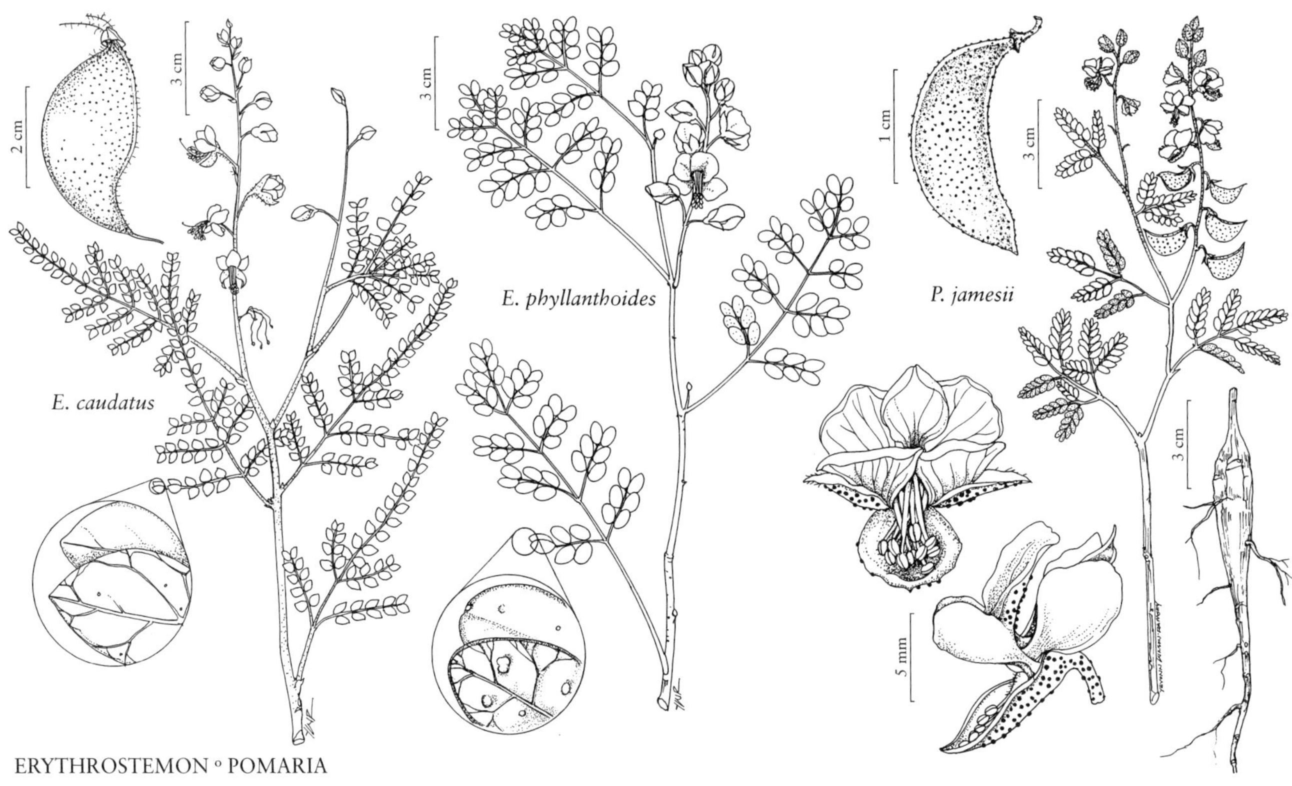

ERYTHROSTEMON ◦ POMARIA

elliptic, median 10–28 × 7–18 mm, terminal 11–35 × 7–18 mm, base inequilateral, margins revolute, slightly thickened, apex obtuse, rounded, truncate or shallowly emarginated, main vein prominent abaxially, secondary veins brochidodromous, surfaces glabrous or moderately pubescent, or abaxially with small tuft of hairs in main vein axis; blades eglandular but with gland-tipped, cone-shaped appendages, clustered into a corona at pinnae insertions and a single gland-tipped appendage proximal to each leaflet pulvinule, these evident on very young foliage. **Inflorescences** 20–30+-flowered, axillary or terminal, compact or long and lax, erect, 4–30 cm; axis, pedicels, and calyces moderately pubescent or glabrous, eglandular; bracts early caducous, ovate, concave, 0.5–2 mm, glabrous with ciliate margins. **Pedicels** articulate 2–7 mm proximal to calyx, 13–30 mm, when pubescent, hairs densest at point of articulation. **Flowers:** calyx base tapering into distal section of pedicel, lobes 6–9 mm, lower lobe cucullate in bud, imbricate in anthesis, inner surface densely pubescent; petals clawed, blade base and claw pubescent; banner spotted or faintly streaked orange-red at base, obovate to cordate, 10–12 × 8–10 mm (including 1–1.5 mm claw), apex emarginate, abaxially stipitate-glandular with yellow or orangish glands on proximal ½, blade base and claw pubescent, claw margins stipitate-glandular, inner surface of claw without appendage or thickened ridge; upper laterals obovate-suborbiculate to cordate, 12–14 × 9–10 mm (including 1.5–2 mm claw), apex emarginate, base of blade and claw glandular abaxially, claw sparsely pubescent inside; lower laterals obovate-elliptic to cordate, apex emarginate; filaments 12–13 mm, pubescent on basal ½–¾; anthers 2 × 0.8 mm; ovary pubescent and eglandular or densely glandular; style curved, 10 mm, pubescent; stigma a terminal, fringed, tubular or funnel-shaped chamber. **Legumes** 4.4–7.5 × 1.4–2 cm (including a 1.5 mm beak), subligneous, glabrous or moderately to sparsely glandular with sessile or short-stalked glands. **Seeds** (1 or)2–5, orbicular or cordate, 9–10 × 7.5–8.5 mm, shiny.

Flowering Jan–Nov. Low, deciduous forests, open semiarid scrub; 10–150 m; Tex.; Mexico (Baja California, Chihuahua, Hidalgo, Jalisco, Nayarit, Nuevo León, Querétaro, San Luis Potosí, Tamaulipas, Veracruz).

Erythrostemon mexicanus is cultivated as an ornamental in tropical and subtropical climates. The native range extends into extreme southern Texas as far northward as Webb County.

4. **Erythrostemon phyllanthoides** (Standley) Gagnon & G. P. Lewis, PhytoKeys 71: 125. 2016 • Bird-of-paradise, dwarf poinciana, south Texas rushpea [C] [F]

Caesalpinia phyllanthoides Standley, Contr. U.S. Natl. Herb. 23: 425. 1922; *Poincianella phyllanthoides* (Standley) Britton & Rose

Herbs or shrubs, clonal, unarmed, woody-based, 0.3–0.8 m, rhizomatous. **Stems** with dense, white, pustular lenticels, puberulous, glabrescent, sparsely glandular or eglandular. **Leaves:** stipules not seen; petiole 1.3–4.1 cm, glabrous or puberulous and with few stipitate glands near base; rachis 2.5–5 cm, glabrous, sometimes with few short-stalked glands; pinnae 3 or 4 pairs, opposite, also with terminal pinna, gland-tipped appendages clustered at pinnae insertions; leaflets in 2 or 3 opposite pairs, petiolulate, a minute gland-tipped appendage at base of each petiolule, blades obovate to elliptic, terminal blades 4.5–11 × 3–7 mm, median blades 4–11 × 3–9 mm, fleshy, margins thickened, often drying purplish, apex rounded to obtuse, venation obscure, main vein evident abaxially, secondary veins brochidodromous, surfaces glabrous; blades eglandular. **Inflorescences** 15–20-flowered, terminal or axillary, axis glabrous, eglandular; bracts ovate, 2.5–4.5 mm, apex acute, puberulous with fimbriate-glandular margins. **Pedicels** articulate 1 mm proximal to calyx, 7–14 mm, puberulous, stipitate-glandular near apex. **Flowers:** calyx abaxial lobe 5–7.5 mm, other four 4.5–6 mm, puberulous and stipitate-glandular, margins fimbriate-glandular; petals clawed; banner ovate-elliptic, 11 × 7–9 mm (including 0.5 mm claw), claw margins pubescent, a small triangle of hairs at claw apex on inner surface, petal without a ridge or flap of thickened tissue at claw apex, a few glands on blade margin near base; upper laterals obovate, 11 × 6 mm (including 1 mm claw), claw sparsely hairy and short-stalked glandular; lower laterals oblanceolate, 12 × 4.5 mm (including 2 mm claw), claw stipitate-glandular, glabrous; filaments 9–10 mm, pubescent on basal ½; anthers 1.5 × 0.8 mm; ovary puberulous, especially on suture, densely short-stalked glandular throughout; style curved, 10.5 mm, glabrous; stigma a terminal, flared or funnel-shaped chamber. **Legumes** 2.5 × 1.3 cm, subligneous, glabrous, with few scattered dark glands. **Seeds** 1 or 2.

Flowering Feb–Aug. Subtropical, arid thorn scrub on limestone outcrops, sandy loam soils; of conservation concern; 30–70 m; Tex.; Mexico (Tamaulipas).

Erythrostemon phyllanthoides is known from Jim Wells and Live Oak counties. The species is in the Center for Plant Conservation's National Collection of Endangered Plants as *Caesalpinia phyllanthoides*.

16. POMARIA Cavanilles, Icon. 5: 1, plate 402. 1799 • [For Dominic Pomar, 1598–1621, botanist and physician to Philip III of Spain]

Beryl B. Simpson

Melanosticta de Candolle

Herbs, perennial, shrubs, or subshrubs, unarmed; from thick taproot, or roots fasciculate, black. **Stems** ascending, pubescent, trichomes often orange drying black, multicellular, glandular-punctate, appearing as dots, or multicellular projections. **Leaves** alternate, odd-bipinnate; stipules present, persistent or tardily deciduous, surfaces often pubescent, also with glandular-punctate trichomes; petiolate; pinnae (3–)5–7, opposite, attachment often marked by ring of orange, glandular-punctate trichomes; leaflets 4–10 per pinna, blade margins entire, surfaces glabrous or pubescent, trichomes simple, conspicuous, orange drying black, glandular-punctate abaxially. **Inflorescences** 6–31-flowered, terminal or axillary, racemes; bracts reduced or absent. **Flowers** caesalpinioid, androecium and gynoecium cupped in lower sepal; calyx decidous in fruit, connate basally, sepals linear, laciniate, valvate in bud, lobes 5, unequal; corolla yellow, often with red markings, petals ± spatulate, claw differentiated from blade; stamens 10, unequal, distinct; anthers dorsifixed, usually red, 1 mm; ovary often villous, densely covered with glandular-punctate trichomes and multicellular projections; style arcuate; stigma impressed, lateral. **Fruits** legumes, stipitate, laterally compressed, oblong, oblong-lanceoloid, lunate, or oval, dehiscent, abruptly narrowed at base, apex mucronate by persistent style, glabrous or pubescent, also glandular-punctate. **Seeds** 1–3[or 4], compressed, oval.

Species 15 (5 in the flora): w, c United States, Mexico, South America, s Africa.

Pomaria was confounded for years with both *Hoffmannseggia* and *Caesalpinia*. The former because species of both genera are small shrubs or perennial herbs and the latter because of *C. caudata* (= *Erythrostemon caudatus*), a species that resembles *Pomaria* (and *Hoffmannseggia*) in habit. *Pomaria* is distinguished readily from both of these genera because the abaxial sepal is larger than the other four and projects between the two lowermost petals; it forms a narrow elongate cup with the stamens and gynoecium nestled inside. Because the ovary and style are horizontal relative to the axis of the plant, the stigma is lateral and faces upward, thus facilitating contact by insect visitors. In addition, the exterior surfaces of the sepals appear striped due to the presence of glandular-punctate trichomes in rows parallel to the midvein and margins. *Pomaria* is distinctive also in having complex multicellular projections on the fruit consisting of a cylindrical stalk bearing plumose lateral and/or apical trichomes. Phylogenetic studies have shown that *Pomaria* is sister to *Erythrostemon*, a segregate of *Caesalpinia* in the broad sense (E. Gagnon et al. 2016).

In descriptions, leaf length includes petiole. No chromosome counts have been reported for any species of *Pomaria*.

SELECTED REFERENCES Simpson, B. B. 1998. A revision of *Pomaria* (Fabaceae) in North America. Lundellia 1: 46–71. Simpson, B. B. et al. 2006. Phylogeny and biogeography of *Pomaria* (Caesalpinioideae: Leguminosae). Syst. Bot. 31: 792–804.

1. Legumes lunate or symmetrically oval in outline, glabrous, puberulent, or pilose, with few or scattered glandular-punctate trichomes, sometimes with scattered multicellular (stellate) projections to 0.4 mm.
   2. Subshrubs; legumes symmetrically oval in outline, glabrous or puberulent and with few glandular-punctate trichomes, margins with black, glandular-punctate trichomes, and many multicellular projections to 1 mm . . . . 4. *Pomaria brachycarpa*
   2. Herbs; legumes lunate in outline, glabrous or pilose and with scattered glandular-punctate trichomes, and scattered multicellular projections to 0.4 mm, each with numerous apical trichomes, appearing stellate, margins densely covered with complex multicellular projections to 0.4 mm. . . . . 5. *Pomaria jamesii*
1. Legumes oblong-lanceolate or obliquely oblong in outline, pilose and with scattered or few glandular-punctate trichomes, or with few, scattered or, sometimes, dense multicellular projections 0.5–2 mm or less than 0.5 mm.
   3. Abaxial sepal with larger punctate trichomes that dry black, and smaller non-punctate hairs remaining orange or red; legume margins with multicellular projections to 1 mm . . . . 3. *Pomaria melanosticta*
   3. Abaxial sepal with evenly sized black, glandular-punctate trichomes; legume margins pilose or with few multicellular projections to 0.5 mm.
      4. Legumes with multicellular projections less than 0.5 mm. . . . . 1. *Pomaria austrotexana*
      4. Legumes with few multicellular projections 0.5–2 mm. . . . . 2. *Pomaria wootonii*

1. Pomaria austrotexana B. B. Simpson, Lundellia 1: 51, fig. 1. 1998

Subshrubs, decumbent at base, 15–60 cm; from thick, woody root-crown. **Mature stems** reddish, ± rugose to striate, densely appressed-pubescent. **Leaves** 55–70 × 15–30 mm; stipules filiform, 3 × 3 mm, margins ± entire to pinnatifid, densely tomentose; pinnae 5–7; leaflets 6–10 per pinna, blades oblong, 3–6 × 1–2.5 mm, apex rounded, surfaces densely, evenly pilose, with numerous glandular-punctate trichomes abaxially, moderately to densely tomentose adaxially. **Racemes** 7–15-flowered, terminal, 7–12 cm. **Flowers** upright, almost bilabiate in outline, 12–20 × 6–10 mm; abaxial sepal 9 × 3 mm; lateral sepals 8 × 4 mm; abaxial sepal pilose and with short, curled trichomes on midveins and margins and mixed with evenly-sized black, glandular-punctate trichomes; banner yellow with dark red blotches, 8 × 3 mm, with small tuft of trichomes in fold of claw and very few glandular trichomes abaxially; lateral petals yellow, 8 × 4 mm, mostly glabrous. **Legumes** upright, oblong-lanceolate in outline, 20–35 × 10 mm, pilose and with few glandular-punctate trichomes and with scattered multicellular projections less than 0.5 mm, with white trichomes radiating apically, margins pubescent with short curled trichomes and with few multicellular projections to 0.5 mm. **Seeds** 2.

Flowering spring. Deep sands; 0–200 m; Tex.; Mexico (Tamaulipas).

Pomaria austrotexana appears to be uncommon in southern Texas and adjacent Mexico.

2. Pomaria wootonii (Britton) B. B. Simpson, Lundellia 1: 69. 1998

Larrea wootonii Britton in N. L. Britton et al., N. Amer. Fl. 23: 315. 1930; *Caesalpinia wootonii* (Britton) Eifert

Shrubs, 45–60 cm; roots unknown. **Mature stems** brown, striate, pilose, also with scattered glandular-punctate trichomes. **Leaves** 27–95 × 22–50 mm; stipules linear, 2–3 × 0.3 mm, margins ± entire, densely pubescent; pinnae 5–7; leaflets 8–10 per pinna, blades oblong, 4–1 × 2–5 mm, apex apiculate, surfaces with short, curled trichomes abaxially, especially on margins and veins, very sparsely pilose adaxially. **Racemes** 6–10-flowered, axillary and terminal, 2–8.9 cm. **Flowers** upright, almost bilabiate in outline, 6–9 × 7–9 mm; abaxial sepal 5.5 × 2.5 mm; lateral sepals 6 × 2–3.5 mm; sepals shortly lanose on margins, sparsely pilose at base and on veins, with few evenly sized black, scattered glandular-punctate trichomes; banner yellow, 3–5.5 × 2 mm, very villous inside fold of claw, sometimes lanose basally and bearing glandular-punctate trichomes sometimes elongate abaxially; lateral petals yellow, 5–6 × 2–3.5 mm, sometimes sparsely villous on inner claw, with few peltate, glandular trichomes abaxially. **Legumes** upright, oblong-lanceolate in outline, 20–21 × 7–8 mm, pilose and with scattered glandular-punctate trichomes and with few multicellular projections 0.5–2 mm with lateral and apical trichomes, margins pilose. **Seeds** 1–3.

Flowering spring–fall. Caliche, shale, or limestone soils; 0–800 m; Tex.; Mexico (Coahuila, Nuevo León, Tamaulipas).

Pomaria wootonii was reported by B. B. Simpson (1998) as occurring only in northern Mexico; specimens seen subsequently have indicated that probably it occurs in southernmost Texas. It may hybridize with *P. austrotexana*.

3. Pomaria melanosticta S. Schauer, Linnaea 20: 748. 1847

Caesalpinia melanosticta (S. Schauer) Fisher; *C. melanosticta* var. *greggii* (Fisher) Fisher; *C. melanosticta* var. *parryi* (Fisher) Fisher; *C. parryi* (Fisher) Eifert; *Hoffmannseggia melanosticta* (S. Schauer) A. Gray; *H. melanosticta* var. *greggii* Fisher; *H. melanosticta* var. *parryi* Fisher; *H. parryi* (Fisher) B. L. Turner; *Larrea melanosticta* (S. Schauer) Britton; *L. parryi* (Fisher) Britton

Subshrubs, 30–60 cm; from roots thickened at ground level. **Mature stems** gray to red-brown, striate, sometimes canescent. **Leaves** 30–75 × 20–45 mm; stipules linear-lanceolate, 2–4 × 0.5–1 mm, margins slightly pectinate to double-laciniate, densely villous; pinnae 5–9; leaflets 4–8 per pinna, blades oblong to oblong-obovate, 3–13 × 2–7 mm, apex rounded to slightly emarginate, surfaces densely white-villous to strigose abaxially, especially margins and midveins, also evenly covered with glandular-punctate trichomes, sparsely pilose adaxially. **Racemes** 10–31-flowered, terminal, 7–30 cm. **Flowers** upright, turbinate in outline, 6–10 × 6–10 mm; abaxial sepal 5–8 × 2–3 mm; lateral sepals 5–9 × 2–3 mm; sepals villous abaxially and marginally, also densely covered with 2 kinds of glandular trichomes, with larger punctate hairs that dry black, and smaller non-punctate hairs that remain orange or red; banner bright yellow with red spots, 4–6 × 1.5–2 mm, villous in fold and abaxial portions of claw, glabrous or with glandular-punctate trichomes abaxially; lateral petals yellow, fading pink or dull red, 5–6 × 2–3 mm, glabrous or villous on abaxial blade claw. **Legumes** upright, obliquely oblong in outline, curved distally, 20–32 × 10–15 mm, pilose and with scattered glandular-punctate trichomes and dense, red columnar multicellular projections to 2 mm, with white trichomes laterally and apically, margins fringed with dense array of similar multicellular projections to 1 mm. **Seeds** 1 or 2.

Flowering summer–early fall. Limestone or gypsum soils; 500–2000 m; Tex.; Mexico (Chihuahua, Coahuila, Hidalgo, Nuevo León, Querétaro, San Luis Potosí, Zacatecas).

Pomaria melanosticta is known from Brewster and Presidio counties.

4. Pomaria brachycarpa (A. Gray) B. B. Simpson, Lundellia 1: 54. 1998 [C] [E]

Hoffmannseggia brachycarpa A. Gray, Smithsonian Contr. Knowl. 3(5): 55. 1852 (as Hoffmanseggia); *Caesalpinia brachycarpa* (A. Gray) Fisher; *Larrea brachycarpa* (A. Gray) Britton

Subshrubs, to 40 cm; from thick taproot. **Mature stems** yellow to brown, striate, with glandular-punctate trichomes. **Leaves** 50–60 × 30–35 mm; stipules oblanceolate, 1.5–3 × 1.5–2 mm, margins slightly serrate to laciniate, ciliate with simple trichomes, mixed with glandular-punctate trichomes; pinnae (3–)5–7; leaflets 6–10 per pinna, blades oblong, 3–7 × 1.2–3 mm, apex rounded, surfaces glabrous or puberulent with scattered glandular-punctate trichomes abaxially, primarily submarginally, glabrous or puberulent adaxially. **Racemes** 6–25-flowered, terminal, 7–13 cm. **Flowers** nutant, turbinate in outline, 6–8 × 6–7 mm; abaxial sepal 5–6 × 2 mm; lateral sepals 5 × 3–3.5 mm; sepals sparsely pilose on margins and abaxial midvein, also with submarginal glandular-punctate trichomes; banner yellow, 5–6 × 2–2.5 mm, tuft of trichomes in fold and at base of claw, also with few glandular-punctate trichomes abaxially on expanded blade; lateral petals yellow, 5.9–5.5 × 3–3.5 mm, glabrous. **Legumes** upright, bilaterally symmetrical, oval in outline, 15–21 × 7–10 mm, glabrous or puberulent and with few glandular-punctate trichomes, margins with black, glandular-punctate trichomes and many multicellular projections to 1 mm, each terminating in radiating trichomes or cap. **Seeds** 1 or 2.

Flowering spring (late fall). Live oak savanna, rocky clay or limestone; of conservation concern; 400–800 m; Tex.

Pomaria brachycarpa is restricted to Crockett, Edwards, Kimball, Kinney, Menard, and Sutton counties on the Edwards Plateau of central Texas. A report of this species from New Mexico by W. C. Martin and C. R. Hutchins (1980) stems from "New Mexico" printed (in error) on the Wright type sheet and thus reported by A. Gray in his description as occurring there (B. B. Simpson 1998).

5. Pomaria jamesii (Torrey & A. Gray) Walpers, Repert. Bot. Syst. 1: 811. 1843 • False mesquite, rush-pea [F]

Hoffmannseggia jamesii Torrey & A. Gray, Fl. N. Amer. 1: 393. 1840 (as Hoffmanseggia); *Caesalpinia jamesii* (Torrey & A. Gray) Fisher; *H. jamesii* var. *popinoensis* Fisher; *Larrea jamesii* (Torrey & A. Gray) Britton

Herbs, to 50 cm; from thick, spindle-shaped taproot. **Mature stems** yellow, striate, puberulent. **Leaves** 42–75 × 25–60 mm; stipules linear to lanceolate, 4 × 5 mm, margins ± entire, pubescent, with few glandular-punctate trichomes; pinnae 5–7; leaflets 8–20 per pinna, blades oblong, 2.5–7 × 1–2.5 mm, apex rounded, surfaces densely strigose or covered with curly trichomes mixed with glandular-punctate trichomes, especially marginally and abaxially, few scattered trichomes to moderately strigose adaxially. **Racemes** 16–26-flowered, axillary and terminal, 12–15 cm. **Flowers** usually nutant at anthesis, turbinate in outline, 6–10 × 9–10 mm; abaxial sepal 7–9 × 4 mm; lateral sepals 6–9 × 9–10 mm; sepals villous abaxially, or with scattered, short, curled, and glandular-punctate trichomes; banner bright yellow with red markings, 5–9 × 2–2.5 mm, villous in fold of claw, also with glandular-punctate trichomes abaxially on claw and on basal portion of blade; lateral petals yellow, sometimes red basally, 6–8 × 3–3.5 mm, sometimes with few glandular-punctate trichomes abaxially at base, slightly villous on inner claw. **Legumes** decumbent, lunate in outline, 20–25 × 8–10 mm, glabrous or pilose, with scattered glandular-punctate trichomes and scattered multicellular projections to 0.4 mm, each with numerous apical trichomes, appearing stellate, primarily apically and on tip, margins densely covered with complex multicellular projections to 0.4 mm. **Seeds** 2.

Flowering summer–early fall. Grasslands, sandy or clay soils; 600–2300 m; Ariz., Colo., Kans., Mo., N.Mex., Okla., Tex.; Mexico (Chihuahua, Coahuila).

17. HOFFMANNSEGGIA Cavanilles, Icon 4: 63, plates 392; 393, fig. 1. 1798 (as Hoffmanseggia), name and orthography conserved • Rush-pea [For Johann Centurius von Hoffmannsegg, 1766–1849, German botanist who explored France, Hungary, Portugal, and Spain]

Beryl B. Simpson

Moparia Britton & Rose

Herbs, perennial, shrubs, or subshrubs, unarmed; with woody taproot or caudex, roots sometimes forming swollen, tuberlike spheres. **Stems** erect, spreading, or decumbent, woody or herbaceous and glabrous, pubescent, or puberulent, sometimes also stipitate-glandular. **Leaves** alternate, odd-bipinnate; stipules present, persistent, margins entire; petiolate; pinnae 1–13, opposite; leaflets 7–27 per pinna, blade margins entire, surfaces glabrous or pubescent. **Inflorescences** 3–27-flowered, terminal or axillary, racemes; bracts reduced or absent. **Flowers** caesalpinioid, zygomorphic; calyx persistent in fruit or jaggedly dehiscent prior to fruiting, slightly imbricate or valvate, lobes 5; corolla yellow, orange-yellow, or yellow-pink to rose, petals spatulate, claw differentiated from blade, banner claw usually concave, sometimes with trichomes in fold, sometimes surfaces and margins with glandular trichomes abaxially; stamens 10, basally connate, subequal, ± length of petals; filaments with clear, multicellular processes primarily basally; anthers dorsifixed, dehiscing introrsely; ovary elongate, laterally compressed; stipe relatively short; style as long as or longer than ovary; stigma terminal or obliquely so, impressed. **Fruits** legumes, stipitate, compressed laterally, falcate, lunate, trapezoidal, rectangular, oblong, suborbicular, or arcuate, dehiscent or indehiscent (when dehiscent, valves separating and flaring outward or each valve twisting spirally around itself), usually puberulent or pubescent. **Seeds** 1–11, compressed, usually ovoid or elliptic in outline, 2–7 × 1.5–6 mm; funiculus attached obliquely to seed creating shoulder at apex. $x = 12$.

Species 22 (7 in the flora): c, s, sw United States, Mexico, South America.

Hoffmannseggia occurs amphitropically in arid and semiarid regions of North America and semiarid and Andean areas of South America.

A molecular phylogenetic study of *Hoffmannseggia* (B. B. Simpson et al. 2004b) has shown that it consists of a woody clade and an herbaceous clade. Biogeographic studies (Simpson et al. 2004c) indicate that there have been four independent colonizations of North America from South America, two in each clade. While species of *Hoffmannseggia* often resemble those of *Caesalpinia* (in the broad sense) and *Pomaria*, phylogenetic studies have shown that the closest relatives of *Hoffmannseggia* are the South American *Balsamocarpon* Clos, *Stenodrepanum* Harms, and *Zuccagnia* Cavanilles (M. J. Nores et al. 2012). *Larrea* Ortega (1797 type *L. glauca* Ortega) was rejected in favor of conservation of *Hoffmannseggia*.

Leaf length given for each species below includes length of the petiole. Glandular trichomes are secretory and usually slightly bulbous at the tip.

SELECTED REFERENCES Fisher, E. M. 1892. Revision of North American species of *Hoffmannseggia*. Contr. U.S. Natl. Herb. 1: 143–150. Simpson, B. B. 1999. A revision of *Hoffmannseggia* (Fabaceae) in North America. Lundellia 2: 14–54. Simpson, B. B. et al. 2004b. Phylogeny and character evolution of *Hoffmannseggia* (Caesalpinieae: Caesalpinioideae: Leguminosae). Syst. Bot. 29: 933–946. Simpson, B. B. et al. 2004c. The biogeography of *Hoffmannseggia* (Leguminosae, Caesalpinioideae, Caesalpineae): A tale of many travels. J. Biogeogr. 31: 1–13. Simpson, B. B. and E. A. Ulibarri. 2006. A synopsis of the genus *Hoffmannseggia* (Leguminosae). Lundellia 9: 7–33.

1. Shrubs; pinnae 3; legumes lunate or falcate in outline (wider in middle), dehiscent, valves simply flaring, slightly twisted, or each spirally twisted around itself.
   2. Shrubs 50–250 cm, erect; terminal pinna longer than laterals; flowers 12–15 mm; calyces falling . . . . 1. *Hoffmannseggia microphylla*
   2. Shrubs to 30 cm, spreading; terminal pinna shorter than laterals; flowers 5–8 mm; calyces persistent . . . . 2. *Hoffmannseggia drummondii*
1. Herbs or subshrubs; pinnae (3–)5–13; legumes trapezoidal, arcuate, broadly oblong to suborbicular, falcate, or rectangular in outline, indehiscent or dehiscent and each valve spirally twisted around itself.
   3. Calyces and pedicels abaxially villous, puberulent to strigose, or densely pubescent and stipitate-glandular.
      4. Banner claw margins sparsely stipitate-glandular; legumes trapezoidal in outline, dehiscent, valves each tightly spirally twisted around itself after separating, pubescent to sparsely villous and stipitate-glandular. . . . . 3. *Hoffmannseggia oxycarpa*
      4. Banner claw margins notably stipitate-glandular; legumes rectangular or arcuate, indehiscent, valves flat, sparsely tomentose and sparsely stipitate-glandular . . . . 7. *Hoffmannseggia glauca*
   3. Calyces and pedicels abaxially pubescent, puberulent, tomentose, or strigose, trichomes eglandular.
      5. Legumes flat, arcuate (sometimes forming nearly a full circle), apices round. . . . . 6. *Hoffmannseggia drepanocarpa*
      5. Legumes ± undulate, broadly oblong, rectangular, or suborbicular, straight, apices acute.
         6. Flowers 6–10 mm; legumes 5–6 mm wide; Texas . . . . 4. *Hoffmannseggia tenella*
         6. Flowers 12–15 mm; legumes 10–20 mm wide; Colorado, Utah . . . . . . 5. *Hoffmannseggia repens*

1. Hoffmannseggia microphylla Torrey in W. H. Emory, Rep. U.S. Mex. Bound. 2(1): 58. 1859 (as Hoffmanseggia)

Caesalpinia virgata Fisher; *Larrea microphylla* (Torrey) Britton

Shrubs, erect, almost aphyllous, 50–250 cm; from woody taproot. **Leaves** 20–50 × 9–26 mm; stipules linear-lanceolate, 0.5–1.5 × 0.2–0.5 mm, margins fringed; pinnae 3, terminal longer than laterals; leaflets 9–23 per pinna, blades oblong to elliptic, 1.5–3.5 × 1–2 mm, surfaces sparsely to densely villous or strigose abaxially, glabrous or sparsely villous adaxially. **Racemes** 10–27-flowered, terminal or axillary, 9–16 cm; rachis and pedicels strigose and, sometimes, sparsely stipitate-glandular. **Flowers** remaining upright, openly flared, 12–15 × 6–12 mm; calyx jaggedly dehiscent before fruiting, distinct portion 4–12 × 5–8 mm, strigose, sometimes also stipitate-glandular; banner yellow and basally with red markings, 5–10 × 4–7 mm, with short, round glandular trichomes abaxially, tuft of trichomes at base of claw adaxially; lateral petals yellow, 5–10 × 3–5 mm, with glandular trichomes abaxially. **Legumes** falcate to lunate in outline, 18–23 × 5–8 mm, dehiscent, margins slightly raised, shortly villous, apex acute to mucronate; valves flaring outward, sometimes each spirally twisted around itself, with jagged ring at base where sepals dehisced, puberulent and stipitate-glandular. **Seeds** 3–6. **2*n*** = 24.

Flowering spring. Sonoran Desert; 0–1000 m; Ariz., Calif.; Mexico (Baja California, Sonora).

In California, *Hoffmannseggia microphylla* occurs in Imperial, Inyo, Riverside, San Bernardino, and San Diego counties.

2. Hoffmannseggia drummondii Torrey & A. Gray, Fl. N. Amer. 1: 393. 1840 (as Hoffmanseggia) • Drummond rush-pea

Caesalpinia drummondii (Torrey & A. Gray) Fisher; *C. texensis* (Fisher) Fisher; *Hoffmannseggia texensis* Fisher; *Larrea drummondii* (Torrey & A. Gray) Britton; *L. texensis* (Torrey & A. Gray) Britton

Shrubs, low, spreading, to 30 cm; from woody taproot. **Leaves** 10–23 × 10–15 mm; stipules ovate, 1 × 1 mm; pinnae 3, terminal shorter than laterals; leaflets 7–13 per pinna, blades oblong, 3–3.3 × 0.5–1.6 mm, surfaces glabrous, sometimes with very few multicellular, glandular trichomes abaxially. **Racemes** 3–8-flowered, terminal or axillary, 2–4 cm; rachis and pedicels sparsely stipitate-glandular. **Flowers** turbinate in outline, 5–8 × 3–8 mm; calyx persistent in fruit, distinct portion 0.5–2 × 4.5 mm, pubescent and sparsely stipitate-glandular;

banner yellow with red markings, 3–7 × 2.5–5 mm, with few multicellular, glandular trichomes abaxially, a few trichomes at base of claw adaxially; lateral petals yellow, 3–7 × 2–3 mm, with few multicellular, glandular trichomes at base abaxially. **Legumes** lunate in outline, 16–20 × 6–8 mm, dehiscent or indehiscent, margins glabrous, apex mucronate; valves thin, flaring outward when dehiscent, glabrous or glabrate. **Seeds** 1 or 2. $2n = 24$.

Flowering spring (year-round). Sandy-clay soils; 0–700 m; Tex.; Mexico (Tamaulipas).

In Texas, *Hoffmannseggia drummondii* is known from the south-central part of the state.

3. Hoffmannseggia oxycarpa Bentham, Smithsonian Contr. Knowl. 3(5): 55. 1852 (as Hoffmanseggia)

Caesalpinia oxycarpa (Bentham) Fisher; *Larrea oxycarpa* (Bentham) Britton

Subspecies 2 (1 in the flora): sw United States, n Mexico.

Subspecies *arida* (Rose) B. B. Simpson occurs in Hidalgo and Querétaro, Mexico, and differs from subsp. *oxycarpa* by being more robust and by legumes having black-tipped, multicellular trichomes.

3a. Hoffmannseggia oxycarpa Bentham subsp. **oxycarpa**

Subshrubs, 10–34(–40) cm; from woody taproot. **Leaves** (7–)11–70(–93) × 16–38 mm; stipules lanceolate, 2–5 × 1–1.5 mm, margins villous, glandular; pinnae (3–)5–9; leaflets 4–9 per pinna, blades ovate to oblong, 2–12 × 1–6 mm, surfaces glabrous. **Racemes** 4–18-flowered, terminal, 0.6–2.1 cm; rachis and pedicels villous and stipitate-glandular. **Flowers** turning downward, broadly turbinate, 8–10.8 × 8 mm; calyx persistent, edges red, distinct portion 5–8 × 1.5–2 mm, villous and stipitate-glandular; banner yellow dotted with red, fading pinkish red, 6–13 × 3–6 mm, glabrous abaxially, with few trichomes at base of claw adaxially or claw margins sparsely hairy; lateral petals yellow, 6–10 × 3–4 mm, glabrous abaxially, eglandular. **Legumes** trapezoidal in outline, elongate, 8–36 × 4–7 mm, dehiscent, margins pubescent, apex acute; valves each spirally twisted around itself after separating, pubescent to sparsely villous, with mixed yellow or orange capitate, multicellular, glandular trichomes. **Seeds** 4–6. $2n = 24$.

Flowering spring (fall, winter). Rocky limestone soils; 600–2300 m; N.Mex., Tex.; Mexico (Coahuila, Nuevo León, Tamaulipas).

4. Hoffmannseggia tenella Tharp & L. O. Williams, Ann. Missouri Bot. Gard. 23: 451. 1936 (as Hoffmanseggia) • Slender rush-pea [C] [E]

Herbs, spreading or decumbent, to 20 cm; from woody taproot. **Leaves** 53–120 × 17–40 mm; stipules ovate, 1.5–2 × 1–1.5 mm; pinnae 5–7; leaflets 5 or 6 per pinna, blades oblong, 3.5–5.5 × 1.5–2 mm, surfaces puberulent to slightly tomentose abaxially (especially margins), glabrous adaxially. **Racemes** 3–7-flowered, terminal, 1.3–10 cm; rachis and pedicels sparsely pubescent, eglandular. **Flowers** narrowly conical, 6–10 × 3–4 mm; calyx persistent, margins reddish, distinct portion 4–5 × 1 mm, shortly pubescent abaxially (including margins), eglandular; banner yellow-pink to rose, folded, 6 × 4 mm, glabrous; lateral petals rose, 4 × 2.5 mm. **Legumes** upright, slightly undulate, straight, edges often red, rectangular, 8–19 × 5–6 mm, indehiscent, base pointed, margins pronounced, puberulent to pubescent, apex acute; valves flat, thin, reticulate, glabrate or puberulent. **Seeds** 2–4.

Flowering spring–fall. Clay soils in coastal prairie grasslands; of conservation concern; 10–20 m; Tex.

Hoffmannseggia tenella is known from Kleberg and Nueces counties in southern Texas. It is in the Center for Plant Conservation's National Collection of Endangered Plants.

5. Hoffmannseggia repens (Eastwood) Cockerell, Muhlenbergia 4: 68. 1908 (as Hoffmanseggia) • Creeping rush-pea [E]

Caesalpinia repens Eastood, Zoë 4: 116, plate 26. 1893; *Moparia repens* (Eastwood) Britton & Rose

Herbs, 9–15 cm; from woody caudex, with spreading, underground rhizomes. **Leaves** 2–10 × 24–30 mm; stipules ovate, 3–5.5 × 1.5–4 mm, pubescent; pinnae 3–9; leaflets 9–15 per pinna, blades obtuse-oblong, 5–9 × 2–4 mm, surfaces puberulent to pubescent abaxially, sparsely pubescent adaxially. **Racemes** 10–15-flowered, terminal, 9.7–14 cm; rachis and pedicels puberulent, eglandular. **Flowers** turning downward, broadly opening, 12–15 × 8–13 mm; calyx persistent, distinct portion 7–11 × 2–5 mm, densely tomentose abaxially, eglandular; banner bright yellow or orange-yellow with red markings, fading pink to pale orange, 13–15 × 6 mm, glabrous abaxially, with tuft of trichomes at base of claw adaxially; lateral petals yellow, fading pinkish, 12–13 ×

3–6 mm, glabrous abaxially. **Legumes** often undulate, straight, green turning red, compressed between seeds, broadly oblong or suborbicular in outline, 20–54 × 10–20 mm, indehiscent, margins pronounced, puberulent, apex acute, often with portion of withered style; valves thin, flat, reticulate, sparsely puberulent. **Seeds** 1–4(–6).

Flowering late spring. Dunes, sandy soils; 900–1900 m; Colo., Utah.

Hoffmannseggia repens usually flowers in spring but will flower sporadically at other times during wet years.

6. **Hoffmannseggia drepanocarpa** A. Gray, Smithsonian Contr. Knowl. 3(5): 58. 1852 (as Hoffmanseggia) • Sickle-pod rush-pea

Caesalpinia drepanocarpa (A. Gray) Fisher; *Larrea drepanocarpa* (A. Gray) Britton

Herbs, 8–30 cm, with very short internodes, appearing almost fasciculate; from taproot. **Leaves** 30–100 × 13–30 mm; stipules lanceolate, 2–3 × 1–1.3 mm; pinnae 7–9; leaflets 9–19 per pinna, blades obtuse-ovate, 1–5.5 × 1–2.3 mm, surfaces glabrous or sparsely strigose abaxially, glabrous or sparsely pubescent adaxially. **Racemes** 3–11-flowered, terminal, 6–27 cm; rachis and pedicels strigose, eglandular. **Flowers** turbinate, 6–9 × 3.5–5 mm; calyx persistent, often roseate to burgundy, distinct portion 3–5 × 1–2 mm, pubescent to strigose abaxially, eglandular; banner yellow, sometimes tinged with red, 5–8 × 2.5–4.5 mm, glabrous abaxially, with small tuft of trichomes at base of claw adaxially; lateral petals yellow, sometimes tinged red, 6.5–8 × 2–5 mm, glabrous abaxially. **Legumes** flat, arcuate, sometimes forming nearly a full circle, pale brown or reddish, falcate, 23–40 × 5–8 mm, indehiscent, margins parallel, pronounced, puberulent, apex round, with remnants of withered style; valves reticulate, puberulent. **Seeds** 6–11. $2n = 24$.

Flowering spring (late summer). Grasslands in sandy or clay limestone soils; 900–2000 m; Ariz., Colo., Kans., N.Mex., Tex.; Mexico (Chihuahua, Coahuila).

7. **Hoffmannseggia glauca** (Ortega) Eifert, Sida 5: 43. 1972 (as Hoffmanseggia) • Hog potato, Indian rush-pea [F] [W]

Larrea glauca Ortega, Nov. Pl. Descr. Dec. 2: 15, plate 2. 1797; *Caesalpinia falcaria* (Cavanilles) Fisher var. *capitata* (Fisher) Fisher; *C. falcaria* var. *pringlei* (Fisher) Fisher; *C. falcaria* var. *rusbyi* (Fisher) Fisher; *Hoffmannseggia densiflora* Bentham; *H. falcaria* var. *capitata* Fisher; *H. falcaria* var. *pringlei* Fisher; *H. falcaria* var. *rusbyi* Fisher; *H. stricta* Bentham; *H. stricta* var. *demissa* A. Gray

Herbs, 5–30(–50) cm; from deep taproot, producing round, tuberlike spheres to 2 cm. **Leaves** 38–150 × 13–42 mm; stipules ovate, 1.5–4 × 1.5–3 mm, ciliate; pinnae 4–13; leaflets 7–27 per pinna, blades obtuse-ovate, 2–6 × 1–4.5 mm, surfaces strigose abaxially, glabrous adaxially. **Racemes** 4–15-flowered, terminal, 5–23 cm; rachis and pedicels puberulent to strigose and stipitate-glandular. **Flowers** turning downward, broadly flared, 10–16 × 10–18 mm; calyx persistent, densely pubescent abaxially, with multicellular, glandular trichomes; banner yellow, drying pink with red markings, 5–14 × 5 mm, conspicuous multicellular, glandular trichomes on claw and abaxial surface, with few hairs at base of folded claw adaxially; lateral petals bright yellow, 13 × 6 mm, with multicellular, glandular trichomes on claw margins and base abaxially. **Legumes** tan, rectangular to arcuate, sometimes expanded near apex, 20–40 × 5–8 mm, indehiscent, margins ± parallel, obscure, apex obtuse to acute; valves flat, sparsely tomentose, with a few scattered multicellular, glandular trichomes appearing as brown dots. **Seeds** 1–10. $2n = 24$.

Flowering spring. Disturbed areas; 0–3000 m; Ariz., Calif., Kans., N.Mex., Okla., Tex.; Mexico; South America (Argentina, Bolivia, Chile, Peru).

Hoffmannseggia glauca is considered a noxious weed in agricultural and pasture lands of the middle and southwestern United States, spreading aggressively by tuberous roots. While it is possible that it was introduced into North America by humans, historical use of the tubers by indigenous people in the American Southwest indicates a long association and, perhaps, natural long-distance dispersal from South America.

Hoffmannseggia falcaria Cavanilles, an illegitimate and superfluous name, pertains here.

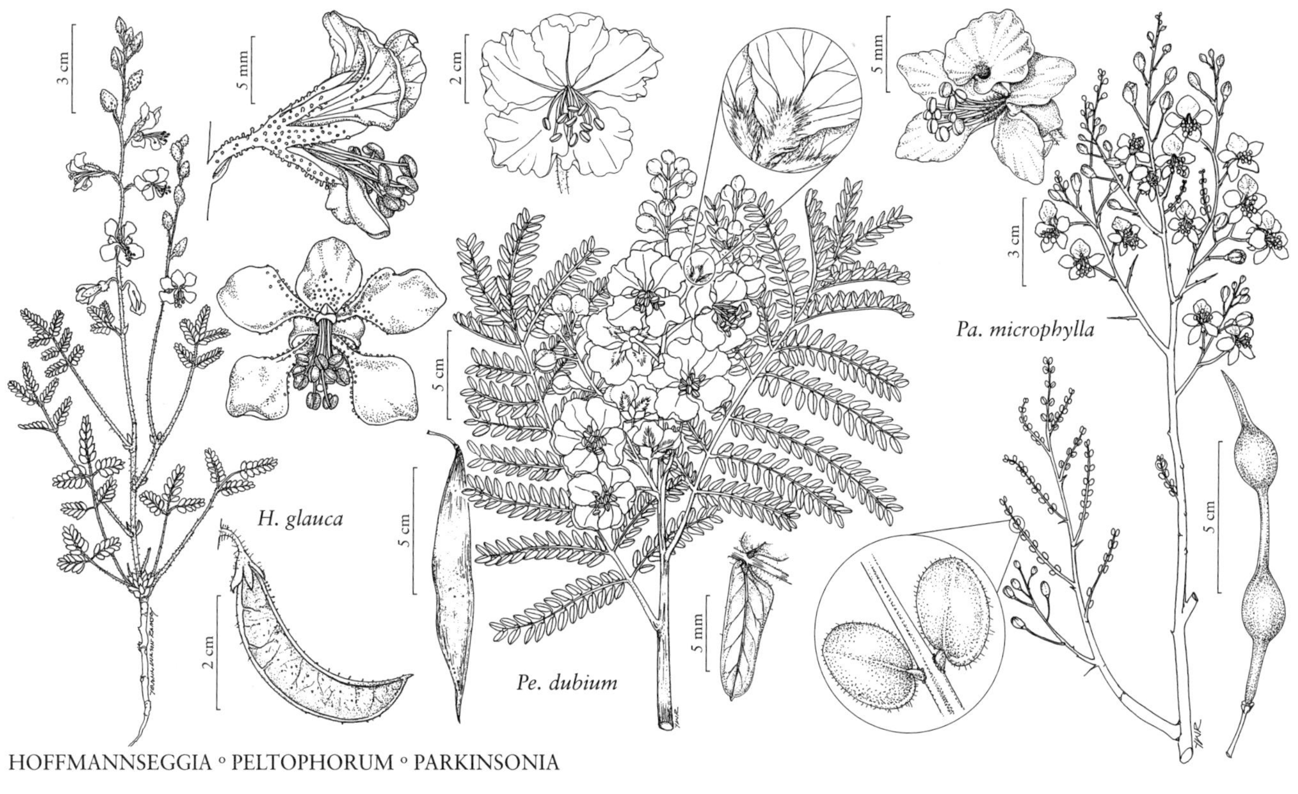

HOFFMANNSEGGIA ◦ PELTOPHORUM ◦ PARKINSONIA

18. PELTOPHORUM (Vogel) Bentham, J. Bot. (Hooker) 2: 75. 1840, name conserved • [Greek, *pelte*, shield, and *phoras*, bearing, alluding to broad, peltate stigma] [I]

Douglas H. Goldman

Caesalpinia Linnaeus sect. *Peltophorum* Vogel, Linnaea 11: 406. 1837

Trees, unarmed. **Branches** spreading. **Stems** pubescent becoming glabrescent, hairs red-brown. **Leaves** alternate, even-bipinnate; stipules present, deciduous, 1 mm, triangular, entire, not pinnatifid or lacerate; petiolate; pinnae [3–](5–)7–22 pairs, opposite; leaflets [6–]16–60 per pinna, stipels absent, blade margins entire, surfaces glabrous or pubescent. **Inflorescences** 30–300-flowered, terminal or axillary, panicles [racemes]; bracts present, early-deciduous to persistent, linear to deltate; bracteoles absent. **Flowers** caesalpinioid, often fragrant; calyx not persistent, ovate, imbricate, pubescent, lobes 5, longer than tube; corolla yellow, petals subequal, to 25 mm diam., not clawed, pubescent near base; stamens 10, distinct, densely pubescent basally; anthers dorsifixed; ovary sessile or nearly so, densely pubescent; style slender, elongate; stigma peltate, broad. **Fruits** legumes, erect to deflexed, short-stipitate, strongly compressed, oblong-ellipsoid, 4–12[–15] cm, with winglike margins, indehiscent, glabrous or finely pubescent. **Seeds** 1–4[–8], strongly compressed, oblong-ellipsoid. x = 13.

Species 5–7 (2 in the flora): introduced, Florida; West Indies, South America, se Asia, s Africa, Australia.

Peltophorum is closely related to the caesalpinioid genera *Delonix* and *Parkinsonia* (A. Bruneau et al. 2008). Species of *Peltophorum* are used as ornaments and for lumber, fuel, medicine, or fodder (G. P. Lewis 2005).

Peltophorum dubium and *P. pterocarpum* are widely cultivated for their attractive flowers, and have escaped and become naturalized in parts of peninsular Florida.

Baryxylum Loureiro, as applied to *Peltophorum*, is a rejected name.

1. Leaflet blades narrowly oblong, (4–)7–15 × (1.5–)2–4.5 mm, lengths usually 3–4 times widths, apices acute or apiculate; larger inflorescence rachises little, if at all, lenticellate . . . . 1. *Peltophorum dubium*
1. Leaflet blades oblong, (7–)10–21 × (3–)5–10 mm, lengths usually 1.5–3 times widths, apices usually retuse, sometimes rounded to blunt, not apiculate; larger inflorescence rachises densely lenticellate . . . . 2. *Peltophorum pterocarpum*

1. Peltophorum dubium (Sprengel) Taubert in H. G. A. Engler and K. Prantl, Nat. Pflanzenfam. 77[III,3]: 176. 1892 • Copperpod, horsebush [F] [I]

Caesalpinia dubia Sprengel, Syst. Veg. 2: 343. 1825

Trees to 10(–25) m. **Leaves** 15–55 cm; pinnae (10–)20–44; leaflets (20–)24–60 per pinna, blade narrowly oblong, (4–)7–15 × (1.5–)2–4.5 mm, length usually 3–4 times width, apex acute or apiculate. **Panicles** 14–40 cm; larger rachises little, if at all, lenticellate. **Flowers:** calyx lobes 6–9 mm; corolla 13–20 mm. **Legumes** narrowly oblong-ellipsoid, rarely weakly constricted between seeds, 4–8(–10) cm, base attenuate, apex acuminate. **Seeds** 1 or 2, obovoid. $2n = 26$.

Flowering Jun–Aug. Disturbed areas; 0–30[–600] m; introduced; Fla.; West Indies; South America.

2. Peltophorum pterocarpum (de Candolle) Backer ex K. Heyne, Nutt. Pl. Ned.-Ind. ed. 2, 2: 755. 1927 • Yellow poinciana [I]

Inga pterocarpa de Candolle in A. P. de Candolle and A. L. P. P. de Candolle, Prodr. 2: 441. 1825

Trees to 10[–35] m. **Leaves** 15–50 cm; pinnae 14–30; leaflets 16–40 per pinna, blade oblong, (7–)10–21 × (3–)5–10 mm, length usually 1.5–3 times width, apex usually retuse, sometimes rounded to blunt, not apiculate. **Panicles** 20–40 cm; larger rachises densely lenticellate. **Flowers:** calyx lobes [5–]7–11 mm; corolla [13–]15–25 mm. **Legumes** oblong-ellipsoid, usually slightly constricted between seeds, 4–12 cm, base cuneate, apex acuminate. **Seeds** 1–4, oblong. $2n = 26$.

Flowering May–Oct. Disturbed areas; 0–10[–300] m; introduced; Fla.; se Asia; Australia; introduced also in tropical and subtropical areas nearly worldwide.

The invalid name *Peltophorum inerme* Náves ex Fernández-Villar has sometimes been used for this species.

19. PARKINSONIA Linnaeus, Sp. Pl. 1: 375. 1753; Gen. Pl. ed. 5, 177. 1754 • Paloverde [For John Parkinson, 1567–1650, apothecary to King James I]

Alexander Krings

Wade Wall

Alice Broadhead

Cercidiopsis Britton & Rose; *Cercidium* Tulasne; *Peltophoropsis* Chiovenda

Trees or shrubs, armed or unarmed. **Stems** and branches green or yellowish green, erect, glabrous or strigulose, glabrescent. **Leaves** clustered, alternate from spurs, even-bipinnate, sometimes appearing pinnate; stipules present, caducous, minute, or spinescent; petiolate or petiole obsolete; pinnae 2(or 3)[4], glands linear, minute, in sparse to dense patches between leaflets, in leaflet axils, or surrounding pulvini; leaflets 2–76, alternate, subopposite, or opposite, blade margins entire, surfaces sparsely pubescent abaxially, glabrate or sparsely pubescent adaxially. **Inflorescences** 2–15-flowered, axillary, racemes [corymbiform]; bracts and bracteoles present. **Flowers** caesalpinoid; calyx actinomorphic, nearly aposepalous, nearly regular, lobes 5; corolla yellow, erose-margined, glabrous except claw pubescent; stamens 10, distinct or monadelphous, villous proximally, much longer than anthers; anthers basifixed. **Fruits** legumes, stipitate, compressed or subterete, sometimes torulose, oblong to linear, indehiscent, glabrous, glabrate, or pubescent. **Seeds** 1–5, oblong to suborbiculate in silhouette, 4–7 mm wide; hilum apical or subapical. $x = 14$.

Species ca. 12 (4 in the flora): s, w United States, Mexico, West Indies, Central America; introduced in South America, Asia, Africa, Australia.

Taxa referable to *Parkinsonia* usually have been treated in *Cercidium* and *Parkinsonia* (C. S. Sargent 1889; I. M. Johnston 1924; L. D. Benson 1940; A. M. Carter 1974, 1974b) or within a broad *Parkinsonia* (S. Watson 1876; J. P. M. Brenan 1963; D. Isely 1975; R. M. Polhill and J. E. Vidal 1981; J. A. Hawkins 1996). Molecular evidence from the chloroplast genome indicated that, together, *Cercidium* and *Parkinsonia* form a strongly supported monophyletic group (E. M. Haston et al. 2005) and a broad circumscription is adopted here.

1. Pinna rachillas (100–)150–600 mm, narrowly winged; leaflets 40–76, alternate, subopposite, or opposite (usually all on same rachilla); raceme axis 8–18 cm . . . . 1. *Parkinsonia aculeata*
1. Pinna rachillas 1.5–40 mm, not winged; leaflets 2–16, opposite; raceme axis 0.4–3.8 cm.
   2. Nodal spines absent, branch tips often spinescent; leaves appearing pinnate; petiole obsolete; leaflets (6–)12–16; rachillas with glandular patches surrounding leaflet pulvini or, at least, on opposing sides; sepal adaxial surfaces pubescent; petals light yellow, except adaxial one white or cream-yellow, not orange-dotted; ovaries densely sericeous; legumes constricted between seeds . . . . 2. *Parkinsonia microphylla*
   2. Nodal spines present; leaves evidently bipinnate; petiole 1.6–3.5 mm; leaflets 2–6 (or 8); rachillas with glandular patches on adaxial side, not surrounding leaflet pulvini; sepal adaxial surfaces glabrous; petals deep yellow, adaxial one often orange-dotted basally; ovaries glabrate or sericeous; legumes either not constricted between seeds or irregularly and indistinctly torulose.
      3. Stems pale green; ovaries glabrate; legumes not constricted between seeds; Arizona, California, Nevada . . . . .3. *Parkinsonia florida*
      3. Stems dark to olive green; ovaries sericeous or glabrate; legumes irregularly and indistinctly torulose; s Texas . . . . .4. *Parkinsonia texana*

1. Parkinsonia aculeata Linnaeus, Sp. Pl. 1: 375. 1753 • Jerusalem thorn, paloverde, retama [I] [W]

Parkinsonia thornberi M. E. Jones

Trees, to 10 m, with nodal spines. **Stems** yellowish green, twigs glabrous or sparsely pubescent (at least around nodes). **Leaves** appearing pinnate; stipules obsolescent or spinescent, spines to 20 mm; petiole obsolete; pinnae 2(or 3); petiolules 0.2–0.3 mm, sparsely pubescent; rachillas (100–) 150–600 mm, narrowly winged, with sparse, glandular patches in leaflet axils; leaflets 40–76, alternate, subopposite, or opposite, blades oblanceolate to oblong, 2–8 × 0.9–3 mm, base attenuate, apex obtuse, apiculate, surfaces sparsely pubescent abaxially, glabrate adaxially. **Racemes** 2–15-flowered, axis 8–18 cm, strigulose to glabrate; bracts linear or lanceolate, 2 × 0.3 mm; bracteoles caducous or subpersistent. **Pedicels** 5.4–13.8 mm, glabrous or sparsely pubescent, joints 1.5–3.5 mm from flower, not bearded, nearer flower than pedicel base. **Flowers:** calyx lobes usually deciduous, sparsely pubescent abaxially, pubescent adaxially; corolla 13–20 mm diam., petals light to deep yellow, adaxial one usually orange-dotted basally; ovary sericeous. **Legumes** subterete, constricted between seeds, 2–12 × 0.5–0.8 cm, glabrous. **Seeds** (1 or)2–5. $2n = 28$.

Flowering Mar–Sep. Low, poorly drained areas, open woods, roadsides, disturbed places; 0–1300 m;

introduced; Ala., Ariz., Calif., Fla., Ga., La., Miss., Nev., N.Mex., S.C., Tex., Utah; Mexico; West Indies; Central America; introduced also in South America, Asia, Africa, Australia.

The original distribution of *Parkinsonia aculeata* is unknown, possibly Central America and southern Mexico (R. S. Felger et al. 2001; G. P. Lewis et al. 2005; J. A. Hawkins et al. 2007). *Parkinsonia aculeata* is now extensively naturalized in the tropics and subtropics. Among native congenerics in the flora area, it shares adaxially pubescent calyx lobes only with *P. microphylla* and can be easily differentiated by the longer, winged rachillas, and 40–76, alternate or opposite leaflets per pinna versus (6–)12–16 and opposite per pinna in *P. microphylla*.

Hybrids between *Parkinsonia aculeata* and *P. microphylla* are known from the flora area. Individuals of *P. aculeata* × *P. microphylla* can be distinguished by the combination of rachillas of intermediate length (usually 2–6 times as long as in *P. microphylla*) and glandular patches completely or nearly completely surrounding the pulvini.

2. **Parkinsonia microphylla** Torrey in War Department [U.S.], Pacif. Railr. Rep. 4(5): 82. 1857 • Yellow paloverde F

Cercidiopsis microphylla (Torrey) Britton & Rose; *Cercidium microphyllum* (Torrey) Rose & I. M. Johnston

Trees or shrubs, 3–4.6 m, without nodal spines, branch tips often spinescent. **Stems** yellowish green, twigs moderately pubescent. **Leaves** appearing pinnate; stipules not spinescent, linear-lanceolate, 1.5 mm; petiole obsolete; pinnae 2(or 3); petiolules 0.2 mm, sparsely pubescent; rachillas 10–40 mm, not winged, with glandular patches surrounding leaflet pulvini or, at least, on opposing sides; leaflets (6–)12–16, opposite, blades elliptic to suborbiculate, 2–3 × 0.9–2.9 mm, base rounded, apex obtuse to rounded, not apiculate, surfaces sparsely pubescent. **Racemes** 2–15-flowered, axis 0.6–3.8 cm, strigulose; bracts ovate to lanceolate, 0.4–0.5 × 0.2–0.3 mm; bracteoles persistent. **Pedicels** 4.6–12.1 mm, pubescent, joints 1–3.6 mm from flower, bearded, distinctly nearer flower than pedicel base. **Flowers:** calyx lobes pubescent; corolla 8–12 mm diam., petals light yellow, except adaxial one white or cream-yellow; ovary densely sericeous. **Legumes** subterete, constricted between seeds, 3–12 × 0.8–1 cm, pubescent at least basally. **Seeds** 1–4. $2n = 28$.

Flowering Mar–May. Coarse soils of plains and hill slopes; 0–1100 m; Ariz., Calif.; Mexico (Baja California, Baja California Sur, Sonora).

Parkinsonia microphylla is the only *Parkinsonia* in the flora area with glandular patches completely around or, at least, on opposing sides of the leaflet pulvini. All other taxa have glandular patches in the leaflet axils (*P. aculeata*) or only adaxially between the leaflets (*P. florida* and *P. texana*).

3. **Parkinsonia florida** (Bentham ex A. Gray) S. Watson, Proc. Amer. Acad. Arts 11: 135. 1876 • Blue paloverde

Cercidium floridum Bentham ex A. Gray, Smithsonian Contr. Knowl. 3(5): 58. 1852; *C. torreyanum* (S. Watson) Sargent; *Parkinsonia torreyana* S. Watson

Trees, 2.5–8(–12) m, with nodal spines. **Stems** pale green, twigs moderately pubescent. **Leaves:** stipules not spinescent; petiole 1.6–3.5 mm, pubescent; pinnae 2; petiolules 0.2 mm, densely pubescent; rachillas 3–7 mm, not winged, with glandular patches on adaxial side, not surrounding leaflet pulvini; leaflets (4 or)6(or 8), opposite, blades elliptic to obovate, 3–7 × 1.6–3 mm, base cuneate to rounded, apex truncate to rounded, not apiculate, surfaces sparsely pubescent abaxially, sparsely pubescent to glabrate adaxially. **Racemes** 2–10-flowered, axis 1.1–3.5 cm, strigulose to glabrate; bracts lanceolate, 0.3–0.4 × 0.2–0.3 mm; bracteoles caducous. **Pedicels** 10–14 mm, sparsely pubescent or glabrate, joints 1–3 mm from flower, bearded, rarely glabrous, usually nearer flower than pedicel base, rarely nearer pedicel base than flower. **Flowers:** calyx lobes sparsely pubescent abaxially, glabrous adaxially; corolla 8–16 mm diam., petals deep yellow, adaxial one sometimes orange-dotted basally; ovary glabrate. **Legumes** compressed, not constricted between seeds, 3.8–12 × 1–1.3 cm, glabrescent. **Seeds** 1 or 2(–4). $2n = 28$.

Flowering Mar–Jun (Aug–Nov). Fine soils along washes and flood plains; 0–1000 m; Ariz., Calif., Nev.; Mexico (Sonora).

Hybrids between *Parkinsonia florida* and *P. microphylla* usually can be recognized by intermediacy (for example, leaflets too large for *P. microphylla* and too numerous for *P. florida*), as well as presence of characteristics from both parents (for example, nodal spines, petiolate leaves, glandular patches surrounding pulvini, pubescent ovaries; A. M. Carter 1974b).

4. Parkinsonia texana (A. Gray) S. Watson, Proc. Amer. Acad. Arts 11: 136. 1876 • Texas paloverde

Cercidium texanum A. Gray, Smithsonian Contr. Knowl. 3(5): 58. 1852

Trees or shrubs, (2–)3–8 m, with nodal spines. **Stems** dark to olive green, twigs moderately to densely pubescent. **Leaves:** stipules not spinescent; petiole 1.8–3.5 mm, pubescent; pinnae 2; petiolules 0.2–0.3 mm, densely pubescent; rachillas 1.5–12 mm, not winged, with glandular patches on adaxial side, not surrounding leaflet pulvini; leaflets 2–6(or 8), opposite, blades oblanceolate to obovate, 2–3.5 × 0.8–1.9 mm, base cuneate to attenuate, apex truncate or rounded, apiculate or not, surfaces sparsely pubescent abaxially, sparsely pubescent to glabrate adaxially. **Racemes** 2–10-flowered, axis 0.4–3.5 cm, strigulose to glabrate; bracts deltate or lanceolate, 0.3–0.5 × 0.2–0.3 mm; bracteoles persistent or caducous. **Pedicels** 4–11.3 mm, sparsely pubescent or glabrate, joints 2–4.2 mm from flower, bearded, equidistant between flower and pedicel base, distinctly nearer pedicel base, or nearer flower than pedicel base. **Flowers:** calyx lobes moderately pubescent abaxially, glabrous adaxially; corolla 7.9–16 mm diam., petals light to deep yellow, adaxial one often orange-spotted basally; ovary sericeous or glabrate. **Legumes** compressed, irregularly and indistinctly torulose, 2.9–5.9 × 0.5–0.8 cm, pubescent, at least basally, or glabrate. **Seeds** 1–4. $2n = 28$.

Varieties 2 (2 in the flora): Texas, ne Mexico.

Essentially restricted to the Tamaulipan thornscrub ecoregion, vars. *macra* and *texana* display a parapatric distribution with only a very narrow zone of apparent overlap. The abruptness of the transition between densely sericeous and glabrate ovaries (that is, a conspicuous absence of populations exhibiting sparsely to moderately sericeous ovaries), as well as the sympatric occurrence of ovaries of both types in a narrow zone where varieties meet, suggests a genetic basis to the variation. Significant relationships between environmental gradients and both ovary vesture and leaflet number suggest an environmental influence in shaping the distribution of genetic variation (A. Krings et al., unpubl.).

1. Leaflets 2 or 4 per pinna; ovaries densely sericeous; legumes pubescent, at least basally . . . . 4a. *Parkinsonia texana* var. *texana*
1. Leaflets 4 or 6 (or 8) per pinna; ovaries glabrate; legumes glabrate . . . . 4b. *Parkinsonia texana* var. *macra*

4a. Parkinsonia texana (A. Gray) S. Watson var. **texana**

Trees or shrubs to 8 m. **Leaflets** 2 or 4 per pinna, blades 2.5–3.5 × 0.8–1.6 mm. **Pedicels** 4.8–7.8 mm. **Flowers:** corolla 7.9–13 mm diam.; ovary densely sericeous. **Legumes** 3.2–5.4 × 0.5–0.6 cm, pubescent, at least basally.

Flowering Mar–Jul. Dry, gravelly soils, semidesert scrub; 80–500[–1800] m; Tex.; Mexico (Coahuila, Nuevo León, Tamaulipas).

4b. Parkinsonia texana (A. Gray) S. Watson var. **macra** (I. M. Johnston) Isely, Mem. New York Bot. Gard. 25(2): 218. 1975

Cercidium macrum I. M. Johnston, Contr. Gray Herb. 70: 64. 1924

Trees or shrubs (2–)3–4 m. **Leaflets** 4 or 6(or 8) per pinna, blades 2–3.4 × 1–1.9 mm. **Pedicels** 4–11.3 mm. **Flowers:** corolla 13–16 mm diam.; ovary glabrate. **Legumes** 2.9–5.9 × 0.6–0.8 cm, glabrate.

Flowering Apr–Jul. Clay loam and sandy soils, semidesert or thornscrub; 0–500[–1100] m; Tex.; Mexico (Nuevo León, Tamaulipas).

Among congenerics in the flora area, var. *macra* and *Parkinsonia florida* are the only taxa with glabrate pistils.

20. DELONIX Rafinesque, Fl. Tellur. 2: 92. 1837 • Flamboyant, flame tree, royal poinciana [Greek *delos*, evident, and *onyx*, claw, alluding to petals] I

Neil A. Harriman†

Trees, unarmed. **Stems** spreading, puberulent. **Leaves** alternate, even-bipinnate; stipules present; petiolate; pinnae 11–20 pairs, opposite; leaflets 20–50[+], blade margins entire, surfaces puberulent or glabrate. **Inflorescences** 20–25-flowered, axillary to subterminal, racemes,

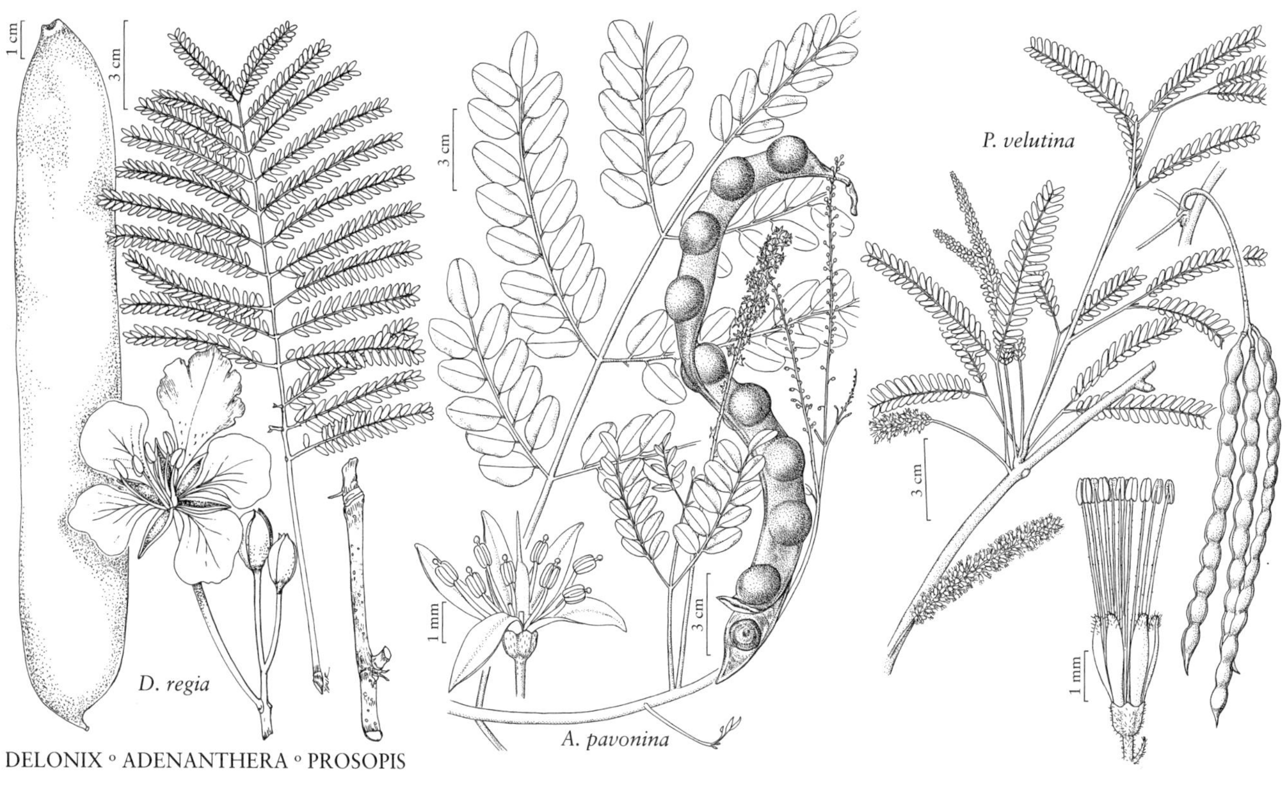

DELONIX ◦ ADENANTHERA ◦ PROSOPIS

corymblike; bracts present, caducous. **Flowers** caesalpinioid; calyx nearly actinomorphic, valvate, lobes 5; corolla scarlet and yellow; stamens 10, declined, slightly connate basally; anthers dorsifixed. **Fruits** legumes, stipitate, compressed, straight, oblong, dehiscent on ground, woody, glabrous. **Seeds** 20–40, slightly compressed, oblong. $x = 14$.

Species 11 (1 in the flora): introduced, Florida; sw Asia, e Africa, Indian Ocean Islands (Madagascar); introduced widely.

Delonix is a genus primarily of Madagascar, with nine species endemic there; one species is endemic to Ethiopia, northern Kenya, and Somalia, and one is widespread in east Africa, Arabia, and India.

1. **Delonix regia** (Bojer) Rafinesque, Fl. Tellur. 2: 92. 1837 [F] [I]

Poinciana regia Bojer, Bot. Mag. 56: plate 2884. 1829

Trees 8–12 m; bark smooth. **Leaves** early deciduous (30–50 cm); stipules early deciduous, pinnate, 5–15 mm; petiole 2–4 cm, with pubescent spheroid projections between pinnae pairs; leaflet blades light green abaxially, elliptic to shortly oblong, 5–10 × 2–4 mm, midrib evident, lateral veins not evident, surfaces initially puberulent. **Pedicels** 5–8 cm, jointed apically. **Flowers:** calyx deeply lobed, red inside, 20–25 mm; lobes subequal and recurving at anthesis, falling with petals, elliptic; corolla somewhat zygomorphic, 80–100 mm diam.; petals 40–70 mm, long-clawed, blade obovate to orbiculate; filaments subequal to petals, tawny-hirsute basally. **Legumes** persistent, 300–600 × 40–65 mm. **Seeds** ivory streaked with brown, 20 mm. $2n = 28$.

Flowering late summer. Waste areas; 0–50 m; introduced, Fla.; Indian Ocean Islands (Madagascar); introduced also in tropical and subtropical regions nearly worldwide.

Delonix regia is a rare endemic of Madagascar but is now widely cultivated throughout the tropics and subtropics. While planted in Arizona, southern California, and Florida, it is known to escape only in Florida, and there sparingly.

Key to Genera of Subfamily Caesalpinioideae, Mimosoid Clade

1. Stamens 5–10.
   2. Shrubs or trees, usually armed with nodal spines or thorns; fruits legumes or loments, indehiscent or dehiscent, elongate, turgid, and often irregularly moniliform, or coiled springlike, rarely irregularly twisted or contorted.
      3. Pinnae 1 or 2 pairs; fruits loments, straight or spirally coiled, seeds distinct nearly to base; inflorescences axillary, spikes or globose heads, 40–100+-flowered, corollas yellow, cream-yellow, purple-brown, greenish white, or yellow-green, all bisexual; sc, sw United States . . . . 22. *Prosopis*, v. 11(1), p. 76
      3. Pinnae 7–15 pairs; fruits legumes, contorted or coiling at maturity; inflorescences axillary, pendent spikes, 50–200-flowered, corollas pale green, distally bisexual with bright yellow anthers, and proximally sterile with purple or white staminodes; introduced, Florida . . . . 26. *Dichrostachys*, v. 11(1), p. 91
   2. Herbs, shrubs, or trees, unarmed, or with internodal prickles which are generally curved and flattened; fruits legumes, dehiscent or segmenting.
      4. Perennial herbs, unarmed, terrestrial or floating-aquatic; stems ascending, decumbent, prostrate, prostrate-ascending, or floating; corollas yellow-green to white; distal flowers often bisexual, proximal flowers sterile with petaloid staminodes (monomorphic in *N. lutea*) . . . . 23. *Neptunia*, v. 11(1), p. 79
      4. Trees, shrubs, subshrubs, or perennial herbs, usually unarmed, sometimes armed, terrestrial; stems erect, ascending, decumbent, prostrate, or sprawling; corollas white, cream, yellow, greenish white, pink, purple, or purple-pink; flowers usually bisexual.
         5. Trees, 5–15(–40) m, unarmed; leaflet blades 15–45 mm, alternate; inflorescences in terminal panicles or axillary spikelike racemes; corollas white to cream; legumes straight to falcate or contorted, swollen around seeds, valves twisting; seeds glossy red, flattened; stipitate anther glands present; introduced, Florida . . . . 21. *Adenanthera*, v. 11(1), p. 75
         5. Trees, shrubs, subshrubs, or herbs, 0.1–3 m, unarmed or armed; leaflet blades 1.5–26(–30) mm, opposite; inflorescences in heads, spikes, or racemes; corollas white, greenish white, pale green, yellow, or pink to purple; legumes straight or curved, not swollen around seeds; seeds not glossy red; stipitate anther glands absent.
            6. Petiole nectar glands absent; legumes often craspedial, segmented into 1-seeded portions separating from persistent sutures (replum), sometimes unsegmented; plants armed with recurved or straight prickles or unarmed; corollas white or pink to purple . . . . 27. *Mimosa*, v. 11(1), p. 93
            6. Petiole nectar gland present (sometimes minute); legumes not craspedial; plants without prickles; corollas white, greenish white, or yellow.
               7. Shrubs or trees, 2–18(–20) m; stems erect; stipules ovate, inconspicuous; inflorescences globose heads; corollas yellow, white, or greenish white; legumes shortly stipitate, linear or oblong, compressed or flat, valves sometimes curling . . . . 24. *Leucaena*, v. 11(1), p. 82
               7. Herbs or shrubs, to 3 m; stems erect to prostrate or decumbent; stipules subulate, small but evident; inflorescences condensed heads or spikes; corollas pale green or white; legumes sessile, linear or falcate, subterete to flattened, splitting along margins at maturity . . . . 25. *Desmanthus*, v. 11(1), p. 84
1. Stamens 14–250.
   8. Filaments distinct (except rarely connate basally in *Acacia*); leaves bipinnate or simple phyllodia.
      9. Leaves simple phyllodia or bipinnate; stipular spines usually absent (except *A. paradoxa*); seeds usually with pulpy aril forming a cap or encircling seed . . . . 28. *Acacia*, v. 11(1), p. 105
      9. Leaves bipinnate; stipular spines present or absent; seeds usually without pulpy aril (except sometimes in *Vachellia*).

10. Stipular spines present, sometimes enlarged and inhabited by ants; ovaries sessile or subsessile; seeds sometimes surrounded by pulp . . . . .29. *Vachellia*, v. 11(1), p. 111
10. Stipular spines absent; ovaries stipitate; seeds not surrounded by pulp.
11. Petiolar glands absent; prickles absent; inflorescences usually in globose heads; corollas greenish white, drying to pink-rose; stamens 175–250, creamy white, anther glands absent . . . . .31. *Acaciella*, v. 11(1), p. 121
11. Petiolar glands usually present; prickles present or absent; inflorescences spikes or heads; corollas white to creamy white or yellow; stamens 35–160, white, small anther glands sometimes present.
12. Prickles usually present; stipules caducous; inflorescences terminal or axillary, heads or spikes, usually in pseudoracemes or pseudopanicles; ovaries stipitate or sessile, with nectariferous disc at base; stamens creamy or yellow, fading to reddish brown . . . . 30. *Senegalia*, v. 11(1), p. 117
12. Prickles absent; stipules persistent; inflorescences axillary, cylindrical spikes; ovaries short-stipitate, nectariferous disc absent; stamens white . . . . .32. *Mariosousa*, v. 11(1), p. 123

[8. Shifted to left margin.—Ed.]

8. Filaments fused into a tube, monadelphous; leaves bipinnate.
13. Legumes usually dehiscent into 2 valves, sometimes craspedial; nectary glands present or absent.
14. Trees, shrubs, or herbs, unarmed; stipular spines absent.
15. Petiole nectary glands present; inflorescences axillary spikes or racemes; legumes straight, flat, membranous, with 2 prominent suture ribs surrounding periphery and detaching after dehiscence (craspedial); exocarp dark purple to blackish, exfoliating . . . . .42. *Lysiloma* (in part), v. 11(1), p. 139
15. Petiole nectary glands absent; inflorescences axillary or terminal heads sometimes in short pseudopanicles; legumes straight or slightly curved, dehiscent longitudinally along sutures, valves strongly recurving; exocarp dark brown to green, not exfoliating.
16. Heads globose; corollas greenish white; stamens 30–60; legumes dehiscing elastically from distal end to proximal end . . . . 33. *Zapoteca*, v. 11(1), p. 124
16. Heads ± hemispheric or obconic; corollas reddish or whitish; stamens (14–)19–28; legumes dehiscing longitudinally along sutures but not elastically . . . . 34. *Calliandra*, v. 11(1), p. 126
14. Shrubs or trees, usually armed; stipular spines present.
17. Legumes recurved to coiled into a circle; seeds with aril; petiolar nectary gland between lowest pair of pinnae; leaflet blade venation pinnate . . . . .38. *Pithecellobium*, v. 11(1), p. 133
17. Legumes straight; seeds without an aril; petiolar nectary gland borne between distalmost pair(s) of pinnae; leaflet blade venation brochidodromous . . . . 36. *Havardia*, v. 11(1), p. 130
13. Legumes indehiscent, dehiscent, or late dehiscent; nectary glands present.
18. Legumes falcate or forming a nearly complete flattened spiral, valves woody, dull light brown to maroon or blackish; inflorescences racemes, pseudoracemes, or heads (fascicles) or flowers solitary.
19. Pinnae 2 or 3 pairs; inflorescences pseudoracemes from short shoots; legumes falcate, light brown to maroon . . . . .37. *Ebenopsis*, v. 11(1), p. 132
19. Pinnae 4–10(–15) pairs; inflorescences heads; legumes forming a nearly complete flattened spiral, blackish . . . . .41. *Enterolobium*, v. 11(1), p. 138
18. Legumes straight or slight curved, valves papery, membranous, leathery, or if woody, glossy red-brown; inflorescences umbels, spikes, racemes, or heads.

[20. Shifted to left margin.—Ed.]

20. Legumes turgid, fleshy, pulpy, margins thickened, septate between seeds; flowers dimorphic, peripheral flowers smaller than central; introduced, Florida . . . . 39. *Samanea*, v. 11(1), p. 135
20. Legumes flat, not fleshy or pulpy, not septate between seeds; flowers sometimes dimorphic; Florida (*Lysiloma*), California (*Paraserianthes*), or widespread (*Albizia*).
    21. Legumes with prominent sutural ribs surrounding periphery and persistent, not separating from the valves (or tardily), seeds released through decay of valves; Florida . . . . 42. *Lysiloma* (in part), v. 11(1), p. 139
    21. Legumes without prominent peripheral ribs, raised over seeds; widespread.
        22. Pinnae 20–30+ pairs; inflorescences axillary, racemes, flowers homomorphic, corollas greenish; stamens ± 90, equaling petals, greenish to lemon yellow; legumes indehiscent or late-dehiscent; introduced, California. . . . . 35. *Paraserianthes*, v. 11(1), p. 129
        22. Pinnae (1 or)2–12 pairs; inflorescences axillary or terminal, heads or corymbs; flowers dimorphic, corollas whitish or pink to yellow-green; stamens 20–70, usually long-exserted, pink or white; legumes dehiscent or late-dehiscent; widespread . . . . 40. *Albizia*, v. 11(1), p. 136

21. ADENANTHERA Linnaeus, Sp. Pl. 1: 384. 1753; Gen. Pl. ed. 5, 181. 1754 • [Greek *adeno*, little gland, and *anthera*, anther, alluding to gland-tipped anthers] [I]

Douglas H. Goldman

Trees [shrubs], unarmed. **Stems** ascending, glabrous [pubescent, hairs sometimes glandular]. **Leaves** alternate, even-bipinnate; stipules present; petiolate; pinnae [2 or]3–6[–8] pairs, alternate; leaflets [2–]8–18(–22), alternate, blade margins entire, surfaces usually glabrous. **Inflorescences** ±100-flowered, axillary or terminal, racemes or panicles; bracts present. **Flowers** mimosoid, often fragrant; calyx not persistent, campanulate, lobes 5; corolla white to cream [yellow or pink-red]; stamens 10, distinct; anthers dorsifixed, stipitate glands present. **Fruits** legumes, sessile or subsessile, compressed, swollen around seeds, straight to falcate or contorted, linear, dehiscent, glabrous, becoming strongly contorted when dehisced. **Seeds** 5–25, obovoid to ellipsoid or suborbicular. $x = 13$.

Species 13 (1 in the flora): introduced, Florida; Asia, Indian Ocean Islands (Madagascar), Pacific Islands, Australia; introduced also in tropical and subtropical regions worldwide.

SELECTED REFERENCE Nielsen, I. C. and P. Guinet. 1992. Synopsis of *Adenanthera* (Leguminosae-Mimosoideae). Nordic J. Bot. 12: 85–114.

1. Adenanthera pavonina Linnaeus, Sp. Pl. 1: 384. 1753 • Red beadtree [F] [I]

Trees to 5–15(–40) m. **Leaves** 20–60 cm; stipules deciduous, relatively small; leaflet blade elliptic to obovate, 15–45 × 10–20 mm, base cuneate to rouned, sometimes inequilateral, apex blunt or rounded to acute. **Inflorescences** terminal panicles or axillary racemes, racemes spike-like, 12–30 cm; bracts usually early-deciduous, filiform to ovate, 0.5–1.5 mm. **Flowers:** calyx lobes rounded to broadly obtuse, 0.2 mm; corolla becoming yellow in age, oblong, 3–5 mm, petals subequal; anthers with terminal gland; ovary glabrous or pubescent; style slender, elongate. **Legumes** erect, 100–300 mm. **Seeds** glossy red, compressed, (7–)8–9 mm. $2n = 26, 28$.

Flowering spring. Disturbed tropical woodlands and woodland margins; 0–10[–600] m; introduced; Fla.; tropical Asia; introduced also in tropical and subtropical regions worldwide.

Adenanthera pavonina has a broad range of uses, including food, industrial lubricants, medicine, and timber; the showy seeds are often used for jewelry (M. A. Luckow 2005). Unlike those of the majority of Mimosoideae, the inflorescences of this species are somewhat lax, with relatively widely spaced flowers and shorter stamens, superficially resembling some caesalpinioid genera.

22. PROSOPIS Linnaeus, Syst. Nat. ed. 12, 2: 282, 293. 1767; Mant. Pl. 1: 10, 68. 1767 • Mesquite [Derivation uncertain; perhaps Greek *prosopon*, mask, alluding to similarity with *Tamarindus* masking identity of *Prosopis*]

Debra K. Trock

Trees or shrubs, usually armed, rarely unarmed; taprooted, forming underground spreading horizontal runners. **Branches** ascending or spreading. **Stems** glabrous or pubescent. **Leaves** alternate, even-bipinnate; stipules present, inconspicuous and early deciduous or modified spines; petiolate, petiole with sessile, circular glands; pinnae 1 or 2(or 3)[–7] pair(s), opposite, apex with scalelike mucro or spine; leaflets 6–60, alternate or opposite, overlapping or not, blade margins entire, surfaces sometimes glaucous, glabrous or pubescent. **Inflorescences** 40–100+-flowered, axillary, spikes or heads [racemes]; bracts absent. **Flowers** mimosoid; calyx campanulate, lobes 5, connate proximally, sometimes striate; corolla yellow, cream-yellow, purple-brown, greenish white, or yellow-green, [reddish], petals connate or distinct, linear; stamens 10 (5 + 5), distinct; anthers dorsifixed, introrse, elliptic, apex pedicellate with a deciduous, capitate gland. **Fruits** loments, stipitate or sessile, straight or spirally coiled, torulose, linear or cylindric, thickened, indehiscent, pubescent, glabrescent, or glabrous. **Seeds** (4 or)5–25+, gray-green, tan, yellow-tan, yellow-brown, or brown, ovoid, reniform-ovoid, ellipsoid, or oblong. $x = 14$.

Species ca. 48 (6 in the flora): sw, sc United States, Mexico, South America (Argentina, Bolivia, Chile, Peru), sw Asia, Africa; deserts, dry subtropical regions; introduced in Australia.

Prosopis was treated by G. Bentham (1842, 1846, 1875) as polymorphic and divided into several sections based on fruit types and derivation of the spines. G. Engelmann and A. Gray (1845), as well as N. L. Britton and J. N. Rose (1928), divided the North American species into two and three genera respectively. A. Burkart (1976) adopted the position of Bentham, and most North American authors have continued to follow his treatment.

In arid countries, species of *Prosopis* are valued for shade, fuel, food, and forage. Due to their hardiness and abundance, they are often an important component of the vegetation in these regions. Some species are invasive and are a problem for ranchers and farmers. At least 27 species are listed as potentially noxious weeds in the United States.

SELECTED REFERENCES Burkart, A. 1976. A monograph of the genus *Prosopis* (Leguminosae subfam. Mimosoideae). J. Arnold Arbor. 57: 219–249. Burkart, A. 1976b. A monograph of the genus *Prosopis* (Leguminosae subfam. Mimosoideae): Catalogue of the recognized species of *Prosopis*. J. Arnold Arbor. 57: 450–524. Isely, D. 1972. Legumes of the U.S. VI. *Calliandra*, *Pithecellobium*, *Prosopis*. Madroño 21: 273–298.

1. Inflorescences globose heads; loments coiled.
    2. Spines 4–9 cm; leaflets touching or overlapping . . . . 4. *Prosopis reptans*
    2. Spines 0.1–2 cm; leaflets 3.5–5 mm apart . . . . 5. *Prosopis strombulifera*
1. Inflorescences amentlike spikes; loments straight or coiled.
    3. Loments coiled; leaflets 10–18. . . . . 3. *Prosopis pubescens*
    3. Loments straight or curved; leaflets 12–60.
        4. Leaflets alternate. . . . . 2. *Prosopis laevigata*
        4. Leaflets opposite.
            5. Leaflets 5–18 mm apart, blades (15–)20–63 mm, surfaces glabrous . . . . . . 1. *Prosopis glandulosa*
            5. Leaflets 3–4 mm apart, blades 4–13 mm, surfaces pubescent . . . . . . 6. *Prosopis velutina*

1. Prosopis glandulosa Torrey, Ann. Lyceum Nat. Hist. New York 2: 192, plate 2. 1827 • Honey mesquite

Prosopis chilensis (Molina) Stuntz var. *glandulosa* (Torrey) Standley; *P. juliflora* (Swartz) de Candolle var. *glandulosa* (Torrey) Cockerell

Trees or shrubs, 3–9(–13) m. **Trunks:** bark thick and shallowly fissured, crooked. **Branches** arching, shrubby form with flexuous branches. **Stems** glabrate to sparsely velutinous. **Leaves:** stipules nodal, solitary or paired, yellowish green, 1–4.5 cm, glabrous; petiole/rachis 1–15 cm; pinnae 2 or 4; leaflets 12–48, opposite, 5–18 mm apart, blades linear to oblong or falcate, (15–)20–63 × 1.4–4.5 mm, usually 5–15 times longer than wide, base cuneate, margins sparsely ciliate, veins prominent, apex obtuse or mucronate, surfaces glabrous. **Peduncles** (0.8–)1–3 cm, glabrous. **Inflorescences** amentlike spikes, ascending or drooping, 5–14 cm. **Flowers:** sepals 1 mm, glabrous; petals connate proximally, cream-yellow, 2.5–3.5 mm, adaxially lanulose; stamens cream-yellow; filaments 6–7 mm, glabrous; anthers 1 mm; ovary stipitate, 2 mm, villous; style 4 mm, glabrous. **Loments** pale yellow to tan or tinged with violet, compressed to nearly cylindric, usually straight, rarely subfalcate, 8–20 × 0.7–1.3 cm, glabrous. **Seeds** yellow-tan, broadly ellipsoid, 4–5 mm.

Varieties 3 (3 in the flora): sc, sw United States, Mexico.

1. Shrubs, usually prostrate, rarely erect . . . . 1b. *Prosopis glandulosa* var. *prostrata*
1. Trees or shrubs, erect.
   2. Leaflets 12–34, blades 20–60 mm, apices obtuse; spines usually solitary . . . . 1a. *Prosopis glandulosa* var. *glandulosa*
   2. Leaflets 16–48, blades 15–25 mm, apices mucronate; spines usually paired . . . . 1c. *Prosopis glandulosa* var. *torreyana*

1a. Prosopis glandulosa Torrey var. **glandulosa** [W]

Trees or shrubs, erect. **Spines** usually solitary. **Leaves:** petiole/rachis 2–15 cm; leaflets 12–34, 7–18 mm apart, blades 20–60 × 1.5–4.5 mm, apex obtuse. **Inflorescences** 5–14 cm. $2n$ = 28, 56, 112.

Flowering Apr–Jun. Open prairies, canyons, roadsides; 0–1900 m; Colo., Kans., La., N.Mex., Okla., Tex.; Mexico (Baja California, Chihuahua, Coahuila, Nuevo León, Sonora, Tamaulipas, Vera Cruz, Yucatán).

Variety *glandulosa* was probably restricted to washes and river drainages prior to the introduction of livestock. Animals are effective seed dispersers and that, along with reduced fire frequency, has allowed the species to invade relatively large areas of dry grassland.

1b. Prosopis glandulosa Torrey var. **prostrata** Burkart, J. Arnold Arbor. 57: 516. 1976

Shrubs, usually prostrate, rarely erect. **Spines** usually solitary. **Leaves:** petiole/rachis 2–13 cm; leaflets 12–34, 8–16 mm apart, blades 20–60 × 1.5–4.5 mm, apex obtuse. **Inflorescences** 5–12 cm.

Flowering Mar–Jun. Prairies, canyons, along streams, roadsides, deep, sandy soils; 0–1900 m; Tex.; Mexico (Tamaulipas).

Variety *prostrata* is known in the flora area from Kleberg County.

1c. Prosopis glandulosa Torrey var. **torreyana** (L. D. Benson) M. C. Johnston, Brittonia 14: 82. 1962 • Western honey mesquite [W]

Prosopis juliflora (Swartz) de Candolle var. *torreyana* L. D. Benson, Amer. J. Bot. 28: 751, plate 1, fig. 4. 1941

Trees or shrubs, erect. **Spines** usually paired. **Leaves:** petiole/rachis 1–8 cm; leaflets 16–48, 5–8 mm apart, blades 15–25 × 1.5–6 mm, apex mucronate. **Inflorescences** 3–12 cm. $2n$ = 28, 56.

Flowering Mar–Jun. Grasslands, alkali flats, washes, sandy alluvial flats; 0–2500 m; Ariz., Calif., Mo., Nev., N.Mex., Tex., Utah; Mexico (Baja California, Chihuahua, Coahuila, Nuevo León, Sonora, Veracruz).

Variety *torreyana* reportedly hybridizes with *Prosopis velutina* in Arizona, Baja California, and Sonora. R. A. Palacios (2006) considered var. *torreyana* to be synonymous with *P. odorata* (= *P. pubescens*).

2. Prosopis laevigata (Humboldt & Bonpland ex Willdenow) M. C. Johnston, Brittonia 14: 78. 1962 • Smooth mesquite [I]

Acacia laevigata Humboldt & Bonpland ex Willdenow, Sp. Pl. 4: 1059. 1806; *Mimosa laevigata* (Humboldt & Bonpland ex Willdenow) Poiret

Varieties 2 (1 in the flora): introduced, Texas; Mexico, South America (Argentina, Bolivia, Peru).

Variety *andicola* Burkart, known from Peru, is a montane plant that is glabrous and has only one pair of pinnae.

2a. Prosopis laevigata (Humboldt & Bonpland ex Willdenow) M. C. Johnston var. **laevigata** [I]

Shrubs [trees], 2–3[6–7] m. **Trunks:** bark flakey, gland-dotted. **Branches** ± flexuous distally. **Stems** sparsely pubescent. **Leaves:** stipules modified paired spines, creamy white, gland-dotted, 0.5–2.5 cm, glabrous; petiole/rachis 0.3–2.5 cm; pinnae 4; leaflets 40–60, alternate, 1–2 mm apart, blades linear-oblong, [2.5–]5–10 [–15] × 1.1–3 mm, base rounded, margins sparsely ciliate, veins prominent, apex obtuse, surfaces glabrous. **Peduncles** 0.4–3 cm, sparsely pubescent. **Inflorescences** amentlike spikes, 4–10(–13) cm. **Flowers:** sepals 1 mm, glabrous; petals connate proximally, greenish white, 3–4 mm, sparsely pubescent adaxially with tufted hairs apically; stamens yellow; filaments 5–6 mm, glabrous; anthers 0.5–0.8 mm; ovary stipitate, 1–1.5 mm, villous; style 0.4–0.6 mm, pubescent proximally. **Loments** mostly yellow, sometimes speckled with violet, linear, straight to slightly curved, submoniliform, 9–17 × 0.7–1.4 cm, glabrous. **Seeds** yellow-brown, ovoid, 3–4 mm. **2*n*** = 28.

Flowering May–Aug. Open fields, roadsides, disturbed areas, mountain ridges and canyons, well-drained or drying soils; 40–2100 m; introduced; Tex.; Mexico (Aguascalientes, Chiapas, Durango, Guanajuato, Guerrero, Hidalgo, Jalisco, Michoacán, Morelos, Nuevo León, Oaxaca, Puebla, Querétaro, San Luis Potosí, Tamaulipas, Veracruz, Zacatecas).

Fruits of var. *laevigata* are edible and are used as fodder in Mexico; plants have also been cultivated as shade trees. In the flora area, var. *laevigata* is known only from Nueces County.

3. Prosopis pubescens Bentham, London J. Bot. 5: 82. 1846 • Screwbean mesquite

Prosopis odorata Torrey & Frémont; *Strombocarpa odorata* (Torrey & Frémont) A. Gray

Trees or shrubs, 2–10 m. **Trunks:** 2–3(–4) dm; bark thin flakey. **Branches** flexuous. **Stems** puberulent. **Leaves:** stipules modified paired spines, white or gray, 0.2–2 cm, glabrous; petiole/rachis 0.6–0.8 cm, densely lanate to glabrescent; pinnae 2(–4), rarely with a terminal leaflet; leaflets 10–18, opposite, 4–5 mm apart, blades elliptic-oblong, (4–)7–12 × 2–4 mm, base rounded or oblique, margins ciliolate, slightly 1–3-veined basally, apex rounded, obtuse, truncate, or mucronulate, surfaces tomentulose. **Peduncles** 1–1.5 cm, lanate. **Inflorescences** amentlike spikes, 4–6(–8) cm. **Flowers:** sepals 1 mm, finely tomentose; petals connate ½ their lengths, yellow, red-tipped, 2–3 mm, pubescent; stamens bright yellow; filaments 3.5–4 mm, glabrous; anthers 0.7–1 mm; ovary stipitate, 1.5–2 mm, densely white-pilose; style 2 mm, glabrous. **Loments** yellow-tan to dark brown (purple spotted), cylindric, coiled 2 or 3 times with 8–24 close-set spirals, 2.5–5.5 × 0.5–0.6 cm, puberulous to glabrescent. **Seeds** tan, reniform-ovoid, 3–3.5 mm. **2*n*** = 56.

Flowering Apr–May (or Jul). Desert riparian woodland, along creeks, washes, and river bottoms in saline and alkaline soils; 60–1600 m; Ariz., Calif., Nev., N.Mex., Tex., Utah; Mexico (Baja California, Chihuahua, Sonora).

Fruits of *Prosopis pubescens* are used as fodder for cattle and the wood as a source of fuel. In Texas, *P. pubescens* is known from the trans-Pecos and Big Bend regions.

4. Prosopis reptans Bentham, J. Bot. (Hooker) 4: 352. 1841 [W]

Varieties 2 (1 in the flora): Texas, n Mexico, South America (Argentina, Peru).

Variety *reptans* has smaller leaves and less pubescence than var. *cinerascens*; var. *reptans* was described from central Argentina and was later discovered to occur in Peru as well.

4a. Prosopis reptans Bentham var. **cinerascens** (A. Gray) Burkart, Darwiniana 4: 75. 1940 • Tornillo

Strombocarpa cinerascens A. Gray, Smithsonian Contr. Knowl. 3(5): 61. 1852; *Prosopis cinerascens* (A. Gray) A. Gray ex Bentham

Shrubs [trees], 0.1–0.3(–0.4) [5–8] m. **Trunks:** bark white-flakey. **Branches** distinctly flexuous. **Stems** puberulent throughout. **Leaves:** stipules modified paired spines, white, 4–9 cm, sparsely short-pubescent; petiole/rachis 15–20 cm; pinnae 2; leaflets 12–22, alternate, touching or overlapping, blades oblong-obovate, 2.5–4 × 1–2 mm, base oblique, margins distinctly ciliate, midvein displaced, apex rounded, surfaces cinereous to glabrate. **Peduncles** 3–4 cm, tomentose to glabrescent. **Inflorescences** globose heads, 1.5 cm. **Flowers:** sepals 2–2.5 mm, glabrous; petals connate proximally, purple-brown with darker tips, ± 4 mm, villous adaxially; stamens tan; filaments 1.5–2 mm; anthers yellow, 1.5–2 mm; ovary sessile, 2.5–3 mm, villous; style 4–4.5 mm, glabrous. **Loments** yellow to light brown, cylindric, coiled (9–12 coils), 4.5–5.5 × 0.6–0.8 cm, sparsely short-pubescent. **Seeds** brown, oblong, 4–4.5 mm. **2*n*** = 28, 56, ± 112.

Flowering Mar–Jun. Sandy bluffs, ocean beaches, grasslands; 0–200 m; Tex.; Mexico (Nuevo León, San Luis Potosí, Tamaulipas).

In Texas, var. *cinerascens* is known from the southern third of the state.

5. **Prosopis strombulifera** (Lamarck) Bentham, J. Bot. (Hooker) 4: 352. 1841 • Argentine screwbean [I]

Mimosa strombulifera Lamarck in J. Lamarck et al., Encycl. 1: 15. 1783; *Acacia strombulifera* (Lamarck) Willdenow; *Strombocarpa strombulifera* (Lamarck) A. Gray

Varieties 2 (1 in the flora): introduced, California; South America (Argentina, Chile).

Variety *ruiziana* Burkart (found in Argentina) has fruits to 2 cm longer than var. *strombulifera*; plants produce only one or two fruits per inflorescence.

5a. **Prosopis strombulifera** (Lamarck) Bentham var. **strombulifera** [I]

Shrubs, 0.2–1.5(–3) m. **Trunks:** bark light to dark brown, deeply fissured and flakey. **Branches** distinctly flexuous. **Stems** glabrous, gland-dotted. **Leaves:** stipules modified paired spines, decurrent, white, 0.1–2 cm, glabrous; petiole/rachis 1.5–4.5 cm; pinnae 2; leaflets 6–16, usually alternate, rarely opposite, 3.5–5 mm apart, blades gray-green, oblong, 2–9 × 0.8–2 mm, base rounded to oblique, margins sparsely ciliate, enervate or slightly 1–3-veined, apex obtuse, surfaces glaucous, puberulous, or glabrescent. **Peduncles** 1.5–6 cm, glabrescent. **Inflorescences** globose heads, 1.5 cm. **Flowers:** sepals 1.5–2.2 mm, puberulous; petals mostly connate, yellow, 3–4 mm, lobes 1 mm, villous adaxially; stamens yellow; filaments 4–5 mm, glabrous; anthers 1.5 mm; ovary short-stipitate, 1.5 mm, sparsely villous; style 1.5–2 mm, glabrous. **Loments** lemon yellow to yellow-tan, cylindric, coiled (8–17 coils), 1.8–5.2 × 0.6–1 cm, puberulous when young. **Seeds** gray-green, ovoid, 4.5–5.4 mm.

Flowering Jul. Disturbed or waste ground; 0–80 m; introduced; Calif.; South America (Argentina, Chile).

Variety *strombulifera* is probably introduced in Imperial County. The fruits are reportedly sold in markets in Chile as an astringent and toothache remedy. The roots produce a brown dye.

6. **Prosopis velutina** Wooton, Bull. Torrey Bot. Club 25: 456. 1898 • Velvet mesquite [F] [W]

Prosopis chilensis (Molina) Stuntz var. *velutina* (Wooton) Standley; *P. juliflora* (Swartz) de Candolle var. *velutina* (Wooton) Sargent

Trees, rarely multi-stemmed shrubs, 1–10(–15) m. **Trunks:** short, bark tan to gray-brown, flakey. **Branches** slightly flexuous distally. **Stems:** new growth short-puberulous. **Leaves:** stipules modified paired spines, tan to light brown, 1–2 cm, hirsute; petiole/rachis 0.6–6 cm, pubescent; pinnae 2–4(–6); leaflets 24–60, opposite, 3–4 mm apart, blades oblong, 4–13 × 2–4 mm, base rounded, margins ciliate, nervate abaxially, apex rounded, surfaces pubescent. **Peduncles** 0.5–0.8 cm, densely villous. **Inflorescences** amentlike spikes, 5–15 cm. **Flowers:** sepals 1 mm, sparsely pubescent; petals connate proximally, yellow-green, 2.5–3 mm, tips villous adaxially; stamens yellow; filaments 3.5–4.5 mm, minutely pubescent; anthers 0.7–0.9 mm; ovary stipitate, 2 mm, villous; style 2.5 mm, glabrous. **Loments** yellow, linear, straight, 10–20 × 0.6–1 cm, pubescent. **Seeds** dark brown, ovoid, 5–6 mm. $2n = 56$.

Flowering Apr–Oct. Creosote deserts, washes, river bottoms, dry flats, canyons, sandy soils; 150–1700 m; Ariz., Calif., N.Mex.; Mexico; introduced in Australia.

Prosopis velutina is introduced in California, where it is known from the Central Coast area and San Joaquin Valley southward.

23. NEPTUNIA Loureiro, Fl. Cochinch. 2: 641, 653. 1790 • Puff [For Neptune, Roman god of water and seas, presumably alluding to aquatic habitat of some species]

Guy L. Nesom

Herbs, perennial, aquatic, semiaquatic, or terrestrial, unarmed; usually from orange taproots when terrestrial. **Stems** erect, ascending, decumbent, prostrate, or prostrate-ascending or -floating, glabrous or pubescent. **Leaves** alternate, even-bipinnate; stipules present, persistent; petiolate; pinnae 2–11 pairs, opposite; leaflets 16–80(–86), opposite, blade nyctinastic, oblong to linear or oblong-lanceolate, margins entire, surfaces glabrous. **Inflorescences** 15–60-flowered, axillary, spikes, single [paired], congested-capitate; bracts present, persistent, mid-peduncle. **Flowers** mimosoid, dimorphic (except monomorphic in *N. lutea*), proximal flowers either staminate or sterile, stamens modified to petaloid staminodes, flowers in distal ½ bisexual; calyx usually persistent, zygomorphic, greenish to yellow, campanulate, lobes 4; corolla yellow-green to white, lobes 5, distinct nearly to base or irregularly coherent; stamens 10 [5], distinct, fertile or sterile and petaloid, exserted, yellow; anthers dorsifixed. **Fruits** legumes, stipitate, flat, broadly oblong to subglobose, dehiscent, glabrous or sparsely short-villous. **Seeds** 1–20, oblong-ellipsoid to obovoid; hilum terminal. x = 7, 9, 13.

Species ca. 12 (5 in the flora): sc, se United States, Mexico, West Indies, Central America, South America, s Asia, Africa, Australia; introduced elsewhere in Asia.

SELECTED REFERENCES Turner, B. L. 1951. Revision of the United States species of *Neptunia* (Leguminosae). Amer. Midl. Naturalist 46: 82–92. Windler, D. R. 1966. A revision of the genus *Neptunia* (Leguminosae). Austral. J. Bot. 14: 379–420.

1. Herbs aquatic, semiaquatic, or terrestrial, usually in wet habitats; floating and submergent stems often inflated and rooting at nodes; spikes with 2(or 3) cordate-clasping bracts, 3–8 mm; leaflet blades without raised-reticulate venation abaxially.
    2. Stems usually prostrate-floating, with little or no branching; petioles eglandular; pinnae 2 or 3(or 4), leaflets 16–40 . . . . 1. *Neptunia oleracea*
    2. Stems usually erect to ascending or floating, often procumbent near water's edge, often highly branched; petioles with a prominent discoid gland at base of, or proximal to, proximalmost pinnae pair; pinnae 2–4(or 5) pairs, leaflets 18–70 . . . . .2. *Neptunia plena*
1. Herbs terrestrial, sometimes of moist sites; stems not inflated, not rooting at nodes; spikes with (0 or)1 or 2 linear-subulate bracts, 1–3 mm; leaflet blades with raised-reticulate venation abaxially.
    3. Spikes subcylindric, 30–60-flowered; flowers monomorphic, anther-bearing, without staminodes; legume stipes 4–14 mm; leaflets 16–36; calyces 1–2 mm (including lobes) . . . . 3. *Neptunia lutea*
    3. Spikes spheric to ovoid, 15–30-flowered; flowers dimorphic, proximal with flattened, petaloid staminodes, distal anther-bearing; legume stipes 1–4 mm; leaflets (16–)28–80(–86); calyces 2–2.7 mm (including lobes).
        4. Legumes 5–13 mm wide, base usually tapering to stipe; stipe 2–4 mm, usually longer than calyx; pinnae (2 or)3–6 pairs per leaf, blade margins ciliate . . . . . . 4. *Neptunia pubescens*
        4. Legumes 8–17 mm wide, base usually rounded to stipe; stipe 1–2(–3) mm, ± equal to calyx; pinnae 2 or 3(or 4) pairs per leaf, blade margins eciliate . . . . 5. *Neptunia microcarpa*

1. Neptunia oleracea Loureiro, Fl. Cochinch. 2: 654. 1790 • Water sensitive plant, water or garden mimosa [I]

Mimosa natans Linnaeus f.; *Neptunia prostrata* Baillon

Herbs aquatic. **Stems** usually prostrate-floating, with little or no branching, often rooting at nodes. **Leaves:** stipules cordate-clasping; petiole 2–7 cm, eglandular; pinnae 2 or 3 (or 4) pairs; leaflets 16–40, blades 5–18 mm, without raised-reticulate venation abaxially or veins obscured, margins eciliate or sparsely ciliate. **Peduncles** 5–20(–30) cm. **Spikes** 30–50-flowered, ovoid to obovoid; bracts 2(or 3), cordate-clasping, 3–7 × 3–6 mm. **Flowers** dimorphic, proximal with flattened, petaloid staminodes, distal anther-bearing; calyx 2–4 mm. **Legumes** 8–10 mm wide, base at right angle to stipe; stipe 4–8 mm, longer than calyx. **Seeds** 4–8. $2n$ = 56.

Flowering Aug–Oct. Streams, lakes, ponds; 100 m; introduced; Ark.; South America; s Asia (India); Africa; introduced also in Mexico, West Indies, Central America, elsewhere in Asia.

Neptunia oleracea is native to tropical Asia, including India, tropical Africa, and South America and is a cosmopolitan tropical weed. It grows wild and is cultivated as a vegetable throughout southeast Asia, particularly Indochina and Thailand. It is a popular Thai vegetable; the young leaves, shoot tips, and young pods are often used in soup or a spicy and sour salad with seafood. In the United States, *Neptunia oleracea* is grown as an aquarium or pond plant.

Neptunia oleracea in Arkansas was encountered in a colony on the Little Maumelle River, floating and intermixed with *Hydrilla verticillata*, near Little Rock (J. H. Peck and B. E. Serviss 2011).

Neptunia natans (Linnaeus f.) Druce (1917), not W. Theobald (1883), pertains here.

2. Neptunia plena (Linnaeus) Bentham, J. Bot. (Hooker) 4: 355. 1841 • Water dead-and-awake [I]

Mimosa plena Linnaeus, Sp. Pl. 1: 519. 1753

Herbs semiaquatic or terrestrial, usually in wet habitats. **Stems** erect to ascending or floating, often procumbent near water's edge, often highly branched, submergent stems often inflated and rooting at nodes. **Leaves:** stipules cordate-clasping; petiole 1–2.5 cm, with a prominent discoid gland at base of, or proximal to, proximalmost pinnae pair; pinnae 2–4(or 5) pairs; leaflets 18–70, blades 3–6(–14) mm, without raised-reticulate venation abaxially or veins obscured, margins eciliate. **Peduncles** 5–8 cm. **Spikes** 30–60-flowered, ovoid; bracts 2, cordate-clasping, 4–8 × 3–8 mm. **Flowers** dimorphic, proximal with flattened, petaloid staminodes, distal anther-bearing; calyx 1.5–2.5 mm. **Legumes** 7–12 mm wide, base attenuate to stipe; stipe 3–9 mm, longer than calyx. **Seeds** 6–20. $2n$ = 72, 78.

Flowering Aug–Oct. Wet habitats, ephemeral lakes, ponds in highway medians; 0–20 m; introduced; Tex.; Mexico; West Indies; Central America; South America; introduced also in Asia.

Neptunia plena is known only from Kenedy County; it was first collected there in 1938 and was collected again in 2007 from a different location in the county.

3. Neptunia lutea (Leavenworth) Bentham, J. Bot. (Hooker) 4: 356. 1841 • Yellow puff [E] [F]

Acacia lutea Leavenworth, Amer. J. Sci. Arts 7: 61. 1824; *Neptunia lutea* var. *multipinnata* B. L. Turner; *N. lutea* var. *tenuis* (Bentham) B. L. Robinson

Herbs terrestrial, sometimes in moist sites. **Stems** erect to decumbent or prostrate. **Leaves:** stipules lanceolate; petiole 1.5–3 cm, eglandular; pinnae 2–11 pairs; leaflets 16–36, blades 3.5–6 mm, with raised-reticulate venation abaxially, margins ciliate. **Peduncles** 5–10 cm. **Spikes** 30–60-flowered, subcylindric; bracts (0 or)1 or 2, linear-subulate, 1–3 × 1–2 mm. **Flowers** monomorphic, anther-bearing, without conspicuous staminodes; calyx 1–2 mm. **Legumes** 10–15 mm wide, base attenuate to stipe; stipe 4–14 mm, longer than calyx. **Seeds** 1–6. $2n$ = 28.

Flowering Apr–Oct. Pine, pine-oak, oak woods, post oak-juniper-pine, post oak ridges, juniper-oak flatwoods, cedar barrens, chalk prairies, sandstone outcrops, blackland prairies, coastal prairies, wet flats and upland prairie, sandstone slopes, marly outcrops, sandy or calcareous soils, gravelly clay loam, roadsides, fields; 0–400 m; Ala., Ark., Kans., La., Miss., Okla., Tex.

The leaflets of *Neptunia lutea*, as well as other species in this genus, show rapid movement in response to touch, but the species generally used to demonstrate this phenomenon is *Mimosa pudica*.

4. Neptunia pubescens Bentham, J. Bot. (Hooker) 4: 356. 1841 • Tropical puff

Neptunia floridana Small; *N. lindheimeri* B. L. Robinson; *N. pubescens* var. *floridana* (Small) B. L. Turner; *N. pubescens* var. *lindheimeri* (B. L. Robinson) B. L. Turner

Herbs terrestrial, sometimes in moist sites. **Stems** erect to decumbent, prostrate, or prostrate-ascending. **Leaves:** stipules lanceolate-acuminate; petiole 1.2–3 cm, eglandular; pinnae (2 or)3–6 pairs; leaflets (16–)28–60(–86), blades 2.3–8.5 mm, with raised-reticulate venation abaxially, margins ciliate. **Peduncles** 2.5–11 cm. **Spikes** 15–30-flowered, spheric to ovoid; bracts 0–2, linear-subulate, 1–3 × 1–2 mm. **Flowers** dimorphic, proximal with flattened, petaloid staminodes, distal anther-bearing; calyx 2–2.7 mm. **Legumes** 5–13 mm wide, base usually tapering to stipe; stipe 2–4 mm, usually longer than calyx. **Seeds** 4–11. $2n$ = 28.

Flowering (Apr–)May–Sep(–Oct). Sand, sandy loam, clay soils, coastal prairies, meadows, live-oak savannas, blackland prairies, beach ridges and strands, silt and shell fill, canal edges, marsh and pond edges, roadsides, lawns; 0–100 m; Ala., Fla., La., Miss., Tex.; Mexico; Central America; South America.

The heteromorphic flowers of *Neptunia pubescens*, and other legume genera as well, result mostly from suppression and modification of structures after they are initiated rather than complete loss of structures (S. C. Tucker 1988).

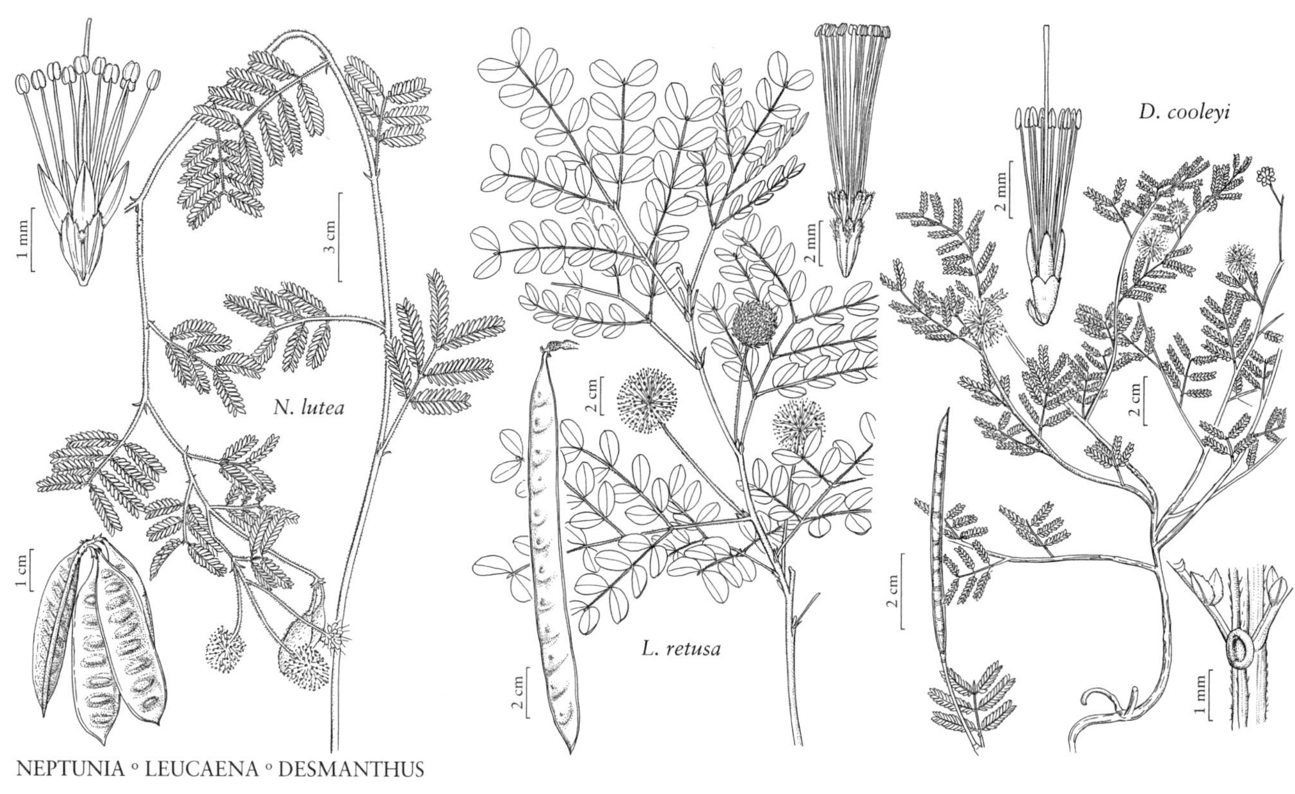

NEPTUNIA ◦ LEUCAENA ◦ DESMANTHUS

5. **Neptunia microcarpa** Rose, Contr. U.S. Natl. Herb. 8: 300. 1905 • Rio Grande puff

Neptunia palmeri Britton & Rose; *N. pubescens* Bentham var. *microcarpa* (Rose) Windler

Herbs terrestrial. **Stems** erect to decumbent or prostrate. **Leaves:** stipules lanceolate-acuminate; petiole 1.5–2 cm, eglandular; pinnae 2 or 3(or 4) pairs; leaflets 30–80, blades 4–6.5 mm, with raised-reticulate venation abaxially, margins eciliate. **Peduncles** 2.5–11 cm. **Spikes** 20–30-flowered, spheric to ovoid; bracts (0 or)1 or 2, linear-subulate, 1–3 × 1–2 mm. **Flowers** dimorphic, proximal with flattened, petaloid staminodes, distal anther-bearing; calyx 2–2.7 mm. **Legumes** 8–17 mm wide, base usually rounded to stipe; stipe 1–2(–3) mm, ± equal to calyx. **Seeds** 5–9. **2*n*** = 28.

Flowering May–Aug(–Oct). Stream edges, floodplains, bottomlands, roadsides, limestone soils, silty gravel, limestone hills; 300–400 m; Tex.; Mexico (Coahuila, Nuevo León, Tamaulipas).

Neptunia microcarpa was treated as conspecific with *N. pubescens* by D. R. Windler (1966). Morphological differences are consistent, and the two taxa are disjunct in geographical range and different in ecology. B. L. Turner (1951) and Turner et al. (2003) treated each at specific rank.

24. LEUCAENA Bentham, J. Bot. (Hooker) 4: 416. 1842 • Lead tree [Greek *leukos*, white, and *ainos*, exceedingly, alluding to flower color in most species]

Neil A. Harriman†

Shrubs or trees, unarmed. **Stems** erect, glabrous, sparsely hirsute, or tomentose. **Leaves** alternate, even-bipinnate; stipules present, persistent or caducous, ovate, inconspicuous, apex acuminate; solitary nectary gland present between or just below proximalmost pinnae, on rachis and rachillae; petiolate; pinnae 2–20 pairs; leaflets 8–60(–140), blade margins entire, surfaces pubescent or glabrous. **Inflorescences** 45–190-flowered, axillary, globose heads, usually fascicled, rarely solitary; bracts present, connate, forming involucre at base of each inflorescence, 2–4-lobed; bracteoles peltate and marcescent, exceeding buds only when very young (except in *L. retusa*). **Flowers** mimosoid; calyx obconic, tubular, or campanulate, lobes 5; corolla yellow, white, or greenish white; stamens 10, distinct; anthers dorsifixed to nearly basifixed. **Fruits** legumes, shortly stipitate, compressed or flat, linear or oblong, dehiscent, valves sometimes curling, membranous to leathery, often succulent when immature, glabrous or pubescent. **Seeds** 8–24, round, ovate, or weakly rhomboidal; pleurogram U-shaped, generally symmetric. x = 26, 28.

Species 22 (3 in the flora): sc, se United States, Mexico, West Indies, Central America, South America; introduced in tropical and subtropical areas worldwide.

Leucaena greggii S. Watson has been ascribed to southern Texas (N. L. Britton and J. N. Rose 1928; C. S. Sargent 1922) but incorrectly so. *Leucaena esculenta* (de Candolle) Bentham has edible pods and seeds and is cultivated in the southwestern United States; it is not known to have escaped (C. E. Hughes 1998). Distinguishing features of *L. esculenta* include corky ridges on young growth and leaves with more than 50 pinnae, each with more than 100 leaflets.

SELECTED REFERENCES Hughes, C. E. 1998. Monograph of *Leucaena* (Leguminosae-Mimosoideae). Syst. Bot. Monogr. 55: 1–244. Hughes, C. E., C. D. Bailey, and S. A. Harris. 2002. Divergent and reticulate species relationships in *Leucaena* (Fabaceae) inferred from multiple data sources: Insights into polyploidy origins and nrDNA polymorphism. Amer. J. Bot. 89: 1057–1073.

1. Pinnae 2–4 pairs; leaflets usually 8–16; se New Mexico, w, c Texas . . . . 1. *Leucaena retusa*
1. Pinnae 4–20 pairs; leaflets 26–60(–140); s Florida, s Texas.
    2. Leaflets 40–60(–140), blades 4–5 mm; anthers glabrous, tips apiculate . . . . 2. *Leucaena pulverulenta*
    2. Leaflets 26–32, blades 8–14 mm; anthers sparsely hairy, tips rounded . . . . 3. *Leucaena leucocephala*

1. Leucaena retusa Bentham, Smithsonian Contr. Knowl. 3(5): 64. 1852 [F]

Caudoleucaena retusa (Bentham) Britton & Rose

Shrubs or trees 2–5(–8) m, glabrous. **Leaves:** stipules long-persistent; petiole 2–5 cm; gland cylindrical; pinnae 2–4 pairs; rachis 4–8 cm; leaflets usually 8–16, rachilla 4.5–5.5 cm, blade elliptic, (15–)20–26(–30) × (8–)10–12(–15) mm. **Peduncles** 2.5–9 cm, densely villous. **Inflorescences** usually in fascicles of 2–4, rarely solitary, 2–2.5 cm diam.; bracts conspicuously exserted in bud. **Flowers:** calyx tube glabrous; petals distinct, yellow, margins ciliolate; anthers glabrous. **Legumes** compressed, linear, 12–25 × 0.8–1.5 cm, coriaceous. $2n$ = 56.

Flowering Apr–Jul, fruiting Jul–Sep. Limestone or igneous hills; 500–2100 m; N.Mex., Tex.; Mexico (Chihuahua, Coahuila).

Leucaena retusa is not uncommon in central and western Texas; in New Mexico it is known only in the Guadalupe Mountains in Eddy County near the ghost town of Queen.

2. Leucaena pulverulenta (Schlechtendal) Bentham, J. Bot. (Hooker) 4: 417. 1842

Acacia pulverulenta Schlechtendal, Linnaea 12: 571. 1838

Shrubs or trees 5–18(–20) m, new growth whitish puberulent. **Leaves:** petiole 5 cm; gland depressed-elliptic; pinnae 10–20 pairs; rachis 11–17 cm; leaflets 40–60(–140), rachilla 5–6 cm, blade oblong, 4–5 × 1 mm. **Peduncles** 2.5–3.5 cm, densely pubescent. **Inflorescences** fascicled in distal axils, 1–2 cm diam.; bracts inconspicuous. **Flowers:** calyx tube densely pubescent; petals connate basally, pale greenish white, pilose; anthers glabrous, tip apiculate. **Legumes** flat, oblong, 8–20 × 1–1.5 cm, membranous. $2n$ = 56.

Flowering Feb–Jul, fruiting Aug–Nov. Coastal plains, roadsides, canal banks, waste ground; 0–100 m; Tex.; Mexico (Hidalgo, Nuevo León, Querétaro, San Luis Potosí, Tamaulipas, Veracruz).

Leucaena pulverulenta is cultivated in California but not escaped. The species is locally abundant and, apparently, native in southern Texas; it is cultivated, but not persistent, farther north.

3. Leucaena leucocephala (Lamarck) de Wit, Taxon 10: 54. 1961 [I]

Mimosa leucocephala Lamarck in J. Lamarck et al., Encycl. 1: 12. 1783

Shrubs or trees 3–15(–20) m, twigs and petioles puberulent. **Leaves:** petiole 2–3 cm; gland saucer-shaped; pinnae 4–8 pairs; rachis 9–11 cm; leaflets 26–32, rachilla 7–8 cm, blade oblong, 8–14 × 2–4.5 mm. **Peduncles** 1–2.5 cm, pubescent. **Inflorescences** fascicled in distal axils, 1–2 cm diam.; bracts inconspicuous. **Flowers:** calyx tube strigose; petals distinct, white, puberulent; anthers sparsely hairy, tip rounded. **Legumes** green becoming red to brown, flat, compressed, 12–21 × 1.4–2 cm. $2n$ = 104.

Flowering and fruiting year-round. Pinelands, roadsides, canal banks, fencerows, waste ground; 0–500 m; introduced; Fla., Tex.; Mexico; West Indies; Central America; South America; introduced also in tropical and subtropical areas worldwide.

Leucaena leucocephala is probably native in the New World tropics and is now pantropical as a weed. It is planted for food and animal forage and is used as firewood. Because it is cultivated in Arizona and California, it should be expected as a weed. *Leucaena leucocephala* is a self-compatible tetraploid.

C. E. Hughes (1998) recognized three subspecies in *Leucaena leucocephala*, two of which occur in North America: subsp. *glabrata* (Rose) Zárate (arborescent) and subsp. *leucocephala* (shrubby), with traits which are not determinable from herbarium specimens; their character states are otherwise overlapping.

25. DESMANTHUS Willdenow, Sp. Pl. 4: 888, 1044. 1806, name conserved • Bundle flower [Greek *desme*, bundle, and *anthos*, flower, alluding to dense, globose inflorescences]

Melissa A. Luckow

Herbs, perennial, or shrubs [trees], unarmed, branched from base; taproot woody. **Stems** prostrate to decumbent or erect, young ones angled with corky ridges, glabrous or pubescent. **Leaves** alternate, even-bipinnate; stipules present, setiform, base usually dilated, auriculate, striate-veined, membranous, 1 auricle sometimes developed into curled tooth under petiole; 1 extrafloral nectary usually present on rachis between proximal pair of pinnae, sometimes also between distal pinnae (in *D. cooleyi*, *D. glandulosus*, *D. leptophyllus*, and *D. velutinus*), rarely absent, sessile or stipitate; petiolate; pinnae 1–18 pairs, opposite; leaflets 10–90, opposite, short-petiolulate, blade margins entire, surfaces usually glabrous, sometimes pubescent or with few, scattered hairs, margins ciliate. **Inflorescences** 3–71-flowered, axillary, condensed spikes or heads, often with sterile flowers proximally, functionally staminate flowers in middle, bisexual flowers distally, sterile or staminate flowers sometimes absent; bracts present, peltate, sometimes grouped into involucel at base of head. **Flowers** mimosoid; calyx cupulate, lobes 5, connate 1/3–1/2 length, dentate, acute; corolla pale green or white, petals distinct, oblanceolate or linear, 1-veined; stamens 5–10, distinct, filaments white or pale pink; anthers dorsifixed to nearly basifixed; ovary sessile, linear [ovate], glabrous [pubescent]; stigma funnelform; staminate flowers with rudimentary ovary; sterile flowers with filamentous staminodia, white or pale pink. **Fruits** legumes, sessile, straight or falcate, subterete to flattened, linear to oblong or falcate, leathery to papery [woody], dehiscent [indehiscent], glabrous. **Seeds** 2–32, ovoid or rhomboid, obliquely, longitudinally, or laterally positioned in pod, testa hard, pleurogram present. x = 14.

Species 25 (13 in the flora): United States, Mexico, West Indies, Central America, South America; introduced in Asia, Africa, Indian Ocean Islands, Pacific Islands, Australia.

Species of *Desmanthus* have been studied over the past several decades as potential food and forage crops in both temperate and tropical areas because of the high protein content of the leaves and seeds, low levels of toxins, and a vigorous growth habit that allows them to persist in harsh environments. Attempts have been made to use *D. illinoensis* as a perennial seed crop, but it has been challenging to develop a reliable method to harvest the seeds from the dense infructescences (P. A. Kulakow 1999). *Desmanthus illinoensis* has been tested also as a temperate forage legume and can be used effectively in polyculture grasslands (V. D. Picasso et al. 2011). Extensive research on species from the *D. virgatus* complex (*D. leptophyllus*, *D. pubescens* B. L. Turner, *D. virgatus*) as a warm area/tropical forage crop has also been conducted, notably in Australia, where cultivars have been developed (W. R. Ocumpaugh et al. 2004).

The center of diversity for *Desmanthus* is in Mexico and the southern United States. Some species have disjunct distributions between the southern United States and southern South America (M. A. Luckow 1993).

Species delimitation in *Desmanthus* is challenging, and both flowering and fruiting material are often necessary for identification. *Desmanthus* is often confused with *Neptunia*. Stipules provide the best differentiating character; in *Desmanthus* they are setiform; in *Neptunia* they are triangular, membranous, and striate. One also often finds *Acaciella angustissima* among *Desmanthus* specimens. Flowering material is easily discerned using stamen number (10 per flower in *Desmanthus*, 15–many in *Acacia*, *Acaciella*, *Mariosousa*, *Senegalia*, and *Vachellia*); *Acaciella angustissima* also lacks a nectary on the petiole.

Desmanthus pernambucanus (Linnaeus) Thellung is planted in tropical climates as a forage crop and is a pantropical weed. It was reported as escaped in Florida by A. W. Chapman (1860; as *D. diffusus* Willdenow) and others, perhaps based on that report. No voucher specimens from Florida have been located so it is excluded here. It would key to *D. leptophyllus*, from which it differs in having 2–4 pinnae per leaf with 18–24 leaflets per pinna, pubescent stipules with curved auricles, and by being relatively few-branched from base, versus 4–8 pairs of pinnae with 32–72 leaflets per pinna, glabrous stipules with straight auricles, and relatively much-branched from base in *D. leptophyllus*. It has often been confused with *D. virgatus*; the latter has a shorter petiole and, usually, more pinnae than *D. pernambucanus*, as well as smaller stature.

SELECTED REFERENCE Luckow, M. A. 1993. Monograph of *Desmanthus* (Leguminosae-Mimosoideae). Syst. Bot. Monogr. 38.

1. Shrubs, 5–25 dm, annual growth terminal on existing branches; heads 23–43-flowered; staminodia showy, 7.5–17 mm . . . . 5. *Desmanthus covillei*
1. Herbs, subshrubs, or shrubs, 1.5–30 dm, new growth usually basal from woody taproot; heads 3–20(–71)-flowered; staminodia often inconspicuous, 0.5–11 mm.
    2. Stamens 5; sterile flowers 0–2 per head; legumes oblong-falcate, and in tight, globose clusters, or straight, linear, and constricted between seeds.
        3. Legumes incurved-falcate, not constricted between seeds, 4.5–7 mm wide, 3–4 times longer than wide, tardily dehiscent along abaxial suture; seeds inserted transversely; heads 20–71-flowered . . . . 7. *Desmanthus illinoensis*
        3. Legumes linear, regularly constricted between seeds, 2.5–4 mm wide, 7+ times longer than wide, readily dehiscent along both sutures; seeds inserted longitudinally; heads 4–10-flowered . . . . 8. *Desmanthus leptolobus*
    2. Stamens 10; sterile flowers 0–20 per head; legumes linear or oblong, not in tight, globose clusters, not or irregularly constricted between seeds.
        4. Leaflet abaxial surface venation raised, reticulate; leaf nectaries usually absent.
            5. Peduncles 2–6.2 cm in fruit; legumes dark brown with slightly raised venation on valves, apex obtuse; leaflet blades pubescent abaxially; sterile flowers 3–7 per head . . . . 10. *Desmanthus obtusus*
            5. Peduncles 7–14 cm in fruit; legumes light brown with conspicuous raised, reticulate venation on valves, apex acute; leaflet blades glabrous abaxially; sterile flowers absent . . . . 11. *Desmanthus reticulatus*
        4. Leaflet abaxial surface with eccentric midvein visible; leaf nectaries usually present.

[6. Shifted to left margin.—Ed.]

6. Heads 21–60-flowered; styles exserted 3–5 mm beyond stamens; staminodia usually showy, 5–11 mm; legumes 4.6–10 cm.
   7. Herbs erect, 1.5–3 m, unbranched or 2 or 3-branched from base; nectaries between proximal pair of pinnae or on petioles between stipels; stipules persistent; peduncles 1.5–3.7 cm . . . . 2. *Desmanthus bicornutus*
   7. Herbs decumbent, to 0.5 m, much-branched from base; nectaries usually between proximal pairs of pinnae, rarely absent or also between more distal pairs of pinnae; stipules deciduous; peduncles 0.5–1.8 cm . . . . 4. *Desmanthus cooleyi*
6. Heads 5–22(–33)-flowered; styles slightly or not exserted beyond stamens; staminodia usually inconspicuous, 0.5–8(–10.5) mm; legumes 2.2–8.5(–10.6) cm.
   8. Peduncles 0–0.5 cm . . . . 3. *Desmanthus brevipes*
   8. Peduncles 0.6–4 cm.
      9. Stems usually velutinous, rarely sparsely pubescent or glabrous; stipules densely villous . . . . 12. *Desmanthus velutinus*
      9. Stems glabrous or densely to sparsely pubescent; stipules glabrous or pubescent but not villous.
         10. Petioles 1–5(–6) mm; herbs prostrate to decumbent.
            11. Legume apex apiculate; leaflets 14–24 per pinna; taproot napiform, bark red . . . . 1. *Desmanthus acuminatus*
            11. Legume apex acute; leaflets 22–46 per pinna; taproot cylindric, bark brown . . . . 13. *Desmanthus virgatus*
         10. Petioles (3–)5–16 mm; herbs or shrubs usually erect, sometimes decumbent.
            12. Leaf nectaries between proximal and distal pairs of pinnae, sometimes between all pairs; Texas . . . . 6. *Desmanthus glandulosus*
            12. Leaf nectaries usually between proximal pairs of pinnae, rarely also between distal pairs; Florida . . . . 9. *Desmanthus leptophyllus*

1. **Desmanthus acuminatus** Bentham, J. Bot. (Hooker) 4: 357. 1841 • Wild tantan

Acuan acuminatum (Bentham) Kuntze; *Desmanthus depressus* Humboldt & Bonpland ex Willdenow var. *acuminatus* (Bentham) Burkart; *D. virgatus* (Linnaeus) Willdenow var. *acuminatus* (Bentham) Isely

Herbs, prostrate to decumbent, much-branched from base, to 3 dm, not woody at base; taproot napiform, bark red, corky. **Stems** densely to sparsely pubescent with short white hairs along ribs, glabrescent. **Leaves** 1–4 cm; stipules persistent, 2.5–6 mm, with prominently veined auricles, one developed into a tooth curved under pulvinus, pubescent, hairs white, relatively long; petiole 3–6 mm; pinnae 2–4 pairs; nectary usually present, sessile, crateriform or flattened, between proximal pair of pinnae; leaflets 14–24, blades 3–5.5 mm, venation obscure except eccentric midvein, surfaces glaucous, glabrous. **Peduncles** 0.6–2 cm, 1–2 cm in fruit. **Heads** 1 per axil, 6–12-flowered; sterile flowers 0–3 per head; staminate and bisexual flowers 5–10 per head. **Flowers:** stamens 10; staminodia 6–8 mm; style slightly exserted beyond stamens. **Legumes** brown to nearly black, ± falcate, linear-oblong, not constricted between seeds, dehiscent along both sutures, 2.7–5 cm × 2.5–4.5 mm, apex apiculate with beak 1–4 mm. **2*n*** = 28.

Flowering and fruiting Apr–May. Post-oak or juniper woodlands, prairies, roadsides; 60–800 m; Tex.; South America (Argentina, Bolivia, Paraguay, Uruguay).

Desmanthus acuminatus occurs in Texas from the coastal plain to the Cross Timbers region. Although recognized by some as a variety of *D. virgatus*, *D. acuminatus* can be distinguished in the flora area by the red, napiform taproot, pubescent stipules with prominent auricles, and longer petiole with flattened nectary.

2. **Desmanthus bicornutus** S. Watson, Proc. Amer. Acad. Arts 21: 426. 1886 • Ruby or two-horn bundleflower

Desmanthus rostratus B. L. Turner; *D. subulatus* (Britton & Rose) Wiggins

Herbs, erect, often unbranched, sometimes 2 or 3-branched from base, 15–30 dm, base woody in age. **Stems** glabrous. **Leaves** 9–18 cm; stipules persistent or late-deciduous, 1.2–7.8 mm, with small, membranous, erose auricles, these sometimes abscising, glabrous; petiole 3–11 mm; pinnae 6–14 pairs; nectary sessile, crateriform, between proximal pair of pinnae or on petiole between stipels; leaflets 40–90, blades 2.7–5.4 mm, venation obscure except for eccentric midvein, surfaces glabrous. **Peduncles** 1.5–3.7 cm, 1.5–5 cm in fruit. **Heads** 1 or 2 per axil, 25–60-flowered; sterile flowers 8–20 per head; staminate and bisexual flowers 16–50 per head. **Flowers:** stamens 10; staminodia 5–11 mm, usually showy; style exserted 3–5 mm beyond stamens. **Legumes** dark warm brown, straight or curved, linear, not constricted between seeds, dehiscent along both sutures, 4.6–10 cm × 2.7–4.5 mm, apex attenuate.

Flowering Aug–Nov, fruiting Sep–Dec. Along washes and roadsides in *Acacia-Prosopis* or *Larrea* scrub; 0–1400 m; Ariz.; Mexico; Central America.

The nectary borne between two stipels on the petiole of *Desmanthus bicornutus* is distinctive and the source of the specific epithet (two-horns). Although the species is widespread in Mexico, it is found in the flora area only in the Pajarito and Patagonia mountains of Santa Cruz County. It has been studied as a forage crop for wildlife.

3. **Desmanthus brevipes** B. L. Turner, Field & Lab. 18: 60. 1950 • Dwarf bundleflower [E]

Desmanthus tatuhyensis Hoehne var. *brevipes* (B. L. Turner) Luckow

Herbs, prostrate to decumbent, much-branched from base, to 4 dm. **Stems** glabrous or sparsely pubescent with short, white hairs along ribs, glabrescent. **Leaves** 2.3–7.5 cm; stipules persistent, 1.4–2.5 mm, with membranous auricles opposite petiole, glabrous; petiole 3–7 mm; pinnae 1 or 2 pairs; nectary sessile, crateriform, between proximal pair of pinnae; leaflets 38–52, blades 2.7–6.5 mm, venation obscure except for eccentric midvein, surfaces glabrous. **Peduncles** 0–0.5 cm, 0.4–0.9 cm in fruit. **Heads** 1 per axil, 7–9-flowered; sterile flowers 1 or 2 per head; staminate and bisexual flowers 5–8 per head. **Flowers:** stamens 10; staminodia 1.5–2 mm; style not exserted beyond stamens. **Legumes** reddish brown to nearly black, ± falcate, linear, not constricted between seeds, dehiscent along both sutures, 3.5–5 cm × 3–3.5 mm, apex acute. $2n = 28$.

Flowering and fruiting Jun–Oct. Beaches, bayfronts, grasslands, roadsides; 0–150 m; La., Tex.

Desmanthus brevipes is a segregate from the *D. virgatus* complex. The species was considered to be a variety of *D. tatuhyensis* by M. A. Luckow (1993), but subsequent study of the latter species in Argentina indicates that *D. brevipes* is distinct from its South American cousin. *Desmanthus brevipes* is easily distinguished by its sessile or very short flowering and fruiting peduncles.

4. **Desmanthus cooleyi** (Eaton) Branner & Coville, Rep. (Annual) Arkansas Geol. Surv. 1888(4): 178. 1891 • Cooley's mimosa or bundleflower [F]

Acacia cooleyi Eaton, Man. Bot. ed. 5, 89. 1829; *Desmanthus jamesii* Torrey & A. Gray; *D. jamesii* var. *fendleri* S. Watson

Herbs, decumbent to erect, much-branched from base, to 5 dm, base slightly woody. **Stems** sparsely pubescent along ridges or glabrous. **Leaves** 2.7–3.6 cm; stipules deciduous, 0.6–2.5 mm, with flared, membranous base, glabrous; petiole 3–7 mm; pinnae 3–7 pairs; nectary usually present, rarely absent, sessile, crateriform, between proximal pair of pinnae, rarely additional glands borne between more distal pairs of pinnae; leaflets 18–32, blades 2.5–4.8 mm, venation obscure except for eccentric midvein, surfaces glabrous. **Peduncles** 0.5–1.8 cm, 0.7–2.5 cm in fruit. **Heads** 1 or 2 per axil, 21–37-flowered; sterile flowers 3–10 per head; staminate and bisexual flowers 15–40 per head. **Flowers:** stamens 10; staminodia 5–10.5 mm, usually showy; style exserted 3–5 mm beyond stamens. **Legumes** brown, straight, linear, often with 1–several irregular constrictions, dehiscent along both sutures, 5–9 cm × 2.9–4.8 mm, apex usually acute, rarely attenuate.

Flowering May–Aug, fruiting Aug–Sep. Shortgrass prairies, oak-juniper-pinyon woodlands, clearings in ponderosa pine forests, roadsides; 900–2300 m; Ariz., Colo., Kans., N.Mex., Okla., Tex.; Mexico (Chihuahua, Durango).

Desmanthus cooleyi differs from *D. velutinus* in having shorter peduncles (0.5–1.8 versus 1.9–4 cm), often two inflorescences per leaf axil, and broader fruits (2.9–4.8 versus 2.1–3.5 cm). The relatively small, deciduous stipules also are diagnostic.

5. **Desmanthus covillei** (Britton & Rose) Wiggins, Field & Lab. 18: 128. 1950 • Coville's bundleflower

Acuan covillei Britton & Rose in N. L. Britton et al., N. Amer. Fl. 23: 135. 1928; *Desmanthus covillei* var. *arizonicus* B. L. Turner; *D. palmeri* (Britton & Rose) Wiggins

Shrubs, erect, much-branched from base, 5–25 dm. **Stems** glabrous. **Leaves** 2–5 cm; stipules persistent, 1.5–2.5 mm, with flared, membranous bases, glabrous; petiole 5–15 mm; pinnae 1–3(or 4) pairs; nectary sessile or stipitate, crateriform, interpinnal between proximal pair of pinnae; leaflets 16–34, blades 4–8 mm, venation obscure except for eccentric midvein, sometimes also 1 short, arcuate vein from base, surfaces glabrous. **Peduncles** 1–2.3 cm, 1–3.5 cm in fruit. **Heads** 1 or 2 per axil, 23–43-flowered; sterile flowers 5–16 per head; staminate and bisexual flowers 8–30 per head. **Flowers:** stamens 10; staminodia 7.5–17 mm, showy; style exserted 3–5 mm beyond stamens. **Legumes** brown, straight to slightly arcuate, linear, constricted between seeds, dehiscent along both sutures, 5.5–13 cm × 2.7–4 mm, apex acute, rarely with short beak to 3 mm.

Flowering Aug–Oct, fruiting Sep–Dec. Coastal plains, arroyos, foothills, canyons, slopes; 700–1000 m; Ariz.; Mexico (Baja California Sur, Sinaloa, Sonora).

Desmanthus covillei is the only shrubby member of the genus in the flora area. It is widespread in western Mexico but known in the flora area only from the Tucson Mountains in Pima County. The relatively large, showy inflorescences and large fruits are diagnostic.

6. Desmanthus glandulosus (B. L. Turner) Luckow, Syst. Bot. Monogr. 38: 77. 1993 • Glandular bundleflower

Desmanthus virgatus (Linnaeus) Willdenow var. *glandulosus* B. L. Turner, Field & Lab. 18: 64, fig. 6. 1950

Herbs, usually erect, sometimes decumbent, sparsely branched, to 7 dm, base often woody. **Stems** sparsely pubescent on ridges or glabrous. **Leaves** 4–8 cm; stipules usually deciduous, rarely persistent, 1.2–6 mm, with small, membranous, erose auricles, glabrous or sparsely pubescent; petiole 4–10 mm; pinnae 3–6 pairs; nectary sessile, crateriform or flattened, between proximal pair of pinnae, usually also between distal pair of pinnae, sometimes between all pairs; leaflets 28–52, blades 4.2–7.4 mm, venation obscure except for eccentric midvein, surfaces glaucous, glabrous. **Peduncles** 1.8–3 cm, 1.8–3.5 cm in fruit. **Heads** (or condensed spikes) 1 per axil, 9–20-flowered; sterile flowers 3–7 per head; staminate and bisexual flowers 5–12 per head. **Flowers:** stamens 10; staminodia 6–8 mm; style not exserted beyond stamens. **Legumes** dark warm brown, straight or curved distally away from axis, linear, not constricted between seeds, dehiscent along both sutures, 5.8–10.6 cm × 3.4–4.6 mm, apex acute or apiculate.

Flowering Jun–Sep, fruiting Jul–Oct. On limestone soils, oak-juniper woodlands, dry desert scrub; 100–2200 m; N.Mex., Tex.; Mexico (Coahuila).

Desmanthus glandulosus is found infrequently in southern New Mexico and the mountains of western Texas.

Originally considered a variety of *Desmanthus virgatus*, *D. glandulosus* differs in having an erect, sparsely branched habit, usually more than one large, flattened nectary per leaf, and deciduous stipules. Also, the fruits of *D. glandulosus* are larger (to 10.5 cm, those of *D. virgatus* usually not exceeding 6 cm).

7. Desmanthus illinoensis (Michaux) MacMillan ex B. L. Robinson & Fernald, Manual ed. 7, 503. 1908 • Illinois or prairie bundleflower, prairie mimosa [E] [F] [W]

Mimosa illinoensis Michaux, Fl. Bor.-Amer. 2: 254. 1803; *Desmanthus illinoensis* var. *glandulosus* (Michaux) J. F. Macbride

Herbs, erect to decumbent, sparsely to much-branched, to 15 dm. **Stems** sparsely pubescent on ridges or glabrous. **Leaves** 3.5–12 cm; stipules persistent, 3.6–12 mm, with small, winged margin at base opposite petiole, glabrous or sparsely pubescent; petiole 2–10 mm; pinnae 5–18 pairs; nectary present or absent, sessile, crateriform, between proximal pair of pinnae; leaflets 30–70, blades 1.7–6 mm, venation obscure except for nearly centric midvein, surfaces glabrous. **Peduncles** 1–6 cm, 1.8–6.5 cm in fruit. **Heads** 1(or 2) per axil, 22–71-flowered, usually all bisexual, occasionally with a few functionally staminate and sterile flowers at base; sterile flowers 0–2 per head; bisexual flowers 22–69 per head. **Flowers:** stamens 5; staminodia 4–6 mm; style not exserted beyond stamens. **Legumes** in tight, globose clusters, dark brown, slightly to strongly incurved-falcate, oblong, not constricted between seeds, tardily dehiscent along abaxial suture, dehiscent initially only along adaxial one, 1.5–3.2 cm × 4.5–7 mm, apex acute or attenuate with beak 1–2 mm. **Seeds** inserted transversely. $2n = 28$.

Flowering May–Jun(–Aug), fruiting Jul–Oct. Edges of swamps and marshes, bottomlands, breaks of rivers, creeks, wet prairies, drier areas with oak, pinyon, mesquite, and yucca, roadsides; 0–1500 m; Ala., Ark., Colo., Fla., Ga., Ill., Ind., Iowa, Kans., Ky., La., Minn., Miss., Mo., Nebr., Nev., N.Mex., N.Dak., Ohio, Okla., Pa., S.C., S.Dak., Tenn., Tex., Utah.

Desmanthus illinoensis is the most common species of the genus in the flora area. It is native in the central part of its range but may be introduced in the farthest eastern and western parts. *Desmanthus illinoensis* is easily recognized by its erect habit with tight clusters of oblong, falcate fruits. It is being studied as a potential food and forage crop for temperate climates.

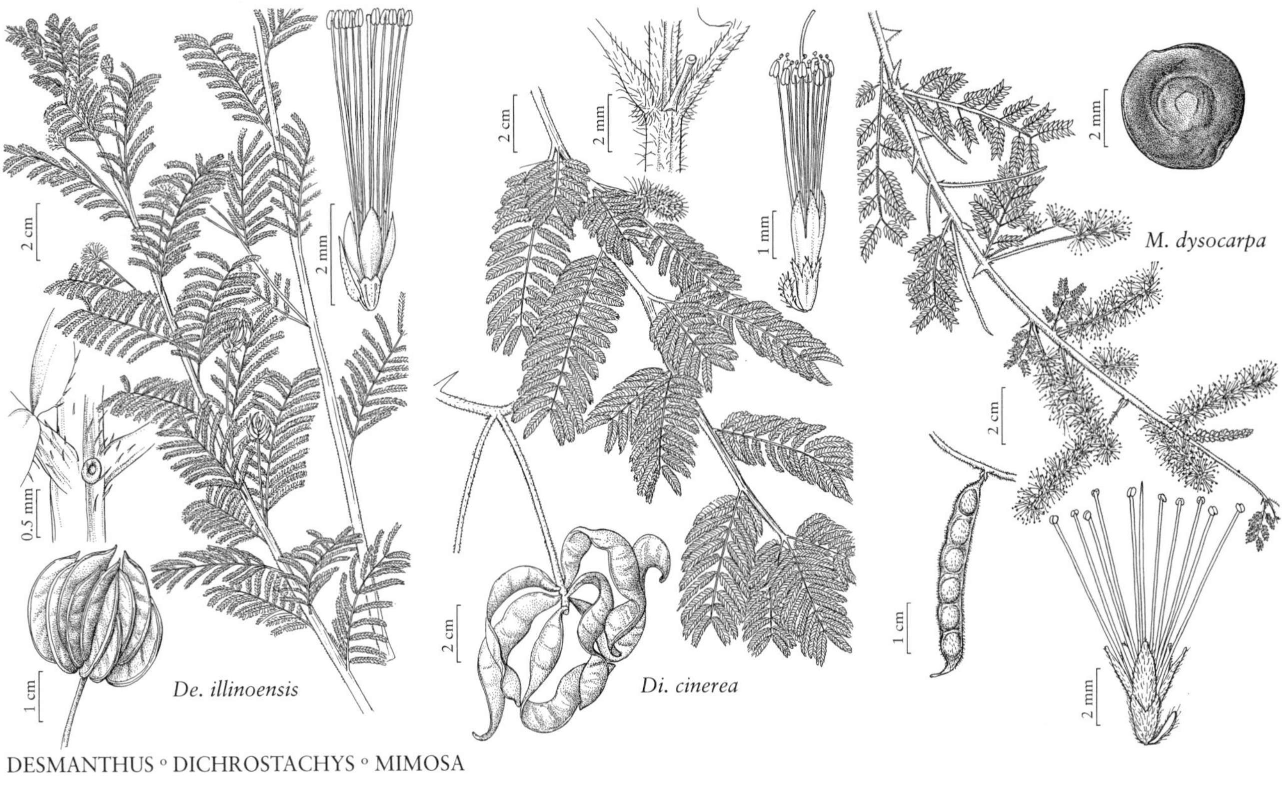

DESMANTHUS ◦ DICHROSTACHYS ◦ MIMOSA

8. **Desmanthus leptolobus** Torrey & A. Gray, Fl. N. Amer. 1: 402. 1840 • Slender-lobed bundleflower, prairie mimosa [E]

Herbs, prostrate or decumbent, much-branched, to 10 dm. **Stems** glabrous. **Leaves** 2.5–6.3 cm; stipules persistent, 2.5–7 mm, without winged margin at base, glabrous; petiole 2–5 mm; pinnae 4–9 pairs; nectary present or absent, sessile, crateriform, interpinnal between proximal pair of pinnae; leaflets 30–44, blades 2–4.5 (–6.8) mm, venation obscure except for eccentric midvein, surfaces glabrous. **Peduncles** 0.6–2 cm, 0.8–2.5 cm in fruit. **Heads** 1 per axil, 4–10-flowered, all bisexual. **Flowers:** stamens 5; style exserted beyond stamens. **Legumes** dark brown, straight, linear, regularly constricted between seeds, edges scalloped, dehiscent along both sutures, 4–7.5 cm × 2.5–3 mm, apex acute to apiculate with beak 1–3 mm. **Seeds** inserted longitudinally. 2*n* = 28.

Flowering May–Aug, fruiting Jun–Sep. Rich blackland prairies and woodlands, roadsides, uncultivated fields, waste areas; 150–300 m; Kans., Mo., Okla., Tex.

In *Desmanthus leptolobus*, the scalloped edges of the legume where it is constricted between the seeds and the longitudinal insertion of the seeds are diagnostic. The Missouri records are from along railroad tracks and likely represent introductions.

9. **Desmanthus leptophyllus** Kunth in A. von Humboldt et al., Nov. Gen. Sp. 6(fol.): 208; 6(qto.): 264. 1824 • Slenderleaf bundleflower [I]

Shrubs, erect, much-branched, 4–30 dm. **Stems** glabrous. **Leaves** 4.4–11 cm; stipules persistent, 3.3–9.5 mm, with small, membranous margins at base, glabrous or pubescent; petiole 3–14 mm; pinnae 4–8 pairs; nectary sessile, crateriform or flattened, between proximal pair of pinnae, rarely also between distal pairs of pinnae; leaflets 32–72, blades 2.1–5.7 mm, venation obscure except for nearly centric midvein, surfaces glabrous. **Peduncles** 0.8–2.7 cm, 1–3.3 cm in fruit. **Heads** 1 per axil, 5–12-flowered; sterile flowers 0(1 or 2) per head; staminate and bisexual flowers 5–11 per head. **Flowers:** stamens 10; staminodia 0.5 mm; style not exserted beyond stamens. **Legumes** reddish brown to nearly black, usually straight, sometimes recurved, linear, not constricted between seeds, dehiscent along both sutures, 5.5–8.5 cm × 3.2–5 mm, apex acute, apiculate with beak to 3 mm.

Flowering and fruiting Sep–Jan. Coastal thickets, marshes, waste places, roadsides; 0–50 m; introduced; Fla.; Mexico; West Indies; Central America; South America.

Part of the *Desmanthus virgatus* complex, *D. leptophyllus* differs from *D. virgatus* in the flora area by having more pinnae and leaflets and an erect rather than decumbent or prostrate habit. In the flora area, it is known from relatively few collections and is likely introduced.

10. Desmanthus obtusus S. Watson, Proc. Amer. Acad. Arts 17: 371. 1882 • Bluntpod bundleflower

Herbs, decumbent to erect, much-branched from base, to 5 dm. **Stems** pubescent throughout or pubescent only along ridges. **Leaves** 1.6–4.1 cm; stipules persistent, 1–4 mm, with an erose, membranous vein curled abaxially under pulvinus (sometimes absent), pubescent; petiole 3–11 mm; pinnae 1–3(or 4) pairs; nectary usually present, rarely absent, sessile, crateriform, interpinnal between proximal pair of pinnae; leaflets 12–30, blades 3–6 mm, venation conspicuous abaxially with raised reticulate midvein, usually also 2 other veins arising from base, raised crossveins also present, surfaces sparsely pubescent abaxially, glabrous adaxially. **Peduncles** 1.3–6 cm, 1.9–6.2 cm in fruit. **Heads** 1 per axil, 6–14-flowered; sterile flowers 3–7 per head; staminate and bisexual flowers 4–10 per head. **Flowers:** stamens 10; staminodia 5–10.5 mm; style exserted beyond stamens. **Legumes** dark brown, straight, linear, often with 1–several irregular constrictions, with slightly raised venation on valves, dehiscent along both sutures, 2.5–5 cm × 2.2–3.2 mm, apex obtuse or apiculate, rarely acute.

Flowering Mar–May (Aug–Sep), fruiting Apr–Jul (Sep–Oct). Pinyon-juniper woodlands, live oak woodlands, mesquite-juniper scrub, mesquite grasslands, old pastures, roadsides, rocky ledges; 100–900 m; N.Mex., Tex.; Mexico (Coahuila, Tamaulipas).

Desmanthus obtusus is most often confused with *D. reticulatus* and *D. velutinus*. It differs from the latter in having fewer pairs of pinnae per leaf (1–3 versus 3–7), raised venation on the abaxial leaf surface, and obtuse rather than acuminate legume apex; it differs from *D. reticulatus* in having a more compact and branched habit, shorter peduncles, fruits darker at maturity, leaflet blades pubescent abaxially rather than glabrous, and 3–7 sterile flowers, rather than being without sterile flowers.

11. Desmanthus reticulatus Bentham, J. Bot. (Hooker) 4: 357. 1841 • Netleaf bundleflower [E]

Herbs, lanky and diffuse, with spreading branches, to 7 dm; taproot narrow, linear, bark orange or brown. **Stems** uniformly pubescent to glabrate. **Leaves** 2.5–6 cm; stipules persistent, 1.7–3.5 mm, with 4 or 5-veined, membranous wing opposite petiole, pubescent; petiole 6–20 mm; pinnae 3 or 4(or 5) pairs; nectary absent or rudimentary, between proximal pair of pinnae; leaflets 10–20, blades 3–6.5 mm, venation conspicuous abaxially with raised eccentric midvein, usually also 2 veins arising from base, raised crossveins also present, surfaces glaucous, glabrous or with few, scattered hairs abaxially. **Peduncles** 5.5–12 cm, 7–14 cm in fruit. **Heads** 1 per axil, 8–20-flowered; sterile flowers absent. **Flowers:** stamens 10; style slightly exserted beyond stamens. **Legumes** light brown, straight, linear, not constricted between seeds, with conspicuous raised, reticulate venation on valves, dehiscent along both sutures, 2–5 cm × 3–4.2 mm, apex acute to attenuate.

Flowering and fruiting Apr–Jun(–Sep). Rich, moist blackland prairies, Tamaulipan scrub, roadsides in agricultural areas; 50–500 m; Tex.

Although not included in the most recent List of the Rare Plants of Texas (J. M. Poole et al., http://www.tpwd.state.tx.us/publications/pwdpubs/media/pwd_rp_w7000_1142.pdf), *Desmanthus reticulatus* is an inconspicuous plant of the blackland prairies of south-central Texas and is seldom collected.

12. Desmanthus velutinus Scheele, Linnaea 21: 455. 1848 • Velvet bundleflower

Herbs, decumbent to erect, much-branched, to 5 dm; taproot cylindric, bark red or brown, 5+ dm. **Stems,** pinnae, and rachises usually uniformly velutinus with spreading, white hairs, rarely sparsely pubescent or glabrous. **Leaves** 2.1–6.8 cm; stipules persistent, 1.7–4.5 mm, with erose, membranous wing curved under petiole, densely villous; petiole 4–12 mm; pinnae 3–7 pairs; nectary sessile, crateriform, between proximal pair of pinnae, sometimes also between distal pairs of pinnae; leaflets 24–44, blades 2.4–5.8 mm, venation obscure except for nearly centric midvein, surfaces glaucous, pubescent abaxially. **Peduncles** 1.9–4 cm, 2.8–6.5 cm in fruit. **Heads** 1 per axil, 15–33-flowered; sterile flowers 7–13 per head; staminate and bisexual flowers 11–20 per head. **Flowers:** stamens 10; staminodia 7.5–10.5 mm;

style slightly exserted beyond stamens. **Legumes** dark brown, straight, linear, sometimes irregularly constricted between seeds, dehiscent along both sutures, 4.2–8.2 cm × 2.1–3.5 mm, apex acute to attenuate with beak 1–6 mm. **2*n*** = 28.

Flowering Apr–Jun (Aug), fruiting May–Jul(–Oct). Oak and juniper woodlands, drier habitats with *Acacia* and *Prosopis*; 200–1900 m; N.Mex., Tex.; Mexico (Coahuila).

Desmanthus velutinus is sometimes confused with 4. *D. cooleyi* and 10. *D. obtusus*; see discussions under those species for distinguishing characteristics. The range of *D. velutinus* is limited to central Texas along the Balcones Fault, southwest to trans-Pecos and Rio Grande plain, southern New Mexico, and adjacent Coahuila, Mexico.

13. Desmanthus virgatus (Linnaeus) Willdenow, Sp. Pl. 4: 1047. 1806 • Wild tantan [W]

Mimosa virgata Linnaeus, Sp. Pl. 1: 519. 1753; *Desmanthus depressus* Humboldt & Bonpland ex Willdenow; *D. virgatus* var. *depressus* (Humboldt & Bonpland ex Willdenow) B. L. Turner

Herbs, prostrate to decumbent, much-branched from base, to 1.5 dm, not woody at base; taproot cylindric, bark brown. **Stems** glabrous or sparsely pubescent with short white hairs along ribs, glabrescent. **Leaves** 1–3[–6.5] cm; stipules persistent, 2.1–9 mm, with membranous, prominently veined auricle opposite petiole, glabrous or pubescent; petiole 1–5 mm; pinnae 2–5 pairs; nectary present, sessile, crateriform, interpinnal between proximal pair of pinnae; leaflets 22–46, blades 2.7–7 mm, venation obscure except for eccentric midvein, surfaces glabrous. **Peduncles** 0.6–4 cm, 1–5.2 cm in fruit. **Heads** 1 per axil, 3–22-flowered, sometimes only bisexual flowers present; sterile flowers 0–8 per head; staminate and bisexual flowers 3–14 per head. **Flowers:** stamens 10; staminodia 1.5–7.5 mm; style not exserted beyond stamens. **Legumes** reddish brown to nearly black, straight or weakly falcate, linear, not constricted between seeds, dehiscent along both sutures, 2.2–6[–8.8] cm × 2.5–4 mm, apex acute to attenuate. **2*n*** = 28.

Flowering and fruiting Apr–Nov. Railroad tracks, pastures, roadsides, along city streets, coastal thickets, beaches; 0–1000 m; Fla., La., Tex.; Mexico; West Indies; Central America; South America.

Desmanthus virgatus was the umbrella species in the genus for any taxon with inconspicuous flowers and unspecialized legumes; *D. acuminatus*, *D. brevipes*, and *D. glandulosus* have at times been considered varieties of this species, and *D. leptophyllus* and *D. pernambucanus* were synonymized with it in the tropics. The confusion is understandable because species differ in characteristics that may be difficult to see on a herbarium specimen, such as habit, degree of branching, taproot color and shape, and sleep movements of the leaves. Common garden studies (M. A. Luckow 1993) demonstrated that such characteristics are not phenotypic plasticity but have a genetic basis. In the flora area, *D. virgatus* is less variable than in Mexico, where one sees more erect forms with larger fruits and more flowers per inflorescence.

Desmanthus virgatus, as here circumscribed, is found throughout warmer areas in the New World; Old World species that have previously been considered *D. virgatus* are best referred to *D. pernambucanus*. *Desmanthus virgatus* has been intensively studied as a potential source of livestock feed for tropical areas.

26. DICHROSTACHYS (de Candolle) Wight & Arnott, Prodr. Fl. Ind. Orient. 1: 271. 1834, name conserved • [Greek *di-*, two, *chroma*, color, and *stachys*, spike, alluding to spikes with yellow stamens distally and white or other color staminodes proximally] [I]

Melissa A. Luckow

Desmanthus Willdenow sect. *Dichrostachys* de Candolle in A. P. de Candolle and A. L. P. P. de Candolle, Prodr. 2: 445. 1825

Shrubs or trees, armed [unarmed], branchlets modified as thorns, branched from base. **Branches** plagiotropic. **Stems:** younger ones rarely angled with corky ridges, pubescent to glabrate; short shoots (brachyblasts) present, clothed in persistent, distichous, connate stipule bases. **Leaves** alternate, even-bipinnate; stipules present, persistent, stramineous, ovate-triangular, striate; extrafloral nectary(ies) present, raised [sessile]; petiolate; pinnae [1 or]7–15[–20] pairs, opposite;

leaflets (8 or)10–40 pairs, opposite, blade margins entire, surfaces pubescent or glabrous. **Inflorescences** pedunculate, pendent, 50–200-flowered, axillary, spikes [condensed], borne 1–3 in axils of new growth or, more frequently, on brachyblasts, sterile flowers proximally, bisexual flowers distally, functionally staminate flowers in between; bracts present; bracteoles carinate, 1-veined, sometimes enlarged and exserted above flowers at anthesis. **Flowers** mimosoid, bisexual, staminate, or sterile; calyx cupulate [obconic], lobes 5, connate; corolla pale green; stamens 10, distinct, inserted at 2 levels; anthers dorsifixed; ovary sessile, oblong, densely strigose with silky white hairs; stigma punctate; staminate flowers with rudimentary ovary or ovary absent. **Fruits** legumes, sessile, coiling or curling, compressed, oblong-linear, indehiscent [elastically dehiscent from apex], glabrate. **Seeds** 2–8, ovoid to rhomboid, positioned obliquely. x = 14.

Species ca. 15 (1 in the flora): introduced, Florida; s Asia, Africa, Indian Ocean Islands (Madagascar), Australia; introduced also in tropical regions.

All but three species of *Dichrostachys* are endemic to Madagascar. The recent treatment of the Leguminosae of Madagascar (J. F. Villiers 2002b) does not correspond with results of phylogenetic studies (M. A. Luckow and D. J. Du Puy 2000; C. E. Hughes et al. 2003). The Malagasy species are easily distinguished by being unarmed and without apical anther glands; *D. cinerea* is the only species with indehiscent fruits.

1. **Dichrostachys cinerea** (Linnaeus) Wight & Arnott, Prodr. Fl. Ind. Orient. 1: 271. 1834 • Sicklebush, bell mimosa, Chinese lantern tree, maribu, Kalahari Christmas tree, aroma [F] [I]

Mimosa cinerea Linnaeus, Sp. Pl. 1: 520, no. 25 [not p. 517, no. 10]. 1753; *Dichrostachys glomerata* (Forsskål) Chiovenda; *D. nutans* (Persoon) Bentham; *D. platycarpa* Welwitsch ex W. Bull

Shrubs or trees 1–8(–10) m, bark light reddish brown, checkered, rough. **Stems** often armed at nodes with single axillary thorn to 8 cm, brachyblasts 0.5–1.5 cm. **Leaves** 1.5–20 cm, from brachyblasts or directly on new growth; petiole 0.5–4 cm; pinnae 1–8[–10] cm; nectary 1+, between first pair of pinnae, usually also between distal ones, narrowly cylindrical to crateriform, apically concave; leaflet blades linear to oblong, 2–5[–14] mm, venation obscure except midvein, sometimes with raised secondary venation. **Peduncles** 2–7 cm. **Spikes** 3.5–7 cm, stout, woody in fruit, 1–3[–6] heads per axil, each 2–5 cm, ca. ½ sterile. **Flowers** 2–5 mm; calyx ¼–½ length of flower; petals lanceolate, distinct basally, connate centrally; anthers bright yellow, oblong to ovate, glands long-stipitate, orbicular; staminodia exserted 5–15 mm from corolla; style white, exserted from stamens. **Legumes** pendent, usually densely crowded in glomerules of 10–20 irregularly contorted, twisted, intertwined pods, light [dark] brown, 8–11(–14) mm wide, valves leathery to slightly woody, rough with raised reticulate venation, usually raised over seeds. **2*n*** = 28 [36, 54, 56, 78].

Flowering and fruiting Jun–Feb. Heavy clay to sandy soils; 0–50 m; introduced; Fla.; Asia (India); Africa; Australia; introduced also in West Indies.

In the flora area, *Dichrostachys cinerea* is known from Lake, Miami-Dade, Monroe, Palm Beach, and Polk counties.

As currently circumscribed, *Dichrostachys cinerea* is widespread and highly variable. Early classifications distinguished species within the *D. cinerea* complex (G. Bentham 1875; E. G. Baker 1926–1930), but J. P. M. Brenan and R. K. Brummitt (1965) subsumed them all [except the Australian *D. spicata* (F. Mueller) Domin] in *D. cinerea*. Their treatment recognized ten subspecies and numerous varieties within some subspecies. This classification was not supported after improved sampling (J. H. Ross 1974). If one adopts the Brenan and Brummitt classification, the Florida introductions are best assigned to *Dichrostachys cinerea* subsp. *africana* Brenan & Brummitt. *Dichrostachys cinerea* has become a pervasive weed in Cuba, to the extent that it has been proposed as a source for biofuel in that country (D. Travieso Pedroso and M. Kaltschmitt, DOI 10.1007/s1339-011-0026-y) and has been banned from Hawaii because of its invasive potential (U.S. Forest Service, http://www.hear.org/pier/).

Dichrostachys cinerea has had many traditional medicinal uses and has recently been tested as an effective antibacterial (M. M. Eisa et al. 2000), antitumor (A. H. S. Abou Zeid et al., DOI: 10.1055/s-0028-1084325), and antiasthmatic (G. Irié-N'guessan et al. 2011) agent. The species is also a nutritious forage plant and an important source of fuel and building wood in Africa (D. A. Hines and K. Eckman 1993).

27. MIMOSA Linnaeus, Sp. Pl. 1: 516. 1753; Gen. Pl. ed. 5, 233. 1754 • [Greek *mimos*, mimicking (animal movement), alluding to sensitive collapse of foliage when touched (thigmotropism) in some species]

Rosaura Grether

Leptoglottis de Candolle ex Torrey & A. Gray; *Mimosopsis* Britton & Rose; *Morongia* Britton; *Schrankia* Willdenow, name conserved

Herbs, perennial, shrubs, or subshrubs [trees], armed or unarmed. **Stems** erect, scandent, decumbent, prostrate, or sprawling, terete, striate, or ribbed, prickles infrastipular, irregular in internodes, or along ribs; short shoots (brachyblasts) sometimes present, glabrous or pubescent. **Leaves** alternate, usually even-bipinnate, rarely some leaves unipinnate (*M. borealis*, *M. turneri*); stipules present; petiolate, petiole eglandular [glandular]; pinnae [0 or]1–14[–33] pairs; leaflets 1–40[–95] pairs, opposite, blade margins entire, surfaces glabrous or pubescent. **Peduncles** unarmed or prickly. **Inflorescences** 5–180-flowered, usually axillary, sometimes also terminal, capitula, spikes, or racemes; bracts present. **Flowers** mimosoid, bisexual, or staminate present at base of inflorescence; calyx campanulate, lobes 4 or 5(or 6), valvate; corolla white, pink, purple, or purple-pink, lobes 4 or 5(or 6), valvate; stamens 8 or 10 (2 times corolla lobes) or 4[5] (as many as corolla lobes), distinct or connate at bases, exserted, white, pink or lilac; anthers dorsifixed, introrse, eglandular; ovary sessile or stipitate; style longer than stamens; stigma poriform, cupuliform, or tubular [obliquely funnelform]. **Fruits** legumes, sessile or stipitate, straight or curved, constricted or not between seeds, linear, oblong, or tetragonal [elliptic], dehiscent, craspedial, glabrous or pubescent, valves segmented with 1 seed each or entire, usually wider than margin, persistent margin usually narrow, sometimes as wide as or wider than valves, prickly or unarmed. **Seeds** 1–18, ± isodiametric, lenticular, elliptic, oblong, or rhomboid, testa smooth or porous. $x = 13$.

Species ca. 530 (20 in the flora): United States, Mexico, West Indies, Central America, South America, Asia, Africa, Indian Ocean Islands (Madagascar), Australia; arid or semiarid areas, tropics, subtropics, temperate regions.

Mimosa is divided into five sections: sect. *Batocaulon* de Candolle, sect. *Habbasia* de Candolle, and sect. *Mimosa* are represented in the United States; sects. *Calothamnos* Barneby and *Mimadenia* Barneby are not found in the flora area.

Mimosa diplotricha C. Wright ex Sauvalle, *M. pigra*, and *M. pudica* Linnaeus are pantropical weeds. *Mimosa diplotricha* and *M. pigra* are noxious weeds, mainly in Australia: the former is found in Hawaii and Puerto Rico but not in the continental United States. *Mimosa pigra* is a noxious weed and a prohibited aquatic plant in the flora. *Mimosa pudica* is cultivated in the United States as an ornamental and is also used for experimental projects due to its sensitive leaves; furthermore, it can be considered as introduced in the flora of Florida and Maryland. Other species of *Mimosa* are widely used as melliferous and medicinal plants, forage for goats, living fences, firewood sources, and for reforestation by rural communities in arid, semiarid, and tropical regions.

SELECTED REFERENCE Barneby, R. C. 1991. Sensitivae censitae. A description of the genus *Mimosa* L. (Mimosaceae) in the New World. Mem. New York Bot. Gard. 65: 1–835.

1. Inflorescences spikes.
  2. Leaves with (1 or)2–4 pinna pairs, 2–4(or 5) leaflet pairs; corollas glabrous; legumes glabrous . . . . 3. *Mimosa distachya*
  2. Leaves with 5–11 pinna pairs, 6–14 leaflet pairs; corollas densely sericeous; legumes tomentose . . . . 4. *Mimosa dysocarpa*
1. Inflorescences capitula.
  3. Legumes segmented, each with 1 seed.
    4. Corolla lobes 4, stamens 4; legumes 3–4 mm wide; leaves with 1 or 2 pairs of digitate pinnae . . . . 14. *Mimosa pudica*
    4. Corolla lobes 4 or 5, stamens 8 or 10; legumes 5–13 mm wide; leaves with 1–14 pairs of non-digitate pinnae.
      5. Subshrubs, scandent; stems ribbed, prickles along ribs . . . . 9. *Mimosa malacophylla*
      5. Herbs or shrubs, erect or procumbent; stems not ribbed, prickles infrastipular or irregular along internodes.
        6. Corollas glabrous; legumes glabrous.
          7. Corolla lobes ⅔ corolla length; legumes oblong . . . . 2. *Mimosa borealis*
          7. Corolla lobes ⅓–½ corolla length; legumes linear . . . . 20. *Mimosa turneri*
        6. Corollas usually tomentose or strigose, rarely glabrous; legumes tomentose, setose, strigose, strigulose, or puberulent.
          8. Corollas tomentose; legumes tomentose and setose; stems tomentose or glabrescent, brachyblasts present . . . . 5. *Mimosa emoryana*
          8. Corollas strigose or glabrous; legumes setose or strigose to strigulose; stems strigose to strigulose or puberulent, brachyblasts absent.
            9. Shrubs, erect, 1–3 m; legumes oblong, segments (4–)7–25 . . . . 13. *Mimosa pigra*
            9. Herbs, procumbent, 0.1–0.5 m; legumes obliquely oblong, segments 1–4 . . . . 18. *Mimosa strigillosa*
  3. Legumes not segmented, valves entire.
    10. Shrubs; prickles infrastipular.
      11. Legumes linear, 3–4 mm wide; corollas tomentose or tomentulose . . . . 1. *Mimosa biuncifera*
      11. Legumes oblong, 5–8 mm wide; corollas glabrous or puberulent, or pilosulous on lobes.
        12. Prickles in groups of 3, 2 straight, 1 recurved; capitula 13–20 mm diam., 50–120-flowered; corollas pilosulous on lobes or glabrous . . . . 6. *Mimosa grahamii*
        12. Prickles usually solitary, rarely 2 or 3, recurved; capitula 8–15 mm diam., 10–30-flowered; corollas glabrous or puberulent . . . . 19. *Mimosa texana*
    10. Herbs or subshrubs; prickles along stem ribs, rarely unarmed.
      13. Leaflet blades with reticulate veins prominent on both surfaces, or at least abaxially.
        14. Inflorescences axillary capitula; legumes linear-oblong, valves 3–6 mm wide . . . . 7. *Mimosa hystricina*
        14. Inflorescences axillary capitula, sometimes also terminal racemes; legumes linear, valves 1–2.5 mm wide.
          15. Inflorescences 20–30 mm diam., 90–140-flowered; peduncles 3.5–9.5 cm; racemes 130–200 mm; stipules 4.5–8 mm . . . . 12. *Mimosa nuttallii*
          15. Inflorescences 15–18 mm diam., 30–50-flowered; peduncles 0.6–1.5 cm; racemes 40–50 mm; stipules 1–2.5 mm . . . . 15. *Mimosa quadrivalvis*
      13. Leaflet blades with 1 vein slightly evident only on abaxial surface.
        16. Petioles shorter than primary rachis; pinnae (3 or)4–9 pairs; legumes linear, to 140 mm.
          17. Leaflet blades obliquely linear, 0.5–1 mm wide, surfaces not glaucous; capitula 60–120-flowered, bracts linear, ⅓–½ corolla length; legumes 1.5–4 mm wide, sessile . . . . 10. *Mimosa microphylla*
          17. Leaflet blades obliquely linear-oblong to oblong, 1–1.5 mm wide, surfaces glaucous; capitula 30–60-flowered, bracts spatulate, ¼–⅓ corolla length; legumes 3–5 mm wide, stipitate . . . . 17. *Mimosa rupertiana*

[16. Shifted to left margin.—Ed.]

16. Petioles as long or longer than primary rachis; pinnae 1–3 or 2–5 pairs; legumes linear-oblong, to 90(–100) mm.
    18. Pinnae 2–5 pairs; capitula 100–180-flowered; legume valves slightly wider than margin . . . . 16. *Mimosa roemeriana*
    18. Pinnae 1–3 pairs; capitula 20–70-flowered; legume valves narrower than margin.
        19. Leaflets 6–9 pairs, blades obliquely linear-oblong to oblong; corolla lobes ½ corolla length; legumes 25–60 × 2.5–4 mm. . . . . 8. *Mimosa latidens*
        19. Leaflets 9–14 pairs, blades obliquely linear; corolla lobes ¼–⅓ corolla length; legumes (45–)70–90(–100) × 4–4.5(–5) mm . . . . 11. *Mimosa monclovensis*

1. Mimosa biuncifera Bentham, Pl. Hartw., 12. 1839 • Wait-a-minute bush, wait-a-bit, catclaw mimosa

Mimosa aculeaticarpa Ortega var. *biuncifera* (Bentham) Barneby; *M. biuncifera* var. *flexuosa* B. L. Robinson; *M. biuncifera* var. *lindheimeri* (A. Gray) B. L. Robinson; *M. lindheimeri* A. Gray; *M. warnockii* B. L. Turner; *Mimosopsis biuncifera* (Bentham) Britton & Rose; *M. flexuosa* (B. L. Robinson) Britton & Rose; *M. lindheimeri* (A. Gray) Britton & Rose

Shrubs, erect, 1–2 m, armed. **Stems** terete, tomentulose or glabrescent; prickles infrastipular, paired, usually recurved, rarely straight. **Leaves:** stipules linear to subulate, 2–4 mm, puberulent; petiole 0.1–0.7 cm; primary rachis 0.3–2 cm; pinnae 2–8 pairs; leaflets 5–9(–12) pairs, blades obliquely oblong, 2–4 × 0.4–1.3 mm, margins ciliate, reticulate veins slightly visible abaxially, apex acute to obtuse, surfaces puberulent or glabrous abaxially, glabrous adaxially. **Peduncles** 0.7–1.5 cm. **Inflorescences** 17–40-flowered, axillary, globose capitula, solitary or in fascicles of 2 or 3, 8–12 mm diam.; bracts spatulate, ¼–½ corolla length. **Pedicels** 0 mm. **Flowers** bisexual; calyx campanulate, lobes 5, (⅓–)½–¾ corolla length; corolla white or purplish pink on lobes, tomentose or tomentulose, lobes 5, ¼–⅓ corolla length; stamens 10, filaments distinct to bases, white; ovary stipitate, glabrous or pubescent; style attenuate at apex; stigma poriform. **Legumes** sessile or stipitate, straight or curved, linear, 25–45 × 3–4 mm, constricted between seeds, valves entire, margin prickly or unarmed, apex acute to acuminate, faces glabrous; stipe 0.5–1.5 mm. **Seeds** 3–8, dark brown, oblong, 3.5–6 × 2–2.7 × 1–1.8 mm, testa smooth or porous, fissural line 40–50%.

Flowering Apr–Aug; fruiting Sep–Dec. Sonoran desert, washes, drainage areas, sandy-clay soils, riparian forest in desert grasslands, scattered oaks in broad canyon bottoms, roadsides; 150–2700 m; Ariz., N.Mex., Tex.; Mexico (Chihuahua, Coahuila, Durango, Nuevo León, San Luis Potosí, Sinaloa, Sonora, Tamaulipas, Zacatecas).

Mimosa flexuosa Bentham is an illegitimate name that pertains here.

Mimosa biuncifera is widely distributed in Arizona. It occurs in the southern half of New Mexico, and in central and western Texas, from McLennon County in the east, Floyd and Lamb counties in the north, Uvalde County in the south, and El Paso County in the west.

2. Mimosa borealis A. Gray, Mem. Amer. Acad. Arts, n. s. 4: 39. 1849 • Fragrant mimosa E

Mimosa fragrans A. Gray

Shrubs, erect, 0.5–2 m, usually armed, rarely unarmed. **Stems** terete, glabrous; prickles irregular along internodes, recurved or straight; brachyblasts present. **Leaves:** some 1-pinnate, with 1 or 2 pairs of leaflets; stipules subulate, 1.5–4 mm, glabrous; petiole 0.2–0.6 cm; primary rachis 0.2–0.5(–1.5) cm; pinnae 1–3(or 4) pairs; leaflets (1 or)2–7(or 8) pairs, blades obliquely oblong or elliptic to obovate, 2.5–6(–6.5) × 1–2.5 mm, margins eciliate, reticulate veins prominent abaxially, apex obtuse to acuminate, surfaces glabrous. **Peduncles** 0.5–1.5(–2.5) cm. **Inflorescences** (5–)10–30-flowered, axillary, globose or semiglobose capitula, solitary, in fascicles of 2 or 3, or in pseudoracemes, 9–15 mm diam.; bracts spatulate, ⅓ corolla length. **Pedicels** 0.5–1 mm. **Flowers** bisexual; calyx campanulate, lobes 4 or 5, ⅓ corolla length; corolla purple, glabrous, lobes 4 or 5, ⅔ corolla length; stamens 8 or 10, filaments connate at bases, pink or lilac; ovary stipitate, glabrous; style attenuate at apex; stigma poriform. **Legumes** stipitate, curved, oblong, 15–45(–60) × 6–7.5(–10) mm, constricted between seeds, valves with (1 or) 2–7(or 8) segments, bulliform, margin unarmed or randomly prickly, apex cuspidate to rostrate, faces glabrous; stipe 5–9 mm. **Seeds** (1 or)2–7(or 8), dark brown, lenticular, 4.5–5.5 × 3.9–4.8 × 2.5–3.5 mm, testa porous, fissural line 75%.

Flowering Mar–Oct; fruiting Apr–Oct. Scrublands with *Juniperus*, *Quercus*, and associated species, rocky soils in mixed prairies, grasslands, dry rocky banks, limestone outcrops and slopes, gravelly hillsides, open areas on canyon rim; 100–1700 m; Colo., Kans., N.Mex., Okla., Tex.

Mimosa borealis has been found in Baca County in Colorado, Barber, Clark, and Meade counties in Kansas, and Chaves, De Baca, Eddy, Guadalupe, Harding, Lincoln, Mora, Otero, Quay, San Miguel, and Union counties in New Mexico but is more frequent in western Oklahoma, and in central, northern, and western Texas.

B. L. Turner (1959) cited *Mimosa borealis* as probably occurring in adjacent Mexico, but no specimens have been seen.

3. **Mimosa distachya** Cavanilles, Icon. 3: 48, plate 295. 1795–1796

Varieties 4 (1 in the flora): Arizona, Mexico, West Indies (Cuba), South America (Colombia, Venezuela).

3a. **Mimosa distachya** Cavanilles var. **laxiflora** (Bentham) Barneby, Mem. New York Bot. Gard. 65: 83. 1991 • Mexican mimosa

Mimosa laxiflora Bentham, London J. Bot. 5: 93. 1846

Shrubs, erect, 1–2.5 m, armed or unarmed. **Stems** terete, glabrous; prickles irregular along internodes, recurved. **Leaves:** stipules subulate, 1–2.5 mm, tomentose; petiole (0.5–)1.5–3 cm; primary rachis (0.5–)3–5 cm; pinnae (1 or)2–4 pairs; leaflets 2–4(or 5) pairs, blades obliquely elliptic to ovate or obovate, (3.5–)5–11 × (1.5–)3.5–8 mm, margins ciliate, reticulate veins visible abaxially, apex obtuse or acute, mucronulate, surfaces glaucous, glabrous or abaxial surface puberulent. **Peduncles** 0.6–1.5 cm. **Inflorescences** 20–55-flowered, axillary, lax spikes, solitary or fascicles of 2, 25–45 mm; bracts spatulate, 1/5–1/4 corolla length. **Pedicels** 0.2–0.5 mm. **Flowers** bisexual; calyx campanulate, lobes 4 or 5, 1/5 corolla length; corolla purple pink, glabrous, lobes 4 or 5, 1/2 corolla length; stamens 8 or 10, filaments connate at bases, pink; ovary stipitate, glabrous; style attenuate at apex; stigma poriform. **Legumes** stipitate, straight or curved, linear to oblong, 25–45 × 5–7.5 mm, constricted between seeds, valves with 4–9 segments, margin unarmed, apex apiculate, faces glabrous; stipe 3–7 mm. **Seeds** 4–9, dark brown to black, lenticular, 3–3.2 × 2.5–2.8 × 1.6–1.8 mm, testa shiny, fissural line 25%.

Flowering Apr–Aug; fruiting Aug–Oct. Thorn scrub and thorn forest with cacti on dry stony hillsides, along desert washes; 200–800 m; Ariz.; Mexico (Chihuahua, Sinaloa, Sonora).

Variety *laxiflora* is restricted to Pima County in Arizona.

4. **Mimosa dysocarpa** Bentham, Smithsonian Contr. Knowl. 3(5): 62. 1852 • Velvetpod mimosa F

Mimosa dysocarpa var. *wrightii* (A. Gray) Kearney & Peebles; *M. wrightii* A. Gray

Shrubs, erect, 0.7–1.5 m, armed. **Stems** terete, tomentose or glabrescent; prickles irregular along internodes, recurved or straight. **Leaves:** stipules linear to subulate, 4–7 mm, tomentose; petiole 0.6–1 cm; primary rachis 2.5–7.5 cm; pinnae 5–11 pairs; leaflets 6–14 pairs, blades obliquely linear-lanceolate or lanceolate-oblong, 3–6 × 1–2.5 mm, margins sericeous, 1 or 2 eccentric veins prominent, apex acute, mucronulate, surfaces light green, sericeous abaxially, dark green, glaucous, sericeous or glabrous adaxially. **Peduncles** 1–1.5(–2) cm. **Inflorescences** 50–150-flowered, axillary, spikes, solitary, in fascicles of 2 or 3, or aggregated in racemes, 20–50(–80) mm; bracts linear-spatulate, 1/3–1/2 corolla length. **Pedicels** 0 mm. **Flowers** bisexual and staminate; calyx campanulate, lobes 4 or 5, 1/2 corolla length; corolla purple-pink, densely sericeous, lobes 4 or 5, 1/3–1/2 corolla length; stamens 8 or 10, filaments distinct to bases, pink; ovary sessile, tomentose; style attenuate at apex; stigma poriform. **Legumes** sessile, straight or curved, linear-oblong, 40–50 × 5–7 mm, constricted between seeds, valves with (2–)4–9 segments, margin unarmed or sparsely prickly, apex apiculate, faces tomentose. **Seeds** (2–)4–9, reddish brown, lenticular, 5 × 4 × 3 mm, testa smooth, fissural line 50%.

Flowering Jun–Sep; fruiting Sep. Dry scrublands, open slopes, desert grasslands, steep rocky slopes with oaks, pines, and grasses; 1200–2200 m; Ariz., N.Mex., Tex.; Mexico (Chihuahua, Durango, Sonora, Zacatecas).

Mimosa dysocarpa is known from Cochise, Pima, Pinal, Santa Cruz, and Yavapai counties in Arizona, Grant, Hidalgo, Luna, and Socorro counties in New Mexico, and Brewster, Jeff Davis, and Presidio counties in Texas.

5. **Mimosa emoryana** Bentham, Trans. Linn. Soc. London 30: 426. 1875

Varieties 2 (1 in the flora): Texas, n Mexico.

Variety *chihuahuana* (Britton & Rose) Barneby occurs in northern Mexico.

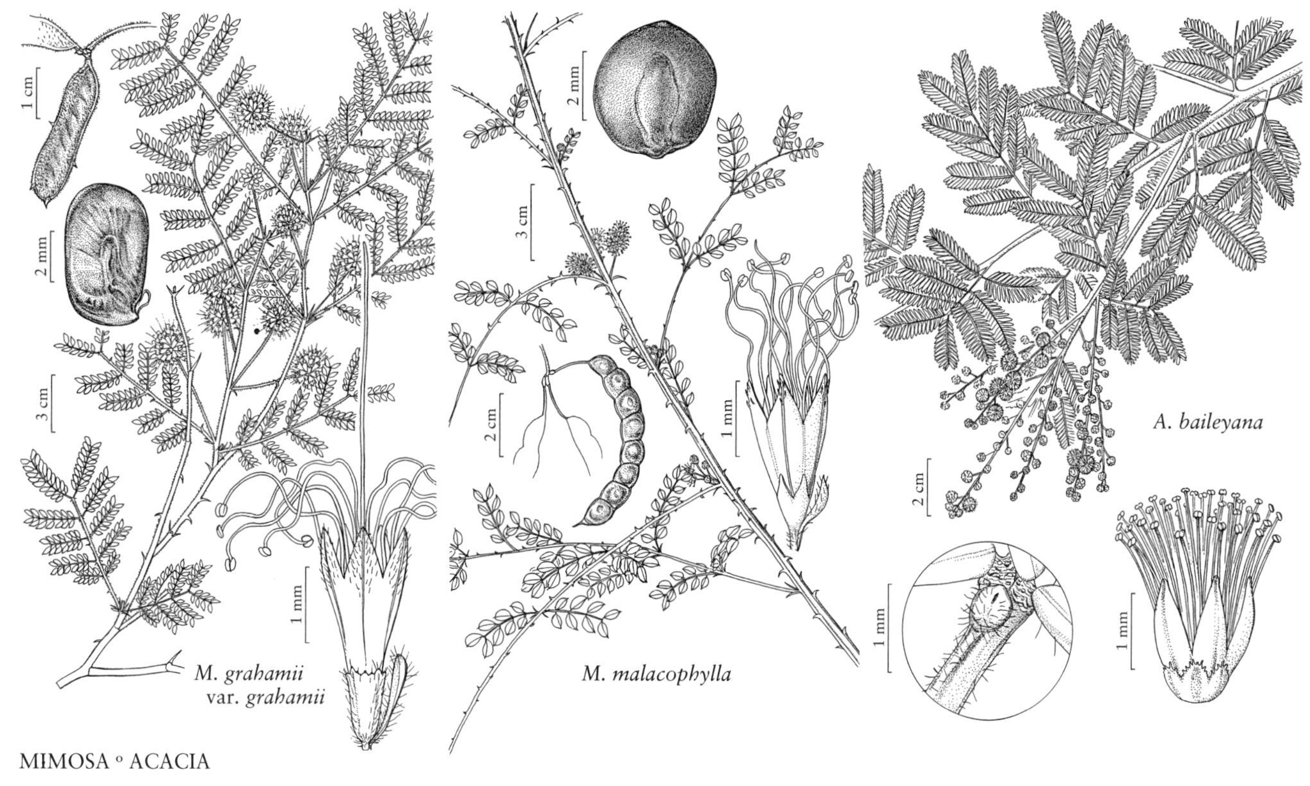

MIMOSA ◦ ACACIA

5a. Mimosa emoryana Bentham var. **emoryana** • Cat claw, Emory's mimosa

Shrubs, erect, 0.5–2 m, armed. **Stems** terete, tomentose or glabrescent; prickles irregular along internodes, recurved; brachyblasts present. **Leaves:** stipules subulate, 1.5–4 mm, tomentose; petiole 0.5–1 cm; primary rachis 0.3–1.5 cm; pinnae 1–3 pairs; leaflets 2–4 pairs, blades obliquely oblong or elliptic, 3–5.5 × 1.3–2 mm, margins tomentose, 1 or 2 veins slightly visible abaxially, apex obtuse or acute to mucronulate, surfaces tomentose. **Peduncles** 1–2.5 cm. **Inflorescences** 25–35-flowered, axillary, globose to subglobose capitula, solitary or fascicles of 2, 15–18 mm diam.; bracts spatulate, ⅓–½ corolla length. **Pedicels** 0.2–0.3 mm. **Flowers** bisexual; calyx campanulate, lobes 5, ¼ corolla length; corolla purplish pink, tomentose, lobes 5, ⅓ corolla length; stamens 10, filaments distinct to bases, violet; ovary stipitate, tomentose; style attenuate at apex; stigma cupuliform. **Legumes** sessile or stipitate, curved, oblong, 35–55 × 6–7 mm, constricted between seeds, valves with 4–7 segments, bulliform, margin sparsely prickly, apex rostrate, faces tomentose and setose; stipe 1 mm. **Seeds** 4–7, dark brown, lenticular or elliptic, 4.5–5 × 3–3.5 × 2–2.5 mm, testa smooth, fissural line 75–80%.

Flowering May–Aug; fruiting Aug–Oct. Scrub on limestone hillsides, gravel plains, rocky calcareous soils, lower grassland transitions; 900–1600 m; Tex.; Mexico (Chihuahua, Coahuila, Durango, Nuevo León).

Variety *emoryana* is known from Brewster, Hudspeth, Presidio, and Terrell counties in western Texas.

6. Mimosa grahamii A. Gray, Smithsonian Contr. Knowl. 5(6): 52. 1853 (as grahami) [F]

Mimosopsis grahamii (A. Gray) Britton & Rose

Varieties 2 (1 in the flora): s United States, n, c Mexico.

Variety *prolifica* (S. Watson) Barneby occurs in northern Mexico.

6a. Mimosa grahamii A. Gray var. **grahamii** • Graham's mimosa [F]

Mimosa grahamii var. *lemmonii* (A. Gray) Kearney & Peebles; *M. lemmonii* A. Gray; *Mimosopsis lemmonii* (A. Gray) Britton & Rose

Shrubs, erect, 0.6–1 m, armed. **Stems** terete, pilose or glabrous; prickles infrastipular, paired and straight, also 1 internodal and recurved. **Leaves:** stipules ligulate to subulate, 2–5 mm, pilose or glabrescent; petiole 0.3–2 cm; primary rachis 3–9 cm; pinnae 5–8 pairs; leaflets 7–16

pairs, blades obliquely oblong to lanceolate-oblong or elliptic, 3–6 × 1–2.5 mm, margins ciliate, reticulate veins prominent abaxially, apex acute, mucronulate, surfaces glaucous, pilosulous or glabrous. **Peduncles** 1.5–3 cm. **Inflorescences** 50–120-flowered, axillary, globose capitula, solitary or fascicles of 2 or 3, 13–20 mm diam.; bracts spatulate, 1/3–1/2 corolla length. **Pedicels** 0.2–0.3 mm. **Flowers** bisexual; calyx campanulate, lobes 5, 1/5–1/3 corolla length; corolla purplish pink, glabrous, lobes 5, 1/4–1/3 corolla length, pilosulous on lobes or glabrous; stamens 10, filaments distinct to bases, white; ovary stipitate, tomentose; style attenuate at apex; stigma poriform. **Legumes** stipitate, straight, oblong, 25–45 × 6–8 mm, not constricted between seeds, valves entire, margin prickly, apex acute, mucronate to rostrate, rostrum 3–4 mm, faces tomentose or glabrous; stipe 1.5–2.5 mm. **Seeds** 3–8, reddish brown, lenticular, oblong, or rhomboid, 5–6 × 4.1–4.6 × 1.8–2 mm, testa porous, fissural line 50%.

Flowering Apr–May; fruiting Aug–Sep. Oak-pine forests, canyon bottoms, rocky canyon slopes, igneous rock banks, arroyos, desert grassland on open hillsides; 1100–2000 m; Ariz., N.Mex.; Mexico (Chihuahua, Durango, Sonora).

Variety *grahamii* is known from Cochise, Pima, Pinal, Santa Cruz, and Yavapai counties in southern Arizona, and from Grant, Hidalgo, and Luna counties in southern New Mexico.

7. Mimosa hystricina (Small ex Britton & Rose) B. L. Turner, Phytologia 76: 414. 1994 [E]

Leptoglottis hystricina Small ex Britton & Rose in N. L. Britton et al., N. Amer. Fl. 23: 139. 1928; *Mimosa quadrivalvis* Linnaeus var. *hystricina* (Small ex Britton & Rose) Barneby; *Schrankia hystricina* (Small ex Britton & Rose) Standley; *S. nuttallii* (de Candolle) Standley var. *hystricina* (Small ex Britton & Rose) Isely

Subshrubs, prostrate, 0.5–1 m, armed. **Stems** ribbed, glabrous or puberulent; prickles along ribs, recurved. **Leaves:** stipules linear to filiform, 5–8 mm, puberulent; petiole 2–5 cm; primary rachis (3–)5–6 cm; pinnae 3–5 pairs; leaflets 11–17 pairs, blades obliquely oblong to elliptic, 4–7 × 1.5–2.5 mm, margins ciliate, reticulate veins prominent abaxially and adaxially, apex acute, mucronate, surfaces glabrous. **Peduncles** 7–13 cm. **Inflorescences** 100–180-flowered, axillary, globose capitula, solitary, 20–30 mm diam.; bracts linear, 3/4 or equal to corolla length. **Pedicels** 0.2–0.5 mm. **Flowers** bisexual and staminate; calyx campanulate, lobes 5, 1/9–1/7 corolla length; corolla purplish pink, glabrous, lobes 5, 1/4–1/3 corolla length; stamens 10, filaments connate at bases, pink; ovary stipitate, glabrous; style attenuate at apex; stigma tubular. **Legumes** stipitate, straight, linear-oblong, tetragonal, 20–45 × 8–10 mm, not constricted between seeds, valves entire, 3–6 mm wide, margin 2–4 mm wide, prickly, prickles connate at bases, apex acute, obtuse, or rostrate, rostrum 2–4 mm, faces glabrous; stipe 1–1.5 mm. **Seeds** 5–14, reddish brown, lenticular or rhomboid, 4–4.9 × 3.6–3.9 × 2–2.5 mm, testa porous, fissural line 90%.

Flowering (Jan–)Mar–Jun(–Oct); fruiting (Mar–)May–Jul(–Nov). Dry sandy soils, pine-post oak hills, moist grassy fields in pinewoods areas; 0–100 m; La., Tex.

Mimosa hystricina occurs in Allen, Beauregard, and Calcasieu parishes in southwestern Louisiana, and in southeastern Texas. Flowering plants are difficult to distinguish from *M. nuttallii*; the latter is more common in Missouri and Texas.

8. Mimosa latidens (Small) B. L. Turner, Phytologia 76: 414. 1994 • Kairn's sensitive-briar

Morongia latidens Small, Bull. New York Bot. Gard. 2: 98. 1901; *Leptoglottis berlandieri* Britton; *L. latidens* (Small) Small ex Britton & Rose; *Mimosa quadrivalvis* Linnaeus var. *latidens* (Small) Barneby; *Schrankia latidens* (Small) K. Schumann

Herbs or subshrubs, prostrate, 0.2–0.5 m, armed. **Stems** ribbed, glabrous; prickles along ribs, recurved. **Leaves:** stipules subulate to narrowly lanceolate, 1.5–4 mm, glabrous; petiole 2–4 cm; primary rachis 0.7–2.5 cm; pinnae 1–3 pairs; leaflets 6–9 pairs, blades obliquely linear-oblong to oblong, 3–6 × 0.8–2 mm, margins ciliate, 1 eccentric vein evident abaxially, apex acute, mucronulate, surfaces glabrous. **Peduncles** 1–3.5 cm. **Inflorescences** 20–70-flowered, axillary, globose capitula, solitary or fascicles of 2, 10–15(–18) mm diam.; bracts linear-lanceolate, 1/7–1/3 corolla length. **Pedicels** 0.2 mm. **Flowers** bisexual and staminate; calyx campanulate, lobes 5(or 6), 1/8–1/5 corolla length; corolla purplish pink, glabrous, lobes 5(or 6), 1/2 corolla length; stamens 10(or 12), filaments distinct to bases, pink; ovary sessile, glabrous; style attenuate at apex; stigma tubular. **Legumes** stipitate, straight, linear-oblong, tetragonal, 25–60 × 2.5–4 mm, not constricted between seeds, valves entire, 1.5–2.5 mm wide, margin 2–3 mm wide, prickly, apex rostrate, rostrum 2–6 mm, faces glabrous; stipe 1–2 mm. **Seeds** 6–9, brown, lenticular or rhomboid, 3.8–4 × 2.5–3 × 1.5–2 mm, testa porous, fissural line 90%.

Flowering Mar–Oct; fruiting Jun–Oct. Red sandy loam, abandoned fields on sand; 0–700 m; La., Tex.; Mexico (Coahuila, Nuevo León, San Luis Potosí, Tamaulipas).

Mimosa latidens is known from southeastern Texas and disjunct in Concho County in central Texas, and Acadia Parish in Louisiana.

9. Mimosa malacophylla A. Gray, Boston J. Nat. Hist. 6: 182. 1850 [F]

Mimosa malacophylla var. *glabrata* Bentham; *M. wootonii* Standley

Subshrubs, scandent, 2–3 m, armed. **Stems** ribbed, tomentulose or glabrous; prickles along ribs, recurved. **Leaves:** stipules subulate, 2–6 mm, glabrous; petiole 1.5–3 cm; primary rachis 3.5–8.5 cm; pinnae 4–6 pairs; leaflets 4–6 pairs, blades obliquely elliptic to obovate, 5–14 × 2.5–6.5 mm, margins ciliate or eciliate, revolute, reticulate veins prominent abaxially and adaxially, apex mucronate, surfaces glabrous or puberulent. **Peduncles** 0.8–1 cm. **Inflorescences** 40–70-flowered, axillary, globose capitula, solitary or in fascicles of 2–5, or aggregated in racemes, 11–15 mm diam.; bracts spatulate, ⅓–½ corolla length. **Pedicels** 0.2–0.5 mm. **Flowers** bisexual; calyx campanulate, lobes (4 or)5, ⅓ corolla length; corolla white, tomentulose or glabrous, lobes (4 or)5, ⅓ corolla length; stamens (5 or 8 or)10, filaments connate at bases, white; ovary stipitate, tomentose; style attenuate at apex; stigma poriform. **Legumes** stipitate, curved, oblong, 4.5–7.5 cm × 6–11 mm, reticulate-veined, constricted between seeds, valves with 6–8 segments, margin sparsely prickly or unarmed, apex apiculate to rostrate, faces glabrous; stipe 10–15 mm. **Seeds** 6–8, dark brown, lenticular, 5 × 4.5–4.8 × 2–2.5 mm, testa porous, fissural line 90%.

Flowering Apr–Nov; fruiting Apr–Dec. Scrub woodlands, thornscrub, caliche ridges, shrub thickets; 10–400 m; Tex.; Mexico (Coahuila, Nuevo León, Tamaulipas).

Mimosa malacophylla is found in Bee, Cameron, Duval, Hays, Hidalgo, Jim Wells, Kinney, and Live Oak counties in southern and south-central Texas.

10. Mimosa microphylla Dryander in J. E. Smith and J. Abbot, Nat. Hist. Lepidopt. Georgia 2: 123, plate 62. 1797 • Prickly red mimosa, littleleaf sensitive-briar [E] [W]

Leptoglottis angustisiliqua Britton & Rose; *L. chapmanii* Small ex Britton & Rose; *L. halliana* Britton & Rose; *L. microphylla* (Dryander) Britton & Rose; *Mimosa quadrivalvis* Linnaeus var. *angustata* (Torrey & A. Gray) Barneby; *Morongia angustata* (Torrey & A. Gray) Britton; *M. microphylla* (Dryander) Britton; *M. uncinata* (Willdenow) Britton; *Schrankia angustata* Torrey & A. Gray; *S. angustata* var. *brachycarpa* Chapman; *S. microphylla* (Dryander) J. F. Macbride; *S. uncinata* Willdenow

Subshrubs, prostrate, 0.9–1 m, armed. **Stems** ribbed, glabrous or puberulent; prickles along ribs, recurved. **Leaves:** stipules narrowly lanceolate, 2–4.5 mm, glabrous; petiole 3–5 cm; primary rachis 6–8.5 cm; pinnae (3–)5–8 pairs; leaflets 10–15(–17) pairs, blades obliquely linear, 2.5–5 × 0.5–1 mm, margins ciliate, 1 eccentric vein evident abaxially, apex acute, mucronulate, surfaces glabrous. **Peduncles** 2–5(–10) cm. **Inflorescences** 60–120-flowered, axillary, globose capitula, solitary or fascicles of 2–4, 10–18 mm diam.; bracts linear, ⅓–½ corolla length. **Pedicels** 0.2–0.3 mm. **Flowers** bisexual and staminate; calyx campanulate, lobes 5, ⅙–⅕ corolla length; corolla purplish pink, glabrous, lobes 5, ⅓–½ corolla length; stamens 10, filaments distinct to bases, pink; ovary stipitate, glabrous; style attenuate at apex; stigma narrowly tubular. **Legumes** sessile, straight, linear, tetragonal, 90–140 × 1.5–4 mm, not constricted between seeds, valves entire, 0.5–2 mm wide, unarmed or prickly, margin 1–2 mm wide, unarmed or prickly, apex rostrate, rostrum 5–30 mm, faces glabrous or puberulent. **Seeds** 18, (mature seeds not seen), dark brown, 4.5 mm, testa porous, fissural line not observed.

Flowering Apr–Aug(–Jan); fruiting Jun–Aug(–Jan). Mixed woodlands, sandy pine-post oak woods, sandy soils of floodplains, roadside banks; 100 m; Ala., Fla., Ga., Ill., Ky., La., Miss., N.C., S.C., Tenn., Tex., Va.

Mimosa microphylla is known from the south and southeastern United States, distributed in DeKalb, Macon, Russell, and Tuscaloosa counties in Alabama, Citrus County in Florida, Bullock, Dade, Hancock, and Taylor counties in Georgia, St. Tammany Parish in Louisiana, Harrison County in Mississippi, Gaston, Guilford, Rockingham, and Rutherford counties in North Carolina, Richland and Spartanburg counties in South Carolina, Wayne County in Tennessee, and Waller County in Texas.

11. Mimosa monclovensis R. Grether & Marc. F. Simon, Phytoneuron 2018-39: 2. 2018

Schrankia subinermis S. Watson, Proc. Amer. Acad. Arts 17: 350. 1882; *Leptoglottis nelsonii* Britton & Rose; *L. subinermis* (S. Watson) Britton & Rose; *Mimosa quadrivalvis* Linnaeus var. *nelsonii* (Britton & Rose) Barneby

Herbs or subshrubs, prostrate, 0.5–1.5 m, armed or unarmed. **Stems** ribbed, glabrous; prickles sparse along ribs, recurved. **Leaves:** stipules linear or filiform, 2–3.5 mm, glabrous; petiole (2–)2.5–3(–4) cm; primary rachis 2.5–3.5 cm; pinnae 1–3 pairs; leaflets 9–14 pairs, blades obliquely linear, 3.5–6 × 0.7–1(–1.4) mm, margins ciliate, 1 eccentric vein evident abaxially, apex acute, mucronulate, surfaces glabrous. **Peduncles** 1–5 cm. **Inflorescences** 35–40-flowered, axillary, globose capitula, solitary, 10–12 mm diam.; bracts spatulate, ¼–⅓ corolla length. **Pedicels** 0.2 mm. **Flowers** bisexual and staminate; calyx campanulate, lobes 5, ⅕–¼ corolla length; corolla pink, glabrous, lobes 5, ¼–⅓ corolla length; stamens 10, filaments connate at bases, pink; ovary stipitate, glabrous; style attenuate at apex; stigma tubular. **Legumes** sessile, straight, linear-oblong, tetragonal, (45–)70–90(–100) × 4–4.5(–5) mm, not constricted between seeds, valves entire, 1–2.5 mm wide, margin 2.5–3.5 mm wide, prickly or unarmed, apex rostrate, rostrum 5–10 mm, faces glabrous. **Seeds** (6–)10–16, dark brown, oblong or subrhomboid, 5–6 × 2.5–3 × 1.5 mm, testa porous, fissural line 90%.

Flowering Apr–Jun; fruiting May–Aug. Dry sandy or gravelly places; 100–200 m; Tex.; Mexico (Coahuila).

Mimosa monclovensis occurs in southern Texas, southward from San Antonio, according to R. C. Barneby (1991, treated as *M. quadrivalvis* var. *nelsonii*).

Mimosa subinermis (S. Watson) B. L. Turner, not *M. subinermis* Bentham (1841), is an illegitimate name that pertains to *M. monclovensis*.

12. Mimosa nuttallii (de Candolle ex Torrey & A. Gray) B. L. Turner, Phytologia 76: 417. 1994 • Sensitive-briar, Nuttall's sensitive-briar [E] [W]

Leptoglottis nuttallii de Candolle ex Torrey & A. Gray, Fl. N. Amer. 1: 696. 1840; *L. mimosoides* Small ex Britton & Rose; *Mimosa quadrivalvis* Linnaeus var. *nuttallii* (de Candolle ex Torrey & A. Gray) Beard ex Barneby; *Schrankia nuttallii* (de Candolle ex Torrey & A. Gray) Standley

Herbs or subshrubs, prostrate or sprawling, 0.5–0.8 m, armed. **Stems** ribbed, usually glabrous, rarely puberulent; prickles along ribs, recurved. **Leaves:** stipules linear to narrowly lanceolate, 4.5–8 mm, glabrous; petiole 2–4 cm; primary rachis 3–7 cm; pinnae 4–7(or 8) pairs; leaflets 11–16 pairs, blades obliquely oblong to elliptic, 4.5–6 × 1.8–2.5 mm, margins ciliate, reticulate veins prominent abaxially, apex acute, mucronate, surfaces glabrous. **Peduncles** 3.5–9.5 cm. **Inflorescences** 90–140-flowered, axillary, globose capitula, solitary and in racemes 130–200 mm, 20–30 mm diam.; bracts spatulate, ⅓–½ corolla length. **Pedicels** 0.2–0.9 mm. **Flowers** bisexual and staminate; calyx campanulate, lobes 5(or 6), ⅒ corolla length; corolla purplish pink, glabrous, lobes 5(or 6), ⅓–½ corolla length; stamens 10(or 12), filaments connate at bases, pink; ovary stipitate, glabrous; style attenuate at apex; stigma narrowly cupuliform or tubular. **Legumes** sessile, straight or curved, linear, 40–120 × 3–4.5 mm, not constricted between seeds, valves entire, 1–2.5 mm wide, margin 2–4 mm wide, prickly, prickles sometimes connate at bases, apex rostrate, rostrum 5–20 mm, faces glabrous. **Seeds** 4–15, reddish brown, lenticular or rhomboid, 4.2 × 3.2 × 2 mm, testa porous, fissural line 90%.

Flowering Apr–Oct; fruiting Jun–Oct. Woods, mesic to xeric prairies, dry woods, oak woods; 0–1300 m; Ark., Colo., D.C., Ill., Iowa, Kans., La., Mich., Mo., Nebr., N.Mex., N.Dak., Okla., Pa., S.Dak., Tex., Wis.

Mimosa nuttallii is the most widespread species of the genus in the United States. It superficially resembles *M. hystricina*, but the two are largely allopatric (B. L. Turner 1994e), although D. Isely (1973) reported occasional intermediates between these two closely related taxa in northern Louisiana. Furthermore, Isely (1986) considered *M. hystricina* as a variety of *M. nuttallii.*

13. Mimosa pigra Linnaeus, Cent. Pl. I, 13. 1755, name conserved [W]

Shrubs, erect, 1–3 m, armed. **Stems** terete, strigose and puberulent; prickles irregular along internodes, straight or recurved. **Leaves:** stipules widely lanceolate to ovate, lanceolate-ovate, or ligulate, 2–5 mm, usually densely strigose to pubescent or puberulent, rarely glabrescent; petiole 0.2–2 cm; primary rachis prickly and with acicular aculei between pinnae, 1–15 (–17) cm; pinnae 4–14 pairs; leaflets 16–40 pairs, blades obliquely linear or linear-oblong, 3–9 × 0.5–2 mm, margins ciliate to setose, 3 or 4 parallel veins prominent abaxially, apex mucronulate or acute to apiculate, surfaces pubescent to strigulose or glabrous abaxially, glabrous adaxially. **Peduncles** 1.5–5 cm. **Inflorescences** 80–100-flowered, axillary, globose or subglobose capitula, solitary and in fascicles of 2–4, or in racemiform branches, 10–18 mm diam.; bracts linear-lanceolate or oblanceolate, 1/4–3/4 corolla length. **Pedicels** 0 mm. **Flowers** bisexual and staminate; calyx irregularly laciniate or campanulate, lobes 4, 1/5–1/2 corolla length; corolla pink, strigose or glabrous, lobes 4, 1/4–1/3 corolla length; stamens 8, filaments connate at bases, lilac; ovary sessile, hispid or pubescent; style attenuate at apex; stigma narrowly cupuliform. **Legumes** sessile or stipitate, straight or curved, oblong, (30–)40–120 × 9–13 mm, not constricted between seeds, valves with (4–)7–25 segments, margin unarmed, apex apiculate or mucronate to cuspidate, faces setose or sparsely strigose and puberulent; stipe 3–7 mm. **Seeds** (4–)7–25, olive-ochre, oblong-elliptic, 5–6.5 × 2.3–3 × 0.8–1.5 mm, testa smooth, fissural line 90%.

Varieties 2 (2 in the flora): s United States, Mexico, Central America, South America, Africa; introduced in tropical Asia.

1. Stipules densely strigose to pubescent, not striate; pinnae 8–14 pairs; corolla lobes densely strigose; legumes with 15–25 segments, valves and margin densely setose . . . . 13a. *Mimosa pigra* var. *pigra*
1. Stipules usually puberulent, rarely glabrescent, striate; pinnae 4–7(or 8) pairs; corolla lobes sparsely strigose or glabrous; legumes with (4–)7–10(–14) segments, valves and margin sparsely strigose and puberulent . . . . 13b. *Mimosa pigra* var. *asperata*

13a. Mimosa pigra Linnaeus var. **pigra** • Catclaw mimosa, giant sensitive plant [W]

Mimosa pellita Humboldt & Bonpland ex Willdenow

Stems densely strigose; prickles recurved, brownish. **Leaves:** stipules widely lanceolate to ovate, 3–5 mm, not striate, densely strigose to pubescent; petiole 0.5–2 cm; primary rachis 8–15(–17) cm; pinnae 8–14 pairs; leaflets 20–40 pairs, blades obliquely linear-oblong, 4–9 × 0.5–2 mm, apex mucronulate, abaxial surface glabrous or pubescent. **Peduncles** 2–5 cm. **Capitula** 10–18 mm diam.; bracts linear-lanceolate, 1/2–3/4 corolla length. **Flowers:** calyx irregularly laciniate, 1/4–1/2 corolla length; corolla lobes densely strigose. **Legumes** sessile, 40–120 × 9–13 mm, segments 15–25, margin densely setose, apex apiculate, faces densely setose. **Seeds** 6–6.5 × 2–2.5 × 1–1.5 mm.

Flowering Jul; fruiting Jul–Aug. Canal ditch banks, blackish water, mangroves; 0–40 m; Fla.; Mexico; Central America; South America; Africa; introduced in tropical Asia, Australia.

The typical variety, registered as *Mimosa pellita* in the USDA Plants website, is included as present in Texas. However, material of this plant from Texas has not been seen. The variety is considered a weed in Florida and Australia.

13b. Mimosa pigra Linnaeus var. **asperata** (Linnaeus) Zarucchi, Vincent & Gandhi, Phytoneuron 2018-70: 2. 2018 • Coatante, corza, zarza

Mimosa asperata Linnaeus, Syst. Nat. ed. 10, 2: 1312. 1759; *M. asperata* var. *berlandieri* (A. Gray) B. L. Robinson; *M. berlandieri* A. Gray in W. H. Emory; *M. catalinae* León; *M. pigra* var. *berlandieri* (A. Gray) B. L. Turner

Stems sparsely strigose; prickles straight, whitish. **Leaves:** stipules lanceolate-ovate or ligulate, 2–3 mm, striate, usually puberulent, rarely glabrescent; petiole 0.2–0.7(–1.5) cm; primary rachis 1–6.5 cm; pinnae 4–7(or 8) pairs; leaflets 16–30 pairs, blades obliquely linear, 3–9 × 0.5–1.2 mm, apex acute to apiculate, abaxial surface pubescent to strigulose. **Peduncles** 1.5–3.5 cm. **Capitula** 10–15 mm diam.; bracts oblanceolate, 1/4–1/2 corolla length. **Flowers:** calyx campanulate, 1/5–1/4 corolla length; corolla lobes sparsely strigose or glabrous. **Legumes** stipitate, (30–)40–65 (–75) × 9–11(–13) mm, segments (4–)7–10(–14), margin sparsely strigose and puberulent, apex mucronate to cuspidate, faces sparsely strigose and puberulent; stipe 3–7 mm. **Seeds** 5–5.3 × 2.3–3 × 0.8–1 mm.

Flowering (Jan–)Mar–Aug(–Oct); fruiting Mar–Sep (–Nov). Disturbed areas near canals, edges of ponds; 0–400 m; Tex.; Mexico; Central America (Belize, Guatemala, Nicaragua).

Variety *asperata* is found in southernmost Texas in Calhoun, Cameron, Hidalgo, Starr, and Zapata counties.

14. Mimosa pudica Linnaeus, Sp. Pl. 1: 518. 1753 • Sensitive plant, shameplant [I]

Mimosa pudica var. *unijuga* (Duchassaing & Walpers) Grisebach

Herbs or subshrubs, erect or decumbent, 0.3–1 m, armed. **Stems** ribbed to striate, hispid or glabrous; prickles infrastipular, paired, also sparse along internodes, recurved. **Leaves:** stipules lanceolate, 7–12 mm, glabrous to sparsely setose; petiole 1–4.5 cm; primary rachis 0–2.5 mm; pinnae 1 or 2 pairs, digitate; leaflets 15–25 pairs, blades obliquely linear-oblong, 5–10 × 2–2.5 mm, margins setose, 1 eccentric vein prominent abaxially, apex acute to mucronate, surfaces glabrous. **Peduncles** 1–3 cm. **Inflorescences** 95–125-flowered, axillary, globose or subglobose capitula, solitary or fascicles of 2 or 3, also disposed in racemiform branches, 10–15 mm diam.; bracts linear to lanceolate, ½–⅔ corolla length. **Pedicels** 0 mm. **Flowers** bisexual; calyx campanulate, lobes 4, 1/10 corolla length; corolla pink, glabrous, lobes 4, ¼ corolla length; stamens 4, filaments distinct to base, lilac; ovary sessile to shortly stipitate, glabrous; style attenuate at apex; stigma poriform. **Legumes** sessile, straight, linear-oblong, 10–15 × 3–4 mm, constricted between seeds, valves with 2–5 segments, margin armed, long-setose, apex acuminate, faces glabrous. **Seeds** 2–5, ochre, lenticular, 3–3.2 × 2.5–3 × 1–1.2 mm, testa smooth or porous, fissural line 90%.

Flowering Jul–Jan; fruiting Jul–Jan. Pinelands, secondary vegetation, burned or cleared pinelands; 0–40 m; introduced; Fla., Md.; Mexico; West Indies; Central America; South America; introduced also in tropical Asia, Africa, Australia.

Mimosa pudica is a pantropical species that has become established in Florida; C. F. Reed (1964) included *M. pudica* in the flora of the chrome and manganese ore piles at Canton, in the Port of Baltimore, Maryland; his record from Newport News, Virginia, cannot be verified, as that is an immature plant, probably corresponding to another species.

Varieties of *Mimosa pudica* were distinguished by J. P. M. Brenan (1959) in tropical East Africa. R. C. Barneby (1991) proposed a modified key to varieties; however, they are not clearly delimited in American populations. Available specimens from the flora area cannot be determined at the infraspecific level.

15. Mimosa quadrivalvis Linnaeus, Sp. Pl. 1: 522. 1753

Varieties 5 (1 in the flora): se United States, Mexico, West Indies (Puerto Rico).

15a. Mimosa quadrivalvis Linnaeus var. **floridana** (Chapman) Barneby, Mem. New York Bot. Gard. 65: 300. 1991 • Florida mimosa [E]

Schrankia floridana Chapman, Fl. South. U.S. ed. 2 repr. 2, 683. 1892; *Leptoglottis floridana* (Chapman) Small ex Britton & Rose; *Morongia floridana* (Chapman) A. Heller; *S. microphylla* (Dryander) J. F. Macbride var. *floridana* (Chapman) Isely

Herbs or subshrubs, scandent, 0.5–1 m, armed. **Stems** ribbed, glabrous or puberulent; prickles sparse along ribs, recurved. **Leaves:** stipules narrowly lanceolate to filiform, 1–2.5 mm, glabrous; petiole 2.5–4.5 cm; primary rachis 3–9.5 cm; pinnae 3–6 pairs; leaflets 13–24 pairs, blades obliquely linear to oblong, 2.5–4.5 × 1–2 mm, margins ciliate or eciliate, reticulate veins prominent abaxially, apex acute, obtuse, or mucronulate, surfaces glabrous. **Peduncles** 0.6–1.5 cm. **Inflorescences** 30–50-flowered, axillary, globose capitula, solitary or fascicles of 2, also in terminal racemes 40–50 mm, 15–18 mm diam.; bracts spatulate, ¼ corolla length. **Pedicels** 0.2–0.3 mm. **Flowers** bisexual and staminate; calyx campanulate, lobes 5, ⅙–⅕ corolla length; corolla pink, glabrous, lobes 5, ⅓–½ corolla length; stamens 10, filaments connate at bases, pink; ovary stipitate, glabrous; style attenuate at apex; stigma narrowly cupuliform or tubular. **Legumes** sessile, straight, linear, 70–150 × 2–3.5 mm, not constricted between seeds, valves entire, 1–1.5 mm wide, sparsely prickly, margin 2.5–3 mm wide, unarmed or sparsely prickly, apex rostrate, rostrum 5–10 mm, faces glabrous or puberulent. **Seeds** 8–18, reddish brown, oblong to elliptic, 6–6.5 × 2–2.5 × 1–1.5 mm, testa porous, fissural line 90%.

Flowering Mar–Oct; fruiting May–Oct. Sandy, scrub oak-pine and open pine-scrub oak areas, woodlands, roadsides, palmetto scrub, white sands; 0–100 m; Fla., Ga.

D. Isely (1986) considered this taxon as a variety of *Schrankia microphylla*; however, this treatment considers this plant a variety of *Mimosa quadrivalvis*, coinciding with R. C. Barneby (1991). The vernacular name fourvalve mimosa, included in USDA plants website, corresponds to *M. quadrivalvis* var. *quadrivalvis*, which is considered as endemic to the state of Veracruz, Mexico (A. Martínez-Bernal et al. 2008).

16. Mimosa roemeriana Scheele, Linnaea 21: 456. 1848 • Sensitive-briar, Roemer's mimosa

Leptoglottis reverchonii Britton & Rose; *L. roemeriana* (Scheele) Britton & Rose; *Mimosa quadrivalvis* Linnaeus var. *platycarpa* (A. Gray) Barneby; *Schrankia platycarpa* A. Gray; *S. roemeriana* (Scheele) Blankinship

Herbs or subshrubs, prostrate, 0.6–0.7 m, armed. **Stems** ribbed, glabrous or puberulent; prickles along ribs, recurved. **Leaves:** stipules narrowly lanceolate, 2–6 mm, ciliate; petiole 2–4 cm; primary rachis 2–4 cm; pinnae 2–5 pairs; leaflets 8–12 pairs, blades obliquely linear to oblong, 4–9.5 × 1–3 mm, margins ciliate, 1 eccentric vein slightly evident abaxially, apex acute, mucronulate, surfaces glabrous. **Peduncles** 2–6 cm. **Inflorescences** 100–180-flowered, axillary, globose capitula, solitary, 15–18 mm diam.; bracts spatulate, ⅕ corolla length. **Pedicels** 0.2–0.5 mm. **Flowers** bisexual and staminate; calyx campanulate, lobes 5, ⅙–⅕ corolla length; corolla purplish pink, glabrous, lobes 5, ⅓–½ corolla length; stamens 10, filaments distinct to bases, pink; ovary stipitate, glabrous or shortly setose; style attenuate at apex; stigma tubular. **Legumes** sessile or stipitate, straight, linear-oblong, 40–70(–100) × 3–5 (–7) mm, not constricted between seeds, valves entire, 3–4(–6) mm wide, densely prickly, margin 0.5–2 mm wide, prickly, apex rostrate, rostrum 1–6(–8) mm, faces glabrous; stipe 3–5 mm. **Seeds** 12–18, dark brown, oblong, 6 × 3 × 1.5 mm, testa porous, fissural line 90%.

Flowering Mar–May(–Sep); fruiting Mar–Aug(–Sep). Dry stony prairies, calcareous prairies, rock, dry, grassy fields, wooded areas on rocky gravel; 100–1300 m; Okla., Tex.; Mexico (Nuevo León, Tamaulipas).

Mimosa roemeriana is distributed in Brewster, Comal, Dallas, Hays, Kerr, Kinney, Tarrant, and Travis counties in Texas. It has been also reported from Bryan County in Oklahoma.

17. **Mimosa rupertiana** B. L. Turner, Phytologia 77: 81. 1995 • Eastern sensitive plant

Morongia occidentalis Wooton & Standley, Contr. U.S. Natl. Herb. 16: 135. 1913, not *Mimosa occidentalis* Britton & Rose 1928; *Leptoglottis occidentalis* (Wooton & Standley) Britton & Rose; *Mimosa quadrivalvis* Linnaeus var. *occidentalis* (Wooton & Standley) Barneby; *Schrankia occidentalis* (Wooton & Standley) Standley

Subshrubs, prostrate, 0.5–1 m, armed or unarmed. **Stems** ribbed, glabrous or puberulent; prickles along ribs, recurved. **Leaves:** stipules lanceolate, 2–3 mm, glabrous; petiole 1–4 cm; primary rachis 4–10 cm; pinnae 4–9 pairs; leaflets (10–)13 or 14 pairs, blades obliquely linear-oblong to oblong, 2.5–6 × 1–1.5 mm, margins ciliate, 1 eccentric vein evident abaxially, apex acute, mucronulate, surfaces glaucous, glabrous. **Peduncles** 1.5–5 cm. **Inflorescences** 30–60-flowered, axillary, globose capitula, solitary or fascicles of 2, 12–18 mm diam.; bracts spatulate, ¼–⅓ corolla length. **Pedicels** 0.3–0.5 mm. **Flowers** bisexual and staminate; calyx campanulate, lobes 5, ⅙–⅕ corolla length; corolla pinkish purple, glabrous, lobes 5, ⅓–½ corolla length; stamens 10, filaments distinct to bases, purple; ovary stipitate, glabrous; style attenuate at apex; stigma tubular. **Legumes** stipitate, straight, linear, 50–110(–140) × 3–5 mm, not constricted between seeds, valves entire, 2–2.5 mm wide, prickly, margin 2–4 mm wide, prickly, apex rostrate, rostrum 5–10 mm, faces puberulent or glabrous; stipe 2–5 mm. **Seeds** (4–)7–12(–18), reddish brown, oblong, 4–9 × 3–5 × 1.5–3 mm, testa porous, fissural line 90%.

Flowering May–Jul; fruiting May–Aug. Sandhills, dunes, sandy desert over low limestone hills, eroded pasture on calcareous clay loam, mesquite-*Yucca* communities, shinnery oak dunes; 500–1400 m; Colo., N.Mex., Okla., Tex.; Mexico (Chihuahua).

Mimosa rupertiana is frequent in Bernalillo, Chaves, Curry, De Baca, Eddy, Grant, Harding, Hidalgo, Lea, Quay, Roosevelt, San Miguel, Torrance, Union, and Valencia counties in New Mexico, and primarily in the panhandle in Texas; in addition, it has been reported from Baca County in southeastern Colorado, and Beaver and Cimarron counties in northwestern Oklahoma.

Mimosa occidentalis (Wooton & Standley) B. L. Turner is an illegitimate name that pertains here.

18. **Mimosa strigillosa** Torrey & A. Gray, Fl. N. Amer. 1: 399. 1840 • Sensitive-briar, powderpuff [W]

Mimosa dolichocephala Harms; *M. dolichocephala* var. *sabulicola* (Chodat & Hassler) Hassler; *M. sabulicola* Chodat & Hassler

Herbs, procumbent, 0.1–0.5 m, armed or unarmed. **Stems** terete, strigose to strigulose; prickles sparse along internodes, recurved. **Leaves:** stipules widely ovate, 2–4.5 mm, striate, glabrous; petiole 1–7.5 cm; primary rachis 1–8 cm; pinnae 3–7 pairs; leaflets (8–)10–15(–19) pairs, blades obliquely linear to oblong, 3–5.5(–8) × 0.5–1.5 mm, margins strigulose, parallel veins prominent abaxially, apex acute to mucronate, surfaces glabrous. **Peduncles** (2–)3–34 cm. **Inflorescences** 80–140-flowered, axillary, subglobose capitula, solitary, 12–30 mm diam.; bracts spatulate, ½ corolla length. **Pedicels** 0 mm. **Flowers** bisexual and staminate; calyx campanulate, lobes 4, ⅙ corolla length; corolla purplish pink, strigose, lobes 4, ⅓ corolla length; stamens 8, filaments connate in a tube ¼–⅓ corolla length, pink; ovary stipitate, strigose; style attenuate at apex; stigma poriform. **Legumes** stipitate, straight, obliquely oblong, 10–28 × 6–9 mm, constricted between seeds, valves with 1–4 segments, margin unarmed, strigose, apex mucronate, faces strigose to strigulose; stipe 1–2 mm. **Seeds** 1–4, brown, elliptic or lenticular, 3.5–6.5 × 2.8–4.2 × 1–1.5 mm, testa porous, fissural line 90–95%.

Flowering Apr–Nov; fruiting May–Nov. Pine woods, along rivers in sandy loam, well-drained, open areas, meadows, dry sandy or clay soils and ditches, sandy roadsides; 0–150 m; Ark., Fla., Ga., La., Miss., Okla., Tex.; Mexico (Tamaulipas, Veracruz); South America (Argentina, Paraguay, Uruguay).

Mimosa strigillosa is widely distributed in the southeastern United States throughout most of Florida, Charlton County in Georgia, scattered parishes in Louisiana, Washington County in Mississippi, and in coastal Texas and scattered counties inland in north, central, and south Texas.

19. Mimosa texana (A. Gray) Small, Bull. New York Bot. Gard. 2: 99. 1901

Mimosa borealis A. Gray var. *texana* A. Gray, Smithsonian Contr. Knowl. 3(5): 61. 1852

Varieties 2 (1 in the flora): sw, sc United States, n Mexico.

Variety *filipes* (Britton & Rose) Barneby is known only from Puebla, Mexico.

19a. Mimosa texana (A. Gray) Small var. **texana** • Texas mimosa

Mimosa wherryana (Britton) Standley; *Mimosopsis wherryana* Britton

Shrubs, erect, 0.3–2 m, armed. **Stems** terete, puberulent or glabrescent; prickles infra-stipular, usually solitary, rarely groups of 2 or 3, recurved; brachyblasts present. **Leaves:** stipules subulate, 1.5–5.5 mm, glabrous; petiole 0.3–1 cm; primary rachis 0.2–0.7 cm; pinnae 1–4 pairs; leaflets 3–7 pairs, blades obliquely oblong to elliptic, 1.5–4.5 × 0.5–2 mm, margins ciliate, reticulate veins prominent abaxially, apex obtuse or acute, surfaces glabrous or abaxial surface puberulent. **Peduncles** 0.5–1.5 cm. **Inflorescences** 10–30-flowered, axillary, globose capitula, solitary or fascicles of 2–5, 8–15 mm diam.; bracts linear to spatulate, 1/3–1/2 corolla length. **Pedicels** 0 mm. **Flowers** bisexual; calyx campanulate, lobes 5, 1/3–1/2(–2/3) corolla length, glabrous to puberulent; corolla purple, glabrous or puberulent, lobes 5, 1/5–1/4(–1/3) corolla length; stamens 10, filaments distinct to bases, white; ovary stipitate, glabrous; style attenuate at apex; stigma poriform. **Legumes** sessile or stipitate, straight, oblong, 20–40 × 5–8 mm, reticulate veins prominent, constricted or not between seeds, valves entire, margin prickly or unarmed, apex acute to acuminate or apiculate, faces glabrous; stipe 0.5–1 mm. **Seeds** 3–6, dark brown, elliptic or lenticular, 4.5–5 × 3.5–3.8 × 1.2–1.5 mm, testa porous, fissural line 50%.

Flowering Mar–Sep; fruiting May–Oct. Dry, rocky plains and streambeds, arroyos, rocky limestone hills; 50–1400 m; N.Mex., Tex.; Mexico (Coahuila, Durango, Nuevo León, San Luis Potosí, Sonora, Tamaulipas).

Variety *texana* is widely distributed in Brewster, McCulloch, Terrell, Travis, Uvalde, Val Verde, and Webb counties in Texas; a new report of this variety from adjacent New Mexico was collected at the environs of Whites City in Eddy County (*R. G. Walter* & *J. M. Ricketson 426*, MO!), just north and northeast of Guadalupe Mountains National Park, Texas.

20. Mimosa turneri Barneby, Brittonia 38: 4, fig. 2 [lower left]. 1986 • Desert mimosa

Shrubs, erect, 0.3–2 m, armed. **Stems** terete, glabrous; prickles infrastipular or irregular along internodes, straight or recurved; brachyblasts present. **Leaves:** some 1-pinnate, with 1 or 2 pairs of leaflets; stipules subulate, 1–2 mm, glabrous; petiole 0.2–0.4 cm, flattened, adaxially bisulcate; primary rachis 0.2–0.4(–0.7) cm; pinnae 1 or 2 pairs; leaflets 2 or 3 pairs, blades obliquely oblong to elliptic, 1.5–3.5 × 0.5–1.5 mm, margins eciliate, pinnate veins prominent abaxially, apex obtuse or retuse to acute, surfaces glabrous. **Peduncles** 0.5–1.7 cm. **Inflorescences** 5–25-flowered, axillary, globose or semiglobose capitula, solitary or fascicles of 2, 9–12 mm diam.; bracts spatulate, 1/5–1/3 corolla length. **Pedicels** 0.5 mm. **Flowers** bisexual; calyx campanulate, lobes 4 or 5, 1/5–1/3 corolla length; corolla purplish pink or white, glabrous, lobes 4 or 5, 1/3–1/2 corolla length; stamens 8 or 10, filaments distinct to bases, lilac-pink; ovary stipitate, glabrous; style attenuate at apex; stigma poriform. **Legumes** stipitate, curved, linear, 30–60 × 5–7 mm, constricted between seeds, valves with (3 or)4–6(–8) segments, bulliform, margin prickly on 1 suture, apex cuspidate to rostrate, rostrum 3–4 mm, faces glabrous; stipe 5–7 mm. **Seeds** (3 or)4–6(–8), brown, lenticular, 4–4.5 × 3–3.5 × 2.5–3 mm, testa porous, fissural line 25%.

Flowering Apr–Aug; fruiting May–Aug. Thorn scrub, calcareous gravelly hillsides and arroyo banks; 600–1400 m; N.Mex., Tex.; Mexico (Coahuila, Nuevo León).

Mimosa turneri is known from Eddy and Otero counties in New Mexico, and from Brewster, Hudspeth, Jeff Davis, Pecos, Presidio, and Val Verde counties in southwestern Texas.

28. ACACIA Miller, Gard. Dict. Abr. ed. 4, vol. 1. 1754, name conserved • [Derivation uncertain, perhaps Greek *ake* or *akis*, sharp point, alluding to spiny stipules of some species, or *a*, absent, and *kakia*, malice, alluding to sacredness or use of wood in making vessels] I

John E. Ebinger

David S. Seigler

Shrubs or trees [rarely vines], usually unarmed, stipular spines present on *A. paradoxa*. **Stems** erect to ascending or pendulous, glabrous or pubescent; twigs not flexuous or slightly so, terete to angled or ridged, short shoots usually absent. **Leaves** alternate (except fascicled or whorled in *A. verticillata*), even-bipinnate or phyllodic, leaves often modified (in age) to polymorphic phyllodes (enlarged, flattened petiole without leaflets), usually glandular on margins and/or apex, saplings often with even-pinnate juvenile leaves often not present at maturity; stipules usually present, usually early deciduous, rarely woody, spinose; petiolate, usually with 1 globose gland; pinnae [1 or] 2–31[–50] pairs, mostly opposite; leaflets 8–70 pairs per pinna, opposite, sessile or subsessile, blade margins entire, surfaces glabrous or pubescent. **Peduncles** usually not elongated in fruit, glabrous or pubescent. **Inflorescences** 20–200+-flowered, terminal or axillary, globose heads or cylindrical spikes, heads solitary, fascicled, or clustered, or arranged in pseudoracemes or pseudopanicles; bracts present. **Flowers** mimosoid; calyx cup-shaped, lobes 4 or 5, triangular, glabrous [pubescent]; corolla yellow to cream, cup-shaped, lobes 4 or 5, triangular, membranous, glabrous [pubescent]; stamens 20–150, rarely connate basally, usually exserted, mostly yellow to gold or creamy white; anthers dorsifixed, mostly eglandular; ovary sessile or short-stipitate; style and stigma filiform. **Fruits** legumes, erect to pendulous, stipitate, stipe usually relatively short, mostly flat, straight to falcate, linear to oblong, apex sometimes beaked, usually dehiscent along sutures, dry, papery to leathery, glabrous or pubescent. **Seeds** usually 6–10, usually flattened, ellipsoid to ovoid, uniseriate, usually with pulpy, bright-colored aril, forming a cap or encircling seed. $x = 13$.

Species ca. 1300 (15 in the flora): introduced; Indian Ocean Islands, Pacific Islands (Kei Islands, New Guinea), Australia; introduced also in South America; introduced elsewhere in tropical and subtropical regions.

Acacia species are indigenous mostly in the Southern Hemisphere, with more than 950 in Australia. None is native to the New World.

To preserve as much current usage as possible, at the 17th International Botanical Congress in 2005, the type of the genus *Acacia* was changed from *Acacia scorpioides* (Linnaeus) W. Wright to the Australian species *Acacia penninervis* Sieber ex de Candolle (B. R. Maslin 2008; J. McNeill and N. J. Turland 2010). Presently, there is considerable evidence that the broadly defined genus *Acacia* is not a natural or monophyletic group (Gill. K. Brown et al. 2008). Therefore, plants of the former *Acacia* subg. *Phyllodineae* remain in the genus *Acacia* (Maslin et al. 2003; Maslin 2008), and other species of the traditional *Acacia* are transferred to the genera *Acaciella*, *Mariosousa*, *Parasenegalia* Seigler & Ebinger, *Pseudosenegalia* Seigler & Ebinger, *Senegalia*, and *Vachellia*.

Members of *Acacia* enumerated here are introduced, exotic species proven to be adventive in the United States by vouchered collections; most are restricted to Arizona, southern California, and Florida. In addition, many Australian *Acacia* species are cultivated in botanical gardens and plant introduction centers and as ornamentals in the nursery trade. Although not clearly established to be adventive, other *Acacia* species may occasionally be found outside of cultivation; D. Isely (1973) mentioned a few of these, including *A. podalyriifolia* A. Cunningham ex G. Don, reported from a non-cultivated stand on Santa Catalina Island, California, and more recently from Orange County. Naturalized individuals of *A. salicina* Lindley and *A. stenophylla* A. Cunningham ex Bentham are known from Maricopa County, Arizona (ASU). *Acacia iteaphylla* F. Mueller ex Bentham is naturalized on the University of California-Riverside campus and is possibly invasive (*Sanders & Morgan 21588*, UCR).

SELECTED REFERENCES Brown, Gill. K. et al. 2008. *Acacia s.s.* and its relationship among tropical legumes, tribe Ingeae (Leguminosae: Mimosoideae). Syst. Bot. 33: 739–751. Maslin, B. R., J. T. Miller, and D. S. Seigler. 2003. Overview of the generic status of *Acacia* (Leguminosae: Mimosoideae). Austral. Syst. Bot. 16: 1–18.

1. Leaves compound.
   2. Leaves with 2–5 pinna pairs; petioles 0–2 mm . . . . 2. *Acacia baileyana*
   2. Leaves with (3–)6–31 pinna pairs; petioles 5–33 mm.
      3. Distance between pinna pairs 7–20 mm; leaflet blades 5–15 mm . . . . 6. *Acacia decurrens*
      3. Distance between pinna pairs 2–7 mm; leaflet blades 1.5–5 mm.
         4. Rachis glands between most pinna pairs . . . . 5. *Acacia dealbata*
         4. Rachis glands scattered, at pinna pair nodes and internodes . . . . 8. *Acacia mearnsii*
1. Leaves phyllodic.
   5. Phyllodes 5–30 mm.
      6. Stipular spines present . . . . 10. *Acacia paradoxa*
      6. Stipular spines absent.
         7. Phyllodes inequilateral, ± triangular, 5–15 mm wide, alternate. . . . . 3. *Acacia cultriformis*
         7. Phyllodes acicular, linear, 0.5–1.5 mm wide, fascicled or whorled . . . . 15. *Acacia verticillata*
   5. Phyllodes (20–)30–250 mm.
      8. Phyllodes with pinnate venation.
         9. Pulvinus 4–8 mm; phyllodes 10–35 mm wide. . . . . 11. *Acacia pycnantha*
         9. Pulvinus 1–3.5 mm; phyllodes 3–14(–25) mm wide.
            10. Globose heads 5–7 diam.; phyllode gland not obvious, not disciform . . . 13. *Acacia retinodes*
            10. Globose heads 8–12 mm diam.; phyllode gland obvious, disciform . . . . . . 14. *Acacia saligna*
      8. Phyllodes with parallel venation.
         11. Inflorescences cylindrical spikes.
            12. Phyllodes falcate; flowers 5-merous . . . . 1. *Acacia auriculiformis*
            12. Phyllodes not falcate; flowers 4-merous . . . . 7. *Acacia longifolia*
         11. Inflorescences globose heads.
            13. Twigs fragrant (vanilla-scented) when crushed, resin-ribbed . . . . 12. *Acacia redolens*
            13. Twigs not fragrant when crushed, not resinous.
               14. Inflorescences pseudoracemes of 2 heads; minor phyllode veins weakly reticulate . . . . 4. *Acacia cyclops*
               14. Inflorescences pseudoracemes of 2–8 heads; minor phyllode veins prominently reticulate . . . . 9. *Acacia melanoxylon*

1. Acacia auriculiformis A. Cunningham ex Bentham, London J. Bot. 1: 377. 1842 (as auriculaeformis)
• Northern black wattle [I]

Trees, erect, to 35 m. **Twigs** gray to dark reddish brown, not flexuous, slightly ridged, glabrous. **Leaves** phyllodic; phyllode flat, falcate, linear to narrowly elliptic, 100–200 × 12–28 mm, venation parallel, mostly with 3 prominent veins, minor veins prominent, apex narrowly obtuse, not apiculate, surfaces glabrous; gland 1, 0–3 mm distal to pulvinus; pulvinus 3–5 mm. **Peduncles** 5–10 mm. **Inflorescences** cylindrical, interrupted spikes, loosely flowered, 50–85 × 4–7 mm, solitary or in fascicles of 2 or 3 in leaf axils, rarely in pseudoracemes. **Flowers** 5-merous, light golden yellow; calyx 0.9–1.3 mm; corolla 1.6–2.4 mm; filaments 2.5–3.5 mm; ovary pubescent. **Legumes** flattened, oblong, 30–160 × 8–18 mm, not constricted between seeds. **Seeds:** aril light yellow, encircling seed. **2*n*** = 26.

Flowering summer, fall. Disturbed areas; 0–20 m; introduced; Fla.; Pacific Islands (Kei Islands, New Guinea); n Australia.

Acacia auriculiformis is known from Collier, Martin, and Miami-Dade counties.

2. Acacia baileyana F. Mueller, Trans. & Proc. Roy. Soc. Victoria 24: 168. 1888 * Cootamundra wattle F I

Shrubs or small trees, erect, to 10 m. **Twigs** dark purplish brown to nearly black, not flexuous, ridged, pruinose, glabrous or pubescent. **Leaves** compound, 10–33 mm; petiole 0–2 mm, glabrous, gland absent; pinnae 2–5 pairs, 10–28 mm, 4–9 mm between pinna pairs; leaflets 8–24 pairs per pinna, blades oblong, 3.5–7.5 × 0.8–1.3 mm, base obtuse, apex obtuse to acute, not apiculate, surfaces glabrous. **Peduncles** 2–6 mm. **Inflorescences** globose heads, densely flowered, 4–8 mm diam., in axillary pseudoracemes of 8–35 heads or terminal pseudopanicles of 1–15 pseudoracemes. **Flowers** 5-merous, bright yellow; calyx 0.4–0.9 mm; corolla 1.2–2 mm; filaments 2.5–3.5 mm; ovary glabrous. **Legumes** flattened, oblong, 30–150 × 7–13 mm, sometimes slightly constricted between some seeds. **Seeds:** aril light yellow, obovate, 2–3 mm, forming small cap on seed. $2n = 26$.

Flowering winter, early spring. Disturbed areas; 100–500 m; introduced; Calif.; se Australia.

Acacia baileyana is known from Alameda, Contra Costa, Los Angeles, Monterey, Napa, Orange, Riverside, San Bernardino, Santa Barbara, Santa Clara, Santa Cruz, San Diego, and Ventura counties.

3. Acacia cultriformis A. Cunningham ex G. Don, Gen. Hist. 2: 406. 1832 • Knife-leaf wattle I

Shrubs, erect, to 4 m. **Twigs** bluish to purplish, not flexuous, ridged, glabrous. **Leaves** phyllodic; phyllode flat, one side nearly straight, the other rounded or angled, inequilateral, often deltate to triangular, 10–30 × 5–15 mm, venation parallel, midvein prominent, minor veins not obvious, apex acute, apiculate, surfaces glabrous; gland 1, prominent, near widest part of leaf; pulvinus 0.3–1 mm. **Peduncles** 2–5 mm. **Inflorescences** globose to slightly elongated heads, densely flowered, 3–7 mm, in pseudoracemes of 5–20 heads, usually solitary in distal leaf axils. **Flowers** 5-merous, golden yellow; calyx 0.5–0.9 mm; corolla 1.3–1.8 mm; filaments 2.7–3.5 mm; ovary glabrous. **Legumes** flattened, linear, 40–90 × 5–8 mm, slightly constricted between some seeds. **Seeds:** aril white, club-shaped, from base.

Flowering winter–summer. Disturbed areas; 0–150 m; introduced; Calif.; e Australia.

Acacia cultriformis is known from Los Angeles, Marin, San Diego, Santa Barbara, and Ventura counties.

4. Acacia cyclops A. Cunningham ex G. Don, Gen. Hist. 2: 404. 1832, name conserved • Western coastal wattle I

Shrubs or small trees, erect, to 6 m. **Twigs** light to dark reddish brown, slightly flexuous, ridged, glabrous. **Leaves** phyllodic; phyllode flat, slightly falcate, narrowly elliptic to oblanceolate, 40–95 × 4–15 mm, venation parallel, with 3–5 prominent veins, minor veins weakly reticulate, apex obtuse, obliquely apiculate, surfaces glabrous; gland 0 or 1, 0–2 mm distal to pulvinus; pulvinus 1–2 mm. **Peduncles** 2–10 mm. **Inflorescences** globose heads, densely flowered, 6–9 mm diam., in short pseudoracemes of 2 heads solitary in leaf axils. **Flowers** 5-merous, golden yellow; calyx 0.9–1.3 mm; corolla 1.3–2 mm; filaments 2.5–3.5 mm; ovary glabrous. **Legumes** elliptic in cross section, oblong, 50–130 × 9–17 mm, not constricted between seeds. **Seeds:** aril orange to scarlet, enlarged, encircling seed in 2 folds.

Flowering year-round. Disturbed areas, coastal dunes; 0–400 m; introduced; Calif.; s Australia.

Acacia cyclops is known from Los Angeles, Marin, Orange, and San Diego counties.

5. Acacia dealbata Link, Enum. Hort. Berol. Alt. 2: 445. 1822 • Silver wattle I

Shrubs or trees, erect, to 30 m. **Twigs** dark purplish brown to black, slightly flexuous, ridged, pruinose, densely puberulent. **Leaves** compound, 80–170 mm; petiole 8–22 mm, densely puberulent, gland present, below proximalmost pinna pair, 0.5–1 mm diam., puberulent; rachis gland between most pinna pairs; pinnae 6–30 pairs, 15–55 mm, 2–7 mm between pinna pairs; leaflets 15–70 pairs per pinna, blades linear, 2–5 × 0.4–0.8 mm, base cuneate, apex obtuse to acute, not apiculate, surfaces densely puberulent. **Peduncles** 2–6 mm. **Inflorescences** globose heads, densely flowered, 6–9 mm diam., in axillary pseudoracemes of 11–30 heads or terminal pseudopanicles of 1–15 pseudoracemes. **Flowers** 5-merous, pale yellow to cream; calyx 0.6–1.1 mm; corolla 1.4–2 mm; filaments 3.5–4.5 mm; ovary glabrous. **Legumes** flattened, oblong, 20–110 × 6–14 mm, constricted between some seeds. **Seeds:** aril light yellow, obovate, 2–3 mm, forming cap on seed. $2n = 26$.

Flowering winter, early spring. Disturbed areas; 0–300 m; introduced; Calif.; se Australia; introduced also in s South America.

Acacia dealbata is known from Butte, Los Angeles, Marin, Monterey, Napa, Riverside, Sacramento, Santa Clara, Santa Cruz, San Bernardino, and San Diego counties.

6. Acacia decurrens Willdenow, Sp. Pl. 4: 1072. 1806 • Green wattle [I]

Shrubs or small trees, erect, to 15 m. **Twigs** dark reddish brown to nearly black, slightly flexuous, ridged, usually glabrous. **Leaves** compound, 70–150 mm; petiole 7–33 mm, glabrous, gland present, below proximalmost pinna pair, 1–2 mm diam., glabrous; rachis glands between most pinna pairs; pinnae 3–13, 35–80 mm, 7–20 mm between pinna pairs; leaflets 15–45 pairs per pinna, blades linear, 5–15 × 0.3–0.6 mm, base cuneate, apex obtuse to acute, not apiculate, surfaces glabrous. **Peduncles** 2–4 mm. **Inflorescences** globose heads, densely flowered, 5–8 mm diam., in axillary pseudoracemes of 10–30 heads or terminal pseudopanicles of 1–15 pseudoracemes. **Flowers** 5-merous, bright yellow; calyx 0.6–1.2 mm; corolla 1.4–2 mm; filaments 2.5–3.5 mm; ovary glabrous. **Legumes** flattened, linear, 20–105 × 4–8 mm, slightly constricted between seeds. **Seeds:** aril light yellow, obovate, 2–3 mm, forming cap on seed. $2n = 26$.

Flowering year-round. Disturbed areas; 500–600 m; introduced; Calif.; se Australia; introduced also in s South America.

Acacia decurrens is known from Mendocino, San Diego, Solano, and Ventura counties, and one possible record in Humboldt County.

7. Acacia longifolia (Andrews) Willdenow, Sp. Pl. 4: 1052. 1806 • Sidney golden wattle [I]

Mimosa longifolia Andrews, Bot. Repos. 3: plate 207. 1802

Shrubs or trees, erect, to 10 m. **Twigs** dark reddish brown, not flexuous, ridged, glabrous. **Leaves** phyllodic; phyllode flat, not falcate, narrowly elliptic, 50–150 × 10–25 mm, venation parallel, with 2–4 prominent veins, minor veins prominent, apex acute to obtuse, apiculate, surfaces glabrous; gland 1, 0–7 mm distal to pulvinus; pulvinus 2–5 mm. **Peduncles** 0–2 mm. **Inflorescences** cylindrical spikes, densely flowered, 20–50 × 5–8 mm, solitary or in fascicles of 2 or 3 in leaf axils. **Flowers** 4-merous, bright yellow; calyx 0.6–0.9 mm; corolla 1.5–2.1 mm; filaments 2.6–3.6 mm; ovary pubescent. **Legumes** elliptic in cross section, linear, 50–150 × 5–9 mm, somewhat constricted between seeds. **Seeds:** aril light yellow, folded several times into thickened, lateral, skirtlike aril covering seed apex.

Flowering winter, spring. Sandy coastal areas; 0–40 m; introduced; Calif.; Pacific Islands (Kei Islands, New Guinea); se Australia; introduced also in s South America.

Acacia longifolia is known from Alameda, Contra Costa, Los Angeles, Marin, Monterey, Orange, Riverside, San Bernardino, San Diego, San Francisco, San Luis Obispo, Santa Barbara, Santa Cruz, Solano, and Ventura counties.

8. Acacia mearnsii De Wildeman, Pl. Bequaert. 3: 61. 1925 (as mearnsi) • Black wattle [I]

Shrubs or small trees, erect, to 10 m. **Twigs** dark purplish brown to black, slightly flexuous, ridged, puberulent. **Leaves** compound, 50–140 mm; petiole 5–30 mm, puberulent, gland present, below proximalmost pinna pair, 0.7–1.5 mm diam., puberulent; rachis glands scattered, with some between pinna pairs (at pinna pair nodes and internodes); pinnae 7–31 pairs, 15–70 mm, 3–7 mm between pinna pairs; leaflets 20–70 pairs per pinna, blades linear, 1.5–3.5 × 0.5–0.8 mm, base cuneate, apex obtuse, not apiculate, surfaces puberulent. **Peduncles** 4–9 mm. **Inflorescences** globose heads, densely flowered, 5–9 mm diam., in axillary pseudoracemes of 20–35 heads or terminal pseudopanicles of 1–10 pseudoracemes. **Flowers** 5-merous, pale yellow to cream; calyx 0.6–1.1 mm; corolla 1.4–2 mm; filaments 3.5–4.5 mm; ovary glabrous. **Legumes** flattened, linear, 30–140 × 4–8 mm, slightly constricted between seeds. **Seeds:** aril light yellow, obovate, 1–2 mm, forming cap on seed. $2n = 26$.

Flowering spring, early summer. Disturbed areas; 0–400 m; introduced; Calif.; se Australia.

Acacia mearnsii is known from Los Angeles, Orange, Riverside, San Diego, and Santa Barbara counties.

9. Acacia melanoxylon R. Brown in W. Aiton and W. T. Aiton, Hortus Kew. 5: 462. 1813 • Blackwood [I]

Trees, erect, to 30 m, usually spreading by root suckers. **Twigs** reddish brown, not flexuous, slightly ridged, glabrous. **Leaves** phyllodic, juvenile compound leaves often persisting on young plants; phyllode flat, straight to slightly falcate, usually narrowly elliptic, rarely oblanceolate, 40–140 × 6–25 mm, venation parallel, with 3–5 prominent veins, minor veins prominently reticulate, apex narrowly obtuse to acute, apiculate, surfaces glabrous; gland 0 (or 1), 0–5 mm distal to pulvinus when present; pulvinus 2–5 mm. **Peduncles** 4–11 mm. **Inflorescences** globose heads, densely flowered, 6–9 mm diam., in solitary pseudoracemes of 2–8 heads in leaf axils. **Flowers** 5-merous, pale yellow; calyx 0.9–1.3 mm; corolla 1.5–2 mm; filaments 2.5–3.5 mm; ovary pubescent. **Legumes** elliptic in cross section, linear, 50–150 × 4–8 mm, not constricted between seeds. **Seeds:** aril yellow to pink to deep red, encircling seed in irregular double fold. $2n = 26$.

Flowering fall, spring. Disturbed areas; 30–300 m; introduced; Calif.; se, e Australia; introduced also in s South America.

Acacia melanoxylon is known from Alameda, Contra Costa, Los Angeles, Marin, Mendocino, Monterey, San Diego, San Francisco, San Luis Obispo, Santa Barbara, Santa Cruz, and Ventura counties.

10. Acacia paradoxa de Candolle, Cat. Pl. Hort. Monsp., 74. 1813 • Kangaroo thorn [I]

Shrubs or small trees, erect, to 4 m. **Twigs** light to dark reddish brown, not flexuous, ridged, densely pubescent; stipular spines present. **Leaves** phyllodic; phyllode undulate, straight, lanceolate to narrowly oblong-elliptic, 7–20 × 2–7 mm, venation pinnate, midvein usually eccentric, minor veins prominent, apex acute to obtuse, not apiculate, spine-tipped, surfaces slightly pubescent or glabrous; gland 1, 2–5 mm distal to leaf base; pulvinus absent. **Peduncles** 5–18 mm. **Inflorescences** globose heads, densely flowered, 8–12 mm diam., 1 (or 2) in leaf axils. **Flowers** 5-merous, bright yellow; calyx 1–1.7 mm; corolla 1.6–2.4 mm; filaments 3.3–4.3 mm; ovary glabrous or pubescent. **Legumes** flattened, oblong, 30–60 × 4–7 mm, not constricted between seeds. **Seeds:** aril yellow, club-shaped, 1–2 mm, forming cap on seed.

Flowering winter, spring. Disturbed areas; 0–300 m; introduced; Calif.; se Australia (Tasmania); introduced also in s South America (Chile).

Acacia paradoxa is known from Alameda, Marin, Monterey, San Francisco, Santa Barbara, and Santa Cruz counties.

11. Acacia pycnantha Bentham, London J. Bot. 1: 351. 1842 • Golden wattle [I]

Shrubs or small trees, erect, to 8 m. **Twigs** reddish brown, slightly flexuous, terete, glabrous. **Leaves** phyllodic; phyllode flat, falcate, narrowly elliptic to oblanceolate, 90–150 × 10–35 mm, venation pinnate, midvein medial, minor veins not obvious, apex obtuse, apiculate, surfaces glabrous; gland 1 (or 2), 3–45 mm distal to pulvinus; pulvinus 4–8 mm. **Peduncles** 2–5 mm. **Inflorescences** globose heads, densely flowered, 7–10 mm diam., usually in solitary pseudoracemes of 20–30 heads in leaf axils. **Flowers** 5-merous, golden yellow; calyx 1.5–2 mm; corolla 2.5–3 mm; filaments 3.5–4.5 mm; ovary glabrous. **Legumes** flattened, linear, 50–130 × 5–7 mm, slightly constricted between seeds. **Seeds:** aril light yellow, obovate, forming cap on seed.

Flowering winter, spring. Disturbed coastal habitats; 0–100 m; introduced; Calif.; se Australia.

Acacia pycnantha is known from Los Angeles, Marin, Orange, San Diego, San Luis Obispo, and Santa Barbara counties.

12. Acacia redolens Maslin, Nuytsia 1: 327, fig. 8. 1974 • Vanilla-scented wattle [F] [I]

Shrubs or small trees, erect, to 5 m. **Twigs** brown to purple-brown, fragrant when crushed (vanilla-scented), not flexuous, ridged (resin-ribbed), glabrous. **Leaves** phyllodic; phyllode flat, straight, oblanceolate, 20–70 × 5–15 mm, venation parallel, with 5–12 prominent veins, minor veins not obvious, apex obtuse, apiculate, surfaces glabrous; gland 1, at edge of pulvinus; pulvinus 1–3 mm. **Peduncles** 2–6 mm. **Inflorescences** globose heads, densely flowered, 3–5 mm diam., solitary or clustered in short pseudoracemes of 2–6 heads in distal leaf axils. **Flowers** 5-merous, light yellow; calyx 0.5–0.8 mm; corolla 1–1.6 mm; filaments 2–3 mm; ovary glabrous. **Legumes** flattened, linear, 30–60 × 2–4 mm, constricted between seeds. **Seeds:** aril cream-white, thickened, forming cap on seed.

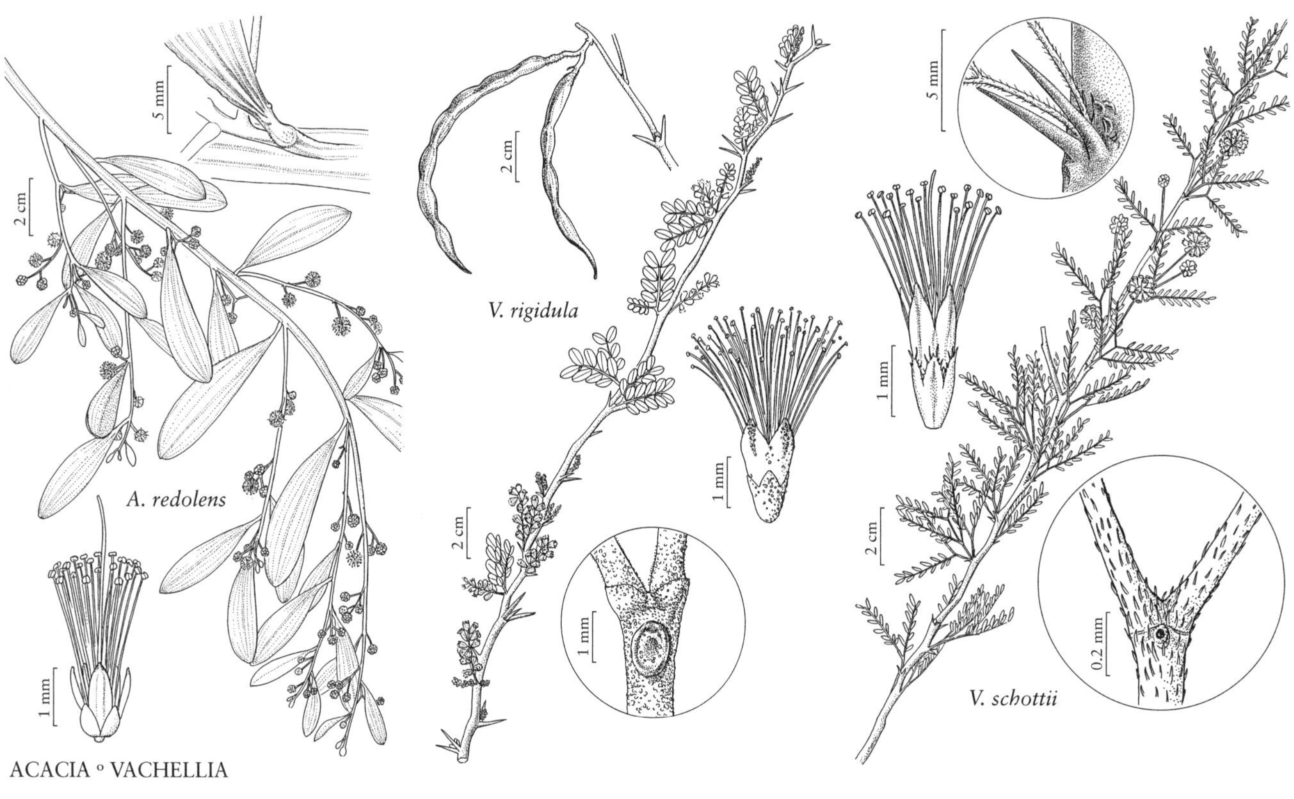

ACACIA ◦ VACHELLIA

Flowering spring–early summer. Disturbed areas; 30–400 m; introduced; Ariz., Calif.; sw Australia.

Acacia redolens is known from Maricopa County, Arizona, and Contra Costa, Orange, Riverside, and San Diego counties, California.

13. Acacia retinodes Schlechtendal, Linnaea 20: 664. 1847 • Swamp or ever-blooming wattle [I]

Shrubs or small trees, erect, to 10 m, often spreading by root suckers. **Twigs** reddish brown, not flexuous, ridged, glabrous. **Leaves** phyllodic; phyllode flat, slightly falcate, linear-lanceolate to narrowly oblanceolate, 30–200 × 3–14 mm, venation pinnate, midvein medial, minor veins not obvious, apex acuminate, apiculate, surfaces glabrous; gland 1, 1–10 mm distal to pulvinus (not obvious, not disciform); pulvinus 1–3 mm. **Peduncles** 2–5 mm. **Inflorescences** globose heads, densely flowered, 5–7 mm diam., in solitary pseudoracemes of 5–9 heads in leaf axils. **Flowers** 5-merous, pale yellow to cream; calyx 0.5–0.9 mm; corolla 1.2–1.7 mm; filaments 2.5–3.5 mm; ovary glabrous. **Legumes** flattened, linear, 40–160 × 4–7 mm, slightly constricted between seeds. **Seeds:** aril light yellow, nearly encircling seed. $2n = 26$.

Flowering year-round. Disturbed coastal habitats; 0–600 m; introduced; Calif., Fla.; se Australia.

Acacia retinodes is known from Los Angeles, Marin, Orange, San Diego, San Luis Obispo, and Santa Barbara counties in California, and from Glades and Monroe counties in Florida.

14. Acacia saligna (Labillardière) H. L. Wendland, Comm. Acac. Aphyll., 26. 1820 • Golden wreath wattle [I]

Mimosa saligna Labillardière, Nov. Holl. Pl. 2: 86, plate 235. 1807

Shrubs or small trees, pendulous, to 6 m. **Twigs** bluish to purplish, slightly flexuous, slightly ridged, glabrous. **Leaves** phyllodic; phyllode flat, straight to slightly curved, linear to narrowly elliptic, 70–250 × 6–25 mm, venation pinnate, midvein prominent, minor veins faint, apex narrowly acuminate, apiculate, surfaces glabrous; gland 1, 0–3 mm distal to pulvinus (obvious, disciform); pulvinus 1–3.5 mm. **Peduncles** 5–15 mm. **Inflorescences** globose heads, densely flowered, 8–12 mm diam., in pseudoracemes of 2–10 heads, 5–40 mm, solitary in distal leaf axils. **Flowers** 5-merous, golden yellow; calyx 1–2 mm; corolla 2.6–3.4 mm; filaments 5–6 mm; ovary glabrous. **Legumes** flattened, linear, 80–140 × 5–8 mm, constricted between seeds. **Seeds:** aril yellow, clavate, obovate, 2–3 mm, forming cap on seed.

Flowering fall–spring. Disturbed areas; 0–600 m; introduced; Calif., Fla., Nev.; sw Australia.

Acacia saligna is known from Los Angeles, Orange, Riverside, San Diego, and Ventura counties in California, Lee and Monroe counties in Florida, and Clark County in Nevada.

15. Acacia verticillata (L'Héritier) Willdenow, Sp. Pl. 4: 1049. 1806 • Prickly Moses [I]

Mimosa verticillata L'Héritier, Sert. Angl., 30. 1789

Shrubs or small trees, erect, to 5 m. **Twigs** dark reddish brown, not flexuous, prominently ridged, glabrous or pubescent. **Leaves** phyllodic; fascicled or whorled; phyllode quadrangular, straight, linear, acicular, 5–20 × 0.5–1.5 mm, venation parallel, midvein prominent, minor veins not obvious, apex acuminate, sharp-pointed, surfaces mostly glabrous; gland 1 (usually not obvious, disc-shaped), 3–6 mm distal to leaf base; pulvinus absent. **Peduncles** 2–12 mm. **Inflorescences** cylindrical spikes, densely flowered, 10–45 × 4–7 mm, solitary in leaf axils. **Flowers** 5-merous, pale yellow; calyx 0.5–0.8 mm; corolla 1.1–1.6 mm; filaments 2.2–3.2 mm; ovary glabrous. **Legumes** flattened, linear, 20–90 × 2.7–5 mm, not constricted between seeds. **Seeds:** aril light yellow, folded and thickened, forming cap on seed. **2*n*** = 26.

Flowering fall, winter. Disturbed areas; 0–100 m; introduced; Calif.; se Australia (including Tasmania).

Acacia verticillata is known from Marin, Monterey, San Francisco, Santa Barbara, and Santa Clara counties.

29. VACHELLIA Wight & Arnott, Prodr. Fl. Ind. Orient. 1: 272. 1834 • Acacia [For Rev. George Harvey Vachell, 1799–1839, plant collector in China]

John E. Ebinger

David S. Seigler

Shrubs or trees, armed. **Stems** erect to spreading, glabrous or pubescent; twigs terete [angulate], some flexuous, short shoots usually present. **Leaves** alternate, even-bipinnate, usually clustered on short shoots, leaves of short shoots usually smaller, with fewer pinna pairs and leaflets than alternately arranged leaves on faster growing branches; stipules present, spinose, paired at nodes, [asymmetric], straight to curved, woody, in some species enlarged and inhabited by ants; petiolate, petiole channeled, glabrous or pubescent, petiolar gland 1–30; pinnae 1–45 [–60] pairs, mostly opposite; leaflets 2–47 pairs per pinna, usually opposite, sessile or subsessile, blade margins entire, surfaces glabrous or pubescent. **Inflorescences** 50–180(–1500+)-flowered, primarily axillary, globose heads or cylindrical spikes, solitary or clustered in leaf axis or on short shoots, sometimes pseudoracemes; bracts present. **Flowers** mimosoid; calyx campanulate, lobes 4 or 5; corolla yellow, white, or cream, lobes 4 or 5; stamens 15–120, distinct, exserted, yellow or white, [gold or creamy white]; anthers dorsifixed, eglandular; ovary sessile or short-stipitate, usually glabrous; style and stigma filiform. **Fruits** legumes, stipitate, flattened to terete, straight to falcate, linear to oblong, usually dehiscing along both sutures, sometimes indehiscent, glabrous or pubescent. **Seeds** 6–10(–20), uniseriate or biseriate, sometimes flattened, ovoid to ellipsoid, sometimes surrounded by pulp; pleurogram U-shaped. x = 13.

Species ca. 160 (10 in the flora): s, sw United States, Mexico, West Indies, Central America, South America, Europe, Asia, Africa, Australia; introduced nearly worldwide in tropical to warm temperate regions.

There is considerable evidence that *Acacia* in the broad sense is not a natural or monophyletic group. Largely because the segregation of *Acacia* in the broad sense into at least five genera would result in requiring a change in generic epithet for about 1000 Australian species of subg. *Phyllodineae* (de Candolle) Seringe, at the 17th International Botanical Congress in 2005, the type of *Acacia* was changed from *A. scorpioides* (Linnaeus) W. F. Wright to the Australian species *A. penninervis* (B. R. Maslin 2008; J. McNeill and N. J. Turland 2010). As a result of this change, plants of former *Acacia* subg. *Acacia* should be placed in *Vachellia* (Maslin et al. 2003; D. S. Seigler and J. E. Ebinger 2005).

SELECTED REFERENCES Clarke, H. D., D. S. Seigler, and J. E. Ebinger. 1989. *Acacia farnesiana* (Fabaceae: Mimosoideae) and related species from Mexico, the southwestern U.S., and the Caribbean. Syst. Bot. 14: 549–564. Clarke, H. D., D. S. Seigler, and J. E. Ebinger. 1990. *Acacia constricta* (Fabaceae: Mimosoideae) and related species from the southwestern U.S. and Mexico. Amer. J. Bot. 77: 305–315. Ebinger, J. E., D. S. Seigler, and H. D. Clarke. 2002. Notes on the segregates of *Acacia farnesiana* (Linnaeus) Willdenow (Fabaceae: Mimosoideae) and related species in North America. SouthW. Naturalist 47: 86–91. Lee, Y. S., D. S. Seigler, and J. E. Ebinger. 1989. *Acacia rigidula* (Fabaceae) and related species in Mexico and Texas. Syst. Bot. 14: 91–100.

1. Inflorescences cylindrical spikes.
    2. Stipular spines enlarged, 4–10 mm wide near base; pinnae 3–14 pairs . . . . 4. *Vachellia cornigera*
    2. Stipular spines 0.6–2.1 mm wide near base; pinnae 1 pair. . . . . 7. *Vachellia rigidula*
1. Inflorescences globose heads.
    3. Leaflet blades 16–28 mm. . . . . 2. *Vachellia choriophylla*
    3. Leaflet blades 1.1–6.3 mm.
        4. Involucral bracts near middle of peduncles.
            5. Leaflet blades linear and subterete . . . . 8. *Vachellia schottii*
            5. Leaflet blades elliptic, oblong, or oval and flat.
                6. Stems not glutinous; pinnae 2–8 pairs . . . . 3. *Vachellia constricta*
                6. Stems glutinous; pinnae 1 or 2(or 3) pairs . . . . .10. *Vachellia vernicosa*
        4. Involucral bracts at base of heads.
            7. Pinnae 12–45 pairs. . . . . 6. *Vachellia macracantha*
            7. Pinnae 1–8 pairs.
                8. Petiolar glands donut-shaped, at or just below lowermost pinnae . . . . 1. *Vachellia bravoensis*
                8. Petiolar glands circular to slightly elongated, not donut-shaped, usually medial on petiole.
                    9. Legumes nearly terete in cross section, not constricted between seeds; seeds biseriate or irregularly arranged . . . . 5. *Vachellia farnesiana* (in part)
                    9. Legumes narrowly elliptic in cross section, constricted between seeds; seeds uniseriate.
                        10. Stems usually slightly flexuous; petioles 6–12(–17) mm . . . . 5. *Vachellia farnesiana* (in part)
                        10. Stems strongly flexuous; petioles 3–7 mm. . . . . .9. *Vachellia tortuosa*

1. Vachellia bravoensis (Isely) Seigler & Ebinger, Phytologia 87: 146. 2006 • Huisachillo

Acacia schaffneri (S. Watson) F. J. Hermann var. *bravoensis* Isely, Sida 3: 383. 1969

Shrubs or trees, erect, to 4 (–6) m; bark grayish brown, shallowly furrowed. **Stems** slightly flexuous, glabrous or sparsely pubescent, not glutinous; short shoots present. **Leaves** 5–20 mm; stipular spines terete, straight, 1–15 (–29) × 0.5–1.5 mm near base; petiole 2–8 mm, usually densely pubescent; petiolar gland 1, at or just below lowermost pinnae, sessile, circular, 0.2–1.1 mm diam., donut-shaped (circular in outline with characteristic central hole); rachis 0–18 mm; pinnae 1–3(or 4) pairs, 7–28 mm; leaflets 10–24 pairs per pinna, blades flat, oblong, 2–4.2(–5) × 0.6–1.1 mm, base oblique and obtuse, apex broadly acute to obtuse, surfaces glabrous. **Peduncles** 7–24 mm. **Inflorescences** globose heads, densely flowered, 8–11 mm diam., solitary or clusters of 2–5 on short shoots; involucre at base of head (not obvious). **Flowers** yellow; calyx 0.8–1.6 mm, glabrous or puberulent; corolla 2–3 mm, glabrous or puberulent; filaments yellow, 3.2–4.2 mm. **Legumes** linear, nearly terete in cross section, 70–160 × 6–9 mm, constricted between seeds. **Seeds** uniseriate. **2*n*** = 26.

Flowering Feb–Apr. Disturbed sites in thorn scrub woodlands, desert grasslands; 0–700 m; Tex.; Mexico (Coahuila, Hidalgo, Nuevo León, San Luis Potosí, Tamaulipas).

Vachellia bravoensis is known from southern Texas from Wharton County north to Blanco County, west to Kinney County, and south to Cameron County.

Many authors have placed *Vachellia bravoensis* with *V. tortuosa* because the fruits are similar, being constricted around the seeds, relatively long and narrow, and pubescent. *Vachellia bravoensis* is easily separated from *V. tortuosa* by the presence of a circular petiolar gland at or immediately below the lowermost pinna pair, and fewer pinna pairs (1–3 versus (2–)4–8).

Vachellia bravoensis hybridizes with *V. rigidula* (*V.* ×*ruthvenii* Seigler & Ebinger). This uncommon hybrid has been found only at the Chaparral Wildlife Management Area, Dimmit County, Texas. It is similar to *V. bravoensis* in having some leaves with two pinna pairs and the pinnae with five to twelve pairs of leaflets.

2. Vachellia choriophylla (Bentham) Seigler & Ebinger, Phytologia 87: 150. 2006 • Cinnecord

Acacia choriophylla Bentham, London J. Bot. 1: 495. 1842

Shrubs or trees, bushy, to 10 m; bark light brown to reddish brown, smooth. **Stems** not flexuous, glabrous, not glutinous; short shoots usually absent. **Leaves** 7–70 mm; stipular spines terete to elliptic, straight, 0.7–1.5(–4.5) × 0.4–1.4 mm near base; petiole 6–15 mm, glabrous; petiolar gland 1, just below lowermost pinnae, short-stalked or sessile, circular, 0.2–0.6 mm diam., apex globose; rachis 0–60 mm; pinnae 1–3(or 4) pairs, 35–60 mm; leaflets 4–8 pairs per pinna, blades flat, elliptic to obovate, 16–28 × 5–15 mm, base acute to obtuse, apex obtuse, surfaces glabrous. **Peduncles** 22–35(–55) mm. **Inflorescences** globose heads, densely flowered, 6–8 mm diam., solitary or clusters of 2–13 in leaf axils, or clusters on leafless axillary shoots; involucre at base of head. **Flowers** yellow; calyx 1–1.6 mm, glabrous; corolla 1.6–2.1 mm, glabrous; filaments yellow, 2.7–3.2 mm. **Legumes** oblong, elliptic in cross section, 40–100 × 14–23 mm, not constricted between seeds. **Seeds** uniseriate. $2n = 26$.

Flowering Jan–Jun. Moist, disturbed sites, open woods, coppices and pine barrens on limestone soils; 0–10 m; Fla.; West Indies (Bahamas, Cuba, Turks and Caicos Islands).

Vachellia choriophylla is known from Miami-Dade and Monroe counties and is reported as spontaneous from Key Largo.

3. Vachellia constricta (Bentham) Seigler & Ebinger, Phytologia 87: 152. 2006, name conserved • Mescat acacia [W]

Acacia constricta Bentham, Smithsonian Contr. Knowl. 3(5): 66. 1852, name conserved; *A. constricta* var. *paucispina* Wooton & Standley

Shrubs or trees, erect, to 6 m; bark dark gray, smooth or shallowly furrowed. **Stems** not flexuous, glabrous or pubescent, not glutinous; short shoots present. **Leaves** 12–35 (–40) mm; stipular spines terete, straight, 5–15(–38) × 0.8–1.2 mm near base; petiole 4–14 mm, sparsely puberulent; petiolar gland 1, at or just below lowermost pinnae, usually sessile, rarely short-stalked, circular, 0.2–0.7 mm diam., donut-shaped; rachis 6–35 mm; pinnae 2–8 pairs, 5–12 mm; leaflets 5–12 pairs per pinna, blades flat, elliptic to oblong or oval, 1.5–3.6 × 0.7–1.3 mm, base oblique and obtuse, apex obtuse to acute, surfaces usually glabrous. **Peduncles** 11–26 mm. **Inflorescences** globose heads, densely flowered, 5.5–9.5 mm diam., solitary or clusters of 2–5 on short shoots; involucre near middle of peduncle. **Flowers** pale yellow; calyx 0.9–1.4 mm, glabrous; corolla 1.7–2.4 mm, glabrous; filaments yellow, 3.5–5 mm. **Legumes** linear, flattened, 50–150 × 3.6–5.6 mm, constricted between seeds. **Seeds** uniseriate. $2n = 52$.

Flowering Apr–Oct. Thorn scrub woodlands, deserts, disturbed and arid sites; 100–2000 m; Ariz., N.Mex., Tex.; Mexico (Baja California Sur, Chihuahua, Coahuila, Durango, Nuevo León, Oaxaca, Puebla, Querétaro, San Luis Potosí, Sonora, Tamaulipas, Veracruz, Zacatecas).

In Texas, *Vachellia constricta* is found in the westernmost part of the state, from El Paso County eastward to Loving and Brewster counties; it is also disjunct in Howard and Midland counties.

Vachellia constricta is closely related to *V. vernicosa*. *Vachellia vernicosa* has glutinous leaves, twigs, and fruits, is mostly glabrous throughout, and has 1 or 2 (or 3) pinna pairs; *V. constricta* is without glutinous leaves, twigs, and fruits, usually is pubescent, and has leaves with 2–8 pinna pairs. A nearly spineless form appears to be common in Arizona and New Mexico (var. *paucispina*). The variation existing in individuals as well as within populations suggests that this characteristic represents random variation, and these plants do not merit varietal status.

4. Vachellia cornigera (Linnaeus) Seigler & Ebinger, Phytologia 87: 153. 2006 • Bullhorn acacia [I]

Mimosa cornigera Linnaeus, Sp. Pl. 1: 520. 1753; *Acacia cornigera* (Linnaeus) Willdenow

Shrubs or trees, erect, to 10(–15) m; bark brown to gray, slightly furrowed. **Stems** not flexuous, puberulent, not glutinous; short shoots absent. **Leaves** 40–160 mm; stipular spines inflated and terete to slightly flattened, straight to slightly reflexed near apex, 30–100 × 4–10 mm near base; petiole 5–20 mm, usually puberulent; petiolar glands 1(or 2), medial to distal on petiole, sessile, elongated, 1–7 narrowing to 1–4 mm distally, canoe-shaped; rachis 30–150 mm; pinnae 3–14 pairs, 30–70 mm; leaflets 15–40 pairs per pinna, blades flat, oblong, 4–11 × 1.3–2.7 mm, base oblique and obtuse, apex obtuse, surfaces glabrous; Beltian bodies present. **Peduncles** 5–15 mm. **Inflorescences** cylindrical spikes, densely flowered, narrowing slightly toward blunt apex, 20–35 × 8–11 mm, solitary or clusters of 2–4 in axil of small, stipular spines on short, usually leafless, axillary branches; involucre at base of peduncle. **Flowers** pale yellow; calyx 0.9–1.4 mm, glabrous or sparsely puberulent; corolla 1–1.5 mm, glabrous; filaments yellow, 1.3–2.3 mm. **Legumes** oblong, nearly terete in cross section, 50–90 × 13–18 mm, not constricted between seeds, apex narrowing to spinelike beak, 20–50 mm. **Seeds** biseriate.

Flowering Jan–Jul. Wet to relatively dry, disturbed habitats; 0–10 m; introduced; Fla.; Mexico; Central America; introduced also in West Indies.

In the flora area, *Vachellia cornigera* is found in Lee and Pinellas counties.

Although the spines of *Vachellia cornigera* are commonly inhabited by ants in Central America and Mexico, this association has not been observed in material introduced into Florida.

Vachellia sphaerocephala (Schlechtendal & Chamisso) Seigler & Ebinger has been reported as an escape from cultivation in Collier and Miami-Dade counties, Florida (R. P. Wunderlin and B. F. Hansen 2000+, vol. 3). It is similar to *V. cornigera* but has leaflets with only the midvein obvious below, and with subglobose inflorescences less than two times longer than wide. In contrast, *V. cornigera* has leaflets with two to three major veins from the base and obvious lateral veins, and with inflorescences more than three times longer than wide.

5. Vachellia farnesiana (Linnaeus) Wight & Arnott, Prodr. Fl. Ind. Orient. 1: 272. 1834 • Huisache

Mimosa farnesiana Linnaeus, Sp. Pl. 1: 521. 1753; *Acacia farnesiana* (Linnaeus) Willdenow

Shrubs or trees, erect or prostrate to ascending, to 8 m; bark dark gray to brown, furrowed. **Stems** usually slightly flexuous, usually glabrous, not glutinous; short shoots present. **Leaves** 7–65 mm; stipular spines terete, straight, 2–35(–55) × 0.5–1.4 mm near base; petiole (3–)6–12(–17) mm, usually sparsely to densely pubescent, hairs erect; petiolar gland 1, usually medial on petiole, sessile or short-stalked, circular to slightly elongated, 0.2–1 mm, apex depressed; rachis 10–55 mm; pinnae 2–6(or 7) pairs, 6–33 mm; leaflets 8–19 pairs per pinna, blades flat, oblong, 1.6–6.3 × 0.5–1.7 mm, base oblique and obtuse, apex broadly acute to obtuse, surfaces glabrous, glabrate, or pubescent abaxially, glabrous adaxially. **Peduncles** 12–36(–45) mm. **Inflorescences** globose heads, densely flowered, 6–10 mm diam., solitary or clusters of 2–5 on short shoots; involucre at base of head (not obvious). **Flowers** bright yellow; calyx 1.1–1.8 mm, glabrous; corolla 1.9–2.8 mm, glabrous; filaments yellow, 3.5–5.5 mm. **Legumes** oblong, nearly terete or elliptic in cross section, 30–170 × 9–18 mm, constricted or not between seeds. **Seeds** biseriate, uniseriate, or irregularly arranged.

Varieties 3 (3 in the flora): s United States, Mexico, West Indies, Central America, c, s South America; introduced in Europe, Africa.

Vachellia farnesiana is the most widespread and morphologically variable species in the genus. Segregate species, subspecies, varieties, and forms have been recognized based on habit, leaflet shape, stem and leaflet pubescence, number of pinna pairs, legume size and shape, and seed position.

1. Shrubs, to 1.5 m, prostrate to ascending; leaflet blades 1.6–3 mm. . . . . 5c. *Vachellia farnesiana* var. *pinetorum*
1. Shrubs or trees, to 8 m, erect; leaflet blades 3–6.3 mm.
   2. Legumes 30–90 mm; seeds biseriate or irregularly arranged . . . . 5a. *Vachellia farnesiana* var. *farnesiana*
   2. Legumes 100–170 mm; seeds uniseriate. . . . . 5b. *Vachellia farnesiana* var. *minuta*

5a. Vachellia farnesiana (Linnaeus) Wight & Arnott var. **farnesiana** • Huisache [W]

Acacia smallii Isely; *Vachellia densiflora* Alexander ex Small

Shrubs or trees, erect, to 8 m. **Stems** slightly flexuous. **Leaves** 30–65 mm, particularly those of fast growing shoots; petiole 6–12(–17) mm, usually sparsely pubescent, hairs erect; pinnae 4–6 pairs, 18–33 mm; leaflet blades 3–6.3 mm, surfaces glabrous or glabrate abaxially. **Legumes** nearly terete in cross section, 30–90 mm, not constricted between seeds. **Seeds** biseriate or irregularly arranged. $2n = 26$.

Flowering year-round. Relatively moist to seasonally dry sites in thickets, open pastures, open fields, disturbed sites; 0–1500 m; Ala., Ariz., Ark., Fla., Ga., La., Miss., S.C., Tex.; Mexico; West Indies; Central America; South America; introduced in Europe, Africa.

Variety *farnesiana* was commonly cultivated in southern Europe for perfume made from the fragrant flowers. In southern Europe and parts of Africa, it is abundant on dry, disturbed sites, and has become a serious pest.

5b. Vachellia farnesiana (Linnaeus) Wight & Arnott var. **minuta** (M. E. Jones) Seigler & Ebinger, Phytologia 87: 157. 2006 • Small acacia

Pithecellobium minutum M. E. Jones, Contr. W. Bot. 18: 38. 1933 (as Pithecollobium)

Shrubs or trees, erect, to 8 m. **Stems** slightly flexuous. **Leaves** 15–30 mm; petiole 6+ mm, usually densely pubescent, hairs erect; pinnae 2–4(or 5) pairs, 6–20 mm; leaflet blades 3–6.3 mm, surfaces pubescent abaxially, hairs erect. **Legumes** elliptic in cross section, 100–170 mm, constricted between seeds. **Seeds** uniseriate, relatively hard partitions between seeds.

Flowering Dec–May. Chaparral, disturbed habitats; 0–150 m; Calif.; Mexico (Baja California, Baja California Sur).

In the flora area, var. *minuta* is known only from San Diego County.

5c. Vachellia farnesiana (Linnaeus) Wight & Arnott var. **pinetorum** (F. J. Hermann) Seigler & Ebinger, Phytologia 87: 157. 2006 • Everglade acacia [E]

Acacia pinetorum F. J. Hermann, J. Wash. Acad. Sci. 38: 237. 1948; *A. farnesiana* (Linnaeus) Willdenow subsp. *pinetorum* (F. J. Hermann) Ebinger & Seigler; *Vachellia insularis* Small; *V. peninsularis* Small

Shrubs, prostrate to ascending, to 1.5 m, diffuse-branched. **Stems** strongly flexuous. **Leaves** 7–35 mm; petiole 3–7 mm, usually glabrous; pinnae 2–6(or 7) pairs, 6–18 mm; leaflet blades 1.6–3 mm, surfaces glabrous. **Legumes** nearly terete in cross section, to 80 mm, not constricted between seeds. **Seeds** biseriate.

Flowering Oct–May. Moist to dry sites in thickets, open pastures, roadsides, successional fields, open pinelands, hammocks; 0–10 m; Fla.

Variety *pinetorum* is relatively common in southern Florida, being found in the Keys, Everglades, and pinelands in Lee, Miami-Dade, and Monroe counties, north to Citrus County. The variety appears to be a diminutive form of *V. farnesiana*; it is easily separated from var. *farnesiana* by the smaller leaflets that are without secondary veins, the strongly flexuous twigs, and the overall smaller size.

6. Vachellia macracantha (Humboldt & Bonpland ex Willdenow) Seigler & Ebinger, Phytologia 87: 160. 2006, name conserved • Cuindora [I]

Acacia macracantha Humboldt & Bonpland ex Willdenow, Sp. Pl. 4: 1080. 1806, name conserved

Trees, erect, to 10 m; bark dark gray to dark brown, shallowly furrowed. **Stems** slightly flexuous, glabrous or sparsely to densely puberulent or lanate, not glutinous; short shoots absent. **Leaves** 70–250 mm; stipular spines terete to oval in cross section, straight, 5–60(–80) × 1–3 mm near base; petiole 5–13 mm, glabrous or puberulent, sometimes lanate; petiolar gland 1, medial to just below lowermost pinnae, stalked, circular or elongated, 0.4–2.3 mm diam., apex flat to globose; rachis 60–240 mm; pinnae 12–45 pairs, 20–45 mm; leaflets 19–47 pairs per pinna, blades flat, linear, 1.7–4.5 × 0.5–1.3 mm, base oblique and obtuse, apex broadly acute to obtuse, surfaces glabrous or sparsely pubescent. **Peduncles** 7–25 mm. **Inflorescences** globose heads, densely flowered, 5–10 mm diam., solitary or clusters of 2–10 in leaf axil; involucre at base of head (not obvious). **Flowers** pale yellow; calyx

0.8–1.5 mm, glabrous; corolla 1.6–2.6 mm, glabrous; filaments yellow, 2.5–4 mm. **Legumes** oblong, flattened to slightly elliptic in cross section, 65–130 × 8–13 mm, not constricted between seeds. **Seeds** uniseriate.

Flowering May–Jan. Shrubby vegetation, successional fields, edge of roads; 0–10 m; introduced; Fla.; Mexico; West Indies; Central America; South America (Argentina, Bolivia, Chile, Colombia, Ecuador, French Guiana, Guyana, Paraguay, Peru, Venezuela).

In Florida, *Vachellia macracantha* has been documented from Hillsborough, Manatee, Miami-Dade, and Monroe counties.

7. **Vachellia rigidula** (Bentham) Seigler & Ebinger, Phytologia 87: 166. 2006 • Black brush [F] [W]

Acacia rigidula Bentham, London J. Bot. 1: 504. 1842

Shrubs or trees, erect, to 4 m; bark light gray to brown, smooth or shallowly furrowed. **Stems** slightly flexuous, glabrous or sparsely puberulent, not glutinous; short shoots present. **Leaves** 2–9 mm; stipular spines terete, straight, 10–50(–80) × 0.6–2.1 mm near base; petiole 2–5(–9) mm, densely puberulent; petiolar gland 1, mostly medial on petiole, sessile, circular, 0.3–0.6 (–1.1) mm diam., apex depressed; rachis 0 mm; pinnae 1 pair, 5–20 mm; leaflets (2 or)3–5 pairs per pinna, blades flat, oblong to elliptic, (4–)6–13(–16) × 2–6 (–8) mm, base oblique and obtuse, apex obtuse, surfaces usually glabrous, rarely sparsely pubescent abaxially. **Peduncles** 0–3 mm. **Inflorescences** cylindrical spikes, loosely flowered, 10–35 mm, solitary or clusters of 2–8 on short shoots; involucre at base of peduncle. **Flowers** white to cream; calyx 0.4–0.8 mm, puberulent; corolla 1.2–1.7 mm, usually glabrous; filaments white, 2.7–4 mm. **Legumes** linear, flattened, 40–100 × 3–6 mm, constricted between seeds. **Seeds** uniseriate. $2n = 26$.

Flowering Feb–Jul. Disturbed sites, rocky slopes, bluffs, fencerows, arroyos, in extensive thickets; 0–1400 m; Tex.; Mexico (Coahuila, Jalisco, Michoacán, Nuevo León, Querétaro, San Luis Potosí, Tamaulipas, Veracruz).

Vachellia rigidula has been documented in southern Texas from Brewster County in the west, southeast to Calhoun County, and south to Mexico.

The name *Acacia amentacea* de Candolle has sometimes been proposed for this taxon. The type of *A. amentacea* is a painting, represented by plate no. 208 of de Candolle. The species represented by this drawing is probably what is now called *Vachellia bilimekii* (J. F. Macbride) Seigler & Ebinger, a species known from southern Mexico. Without a specimen, no accurate determination can be made (Y. S. Lee et al. 1989). Plants of *V. rigidula* occasionally harbor ants in the spines (Lee et al.). This does not appear to represent a highly co-adaptive interaction such as exists in other, better known ant acacias, for the ant species is found on a number of unrelated plants (Lee et al.).

Vachellia rigidula hybridizes with *V. bravoensis* (*V.* ×*ruthvenii*); it is an uncommon hybrid found only at the Chaparral Wildlife Management Area in Dimmit County, Texas.

8. **Vachellia schottii** (Torrey) Seigler & Ebinger, Phytologia 87: 167. 2006 • Schott's acacia [E] [F]

Acacia schottii Torrey in W. H. Emory, Rep. U.S. Mex. Bound. 2(1): 62. 1859

Shrubs, erect, to 3 m; bark dark gray, smooth. **Stems** not flexuous, glabrous or sparsely pubescent, hairs appressed, not glutinous; short shoots present. **Leaves** 4.8–17.5 mm; stipular spines terete, slightly recurved, 4–15(–22) × 0.6–0.9 mm near base; petiole 4–10 mm, sparsely puberulent, hairs appressed; petiolar gland 1, just below lowermost pinnae, sessile, circular, 0.1–0.4 mm diam., donut-shaped; rachis 0–8 mm; pinnae 1(or 2) pairs, 9–25 mm; leaflets 6–14 pairs per pinna, blades subterete, linear, 2.8–6.1 × 0.3–0.6 mm, base cuneate, apex acute, surfaces glabrous. **Peduncles** 20–28 mm. **Inflorescences** globose heads, densely flowered, 5.5–7.5 mm diam., solitary or clusters of 2–5 on short shoots; involucre near middle of peduncle. **Flowers** pale yellow; calyx 0.8–1.2 mm, glabrous or sparsely puberulent; corolla 1.8–2.2 mm, glabrous; filaments yellow, 3–4 mm. **Legumes** linear, flattened, 40–90 × 5.5–7.8 mm, sometimes constricted between seeds. **Seeds** uniseriate.

Flowering Apr–Aug. Washes, on slopes in open thorn scrub; 800–1200 m; Tex.

Within its very restricted range, *Vachellia schottii* is a common species, often occurring in large, relatively pure thickets over extensive areas, apparently being quite successful within this small area. These areas of thorn scrub are located on limestone or gypsum derived soils. *Vachellia schottii* is known only from the Big Bend region in Brewster and Presidio counties. This species probably occurs to the south in adjacent Mexico, though the authors have seen no specimens from that region.

9. Vachellia tortuosa (Linnaeus) Seigler & Ebinger, Phytologia 87: 168. 2006 • Twisted acacia [I]

Mimosa tortuosa Linnaeus, Syst. Nat. ed. 10, 2: 1312. 1759; *Acacia tortuosa* (Linnaeus) Willdenow

Shrubs or trees, erect, to 6 m; bark dark gray to dark brown, shallowly furrowed. **Stems** strongly flexuous, usually pubescent, not glutinous; short shoots present. **Leaves** 12–45 mm; stipular spines terete, straight, 5–40(–55) × 0.7–1.5 mm near base; petiole 3–7 mm, usually densely pubescent, hairs erect; petiolar gland 1, variable between medial to near basal positions of lowermost pinnae, sessile, elongated to circular, 0.3–2 mm, apex depressed; rachis 5–40 mm; pinnae 2–8 pairs, 12–23 mm; leaflets 11–19 pairs per pinna, blades flat, oblong, 3–5.5 × 0.9–1.5 mm, base oblique and obtuse, apex broadly acute to obtuse, surfaces glabrous. **Peduncles** 12–36 mm. **Inflorescences** globose heads, densely flowered, 6–9 mm diam., solitary or clusters of 2–5 on short shoots; involucre at base of head (not obvious). **Flowers** pale yellow; calyx 1.1–1.8 mm, pubescent; corolla 1.5–2.4 mm, pubescent; filaments yellow, 3.5–4.5 mm. **Legumes** linear, elliptic in cross section, 65–150 × 5–9 mm, constricted between seeds. **Seeds** uniseriate. $2n = 26$.

Flowering year-round. Thickets, open pastures, successional fields, dry sites; 0–10 m; introduced; Fla.; West Indies; Central America (Panama); South America.

Vachellia tortuosa is a lowland species, occurring at or near sea level in southern Florida and the West Indies where it is the dominant and co-dominant of the woody vegetation in scrub thickets. Its presence in extreme southern Florida (Collier, Miami-Dade, and Monroe counties) was probably the result of pre-Columbian introduction, as this species was always associated with sites of human occupation. It is not known from Mexico or most of Central America (H. D. Clarke et al. 1989).

10. Vachellia vernicosa (Britton & Rose) Seigler & Ebinger, Phytologia 87: 169. 2006 • Shiny acacia

Acaciopsis vernicosa Britton & Rose in N. L. Britton et al., N. Amer. Fl. 23: 96. 1928, based on *Acacia vernicosa* Standley, Contr. U.S. Natl. Herb. 20: 187. 1919, not W. Fitzgerald 1904; *A. constricta* Bentham var. *vernicosa* (Britton & Rose) L. D. Benson; *A. neovernicosa* Isely

Shrubs, erect, to 3 m; bark dark gray to dark reddish gray, smooth. **Stems** not flexuous, glabrous, glutinous; short shoots present. **Leaves** 3–12 mm; stipular spines terete, straight to slightly reflexed, 3–11(–25) × 0.7–1.1 mm near base; petiole 3–10 mm, glabrous, glutinous; petiolar gland 1, at or just below lowermost pinnae, sessile, circular, 0.1–0.4 mm diam., donut-shaped; rachis 0–9 mm; pinnae 1 or 2(or 3) pairs, 4.5–13 mm; leaflets 4–12 pairs per pinna, blades flat, elliptic to oval, 1.1–2.7 × 0.5–0.9 mm, base oblique and obtuse, apex obtuse, surfaces glabrous, glutinous. **Peduncles** 10–25(–30) mm. **Inflorescences** globose heads, densely flowered, 6–8 mm diam., solitary or clusters of 2–5 on short shoots; involucre near middle of peduncle. **Flowers** pale yellow; calyx 0.6–1.2 mm, glabrous; corolla 1.4–2.1 mm, glabrous; filaments yellow, 2.7–4 mm. **Legumes** linear, flattened, 38–90 × 2.1–3.8 mm, usually constricted between seeds. **Seeds** uniseriate. $2n = 26$.

Flowering Mar–Sep. Disturbed, arid sites of slopes and plains in sandy and gravelly calcareous and gypseous soils; 700–1700 m; Ariz., N.Mex., Tex.; Mexico (Baja California, Chihuahua, Coahuila, Durango, Querétaro, San Luis Potosí, Sonora, Tamaulipas, Zacatecas).

Vachellia vernicosa is sometimes confused with *V. constricta,* and originally both were considered within the concept of *V. constricta*. These species are not separated geographically, nor apparently ecologically, but there is no evidence of intermediacy.

30. SENEGALIA Rafinesque, Sylva Tellur., 119. 1838 • Acacia [From species name *Mimosa senegal* Linnaeus, alluding to nativity]

David S. Seigler

John E. Ebinger

Shrubs or trees [lianas], armed, rarely unarmed. **Stems** usually erect [spreading or climbing], pubescent or glabrous; twigs terete to angulate, usually straight, short shoots present or absent. **Leaves** alternate, even-bipinnate; stipules present, caducous, herbaceous; petiolate, petiole channeled, gland present [absent] in channel; pinnae 1–30(–43) pairs, mostly opposite; leaflets 3–55 pairs per pinna, opposite, sessile or subsessile, blade margins entire, surfaces glabrous or pubescent. **Inflorescences** 6–250+-flowered, terminal or axillary, heads or spikes, usually in pseudoracemes or pseudopanicles; bracts present. **Flowers** mimosoid; calyx campanulate, lobes 5; corolla white, creamy white, or yellow, lobes 5; stamens 40–160, distinct, exserted, creamy or yellow, fading reddish brown; anthers dorsifixed, dehiscing longitudinally, sometimes with a small stalked gland; ovary stipitate or sessile with nectiferous disc at base, usually pubescent; style and stigma filiform. **Fruits** legumes, stipitate or sessile, mostly flattened, straight to falcate, oblong [linear], usually dehiscent along sutures, glabrous or pubescent. **Seeds** 3–16[–25], uniseriate, sometimes flattened, ovoid to ellipsoid, not surrounded by pulp; pleurogram usually U-shaped. $x = 13$.

Species ca. 235 (6, including 2 hybrids, in the flora): sw, sc United States, Mexico, West Indies, Central America, South America, Asia, Africa, Pacific Islands, Australia; nearly worldwide in tropical to warm temperate areas.

Senegalia is separated from related genera by the presence of prickles, the absence of stipular spines, a nectiferous disk at the base of the stipitate ovary, and portate pollen. Based on morphological evidence, L. Pedley (1978, 1986) separated *Senegalia* from other members of *Acacia* in the broad sense. The separation was further supported by phylogenetic analysis of chloroplast *mat*K and *trn*l sequence datasets, in which species of *Senegalia* formed a monophyletic clade (D. S. Seigler et al. 2006b).

SELECTED REFERENCE Seigler, D. S., J. E. Ebinger, and J. T. Miller. 2006b. The genus *Senegalia* (Fabaceae: Mimosoideae) from the New World. Phytologia 88: 38–93.

1. Leaflets 25–55 pairs per pinna . . . . 1. *Senegalia berlandieri*
1. Leaflets 3–21 pairs per pinna.
    2. Inflorescences cylindric spikes, lengths 3+ times widths.
        3. Leaflet blades usually 2.8–5.5 mm; flowers sessile or short-pedicellate, pedicels 0–0.6 mm . . . . 3. *Senegalia greggii*
        3. Leaflet blades usually 5.5–9.2 mm; flowers pedicellate, pedicels 0.5–2.1 mm . . . . 6. *Senegalia wrightii*
    2. Inflorescences globose or subglobose heads, lengths less than 2 times widths.
        4. Leaflets 3–10 pairs per pinna, blades usually obovate, rarely oblong . . . . 4. *Senegalia roemeriana*
        4. Leaflets 13–21 pairs per pinna, blades oblong.
            5. Mature leaflet blades mostly less than 5.4 mm (3–7 mm) . . . . 2. *Senegalia* ×*emoryana*
            5. Mature leaflet blades mostly more than 5.4 mm (5.1–9.3 mm) . . . . 5. *Senegalia* ×*turneri*

1. Senegalia berlandieri (Bentham) Britton & Rose in N. L. Britton et al., N. Amer. Fl. 23: 109. 1928 • Guajillo [W]

Acacia berlandieri Bentham, London J. Bot. 1: 522. 1842

Shrubs or trees to 6 m; bark light to dark gray, smooth; prickles absent or ± straight, widely scattered along twigs, petioles, and rachises. **Stems** not flexuous, with decurrent lines from leaf bases, usually puberulent, rarely glabrous; short shoots absent. **Leaves** 35–165 mm; stipules linear, to 4.5 mm, puberulent; petiole 7–28 mm, usually puberulent; petiolar gland adnate to expanded petiole channel, narrowly elliptic, 1.2–3.5 mm; rachis 25–145 mm; pinnae 7–14(–19) pairs, 30–75 mm; leaflets 25–55 pairs per pinna, blades linear, 2.8–7.2 × 0.7–1.4(–1.8) mm, base oblique and obtuse, apex acute, surfaces glabrous or puberulent. **Peduncles** 6–30 mm. **Inflorescences** densely flowered, globose heads, 12–18 mm diam., 1 in leaf axils or in terminal pseudoracemes or pseudopanicles, to 250 mm. **Flowers** sessile; calyx 1.2–2 mm, puberulent; corolla white, 2–3 mm, puberulent; filaments 6–8 mm. **Legumes** 70–160 × 15–30 mm, not constricted between seeds. $2n = 26$.

Flowering Feb–May. Dry, mostly calcareous soils, thorn scrub, desert grasslands; 50–1400 m; Tex.; Mexico (Chihuahua, Coahuila, Durango, Guanajuato, Guerrero, Hidalgo, Nuevo León, Querétaro, San Luis Potosí, Tamaulipas, Zacatecas).

Senegalia berlandieri is common on limestone ridges and caliche cuestas of central and southern Texas, where it commonly dominates the vegetation. It hybridizes with *S. greggii* (= *S.* ×*emoryana*) and *S. wrightii* (= *S.* ×*turneri*).

2. Senegalia ×emoryana (Bentham) Britton & Rose in N. L. Britton et al., N. Amer. Fl. 23: 109. 1928, as species • Catclaw

Acacia emoryana Bentham, Trans. Linn. Soc. London 30: 522. 1875

Shrubs or trees to 5 m; bark light brown, shallowly furrowed; prickles absent or slightly recurved, scattered along twigs. **Stems** slightly flexuous, usually puberulent; short shoots mostly absent. **Leaves** 25–65 mm; stipules linear, to 3.5 mm, puberulent; petiole 3–22 mm, puberulent; petiolar gland in expanded channel, margins raised, orbiculate to elliptic, 0.6–1.7 mm; rachis 15–50 mm; pinnae 2–7 pairs, 15–35 mm; leaflets 15–20 pairs per pinna, blades oblong, 3–7 × 0.7–1.7 mm, base oblique and obtuse, apex acute, surfaces usually appressed-puberulent. **Peduncles** 8–25 mm. **Inflorescences** densely flowered, globose or subglobose heads, 10–15 mm diam., length less than 2 times width, 1–4 in leaf axils. **Flowers** sessile; calyx 1–2 mm, puberulent; corolla white, 2–3 mm, puberulent; filaments 5–7 mm. **Legumes** 40–160 × 20–35 mm, sometimes constricted between some seeds.

Flowering Apr–Jun. Dry, mostly calcareous soils, thorn scrub, desert grasslands; 100–1400 m; Tex.; Mexico (Chihuahua, Coahuila, Durango, Sonora).

Senegalia ×emoryana is a fertile hybrid between *S. berlandieri* and *S. greggii* and is relatively common where the parents are sympatric in southern Texas and Mexico. Backcrosses of the hybrid with either parent are occasionally encountered and appear to be fertile.

3. Senegalia greggii (A. Gray) Britton & Rose in N. L. Britton et al., N. Amer. Fl. 23: 110. 1928 • Catclaw W

Acacia greggii A. Gray, Smithsonian Contr. Knowl. 3(5): 65. 1852; *A. durandiana* Buckley; *A. greggii* var. *arizonica* Isely

Shrubs or trees to 6 m; bark dark gray to brown, shallowly furrowed; prickles recurved, scattered along twigs. **Stems** slightly flexuous, glabrous or pubescent; short shoots present. **Leaves** 3–23 mm; stipules narrowly triangular, to 1.1 mm, glabrous; petiole 3–11 mm, glabrous or pubescent; petiolar gland oval to orbiculate, 0.2–0.5 mm; rachis 0–12 mm; pinnae 1–3(–5) pairs, 5–14 mm; leaflets 3–6(–8) pairs per pinna, blades oblong to obovate, 2.8–5.5 × 0.9–3.2 mm, base oblique and obtuse, apex obtuse to acute, surfaces glabrous or pubescent. **Peduncles** 8–30 mm. **Inflorescences** loosely to densely flowered, cylindric spikes, 15–40 mm, length 3+ times width, 1–4 from short shoots. **Flowers** sessile or short-pedicellate, pedicel 0–0.6 mm; calyx 1.3–2 mm, usually glabrous; corolla creamy white to yellowish, 1.8–3.1 mm, glabrous; filaments 5–7 mm. **Legumes** 40–150 × 13–21 mm, constricted between some seeds. $2n = 26$.

Flowering May–Sep. Dry, mostly calcareous soils, thorn scrub, pinyon-juniper woodlands, desert grasslands; 0–1500 m; Ariz., Calif., Nev., N.Mex., Tex.; Mexico (Baja California, Chihuahua, Coahuila, Durango, Nuevo León, Sonora, Tamaulipas).

In Nevada, *Senegalia greggii* is known from Clark and Lincoln counties, and in New Mexico from Eddy and Hidalgo counties.

Senegalia greggii is common in thorn scrub vegetation and is frequently dominant. Typically, leaves growing from short shoots are smaller than the leaves of fast-growing branches. D. Isely (1973) recognized var. *arizonica* by the presence of leaflet indument; this characteristic is highly variable and cannot be used for consistent separation. *Senegalia greggii* hybridizes with *S. berlandieri* (= *S. ×emoryana*).

4. Senegalia roemeriana (Scheele) Britton & Rose in N. L. Britton et al., N. Amer. Fl. 23: 115. 1928 • Catclaw F

Acacia roemeriana Scheele, Linnaea 21: 456. 1848; *A. palmeri* S. Watson; *Senegalia lozanoi* Britton & Rose; *S. saltilloensis* Britton & Rose

Shrubs or trees to 6 m; bark dark gray or grayish brown, shallowly furrowed; prickles sometimes paired at nodes, recurved, scattered along twigs, petioles, and rachises. **Stems** slightly flexuous, usually glabrous; short shoots present. **Leaves** 4–80 mm; stipules narrowly triangular, to 1.1 mm, glabrous; petiole 3–30 mm, usually glabrous; petiolar gland oval to orbiculate, 0.3–1.5 mm; rachis 0–40 mm; pinnae 1–4 pairs, 10–80 mm; leaflets 3–10 pairs per pinna, blades usually obovate, rarely oblong, 5–14 × 2–7 mm, base oblique and obtuse, apex obtuse, surfaces usually glabrous. **Peduncles** 17–30 mm. **Inflorescences** densely flowered, globose heads, 11–15 mm diam., length less than 2 times width, usually 1–6 from short shoots. **Flowers** sessile or short-pedicellate; calyx 1.4–2.1 mm, usually glabrous, rarely puberulent; corolla creamy white to yellow, 2.4–3.1 mm, mostly glabrous; filaments 5–7.5 mm. **Legumes** 70–170 × 17–26 mm, not constricted between seeds.

Flowering Mar–Jun. Dry, mostly calcareous soils, thorn scrub, oak-juniper forests, disturbed dry areas; 100–1500 m; N.Mex., Tex.; Mexico (Chihuahua, Coahuila, Nuevo León, Tamaulipas).

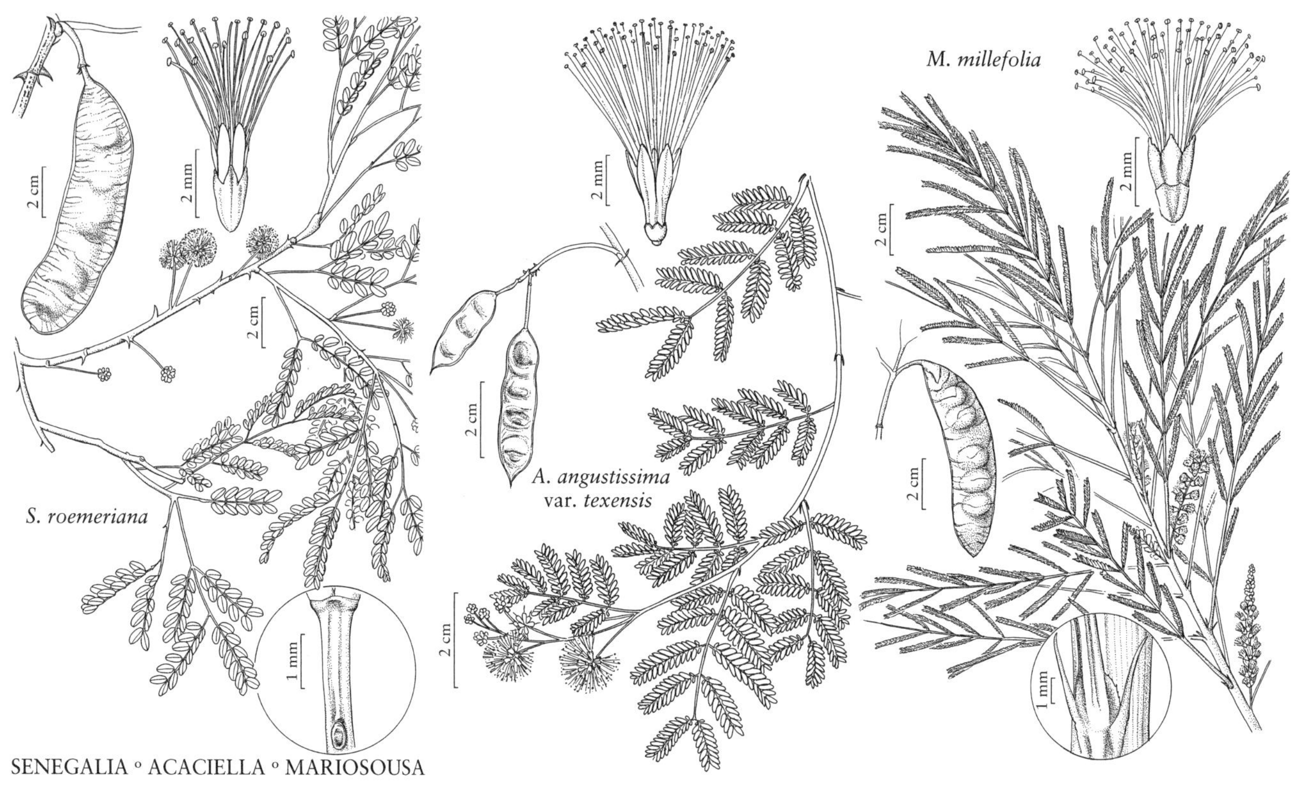

SENEGALIA ◦ ACACIELLA ◦ MARIOSOUSA

Senegalia roemeriana is mostly uncommon and scattered and is rarely dominant. Typically, leaves growing from short shoots are smaller than the leaves of fast-growing branches.

5. Senegalia ×turneri Seigler, Ebinger & C. E. Glass, Phytologia 97: 292. 2015 • Turner's senegalia [E]

Shrubs or trees to 5 m; bark light to dark brown, shallowly furrowed; prickles absent or slightly recurved, scattered along twigs. **Stems** not flexuous, usually puberulent; short shoots mostly absent. **Leaves** 25–70 mm; stipules narrowly triangular to linear, to 2.1 mm, puberulent; petiole 5–20 mm, puberulent; petiolar gland in expanded channel, margins raised, orbiculate to elliptic, 0.8–2.1 mm; rachis 15–45 mm; pinnae 2–7 pairs, 20–45 mm; leaflets 13–21 pairs per pinna, blades oblong, 5.1–9.3 × 0.7–2.6 mm, base oblique and obtuse, apex acute, surfaces glabrous or lightly appressed-puberulent. **Peduncles** 7–25 mm. **Inflorescences** densely flowered, subglobose heads, 8–13 mm diam., length less than 2 times width, 1 or 2 in leaf axils. **Flowers** sessile or subsessile; calyx 1–2 mm, puberulent; corolla white, 2–3 mm, puberulent; filaments 5–7 mm. **Legumes** 40–160 × 20–35 mm, usually constricted between some seeds.

Flowering Apr–Jun. Dry, mostly calcareous soils, thorn scrub, desert grasslands; 20–600 m; Tex.

Senegalia ×*turneri*, a fertile hybrid between *S. berlandieri* and *S. wrightii*, is rare even where the ranges of the parental species overlap in southern Texas. Backcrosses of the hybrid with either parent are occasional and appear fertile.

6. Senegalia wrightii (Bentham) Britton & Rose in N. L. Britton et al., N. Amer. Fl. 23: 110. 1928 • Catclaw acacia

Acacia wrightii Bentham, Smithsonian Contr. Knowl. 3(5): 64. 1852; *A. greggii* A. Gray var. *wrightii* (Bentham) Isely

Shrubs or trees to 12 m; bark dark gray or dark brown, shallowly furrowed; prickles recurved, scattered along twigs. **Stems** not flexuous, usually glabrous; short shoots present. **Leaves** 2–35 mm; stipules narrowly triangular, to 1.1 mm, puberulent; petiole 2–20 mm, usually glabrous; petiolar gland oval to oblong, 0.3–1.1 mm; rachis 0–24 mm; pinnae 1–3 pairs, 3–22 mm; leaflets 3–7(–9) pairs per pinna, blades oblong or obovate to oblanceolate, 5.5–9.2 × 2.2–4.5 mm, base oblique and obtuse, apex obtuse, surfaces usually pubescent. **Peduncles** 10–40 mm. **Inflorescences**

loosely to densely flowered, cylindric spikes, 20–70 mm, length 3+ times width, 1–4 from short shoots. **Flowers** pedicellate, pedicel 0.5–2.1 mm; calyx 1.2–2 mm, glabrous or puberulent; corolla creamy white to yellow, 1.8–2.8 mm, glabrous; filaments 5–7 mm. **Legumes** 40–150 × 15–25 mm, constricted between some seeds.

Flowering Apr–Jun. Dry, mostly calcareous soils, thorn scrub, desert grasslands, disturbed sites; (20–) 100–1100 m; Ariz., Tex.; Mexico (Baja California Sur, Chihuahua, Coahuila, Nuevo León, Tamaulipas).

Senegalia wrightii is closely related to *S. greggii*, under which *S. wrightii* is sometimes treated as a synonym or variety. *Senegalia wrightii* is distinguished from *S. greggii* in being usually more robust, with larger leaves, petioles, and petiolar glands, and leaflet blades are obovate to oblanceolate; *S. greggii* is smaller and leaflet blades are mostly oblong to only slightly obovate. Both hybridize with *S. berlandieri*, and probably with each other. Typically, leaves growing from short shoots of *S. wrightii* are smaller than the leaves of fast-growing branches. *Senegalia wrightii* hybridizes with *S. berlandieri* (= *S.* ×*turneri*).

31. ACACIELLA Britton & Rose in N. L. Britton et al., N. Amer. Fl. 23: 96. 1928 • [Genus *Acacia* and Latin *-ella*, diminutive, alluding to resemblance]

John E. Ebinger

David S. Seigler

Trees, shrubs, [herbs or subshrubs], unarmed. **Stems** erect [to spreading], glabrous or pubescent; twigs terete to angulate, straight, short-shoots absent. **Leaves** alternate, even-bipinnate; stipules present, caducous or persistent, herbaceous; petiolate, petiole channeled; pinnae 1–32 pairs, mostly opposite; leaflets 2–numerous pairs per pinna, opposite, sessile or subsessile, blade margins entire, surfaces glabrous [pubescent]. **Inflorescences** [4–]10–40[–50]-flowered, terminal or axillary, heads, globose to slightly elongated, solitary or clustered, sometimes in pseudoracemes or pseudopanicles; bracts present. **Flowers** mimosoid; calyx campanulate, lobes 5; corolla greenish white, drying pale pink, lobes 5; stamens 175–250, distinct, exserted, creamy white [yellow, pink]; anthers dorsifixed, eglandular; ovary short-stipitate, glabrous; style and stigma filiform. **Fruits** legumes, stipitate, flattened, straight, linear [oblong], usually dehiscent along sutures, glabrous. **Seeds** 3–15[–20], uniseriate, strongly flattened, ovate to orbiculate, not surrounded by pulp; pleurogram U-shaped. $x = 13$.

Species 15 (2 in the flora): sw, c, se United States, Mexico, Central America, s South America (Argentina).

Acaciella has only recently come into common use following the division of *Acacia* in the broad sense into several genera, based on molecular studies (J. T. Miller and R. J. Bayer 2000; S. Gómez-Acevedo et al. 2010) and a revision by M. L. Rico-Arce and S. Bachman (2006). The following characteristics separate this genus from other members of *Acacia* in the broad sense (*Acacia*, *Mariosousa*, *Senegalia*, and *Vachellia*): absence of prickles and stipular spines, absence of petiolar and rachis nectaries, relatively numerous stamens (175–200+ per flower), and stalked flowers (usually in globose heads).

SELECTED REFERENCE Rico-Arce, M. L. and S. Bachman. 2006. A taxonomic revision of *Acaciella* (Leguminosae, Mimosoideae). Anales Jard. Bot. Madrid 63: 189–244.

1. Leaflet blades 2–3.5(–4) × 0.5–1.3 mm, only midveins prominent abaxially . . . . 1. *Acaciella angustissima*
1. Leaflet blades 4–13 × 1.5–3.1 mm, lateral veins and midveins prominent abaxially. . . . . 2. *Acaciella lemmonii*

1. Acaciella angustissima (Miller) Britton & Rose in N. L. Britton et al., N. Amer. Fl. 23: 100. 1928 • Fern acacia [F]

Mimosa angustissima Miller, Gard. Dict. ed. 8, Mimosa no. 19. 1768; *Acacia angustissima* (Miller) Kuntze; *Senegalia angustissima* (Miller) Pedley

Shrubs or trees [subshrubs], to 12 m. **Stems** flexuous, glabrous or puberulent. **Leaves** 10–210 mm; stipules linear, to 6.5 mm, margins ciliate; petiole 3.5–65 mm, glabrous or appressed-pubescent to pilose; pinnae 2–17[–32] pairs, 6–50[–105] mm; rachis 5–200 mm; leaflets 7–85 pairs per pinna, blades linear, 2–3.5[–4] × 0.5–1.3 mm, base oblique and obtuse, only midvein prominent abaxially, apex broadly acute to obtuse. **Peduncles** 5–21 mm. **Inflorescences** usually solitary, rarely 2 or 3, axillary or terminal, pseudoracemes or pseudopanicles, to 280 mm, 9–18 mm diam.; pedicels present. **Flowers:** calyx 0.6–1.2 mm; corolla 1.9–4.5 mm; filaments 3–7.6 mm. **Legumes** 25–90 × 5.5–17 mm, rarely constricted between seeds.

Varieties 3 (2 in the flora): sw, c United States, Mexico, Central America, s South America (Argentina).

Acaciella angustissima is the most widespread and morphologically variable species of *Acaciella*. Segregate species, subspecies, varieties, and forms have been recognized based on habit, leaflet shape, stem and leaflet indument, stem striations, number of pinnae, and leaflets per pinna. *Acaciella angustissima* is common in disturbed habitats, particularly roadsides and pastures, and it is becoming common throughout much of the tropical and subtropical regions where it was introduced originally as a forage crop. With a geographic range that extends from the southern and central United States to northern Argentina, *A. angustissima* is highly variable in many characteristics, one of the most obvious being plant size, which ranges from subshrubs that are sometimes nearly herbaceous, to trees exceeding ten meters. M. L. Rico-Arce and S. Bachman (2006) recognized three varieties and indicated that all three occur in North America north of Mexico. The two varieties described here are common in the central and southwestern United States. No specimens of the third variety [var. *filicioides* (Cavanilles) L. Rico] in the flora area have been located.

1. Leaflets (20–)23–40 pairs per pinna; pinna 9–17 pairs; stems white-puberulent or yellow-hirsute .... 1a. *Acaciella angustissima* var. *angustissima*
1. Leaflets 7–20(–22) pairs per pinna; pinnae 2–6(or 9) pairs; stems glabrous.................... .... 1b. *Acaciella angustissima* var. *texensis*

1a. Acaciella angustissima (Miller) Britton & Rose var. **angustissima**

Acacia angulosa Bertoloni; *A. angustissima* (Miller) Kuntze var. *hirta* (Nuttall) B. L. Robinson; *A. angustissima* subsp. *smithii* (Britton & Rose) Wiggins; *A. angustissima* var. *smithii* (Britton & Rose) M. L. Rico; *A. angustissima* subsp. *suffrutescens* (Rose) Wiggins; *A. angustissima* var. *suffrutescens* (Rose) Isely; *A. boliviana* Rusby; *A. delicata* (Britton & Rose) Bullock; *A. hirta* Nuttall; *A. hirta* var. *glabrior* Engelmann & A. Gray; *A. hirta* var. *suffrutescens* (Rose) Kearney & Peebles; *A. suffrutescens* Rose; *Acaciella angustissima* var. *hirta* (Nuttall) B. L. Turner; *A. breviracemosa* Britton & Rose; *A. ciliata* Britton & Rose; *A. costaricensis* Britton & Rose; *A. delicata* Britton & Rose; *A. elongata* Britton & Rose; *A. ferrisiae* Britton & Rose; *A. hirta* (Nuttall) Britton & Rose; *A. rensonii* Britton & Rose; *A. santanderensis* Britton & Killip; *A. smithii* Britton & Rose; *A. stipellata* (Schlechtendal) Britton & Rose; *A. suffrutescens* (Rose) Britton & Rose; *A. talpana* Britton & Rose

Shrubs or trees, to 12 m. **Stems** flexuous, glabrous or white-puberulent or yellow-hirsute. **Leaves** 50–210 mm; petiole 12–35 mm, glabrous or pubescent, hairs white; pinnae 7–32 pairs, 25–50 mm; rachis 65–200 mm, glabrous or pubescent, hairs white; leaflets 20–40 pairs per pinna, blades 3.3–6.2 × 0.6–1.5 mm, surfaces usually glabrous, sometimes pubescent, hairs white.

Flowering year-round. Dry to relatively moist sites on limestone, open oak or pine woods, secondary deciduous forests, dry thorn scrub, sandhills, disturbed sandy areas, dunes, disturbed sites; 0–2000 m; Ariz., Ark., Fla., Kans., La., Mo., N.Mex., Okla., Tex.; Mexico; Central America; s South America (Argentina).

Specimens from the flora area previously identified as *Acaciella angustissima* var. *filicioides* (Cavanilles) L. Rico (M. L. Rico-Arce and S. Bachman 2006) proved to be specimens of var. *angustissima*.

1b. Acaciella angustissima (Miller) Britton & Rose var. **texensis** (Torrey & A. Gray) L. Rico in N. Diego-Pérez et al., Fl. Guerrero 25: 44. 2005 • Fern acacia [F]

Acacia texensis Torrey & A. Gray, Fl. N. Amer. 1: 404. 1840; *A. angustissima* (Miller) Kuntze var. *chisosiana* Isely; *A. angustissima* var. *oaxacana* B. L. Turner; *A. angustissima* var. *texensis* (Torrey & A. Gray) Isely; *A. cuspidata* Schlechtendal; *Acaciella angustissima* (Miller) Britton & Rose var. *chisosiana* (Isely) B. L. Turner; *A. texensis* (Torrey & A. Gray) Britton & Rose

Subshrubs or shrubs, 0.2–0.8(–1.5) m, with thick, woody caudex, forming colonies by woody rhizomes. **Stems** strongly flexuous, glabrous or puberulent to pilose. **Leaves** 10–60 mm; petiole 3.5–18 mm, glabrous or puberulent; pinnae 2–6(or 9) pairs, 6–25 mm; rachis 5–75 mm, usually glabrous; leaflets 7–20(–22) pairs per pinna, blades 2–5.4 × 0.7–1.7 mm, surfaces usually glabrous, margins sometimes short-ciliate.

Flowering year-round. Dry sites on limestone, thorn scrub, dry prairies, disturbed sites; 300–2400 m; Ariz., N.Mex., Tex.; n, c Mexico.

2. **Acaciella lemmonii** (Rose) Britton & Rose in N. L. Britton et al., N. Amer. Fl. 23: 103. 1928 (as lemmoni)

Acacia lemmonii Rose, Contr. U.S. Natl. Herb. 12: 409. 1909 (as lemmoni); *A. angustissima* (Miller) Kuntze subsp. *lemmonii* (Rose) Wiggins; *A. angustissima* var. *shrevei* (Britton & Rose) Isely; *Acaciella shrevei* Britton & Rose

Shrubs, to 3 m. **Stems** slightly flexuous, usually pubescent. **Leaves** 30–170 mm; stipules linear, to 7.5 mm, margins long-ciliate; petiole 15–41 mm, glabrous or appressed-pubescent; pinnae 4–12 pairs, 30–70 mm; rachis 25–140 mm; leaflets 10–30 pairs per pinna, blades oblong, 4–13 × 1.5–3.1 mm, base oblique and truncate, midvein and lateral veins prominent abaxially, apex acute. **Peduncles** 6–21 mm. **Inflorescences** usually solitary, rarely 2 or 3, axillary or terminal, pseudoracemes, to 175 mm, 12–17 mm diam.; pedicels present. **Flowers:** calyx 0.4–1.1 mm; corolla 1.9–3.8 mm; filaments 5.5–7.5 mm. **Legumes** 30–70 × 6–13 mm, not constricted between seeds.

Flowering May–Sep. Dry sites on limestone, thorn scrub, desert grasslands; 900–1600 m; Ariz.; Mexico (Durango, Jalisco, Nuevo León, Sinaloa, Sonora).

Acaciella lemmonii is known from Cochise and Pima counties.

32. MARIOSOUSA Seigler & Ebinger, Novon 16: 415. 2006 • Acacia [For Mario Sousa Sánchez, 1940–2017, former Director of the Herbarium of the Instituto de Biología, Universidad Nacional Autónoma de México]

David S. Seigler

John E. Ebinger

Trees or shrubs, unarmed. **Stems** erect to spreading, usually lightly puberulent; twigs straight. **Leaves** deciduous [persistent], alternate, even-bipinnate; stipules present, persistent, herbaceous; petiolate, petiole channeled, petiolar gland usually present; pinnae 1–30 pairs, mostly opposite; leaflets [4–]20–40(–45)[–65] pairs per pinna, opposite, sessile or subsessile, blade margins entire, surfaces lightly pubescent abaxially, glabrous adaxially. **Inflorescences** 30–140-flowered, axillary, cylindrical spikes, sometimes in pseudoracemes; bracts present. **Flowers** mimosoid; calyx campanulate, lobes 5; corolla creamy white, lobes 5; stamens 35–120, distinct, exserted, white or cream; anthers dorsifixed, with small, stalked gland; ovary short-stipitate, glabrous; style and stigma filiform. **Fruits** legumes, stipitate, flattened, straight, oblong [linear], dehiscent along sutures, glabrous. **Seeds** 3–12[–15], ovoid to ellipsoid, not surrounded by pulp; pleurogram U-shaped.

Species 13 (1 in the flora): sw United States, Mexico, Central America (Costa Rica).

Species of *Mariosousa* were historically included in *Acacia*, in the broad sense, which is now considered to be a polyphyletic assemblage of at least five, mostly unrelated, groups. A combination of characteristics (non-scandent habit, absence of prickles and stipular spines, persistent stipules, and inflorescences cylindrical spikes) is used to separate *Mariosousa* from other closely related genera. Recent data derived from both morphological and molecular studies have lead to a better understanding of the probable relationships within the Mimosoideae. One result is that the species here included in *Mariosousa*, which commonly have been referred to as the *Acacia coulteri* Bentham group, should be placed in a separate genus (D. S. Seigler et al. 2006; Gill. K. Brown et al. 2008).

Mariosousa heterophylla (Bentham) Seigler & Ebinger [*M. willardiana* (Rose) Seigler & Ebinger], with papery, exfoliating bark and found at lower elevations in desert scrub vegetation of Sonora, Mexico, is sometimes planted in the southwestern United States (Arizona and California). At present, it is not known to be naturalized there.

SELECTED REFERENCE Jawad, J. T., D. S. Seigler, and J. E. Ebinger. 2000. A systematic treatment of *Acacia coulteri* (Fabaceae, Mimosoideae) and similar species in the New World. Ann. Missouri Bot. Gard. 87: 528–548.

1. **Mariosousa millefolia** (S. Watson) Seigler & Ebinger, Novon 16: 419. 2006 • Milfoil wattle [F]

Acacia millefolia S. Watson, Proc. Amer. Acad. Arts 21: 427. 1886; *Senegalia millefolia* (S. Watson) Britton & Rose

Trees or shrubs to 3 m; bark gray, fissured. **Stems** not flexuous, terete, puberulent; short shoots absent. **Leaves** 60–230 mm; stipules linear, to 6.5 mm, glabrous; petiole 15–75 mm, channeled, glabrous or nearly so; rachis 5–19 cm; pinnae 20–55 mm; leaflet blades linear, 2–6.5 × 0.7–1.4 mm, base oblique and obtuse, apex acuminate. **Peduncles** 5–15 mm. **Inflorescences** 30–75 mm. **Flowers** sessile; calyx 1.1–1.6 mm, glabrous; corolla 2–2.7 mm, glabrous; stamens 4.5–6.5 mm; anthers 0.1–0.3 mm. **Legumes** yellowish brown, 70–170 × 12–21 mm, not constricted between seeds.

Flowering Jun–Aug. Thorn scrub, desert grassland, open oak woodlands; 700–1700 m; Ariz., N.Mex.; Mexico (Chihuahua, Sonora).

Mariosousa millefolia is found in Cochise, Gila, Maricopa, Pima, Pinal, and Santa Cruz counties in Arizona, and in Hidalgo County in New Mexico.

Mariosousa millefolia is rarely a dominant member of the vegetation, with most collections indicating scattered individuals. Though numerous specimens are available from throughout most of the geographic range of this taxon, no specimens, other than the type collection, are known from Chihuahua. This taxon may be extremely rare in southwestern Chihuahua, or it is possible that the collection data on the type specimens is incorrect. This collection, which was lectotypified by D. Isely (1969), is from more than 100 km east of any specimens of *M. millefolia* seen by the authors.

33. ZAPOTECA H. M. Hernández, Ann. Missouri Bot. Gard. 73: 757, figs. 1, 3, 4, 7, 11. 1987 • Barba de chivo, cabellito de ángel, pelo de ángel, guaje, guajillo [For the Zapotec ethnic group of Oaxaca, Mexico]

Héctor M. Hernández

Calliandra Bentham ser. *Laetevirentes* Bentham

Shrubs [trees], unarmed [armed]. **Stems** erect, scandent, or prostrate, glabrous, densely pubescent, or pilose. **Leaves** alternate, even-bipinnate; stipules present, foliose [spinescent]; petiolate, petiole extrafloral nectaries usually absent; pinnae 1 or 2(or 3)[4–8] pairs, opposite, sessile; leaflets [2–](6 or)8–34(–44)[–134], blade margins entire, surfaces glabrous or pubescent. **Peduncles** solitary or fasciculate at distal nodes. **Inflorescences** 10–22-flowered, usually axillary, rarely terminal, usually globose heads, rarely pseudopanicles; bracts present. **Flowers** mimosoid; calyx campanulate, lobes 5; corolla greenish white; stamens 30–60, connate proximally into tube; anthers dorsifixed. **Fruits** legumes, sessile or short-stipitate, compressed, linear, dehiscing elastically from base to apex, glabrous [puberulent, pubescent, or villous]. **Seeds** 1–12, ovoid to rhomboid [ellipsoid], pleurogram present. x = 13.

Species 22 (2 in the flora): sw United States, Mexico, West Indies, Central America, South America; tropical and subtropical areas.

Zapoteca was segregated from *Calliandra* and has been recognized as a well-circumscribed genus within the tribe Ingeae. The area of highest species concentration for *Zapoteca* is in southern Mexico.

SELECTED REFERENCES Guinet, P. and H. M. Hernández. 1989. Pollen characters in the genera *Zapoteca* and *Calliandra* (Leguminosae, Mimosoideae): Their systematic and phylogenetic relevance. Pollen & Spores 31: 5–22. Hernández, H. M. 1989. Systematics of *Zapoteca* (Leguminosae). Ann. Missouri Bot. Gard. 76: 781–862.

1. Leaflets (10–)14–34(–44), blades oblong to elliptic; sw Texas . . . . 1. *Zapoteca media*
1. Leaflets (6 or) 8–12 (or 14), blades oblong-obovate; s Arizona . . . . 2. *Zapoteca formosa*

1. Zapoteca media (M. Martens & Galeotti) H. M. Hernández, Ann. Missouri Bot. Gard. 73: 757. 1987 • Cabellito de ángel, Coulter's stickpea

Acacia media M. Martens & Galeotti, Bull. Acad. Roy. Sci. Bruxelles 10: 316. 1843; *Calliandra coulteri* S. Watson

Shrubs to 1.5(–3) m. **Leaves:** stipules lanceolate to ovate-lanceolate, to 7 mm; pinnae 1 or 2(or 3) pairs; leaflets (10–)14–34(–44), blades oblong to elliptic, 4–13 × 1–5.5 mm. **Peduncles** (1–)1.6–7(–10.5) cm at anthesis. **Inflorescences** usually axillary, rarely terminal in short pseudopanicles. **Flowers:** calyx 1.5–2 mm; corolla 3–3.5 mm; filaments 20 mm, white in proximal ½, red-purple in distal ½. **Legumes** to 100 × 6 mm. **Seeds** flattened, widely rhomboid to widely ovoid, 4 × 3 mm. **2*n*** = 26.

Flowering spring–summer. Dry, rocky calcareous slopes in desert scrub; 1200–2000 m; Tex.; Mexico.

Zapoteca media has been recorded in disjunct localities throughout the Chihuahuan Desert, as well as in the semiarid areas of Puebla and Oaxaca.

2. Zapoteca formosa (Kunth) H. M. Hernández, Ann. Missouri Bot. Gard. 73: 757. 1987 [F]

Acacia formosa Kunth, Mimoses, 102. 1822

Subspecies 8 (1 in the flora): Arizona, Mexico, West Indies, Central America, South America.

Zapoteca formosa consists of eight subspecies relatively well arranged geographically; they can be distinguished primarily by leaf (leaflet shape and size) and flower (stamen color) characters. Subspecies *schottii* can be distinguished from the remaining subspecies by its usually smaller stature, fewer and smaller leaflets, and smaller pods.

2a. Zapoteca formosa (Kunth) H. M. Hernández subsp. **schottii** (Torrey ex S. Watson) H. M. Hernández, Ann. Missouri Bot. Gard. 76: 852. 1989 • Schott's stickpea [F]

Calliandra schottii Torrey ex S. Watson, Proc. Amer. Acad. Arts 20: 364. 1885

Shrubs to 1.5(–2) m. **Leaves:** stipules narrowly triangular to lanceolate, sometimes slightly curved, to 5 mm; pinnae 1 or 2 pairs; leaflets (6 or)8–12 (or 14), blades oblong-obovate, 4–12(–14) × 2–6(–7) mm. **Peduncles** 1.8–4.5(–6) cm at anthesis. **Inflorescences** axillary. **Flowers:** calyx 1.5–2 mm; corolla 3 mm; filaments white in proximal ½, pink in distal ½. **Legumes** to 70 × 6 mm. **Seeds** rhomboid-ovoid, 5–8 × 3.5–5 mm.

Flowering spring–summer. Dry, rocky slopes in desert scrub; 1100–1400 m; Ariz.; Mexico (Sonora).

The area occupied by subsp. *schottii* in southern Arizona and northern Sonora corresponds to the northernmost distribution limit of *Zapoteca formosa*. Intergradation of leaf characters between subspp. *schottii* and *rosei* (Wiggins) H. M. Hernández is evident in Sonora, making difficult the determination at the subspecies level.

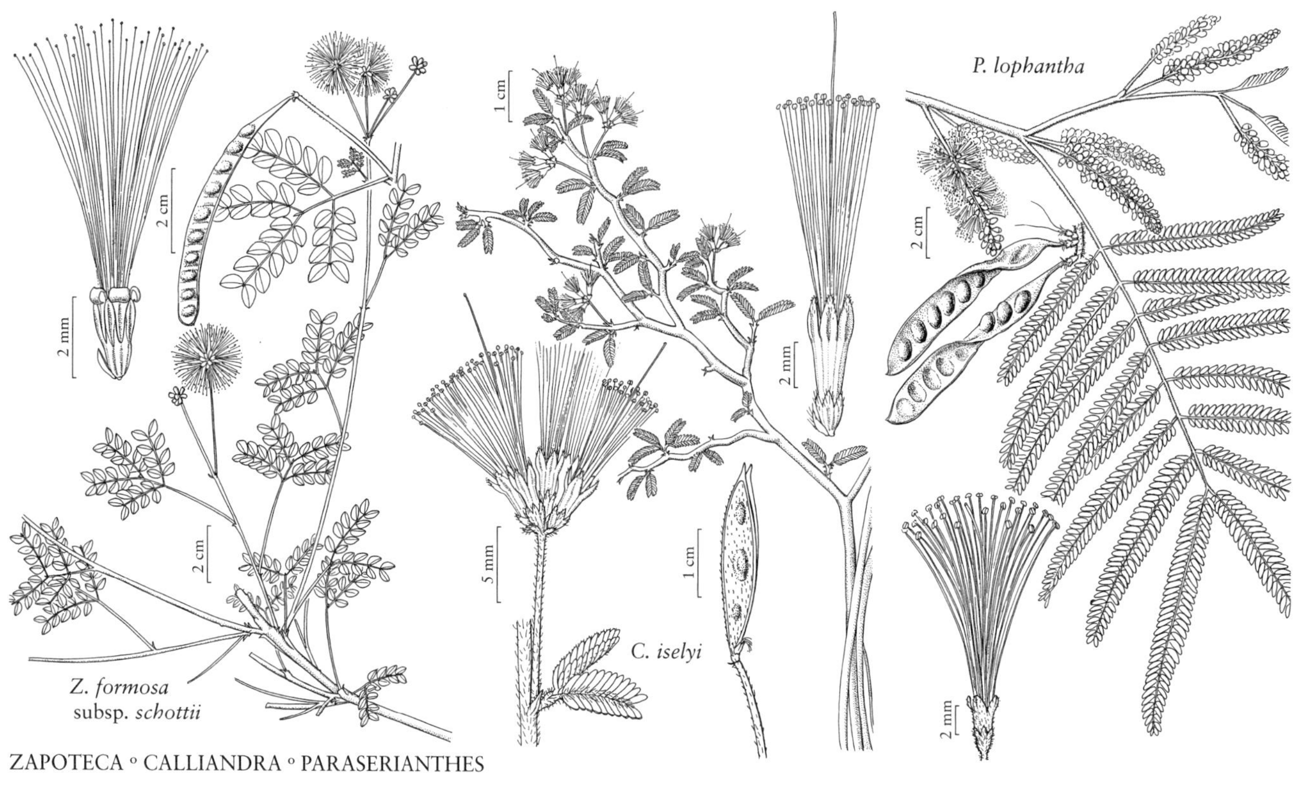

ZAPOTECA ◦ CALLIANDRA ◦ PARASERIANTHES

34. CALLIANDRA Bentham, J. Bot. (Hooker) 2: 138. 1840, name conserved • Tabardillo, fairy duster, mock mesquite, mesquite weed, small huizache [Greek *kallos*, beautiful, and *adras*, man, alluding to showy stamens]

Héctor M. Hernández

Anneslia Salisbury, name rejected

Herbs, perennial, or shrubs [trees], unarmed [armed]. **Stems** erect, ascending, or prostrate, glabrous or hairy. **Leaves** alternate, even-bipinnate; stipules present, foliose [spinescent], usually persistent; petiolate; pinnae 1–7[–26] pairs, opposite, sessile; leaflets [2–]8–40[–200], opposite, blade margins entire, surfaces glabrous, glabrate, or strigose. **Inflorescences** (1 or) 2–12[+]-flowered, axillary or terminal, heads [umbels or pseudoracemes]; bracts present. **Flowers** mimosoid; calyx campanulate, membranous [leathery], lobes usually 5; corolla reddish or whitish; stamens (14–)19–28[+], monadelphous, filaments white, pink, or red, sometimes white proximally and pink or red distally; anthers dorsifixed. **Fruits** legumes, sessile [stipitate], compressed, straight or slightly curved, linear-lanceolate, oblanceolate, or oblong-oblanceolate, dehiscent longitudinally along sutures, valves strongly recurving, glabrous or pubescent, hairs short, white. **Seeds** 1–6, obovoid or rhomboid; pleurogram present. x = 8, 11.

Species 130 (4 in the flora): w, sw United States, Mexico, West Indies, Central America, South America; tropical and subtropical areas.

After publication of the treatment of suborder Mimoseae by G. Bentham (1875), *Calliandra* was understood to be a genus of both the New and Old worlds. Over the last three decades this concept has been modified. Species of ser. *Laetevirentes*, together with other species, were segregated in the Neotropical *Zapoteca* (H. M. Hernández 1986, 1989); species from

Madagascar were placed in *Viguieranthus* (J. F. Villiers 2002). On the other hand, the African species, *C. redacta* (J. H. Ross) Thulin & Asfaw and *C. gilbertii* Thulin & Asfaw, have been transferred to the new genus *Afrocalliandra* É. R. Souza & L. P. Queiroz (É. R. Souza et al. 2013), and *C. cynometroides* Beddome, from India, to *Sanjappa* É. R. Souza & M. V. Krishnaraj (Souza et al. 2016). The remaining New World species of *Calliandra* were grouped by R. C. Barneby (1998) into five sections. Most of the North American and Central American species, including the four in the flora area, belong to sect. *Androcallis* Barneby. *Calliandra eriophylla*, *C. humilis*, and *C. iselyi* belong to ser. *Androcallis* Barneby; *C. biflora* belongs to ser. *Biflorae* Barneby.

SELECTED REFERENCES Barneby, R. C. 1998. Silk tree, guanacaste, monkey's earring. A generic system for the synandrous Mimosaceae of the Americas. Part III. *Calliandra*. Mem. New York Bot. Gard. 74(3): 1–223. Guinet, P. and H. M. Hernández. 1989. Pollen characters in the genera *Zapoteca* and *Calliandra* (Leguminosae, Mimosoideae). Their systematic and phylogenetic relevance. Pollen & Spores 31: 5–22. Souza, É. R. et al. 2013. Phylogeny of *Calliandra* (Leguminosae: Mimosoideae) based on nuclear and plastid molecular markers. Taxon 62: 1200–1219.

1. Shrubs; heads loose, ± hemispheric.
   2. Stems to 60(–120) cm, erect or ascending; pinnae 1–3(or 4) pairs; peduncles 0.4–1.2 (–1.8) cm; corollas usually strigose, rarely glabrate; filaments 15–25 mm; legumes to 9[–10] cm, thickly papery, not translucent, dark brown . . . . 1. *Calliandra eriophylla*
   2. Stems to 30 cm, prostrate; pinnae 1 pair; peduncles 0.9–2.6 cm; corollas usually glabrous, rarely sparsely hairy apically; filaments 10–11 mm; legumes to 3.7 cm, thinly papery, translucent, light brown or light green . . . . 2. *Calliandra iselyi*
1. Herbs; heads compact, obconic.
   3. Stems prostrate or ascending; pinnae (1 or)2–7[–12] pairs; peduncles 0–2.9(–4) cm; heads obconic, (2–)5–12-flowered; filaments to 13 mm. . . . . 3. *Calliandra humilis*
   3. Stems erect; pinnae 1–3 pairs; peduncles 0.4–1(–1.2) cm; heads 1 or 2 (or 3)-flowered; filaments to 24 mm . . . . .4. *Calliandra biflora*

1. Calliandra eriophylla Bentham, London J. Bot. 3: 105. 1844

Calliandra chamaedrys Engelmann; *C. conferta* Bentham; *C. eriophylla* var. *chamaedrys* Isely

Shrubs, profusely branched, sometimes ± leafless at anthesis. **Stems** erect or ascending, to 60 (–120) cm, glabrous or sparsely to densely hairy. **Leaves:** stipules linear-lanceolate to subulate, to 5 mm; pinnae 1–3(or 4) pairs; leaflets 16–20(–28), blades oblong to linear, 2–5 × 0.8–1.4 mm, surfaces strigose to glabrate abaxially, glabrous adaxially. **Peduncles** solitary or fasciculate, axillary or from brachyblasts, 0.4–1.2(–1.8) cm. **Heads** (2–)6–8-flowered, loose, hemispherical. **Flowers** sessile; calyx [0.5–]1–2[–2.5] mm, strigose; corolla [3–]4–6 mm, usually strigose, rarely glabrate; filaments 19–23, white, pink, or red, or white in proximal ½ and red or pink in distal ½, 15–25 mm. **Legumes** dark brown, linear-lanceolate or oblanceolate, to 9[–10] × 0.7[–1] cm, thickly papery, not translucent, pubescent to densely so. **Seeds** 1–6, obovoid, 5–6 × 3–4.5 mm.

Flowering and fruiting winter, spring–fall. Dry, rocky hillsides, along watercourses and desert pavements, on limestone or igneous soils, in creosote and mesquite scrub; 30–1600 m; Ariz., Calif., Nev., N.Mex., Tex.; Mexico.

Calliandra eriophylla is relatively common in the United States portions of the Chihuahuan and Sonoran deserts, and in parts of the Mojave Desert, in Arizona, California, Nevada, New Mexico, and Texas. It is also widespread throughout the desert areas of northern and central Mexico, extending to Guerrero, Oaxaca, and in tropical deciduous forest areas in Chiapas.

The considerable morphological variation of *Calliandra eriophylla*, especially in the leaves (number of pairs of pinnae), inflorescences (peduncle length) and flowers (calyx and corolla length), has caused considerable taxonomic confusion, especially regarding its relationship to *C. conferta*.

Calliandra conferta was described on the basis of specimens from Val Verde county, Texas (*Wright 166*, NY, GH, US, *167*, GH, US). The syntypes resemble *C. eriophylla* in most respects, making separation of these two species difficult. D. Isely (1973), R. C. Barneby (1998), and B. L. Turner (2000b) recognized *C. conferta* as a distinct species, basically by the 1-paired leaves, as found in most individuals in Texas. Specimens from across the range of *C. eriophylla* show that 1-paired leaves often occur intermixed with plants with 2 or 3 pairs of leaves. *Calliandra conferta* cannot be separated from *C. eriophylla* if the full morphological spectrum of the latter is considered.

2. Calliandra iselyi B. L. Turner, Lundellia 3: 17, figs. 3, 4 [lower]. 2000 [F]

Shrubs, profusely branched. **Stems** prostrate, to 30 cm, usually strigose, glabrescent; from thick, woody rhizome. **Leaves:** stipules triangular-lanceolate, to 2–3 mm; pinnae 1 pair; leaflets (8 or)10–22, blades linear to linear-lanceolate, 2–4 × 0.8–1 mm, margins ciliate, surfaces strigose to glabrate abaxially, glabrous adaxially. **Peduncles** solitary, axillary, 0.9–2.6 cm. **Heads** (5 or) 6–8-flowered, loose, ± hemispheric. **Flowers** sessile; calyx 1–1.5 mm, sparsely strigose, at least near apex; corolla 4–4.5 mm, usually glabrous, rarely sparsely hairy apically; filaments 25, light yellow, 10–11 mm; style 2–3 mm longer than filaments. **Legumes** light brown or light green, oblanceolate, 2.2–3.7 × 0.5–0.6 cm, thinly papery, translucent, pubescent. **Seeds** 1–3, obovoid, 4 × 2.5–3 mm.

Flowering and fruiting summer. Rocky slopes, ledges, on limestone or igneous soils, in *Yucca* scrub and desert grassland, below pine and oak belts; 600–1500 m; Tex.; Mexico (Chihuahua, Coahuila).

Calliandra iselyi is known from the Big Bend area in Texas and from Chihuahua and Coahuila. It appears to be uncommon and local.

Calliandra iselyi appears to be closely related to, and very likely derived from, *C. eriophylla*. These species can be distinguished by the shorter stature, consistent 1-paired leaves, longer peduncles, essentially glabrous flowers with shorter filaments, and the smaller, translucent, thin-textured, light-colored legumes of *C. iselyi*. *Calliandra eriophylla* usually are taller shrubs, with 1–3(or 4)-paired leaves, shorter peduncles, flowers with a variable vesture and longer filaments, and usually larger, not translucent, thicker, dark brown legumes.

3. Calliandra humilis Bentham, London J. Bot. 5: 103. 1846 • False mesquite

Herbs, profusely branched from base. **Stems** prostrate or ascending, to 15(–32) cm, strigose or glabrous. **Leaves:** stipules linear-lanceolate or elliptic-ovate, to 5[–7] mm; pinnae (1 or) 2–7[–12] pairs; leaflets 10–40[–54], blades widely elliptic, elliptic-ovate, lanceolate, or linear-lanceolate, 3.5–14 × 1–6 mm, surfaces strigose or glabrous abaxially, glabrous adaxially. **Peduncles** solitary, axillary, 0–2.9(–4) cm. **Heads** (2–)5–12-flowered, compact, obconic. **Flowers** sessile or pedicellate, pedicels 0–2 mm; calyx (1–)2–3 mm, sparsely hairy apically; corolla 4–5[–7.5] mm, with few hairs near apex; filaments 19–28, white (drying pink), 9–13 mm. **Legumes** brown, linear-lanceolate or oblanceolate, to 5.8 × 0.6 cm, thickly papery, weakly translucent, glabrous or sparsely strigose. **Seeds** 1–6, obovoid, 5–6 × 3–4 mm.

Varieties 3 (2 in the flora): sw United States, n, c Mexico.

Calliandra humilis ranges from central Mexico to Puebla and to southwestern United States; at the local level, it appears to be uncommon.

Variety *gentryana* Barneby is known from northern Mexico.

Calliandra humilis can be readily distinguished by being a perennial herb with relatively short stems, relatively small, obconic heads, and relatively short filaments. It shares with *C. biflora* the unusual condition of being herbaceous; however, the two species appear not to be phylogenetically related. These two species can be distinguished by the more numerous, shorter stems, leaves with usually more pairs of pinnae (var. *humilis*), obconic heads with more numerous flowers, and flowers with shorter filaments of *C. humilis*.

1. Pinnae (2 or)3–7[–12] pairs; leaflets 18–40[–54], blades 3.5–6 × 1–1.8 mm, venation perceptible with magnification . . . 3a. *Calliandra humilis* var. *humilis*
1. Pinnae 1–3 pairs; leaflets 10–22, blades 6–14 × 2–6 mm, venation perceptible without magnification . . . . 3b. *Calliandra humilis* var. *reticulata*

3a. Calliandra humilis Bentham var. **humilis**

Calliandra herbacea Engelmann

Stems to 23(–32) cm. **Leaves:** pinnae (2 or)3–7[–12] pairs; leaflets 18–40[–54], imbricate along rachilla, blades 3.5–6 × 1–1.8 mm, venation perceptible only with magnification.

Flowering and fruiting spring–fall. Igneous or limestone soils, rocky slopes, grasslands or open grassy sites in oak woodlands, juniper-pinyon or juniper-ponderosa pine forests; 1500–2700 m; Ariz., N.Mex., Tex.; Mexico.

Variety *humilis* can be readily distinguished from var. *reticulata* by its usually longer stems, leaves with more pairs of pinnae, and smaller, more numerous leaflets. The leaflets in this variety, which are imbricate along the rachilla, have inconspicuous venation. There are numerous instances where vars. *humilis* and *reticulata* intergrade, making identification difficult; although they overlap in portions of their ranges, they do not appear to grow side by side.

3b. Calliandra humilis Bentham var. **reticulata** (A. Gray) L. D. Benson, Amer. J. Bot. 30: 630. 1943

Calliandra reticulata A. Gray, Smithsonian Contr. Knowl. 5(6): 53. 1853

Stems to 15 cm. **Leaves:** pinnae 1–3 pairs; leaflets 10–22, usually well separated along rachilla, blades 6–14 × 2–6 mm, venation perceptible without magnification.

Flowering and fruiting summer–fall. Grasslands and open areas in pine-oak woodlands and pine forests; 1500–2400 m; Ariz., N.Mex.; Mexico.

Variety *reticulata* can be distinguished from the typical variety by its usually shorter stems, the leaves with few pairs of pinnae, and the fewer and larger leaflets, which are usually well spaced along the rachilla and have a conspicuous venation.

4. Calliandra biflora Tharp, Rhodora 56: 132. 1954

Herbs, not profusely branched. **Stems** erect, to 40(–60) cm, strigose throughout. **Leaves:** stipules linear-lanceolate, to 5 mm; pinnae 1–3 pairs; leaflets 8–20 (–24), blades oblong to ovate-lanceolate, 2.5–6 × 1–2 mm, surfaces strigose abaxially, glabrous adaxially. **Peduncles** solitary or fasciculate, axillary, in short, terminal pseudo-panicles prior to anthesis, 0.4–1(–1.2) cm. **Heads** 1 or 2 (or 3)-flowered units. **Flowers** sessile; calyx 1.5–2.5 mm, strigose; corolla 4–6 mm, strigose; filaments (14–)19–24, red or white, to 24 mm. **Legumes** dark brown, oblong-lanceolate or oblanceolate, to 7.3 × 0.8(–1) cm, thickly papery, not translucent, strigose. **Seeds** 1–3(–6), rhomboid, 7–8 × 5–6 mm.

Flowering and fruiting spring–summer. Sandy or loamy soils over caliche, in Tamaulipan thorn scrub or grassland; 30–150 m; Tex.; Mexico (Tamaulipas).

Calliandra biflora has been recorded from a relatively small area in DeWitt, Goliad, and Victoria counties, and from eastern Tamaulipas, Mexico. *Calliandra biflora* and *C. humilis* are unusual among members of *Calliandra* by being perennial herbs.

35. PARASERIANTHES I. C. Nielsen, Bull. Mus. Natl. Hist. Nat., B, Adansonia 5: 326, plate 1, fig. 3. 1984 • Plume albizia [Greek *para-*, near, and generic name *Serianthes*, a Malaysian tree genus, alluding to affinity] [I]

Debra K. Trock

Trees [shrubs], unarmed. **Stems** ascending, tomentose, young growth densely puberulent to woolly. **Leaves** alternate, even-bipinnate; stipules present, caducous; petiolate, with gland at petiole base; pinnae 7–15 pairs, opposite; leaflets 40–100+, opposite, blades pale green abaxially, dark green adaxially, margins entire, surfaces glabrous or strigulose. **Inflorescences** 25–50+-flowered, axillary, racemes [spikes]; bracts present. **Flowers** mimosoid; calyx campanulate, lobes 5; corolla greenish; stamens ± 90, monadelphous, fused at base into tube ± equaling petals, greenish to lemon yellow; anthers dorsifixed, quadrangular, dehiscent longitudinally; ovary sessile or stipitate, solitary, compressed, shallowly sulcate laterally, glabrous; style tapering distally to a poriform stigma. **Fruits** legumes, stipitate, strongly compressed, elevated over seeds, straight, broadly linear to narrowly oblong, indehiscent or late-dehiscent, glabrous or glabrate, not glandular, membranous, leathery, not fleshy or pulpy, not septate between seeds. **Seeds** 8–11, ellipsoid; hilum basal, dull black.

Species 4 (1 in the flora): introduced, California; Pacific Islands (Malesia), w Australia; introduced also in South America (Colombia, Ecuador), Europe (France, Italy, Portugal), s Africa, Atlantic Islands (Azores), Pacific Islands (Hawaii, New Zealand).

Paraserianthes is cultivated throughout the tropics. It is a relatively fast growing tree, reaching 45 meters in height, used to provide shade for plantation crops, as a windbreak, to prevent soil erosion, and as an ornamental (I. C. Nielsen et al. 1983).

1. Paraserianthes lophantha (Willdenow) I. C. Nielsen, Bull. Mus. Natl. Hist. Natl., B, Adansonia 5: 326. 1984 F I

Acacia lophantha Willdenow, Sp. Pl. 4: 1070. 1806, based on *Mimosa distachya* Ventenat, Descr. Pl. Nouv., 20, plate 20. 1801, not Cavanilles 1795; *Albizia lophantha* (Willdenow) Bentham

Trees to 8 m. **Stems** with brownish hairs, hairs 0.2–0.3 mm. **Leaves:** stipules narrowly lanceolate, 2–3 mm; leaflet blades linear to subulate, 5–10 × 1.5–3 mm. **Peduncles** 1–2 cm. **Racemes** 5.5–7.5 cm; bracts caducous, rhombic to obovate, 1–2[–7] mm. **Flowers:** calyx 2–3 mm, lobes deltate, 0.5–1 mm, strigulose; corolla 5–7.5 mm, lobes ovate, strigulose; stamens 13–16+ mm, anthers 0.2–0.3 mm; ovary stipe to 1 mm. **Legumes** yellow to reddish or ochre, 5–9(–10) cm.

Flowering Oct–Mar. Disturbed sites, coastal and urban areas; 0–1000 m; introduced; Calif.; sw Australia; introduced also in South America (Chile, Colombia, Ecuador, Peru), Europe (France, Italy, Portugal), s Africa, Pacific Islands (Hawaii, New Zealand), elsewhere in Australia.

Paraserianthes lophantha is native to southwestern Australia and has been introduced to the rest of the continent; it has the potential to become weedy (although it does not do well above 300 m) and is considered an invasive species in New South Wales, New Zealand, South Africa, and Tasmania.

Albizia distachya J. F. Macbride is an illegitimate name that pertains here.

36. HAVARDIA Small, Bull. New York Bot. Gard. 2: 91. 1901 • Huajillo [For Valery Havard, 1846–1927, U.S. Army officer and botanist]

María de Lourdes Rico-Arce

Painteria Britton & Rose; *Pithecellobium* Martius sect. *Ortholobium* Bentham; *Sphinga* Barneby & J. W. Grimes

Shrubs [trees], armed, stipules spinescent. **Stems** ascending, twigs glabrous or puberulent, resting buds absent, short shoots absent. **Leaves** alternate, even-bipinnate, not sensitive to touch; stipules present; petiolate, petiole with extrafloral nectaries; pinnae (3–)4–6 pairs, opposite, extrafloral nectary present between distalmost 1 or 2 pair(s); leaflets (22–)30, opposite, blade margins entire, venation brochidodromous, surfaces glabrous or glabrate. **Inflorescences** 14-flowered, axillary, heads, sometimes forming pseudoracemes; bracts present. **Flowers** mimosoid, actinomorphic, homomorphic; calyx campanulate, lobes 5 or 6, calyx and corolla connate, valvate; corolla greenish; stamens 25–30[–50], monadelphous, connate into a tube; anthers dorsifixed. **Fruits** legumes, usually stipitate, laterally compressed, straight, broadly linear-oblong in outline,

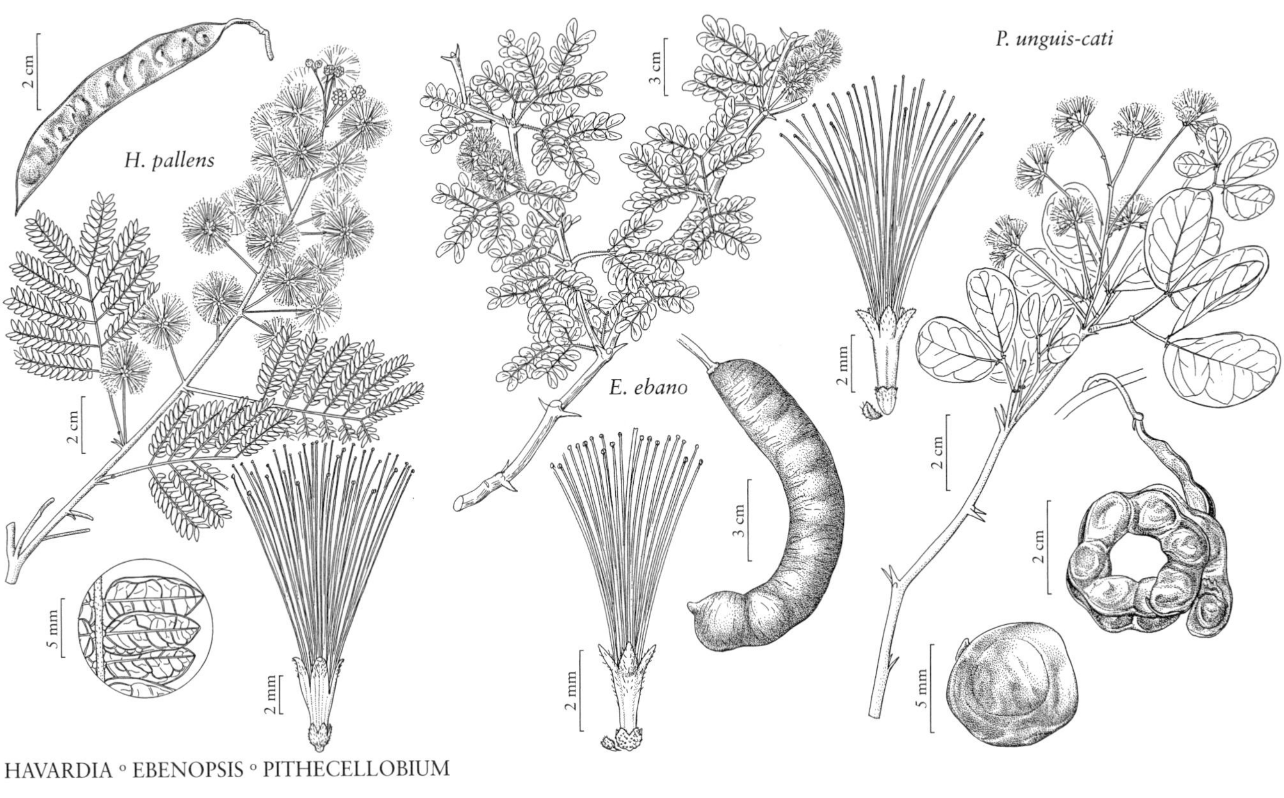

HAVARDIA ◦ EBENOPSIS ◦ PITHECELLOBIUM

dehiscing along margin, glabrous; not constricted between seeds, undulate above seeds. **Seeds** (8–)10–15, flattened, oblong to circular in outline; pleurogram present, aril absent. x = 13.

Species ca. 11 (1 in the flora): Texas, Mexico, Central America, South America.

1. Havardia pallens (Bentham) Britton & Rose in N. L. Britton et al., N. Amer. Fl. 23: 42. 1928 • Tenaza [F]

Calliandra pallens Bentham, London J. Bot. 5: 102. 1846; *Feuilleea brevifolia* (Bentham) Kuntze; *Havardia brevifolia* (Bentham) Small; *Pithecellobium brevifolium* Bentham; *Pithecellobium pallens* (Bentham) Standley; *Zygia brevifolia* (Bentham) Sudworth

Shrubs to 50 dm, crown usually rounded. **Stems** lenticellate, without conspicuous short shoots; bark light gray, smooth. **Leaves** 9.5–13 cm; stipules spinescent, straight, 8 mm; petiole with flat proximal elliptic gland, 1–2 cm, glabrescent; pinnae 2–4 cm, rachis with gland between 1 or 2 distalmost pair of pinnae, sometimes puberulent; leaflet blades oblong, 5–6 × 2 mm, base oblique-rounded, apex acute with small mucro. **Peduncles** in groups of 2 or 3, 1.8 cm, strigulose. **Inflorescences** capitate, 2 or 3 per node, on short axis, strigulose, flower heads 2.5–4 cm diam.; bract caducous, linear-lanceolate, 0.7 mm. **Flowers** sessile; bracteole caducous, proximal, 1 mm; calyx 1.2 mm, estrigulose toward apex; corolla campanulate, 4.3 mm, 4- or 5-lobed, strigulose toward apex; stamens white or brownish cream, 10 mm, tube 3 mm; ovary 1 mm, glabrous. **Legumes** 6.5–9 × 1–1.5 cm, margins thin, base rounded, apex apiculate, beak to 7 mm, valves membranous, fuscous-ferruginous; stipe to 1.2 cm. **Seeds** 7 × 5 mm.

Flowering spring–early fall. Mesquite brush thickets, dry forests, rocky grounds, roadsides, sandy plains, clay soils; 0–100 m; Tex.; Mexico (Chihuahua, Coahuila, Durango, Hidalgo, Nuevo León, Oaxaca, San Luis Potosí, Tamaulipas, Veracruz, Yucatán).

Havardia pallens is planted as an ornamental in the southwestern United States as a part of xeriscape landscaping; it is summer deciduous if conditions are dry. The native range is confined to southern Texas in the lower Rio Grande Valley (Cameron, Hidalgo, and Starr counties), northward through Willacy, Kenedy, Kleberg, and Jim Wells counties, to San Patricio County.

37. EBENOPSIS Britton & Rose in N. L. Britton et al., N. Amer. Fl. 23: 33. 1928 • Texas ebony [Greek *ebenos*, ebony tree, and *-opsis*, resemblance, alluding to habit or wood structure]

María de Lourdes Rico-Arce

Siderocarpos Small, Bull. New York Bot. Gard. 2: 91. 1901, not *Siderocarpus* Pierre 1890 [Sapotaceae]

Trees [shrubs], armed, stipules spiny. **Stems** ascending and spreading, glabrous [puberulent], without resting buds, short shoots (brachyblasts) present. **Leaves** alternate, even-bipinnate, not sensitive to touch; stipules present; petiolate, petiole without extrafloral nectaries; pinnae 2 or 3 pairs, opposite, extrafloral nectary present between pinnae; leaflets 6–10(or 12), opposite, blade margins entire, palmate brochidodromous venation, more conspicuous abaxially, main vein central, surfaces glabrous. **Inflorescences** pedunculate, 20–35-flowered, axillary, spikes [heads], forming pseudoracemes over short shoots; bracts present. **Flowers** mimosoid, actinomorphic, homomorphic; calyx campanulate, lobes 4 or 5, calyx and corolla connate, valvate; corolla greenish; stamens ca. 50, connate into a tube; anthers dorsifixed. **Fruits** legumes, sessile, turgid, sausagelike, slightly curved or falcate, broadly linear-oblong in outline, indehiscent, woody, glabrous, without thickened margins; exocarp light brown to maroon; exocarp and endocarp well developed, with seed chambers, without constriction between seeds, undulate [or not] above seeds. **Seeds** 8–12, turgid, plump, oblong in outline, ± spherical or rhomboid; pleurogram present, aril and endosperm absent, embryonic axis rounded. $x = 13$.

Species 3 (1 in the flora): Texas, n, e Mexico.

Ebenopsis confinis (Standley) Britton & Rose occurs in southeastern Baja California and Baja California Sur, Mexico; *E. caesalpinioides* (Standley) Britton & Rose is known only from the coastal plain near Mazatlán, Sinaloa, Mexico (R. C. Barneby and J. W. Grimes 1996).

1. Ebenopsis ebano (Berlandier) Barneby & J. W. Grimes, Mem. New York Bot. Gard. 74(1): 175. 1996 • Ebony black-seed, ebano [F]

Mimosa ebano Berlandier in P. de La Llave, Mosaico Mex. 4: 418. 1840; *Acacia flexicaulis* Bentham; *Chloroleucon ebano* (Berlandier) L. Rico; *Ebenopsis flexicaulis* (Bentham) Britton & Rose; *Pithecellobium ebano* (Berlandier) C. H. Muller; *P. flexicaule* (Bentham) J. M. Coulter; *P. texense* J. M. Coulter; *Samanea flexicaulis* (Bentham) J. F. Macbride; *Siderocarpos flexicaulis* (Bentham) Small; *Zygia flexcaulis* (Bentham) Sudworth

Trees 4–6(–20) m, with rounded crown. **Stems** gray-ochre, with few horizontal lenticels; bark with vertical fissures. **Leaves:** stipules persistent, to 1 cm; petiole to 0.7–1.5 cm, glabrous; rachis to 1 cm; pinna rachis 2–3.5 cm, with cylindric, elevated gland between pinnae; leaflet blades oblong to rhombic-oblong, 5–12 × 2.5–8 mm, base oblique to semicordate, apex rounded. **Peduncles** 2–6 grouped, ebracteate, pubescent. **Spikes:** axis 2–5 cm, pubescent; bract triangular, 0.5 mm, pubescent abaxially. **Flowers:** calyx 1 mm; corolla campanulate, 4–5 mm, 4–6-lobate, glabrescent; stamens white or cream, staminal tube to 5 mm; ovary subsessile, to 1.5 mm, glabrous. **Legumes** falcate, 11–13.5(–22) × 2.5–3 cm, base rounded, apex cuspidate with recurved beak to 5 mm, valves woody, smooth, surface cracking with age into a mosaic like pattern, sometimes with few verruca; mesocarp well developed, endocarp forming pithy septa between seeds, without visible margin. **Seeds** maroon, 17–22.5 × 9–13 mm, pleurogram closed, testa thin.

Flowering summer. Roadside thickets, scrub; 0–150 m; Tex.; Mexico (Nuevo León, San Luis Potosí, Tamaulipas, Yucatán).

Ebenopsis ebano is found in southern Texas and is cultivated in the southeastern United States as an ornamental. The wood of this species is extremely hard.

38. PITHECELLOBIUM Martius, Flora 20(2,Beibl.): 114. 1837 (as Pithecollobium), name and orthography conserved • [Greek *pithekos*, monkey, and *ellobion*, earring, alluding to pendulous, contorted fruits]

María de Lourdes Rico-Arce

Shrubs or trees, armed, stipules spiny (except *P. keyense*). **Stems** and twigs spreading, glabrous or hairy, without resting buds, with or without short shoots (brachyblasts), bark smooth to rough, crown usually rounded. **Leaves** alternate, even-bipinnate, not sensitive to touch; stipules present; petiolate; pinnae 2(or 4), opposite, extrafloral nectaries present between pinnae and leaflets; leaflets 2, opposite, blade margins entire, surfaces glabrous or glabrescent. **Inflorescences** pedunculate, 15–50+-flowered, axillary, heads or spikes, forming pseudoracemes; bracts absent or present, glandular. **Flowers** mimosoid, sessile, valvate; calyx greenish, campanulate or tubular, lobes 5 or 6, calyx and corolla connate; corolla greenish; stamens 15+, monadelphous, connate proximally into a tube, filaments white or pinkish; anthers dorsifixed. **Fruits** legumes, sessile or stipitate, turgid, recurved to coiled, oblong, without thickened margins, dehiscent, leathery, rugose to reticulate, hairy or glabrous; ± constricted between seeds. **Seeds** 5–12[–16], elliptic to ovate or obovate in outline, strongly biconvex; aril present. $x = 13$.

Species ca. 20 (3 in the flora): s United States, Mexico, West Indies, Central America, n South America; introduced in Asia, Africa, Pacific Islands (Guam, Hawaii, Philippines).

SELECTED REFERENCE Barneby, R. C. and J. W. Grimes. 1997. Silk tree, guanacaste, monkey's earring: A generic system for the synandrous Mimosaceae of the Americas. Part II. *Pithecellobium*. Mem. New York Bot. Gard. 74(2): 2–36.

1. Stem nodes with conspicuous short shoots; peduncles pubescent, less than 2 cm; aril white or pinkish, covering nearly all of seed . . . . 2. *Pithecellobium dulce*
1. Stem nodes without short shoots; peduncles glabrescent or glabrous, (1.5–)1.8–7 cm; aril white or red, covering proximal ⅓ of seed.
   2. Trees, unarmed; peduncles flattened; petioles shorter than rachises; aril red . . . . 1. *Pithecellobium keyense*
   2. Shrubs or trees, armed; peduncles not flattened; petioles longer than rachises; aril white . . . . 3. *Pithecellobium unguis-cati*

1. Pithecellobium keyense Britton in N. L. Britton et al., N. Amer. Fl. 23: 22. 1928

Trees, to 6(–7) m, unarmed. **Stems,** branches, and twigs densely covered with conspicuous lenticels, glabrescent; short shoots absent. **Leaves:** stipules to 1 mm, not spiny, caducous, hard, triangular-subulate, glabrous; petiole 0.4–1.5(–2) cm, shorter than rachis, subglabrous; pinnae 2(or 4), rachis 8–13 mm; leaflets 2 per pinna, blades obovate to oblanceolate-elliptic, 3–8.5(–9) × 1.5–5(–7) cm, base oblique, margins entire, usually revolute, apex rounded with a very small mucro, brochidodromous venation conspicuous on both surfaces, main vein subcentral, surfaces glabrous. **Peduncles:** primary peduncle flattened, axis to 7 cm, glabrescent, secondary peduncles (2.5–)4.5–6 cm, glabrous; bract absent. **Heads** on secondary peduncles 15–30-flowered, sometimes elongated. **Bracteoles** triangular, 0.8 mm, puberulous abaxially. **Flowers:** calyx campanulate or tubular, 1.5–2 mm, lobes 0.5 mm, glabrescent; corolla campanulate or funnelform, to 5.5 mm, lobes 4 or 5; stamens white, dirty cream, or pink, tube to 3–3.5 mm; ovary 1–1.5 mm, glabrous, stipe to 1.5 mm. **Legumes** slightly recurved to 1-coiled (especially at dehiscence), slightly constricted between seeds, 8–20 × 1–1.5 cm, margin not evident, base attenuate, apex cuspidate without beak, glabrous, veins faint; without stipe. **Seeds** 6–12, usually not pendulous, 6–9 × 5–6 mm; aril red, covering proximal ⅓ of seed. $2n = 26$.

Flowering spring. Coastal thickets; 0–20 m; Fla.; West Indies (Bahamas, Cuba, Turks and Caicos Islands); Central America (Belize).

Pithecellobium keyense is known from southern Florida in Broward, Martin, Miami-Dade, and Monroe counties where it is restricted to coastal areas. The species is usually five-merous, but some corollas are four-lobed. Of the three North American *Pithecellobium* species, *P. keyense* has the fewest stamens.

2. Pithecellobium dulce (Roxburgh) Bentham, London J. Bot. 3: 199. 1844 (as Pithecolobium) • Manila tamarind, humuchil, guaymuchil [I]

Mimosa dulcis Roxburgh, Pl. Coromandel 1: 67, plate 99. 1798

Trees, to 12 m, armed. **Stems,** branches, and twigs with few lenticels, rarely hairy; short shoots present. **Leaves:** stipules 5+ mm, spiny (on most branches proximal to inflorescences); petiole to 1.2–5.5 cm, longer than rachis, strigulose or glabrous; pinnae 2, rachis 8–13 (–17) mm; leaflets 2 per pinna, blades obliquely elliptic or oblong- to ovate-elliptic, 1.8–3(–5.5) × 0.7–1.7 (–3) cm, base oblique to slightly semicordate, margins entire, flat, apex usually acute, rarely ± rounded and slightly emarginate, brochidodromous venation more conspicuous adaxially, main vein subcentral, surfaces glabrous, abaxially rarely glabrescent. **Peduncles:** primary peduncle terete, axis to 10 cm, pubescent, secondary peduncles to 2 cm, pubescent; glandular bract present at base. **Heads** spherical capitula, 15–30-flowered. **Bracteoles** triangular, 0.8 mm, puberulous abaxially. **Flowers:** calyx campanulate, 1.5–2 mm, lobes 0.5 mm, strigulose; corolla campanulate, to 3–4.5 mm, lobes 5 or 6; stamens white or dirty cream, tube to 2–3.5 mm; ovary to 2 mm, pubescent, stipe to 1.8 mm. **Legumes** recurved to coiled (especially at dehiscence), margin constricted between seeds, 10–20 × 1–1.5 cm, base attenuate, apex cuspidate, without a beak, puberulous, veins reticulate; stipe less than 1 cm. **Seeds** 8–12, slightly pendulous, 7–11 × 6–12 mm; aril white or pinkish, covering nearly all of seed. $2n$ = 26.

Flowering year-round. Disturbed areas; 0–100 m; introduced; Fla., Tex.; Mexico (Baja California, Guerrero, Jalisco, Michoacán, Morelos, Nayarit, Oaxaca, Puebla, Quintana Roo, Sinaloa, Sonora, Yucatán); Central America; South America (Brazil, Colombia, Guyana, Venezuela); introduced also in West Indies (Bahamas, Greater Antilles, Lesser Antilles), Asia (Bangladesh, China), Africa, Pacific Islands (Guam, Hawaii, Philippines).

Pithecellobium dulce is introduced and naturalized widely in the tropics, where it is planted as a source of dye, food, and forage.

3. Pithecellobium unguis-cati (Linnaeus) Bentham, London J. Bot. 3: 200. 1844 (as Pithecolobium) • Cat's claw, black bead, uña de gato [F]

Mimosa unguis-cati Linnaeus, Sp. Pl. 1: 517. 1753; *Feuilleea unguis-cati* (Linnaeus) Kuntze; *Inga unguis-cati* (Linnaeus) Willdenow; *Zygia unguis-cati* (Linnaeus) Sudworth

Shrubs or trees, to 8 m, armed. **Stems,** branches, and twigs with few lenticels, glabrous; short shoots absent or inconspicuous and few. **Leaves:** stipules to 10(–15) mm, spiny (at least on some branches); petiole to 1–2.5 cm, longer than rachis, glabrous; pinnae 2, rachis 5–10(–16) mm; leaflets 2 per pinna, blades asymmetric-oblong or obovate- to ovate-elliptic, 1.7–2.4(–4.5) × 1.3–2.5(–3.5) cm, base oblique, margins entire, flat, apex rounded, obtuse, or rarely slightly emarginate, brochidodromous venation more conspicuous abaxially, main vein submarginal, surfaces glabrous, abaxially rarely glabrescent. **Peduncles:** primary peduncle not flattened, axis to 8 cm, subglabrous, secondary peduncles 1.8–3 cm, usually glabrous; glandular bract present at base, inconspicuous. **Heads** 8–25(–35)-flowered, sometimes elongated. **Bracteoles** triangular, to 1.2 mm, puberulous abaxially. **Flowers:** calyx campanulate, 1–1.2 mm, lobes 0.5 mm, pubescent; corolla campanulate, 5 mm, lobes 5 or 6, pubescent; stamens white or dirty cream, tube to 5.5 mm; ovary 2.5 mm, glabrous, stipe 2.5 mm. **Legumes** reddish or maroon, recurved to coiled several times (especially at dehiscence), constricted between seeds, 5–10(–15) × 1–1.5 cm, base attenuate, margin thickened, apex acute, glabrous, veins irregular, reticulate; stipe 0–5 mm. **Seeds** 5–8, 6–7 × 5–8 mm; aril white, covering proximal ⅓ of seed; exposed seeds pendulous. $2n$ = 26.

Flowering spring–summer. Shrublands, sand ridges, roadsides; 0–50 m; Fla.; Mexico (Guerrero, Michoacán, Oaxaca, Yucatán); West Indies; South America (Bolivia, Brazil, French Guiana, Guyana, Surinam, Venezuela); introduced in Africa.

Pithecellobium unguis-cati is widespread in the Caribbean, Yucatán Peninsula, and in southwestern Mexico. Its fruits open more widely than those of *P. dulce* and *P. keyense*, exposing the inside of the fruit wall.

39. SAMANEA (Bentham) Merrill, J. Wash. Acad. Sci. 6: 46. 1916 • [Venezuelan saman, colloquial name for *S. saman*] [I]

María de Lourdes Rico-Arce

Pithecellobium Martius sect. *Samanea* Bentham, London J. Bot. 3: 197. 1844 (as Pithecolobium)

Trees, unarmed, strigulose. **Stems** with straight bole, young growth white-puberulent to tomentose, resting buds present, ferruginous or yellowish. **Leaves** alternate, even-bipinnate, not sensitive to touch; stipules present, not spinescent; rachis and pinnae with extrafloral nectaries; petiolate; pinnae 6–10 pairs, opposite, terminal pair heteromorphic; leaflets 12–24, opposite, blade margins entire, surfaces slightly pubescent abaxially, glabrous adaxially. **Inflorescences** 12–25-flowered, axillary or terminal, umbels [corymbs]; bracts present. **Flowers** mimosoid, actinomorphic, dimorphic, 7 or 8-merous, peripheral flowers smaller than central; calyx campanulate, lobes 5–8, calyx and corolla connate, valvate; corolla white and pink; stamens 40+, connate into a tube; anthers dorsifixed, eglandular. **Fruits** legumes, sessile, glossy red-brown, turgid, straight or slightly curved, oblong, indehiscent, fleshy, pulpy, glabrescent, margins thickened; exocarp separating from mesocarp when old, endocarp woody with septae between seeds. **Seeds** 8–20, elliptic, strongly biconvex; pleurogram present, aril and endosperm absent; cotyledons large, radicle curved. $x = 13$.

Species 3 (1 in the flora): introduced, Florida; Central America, South America; introduced also in tropical and subtropical areas nearly worldwide.

1. Samanea saman (Jacquin) Merrill, J. Wash. Acad. Sci. 6: 47. 1916 • Mimosa, rain or silk tree, carreto, cenicero, cenízaro, zorra [F] [I]

Mimosa saman Jacquin, Fragm. Bot., 15, plate 9. 1800/1801; *Albizia nicoyana* Britton & Rose; *A. saman* (Jacquin) F. Mueller; *Pithecellobium saman* (Jacquin) Bentham

Trees to 30 m; branches and twigs densely pubescent to glabrescent; resting buds densely pubescent. **Leaves:** stipules early caducous, 5–6 mm, strigulose; petiole 4–8 cm, eglandular, strigulose; pinnae 4.5–9.5(–18) cm, with gland between each pair; leaflet blades oblique-oblong to obovate, 15–35(–45) × 9–20 mm, base acute, apex rounded, mucronate, venation brochidodromous, main vein central; terminal pinna blades rhombic-elliptic, to 55 × 35 mm, apex rounded or acute; nectaries between each pair of pinnae and leaflets. **Peduncles** 5–7 cm, densely strigulose. **Inflorescences** terminal or axillary, densely strigulose; bracts 3 or 4, deltate, (5–)7 mm, densely strigulose; bract 5 mm, clavate, strigulose. **Flowers:** peripheral flowers pedicellate, pedicels 2–3 mm, strigulose; calyx 6 mm, densely strigulose; corolla campanulate, 10–12 mm; stamens white proximally, pink distally, staminal tube to 8 mm, ovary 4 mm; central flowers: calyx 10 mm, lobes 8; corolla 13–15 mm, lobes 5; staminal tube 12 mm, ovary 4 mm. **Legumes** 15–20 × 1.5–2.3 cm, base rounded, margins entire, apex rounded with slightly curved beak to 8 mm, valves leathery, smooth or slightly rough.

Flowering spring–early summer. Disturbed areas; 0–20 m; introduced; Fla.; Central America; South America; introduced also in tropical and subtropical areas nearly worldwide.

Samanea saman is introduced in the paleotropics as an ornamental, timber, and forage tree. The species is considered invasive in Fiji and Vanuatu; elsewhere in the Pacific, it is naturalized but rarely considered problematic.

40. ALBIZIA Durazzini, Mag. Tosc. 3(4): 13, plate [opp. p. 1]. 1772 • [For Filippo degli Albizzi, 1724–1789, Italian naturalist] [I]

María de Lourdes Rico-Arce

Trees [shrubs], unarmed. **Stems** usually straight, spreading, young growth white-puberulous to tomentose, resting buds absent. **Leaves** alternate, even-bipinnate, not sensitive to touch; stipules present, early caducous, not spinescent; petiole, rachis, and pinnae often with extrafloral nectaries; petiolate; pinnae (1 or)2–12 pairs, opposite; leaflets 10–44(–72), opposite, usually asymmetric, terminal pair usually heteromorphic, blade margins entire, surfaces pubescent. **Inflorescences** 15–40-flowered, axillary or terminal, capitula or capitulalike corymbs, arranged in panicles; bracts present, deltate, densely strigillose. **Flowers** mimosoid, when dimorphic, central flowers sessile, larger than peripheral, 5 or 7 or 8-merous; peripheral flowers usually pedicellate, 5-merous; calyx campanulate or tubular, lobes 5 or 6, calyx and corolla connate, valvate; corolla whitish or pink to yellow-green; stamens 20–70, filaments sometimes connate, usually long-exserted; anthers dorsifixed, eglandular. **Fruits** legumes, stipitate or sessile, usually straight, flat, oblong, margins slightly thickened, sometimes winged, dehiscent or late dehiscent, glabrous or pubescent; not fleshy or pulpy, not septate between seeds. **Seeds** 4–12[–20], globose, obovoid, or wide elliptic; strongly biconvex, with open pleurogram, aril and endosperm absent. $x = 13$.

Species ca. 140 (4 in the flora): introduced; South America, Asia, Africa, Australia; introduced also in Mexico, West Indies, Bermuda, Central America, s Europe, Pacific Islands (Hawaii, New Zealand).

Albizia is a pantropical genus that includes at least 470 names. M. L. Rico-Arce et al. (2008) confirmed a figure between 120 and 140 species; in Africa there are about 36 endemic species.

1. Petiole gland elliptic, length 3 times width; leaflet blades bicolored . . . . 4. *Albizia procera*
1. Petiole gland ± circular, length to 1.5 times width; leaflet blades not or slightly bicolored.
   2. Leaflet blades: midvein subcentral; pedicels, except of central flowers, 1.5–4.5 mm . . . . 2. *Albizia lebbeck*
   2. Leaflet blades: midvein marginal or submarginal; pedicels to 1 mm.
      3. Petiole gland proximal or sub-basal; pinnae (4 or)5–12 pairs . . . . 1. *Albizia julibrissin*
      3. Petiole gland near middle; pinnae 2 or 3(or 4) pairs . . . . 3. *Albizia kalkora*

1. Albizia julibrissin Durazzini, Mag. Tosc. 3(4): 13, plate [opp. p. 1]. 1772 • Silk tree, mimosa [F] [I]

Trees to 6 m. **Stems** strigillose, bark light gray, smooth, with inconspicuous scattered, brownish lenticels. **Leaves** 20–32 cm; stipules 2 mm; petiole 3–7.5 cm, glabrescent or puberulent; gland proximal or sub-basal, elliptic, length to 1.5 times width; pinnae (4 or)5–12 pairs, 5.5–10 cm, with gland between 1 or 2 distal pairs; leaflets (13–)17–22(–36) pairs, blades not bicolored, oblong, 0.7–1.5 cm, venation palmate, midvein marginal or submarginal, base strongly asymmetric, truncate, apex acute, short-mucronate, surfaces glabrous or sparsely pubescent; terminal pair not heteromorphic. **Peduncles** 3–9 cm, densely strigulose; bracts linear-lanceolate, 2(–5) mm. **Inflorescences** 18–25-flowered, terminal or axillary, capitula; axis densely strigillose. **Pedicels** to 1 mm. **Flowers:** calyx campanulate, (2.5–)6 mm, lobes 5 or 6, glabrescent; corolla campanulate, (8–)12 mm, lobes 4 or 5, strigillose distally; stamens 32, white proximally, pink distally, 30–35 mm, tube (10–)12 mm; terminal or central flower calyx 3 mm, lobes 5, glabrous; corolla 9–12 mm, lobes 5; stamens 28 mm, tube long-exerted, to 18 mm. **Legumes** fuscous-ferruginous, 10–20 × 1.5–2.6 cm, margins straight or slightly constricted, base acute, apex rounded, narrowing to a beak to 1.5 cm, valves membranous, glabrescent, smooth or slightly rough. **Seeds** 6–8(–10), 9 × 5 mm. $2n = 26, 52$.

Flowering spring–summer; fruiting summer–fall. Disturbed roadsides, thickets, riverbanks; 100–700 m; introduced; Ala., Ark., Calif., Conn., Fla., Ga., Ill., Ind., Kans., La., Md., Miss., Mo., N.J., N.Mex., N.Y., N.C., Ohio, Okla., Pa., S.C., Tenn., Tex., Va., W.Va.; sw Asia;

introduced also in Mexico, West Indies (Jamaica), South America (Argentina, Brazil, Peru, Uruguay), s Europe, s, se Asia, Africa, Pacific Islands (New Zealand).

Albizia julibrissin is commonly cultivated and is thought to be the hardiest of the *Albizia* species. It is especially attractive when flowering; staminal filaments are deep pink, grading to white at the base. *Albizia julibrissin* forma *rosea* (Carrière) Rehder is a dwarf, bushier plant with bright pink flowers.

2. Albizia lebbeck (Linnaeus) Bentham, London J. Bot. 3: 87. 1844 (as Albizzia) • Woman's tongue tree [I]

Mimosa lebbeck Linnaeus, Sp. Pl. 1: 516. 1753; *Acacia speciosa* (Jacquin) Willdenow; *M. speciosa* Jacquin

Trees to 10 m, crown rounded. **Stems** pilosulous to glabrescent, bark light tan, fissured in rectangular plate, with conspicuous pale lenticels on young branches. **Leaves** 6–24 cm; stipules 2–4 mm; petiole 6–7(–9.5) cm, ribbed to channeled, sometimes pilose; gland proximal, ± circular; pinnae 2 or 3 pairs, 7–14 cm, with gland between distal pair; leaflets 5–7 pairs, blades not bicolored, oblong to ovate, 2–4(–5) cm, venation palmate-pinnate, midvein subcentral, base acute, apex rounded, mucronate, surfaces usually glabrous, sometimes translucent, pilose abaxially; terminal pair not heteromorphic. **Peduncles** 7–8 cm, pilose; bracts linear, 3 mm. **Inflorescences** 30–40-flowered, (1 or)2 or 3 per node, axillary, capitula; axis pilose; floral bracts linear, 2 mm. **Pedicels,** except central flowers, 1.5–4.5 mm. **Flowers:** calyx tubular, 3–6 mm, lobes 5 or 6, short-pubescent; corolla campanulate, 4–10 mm, lobes 4 or 5, glabrous except for lobes; stamens 30, white, 15–25 mm, tube to 4 mm; central flowers: sessile, calyx to 5.5 mm, lobes 5, pilose; corolla 10–11 mm, campanulate, lobes 5; stamens 20–30, to 23 mm, tube to 10 mm. **Legumes** sessile, ochre-brown, 1.2–18.6 (–25) × 3.7–6 cm (including beak), margins straight to slightly constricted between seeds, base rounded, apex acute, with 10 mm beak, glabrescent, usually dehiscent along 1 suture, valves undulating, raised over seeds. **Seeds** 4–11, 7–8(–12) × 7–9 mm. $2n$ = 26.

Flowering spring–early summer; fruiting spring–fall. Disturbed thickets, roadsides; 0–100 m; introduced; Calif., Fla., Tex.; Asia; introduced also in Mexico, West Indies (Bahamas, Greater Antilles, Lesser Antilles), Bermuda, Central America, South America, Africa, Pacific Islands (Fiji, Guam, Hawaii, New Zealand), Australia.

Albizia lebbeck is widely cultivated as an ornamental and shade tree; it is naturalized in the subtropics and tropics and is abundant in central and southern Florida. The rattling pods are persistent during the winter while the trees are leafless (D. Isely 1998).

3. Albizia kalkora (Roxburgh) Prain, J. Asiat. Soc. Bengal, Pt. 2, Nat. Hist. 66: 511. 1897 (as Albizzia) [I]

Mimosa kalkora Roxburgh, Fl. Ind. ed. 1832, 2: 547. 1832

Trees (3–)5–7 m. **Stems** glabrous, bark brown, rough, with protuberant lenticels. **Leaves** 23–30 cm; stipule length unknown; petiole 3–7.5 cm, glabrous; gland near middle, elliptic, length to 1.5 times width; pinnae 2 or 3(or 4) pairs, 8.5–13 cm, rachis without glands; leaflets (5–)8–10(–14) pairs, blades slightly bicolored, oblong, slightly asymmetric, 2.5–3.5(–4.5) cm, surfaces with conspicuous palmate venation, midvein marginal or submarginal, base rounded or slightly acute, apex rounded, mucronate, surfaces glabrous; terminal pair slightly heteromorphic, not larger. **Peduncles** 4–7 cm, glabrous; bracts basal. **Inflorescences** 15–20-flowered, terminal or axillary, capitulalike corymbs; axis glabrous. **Pedicels** to 1 mm. **Flowers:** calyx tubular, 3 mm, lobes 5, sparsely strigillose; corolla infundibuliform, 7–9 mm, lobes 5, sparsely strigillose; stamens 30, 15 mm, tube to 5 mm; central flowers sessile, calyx tubular, 4 mm, lobes 5; corolla infundibuliform, 12 mm, lobes 5, sparsely strigillose; stamens 30–35, 20 mm, tube 17 mm. **Legumes:** stipe to 1 cm, ochre or reddish brown, 0.7–2 × 1.5–3 cm, margins inconspicuous, base and apex acute, valves membranous, shortly pubescent or glabrescent. **Seeds** 4–12, 6 × 4 mm. $2n$ = 26.

Flowering spring–early summer; fruiting summer–fall. Disturbed thickets, roadsides; 100–200 m; introduced; N.C.; Asia.

Young leaflets of *Albizia kalkora* are yellow-green, while those of *A. julibrissin* are dark green; *A. kalkora* has fewer pinnae [2 or 3(or 4) pairs] and leaflets (5–14 pairs), compared to *A. julibrissin* (4–12 pairs of pinnae with 13–36 leaflet pairs per pinna); flowers of *A. kalkora* are paler and more creamy than pink, while those of *A. julibrissin* are more commonly pink to dark pink.

Some specimens from Durham County in North Carolina (where *Albizia kalkora* grows near *A. julibrissin*) exhibit intermediate characteristics and may represent hybrids.

4. Albizia procera (Roxburgh) Bentham, London J. Bot. 3: 89. 1844 (as Albizzia) • White siris [I]

Mimosa procera Roxburgh, Pl. Coromandel 2: 12, plate 121. 1799

Trees 4–15(–25) m. **Stems** to 8.5 cm diam., glabrous, bark greenish, smooth, thin, with scattered, orange lenticels. **Leaves** 9–35 cm; stipules 2 mm; petiole to 6 cm, glabrescent; gland ± proximal, elliptic, length 3 times width; pinnae (1–)3–6 pairs, 10–21 cm, with gland between 1 or 2 distal pairs; leaflets 6–9 pairs, blades bicolored, inequilaterally oval or oblong, 2–5 cm, venation palmate, midvein submarginal, base acute, apex rounded, mucronate, surfaces glabrous or sparsely appressed-puberulous, adaxially darker; terminal pair not heteromorphic. **Peduncles** 1–2 cm, densely strigillose; bracts caducous, proximal, linear lanceolate, 1.3 mm, densely strigillose. **Inflorescences** 20–25-flowered, axillary, capitula; axis densely strigillose. **Pedicels** to 1 mm. **Flowers:** calyx campanulate, 2 mm, lobes 5 or 6, densely strigillose; corolla infundibuliform, 5.3 mm, lobes 5, strigillose; stamens 45, 15 mm, tube 2 mm; terminal or central flower calyx 2.5 mm, lobes 5, glabrous; corolla to 7 mm, lobes 5, densely strigillose; stamens 70, 28 mm, staminal tube to 6 mm. **Legumes** reddish brown, 13–16 × 1.5–3 cm, base acute, apex rounded to a beak to 1 cm, valves membranous, glabrescent, smooth with faint reticulations. **Seeds** 4–8(–12), 6.5–8.5 × 4–6.5 mm. $2n = 26$.

Flowering fall; fruiting winter. Roadsides, thickets; 0–10 m; introduced; Fla.; se Asia; Australia; introduced also in West Indies (Bahamas, Greater Antilles, Lesser Antilles), Central America (Panama), South America (Brazil, Venezuela), Africa.

Albizia procera is cultivated in southern Florida and is found outside cultivation in Miami-Dade County. In its native range, wood from the species is used for furniture and general construction.

41. ENTEROLOBIUM Martius, Flora 20(2,Beibl.): 117. 1837 • [Greek *enteron*, intestine, and *lobion*, pod or capsule, alluding to curved fruit] [I]

Richard P. Wunderlin

Trees, unarmed. **Stems** ascending, glabrous or sparsely pubescent. **Leaves** alternate, even-bipinnate; stipules present, caducous, inconspicuous; rachis glandular mostly distally; petiolate; pinnae 4–10(–15) pairs, opposite; leaflets (24–)30–60, opposite, blade margins entire, surfaces glabrous or sparsely pubescent. **Inflorescences** ca. 50-flowered, axillary, heads [racemes, fascicles, or flowers solitary]; bracts present. **Flowers** mimosoid; calyx valvate, campanulate to funnelform, lobes 5; corolla white or cream, lobes 5, valvate, lobes and tube subequal; stamens [10–] ca. 80, connate proximally into short staminal tube; anthers dorsifixed; style slender. **Fruits** legumes, sessile, compressed, deeply reniform [or circinate], forming a nearly complete spiral, constricted between seeds, indehiscent, woody, glabrous. **Seeds** (5–)8–9(–14), ellipsoid, transverse, on filiform funicle. $x = 13$.

Species 11 (1 in the flora): introduced, Florida; West Indies, Central America, South America; introduced also in Africa.

Enterolobium cyclocarpum (Jacquin) Grisebach and *E. contortisiliquum* are cultivated in temperate and tropical areas of the Old World and New World and sometimes naturalized; only the latter is naturalized in North America. The species can easily be distinguished by their fruits; reniform, plump, blackish, dull, and glaucous in *E. contortisiliquum*; curved to form a complete circle, flattened, dark brown, and lustrous in *E. cyclocarpum*. The wood of *E. cyclocarpum* is used commercially; the pods are fed to livestock; the gum is a substitute for gum arabic; the bark and fruits are used for tanning and in soap; and the bark is used medicinally.

SELECTED REFERENCE Mesquita, A. L. 1990. Revisão Taxonômica do Gênero *Enterolobium* Mart. (Mimosoideae) para a Região Neotropical. M.S. thesis. Universidade Federal Rural de Pernambuco.

1. **Enterolobium contortisiliquum** (Vellozo) Morong, Ann. New York Acad. Sci. 7: 102. 1893 • Earpod tree [F] [I]

Mimosa contortisiliqua Vellozo, Fl. Flumin., plate vol. 11, 25. 1831; *Feuilleea contortisiliqua* (Vellozo) Kuntze

Trees to 30 m. **Bark** smooth. **Leaves:** stipules linear-subulate, 2–3 mm; petiole 3–5(–8) cm, glabrous or sparsely pubescent, with sessile, elliptic gland distal to middle; rachis pubescent or glabrous; stipels distal to secondary pulvinus, linear-subulate, 1 mm; leaflet blade asymmetrical, linear-oblong to subfalcate, 8–15 × 3–4 mm, base obliquely rounded, apex obliquely acute to obtuse, mucronate. **Peduncles** 0.5–2 cm. **Inflorescences:** heads (on secondary branches) 0.5–1 cm, 1–2 cm diam. **Pedicels** 1 mm. **Flowers:** calyx 2 mm, 5-ribbed, pubescent on outer surface, lobes triangular, 0.25 mm; corolla funnelform, 5–6 mm, pubescent on outer surface, lobes linear-lanceolate, 2 mm; stamens ca. 80, 8–10 mm, white or cream, glabrous; filaments connate 4 mm proximally. **Fruits** blackish, (55–)60–70(–80) × (40–)50–60 mm, dull, glaucous. **Seeds** dark brown, flattened, 10 × 5 mm, with evident pleurogram. $2n$ = 26 (South America).

Flowering spring–summer. Disturbed areas; 0–50 m; introduced; Fla.; South America (Argentina, Bolivia, Brazil, Paraguay, Uruguay); introduced also in West Indies, Africa.

Enterolobium contortisiliquum is known from central peninsular Florida.

Enterolobium contortisiliquum is cultivated in tropical and subtropical areas of the Americas and Africa. The species is used for wood in construction and cabinetry and is often cultivated as a shade tree in the tropics and subtropics. The seeds contain toxic saponins.

42. LYSILOMA Bentham, London J. Bot. 3: 82. 1844 • [Greek *lysis*, loosening, separation, and *loma*, border, margin, alluding to separation of continuous, thickened margins from legume valves as they disintegrate]

Ralph L. Thompson

Trees or shrubs, unarmed. **Stems** erect to ascending; bark smooth to furrowed, scaly, or flaking on older branches or trunk; branchlets glabrous or pubescent. **Leaves** alternate, even-bipinnate; stipules present; petiolate, petiole terete, rachis and rachilla terete-trigonous, pulvinate; nectaries present; pinnae [1 or]2–10[–50] pairs, opposite; leaflets 6–56, opposite, blade margins entire, surfaces pilose, glabrescent, or glabrous. **Peduncles** 2–7, from leaf axils or in relatively small, axillary racemes. **Inflorescences** 28–70-flowered, axillary, spikes or racemes, solitary or fasciculate; bracts present or absent; bracteoles present. **Flowers** mimosoid, actinomorphic, buds green-canescent; calyx campanulate or campanulate-tubular, lobes 5, synsepalous, valvate in bud; corolla sympetalous, red, white, greenish white, or yellowish green, valvate in bud; stamens 14–36, exserted, monadelphous, connate basally into slender tube; filaments conspicuous, filiform, white to greenish or yellowish white; anthers versatile, oblong, eglandular; ovary superior, free, glabrous; style subulate-filiform; stigma terminal, concave, glabrous. **Fruits** legumes, stipitate, laterally compressed, straight, broadly to narrowly oblong, dehiscent or indehiscent or craspedial, glabrous, strongly compressed over seeds, not septate between seeds; sutures prominent, exocarp dark purple to ripe-nigrescent, exfoliating, endocarp pale stramineous, papery to leathery, not exfoliating, not fleshy or pulpy, margins wiry. **Seeds** 7–15, compressed, oval or oblong to ellipsoid, smooth, hard, opaque; pleurogram distinct; endosperm absent. x = 13.

Species 9 (3 in the flora): s United States, Mexico, West Indies, Central America.

Legumes in *Lysiloma* are either dehiscent (readily dehiscent at maturity, with undivided margins separating from the valves, and seeds that are released through dehiscence of the valve sutures) or indehiscent (indehiscent at maturity, with valves tardily separating from the persistent margins, and seeds that are released through decay of the valves on the ground).

SELECTED REFERENCE Thompson, R. L. 1980. Revision of the Genus *Lysiloma* (Leguminosae). Ph.D. dissertation. Southern Illinois University, Carbondale.

1. Legumes dehiscent, stipes 0.3–1.3 cm; Arizona . . . . 1. *Lysiloma watsonii*
1. Legumes indehiscent, stipes 0.8–3.8 cm; Florida.
    2. Leaflets 6–12, blades elliptic to obovate, apex obtuse to retuse, 12–35 × 7–23 mm, venation palmate-pinnate; pinnae 6–10; stipule base cuneate-flabellate; peduncles ebracteate; pedicels present; legume apex rounded to emarginate; pleurogram elliptic . . . . 2. *Lysiloma sabicu*
    2. Leaflets 30–56, blades oblong, apex acute to narrowly obtuse, 8–15 × 3–6 mm, venation pinnate; pinnae 4–12; stipule base auriculate-semicordate; peduncles bracteate; pedicels absent; legume apex acuminate; pleurogram U-shaped . . . . 3. *Lysiloma latisiliquum*

1. Lysiloma watsonii Rose, Contr. U.S. Natl. Herb. 1: 99. 1891 (as watsoni) • Littleleaf false tamarind, featherbush, tepeguaje, tepeguajo

Lysiloma acapulcense Bentham var. *brevispicatum* Rose; *L. brevispicatum* (Rose) Britton & Rose; *L. microphyllum* Bentham var. *thornberi* (Britton & Rose) Isely; *L. thornberi* Britton & Rose; *L. watsonii* subsp. *thornberi* (Britton & Rose) Felger & C. H. Lowe

Trees or shrubs, to 10 m, trunk often multi-stemmed from base. **Leaves** deciduous, pinnae 8–20; stipules caducous, pale yellowish green, subfoliaceous, dimidiate-cordate, 0.8–1.1 × 0.4–0.6 mm, base oblique, apex acuminate, surfaces puberulent; petiole yellowish brown to yellowish olive, 0.7–2.2 cm, pilose; petiolar nectary medial to distal of first pinnae, yellowish brown to reddish brown, conical, 0.5–1.2 × 1–1.5 mm; rachis yellowish brown to yellowish olive, 3–10 cm, pilose to glabrescent; rachilla opposite, yellowish brown to yellowish olive, 2.5–9 cm, pilose to glabrescent; pulvinules 0.2–0.4 mm; leaflets 20–38 per pinna, blade oblong, 3.8–8.5 × 1.5–2.9 mm, papery, base obliquely rounded to truncate, venation palmate-pinnate, midvein slightly eccentric, apex obtuse, surfaces subappressed-pilose to glabrescent, margins ciliate. **Peduncles** dark yellowish brown, 2.2–3.8 cm, spreading-pilose to densely pilose. **Inflorescences** 50–70-flowered, racemes, ovoid-cylindrical; bracts caducous, brown, spatulate, 1.2–5.5 × 0.2–4.5 mm. **Pedicels** 0.2–1 mm, canescent. **Flowers:** calyx pale white to yellowish white maculate, 2.3–3.2 × 1.2–1.7 mm, puberulent; lobes cucullate, 0.4–0.9 mm, apex acute to obtuse, canescent; corolla pale yellowish green maculate, campanulate-infundibular, 3.3–4.4 × 1.2–1.7 mm, canescent; lobes cucullate, 0.8–1.2 mm, apex acute to obtuse, canescent; stamens 24–36, white to pale yellowish white, 7.4–9.2 mm, mostly connate 2.2–3.7 mm; ovary subsessile. **Legumes** dark reddish brown to brownish black, slightly falcate, 8–20 × 1.5–3 cm, dehiscent, crustaceous, base attenuate, apex acuminate, surfaces glaucescent, glabrous; stipe 0.3–1.3 cm. **Seeds** dark brown to dark olive brown, oval, 6.4–10.2 × 5–8 mm; pleurogram oval, nearly complete. $2n = 26$.

Flowering Mar–May. Temperate upland shrub grasslands, crassicaulescent deserts; 600–1600 m; Ariz.; Mexico (Chihuahua, Sinaloa, Sonora).

Natural distribution of *Lysiloma watsonii* is restricted to southern Arizona (Pima County) and northern Mexico; it is widely introduced in Maricopa, Pima, and Pinal counties in the greater Phoenix area.

The bark of *Lysiloma watsonii* is used locally as an astringent, purgative, and tea. Roasted seeds are made into atole. The hard wood is utilized in woodworking and in general construction. The species is also planted as a landscape ornamental in Arizona.

2. Lysiloma sabicu Bentham, Hooker's J. Bot. Kew Gard. Misc. 6: 236. 1854 • Horseflesh, horseflesh mahogany, sabicú, jigüe, jiqui, Cuban sabicú or lysiloma [I]

Acacia latisiliqua (Linnaeus) Willdenow var. *paucifoliola* de Candolle; *Lysiloma paucifoliolum* (de Candolle) Hitchcock ex Northrop

Trees, to 20 m, single trunk to 1 m diam. **Leaves** semi-deciduous, pinnae 6–10; stipules persistent, pale yellowish green, foliaceous, obovate-ovate, 9–22 × 5–14 mm, base cuneate-flabellate, apex acute to obtuse, surfaces glabrous; petiole yellowish brown to grayish brown, 1.6–4 cm, glabrous; petiolar nectary medial to distal of first pinnae, yellowish brown to grayish brown, sauceriform, 0.3 × 1 mm; rachis yellowish brown to grayish brown, 2.4–9 cm, glabrous; rachilla opposite to subopposite, 2.8–6.5 cm, glabrous; pulvinules 1–2.2 mm; leaflets 6–12 per pinna, blade elliptic to obovate, 12–35 × 7–23 mm, papery, base obliquely obtuse, apex obtuse to retuse, venation palmate-pinnate, midvein slightly excentric, apex obtuse, surfaces subappressed-pilose to glabrescent, margins glabrous. **Peduncles** yellowish brown to yellowish green, 2.5–6.6 cm, glabrous. **Inflorescences** 28–48-flowered, racemes, globose-capitate; bracts absent. **Pedicels** 0.6–1.2 mm, puberulent. **Flowers:** calyx white to greenish white, 2.2–3.1 × 1.2–1.8 mm, glabrous except lobes; lobes cucullate, 0.4–1.1 mm, apex acute, puberulent; corolla white to greenish white, infundibular-tubular, 4.4–6.2 × 1.5–2.2 mm, glabrous except lobes; lobes cucullate, 1.2–2 mm, apex acute, puberulent; stamens 14–20, white to pale greenish white, 12–18 mm, connate 2.2–5.4 mm; ovary subsessile. **Legumes** blackish brown to reddish black, straight, 8–15 × 2.3–3.9 cm, indehiscent, membranous, base attenuate to cuneate, apex rounded to emarginate, surfaces glabrous; stipe 1.3–3.8 cm. **Seeds** dark brown to brownish black, oblong to ellipsoid, 5.2–8 × 2.9–4 mm; pleurogram elliptic, complete. $2n = 26$.

Flowering Mar–Jun. Limestone coppice thickets, tropical needleleaf forests; 0–10 m; introduced; Fla.; West Indies (Bahamas, Cuba, Hispaniola); introduced also in Puerto Rico.

Lysiloma sabicu is an important timber tree in the Bahamas and Cuba. The lustrous chestnut-brown, dark-striped coppery heartwood is highly valued for fine furniture and paneling. The sapwood is thin, white, and sharply demarcated from the heartwood (S. J. Record and C. D. Mell 1924). In the flora area, *L. sabicu* is known only from Miami-Dade County.

3. **Lysiloma latisiliquum** (Linnaeus) Bentham, Trans. Linn. Soc. London 30: 534. 1875 (as latisiliqua) • Wild tamarind, Bahama lysiloma, singing bean, wild locust, dormido, salam, salom, tzalam [F]

Mimosa latisiliqua Linnaeus, Sp. Pl. 1: 519. 1753; *Acacia bahamensis* (Bentham) Grisebach; *A. latisiliqua* (Linnaeus) Willdenow; *Leucaena latisiliqua* (Linnaeus) Gillis; *Lysiloma bahamense* Bentham

Trees, to 20 m, single main trunk to 1.5 m diam. **Leaves** deciduous, pinnae 4–12; stipules caducous, yellowish green abaxially, dark green adaxially, foliaceous, dimidiate-cordate, 1.3–2.5 × 0.5–1.5 mm, base auriculate-semicordate, apex acuminate to acute, surfaces glabrous; petiole yellowish brown to dark brown, 1.8–5 cm, glabrous or slightly pilose; petiolar nectary medial to proximal to first pinna, dark brown to blackish red, columnar, 0.7–1 × 0.5–0.8 mm; rachis yellowish brown to dark olive brown, 1.7–7.5 cm, glabrous or slightly pilose; rachilla opposite, yellowish brown to dark olive brown, 4–9.5 cm, glabrous or slightly pilose; pulvinules 0.2–0.5 mm; leaflets 30–56 per pinna, blade oblong, 8–15 × 3–6 mm, papery, base obliquely rounded to truncate, venation pinnate (obscure adaxially), mid-vein centric, apex acute to narrowly obtuse, surfaces glabrous except for basal villous tuft, margins glabrous or slightly ciliate. **Peduncles** yellowish green to olive brown, 2–4 cm, glabrous or finely puberulent. **Inflorescences** 33–50-flowered, spikes, globose-capitate; bracts persistent, greenish brown, lanceolate, 4–5.5 × 2–4.5 mm. **Pedicels** absent. **Flowers:** calyx white or greenish maculate, 1.7–2.5 × 1–1.8 mm, puberulent; lobes cucullate, 0.4–1 mm, apex acute, canescent; corolla red maculate, campanulate-infundibular, 2.9–4.3 × 1.2–1.9 mm, puberulent; lobes cucullate, 0.8–1.5 mm, apex acute to obtuse, canescent; stamens 15–26, white to greenish white with pink base, 9–13 mm, connate 1–2.5 mm; ovary sessile. **Legumes** brownish black to grayish black, straight, 8–17 × 3–5 cm, indehiscent, papery, base attenuate, apex acuminate, surfaces glabrous; stipe 0.8–2.8 cm. **Seeds** brownish black to blackish red, oblong to ellipsoid, 6–7.3 × 3–3.5 mm; pleurogram U-shaped. $2n = 26$.

Flowering Mar–Jun. Rockland hammocks, limestone coppice, pine flatlands, scrub thickets; 0–10 m; Fla.; Mexico (Quintana Roo, Yucatán); West Indies (Bahamas, Cuba, Haiti); Central America (Belize, Guatemala).

In the flora area, *Lysiloma latisiliquum* is known from Collier, Miami-Dade, and Monroe counties. It is a timber tree of minor importance in the West Indies. The wood is used for furniture, interior housing trim, and boat building. In Mexico and Belize, the bark is used for tanning of leather and for medicinal teas. The lustrous, rich brown heartwood is tinged with red and contains inconspicuous medullary rays; the sapwood is white (S. J. Record and R. W. Hess 1943).

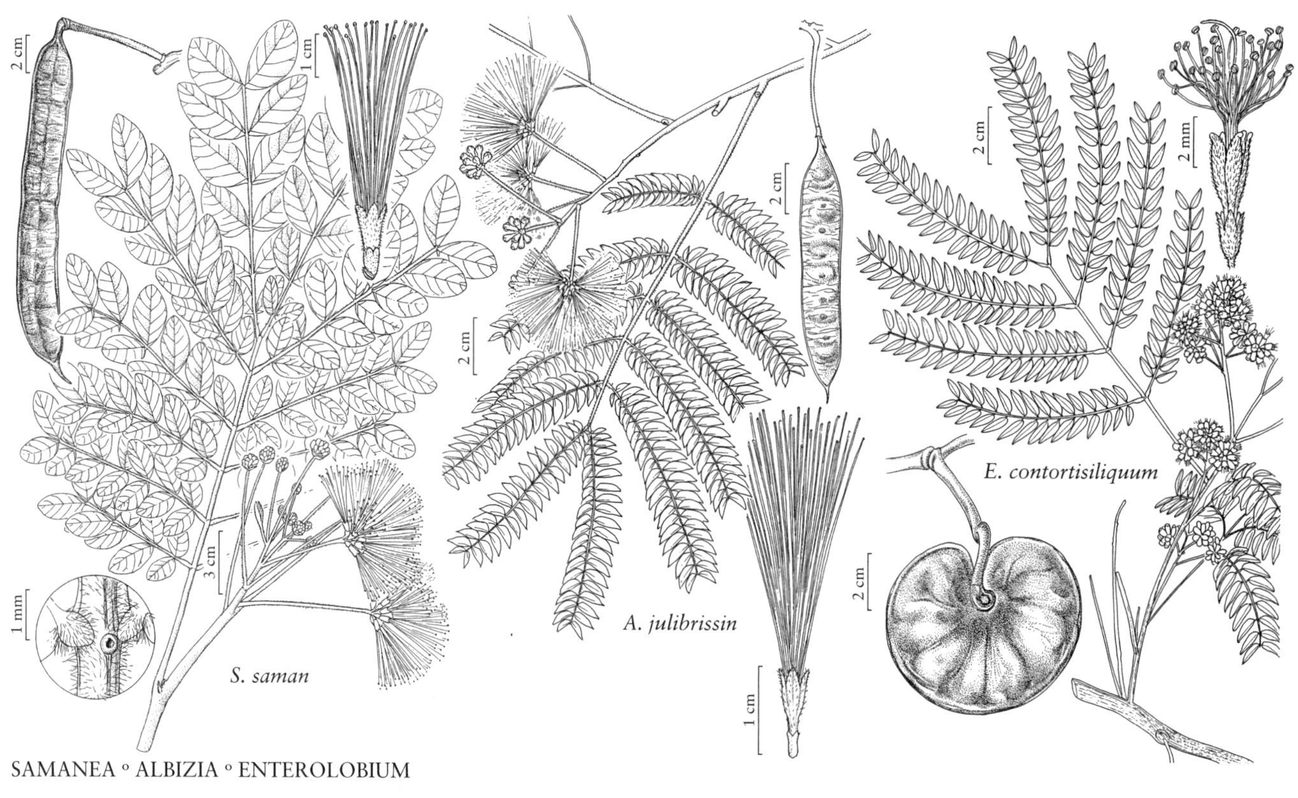

SAMANEA ◦ ALBIZIA ◦ ENTEROLOBIUM

d. FABACEAE Lindley subfam. FABOIDEAE Rudd, Rhodora 70: 496. 1968

Papilionoideae de Candolle

Trees, shrubs, lianas, herbs, or vines, unarmed or armed. **Extrafloral nectaries** absent on petiole and rachis, sometimes stipular, stipellar, or bracteal, rarely on sepals. **Stipules** lateral, free, or absent. **Leaves** pinnate, palmate, unifoliolate, or 3-foliolate, rarely 2 or 4-foliolate, not bipinnate. **Flowers** usually papilionaceous, rarely nonpapilionaceous (in *Amorpha*, *Parryella*, sometimes *Clitoria*), bilateral, rarely asymmetrical, or radial; sepals connate at least basally; petals 5(or 6), rarely only 1 (banner) present or 0; stamens (1–9)10(+), filaments connate, or adaxial filament ± distinct, rarely all filaments distinct, usually heteromorphic, anthers basifixed or dorsifixed; pollen in monads. **Fruits** legumes, dehiscent or indehiscent, or loments, drupes, or samaroid. **Seeds** with complex hilar valve, hilum elongate, pleurogram absent; embryo usually curved, rarely straight. ***x*** = 5, 6, 7, 8, 9, 10, 11, 12.

Genera ca. 503, species ca. 14,000 (111 genera, 1162 species in the flora): nearly worldwide.

SELECTED REFERENCES Allan, G. J. and J. M. Porter. 2000. Tribal delimitation and phylogenetic relationships of Loteae and Coronilleae (Faboideae: Fabaceae) with special reference to *Lotus*: Evidence from nuclear ribosomal ITS sequences. Amer. J. Bot. 87: 1871–1881. Endo, Y. and H. Ohashi. 1997. Cladistic analysis of phylogenetic relationships among tribes Cicereae, Trifolieae, and Vicieae (Leguminosae). Amer. J. Bot. 84: 523–529. Heyn, C. C. 1981. Trifolieae. In: R. M. Polhill and P. H. Raven, eds. 1981. Advances in Legume Systematics. Parts 1 and 2. 2 vols. Kew. Vol. 1, pp. 383–385. Lassen, P. 1989. A new delimitation of the genera *Coronilla*, *Hippocrepis*, and *Securigera* (Fabaceae). Willdenowia 19: 49–62. Lavin, M. and M. Sousa S. 1995. Phylogenetic systematics and biogeography of the tribe Robinieae. Syst. Bot. Monogr. 45. McMahon, M. 2005. Phylogenetic relationships and floral evolution in the papilionoid clade Amorpheae. Brittonia 57: 397–411. McMahon, M. and L. Hufford. 2004. Phylogeny of Amorpheae (Fabaceae, Papilionoideae). Amer. J. Bot. 91: 1219–1230. Rydberg, P. A. 1924. Genera of North American Fabaceae. II. Tribe Galegeae (continued). Amer. J. Bot. 11: 470–482. Steele, K. P. and M. F. Wojciechowski. 2003. Phylogenetic analyses of tribes Trifolieae and Vicieae, based on sequences of the plastid gene, *matK* (Papilionoideae: Leguminosae). In: B. B. Klitgaard and A. Bruneau, eds. 2003. Advances in Legume Systematics. Part 10. Kew. Pp. 355–370. Wojciechowski, M. F. et al. 2000. Molecular phylogeny of the “temperate herbaceous tribes” of papilionoid legumes: A supertree approach. In: P. S. Herendeen and A. Bruneau, eds. 2000. Advances in Legume Systematics. Part 9. Kew. Pp. 277–298.

Key to Genera of Subfamily Faboideae

1. Trees, shrubs (sometimes suffrutescent), or woody vines.
   2. Leaves palmately foliolate or appearing so, or all or mostly unifoliolate, or reduced to phyllodes.
      3. Leaves reduced to spinelike phyllodes; corollas yellow; fruits legumes, partly enclosed by persistent calyx, densely villous . . . . 59. *Ulex*, v. 11(1), p. 256
      3. Leaves not reduced to spinelike phyllodes; corollas white, creamy white, pink, reddish to blue-purple, orange-yellow, or yellow; fruits legumes or loments, usually visible, glabrous, glabrate, or pubescent.
         4. Leaves all unifoliolate, often reduced or deciduous and absent.
            5. Shrubs or small trees with erect or scandent stems; leaflet blades 25–80 mm, elliptic or ovate; corollas white, creamy white, or yellowish, sometimes pinkish; fruits indehiscent; Florida. . . . . 73. *Dalbergia* (in part), v. 11(1), p. 327
            5. Trees or shrubs with erect stems; leaflet blades 2–35 mm, sometimes early deciduous; corollas white, yellow, pink to reddish purple, or blue to violet-purple; fruits dehiscent or indehiscent; sw, w United States.
               6. Stems green, rushlike, unarmed; corollas yellow; fruits dehiscent with twisting valves; introduced, w United States . . . . . 58. *Spartium* (in part), v. 11(1), p. 256
               6. Stems brownish green, branched, armed; corollas pinkish, blue, or purplish, sometimes white; fruits indehiscent; desert Southwest.
                  7. Fruits legumes, enclosed in calyx or exserted, plump to compressed, gland-dotted; seeds usually 1; corollas blue to purple or violet, sometimes white; stems gland-dotted . . .64. *Psorothamnus* (in part), v. 11(1), p. 274
                  7. Fruits loments, exserted, terete, moniliform (constricted between seeds), not gland-dotted, glabrous; seeds (1 or)2–8(–10); corollas pinkish to reddish purple; stems not gland-dotted. . . . . .141. *Alhagi*, v. 11(2), p. 907
         4. Leaves palmate or appearing palmate, sometimes unifoliolate (sometimes mixed with pinnate leaves).
            8. Leaves unifoliolate (sometimes mixed with pinnate leaves), or appearing palmate.
               9. Leaves unifoliolate or odd-pinnate; stipules subspinescent; stems broomlike, green; inflorescences mostly solitary flowers in axils of distal unifoliolate leaves; legume valves elastically dehiscent; trans-Pecos Texas . . . . 131. *Genistidium*, v. 11(2), p. 554
               9. Leaves appearing palmate; stipules and leaf rachis spinescent or spine-tipped; stems not broomlike, brownish; inflorescences 1–4(or 5)-flowered, flowers solitary or in fascicles; legume valves twisting in dehiscence; Alaska, B.C., Alberta, Quebec, c, e United States . . . . 139. *Caragana* (in part), v. 11(2), p. 903
            8. Leaflets 1–11(–17).
               10. Leaves (1–)5–11(–17)-foliolate; stipules adnate to petiole; keel attenuate; stamens monadelphous. . . . . 53. *Lupinus* (in part), v. 11(1), p. 193
               10. Leaves 1–5-foliolate; stipules usually not adnate to petiole or absent; keel not attenuate; stamens distinct or monadelphous.
                   11. Stamens distinct; corollas reddish purple; shrubs with thorn-tipped stems; rarely fruiting; California native . . . . . 49. *Pickeringia*, v. 11(1), p. 169
                   11. Stamens monadelphous; corollas white or yellow; shrubs or trees, unarmed; introduced widely.

12. Trees or large shrubs; inflorescences axillary, pendulous racemes; leaves palmately trifoliolate; corollas yellow; legumes pendulous, constricted between seeds; introduced, British Columbia, California, Maine, Massachusetts, Oregon, Utah, Washington . . . . 54. *Laburnum*, v. 11(1), p. 248
12. Shrubs; inflorescences axillary or terminal, racemes or glomerules or flowers solitary, or clustered on short axillary shoots; distal leaves often reduced and unifoliolate; corollas yellow or white; legumes pendulous or erect, not constricted between seeds; introduced widely.
    13. Calyx cylindric, 8–9 mm; corollas white; twigs erect becoming pendent . . . . 55. *Cytisus* (in part), v. 11(1), p. 250
    13. Calyx campanulate, 3–7(–15) mm; corollas yellow or white; twigs erect or ascending, sometimes becoming pendent.
        14. Corollas white;· styles incurved; calyx bilabiate, adaxial lip 2-lobed; stems nearly leafless . . .56. *Retama*, v. 11(1), p. 253
        14. Corollas yellow or white; styles abruptly incurved; calyx bilabiate or barely or scarcely lobed; stems generally leafy; seeds with appendage.
            15. Styles abruptly curved near middle; calyx lobes connate most of their length, shallowly lobed; leaves not caducous; corollas yellow or white; legumes laterally compressed or inflated, explosively dehiscent . . . . 55. *Cytisus* (in part), v. 11(1), p. 250
            15. Styles abruptly incurved distally; calyx abaxial lip 3-lobed, adaxial lip 2-lobed; leaves often caducous; corollas yellow; legumes inflated, not explosively dehiscent. . . . . .57. *Genista*, v. 11(1), p. 253

[2. Shifted to left margin.—Ed.]

2. Leaves pinnate, not reduced, rarely unifoliolate; leaflets 3–61(–96+).
    16. Leaves pinnately 3-foliolate, usually not unifoliolate or reduced to spines.
        17. Vines trailing, twining and high climbing, or creeping; inflorescences pseudoracemes.
            18. Calyx 5.5–7.5 mm; leaflet margins entire, not lobed or sinuate; stipules 2.5–3 mm; legumes indehiscent; lianas to 5 m. . . . . 84. *Lackeya*, v. 11(1), p. 370
            18. Calyx 6–18 mm; leaflet margins usually lobed, toothed, or sinuate, sometimes entire; stipules 5–16(–25) mm; legumes dehiscent; vines 2–30 m.
                19. Herbaceous vines, 2–5(–10) m; stipules linear-lanceolate, 5–11 mm; inflorescence bracts setaceous; introduced, Florida . . . . 93. *Pachyrhizus* (in part), v. 11(1), p. 396
                19. Woody or coarsely herbaceous vines, climbing and creeping, to 30 m; stipules peltate, 8–16(–25) mm; inflorescence bracts ovate to lanceolate; introduced widely . . . . 94. *Pueraria* (in part), v. 11(1), p. 397
        17. Shrubs, suffrutescent subshrubs, or trees, not creeping; inflorescences pseudoracemes or racemes.
            20. Fruits indehiscent; seeds 1.
                21. Shrubs; stems and leaves not gland-dotted; fruits loments with 1 article, elliptic to suborbicular, pubescent, without swordlike beak; inflorescences pseudoracemes (each cluster 2–4-flowered), rarely capitate; widespread . . . . .108. *Lespedeza* (in part), v. 11(1), p. 431
                21. Suffrutescent subshrubs; stems and leaves gland-dotted; fruits legumes, ovoid, with swordlike beak; inflorescences dense, headlike racemes; introduced, California . . . . .117. *Aspalthium*, v. 11(1), p. 494
            20. Fruits dehiscent or indehiscent; seeds 1–12.

22. Shrubs or subshrubs; inflorescences axillary racemes, 8–60+-flowered, often appearing spicate; hairs biramous (2-branched); legumes not constricted between seeds . . . . .76. *Indigofera* (in part), v. 11(1), p. 335
22. Trees or shrubs; inflorescences terminal or axillary racemes or pseudoracemes, 1–80[–100]-flowered; hairs not biramous; legumes depressed or constricted between seeds.
23. Shrubs, short-lived, unarmed; stipels setiform; leaflet blades gland-dotted abaxially; corollas yellow, orange, red, or purplish; legumes depressed between seeds; seeds white to cream and brown, purplish, or almost black, sometimes mottled . . . . 90. *Cajanus*, v. 11(1), p. 390
23. Trees or shrubs, armed with recurved prickles; stipels swollen, gland-like; leaflet blades not gland-dotted; corollas red; legumes regularly or irregularly constricted between seeds; seeds red to orange-red or orange, sometimes with black markings . . . . 91. *Erythrina* (in part), v. 11(1), p. 391

[16. Shifted to left margin.—Ed.]

16. Leaves odd- or even-pinnate, rarely subpinnate or unifoliolate, leaflets (1–)3–96+.
24. Flowers apetalous or corollas with banner only; surfaces gland-dotted; inflorescences terminal, racemes or spikes; seeds 1 or 2.
25. Corollas with banner only, blue, purple, or white. . . . . 61. *Amorpha* (in part), v. 11(1), p. 258
25. Corollas absent or only banner present, yellow.
26. Leaflet blades linear-filiform or oblong-elliptic; calyx tube not 10-ribbed; corolla absent; legumes prominently gland-dotted; seeds 1 or 2; sw United States (Colorado Plateau) . . . . .60. *Parryella*, v. 11(1), p. 258
26. Leaflet blades suborbiculate to oblong-ovate; calyx tube 10-ribbed; corolla absent or vestigial banner present, yellow; legumes with scattered glands; seed 1; ne Arizona . . . . 62. *Errazurizia*, v. 11(1), p. 270
24. Flowers with corollas; surfaces glandular or not; inflorescences terminal or axillary, usually racemes, panicles, fascicles, or flowers solitary, rarely pseudoracemes, corymbs, or spikes; seeds 1–40.
27. Stamens distinct or connate proximally.
28. Legumes indehiscent; bracteoles present; corollas purple, blue-purple, lilac, lavender, yellow, pink, or white; seeds usually red, dull red, reddish brown, or black, rarely orange or yellow.
29. Leaflet blades not leathery; inflorescences racemes or panicles; calyx truncate; corollas usually white or yellow, rarely pink or purple; stamens 8; legumes fleshy, straight to curved, moniliform; seeds black . . . . .44. *Styphnolobium*, v. 11(1), p. 160
29. Leaflet blades leathery; inflorescences racemes; calyx with obvious lobes; corollas usually shades of purple, rarely white; stamens 10; legumes papery, leathery, or woody, torose to torulose, straight to slightly curved or subglobose to cylindric; seeds usually red or dull red to reddish brown, rarely orange or yellow . . . . 45. *Dermatophyllum*, v. 11(1), p. 162
28. Legumes dehiscent; bracteoles present or absent; corollas white, creamy white, or yellow; seeds light brown to yellow.
30. Leaflet blades densely villous, sericeous, or glabrescent adaxially (in *S. tomentosa*); stipules usually present, caducous; legumes not compressed, narrowly oblong-moniliform; coastal near beaches . . . 46. *Sophora* (in part), v. 11(1), p. 164
30. Leaflet blades glabrous adaxially; stipules absent; legumes compressed laterally, elliptic to linear or lanceolate, not moniliform; inland in forests.
31. Leaflets alternate; axillary buds enclosed in petiole base; inflorescences pendulous panicles; calyx tubular, slightly zygomorphic; legumes not winged along margin; seeds 5–8, reniform, brown . . . . . .43. *Cladrastis*, v. 11(1), p. 159
31. Leaflets opposite or subopposite; axillary buds exposed; inflorescences erect racemes; calyx campanulate; legumes winged along one suture; seeds 1–3, ellipsoidal, yellow. . . . . .47. *Maackia*, v. 11(1), p. 167

[27. Shifted to left margin.—Ed.]

27. Stamens monadelphous, submonadelphous, diadelphous, or connate at least ½ their length.
   32. Stamens monadelphous, submonadelphous, or connate ½ their length (vexillary stamen may be distinct at base or absent).
      33. Trees, shrubs, or vines; stamens 9 or 10; seeds 1 or 3–8; Florida.
         34. Woody or suffrutescent vines; leaves even-pinnate; seeds red, black, red and black, black and white, or whitish; stamens 9 (vexillary stamen absent); fruits legumes, curved, beaked, elastically dehiscent; seeds (1–)3–7 . . . . 81. *Abrus*, v. 11(1), p. 355
         34. Shrubs or trees; leaves odd-pinnate; seeds reddish brown to dark brown; stamens 10; fruits legumes or loments, straight, not beaked, indehiscent or tardily dehiscent; seeds 1 or 3–8.
            35. Fruits loments, leathery, wings papery (10–20 mm wide); calyx with 5 short lobes; seeds 3–8; s Florida coastal hammocks . . . . .78. *Piscidia*, v. 11(1), p. 345
            35. Fruits legumes, woody or rigidly leathery, without wings; calyx truncate, lobes obsolete; seed 1; introduced in Florida, waste places and thickets . . . . 79. *Millettia*, v. 11(1), p. 346
      33. Shrubs or subshrubs; stamens (4 or)5, 9, or 10; seeds 1(or 2); widespread, including Florida.
         36. Flowers papilionaceous, petals all arising from receptacle (hypanthium rim), wings and keel not epistemonous; banner reflexed less than 90°; shrubs, subshrubs, or trees, armed or unarmed, sterile shoots sometimes sharp-tipped; deserts, sw United States . . . . .64. *Psorothamnus* (in part), v. 11(1), p. 274
         36. Flowers conventionally papilionaceous or not, only banner arising from receptacle (hypanthium rim), wings and keel epistemonous, arising laterally or terminally from stamen column; banner reflexed 90°; herbs, shrubs, or subshrubs, usually unarmed (rarely thorns present in *Dalea*); widespread.
            37. Calyx ribs not anastomosing; leaflet blades with pale sinuous lines, single gland between petiolules; trichomes stiff, short, not spirally twisted; fruits loments, stipitate; se Arizona . . . . 65. *Marina* (in part), v. 11(1), p. 280
            37. Calyx ribs usually anastomosing, forming closed arches; leaflet blades without sinuous lines, 2 adaxial intrapetiolular glands and 2 abaxial postpetiolular glands often present between opposing leaflets; trichomes spirally twisted; fruits legumes, sessile; widespread . . . . . 66. *Dalea* (in part), v. 11(1), p. 283
   32. Stamens diadelphous (vexillary stamen sometimes slightly proximally attached to others).
      38. Leaves mostly even-pinnate, rarely odd-pinnate (or leaflets irregularly arranged).
         39. Trees or shrubs, armed with spine-tipped, persistent leaf rachises, or sometimes with spinescent stipules.
            40. Trees to 10 m; stipules 4–10 mm, spinescent; leaves even- or odd-pinnate, leaflets (8 or)9–21(–24); corollas whitish to purplish; styles with pollen brush surrounding distal ½; legumes stipitate-glandular; Arizona, California . . . . 127. *Olneya*, v. 11(2), p. 544
            40. Shrubs 1–3 m; stipules 1–4 mm, sometimes spinescent; leaves even-pinnate, leaflets 2 or 4(–10); corollas purple to lilac or white; styles without pollen brush; legumes glabrous; introduced, Saskatchewan, California, Utah. . . . . 140. *Halimodendron*, v. 11(2), p. 906
         39. Shrubs, usually unarmed, sometimes weakly prickly or spiny.
            41. Inflorescences fascicles or short racemes of 1–5 flowers.
               42. Corollas mostly whitish, sometimes tinged pinkish; styles tufted with pollen brush; stipules 3–5 mm, subulate; legumes constricted between seeds; s Texas . . . . 129. *Coursetia* (in part), v. 11(2), p. 549
               42. Corollas yellow; styles without pollen brush; stipules 5–9 mm, sometimes spine-tipped; legumes not constricted between seeds; introduced widely . . . . 139. *Caragana* (in part), v. 11(2), p. 903
            41. Inflorescences longer racemes or panicles, with 1–40+ flowers.

43. Calyx lobes shorter than tube; corollas white, pale yellow to orange or red, with or without purple spots; styles with spreading hairs; leaflets folding closed at night; legumes not glandular, with spongy mesocarp, bladdery-inflated, sometimes winged. . . . . 118. *Sesbania* (in part), v. 11(1), p. 496
43. Calyx lobes equal to or longer than tube; corollas mostly whitish; styles with tufted or lateral pollen brush; leaflets not folding; legumes glandular, not spongy, inflated, or winged. . . . . 129. *Coursetia* (in part), v. 11(2), p. 549

[38. Shifted to left margin.—Ed.]

38. Leaves odd-pinnate (sometimes irregularly so).
44. Inflorescences racemes, flowers fascicled or in viscid-glandular racemes; Arizona . . . . 129. *Coursetia* (in part), v. 11(2), p. 549
44. Inflorescences racemes, panicles, corymbs, or solitary flowers, glandular or eglandular.
45. Corollas not typically papilionaceous, petals scarcely differentiated, subequal, white, sometimes becoming purple; stamens visible; inflorescences spikelike racemes; legumes indehiscent; seeds 1(or 2) . . . . 63. *Eysenhardtia*, v. 11(1), p. 271
45. Corollas papilionaceous, white, creamy, yellow, pink to purple, azure, or rose; stamens generally hidden within keel; inflorescences racemes, panicles, corymbs, or solitary flowers; legumes dehiscent or indehiscent; seeds 1–10(–16).
46. Legumes sessile, laterally compressed, tardily dehiscent; trees or shrubs, often armed with spinescent stipules; corollas whitish or pinkish . . . . . . 128. *Robinia*, v. 11(2), p. 545
46. Legumes stipitate, inflated or compressed, dehiscent or indehiscent; trees, shrubs, or vines, unarmed; corollas yellow, white, creamy white, pink to purple, reddish purple, azure, or rose.
47. Legumes bladdery-inflated; corollas bright yellow, banner sometimes with red markings . . . . .136. *Colutea*, v. 11(2), p. 901
47. Legumes flattened, compressed, slightly inflated, plump, or cylindric, not bladdery-inflated; corollas yellow, white, creamy white, pink to purple, reddish purple, azure, or rose.
48. Inflorescences axillary, flowers solitary; leaflets (19–)23–59; corollas yellow; seeds 1 or 2; sw Texas. . . . . .48. *Brongniartia*, v. 11(1), p. 168
48. Inflorescences axillary or terminal, racemes; leaflets 1–25; corollas yellowish, white, creamy white, pink to purple, reddish purple, azure, or rose; seeds 1–14; Arizona and se United States.
49. Racemes 4–7-flowered; peduncles and pedicels glandular-hirsute; calyx tubular; corollas usually yellowish; legumes oblong, slightly inflated; s Arizona. . . . . 75. *Diphysa*, v. 11(1), p. 334
49. Racemes 10–100-flowered; peduncles and pedicels eglandular (except sometimes *Wisteria* pedicels with clavate glands); calyx campanulate; corollas yellowish, white, creamy white, pink to purple, reddish purple, azure, or rose; legumes linear, oblong to elliptic, oblanceolate, subreniform, or subglobose, plump, cylindric, compressed, or flattened; c, e, s United States.
50. Legumes narrowly ellipsoid to oblong, compressed, often winged, samaroid; seeds 1 or 2(–4); leaflets 3 or 5; trees; introduced, s Florida . . . . 73. *Dalbergia* (in part), v. 11(1), p. 327
50. Legumes linear, ovoid, linear-oblong, oblong-elliptic, oblanceolate, or subglobose, not narrowly ellipsoid, not winged; seeds 1–10; leaflets (7 or)9–21(–25); trees or vines, rarely shrubs; c, s, e United States.
51. Legumes drupaceous, pendent, indehiscent; trees; introduced, Florida . . . . 67. *Andira*, v. 11(1), p. 316
51. Legumes not drupaceous, erect, dehiscent; trees or woody vines; c, s, e United States.

52. Twining woody vines; inflorescences terminal, pendent racemes; calyx obviously lobed; legumes flattened or cylindric, torulose; c, s, e United States . . . 77. *Wisteria*, v. 11(1), p. 342
52. Trees; inflorescences axillary racemes; calyx lobes inconspicuous; legumes laterally compressed, linear, not torulose; introduced, Florida. . . . . . 126. *Gliricidia*, v. 11(2), p. 543

1. Herbs or herbaceous vines, stems annual, biennial, or perennial.
53. Leaves all or mostly unifoliolate (or leaflets obsolescent).
54. Stamens monadelphous.
55. Suffrutescent subshrubs, gland-dotted when young, sterile shoots usually sharp-tipped; inflorescences loosely 1–20+-flowered, with thornlike tip; corollas usually blue to blue-purple, rarely white, banner with yellow eye; legumes gland-dotted; seeds usually 1, rarely 2; sw deserts . . .64. *Psorothamnus* (in part), v. 11(1), p. 274
55. Herbs, not gland-dotted when young, short shoots absent; inflorescences loose or not, 1–100-flowered, unarmed; corollas usually blue, pink, rose, yellow, or white, rarely orangish or lavender, banner spot white, cream, pink, maroon, or dark blue; legumes not gland-dotted; seeds 1–70; widespread.
56. Stems persistently green, photosynthetic, glabrous, rushlike; leaves unifoliolate or obsolescent; corollas yellow; legumes linear-oblong; seeds 6–18; introduced, California, Oregon, Texas, Washington. . . . . .58. *Spartium* (in part), v. 11(1), p. 256
56. Stems not persistently green and photosynthetic, glabrous or pubescent, not rushlike; leaves palmately compound or unifoliolate; corollas usually blue, pink, rose, yellow, or white, rarely orangish or lavender; legumes oblong, ovoid, ellipsoid, cylindric, or globose; seeds 1–70; widespread.
57. Leaflet blades 5–150 mm; corollas usually yellow, sometimes orangish, rarely white, blue, or lavender; legumes usually inflated; seeds 1–70, oblique-cordiform to oblong-reniform; widespread. . . . . .52. *Crotalaria* (in part), v. 11(1), p. 185
57. Leaflet blades (10–)20–270 mm; corollas pink, rose, or purple; legumes usually oblong, not inflated; seeds 2–7, spheric, lentiform or angulate; Florida . . . . 53. *Lupinus* (in part), v. 11(1), p. 193
54. Stamens diadelphous (except *Orbexilum* sometimes monadelphous proximally).
58. Herbs, annual; leaves sessile; inflorescences axillary, flowers solitary; corollas pinkish; seeds 4-angled with vertical constriction; Arizona. . . . . .132. *Sphinctospermum*, v. 11(2), p. 555
58. Herbs, annual, perennial, or suffrutescent, or vines; leaves petiolate; inflorescences axillary, terminal, or leaf-opposed, usually pseudoracemes, racemes, or spikes, rarely panicles; corollas purple, blue, pink, red, orange, or yellow; seeds reniform, oblong, subglobose, ovoid to ellipsoid, obovate, or 4-angled, without constriction; c, e, se United States.
59. Herbs, not gland-dotted; stems uncinulate-pubescent; corollas red to reddish blue, reddish violet, orange, orange-buff, pink, pinkish lavender, or white; fruits loments; seeds 2–8; introduced, Alabama, Florida, Georgia, Louisiana, Mississippi, North Carolina, Texas. . . . . .111. *Alysicarpus*, v. 11(1), p. 465
59. Herbs or vines, mostly gland-dotted; stems not uncinulate-pubescent; corollas yellow, yellow-orange, violet, purple, or purplish blue; fruits legumes; seeds 1 or 2; c, e, se United States.
60. Legumes dehiscent, not rugose; corollas yellow or yellow-orange; herbaceous vines; inflorescences usually axillary, rarely terminal, usually racemes, sometimes heads or clustered, 1–3-flowered; c, e, se United States . . . . .89. *Rhynchosia* (in part), v. 11(1), p. 382
60. Legumes indehiscent, rugose; corollas violet, purple, or purplish blue; erect herbs; inflorescences terminal, spikes, 5–50-flowered; Florida, Georgia . . . . 112. *Orbexilum* (in part), v. 11(1), p. 467

[53. Shifted to left margin.—Ed.]

53. Leaves 3–96+-foliolate, distalmost leaves sometimes reduced and unifoliolate.
    61. Herbs, sometimes subshrubs; leaves mostly palmately compound; leaflets (1–)3–11(–17), sometimes unifoliolate or pseudopalmate, rarely phyllodic.
        62. Stamens distinct.
            63. Legumes laterally compressed, valves papery, slowly dehiscent; ovaries short-stipitate; corollas yellow. . . . . .50. *Thermopsis*, v. 11(1), p. 170
            63. Legumes inflated, valves leathery, indehiscent; ovaries long-stipitate; corollas white, yellow, violet, or blue. . . . . 51. *Baptisia*, v. 11(1), p. 177
        62. Stamens monadelphous or diadelphous.
            64. Stamens monadelphous.
                65. Fruits bristly loments (with 2–15 segments); leaflets 2 or 4, blade surfaces sometimes punctate; corollas yellow or orange-yellow; inflorescences subtended by enlarged bracts; filaments equal . . . . 68. *Zornia*, v. 11(1), p. 317
                65. Fruits legumes, not bristly; leaflets 1–11(–17), blade surfaces not punctate; corollas yellow, white, purple, or blue, sometimes orangish, lavender, or rose; inflorescence bracts present but not enlarged; filaments alternately long and short.
                    66. Legumes usually inflated; corollas yellow, sometimes orangish; leaflets 1 or 3; seeds 1–70, oblique-cordiform to oblong-reniform, becoming loose at maturity; aril sometimes conspicuous; mostly e United States . . . . .52. *Crotalaria* (in part), v. 11(1), p. 185
                    66. Legumes laterally compressed; corollas blue to purple, sometimes white, yellow, pink, or rose; leaflets (1–)5–11(–17); seeds 2–12, spheric, lentiform, or angulate, not becoming loose; aril absent; mostly w North America . . . . 53. *Lupinus* (in part), v. 11(1), p. 193
            64. Stamens diadelphous.
                67. Fruits spirally coiled. . . . . 149. *Medicago* (in part), v. 11(2), p. 983
                67. Fruits straight or curved.
                    68. Herbs, especially leaves, calyx, and fruits, usually gland-dotted or glandular-pubescent.
                        69. Calyx not enlarging as fruit matures; leaves sometimes deciduous by anthesis except basally, leaflets (1 or)3–5. . . . . . . 115. *Ladeania*, v. 11(1), p. 475
                        69. Calyx enlarging, often somewhat inflating with fruit maturation; leaves persistent, leaflets (1–)3–7(or 8).
                            70. Fruits rugose, glabrous, sometimes glandular-punctate, well exserted beyond the calyx; calyx campanulate in fruit . . . . 112. *Orbexilum* (in part), v. 11(1), p. 467
                            70. Fruits not rugose, usually pubescent, included in calyx except for beak; calyx gibbous-campanulate in fruit . . . . 116. *Pediomelum* (in part), v. 11(1), p. 476
                    68. Herbs not gland-dotted.
                        71. Fruits enclosed within calyx or corolla, or slightly exserted.
                            72. Hairs silvery, dolabriform (branched in middle); leaflet blade margins entire; herbs subacaulescent and tufted, or prostrate or cushion-forming; flowers in short racemes of 2–6(–10) flowers . . . . .135. *Astragalus* (in part), v. 11(2), p. 584
                            72. Hairs not dolabriform; leaflet blade margins usually toothed or entire, rarely lobed; herbs caulescent or acaulescent, usually erect or ascending, sometimes decumbent to prostrate, rarely mat-forming; flowers in umbels, headlike racemes, or spikes, rarely solitary.
                                73. Stipules absent or glandular . . . . . . 123. *Acmispon* (in part), v. 11(1), p. 507
                                73. Stipules conspicuous, not glandular . . . . 145. *Trifolium* (in part), v. 11(2), p. 914

71. Fruits well exserted from calyx or corolla.
74. Stipules absent or glandular . . . . 123. *Acmispon* (in part), v. 11(1), p. 507
74. Stipules conspicuous, not glandular.
75. Fruits elliptic or broadly ovate to ± globose, not reniform; leaflet blade margins entire throughout; inflorescences small, axillary clusters (pseudoracemes), with 1–4 flowers; corollas with pink-purple banner, white wings, keel apex purple . . . . 107. *Kummerowia*, v. 11(1), p. 429
75. Fruits falcate to reniform-incurved; leaflet blade margins partly serrate; inflorescences cylindrical heads with (5–)15–50 flowers; corollas yellow. . . . 149. *Medicago* (in part), v. 11(2), p. 983

[61. Shifted to left margin.—Ed.]

61. Vines, herbs, or subshrubs; leaves usually pinnate, rarely unifoliolate or phyllodic; leaflets (1 or)3–80(–96+).
76. Leaves mostly unifoliolate or 3-foliolate.
77. Herbs with separate foliose and flowering stems.
78. Corollas red; leaves alternate; fruits legumes; s United States . . . . 91. *Erythrina* (in part), v. 11(1), p. 391
78. Corollas usually pink, rarely white; leaves usually 4–7-whorled, sometimes scattered on stems; fruits loments; North America, Great Plains, and eastward. . . . . 110. *Hylodesmum* (in part), v. 11(1), p. 462
77. Vines, herbs, or subshrubs without separate foliose and flowering stems.
79. Stamens monadelphous at anthesis (vexillary stamen becoming distinct in *Hoita*).
80. Wings and keel epistemonous, attached terminally or laterally to stamen tube.
81. Ovule 1; stems eglandular; leaflet blade surfaces with sinuous lines (lineolate); calyx ribs not anastomosing; trichomes stiff, short; California . . . . 65. *Marina* (in part), v. 11(1), p. 280
81. Ovules 2; stems gland-dotted; leaflet blade surfaces not lineolate; calyx ribs anastomosing distally; trichomes flexuous, spirally twisting; widespread . . . . 66. *Dalea* (in part), v. 11(1), p. 283
80. Wings and keel not epistemonous, attached below staminal tube.
82. Fruits indehiscent, not exserted from calyx, apiculate or beaked, eglandular or sparsely glandular; seed 1; Pacific States, British Columbia.
83. Corollas purple or purplish-tinged; calyx not enlarging in fruit, becoming papery; fruits with secondary internal wall of sclereids; California . . . . 113. *Hoita*, v. 11(1), p. 470
83. Corollas cream or yellow; calyx enlarging and concealing fruit, not becoming papery; fruits without secondary internal wall of sclereids; Pacific states, British Columbia . . . . 114. *Rupertia*, v. 11(1), p. 472
82. Fruits dehiscent or indehiscent, exserted from calyx, apiculate-beaked or not, eglandular; seeds 1–15; widespread.
84. Fruits loments, indehiscent.
85. Stipules amplexicaul, adnate to petioles for most of its length; inflorescences short spikes or solitary flowers, 1–15-flowered; bracts foliaceous, persistent; corollas yellow or orange-yellow. . . . . 71. *Stylosanthes*, v. 11(1), p. 322
85. Stipules free from petioles; inflorescences simple or compound racemes or pseudoracemes, or long spikes, (1 or)2–51-flowered; bracts not foliaceous, persistent or deciduous; corollas usually pink, blue, shades of purple, or white, rarely yellow.

86. Stipels present, persistent; calyx lobes longer than tube; loments with (1 or)2–10 segments, stipitate or sessile . . . . 109. *Desmodium* (in part), v. 11(1), p. 442

86. Stipels absent or early-deciduous; calyx lobes shorter than tube; loments with 2–5 segments, distinctly stipitate . . . . 110. *Hylodesmum* (in part), v. 11(1), p. 462

84. Fruits legumes, dehiscent or indehiscent.

87. Herbs, thorns present or absent; stipules adnate to petiole; leaflet margins usually serrulate at least distally, rarely entire; inflorescences racemes, with 1–3 flowers; legumes usually not exceeding calyx . . . . 146. *Ononis*, v. 11(2), p. 975

87. Vines, trailing or climbing, or herbs, unarmed; stipules not adnate to petiole; leaflet margins entire or lobed; inflorescences pseudoracemes or panicles, with 8–50 flowers; legumes larger, well exceeding calyx.

88. Stipules caducous, deltate, or obsolete; ventral margin of fruit 3–5 ribbed; inflorescences panicles, with 8–50 flowers . . . . 82. *Canavalia*, v. 11(1), p. 356

88. Stipules present, conspicuous, peltate; ventral margin of fruit not ribbed; inflorescences pseudoracemes, with 15–40 flowers . . . . 94. *Pueraria* (in part), v. 11(1), p. 397

[79. Shifted to left margin.—Ed.]

79. Stamens usually diadelphous, rarely distinct (except becoming diadelphous in *Pueraria* as fruit expands).

89. Corollas large (20–60+ mm); banners much larger than wings and keel (more than 2 times); inflorescences 1 or 2(–4)-flowered, axillary pseudoracemes; flowers resupinate.

90. Calyx funnelform, lobes shorter than tube; wings extending beyond the keel; styles geniculate distally; fruits 6–11 mm wide, convex and depressed between seeds or flat . . . . 85. *Clitoria* (in part), v. 11(1), p. 371

90. Calyx campanulate, lobes equal to or longer than tube; wings subequal to keel; styles incurved, broadly U-shaped; fruits 3–6 mm wide, flat with raised rib near margin . . . . 86. *Centrosema*, v. 11(1), p. 376

89. Corollas smaller, or if not, then banner not much larger than other petals; inflorescences 1–500+-flowered, axillary or terminal racemes, pseudoracemes, fascicles, panicles, umbels, heads, or flowers solitary; flowers not resupinate.

91. Leaflet margins usually at least partly dentate or serrate, lateral vein tips slightly exserted; fruits indehiscent (or breaking crosswise or irregularly), sometimes prickly and spirally coiled; seeds 1–few; corollas 2–27 mm.

92. Fruits spirally coiled, sometimes only falcate, with or without prickles . . . . 149. *Medicago* (in part), v. 11(2), p. 983

92. Fruits not spirally coiled, without prickles.

93. Fruits included in marcescent corolla or slightly exserted, usually papery or membranous; flowers usually in umbellate racemes. . . . . 145. *Trifolium* (in part), v. 11(2), p. 914

93. Fruits exserted beyond corolla remnants, thickly leathery; flowers in slender or short racemes.

94. Stems usually erect or ascending, sometimes decumbent; inflorescences elongate, axillary racemes; seeds 1 or 2(or 3) . . . . 147. *Melilotus*, v. 11(2), p. 977

94. Stems usually decumbent, procumbent, or prostrate, sometimes ascending or erect; inflorescences racemes or heads, sometimes umbellate, or flowers solitary; seeds 1–30.

95. Corollas 5.5–18 mm, banner without major veins; legumes linear to ovoid or rhomboid-obovoid; seeds oblong to ovoid . . . . .148. *Trigonella*, v. 11(2), p. 981

95. Corollas 2–4(–6) mm, banner with major basal vein; legumes terete, compressed, or flat; seeds mostly reniform . . . . 149. *Medicago* (in part), v. 11(2), p. 983

[91. Shifted to left margin.—Ed.]

91. Leaflet margins entire, rarely lobed, or if dentate, vein tips not exserted (sometimes exserted in a few teeth in *Pachyrhizus*); fruits dehiscent through sutures or indehiscent; seeds 1–25 (–30); corollas often greater than 27 mm.

96. Keel incurved 90–180° or spirally coiled.

97. Stipules auriculate or peltate; corollas yellow, purple, or white; legumes resupinate by twisting of pedicel; seeds mostly with a white aril (protruding hilum) . . . . 99. *Vigna* (in part), v. 11(1), p. 405

97. Stipules not auriculate or peltate; corollas usually pink, purple, red, or orange, rarely yellow or white; legumes not resupinate; seeds usually without aril.

98. Hairs finely uncinate, minutely hooked; floral nodes not swollen; pedicels equal to or longer than calyx tube; keel beaked, apex laterally and tightly coiled 1.5–2 turns. . . . . 104. *Phaseolus*, v. 11(1), p. 414

98. Hairs not uncinate, straight, loosely tangled, or glandular; floral nodes swollen; pedicels mostly shorter than calyx tube; keel incurved or rarely coiled but not laterally.

99. Wing petals oblong, not projected beyond distal bend of keel; hilum elongated ½ length of seed or longer.

100. Keel petals connate along upper margin without forming a gibbosity or hump proximal to the beak; banner with two prominent appendages on inner face; calyx 5-lobed; inflorescences pseudoracemes with 50–60+ flowers; bracts and bracteoles usually caducous; corollas greenish yellow to purple; introduced, Texas. . . . . . 103. *Oxyrhynchus*, v. 11(1), p. 412

100. Keel petals connate along upper margin where a gibbosity or hump forms proximal to the beak; banner without appendages on inner face; calyx with 4 acute-attenuate lobes; inflorescences pseudoracemes, on long peduncle, with 1–12(–22) flowers; secondary bracts and bracteoles persistent, bracteoles conspicuous, equal to or longer than the calyx tube; corollas pink; c, e United States. . . . . 105. *Strophostyles* (in part), v. 11(1), p. 423

99. Wing petals oblong, obovate, ovate, or spatulate, conspicuously projected beyond distal bend of keel; hilum not elongated.

101. Petals connate, keel beak hooked, tip of beak hidden by wing petals; corollas salmon-orange, red, or purple-black; one wing petal directed upward to adopt function of banner . . . . 106. *Macroptilium*, v. 11(1), p. 426

101. Petals distinct, keel beak widely curved, openly hooked, or sigmoidally curved, tip of keel not hidden by wing petals; corollas usually pink to purple, lilac, or white, rarely lavender; wings not directed upward.

102. Keel beak gradually twisted into a hook shape, with conspicuous interlocking marginal hairs, distalmost portion of keel beak folded back on itself; legumes short-beaked distally, mostly erect . . . . .100. *Ancistrotropis*, v. 11(1), p. 408

102. Keel beak sigmoid-curved or tightly coiled, not folded back distally.

103. Keel beak very tightly coiled distally, projected downward rather than laterally; inflorescences with 50 flowers; corollas usually light pink to purple, sometimes white becoming yellowish, wings with purple pattern; introduced, Florida . . . . 101. *Leptospron*, v. 11(1), p. 409

103. Keel beak distinctly sigmoid-curved (S-shaped); inflorescences with 2–10 flowers; corollas light to deep purple or deep lilac, wings without purple pattern; Florida . . . . 102. *Sigmoidotropis*, v. 11(1), p. 410

[96. Shifted to left margin.—Ed.]

96. Keel incurved to ca. 90°, not coiled.

104. Leaflets evidently stipellate at maturity.

105. Fruits loments; inflorescence rachis mostly uncinate-pubescent . . . . 109. *Desmodium* (in part), v. 11(1), p. 442

105. Fruits legumes; inflorescence rachis not uncinate-pubescent.

106. Stems usually twining or trailing, prostrate, or rarely ascending or erect; calyx tubular; keel and style slightly to strongly incurved; cleistogamous flowers (with reduced corollas and stamens) usually present along with purple or purplish blue chasmogamous flowers; sc, sw United States. . . . . 92. *Cologania* (in part), v. 11(1), p. 393

106. Stems ascending, erect, spreading, climbing to prostrate, twining, or procumbent; calyx usually campanulate, rarely 2-lipped or tubular; keel and style incurved or not; cleistogamous flowers usually absent (except *Amphicarpaea*) and chasmogamous present with corollas yellow to orange, shades of purple, pink, blue, or white; widespread.

107. Herbs, subshrubs, or vines, gland-dotted; legumes pubescent; corollas yellow or yellow-orange; seeds 1 or 2; sc, se United States . . . . 89. *Rhynchosia* (in part), v. 11(1), p. 382

107. Herb, shrubs, lianas, or vines, not gland-dotted; legumes glabrous or pubescent; corollas usually violet, pink, blue, lavender, purple, greenish yellow, or white, rarely yellow; seeds 1–25; widespread.

108. Stipules persistent and conspicuous.

109. Herbs; stems erect, pilose-pubescent; inflorescences short racemes, flowers 5–8; corollas 4.5–7(–10) mm; seeds 2–4 . . . . 96. *Glycine*, v. 11(1), p. 401

109. Vines; stems prostrate, twining, or creeping, glabrous or pubescent; inflorescences racemes or pseudoracemes, flowers 1–40; corollas 3.6–30 mm; seeds 1–25.

110. Calyx (6–)10–18 mm (including lobes); leaflet blades 8–20(–26) cm, margins usually 3-lobed; vines coarse, climbing or creeping, to 30 m. . . . . 94. *Pueraria* (in part), v. 11(1), p. 397

110. Calyx 1.3–8 mm; leaflet blades 1.3–5.6(–7.2) cm, margins usually entire, sometimes shallowly deeply incised or lobed; vines prostrate, climbing, or trailing, 1–3 m.

111. Bracteoles obsolescent or absent; flowers 6–24, distributed along axis; styles glabrous . . . . 95. *Amphicarpaea*, v. 11(1), p. 399

111. Bracteoles calyx-like, usually persistent to anthesis; flowers 1–4 distally congested on long peduncle or rachis much contracted; styles bearded.

112. Corollas 25–30 mm; stipules conspicuously retrorse-auriculate. . . . . 99. *Vigna* (in part), v. 11(1), p. 405
112. Corollas 3.6–15 mm; stipules entire, without retrorse lobe.
113. Corollas pale yellow with reddish veins; bracteoles minute or deciduous; legumes pendulous; Florida. . . . . 99. *Vigna* (in part), v. 11(1), p. 405
113. Corollas pink or pinkish, keel beak dark purple; bracteoles persistent; legumes held horizontally or somewhat drooping; widespread . . . . 105. *Strophostyles* (in part), v. 11(1), p. 423
108. Stipules small, relatively inconspicuous, or obsolescent.
114. Corollas 30–65 mm; legumes often with stinging hairs, compressed between seeds; seeds 10–20 mm diam., with conspicuous lateral hilum; se United States . . . 88. *Mucuna*, v. 11(1), p. 380
114. Corollas 6–15(–17) mm; legumes without stinging hairs, not compressed between seeds; seeds 3–13 mm, lateral hilum inconspicuous or absent; c, e, s, se, sw United States.
115. Styles glabrous; bracteoles generally caducous; herbs, from a woody taproot. . . 83. *Galactia* (in part), v. 11(1), p. 358
115. Styles bearded or with 2 lines of hairs; bracteoles present; vines (from a woody base) or herbs.
116. Vines (from a woody base); stems twining and climbing; pedicels longer than calyx tube; banners with 1 prominent appendage at base; styles with 2 lines of hairs; bracteoles lanceolate, persistent; legumes 3–5 cm, ventral suture not verrucose; seeds 4–7 mm, black or brown, hilum 2.5–3 mm with aril. . . . . .97. *Dipogon*, v. 11(1), p. 402
116. Herbs; stems climbing or suberect; pedicels shorter than calyx tube; banners with 2 prominent appendages at base; styles bearded; bracteoles elliptic-rounded, subpersistent; legumes 5–10 cm, ventral suture verrucose; seeds 9–13 mm, white or reddish brown to black, hilum and large white aril extending more than ½ seed length. . . . . 98. *Lablab*, v. 11(1), p. 404

[104. Shifted to left margin.—Ed.]

104. Leaflet stipels absent or deciduous.
117. Fruits dehiscent, (1 or)2–numerous-seeded.
118. Fruits 6–15 cm; corollas 14–22 mm . . . . 93. *Pachyrhizus* (in part), v. 11(1), p. 396
118. Fruits 1–4 cm; corollas 2.5–12(–14) mm.
119. Herbs, with pilose hairs; corollas salmon reddish, 5 mm; seeds 3–6 . . . . .76. *Indigofera* (in part), v. 11(1), p. 335
119. Herbs or vines, without pilose hairs; corollas yellow, orange-yellow, or green-yellow, (4–)6–12(–14) mm; seeds 1 or 2. . . .89. *Rhynchosia* (in part), v. 11(1), p. 382
117. Fruits indehiscent or irregularly dehiscent, either 1-seeded loments or legumes or several-seeded and -segmented loments.
120. Loments with (1 or)2–10 segments, with 1 seed per segment, splitting between indehiscent segments . . . . 109. *Desmodium* (in part), v. 11(1), p. 442
120. Loments or legumes with a single segment, 1-seeded, indehiscent or irregularly dehiscent.

121. Bodies of fruits included in enlarged calyx except for projecting beak . . . . 116. *Pediomelum* (in part), v. 11(1), p. 476
121. Bodies of fruits usually not included in calyx, subequal to calyx lobes or exserted above them.
122. Loment walls papery; bracteoles present; herbs or shrubs, not gland-dotted . . . . 108. *Lespedeza* (in part), v. 11(1), p. 431
122. Legume walls thickly leathery; bracteoles absent; herbs, commonly gland-dotted . . . . 112. *Orbexilum* (in part), v. 11(1), p. 467

[76. Shifted to left margin.—Ed.]

76. Leaves mostly 3–96-foliolate (reduced leaves may have only 2 or 3 leaflets).
123. Leaves even-pinnate; herbs annual, perennial, or biennial.
124. Fruits geocarpic, ± indehiscent; stamens monadelphous, with 8 functional anthers and 2 sterile filaments . . . . 72. *Arachis* (in part), v. 11(1), p. 324
124. Fruits borne above ground, dehiscent or indehiscent; stamens diadelphous, uniform.
125. Leaflets all 2 and/or 4 in number.
126. Styles terete, with a dense ring of hairs just proximal to stigma; corollas 2–8 mm (8–12 mm in *V. ocalensis*); leaflets usually both 2 and 4 . . . . 150. *Vicia* (in part), v. 11(2), p. 994
126. Styles abaxially compressed; corollas 10 mm or more; leaflets all either 2 or 4.
127. Leaflets 2, usually with several longitudinal veins in addition to midrib; inflorescence bracts absent . . . . . 152. *Lathyrus* (in part), v. 11(2), p. 1008
127. Leaflets 4, without major longitudinal veins in addition to midrib; inflorescence bracts present, caducous . . . . 153. *Pisum* (in part), v. 11(2), p. 1030
125. Leaflets (0 or)2–30(–96+), if mostly 2 or 4, some leaves with more than 4 leaflets.
128. Tendrils absent, rachis slightly or evidently extended as a short bristle or mucronate tendril; legumes bladdery-inflated, terete, or flattened, dehiscent or indehiscent.
129. Calyx undulate-truncate or with 5 short lobes 1/4-1/3 as long as tube; stipules narrowly triangular, caducous; legumes terete, elliptic, or 4-angled, flat, inflated, or winged, glabrous; leaflets 10–96+, folding forward to close at night. . . . . 118. *Sesbania* (in part), v. 11(1), p. 496
129. Calyx 2 lipped with some or all lobes at least 1/2 as long as tube; stipules foliose, persistent; legumes linear, sparsely pubescent; leaflets 2–6, not folding . . . . 150. *Vicia* (in part), v. 11(2), p. 994
128. Tendrils present on some or all leaves; legumes laterally compressed (-turgid), dehiscent.
130. Stipules foliaceous, usually larger than leaflets; leaflets 4 or 6; styles folded longitudinally, bearded laterally; stems not winged . . . . 153. *Pisum* (in part), v. 11(2), p. 1030
130. Stipules foliaceous or inconspicuous, not larger than leaflets; leaflets 2–30; styles not longitudinally folded, either laterally bearded or with apical tuft of hairs; stems angled or winged.
131. Calyx lobes 2–4 times longer than tube; herbs conspicuously pilose; flowers 10–15 mm, 1–3 at or near apex of axillary racemes; stems angled, not winged . . 151. *Lens*, v. 11(2), p. 1007
131. Calyx lobes all or some less than 2 times as long as tube, usually shorter than tube; herbs glabrous or pubescent, rarely pilose; flowers 2–35 mm, mostly axillary; stems angled or winged.

132. Styles terete with a distal tuft of hairs (rarely absent) on abaxial side or encircling; stems angled . . . . 150. *Vicia* (in part), v. 11(2), p. 994

132. Styles abaxially compressed, laterally to apically bearded on adaxial side; stems angled and/or winged . . . . 152. *Lathyrus* (in part), v. 11(2), p. 1008

[123. Shifted to left margin.—Ed.]

123. Leaves odd-pinnate; herbs, subshrubs, or vines, usually perennial.

133. Flowers not papilionaceous, wing and keel petals epistemonous, arising from apex of the stamen tube or laterally from it, or wings and keel absent, corolla then consisting only of banner; herbs or shrubs often conspicuously gland-dotted.

134. Corollas consisting only of banner, keel and wings absent; suffrutescent herbs, mostly canescent . . . . 61. *Amorpha* (in part), v. 11(1), p. 258

134. Corollas with 5 petals, epistemonous keel and wings either scarcely differentiated, ovate-oblong to lanceolate and arising from apex of stamen tube, or differentiated and arising laterally from stamen tube; herbs or shrubs, not canescent.

135. Ovules 1 and seed 1; inflorescences racemes; leaflet blades with sinuous lines; calyx ribs not anastomosing distally; sw United States . . . . 65. *Marina* (in part), v. 11(1), p. 280

135. Ovules 2 and seeds 1 or 2; inflorescences spikes; leaflet blades without sinuous lines; calyx ribs anastomosing distally; widespread. . . . . 66. *Dalea* (in part), v. 11(1), p. 283

133. Flowers papilionaceous (-subpapilionaceous), wings and keel arising from receptacle, all petals present; herbs, shrubs, vines, or trees, glandular or eglandular.

136. Stamens distinct or proximally connate; corollas white, creamy white, yellow, or purple; perennial herbs . . . . 46. *Sophora* (in part), v. 11(1), p. 164

136. Stamens monadelphous or diadelphous, usually basally connate; corollas white, yellow, pink to salmon, orange, shades of purple, blue, or red; usually annual or perennial herbs, vines, or subshrubs.

137. Subshrubs, armed, glandular nearly throughout; inflorescence rachis with thornlike tip in anthesis; Nevada . . . . .64. *Psorothamnus* (in part), v. 11(1), p. 274

137. Herbs, subshrubs, or vines, usually unarmed (except *Peteria* armed, stipules and stipels spinescent and bracts spine-tipped), usually eglandular; inflorescence rachis without thornlike tip; widespread.

138. Fruits loments.

139. Inflorescences umbels.

140. Leaflets 11–25; corollas white, pink, purple, or bicolored; perennial herbs; introduced, widespread. . . . . .119. *Securigera*, v. 11(1), p. 501

140. Leaflets 5–7; corollas yellow; shrubby herbs; introduced, California . . . . 120. *Coronilla*, v. 11(1), p. 502

139. Inflorescences fascicles, racemes, panicles, spikes, or heads, rarely solitary flowers.

141. Flowers sub-papilionaceous, wings much smaller than other petals; loments indehiscent, coarsely reticulate, winged, prickly edged; seed 1. . . . . 143. *Onobrychis*, v. 11(2), p. 912

141. Flowers papilionaceous, wings not significantly smaller than other petals; loments dehiscent or indehiscent, not coarsely reticulate, not or moderately winged, not prickly edged (surfaces sometimes prickly in *Hedysarum boreale*); seeds 1–9.

[142. Shifted to left margin.—Ed.]

142. Vines, twining; distal segment of loment sterile, flat, winglike (except *N. wislizeni*); sw United States . . . . 69. *Nissolia*, v. 11(1), p. 319
142. Herbs, not twining; distal segment of loment not produced into a wing; se United States or widespread.
    143. Loments geocarpic, ± indehiscent; stamens monadelphous, with 8 functional anthers and 2 sterile filaments . . . . 72. *Arachis* (in part), v. 11(1), p. 324
    143. Loments not geocarpic, dehiscent or indehiscent; stamens monadelphous or diadelphous, 10, all functional.
        144. Plants annual; inflorescences umbellate heads; loment segments oblong or elliptic-oblong; flowers with inconspicuous keel. . . . . 122. *Ornithopus*, v. 11(1), p. 505
        144. Plants annual or perennial; inflorescences racemes (sometimes subcapitate) or panicles, rarely solitary flowers; loment segments flattened, subglobose, subquadrate, or cylindric; flowers with conspicuous or inconspicuous keel.
            145. Inflorescences terminal and axillary panicles; stipules petiolate . . . . 70. *Chapmannia*, v. 11(1), p. 320
            145. Inflorescences axillary racemes; stipules sessile.
                146. Stipules peltate; inflorescences with 1–5(–15) flowers; keel acute, included, bent, or curved; corollas yellowish; stems often with glandular hairs; se, sw United States to Missouri. . . . . 74. *Aeschynomene*, v. 11(1), p. 329
                146. Stipules ± connate-sheathing, lanceolate; inflorescences with 5–60 flowers; keel broadly truncate, much exceeding other petals; corollas usually pink, reddish, or purple, or yellow, rarely white; stems without glandular hairs; w, ne United States, Canada . . . . 142. *Hedysarum*, v. 11(2), p. 908

[138. Shifted to left margin.—Ed.]

138. Fruits legumes.
    147. Leaflet margins conspicuously dentate; legumes inflated and densely glandular-pubescent; seeds 1 or 2, ovoid-globular . . . . 144. *Cicer*, v. 11(2), p. 913
    147. Leaflet margins entire; legumes inflated or not, glabrous or pubescent, not glandular; seeds 1–77(–84), globose to cuboid, oblong, ovoid, obovoid, reniform, ellipsoid, or terete.
        148. Inflorescences headlike racemes or umbels; flowers subtended by a reduced lobed bract (prophyll); corollas usually yellow; terminal leaflet usually considerably longer than laterals; legumes included in calyx; seeds 1 or 2, globose to ovoid. . . . . 121. *Anthyllis*, v. 11(1), p. 503
        148. Inflorescences racemes or pseudoracemes or flowers solitary, rarely umbellate or fasciculate; flowers without prophylls; corollas purple to blue, pink, reddish, maroon, orange, yellow, cream, or white; terminal leaflets usually not considerably longer than laterals; legumes included in calyx or not; seeds 1–77(–84), globose to cuboid, oblong, ovoid, obovoid, reniform, ellipsoid, or terete.
            149. Leaflets 3(or 5); vines, twining; corollas usually purple to pink-purple or bluish, rarely magenta; keel slightly incurved; sw United States . . . . 92. *Cologania* (in part), v. 11(1), p. 393
            149. Leaflets 1–45(–70); herbs, rarely vines or shrubs, not twining (except *Apios*); corollas purple to blue, pink, reddish, maroon, orange, yellow, cream, or white; keel straight to suberect (except incurved in *Apios*); widespread.
                150. Banners 40–55 mm, much larger than other petals and arising from lower side of resupinate flower; leaflets 5 or 7, stipellate; stipules persistent, striate; inflorescences usually bearing a single resupinate flower . . . . 85. *Clitoria* (in part), v. 11(1), p. 371
                150. Banners 4–26 mm, nearly equal to or only moderately larger than other petals; leaflets 1–45(–70), stipellate or not; stipules persistent or deciduous, not striate; inflorescences without resupinate flowers.

[151. Shifted to left margin.—Ed.]

151. Inflorescences umbels or solitary flowers; legumes narrowly oblong or linear, subterete to quadrate; leaflets 3–25.
    152. Leaflets 3–19, proximal pair not in stipular position; stipules leafy and scarious; corollas yellow, cream, white, pink, purple, red, or lurid; w North America . . . . 124. *Hosackia*, v. 11(1), p. 532
    152. Leaflets 5, proximal pair in stipular position, others palmately arranged; stipules glandlike; corollas yellow, usually marked with red; introduced, widespread . . . . 125. *Lotus*, v. 11(1), p. 538
151. Inflorescences racemes or pseudoracemes; legumes linear to oblong, cylindric, ellipsoid, ovoid, lanceoloid, or globose; leaflets 1–45(–70).
    153. Stipules deeply sagittate-lobed, persistent; bracts subulate, persistent after anthesis; stamens monadelphous; legumes linear-cylindric, torulose . . . . 138. *Galega*, v. 11(2), p. 902
    153. Stipules not sagittate, not lobed, persistent or deciduous; bracts when present usually deltate, lanceolate, linear, or setaceous, rarely subulate, persistent or caducous; stamens monadelphous or diadelphous; legumes linear to oblong, cylindric, ellipsoid, ovoid, lanceoloid, or globose, not torulose.
        154. Leaf blades glandular-punctate; legumes glabrous or with hooked setae; corollas yellow-white, purple-tinged, or bluish . . . . 133. *Glycyrrhiza*, v. 11(2), p. 556
        154. Leaf blades not glandular-punctate; legumes glabrous or pubescent, without hooked setae; corollas white, cream, yellow, pink, blue to purple, maroon, pale green, violet, lavender, or lilac.
            155. Hairs dolabriform (2-branched from middle) in part or throughout; stipules free, not connate; corollas pink to red, salmon to maroon, orange-mauve to orange, or greenish yellow to ochroleucous, rarely white; anthers apiculate and initially gland-tipped . . . . . . .76. *Indigofera* (in part), v. 11(1), p. 335
            155. Hairs basifixed; stipules adnate to petiole or free; corollas white, cream, yellow, pink, blue to purple, maroon, pale green, violet, lavender, or lilac; anthers not apiculate.
                156. Herbs or vines prostrate, twining, or clambering.
                    157. Inflorescences terminal or leaf-opposed; leaflets (3 or)5–11 (or 13), with numerous (8–15) parallel, straight, lateral veins extending to margins . . . . 80. *Tephrosia* (in part), v. 11(1), p. 347
                    157. Inflorescences axillary; leaflets 1–7(or 9), without numerous parallel, lateral veins.
                        158. Keels carinate or moderately incurved; styles filiform, not coiled; inflorescences few-flowered at apex of peduncle or reduced to 1 or 2 flowers in leaf axils; leaflet blades 20–55 mm; rhizomes not tuber-bearing. . . . . 83. *Galactia* (in part), v. 11(1), p. 358
                        158. Keels incurved to strongly incurved; styles spirally coiled; inflorescences many-flowered, nodose pseudoracemes, often flowering ½+ axis length; leaflet blades 47–100 mm; rhizomes tuber-bearing . . . . 87. *Apios*, v. 11(1), p. 378
                156. Herbs usually erect, ascending, prostrate, or decumbent, rarely scandent, not vining.
                    159. Inflorescences pseudoracemes, usually leaf-opposed, with (1 or)2–45 flowers; legumes laterally compressed, flat; styles bearded (except *T. angustissima*) . . . . . . 80. *Tephrosia* (in part), v. 11(1), p. 347
                    159. Inflorescences terminal or axillary racemes; legumes usually bladdery-inflated (except *Peteria* laterally compressed); styles glabrous, sometimes bearded distally.

[160. Shifted to left margin.—Ed.]

160. Stipules spinescent; inflorescences leaf-opposed racemes, appearing terminal; styles slightly bearded; seeds cylindric; w, sc United States . . . . 130. *Peteria*, v. 11(2), p. 552
160. Stipules not spinescent; inflorescences racemes, not leaf-opposed, axillary or terminal; styles glabrous or bearded; seeds reniform; widespread.
    161. Plants with both conspicuously beaked (porrect) keel tips and scapose racemes, often spikelike; plants usually cespitose; styles glabrous. . . . . .134. *Oxytropis*, v. 11(2), p. 557
    161. Plants not with both beaked keels and scapose racemes; styles bearded or glabrous.
        162. Styles glabrous; legumes dehiscent throughout or apically, compressed to bladdery-inflated; corollas violet, blue-purple, purple, red-purple, pink-purple, pink, lilac, reddish, whitish, yellowish, cream, ochroleucous, or greenish; plants with or without creeping rhizomes; widespread, especially in w United States . . . . .135. *Astragalus* (in part), v. 11(2), p. 584
        162. Styles distally bearded; legumes indehiscent, bladdery-inflated; corollas orange-red or brick-red; plants without creeping rhizomes; introduced, w, c North America . . . . 137. *Sphaerophysa*, v. 11(2), p. 902

43. CLADRASTIS Rafinesque, Cincinnati Lit. Gaz. 1(8): 60. 1824 • Yellowwood [Greek *klados*, branch, and *thraustos*, fragile, alluding to brittle branches]

Matthew L. Duley

Trees, unarmed. **Stems** ascending, glabrous. **Leaves** alternate, odd-pinnate, axillary buds enclosed in petiole base; stipules absent; petiolate; leaflets 5–9[–15], alternate, stipels absent, blade margins entire, surfaces pubescent abaxially, glabrous adaxially. **Inflorescences** 25–75+-flowered, terminal, panicles, pendulous; bracts absent. **Flowers** papilionaceous; calyx slightly zygomorphic, tubular, lobes 5, connate basally ½ length; corolla white [pink]; stamens 10, monadelphous, slightly connate at base; anthers dorsifixed. **Fruits** legumes, sessile, compressed laterally, straight, elliptic to linear, apex acute, dehiscent, glabrous or slightly pubescent. **Seeds** [1–]5–8, brown, reniform. $x = 14$.

Species 6 (1 in the flora): sc, se United States, e Asia.

SELECTED REFERENCES Duley, M. L. and M. A. Vincent. 2003. A synopsis of the genus *Cladrastis* (Leguminosae). Rhodora 105: 205–239. Robertson, K. R. 1977. *Cladrastis*: The yellow woods. Arnoldia (Jamaica Plain) 37: 137–150.

1. Cladrastis kentukea (Dumont de Courset) Rudd, Phytologia 21: 327. 1971 (as kentuckea) [E] [F]

Sophora kentukea Dumont de Courset, Bot. Cult. ed. 2, 6: 56. 1811; *Cladrastis fragrans* Rafinesque; *C. lutea* (F. Michaux) K. Koch; *C. tinctoria* Rafinesque; *Virgilia fragilis* Rafinesque; *V. lutea* F. Michaux

Trees to 20 m, canopy to 16 m, rounded; bark gray to gray-brown, thin, smooth. **Stems** reddish brown when young. **Leaves** 20–26 cm; buds pubescent, hairs rusty; petiole green to greenish brown, (1–)3.3–5 cm, glabrous; leaflets: pulvinus glabrous or sparsely pubescent, hairs yellow to rusty; proximal blades ovate, 30–95 × 25–60 mm, terminal blades obovate, ovate, elliptic, or broadly elliptic, 60–170 × 50–110 mm, base rounded or acute, apex acuminate, surfaces sparsely to densely pubescent abaxially at base near or on midvein, hairs white, glabrous adaxially. **Peduncles** 1.5–8 cm. **Panicles** pendulous, 20–50 × 7–22 cm. **Pedicels** 1–2 cm. **Flowers:** calyx 7.2–11.2 × 9.6–14.9 mm, densely pubescent, hairs white to yellow; abaxial lobe 0.4–2.4 × 0.9–2.7 mm; lateral lobes 1.1–2.5 × 2.2–3.2 mm; adaxial lobes 1–2.4 × 2.4–6.7 mm; corolla 10–19 mm, banner reflexed, orbiculate, 12.3–18.3 × 10–15.7 mm, base cuneate, claw 4–7 mm; wings lanceolate, 12–18.9 × 5.1–7.7 mm, base auriculate, claw 5–8 mm; keel lanceolate, 10.7–18.2 × 6.1–9 mm, base auriculate, margins overlapping, folded together; stamens unequal; ovary densely pubescent, hairs white or yellow. **Legumes** 70–80 mm, base cuneate, apex acute. $2n = 28$.

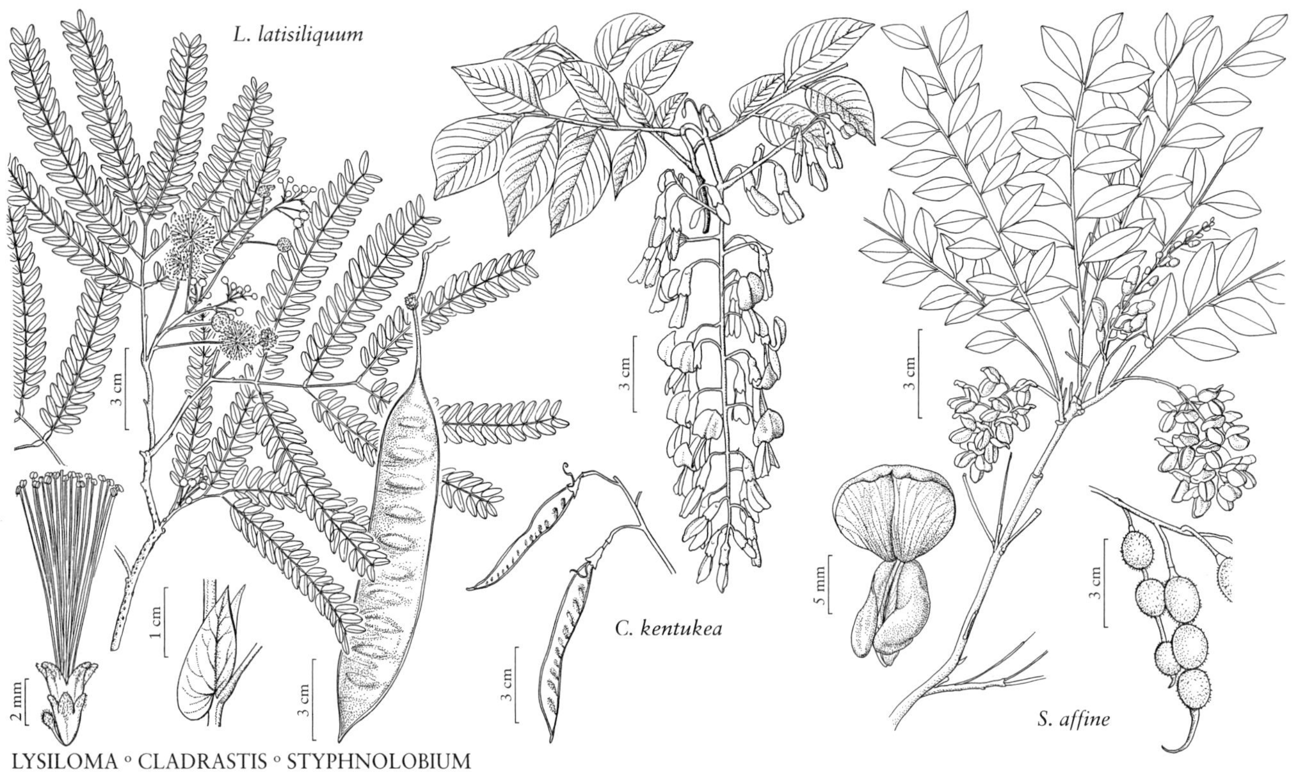

LYSILOMA ◦ CLADRASTIS ◦ STYPHNOLOBIUM

Flowering May; fruiting Sep–Oct. Mesic broadleaf forests; 20–1200 m; Ala., Ark., Ga., Ill., Ind., Ky., La., Miss., Mo., N.C., Okla., S.C., Tenn.

Populations of *Cladrastis kentukea* in Brown County State Park and the Yellowwood State Forest in Indiana are the northernmost native occurrences (H. H. Huffman 1986). Reports from Connecticut, Iowa, Maine, Massachusetts, New York, Ohio, Ontario, Pennsylvania, and Rhode Island appear to be from cultivated and/or escaped plants.

The habitat of *Cladrastis kentukea* varies; it is typically found along river bluffs and in openings in mesophytic cove forests in association with major drainage areas (J. D. Pittillo 1963; H. H. Huffman 1986). It is not a common tree in the wild but is widely cultivated as an ornamental (G. Krüssmann 1984–1986, vol. 1; D. R. Hershey 1977; M. Griffiths 1994; E. F. Gilman 1997).

Cladrastis albiflora Rafinesque and *Virgilia dumontii* Rafinesque are superfluous and illegitimate names that pertain here.

44. STYPHNOLOBIUM Schott, Wiener Z. Kunst 1830(3): 844. 1830 • Pagoda tree [Greek *styphnos*, astringent, and *lobos*, pod, alluding to taste of fleshy pulp]

James C. Sugar

Alexander Krings

Trees or shrubs, unarmed. **Stems** erect, glabrous or moderately pubescent, glabrescent; bark smooth, fissured, or flakey. **Leaves** alternate, odd-pinnate; stipules present, caducous; petiolate; leaflets (7–)11–19+, opposite proximally and alternate distally, all opposite, or all alternate, stipels present, blade margins entire, surfaces glabrous or pubescent. **Inflorescences** 5–100+-flowered, axillary or terminal, racemes or panicles; bracts and bracteoles present, caducous. **Flowers** papilionaceous; calyx zygomorphic, campanulate or hip-shaped, truncate, lobes 5; corolla usually white or yellow, rarely pink or purple [cream]; stamens 10, distinct; anthers basifixed, dehiscing apically; ovary sericeous; style glabrous; stigma attenuate, terminal. **Fruits** legumes, stipitate, straight to curved, moniliform [torulose], indehiscent, fleshy, glabrescent. **Seeds** 1–5 (–8), black, compressed, subreniform to oblong; hilum lateral. *x* = 14.

Species ca. 9 (2 in the flora): c, e United States, Mexico, Central America, nw South America (Colombia), Asia; introduced elsewhere in temperate and subtropical regions.

SELECTED REFERENCE Sousa S., M. and V. E. Rudd. 1993. Revisión del género *Styphnolobium* (Leguminosae: Papilionoideae: Sophoreae). Ann. Missouri Bot. Gard. 80: 273–280.

1. Leaflet blades narrow to broadly elliptic or obovate; inflorescences racemes, axillary; ovaries densely sericeous; hairs of petioles, inflorescence axes, and pedicels translucent to white; flowering Mar–May . . . . 1. *Styphnolobium affine*
1. Leaflet blades usually lanceolate to ovate, sometimes elliptic; inflorescences panicles, terminal; ovaries sparsely sericeous; hairs of petioles, inflorescence axes, and pedicels white, translucent, brown, and/or golden brown; flowering Jun–Sep . . . . 2. *Styphnolobium japonicum*

1. Styphnolobium affine (Torrey & A. Gray) Walpers, Repert. Bot. Syst. 1: 807. 1843 • Eve's necklace [E] [F]

Sophora affinis Torrey & A. Gray, Fl. N. Amer. 1: 390. 1840

Trees or shrubs, to 10 m. **Leaves:** stipules linear, 2 mm; petiole 1.8–2.5 cm, sparsely to moderately pubescent, hairs antrorse-appressed, translucent to white; leaflets (9–)13–19, petiolules 1–2 mm, blades narrow to broadly elliptic or obovate, (0.6–)1–3.7(–4.5) × (0.3–)0.6–1.7(–2) cm, apex obtuse to rounded, mucronate, surfaces evenly sparsely to densely pubescent abaxially, glabrous or glabrate adaxially. **Inflorescences** axillary, racemes, axis moderately to densely pubescent, hairs antrorse-appressed, translucent to white; axis (2–)7–10 cm; bracts linear, 0.5–1.2 mm; bracteoles linear, 0.5–2 mm. **Pedicels** 5–20 mm, densely pubescent, hairs antrorse-appressed, translucent to white. **Flowers:** calyx 2.5–5 mm, moderately to densely pubescent, lobes broadly rounded; corolla white to yellow, pink, or purple, 1–1.4 cm; ovary densely sericeous. **Legumes** 3–5(–15) × 0.8–1 cm; stipe 10–20 mm. **Seeds** 1–4(–8), 5.2–7 × 4–5 mm. **2*n*** = 28.

Flowering Mar–May. Woodlands, floodplains, stream margins, rocky uplands, roadsides; 0–600 m; Ark., La., Okla., Tex.

The flowers of *Styphnolobium affine* are showy, and the persistent fruit resembles a black string of pearls. It is cultivated as an ornamental within its native range. The seeds are reputed to be poisonous.

2. Styphnolobium japonicum (Linnaeus) Schott, Wiener Z. Kunst 1830(3): 844. 1830 • Scholar tree [I]

Sophora japonica Linnaeus, Syst. Nat. ed. 12, 2: 287. 1767; Mant. Pl. 1: 68. 1767

Trees, to 25 m. **Leaves:** stipules linear, 3–4 mm; petiole 1.7–3 cm, sparsely to densely strigose, hairs antrorse, spreading, and retrorse, translucent or brown; leaflets (7–)11–17, petiolules 2–3 mm, blades usually lanceolate to ovate, sometimes elliptic, (1–)1.9–5.6(–6.7) × (0.4–)1.3–2.5(–2.7) cm, apex acute or obtuse, mucronate, surfaces moderately to densely, appressed-pubescent abaxially, moderately to densely pubescent to glabrate adaxially. **Inflorescences** terminal, panicles, axis sparsely to moderately or densely pubescent, hairs antrorse-appressed, some spreading, white, translucent, and golden brown; axis (1–)3.5–14 cm; bracts deltate-attenuate, 1–1.5 mm; bracteoles deltate-attenuate, 0.3–1 mm. **Pedicels** 2–3 mm, densely pubescent, hairs antrorse-appressed, white, translucent, and golden brown. **Flowers:** calyx 3–6 mm, sparsely sericeous, lobes acute to broadly rounded; corolla white to pale yellow, 1–1.5 cm; ovary sparsely sericeous. **Legumes** 2–8[–12] × 0.4–1.1 cm; stipe 4–17 mm. **Seeds** 1–5(–8), 6.9–8 × 4–6.2 mm. **2*n*** = 28.

Flowering Jun–Sep. Roadsides, woodland borders, river bluffs; 0–900 m; introduced; D.C., Md., N.C., Ohio, Pa., Va.; Asia (China); introduced also in Mexico, Central America, South America, Europe, Africa, Australia.

Styphnolobium japonicum is widely cultivated for ornamental use. It contains high concentrations of rutin, which has lectinic and antihypotensive properties, and is used in traditional medicines (W. H. Lewis and M. P. F. Elvin-Lewis 2003).

45. DERMATOPHYLLUM Scheele, Linnaea 21: 458. 1848 • Necklacepod, Mescal bean [Greek *dermatos*, skin, and *phyllon*, leaf, alluding to leathery leaves of *D. speciosum,* the type species]

Michael A. Vincent

Denis M. Kearns

Shrubs or trees, unarmed. **Stems** erect, twigs densely pubescent or glabrescent. **Leaves** alternate, odd-pinnate; stipules present, caducous, linear to deltate; petiolate, petiole 1–1.5 cm; leaflets 5–13[–17], alternate to subopposite, stipels minute or absent, linear, blade leathery, margins entire, thickened, surfaces pubescent or glabrescent. **Inflorescences** 2–15[–75]-flowered, terminal or axillary, racemes; bracts present, caducous; bracteoles persistent or caducous, 2. **Flowers** papilionaceous; calyx campanulate (sometimes gibbous), lobes 5, sometimes connate adaxially; corolla usually purple, blue-purple, lilac, or lavender [violet], rarely white, glabrous; keel petals usually partly connate; stamens 10, distinct or connate proximally; anthers dorsifixed. **Fruits** legumes, stipitate, torose to torulose, straight to slightly curved, compressed and oblong, or subglobose to cylindrical, indehiscent, papery, leathery, or woody, appressed-pubescent. **Seeds** 1–10, usually red or dull red to reddish brown, rarely orange or yellow, reniform to subglobose, margins angular. $x = 9$.

Species 6 (3 in the flora): sc, sw United States, Mexico.

Two other generic names have been used for taxa now placed in *Dermatophyllum*, in addition to their placement in *Sophora*: *Agastianis* Rafinesque and *Calia* Terán & Berlandier (G. P. Yakovlev 1968). *Agastianis* is superfluous and an illegitimate substitute for the nomenclaturally rejected name *Broussonetia* Ortega (1798). *Calia* is considered a later homonym of *Calea* Linnaeus (1763, Asteraceae; K. N. Gandhi et al. 2011).

Dermatophyllum is a segregate from *Sophora*. It is considered distinct from *Sophora* by its woody habit; thick, leathery leaflets; blue, violet, or white petals; calyx with obvious teeth or lobes; flattened to terete legumes; and geographic range. The distinction is supported by molecular data indicating that *Dermatophyllum* (as *Calia*) falls into a separate clade from *Styphnolobium* and other *Sophora* species (K. N. Gandhi et al. 2011; G. P. Lewis et al. 2005; R. T. Pennington et al. 2001; M. F. Wojciechowski et al. 2004).

1. Leaflet blades (2–)2.5–5(–8) cm; pedicels 10–15 mm; legumes woody, subglobose to cylindrical, torulose . . . . 3. *Dermatophyllum secundiflorum*
1. Leaflet blades 1–2.5(–4) cm; pedicels 2–5 mm; legumes papery to almost leathery, compressed and oblong, torose.
    2. Leaflets 5–11, blades lanceolate to elliptic, apices acute, apiculate; floral bracts lanceolate, apices acute . . . . 2. *Dermatophyllum arizonicum*
    2. Leaflets 9–13, blades elliptic to ovate, apices rounded, often emarginate, rarely apiculate; floral bracts lanceolate to elliptic, apices acute to rounded, abruptly apiculate . . . . 2. *Dermatophyllum guadalupense*

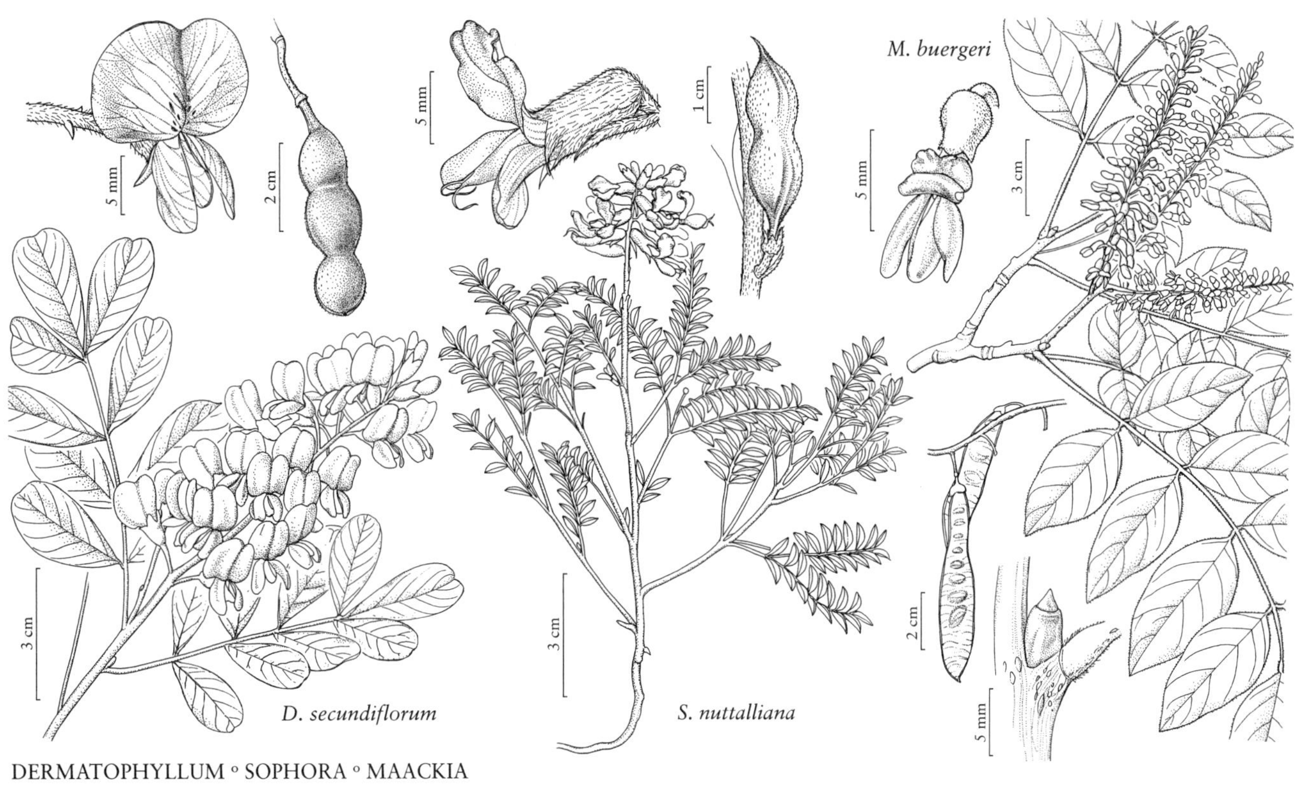

DERMATOPHYLLUM ◦ SOPHORA ◦ MAACKIA

1. Dermatophyllum arizonicum (S. Watson) Vincent, Phytoneuron 2011-57: 2. 2011 • Arizona necklacepod E

Sophora arizonica S. Watson, Proc. Amer. Acad. Arts 11: 135. 1876; *Calia arizonica* (S. Watson) Yakovlev; *C. formosa* (Kearney & Peebles) Yakovlev; *S. formosa* Kearney & Peebles

Shrubs, 1–3 m, twigs strigulose-tomentose. **Leaves:** rachis 3–7 cm; leaflets 5–11, blades lanceolate to elliptic, 1–2.5(–4) × 0.4–1.3 cm, base cuneate to rounded, apex acute, apiculate. **Racemes** 2–8-flowered, congested, 2.5–4 cm; bracts lanceolate, apex acute. **Pedicels** 2–5 mm. **Flowers** ascending, 16–24 mm; calyx obconic, 10–11(–15) mm; corolla usually purple or lilac, rarely white. **Legumes** tan, torose, straight to slightly curved, compressed, oblong, 5–10(–12) × 1–1.4 cm, papery to almost leathery. **Seeds** 3–7(–10), dull red to reddish brown, 7–11 mm. $2n = 18$.

Flowering Mar–May. Limestone soils, foothills, desert washes, canyon slopes, with creosote bush, pinyon, juniper, oak, yucca; 700–1600 m; Ariz.

Dermatophyllum arizonicum is known from Graham, Mohave, and Yavapai counties. This species, *D. guadalupense*, and the Mexican *D. gypsophilum* (B. L. Turner & A. M. Powell) Vincent, *D. juanhintonianum* (B. L. Turner) B. L. Turner, and *D. purpusii* (Brandegee) Vincent, form a closely related group (M. Izaddoost 1975; D. K. Northington 1976; V. E. Rudd 1972; B. L. Turner 2012). D. Isely (1981) suggested that some of these taxa may not deserve recognition as distinct species.

2. Dermatophyllum guadalupense (B. L. Turner & A. M. Powell) B. L. Turner, Phytoneuron 2012-3: 1. 2012 • Guadalupe Mountain necklacepod C E

Sophora gypsophila B. L. Turner & A. M. Powell var. *guadalupensis* B. L. Turner & A. M. Powell, Phytologia 22: 421. 1972; *Dermatophyllum gypsophilum* subsp. *guadalupense* (B. L. Turner & A. M. Powell) Vincent

Shrubs, 0.5–2 m, twigs silvery-pubescent. **Leaves:** rachis 3–6 cm; leaflets 9–13, blades elliptic to ovate, (1–)1.5–2 × 0.8–1.4 cm, base rounded, apex rounded, often emarginate, rarely apiculate, adaxial surface persistently strigose. **Racemes** 2–8-flowered, congested, 2.5–4 cm; bracts lanceolate to elliptic, apex acute to rounded, abruptly apiculate. **Pedicels** 2–5 mm. **Flowers** ascending, 19–28 mm; calyx obconic, 10–14 mm; corolla lavender to purple. **Legumes** tan, torose, straight to slightly curved, compressed, oblong, 5–14 × 1–1.5 cm, almost leathery. **Seeds** 3–10, dull reddish, 7–10 mm. $2n = 18$.

Flowering Apr–May. Slightly gypseous sandstone lenses within limestone, canyons; of conservation concern; 1500–2000 m; N.Mex., Tex.

Dermatophyllum guadalupense is known from the Guadalupe and Brokeoff mountains of Eddy and Otero counties, New Mexico, and Culberson County, Texas. It differs from the Mexican species *D. gypsophilum* in the number of leaflets (9–13 versus 15–17), the width of the fruit (1–1.5 versus 1 cm), and the length of the seeds (7–10 versus 5–6 mm).

3. **Dermatophyllum secundiflorum** (Ortega) Gandhi & Reveal, Phytoneuron 2011-57: 2. 2011 • Mescal bean, mountain laurel [F]

Broussonetia secundiflora Ortega, Nov. Pl. Descr. Dec., 61, plate 7. 1798; *Agastianis secundiflora* (Ortega) Rafinesque; *Calia erythrosperma* Terán & Berlandier; *Cladrastis secundiflora* (Ortega) Rafinesque; *Dermatophyllum speciosum* Scheele; *Sophora secundiflora* (Ortega) Lagasca ex de Candolle; *S. speciosa* (Scheele) Bentham; *Virgilia secundiflora* (Ortega) Cavanilles

Shrubs or trees, 1–5(–6) m, twigs tomentose. **Leaves:** rachis 6–15 cm; leaflets (5 or)7–11, blades elliptic-obovate or oblong, (2–)2.5–5(–8) × 0.7–3.6 cm, base cuneate, apex rounded to emarginate. **Racemes** 4–15-flowered, dense, 5–10 cm; bracts linear-lanceolate, apex acute. **Pedicels** 10–15 mm. **Flowers** ascending to spreading, 10–20 mm; calyx broadly obconic or turbinate, asymmetric, 8–11 mm; corolla usually blue-purple, rarely white. **Legumes** brown, torulose, subglobose to cylidrical, 2–5(–10) × 1–1.5(–2) cm, woody. **Seeds** 1–4(–8), usually red, rarely orange or yellow, 10–15 mm. **2*n*** = 18.

Flowering Feb–Apr. Rocky slopes, canyons, ravines, limestone hills, canyons; 0–1500 m; N.Mex., Tex.; Mexico (Chihuahua, Coahuila, Durango, Hidalgo, Nuevo León, Puebla, San Luis Potosí, Zacatecas).

Dermatophyllum secundiflorum is widely distributed across the southern half of Texas and extends into southeastern New Mexico.

Flowers of *Dermatophyllum secundiflorum* have been described as offensively fragrant and have a scent reminiscent of artificial grape flavoring. Their odor can produce headaches and, sometimes, nausea (E. D. Schulz 1928). The flowers are a source of honey (E. H. Graham 1941). The dull red seeds, poisonous to humans and livestock, were used by Amerindian groups for beads (trade items). Powdered and mixed with mescal, the seeds were employed to produce intoxication, delirium, excitement, and a deep sleep of two to three days (J. M. Kingsbury 1964; R. A. Vines 1960). Bactericidal and fungicidal activities have been reported from seed extracts of mescal bean (D. Pérez-Laínez et al. 2008). The slow growing plants are used as ornamentals.

46. SOPHORA Linnaeus, Sp. Pl. 1: 373. 1753; Gen. Pl. ed. 5, 175. 1754 • Necklacepod [Arabic *sofera*, name of yellow-flowered plant, possibly *Cassia sophera*; Greek *sophorum*, wise men, alluding to occurrence of distinct stamens in papilionaceous flower as unnatural and to circumscription of papilionaceous group]

Michael A. Vincent

Denis M. Kearns

Pseudosophora (de Candolle) Sweet; *Radiusia* Reichenbach; *Vexibia* Rafinesque; *Zanthyrsis* Rafinesque

Herbs, perennial, shrubs, or trees, unarmed. **Stems** erect, pubescent or glabrous. **Leaves** alternate, odd-pinnate; stipules usually present, caducous, linear to deltate; petiolate, petiole 5–30 mm; leaflets (7 or)9–23[–50], alternate or subopposite, stipels absent or minute and linear, blade margins entire, surfaces pubescent or glabrous (densely villous, sericeous, or glabrescent adaxially in *S. tomentosa*). **Inflorescences** 5–75[+]-flowered, terminal or axillary, racemes or panicles; bracts present, caducous; bracteoles caducous or absent. **Flowers** papilionaceous; calyx campanulate, lobes 5, subequal, acute to truncate, sometimes gibbous, adaxial lobes often connate in part; corolla white, creamy white, yellow, or purple, glabrous; keel usually connate in part; stamens 10, distinct or proximally connate; anthers dorsifixed; pistil linear to lanceolate.

Fruits legumes, sessile or short-stipitate, narrowly oblong-moniliform, cylindric [compressed], fusiform, or torulose, dehiscent, pubescent [glabrous]. **Seeds** 1–15, light brown to mustard-yellow, globose to subglobose. $x = 9$.

Species ca. 50 (4 in the flora): United States, Mexico, West Indies (Antilles, Bahamas), Central America, South America, Eurasia, Africa, Pacific Islands, Australia.

Sophora as traditionally circumscribed is recognized as an unnatural assemblage. Molecular studies have elucidated the relationships among taxa in *Sophora* in the broad sense, resulting in recognition of several smaller genera. In the flora area, *Sophora*, as currently circumscribed, comprises herbaceous plants arising from a woody root, and the woody species *S. tomentosa*. Two species in the flora area that formerly were included in *Sophora* are now included in *Dermatophyllum* (*D. arizonicum* and *D. secundiflorum*), as is the closely related Mexican species *D. gypsophilum* and two others are placed in *Styphnolobium* (*S. affine* and *S. japonicum*). *Styphnolobium* is distinct from *Sophora* (in the narrow sense) in molecular studies, falling into the *Cladrastis* clade; *Dermatophyllum* is in a separate lineage from the *Cladrastis* clade and outside a clade in which the North American taxa of *Sophora* (in the narrow sense) fall (J. J. Doyle et al. 1996; R. T. Pennington et al. 2001; M. F. Wojciechowski et al. 2004).

The seeds and foliage of some species of *Sophora* contain neurotoxic alkaloids. Although neurotoxicity has not been demonstrated in native *Sophora* species, G. E. Burrows and R. L. Tyrl (2013) discussed possible teratogenic effects.

SELECTED REFERENCES Crowder, C. A. 1982. Systematics and Phylogeny of the Herbaceous North American and Inland Argentine Sophoras (Fabaceae). Ph.D. thesis. Texas Tech University. Heenan, P. B., M. I. Dawson, and S. J. Wagstaff. 2004. The relationship of *Sophora* sect. *Edwardsia* (Fabaceae) to *Sophora tomentosa*, the type species of the genus *Sophora*, observed from DNA sequence data and morphological characters. Bot. J. Linn. Soc. 146: 439–446.

1. Shrubs or small trees; corollas creamy white to yellow; coastal near beaches or in pinelands . . . . 4. *Sophora tomentosa*
1. Herbs; corollas purple (fading blue), white, or creamy white; inland.
    2. Leaflet blades narrowly linear; leaf rachises 2–4 cm; corollas purple (fading blue) . . . . 1. *Sophora stenophylla*
    2. Leaflet blades obovate to oblong or ovate to oblanceolate; leaf rachises (3–)5–17 cm; corollas white or creamy white.
        3. Inflorescences 7–15 cm; leaflet blades villous-tomentose abaxially, appressed-pubescent adaxially. . . . . 2. *Sophora leachiana*
        3. Inflorescences 20–80 cm; leaflet blades sericeous abaxially, glabrous adaxially. . . . . 3. *Sophora nuttalliana*

1. Sophora stenophylla A. Gray in J. C. Ives, Rep. Colorado R. 4: 10. 1861 • Blue or silvery sophora, fringeleaf necklacepod [E]

Vexibia stenophylla (A. Gray) W. A. Weber

Herbs, 0.1–0.4 m, sericeous to subvillous, rhizomatous. **Leaves:** rachis 2–4 cm; leaflets 9–15, blades narrowly linear, 0.5–3 cm, surfaces subsericeous. **Inflorescences** 5–35-flowered, crowded or loose, 5–20 cm; bracteoles 0. **Pedicels** 5–6 mm. **Flowers** ascending-divergent, 16–25 mm; calyx broadly campanulate, asymmetrically pouched, 5–9 mm; corolla purple, fading blue; ovary pubescent. **Legumes** tan to light brown, cylindric, torulose, 2–6 × 0.6–0.8 cm, papery to almost leathery. **Seeds** 1–6, mustard-yellow, 6–7 mm.

Flowering Apr–Jun. Deep sand, dunes, with sage, juniper, and *Ephedra*; 900–1900 m; Ariz., N.Mex., Utah.

Sophora stenophylla is known from Utah in all counties from Uintah County southwestward to Washington County and counties east, from the three northeastern counties (Apache, Coconino, and Navajo) of Arizona, and from northwestern and south-central New Mexico. The species has pleasantly fragrant flowers. It grows in dunes or areas of loose to compacted sands.

A report of *Sophora stenophylla* from Nevada (V. E. Rudd 1972) could not be verified.

2. Sophora leachiana M. Peck, Madroño 6: 13. 1941 • Western sophora or necklacepod [C] [E]

Vexibia leachiana (M. Peck) W. A. Weber

Herbs, 0.2–0.4 m, finely gray-tomentose, rhizomatous. **Leaves:** rachis 8–17 cm; leaflets 16–21, blades obovate to oblong, 1.5–2.6 cm, surfaces villous-tomentose abaxially, appressed-pubescent adaxially. **Inflorescences** 14–64-flowered, lax, 7–15 cm; bracteoles 1 or 2. **Pedicels** 2–6 mm. **Flowers** divergent or soon declined, 13–16 mm; calyx tubular-campanulate, asymmetrically pouched, 6–8 mm; corolla creamy white; ovary pubescent. **Legumes** light brown, cylindric, fusiform, or torulose, 3–4 × 0.4 cm, leathery. **Seeds** 1 or 2, often dull mustard-yellow, sometimes light brown, 4–5 mm. **2*n*** = 36, 54.

Flowering May–Jun. Open mixed forests, roadsides; of conservation concern; 400–500 m; Oreg.

Sophora leachiana is known from the Siskiyou Mountains of Josephine County along the drainages of Briggs, Galice, and Taylor creeks, in dry, often disturbed sites, both natural and human-derived, and surrounded by pine, Douglas-fir, oak, and hardwood forests. It aggressively colonizes open areas and dies out once the forest cover is reestablished; seed-set is low (C. A. Crowder 1978). *Sophora leachiana* is hypothesized to be closely related to the North American species *S. nuttalliana* and *S. stenophylla*, and to the Asian species *S. alopecuroides* Linnaeus (Crowder 1982).

SELECTED REFERENCE Crowder, C. A. 1978. The Ecology and Reproduction of *Sophora leachiana* (Fabaceae). M.S. thesis. Oregon State University.

3. Sophora nuttalliana B. L. Turner, Field & Lab. 24: [42]. 1956 • Silky or white sophora, white loco [F]

Sophora sericea Nuttall, Gen. N. Amer. Pl. 1: 280. 1818, not Andrews 1806; *Patrinia sericea* Rafinesque; *Pseudosophora sericea* (Rafinesque) Sweet; *Radiusia sericea* (Rafinesque) Heynhold; *Vexibia nuttalliana* (B. L. Turner) Yakovlev; *V. sericea* (Rafinesque) Rafinesque

Herbs, 0.1–0.4(–0.7) m, sericeous to irregularly spreading-pubescent, rhizomatous. **Leaves:** rachis (3–)5–8 cm; leaflets (7–)11–23, blades ovate to oblanceolate, 0.5–1.5 cm, surfaces sericeous abaxially, glabrous adaxially. **Inflorescences** 6–35-flowered, loose to dense, 2–8 cm; bracteoles 2. **Pedicels** 1–2 mm. **Flowers** ascending, becoming spreading or descending, 12–16 mm; calyx asymmetrically tubular, asymmetrically pouched, 5–8 mm; corolla white to creamy white; ovary pubescent. **Legumes** light brown, cylindric, torulose, 3–7 × 0.5–1 cm, firmly papery. **Seeds** (1 or)2–4(–6), mustard-yellow or olivaceous to brown, 4.5–5 mm. **2*n*** = 36.

Flowering Apr–Jun. Grasslands, plains, rocky hillsides, stream beds, canyon floors; 500–2100 m; Ariz., Colo., Kans., Nebr., N.Mex., Okla., S.Dak., Tex., Utah, Wyo.; Mexico (Chihuahua).

Clonal patches of *Sophora nuttalliana* are widespread in the short-grass prairies of the Great Plains and adjacent areas. When in flower, it has an aspect reminiscent of *Astragalus*. Like that genus, it and other *Sophora* species are considered toxic (G. E. Burrows and R. L. Tyrl 2013). However, experiments involving feeding large amounts of plant material to horses failed to provoke symptoms (J. M. Kingsbury 1964). Roots of *S. nuttalliana* reportedly have been used by Native American groups as a sweetener and special food treat, and the plants have been used as forage for sheep (D. E. Moerman 1998).

The name *Sophora carnosa* (Pursh) Yakovlev is based on an illegitimate name, *Astragalus carnosus* Pursh, with which *A. crassicarpus* Nuttall was cited in synonymy. The fruit described for *A. carnosus* is that of *A. crassicarpus*, while the rest of the description is based on flowers and foliage of *S. nuttalliana*.

4. Sophora tomentosa Linnaeus, Sp. Pl. 1: 373. 1753 • Yellow necklacepod

Shrubs or small trees, 1–3(–6) m, tomentulose to deeply sericeous. **Leaves:** rachis 10–25 cm; leaflets 11–21, blades obovate, oblong, elliptic, or suborbiculate, 2–4(–5) cm, surfaces villous to sericeous abaxially, densely villous, sericeous, or glabrescent adaxially. **Inflorescences** 35–75-flowered, crowded, 12–32 cm; bracteoles 0. **Pedicels** 4–10 mm. **Flowers** spreading, (17–)20–25 mm; calyx broadly campanulate, 5–8[–10] mm; corolla creamy white to yellow; ovary pubescent. **Legumes** black, narrowly oblong-moniliform, 5–15(–20) × 0.5–1 cm, leathery. **Seeds** 1–15, light brown, 4–8 mm. **2*n*** = 18.

Subspecies ca. 7 (2 in the flora): sc, se United States, Mexico, West Indies, Central America, n South America, se Asia, Africa, Pacific Islands, Australia.

Sophora tomentosa is polymorphic and has a worldwide distribution along tropical and subtropical seashores. The seeds are considered toxic and have diuretic, sudorific, and purgative properties; they are also used for other medicinal purposes (R. A. Vines 1960).

1. Leaflet blades mostly obovate or oblong; flowers (17–)20–23 mm .... 4a. *Sophora tomentosa* subsp. *bahamensis*
1. Leaflet blades broadly elliptic or suborbiculate; flowers 23–25 mm .... 4b. *Sophora tomentosa* subsp. *occidentalis*

4a. Sophora tomentosa Linnaeus subsp. **bahamensis** Yakovlev, Trudy Leningradsk. Khim.-Farm. Inst. 26: 99. 1968

Sophora arenicola Nees; *S. tomentosa* var. *truncata* Torrey & A. Gray; *Zanthyrsis paniculata* Rafinesque

Leaflet blades mostly obovate or oblong, base cuneate to rounded, usually strongly asymmetrical, surfaces sparsely pubescent abaxially. **Flowers** (17–)20–23 mm; calyx 5–7 mm.

Flowering year-round. Sandy coastal dunes, hammocks, pinelands, roadside ditches; 0–10 m; Fla.; West Indies (Antilles, Bahamas); n South America.

Subspecies *bahamensis* is known from coastal counties in peninsular Florida. The littoral habitat of subsp. *bahamensis* has declined with the intensive development of the Florida coastline; the plants persist along roadsides and other disturbed areas.

4b. Sophora tomentosa Linnaeus subsp. **occidentalis** (Linnaeus) Brummitt, Kirkia 5: 265. 1966

Sophora occidentalis Linnaeus, Syst. Nat. ed. 10, 2: 1015. 1759; *S. havanensis* Jacquin

Leaflet blades broadly elliptic or suborbiculate, base subcordate, slightly asymmetrical, surfaces tomentulose abaxially. **Flowers** 23–25 mm; calyx 7–8 mm.

Flowering Mar–Oct (year-round). Sandy coastal ridges, flats behind dunes, among coastal rocks; 0–10 m; Fla., Tex.; Mexico (Baja California Sur); Central America; n South America; w Africa.

Subspecies *occidentalis* is known from peninsular Florida, where it is considered rare, from Martin, Miami-Dade, Pinellas, and Sarasota counties. In Texas, the subspecies is known from coastal areas from Refugio County southward to Cameron County.

47. MAACKIA Maximowicz & Ruprecht, Bull. Cl. Phys.-Math. Acad. Imp. Sci. Saint-Pétersbourg 15: 128, 143. 1856 • [For Richard Otto Maack, 1825–1886, Russian naturalist, geographer, and anthropologist] [I]

Michael A. Vincent

Carolyn K. Levings

Trees [shrubs], unarmed. **Stems** erect, pubescent or glabrous. **Leaves** alternate, odd-pinnate; axillary buds exposed; stipules absent; petiolate; leaflets (7 or)9–13, opposite or subopposite [alternate], blade margins entire, surfaces glabrous [pubescent]. **Inflorescences** [15–]50–100+-flowered, terminal, racemes, simple or compound, erect; bracts absent; bracteoles present. **Flowers** papilionaceous; calyx campanulate, lobes 4 or 5; corolla white, often yellowish in age, callus present at point where banner reflexes; stamens 10, connate proximally; anthers dorsifixed. **Fruits** legumes, sessile, compressed laterally, straight or curved, lanceolate, winged along one suture, dehiscent, pubescent. **Seeds** 1–3[–5], yellow, ellipsoidal. x = 9, [10].

Species 10 (1 in the flora): introduced, North Carolina; e Asia (China, Japan, Korea, e Russia, Taiwan); temperate areas.

Some *Maackia* species have been used as ornamental landscape trees.

SELECTED REFERENCE Levings, C. K. 2006. A Monograph of the Genus *Maackia*. M.S. thesis. Miami University.

1. Maackia buergeri (Maximowicz) Tatewaki, Trans. Sapporo Nat. Hist. Soc. 16: 4. 1939 • Japanese maackia [F] [I]

Cladrastis amurensis (Maximowicz & Ruprecht) Bentham ex Maximowicz var. *buergeri* Maximowicz, Bull. Acad. Imp. Sci. Saint-Pétersbourg 18: 400. 1873

Trees to 14 m. **Leaves** 12–27.5 cm; petiole 1.5–4 cm; leaflet blades ovate or obovate to elliptic, 2–8 × 1–6 cm, base cuneate, apex acute or attenuate, surfaces pubescent abaxially, glabrescent adaxially. **Racemes** 4–13.5 × 2–4 cm; bracteoles triangular-ovate, 1.2–2.3 × 0.2–0.5 mm, pubescent. **Pedicels** 3–9 mm. **Flowers:** calyx 1.9–4.5 mm; corolla: banner blade 4.7–6.9 mm, apex emarginate, callus thick and cartilaginous, claw 1.5–5.1 mm; wing and keel blades 5.4–7.8 × 2.1–3.3 mm. **Legumes** symmetric, 4–7.3 × 0.8–1.4 cm, suture wing 0.2–0.6 mm wide. **Seeds** 5.5–7.1 × 3.1–3.8 mm. $2n = 18$.

Flowering Apr–May. Disturbed secondary forests; 90–110 m; introduced; N.C.; e Asia (Japan).

Maackia buergeri is widely cultivated, although not as commonly as *M. amurensis* Maximowicz & Ruprecht. The latter species can be distinguished from the former by its glabrous petioles and the wider wings (to 1.4 mm) on its fruits.

48. BRONGNIARTIA Kunth in A. von Humboldt et al., Nov. Gen. Sp. 6(fol.): 364; 6(qto.): 465; plates 587, 588. 1824 • [For Adolphe-Théodore Brongniart, 1801–1876, French botanist]

Óscar Dorado

Shrubs [small trees], unarmed. **Stems** erect and spreading, branches glabrous or pubescent. **Leaves** alternate, odd-pinnate; stipules present; petiolate; leaflets [3–](19–)23–59, blade margins entire, surfaces glabrous or sparsely pilose [tomentose]. **Inflorescences** solitary flowers, axillary; bracts absent; bracteoles present. **Flowers** papilionaceous; calyx campanulate, lobes 5; corolla yellow [maroon, red, blue, purple, pink]; stamens 10, diadelphous; anthers dorsifixed. **Fruits** legumes, stipitate, compressed, elliptic to broadly elliptic [oblong], dehiscent, glabrous. **Seeds** 1 or 2, broadly ellipsoid to orbiculate. $x = 9$.

Species ca. 65 (1 in the flora): Texas, Mexico, South America (Bolivia).

Brongniartia is known mainly from the western and southern states of Mexico, mostly in tropical dry forest; the geographically nearest species (*B. riesebergii* Dorado) is known from the state of Durango, Mexico.

Brongniartia belongs to tribe Brongniartieae Hutchinson, which comprises 15 genera (L. P. de Queiroz et al. 2017).

1. Brongniartia minutifolia S. Watson, Proc. Amer. Acad. Arts 20: 360. 1885 • Littleleaf brongniartia [C] [F]

Brongniartia shrevei Wiggins

Shrubs 1–1.2(–3) m. **Stems:** several branched from base, younger branches beige, older branches usually reddish and glabrescent, rarely sparsely pilose. **Leaves** 1.8–8(–11.5) cm, curved upward; stipules persistent, symmetrically lanceolate to linear-lanceolate, 2–4.5(–5.5) × 0.4–0.9(–1.8) mm, venation inconspicuous, often only midvein slightly conspicuous, glabrous or sparsely pilose, hairs whitish; petiole 1.2–4(–9) mm, glabrous or sparsely pilose; rachis 1.3–6.8(–11.5) cm, glabrous or sparsely pilose, stipels absent or minute; petiolule (0.1–)0.3–1(–1.5) mm; leaflets opposite or subopposite, blades often terete, linear-elliptic to linear, or folding, (2–)3–9(–11) × 0.2–0.8 (–1.6) mm, venation inconspicuous, often only midvein conspicuous adaxially, base acute, apex acute, surfaces glabrous or sparsely pilose, hairs whitish. **Pedicels** ascending, (3.5–)5–10(–12) mm, glabrous; bracteoles linear or triangular, 0.3–1.1(–1.5) mm. **Flowers:** calyx 8–12 × (2.5–)3–4.5 mm, glabrous, sparsely strigulose, or pilose; corolla: banner 12–15 × 8–12 mm, reflexed 90°, blade broadly ovate, base rounded, not auriculate; wings obliquely oblanceolate, 8–11 × 2.8 mm, base

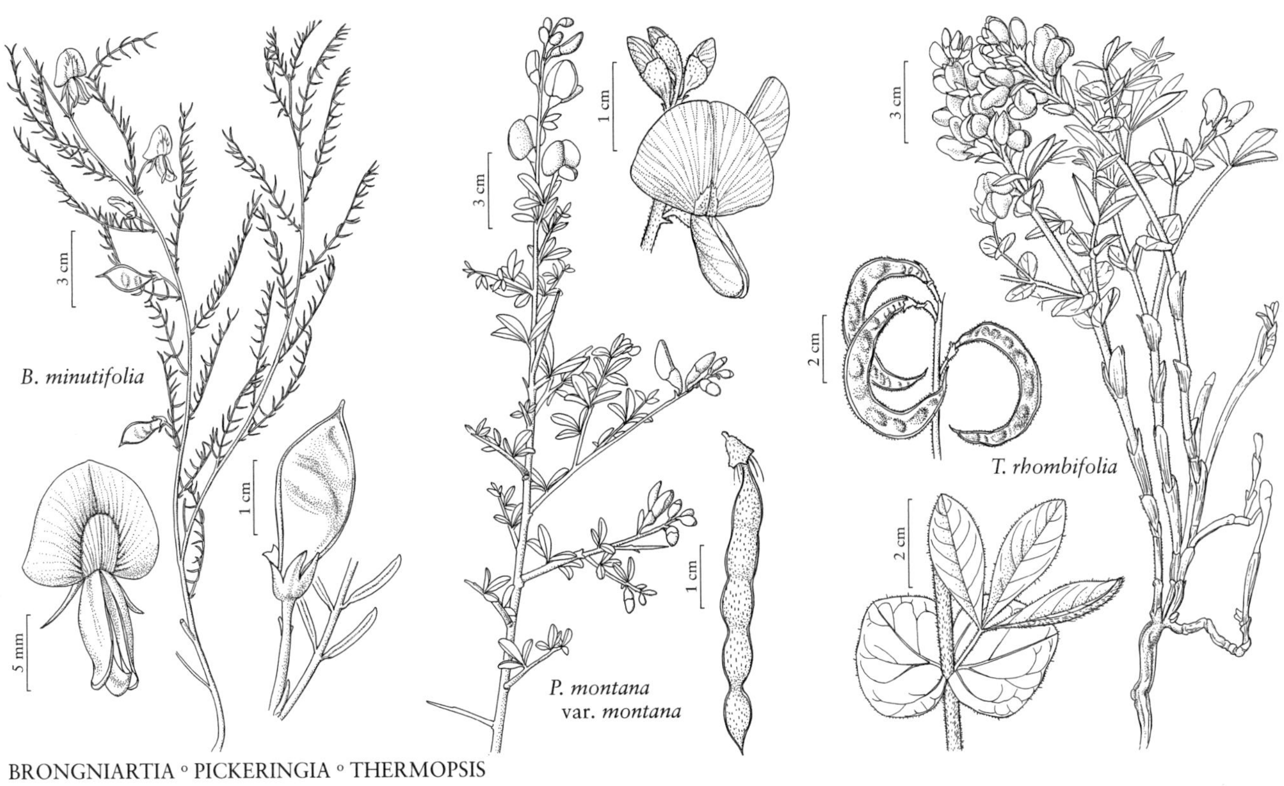

BRONGNIARTIA ◦ PICKERINGIA ◦ THERMOPSIS

usually auriculate; keel semilunate, 9–13 × 3.5–5.5 mm, base auriculate; stamens 12 mm, anthers 1.4–1.5 mm; ovary 14–16 mm, with annular disc at base, style 7.2–7.5 mm. **Legumes** 2.5–3.2 × 1.1–1.7 cm, mucro 1.5–2 mm, wing 0.5–0.7 mm wide; stipe 2–4.5 mm. **Seeds** light brown, 5.4–5.6 × 5–5.8 mm. **2*n*** = 18.

Flowering May–Sep. Xerophyllous shrublands; of conservation concern; 700–1000 m; Tex.; Mexico (Sonora).

Brongniartia minutifolia is known from about 30 km north of the Mexican border (Big Bend National Park, Brewster County, southwestern Texas) and is also disjunctly distributed in northern Sonora, Mexico. In Mexico, *B. minutifolia* inhabits woodland with *Fouquieria macdougallii* Nash, *Vachellia constricta*, and species of *Cercidium* and *Mimosa* (Ó. Dorado 1988).

49. PICKERINGIA Nuttall ex Torrey & A. Gray, Fl. N. Amer. 1: 388. 1840, name conserved • [For Charles Pickering, 1805–1878, botanist with Wilkes Exploring Expedition to California]

Velva E. Rudd†

Michael A. Vincent

Xylothermia Greene

Shrubs, armed. **Stems** erect to semiprostrate, branchlets thorn-tipped, glabrous or pubescent. **Leaves** alternate, unifoliolate or odd-pinnate; stipules absent or present; subsessile; leaflets 1 or 3, subsessile, stipels absent, blade margins entire, surfaces glabrous or pubescent. **Inflorescences** 1–7-flowered, terminal or subterminal, racemes or flowers solitary; bracts present, bracts and bracteoles acicular. **Flowers** papilionaceous; calyx campanulate, lobes 5; corolla usually reddish purple, rarely whitish; stamens 10, distinct; anthers dorsifixed. **Fruits** legumes, stipitate, compressed, linear, dehiscent, pubescent, valves 2. **Seeds** 1–10, reniform; hilum minute, lateral or subapical. $x = 14$.

Species 1: California, nw Mexico.

The relationships of *Pickeringia* to other genera are unclear; fruiting specimens are rare. Apparently, reproduction is chiefly by fire-resistant underground stems.

1. Pickeringia montana Nuttall in J. Torrey and A. Gray, Fl. N. Amer. 1: 389. 1840 • Chaparral pea, stingoree bush [F]

Xylothermia montana (Nuttall) Greene

Shrubs to 2.5 m. **Leaves:** stipules (when present) caducous, minute; blade discolorous, obovate to elliptic, 5–30 × 2–10 mm, leathery, base cuneate, apex acute or obtuse, surfaces glabrous, sericeous, or tomentose abaxially, shiny, glabrous, sparsely appressed-pubescent to sericeous or tomentose adaxially. **Pedicels** 2–3 mm. **Flowers:** calyx subactinomorphic, 5–7 mm, sparsely appressed-pubescent to tomentose; corolla 10–20 mm, glabrous, petals distinct or keel connate apically; filaments alternately subequal; anthers ellipsoid; style glabrous or with minute ring of hairs proximally; stigma terminal. **Legumes** light brown, 20–50 × 4–5 mm. **Seeds** brownish black, 3–4 × 2 mm, sublustrous. $2n = 28$.

Varieties 2 (2 in the flora): California, nw Mexico.

There is some intergradation between the varieties in contact areas.

1. Shrubs glabrous, sericeous, or appressed-pubescent; pinna blades obovate, 3–7 mm wide . . . . 1a. *Pickeringia montana* var. *montana*
1. Shrubs tomentose; pinna blades elliptic, 2–10 mm wide . . . . 1b. *Pickeringia montana* var. *tomentosa*

1a. Pickeringia montana Nuttall var. **montana** [E] [F]

Shrubs glabrous, appressed-pubescent, or sericeous. **Leaflet blades** obovate, 3–7 mm wide.

Flowering Mar–Aug. Rocky areas, mountain slopes, chaparral, oak woodlands; 60–1700 m; Calif.

Variety *montana* is known from the North Coast Ranges southward to the San Gabriel Mountains, the northern Sierra Nevada foothills, and the northern Channel Islands.

1b. Pickeringia montana Nuttall var. **tomentosa** (Abrams) I. M. Johnston, Contr. Gray Herb. 68: 84. 1923

Xylothermia montana (Nuttall) Greene subsp. *tomentosa* Abrams, Bull. Torrey Bot. Club 34: 263. 1907; *Pickeringia montana* subsp. *tomentosa* (Abrams) Abrams

Shrubs tomentose. **Leaflet blades** elliptic, 2–10 mm wide.

Flowering Mar–May. Canyons, rocky stream beds, chaparral; 300–500 m; Calif.; Mexico (Baja California).

Variety *tomentosa* is known in the flora area in southwestern California from the San Bernardino Mountains, Peninsular Ranges, and San Jacinto Mountains.

50. THERMOPSIS R. Brown in W. Aiton and W. T. Aiton, Hortus Kew. 3: 3. 1811 • [Greek *thermos*, lupine, and *-opsis*, similarity, alluding to flower heads resembling yellow lupines]

Billie L. Turner†

Drepilia Rafinesque; *Scolobus* Rafinesque

Herbs, perennial, unarmed, usually rhizomatous. **Stems** erect, ascending, or spreading, glabrate to pubescent. **Leaves** alternate, odd-pinnate; stipules present, usually persistent, ± foliaceous, dimorphic, proximalmost amplexicaul, scarious, and not blade-bearing, distal ones smaller and narrower, subtending leaves; petiolate; leaflets 3, stipels absent, subpetiolulate, blade margins entire, not glandular-punctate, surfaces glabrous or pubescent. **Inflorescences** 5–90-flowered, usually terminal, sometimes lateral, racemes; bracts present, deciduous or persistent, apex acute to acuminate; bracteoles absent. **Flowers** papilionaceous; calyx campanulate, lobes 5, appearing 4-lobed, subequal, abaxial lobes deltate to lanceolate, adaxial lobe double, broader, slightly longer, apex truncate to emarginate; corolla yellow, banner widely ovate, shorter than wing and keel petals, apex usually cleft, sometimes emarginate or short-mucronate, claw cuneate to oblong, replicate to reflexed, wings not adnate to keel, often asymmetric, auriculate, ± length of keel, claw narrowly oblong, keel petals usually asymmetric, auriculate, posteriorly fused, without beak, claw narrowly oblong; stamens 10, distinct, uniform; anthers dorsifixed; ovary short-stipitate, oblong, usually longer than style, pubescent, velutinous, villous, or tomentose [villosulous]; style glabrous; stigma minute. **Fruits** legumes, persistent, stipitate, stipe 2–4 mm, erect, ascending, or divergent, tan to brown, laterally compressed, straight, arcuate, or, rarely, annular, narrowly elliptic, margins straight, or sinuate or lomentaceous from ovule abortion, papery, not elastic, slowly dehiscent, valves separating from apex through both sutures, sericeous, tomentose, velutinous, villous, glabrate, villosulous, or pubescent. **Seeds** 1–16, oblong, elliptic, or reniform; often with minute, membranous rim-aril. $x = 9$.

Species 23 (10 in the flora): North America, Asia.

Thermia Nuttall is an illegitimate name that pertains here.

SELECTED REFERENCES Chen, C. J., M. G. Mendenhall, and B. L. Turner. 1994. Taxonomy of *Thermopsis* (Fabaceae) in North America. Ann. Missouri Bot. Gard. 81: 714–742. Larisey, M. M. 1940b. A revision of the North American species of the genus *Thermopsis*. Ann. Missouri Bot. Gard. 27: 245–258.

1. Stipules 0.3–0.8 cm wide, base cuneate, not cordate or clasping.
   2. Stems from single, woody rootstock; pedicels glabrate, 7–17 mm, at least as long as bracts; legumes inconspicuously appressed-pubescent; racemes terminal or lateral; plants montane, (300–)700–1600 m . . . . 3. *Thermopsis fraxinifolia*
   2. Stems from extensive rhizomes; pedicels villosulous, 4–6 mm, shorter than bracts; legumes densely appressed-pubescent; racemes terminal; plants mostly of piedmont, 300–800 m . . . . 6. *Thermopsis mollis*
1. Stipules 0.5–6 cm wide, base cordate and/or amplexicaul, sometimes acute.
   3. Legumes ascending or erect.
      4. Leaflet blade surfaces densely pubescent; seeds 1–7(–10); stipules 0.7–6 cm wide.
         5. Herbs (2.5–)3–8(–9) dm; stems slender, from rhizomes; racemes 7–30(–35) cm, 10–40-flowered; legumes ascending; widespread in California . . . . 1. *Thermopsis californica*
         5. Herbs 12–23 dm; stems thick, from woody rootstock; racemes 25–60 cm, 30–90-flowered; legumes erect; Santa Ynez Mountains, California . . . 5. *Thermopsis macrophylla*
      4. Leaflet blade surfaces sparsely pubescent or glabrous; seeds 6–16; stipules 0.7–2.5 cm wide.
         6. Herbs 2–8(–10) dm; stems slender; pedicels 3.5–5 mm; calyx 9–11 mm, lobes 3–5 mm; Rocky Mountains northwest to Washington and Oregon coast, Newfoundland and Quebec . . . . 7. *Thermopsis montana*
         6. Herbs 6–18 dm; stems thick; pedicels 2–3 mm; calyx 7–8 mm, lobes 2–3 mm; e, se United States. . . . . 10. *Thermopsis villosa*
   3. Legumes divergent.
      7. Herbs 1.2–3 dm; leaflets 1.7–3.3 × 0.6–2 cm, lateral veins 5–7 pairs; peduncles 1–4 cm; legumes strongly arcuate to annular . . . . 8. *Thermopsis rhombifolia*
      7. Herbs 3–18 dm; leaflets 3–11 × (0.5–)2–6.5 cm, lateral veins 6–12 pairs; peduncles 3–10(–11) cm; legumes straight or arcuate.
         8. Herbs 8–18 dm; stems thick; leaflet blades 6.5–11 × 2.5–6.5 cm, surfaces tomentose; flowers 1.6–1.8 cm; legumes densely tomentose; Humboldt and Siskiyou counties, California . . . . 9. *Thermopsis robusta*

[8. Shifted to left margin.—Ed.]

8. Herbs 3–8(–9) dm; stems slender; leaflet blades 3–7(–8) × 0.5–3.2 cm, surfaces glabrous or glabrate to puberulent; flowers 2–2.9 cm; legumes inconspicuously pubescent; n California to Yamhill County, Oregon, n, e Rocky Mountains, adjacent Great Plains.
   9. Branches ascending, weakly to moderately or strongly zigzag; leaflet blades 0.5–2.5 cm wide, apex not emarginate; petioles 1–2.5 cm; legumes usually arcuate or annular, sometimes straight; n, e Rocky Mountains, adjacent Great Plains . . . . 2. *Thermopsis divaricarpa*
   9. Branches spreading, moderately to strongly zigzag; leaflet blades 2–3.2 cm wide, apex sometimes emarginate; petioles 2.5–4(–5) cm; legumes straight; n California, w Oregon . . . . 4. *Thermopsis gracilis*

1. Thermopsis californica S. Watson, Proc. Amer. Acad. Arts 11: 126. 1876 E

Herbs robust, (2.5–)3–8(–9) dm, sericeous, villous, or tomentose. **Stems** slender, erect, clustered, many-branched, from rhizomes; branches ascending at 20–45°, weakly to strongly zigzag. **Leaves:** stipules persistent, widely ovate to lanceolate, 1.5–6.5 × 0.7–5 cm, base cuneate to cordate or amplexicaul, apex acuminate; petiole 1–3.5 cm; leaflet blades elliptic, obovate, or rhombic, 3–7(–9) × 1.2–4(–4.5) cm, lateral veins 6–9 pairs, conspicuously net-veined abaxially, apex obtuse to acute, surfaces silvery-sericeous or tomentose to villous. **Peduncles** 2–10 cm; bracts semipersistent, ovate to lanceolate, 6–15(–30) × 2.5–15(–20) mm. **Racemes** 10–40-flowered, 7–30(–35) cm; flowers mostly in whorls of 3–5. **Pedicels** 2–6 mm, sericeous or tomentose. **Flowers** 1.5–2 cm; calyx 5–9(–10) × 5–9 mm at limb, lobes 2.5–5 mm, equal to or longer than tube; wing and keel petals asymmetrically oblong-elliptic or, sometimes, reniform (var. *argentata*); ovary velutinous; ovules 5–11. **Legumes** ascending (irregularly divaricate when young), straight, 2–6(–7) × (0.5–)0.6–0.9 cm, sericeous, tomentose, or velutinous. **Seeds** 1–6(–10), brown, oblong, 4–5(–5.5) × (2.5–)2.8–4 mm, short-beaked.

Varieties 3 (3 in the flora): California.

1. Stipules widely to narrowly ovate, 1.5–5 cm wide; floral bracts 3–15 (–20) mm wide; peduncles (4–)6–10 cm . . . . 1a. *Thermopsis californica* var. *californica*
1. Stipules ovate to lanceolate, 0.7–2.5 cm wide; floral bracts 2.5–6 mm wide; peduncles 2–7 (–10) cm.
   2. Herbs silvery-sericeous; wing and keel petals oblong-elliptic to reniform; Kern, Lassen, Los Angeles, Modoc, Santa Barbara, Shasta, Siskiyou, Ventura counties . . . . 1b. *Thermopsis californica* var. *argentata*
   2. Herbs densely silvery-tomentose; wing and keel petals oblong-elliptic; San Diego County . . . . 1c. *Thermopsis californica* var. *semota*

1a. Thermopsis californica S. Watson var. **californica** E

Herbs 3–8(–9) dm, sparsely to densely tomentose or villous. **Branches** weakly to moderately zigzag. **Leaves:** stipules widely to narrowly ovate, 2.5–6.5 × 1.5–5 cm, base cuneate to amplexicaul; petiole 1.5–3.5 cm; leaflet blades elliptic to obovate or rhombic, 3.5–7(–9) × 2–4(–4.5) cm, apex obtuse to acute. **Peduncles** (4–)6–10 cm; bracts widely ovate to nearly lanceolate, 6–15(–30) × 3–15(–20) mm. **Racemes** 12–40-flowered, 10–30(–35) cm. **Flowers:** calyx 5–8(–9) × 6–9 mm at limb, lobes 2.5–5 mm; wing and keel petals oblong-elliptic; ovules 5–8. **Legumes** 3–5.5 × 0.6–0.7 cm. **Seeds** 3–5(–10), 4 × 2.8 mm.

Flowering May–Jun. Chaparral; 0–1000 m; Calif.

Variety *californica* is the more commonly encountered and more variable taxon of the *Thermopsis californica* complex. It is distinguished from vars. *argentata* and *semota* by its larger habit, broader stipules and bracts, and sparsely to densely tomentose vestiture.

Variety *californica* occurs in coastal regions of central California, mostly in chaparral.

1b. Thermopsis californica S. Watson var. **argentata** (Greene) C. J. Chen & B. L. Turner, Ann. Missouri Bot. Gard. 81: 719. 1994 E

Thermopsis argentata Greene, Erythea 3: 18. 1895; *T. macrophylla* Hooker & Arnott var. *argentata* (Greene) Jepson

Herbs (2.5–)3–5 dm, silvery-sericeous throughout. **Branches** weakly to moderately zigzag. **Leaves:** stipules ovate to lanceolate, 1.5–6 × 0.8–2.5 cm, base cuneate to cordate; petiole 1.3–2.1 cm; leaflet blades obovate to elliptic, 3–6.5 × 1.2–3.5 cm, apex obtuse to acute, sometimes short-mucronate. **Peduncles** 4–7 (–10) cm; bracts ovate to lanceolate, 7–15 × 2.5–5 mm. **Racemes** 10–30-flowered, 8–20(–25) cm. **Flowers:** calyx

7–9(–10) × 5–8 mm at limb, lobes 3.5–4.5(–5) mm; wing and keel petals oblong-elliptic to reniform; ovules 8–11. **Legumes** 3–6(–7) × (0.5–)0.7–0.9 cm. **Seeds** 1–6, 4–5(–5.5) × (2.5–)3.5–4 mm. **2*n*** = 18.

Flowering May–Jun. Montane chaparral, pine forests; 1200–2200 m; Calif.

Variety *argentata* differs from the more widespread, more variable var. *californica* in its smaller habit and closely appressed, silvery vestiture.

Variety *argentata* is found in the northeasternmost counties (southeastern Siskiyou and closely adjacent Lassen, Modoc, and Shasta counties), and again in southwestern counties (Kern, Los Angeles, Santa Barbara, and Ventura counties), in mostly interior montane chaparral and pine forest.

1c. Thermopsis californica S. Watson var. **semota** (Jepson) C. J. Chen & B. L. Turner, Ann. Missouri Bot. Gard. 81: 722. 1994 C E

Thermopsis macrophylla Hooker & Arnott var. *semota* Jepson, Fl. Calif. 2: 245. 1936; *T. macrophylla* subsp. *semota* (Jepson) R. M. Beauchamp

Herbs 3–5(–6) dm, densely silvery-tomentose. **Branches** moderately to strongly zigzag. **Leaves:** stipules ovate to lanceolate, 1.5–5.5 × 0.7–2.4 cm, base cuneate to cordate; petiole 1–2 cm; leaflet blades elliptic to narrowly so, 3–6.5(–7.5) × 1.2–3.5(–3.8) cm, apex acute to obtuse, short-mucronate. **Peduncles** 2–6(–9) cm; bracts ovate to nearly lanceolate, 6–11 × 3.5–6 mm. **Racemes** 10–30-flowered, 7–20(–30) cm. **Flowers:** calyx 5–8(–9) × 5–8 mm at limb, lobes 3–5 mm; petals: banner shallowly emarginate or short-mucronate, wings and keel oblong-elliptic; ovules 5–7. **Legumes** 2–4 × 0.6–0.7 cm. **Seeds** 1 or 2 (fully matured not seen).

Flowering Apr–Jun. Grassy oak woodlands; of conservation concern; 1000–1500 m; Calif.

Variety *semota* is restricted to interior portions of San Diego County.

2. Thermopsis divaricarpa A. Nelson, Bot. Gaz. 25: 275, plate 18, fig. 3. 1898 E

Thermopsis rhombifolia (Nuttall ex Pursh) Richardson var. *divaricarpa* (A. Nelson) Isely

Herbs delicate, 3–6(–9) dm, glabrate or puberulent. **Stems** slender, erect, clustered, several-branched, from thick woody rootstock or rhizomes; branches ascending at 20–35°, weakly to moderately or strongly zigzag. **Leaves:** stipules persistent, ovate to narrowly elliptic, 2–3.5(–4) × 0.7–3 cm, base cuneate to cordate, apex acute; petiole 1–2.5 cm; leaflet blades elliptic to narrowly elliptic or rhombic, 3–7 × 0.5–2.5 cm, lateral veins 7–10 pairs, conspicuously net-veined abaxially, apex acute to obtuse, surfaces glabrate to puberulent. **Peduncles** 3–5 cm; bracts deciduous, ovate to lanceolate, 7–14 × 3–5 mm. **Racemes** 5–15-flowered, 7–15 cm; flowers usually in whorls of 2–4. **Pedicels** 5–8 mm, glabrate to puberulent. **Flowers** 2.5–2.9 cm; calyx 8–11 × 6–8 mm at limb, lobes 2–5 mm, equal to or shorter than tube; wing and keel petals elliptic to asymmetrically oblong-elliptic; ovary appressed-pubescent; ovules 10–18. **Legumes** divergent, straight to arcuate, to ca. 45°, 6.5–9 × 0.6–0.8 cm, inconspicuously appressed-pubescent. **Seeds** (6–)10–14, brown-black, elliptic, 4–5 × 2–2.5 mm, beaked. **2*n*** = 36.

Flowering (Apr–)May–Jun(–Jul). Pine or spruce forests, streamsides, moist, open areas; 2000–3000 m; Colo., N.Mex., Wyo.

3. Thermopsis fraxinifolia (Nuttall) M. A. Curtis, Amer. J. Sci. Arts 44: 81. 1843 E

Baptisia fraxinifolia Nuttall in J. Torrey and A. Gray, Fl. N. Amer. 1: 387. 1840; *Thermopsis mollis* (Michaux) M. A. Curtis var. *fraxinifolia* (Nuttall) Isely

Herbs delicate, 5–10 dm, glabrate to sparsely puberulent. **Stems** slender, erect, clustered, many-branched, from single, woody rootstock; branches spreading at 45–80°, strongly zigzag. **Leaves:** stipules sometimes persistent, lanceolate to narrowly ovate, 1–3.5 × 0.3–0.8 cm, base cuneate, apex acuminate; petiole 1.6–3 cm; leaflet blades elliptic, 4.5–8 × 2–3.5 cm, lateral veins 9–12 pairs, conspicuously net-veined abaxially, apex acute to acuminate, surfaces glabrous or sparsely puberulent. **Peduncles** 2.5–5.5 cm; bracts persistent, lanceolate, 8–12 × 1–3 mm. **Racemes** terminal or lateral, scattered, 12–25 cm; flowers 7–25-flowered. **Pedicels** 7–17 mm, glabrate. **Flowers** 1.6–1.9 cm; calyx 7–9 × 4–5 mm at limb, lobes 2–3 mm, much shorter than tube; wing petals elliptic to asymmetrically oblong-elliptic, keel petals asymmetrically oblong-elliptic; ovary appressed-pubescent; ovules (6–)12–16. **Legumes** irregularly divergent, straight, (3–)5.5–7.5 × 0.3–0.5 cm, inconspicuously appressed-pubescent. **Seeds** (5–)10–15, brown, reniform, 4 × 2.5 mm, short-beaked. **2*n*** = 18.

Flowering (Apr–)May–Jul. Rich woodlands, upper hillsides along streams, lower elevations along floodplains; (300–)700–1600 m; Ala., Ga., N.C., S.C., Tenn.

Thermopsis fraxinifolia is partially sympatric with *T. mollis*; in regions of overlap *T. fraxinifolia* usually occurs at higher elevations along upper slopes of mountainous ridges and hills of the Appalachians. The plant may also occur at lower elevations on alluvial deposits along at least some of the rivers in this region.

Thermopsis fraxinifolia can be distinguished from *T. mollis* by its more robust and more branching habit, lateral (as well as terminal) inflorescences, and relatively longer pedicels. Furthermore, *T. mollis* propagates by extensive, vigorous rhizomes, which are absent in *T. fraxinifolia*.

4. Thermopsis gracilis Howell, Erythea 1: 109. 189 [E]

Thermopsis macrophylla Hooker & Arnott var. *venosa* (Eastwood) Isely; *T. montana* Nuttall var. *venosa* (Eastwood) Jepson

Herbs robust, 3–8 dm, glabrous or sparsely villous. **Stems** slender, erect, solitary or clustered, many-branched, from woody rootstock or rhizomes; branches spreading at 30–70°, moderately to strongly zigzag. **Leaves:** stipules persistent, asymmetrically ovate-elliptic, 2.5–3.5 × 1.5–3 cm, base cuneate to cordate, apex acuminate; petiole 2.5–4(–5) cm; leaflet blades elliptic to obovate or rhombic, 3–6(–8) × 2–3.2 cm, lateral veins 6–9 pairs, conspicuously net-veined abaxially, apex acute, obtuse, or emarginate, surfaces glabrous. **Peduncles** 4–9(–11) cm; bracts semipersistent, ovate, 6–8 × 3–5 mm. **Racemes** 7–30-flowered, 12–20 (–30) cm; flowers scattered. **Pedicels** 6–16 mm, glabrous or sparsely villous. **Flowers** 2–2.3 cm; calyx 8–10 × 7–8 mm at limb, lobes 2–3 mm, much shorter than tube; wing petals elliptic, keel petals asymmetrically oblong-elliptic; ovary sparsely villous; ovules 9–14. **Legumes** irregularly divergent, straight, 3–6 × 0.4–0.6 cm, inconspicuously pubescent. **Seeds** 2–8, tan, oblong, 3–4 × 2 mm, short-beaked. **2*n*** = 36.

Flowering (Apr–)May–Jun. Mesophytic lower montane evergreen forests; 100–1200 m; Calif., Oreg.

Thermopsis gracilis is readily distinguished from the closely allopatric *T. californica* and *T. montana* by its divergent fruits, spreading branches, and glabrous to sparsely pubescent foliage. The species is most closely related to *T. robusta*, which also has divergent fruits but which differs in its very robust habit, densely pilose vestiture, and longer calyx lobes.

5. Thermopsis macrophylla Hooker & Arnott, Bot. Beechey Voy., 329. 1838 [C] [E]

Thermopsis macrophylla var. *agnina* J. T. Howell

Herbs robust, 12–23 dm, tomentose. **Stems** thick, erect, solitary or few-clustered, several-branched, from woody rootstock; branches ascending at 45°, moderately zigzag. **Leaves:** stipules persistent, widely ovate, 3–9 × 2–6 cm, base amplexicaul to cordate, apex acuminate; petiole 2–5(–7) cm; leaflet blades elliptic, 4–10 × 2–5 cm, lateral veins 6–8 pairs, not conspicuously net-veined abaxially, apex acute, surfaces villous. **Peduncles** 8–15 cm; bracts persistent, ovate to lanceolate, 8–10 × 3–5 mm. **Racemes** 30–90-flowered, 25–60 cm; flowers in whorls of 3–5. **Pedicels** 2.5–4 mm, villous. **Flowers** 1.7–2.2 cm; calyx 7–9 × 7–8 mm at limb, lobes 3–4 mm, equal to or shorter than tube; wing petals elliptic, keel petals obovate; ovary velutinous; ovules 7–9. **Legumes** erect, straight, 3.5–5 × 0.5–0.7 cm, villous. **Seeds** 5–7, brown-black, widely elliptic, 4–5 × 2.5–3 mm, short-beaked. **2*n*** = 18.

Flowering May–Jun. Sandy granitic soils; of conservation concern; 1000–1400 m; Calif.

Thermopsis macrophylla is known only from the Santa Ynez Mountains in Santa Barbara County; it is in the Center for Plant Conservation's National Collection of Endangered Plants.

6. Thermopsis mollis (Michaux) M. A. Curtis, Mem. Amer. Acad. Arts, n. s. 3: 47. 1846 [E]

Podalyria mollis Michaux, Fl. Bor.-Amer. 1: 264. 1803; *Thermopsis hugeri* (Small) Small

Herbs delicate, 3–6 dm, sparsely appressed-pubescent. **Stems** slender, ascending or spreading, solitary or clustered, several-branched, from extensive rhizomes; branches spreading at 45–80°, strongly zigzag. **Leaves:** stipules caducous, narrowly elliptic to linear, 1.5–2 × 0.3–0.5(–0.8) cm, base cuneate, apex acuminate; petiole 0.7–1.7 cm; leaflet blades elliptic, 3.5–8 × 1–4 cm, lateral veins 7–9 pairs, conspicuously net-veined abaxially, apex acute to acuminate, surfaces sparsely appressed-pubescent (especially on veins), sometimes glabrate adaxially. **Peduncles** 3–7 cm; bracts persistent, lanceolate, 8–13 × 2–4 mm. **Racemes** terminal, 5–17-flowered, 7–20 cm; flowers scattered. **Pedicels** 4–6 mm, villosulous. **Flowers** 1.6–1.9 cm; calyx 7.5–8 × 6–7 mm at limb, lobes 2–3 mm, shorter than tube; wing petals elliptic to asymmetrically oblong-elliptic, keel petals asymmetrically oblong-elliptic; ovary densely appressed-pubescent; ovules (8–) 12–16. **Legumes** divaricate, arcuate to straight, (3–) 4–9 × 0.4–0.6 cm, densely appressed-pubescent. **Seeds** 6–12, tan to brown-black, oblong, 2.5–3.5 × 1.5–2 mm, beaked. **2*n*** = 18.

Flowering (Apr–)May–Jun. Rich, sandy, dry woods and ridges; 300–800 m; Ala., Ga., Ky., N.C., S.C., Tenn., Va.

7. Thermopsis montana Nuttall in J. Torrey and A. Gray, Fl. N. Amer. 1: 388. 1840 E

Thermopsis rhombifolia (Nuttall ex Pursh) Richardson var. *montana* (Nuttall) Isely

Herbs delicate, 2–8(–10) dm, glabrate, appressed-pubescent, or thinly villous. **Stems** slender, erect, solitary or clustered, moderately or few-branched, from woody rootstock or rhizomes; branches ascending at 20–45°, weakly or moderately zigzag. **Leaves:** stipules persistent, widely ovate or elliptic, 1.7–4.5 × 0.7–2.5 cm, base oblique to cuneate, apex acuminate or acute; petiole 1–4 cm; leaflet blades elliptic or obovate, 3.5–8 × 0.7–3(–5) cm, lateral veins 6–11 pairs, conspicuously net-veined abaxially or not, apex acute or obtuse, sometimes short-mucronate or emarginate, surfaces sparsely appressed-pubescent or glabrous. **Peduncles** 2–8 cm; bracts semipersistent, narrowly elliptic or elliptic to widely ovate, 6–10 × 2.5–6 mm. **Racemes** 6–25-flowered, 4–25 cm; flowers in whorls of 2 or 3 or scattered. **Pedicels** 3.5–5 mm, villosulous. **Flowers** 1.6–2.2 cm; calyx 9–11 × 5–8 mm at limb, lobes 3–5 mm, shorter than tube; wings and keel petals asymmetrically oblong-elliptic; ovary velutinous or densely appressed-pubescent; ovules 10–16. **Legumes** ascending, straight, 4.5–6.5 × 0.4–0.6 cm, villosulous or appressed-pubescent. **Seeds** 6–16, brown-black, oblong, 3.5–5 × 2.5–3 mm, beaked.

Varieties 2 (2 in the flora): North America.

The strictly erect fruits distinguish *Thermopsis montana* from *T. gracilis* and from the superficially similar *T. divaricarpa*. Intermediate populations and possible hybrids are discussed under *T. divaricarpa* by C. J. Chen et al. (1994).

1. Herbs 2–7 dm, appressed-pubescent to thinly villous; stems solitary or clustered, few-branched, from woody rootstock or rhizomes; leaflet blades not conspicuously net-veined abaxially; floral bracts elliptic to widely ovate . . . . 7a. *Thermopsis montana* var. *montana*
1. Herbs 5–8(–10) dm, glabrate to sparsely appressed-pubescent; stems clustered, several-branched, from woody rootstock; leaflet blades conspicuously net-veined abaxially; floral bracts narrowly elliptic . . . 7b. *Thermopsis montana* var. *ovata*

7a. Thermopsis montana Nuttall var. **montana** E

Herbs 2–7 dm, appressed-pubescent to thinly villous. **Stems** stiffly erect, solitary or clustered, few-branched, from woody rootstock or rhizomes; branches moderately zigzag. **Leaves:** petiole 1–2.5 cm; leaflet blades elliptic, narrowly elliptic, or obovate, 3.5–8 × 0.7–2.5 cm, not conspicuously net-veined abaxially, surfaces appressed-pubescent. **Racemes** 4–18 cm; bracts elliptic to widely ovate. **Flowers** 1.6–2 cm. **Legumes** villosulous. **2*n*** = 18.

Flowering May–Jun. Open moist margins of creeks and lakes, swales, meadows, pine woodland, sagebrush or pinyon; 2000–3200 m; Ariz., Colo., Idaho, Mont., Nev., N.Mex., Oreg., Utah, Wash., Wyo.

Variety *montana* is widespread and highly variable; it can usually be distinguished from var. *ovata* by its smaller habit, narrower leaflets and bracts, and greater tendency to spread by rhizomes. In southwestern Oregon, the two varieties appear to intergrade.

7b. Thermopsis montana Nuttall var. **ovata** (B. L. Robinson ex Piper) H. St. John, Torreya 41: 112. 1941 E

Thermopsis montana subsp. *ovata* B. L. Robinson ex Piper, Contr. U.S. Natl. Herb. 11: 349. 1906; *T. gracilis* Howell var. *ovata* (B. L. Robinson ex Piper) M. G. Mendenhall; *T. macrophylla* Hooker & Arnott var. *hitchcockii* Isely; *T. montana* var. *hitchcockii* (Isely) M. G. Mendenhall; *T. rhombifolia* (Nuttall ex Pursh) Richardson var. *ovata* (B. L. Robinson ex Piper) Isely

Herbs 5–8(–10) dm, glabrate to sparsely appressed-pubescent. **Stems** erect, clustered, several-branched, from woody rootstock; branches weakly to moderately zigzag. **Leaves:** petiole 3.2–4 cm; leaflet blades broadly to narrowly elliptic or obovate, 4.5–6(–8) × 1.5–3(–5) cm, conspicuously net-veined abaxially, surfaces sparsely appressed-pubescent abaxially, glabrous adaxially. **Racemes** 12–25 cm; bracts narrowly elliptic. **Flowers** 1.9–2.2 cm. **Legumes** appressed-pubescent.

Flowering May–Jun. Moist soils, along streams and ditches, meadows, dry sagebrush plains; 10–2000 m; Nfld. and Labr. (Nfld.), Que.; Idaho, Mont., Oreg., Wash.

Variety *ovata* is distinguished from var. *montana* by having a relatively robust habit, several-branched stems, and broader leaflets and bracts. It is introduced in Newfoundland and Quebec.

8. Thermopsis rhombifolia (Nuttall ex Pursh) Richardson in J. Franklin, Narr. Journey Polar Sea, 737. 1823 [E] [F] [W]

Cytisus rhombifolius Nuttall ex Pursh, Fl. Amer. Sept. 2: 741. 1813

Herbs dwarf and robust, 1.2–3 dm, glabrate to appressed-pubescent. **Stems** slender, erect or ascending, solitary or clustered, few-branched, from woody rootstock or rhizomes; branches ascending at 25–50°, weakly zigzag. **Leaves:** stipules persistent, ovate to widely ovate or elliptic to widely elliptic, 1–2.6 × 0.5–1.5(–2.2) cm, base cuneate to oblique, apex acute to obtuse, short-mucronate; petiole 0.8–2.2 cm; leaflet blades elliptic to obovate or narrowly elliptic, 1.7–3.3 × 0.6–2 cm, lateral veins 5–7 pairs, conspicuously net-veined abaxially, apex acute to obtuse, sometimes short-mucronate, surfaces appressed-pubescent to sparsely tomentose or glabrate abaxially, glabrous adaxially. **Peduncles** 1–4 cm; bracts deciduous, elliptic to obovate, 5–9 × 3–5 mm. **Racemes** 5–15-flowered, 4–12 cm; flowers in whorls of 2 or 3 or scattered. **Pedicels** 3–7 mm, glabrate to densely appressed-pubescent. **Flowers** 1.9–2.1 cm; calyx (6–)8–10(–12) × 4.5–6 mm at limb, lobes (3–)4–5 mm, equal to or shorter than tube; wing petals asymmetrically oblong to very widely ovate, keel petals asymmetrically oblong-widely elliptic; ovary glabrate to appressed-puberulent; ovules 12–14. **Legumes** divergent, strongly arcuate to annular, 3–7 × 0.4–0.7 cm, glabrate to sparsely tomentose. **Seeds** 2–10, brown, elliptic, 3.5–4 × 2.5 mm, beaked. $2n = 18$.

Flowering May–Jun. Xeric grasslands in deep alluvial soils and lower canyons, roadsides; 2000–3000; Alta., B.C., Man., Ont., Sask.; Colo., Mont., Nebr., N.Mex., N.Dak., Okla., S.Dak., Utah, Wis., Wyo.

9. Thermopsis robusta Howell, Erythea 1: 109. 1893 [C] [E]

Herbs robust, 8–18 dm, densely tomentose. **Stems** thick, erect, clustered, many-branched, from woody rootstock; branches ascending at 30–50°, strongly zigzag. **Leaves:** stipules persistent, widely ovate to nearly lanceolate, 1.5–5.5 × 0.7–3 cm, base oblique to cuneate, apex acuminate; petiole 2.2–3.5 cm; leaflet blades elliptic to widely elliptic or ovate, 6.5–11 × 2.5–6.5 cm, lateral veins 9–12 pairs, not conspicuously net-veined abaxially, apex acute to acuminate, short-mucronate, surfaces tomentose. **Peduncles** 7–10 cm; bracts persistent, ovate, 8–14 × 3–8 mm. **Racemes** 20–40-flowered, 20–45 cm; flowers in whorls of 2–5 or scattered. **Pedicels** 4–8 mm, densely tomentose. **Flowers** 1.6–1.8 cm; calyx 7–9 × 5–8 mm at limb, lobes 2–4 mm, equal to or shorter than tube; wing and keel petals asymmetrically oblong-rhombic; ovary densely tomentose; ovules 10–13. **Legumes** divergent, arcuate, 4.5–6.5 × 0.4–0.5 cm, densely tomentose. **Seeds** 5–10, brown, reniform, 3.5–4 × 2 mm, not beaked.

Flowering May–Jun. Ridgetops; of conservation concern; 150–1500 m; Calif.

Thermopsis robusta is a localized, robust taxon known only from Humboldt and Siskiyou counties.

10. Thermopsis villosa (Walter) Fernald & B. G. Schubert, Rhodora 50: 201. 1948 [E] [F]

Sophora villosa Walter, Fl. Carol., 134. 1788; *Baptisia villosa* (Walter) Elliott; *Thermopsis caroliniana* M. A. Curtis

Herbs 6–18 dm, glabrate (except racemes densely villous). **Stems** thick, erect, solitary or clustered, few-branched, from woody rootstock; branches spreading at 45–60°, moderately zigzag. **Leaves:** stipules persistent, elliptic to ovate, 1.5–4.5 × 0.9–2.4 cm, base oblique to cuneate, apex acute to obtuse; petiole 2–5(–6) cm; leaflet blades elliptic, 4–9.5 × 1.8–4.4 cm, lateral veins 6–8 pairs, conspicuously net-veined abaxially, apex acute to obtuse, surfaces sparsely villous abaxially, glabrate adaxially. **Peduncles** 6–13 cm; bracts deciduous, widely ovate to widely obovate, 5–7 × 5–6(–8) mm. **Racemes** 10–50-flowered, 15–50 cm; flowers in whorls of 2 or 3 or scattered. **Pedicels** 2–3 mm, densely villous. **Flowers** 1.7–1.9 cm; calyx 7–8 × 5–6.5 mm at limb, lobes 2–3 mm, much shorter than tube; wing and keel petals asymmetrically oblong-rhombic; ovary velutinous; ovules 12–16. **Legumes** ascending, straight to slightly arcuate, 4–5.5 × 0.4–0.6 cm, densely tomentose to villous. **Seeds** 7–12, olive brown, elliptic, 3–3.5 × 1.8–2 mm, beaked. $2n = 18$.

Flowering May–Jun(–Jul). Open areas of deciduous oak woodlands; 1000–1600 m; Ala., Conn., Ga., Maine, Md., Mass., N.H., N.J., N.Y., N.C., Pa., S.C., Tenn., Vt., Va.

Thermopsis villosa is a distinctive, stiffly erect species of the southern Appalachian ridges and upper valleys. Locally naturalized populations occur where the species has been cultivated farther north.

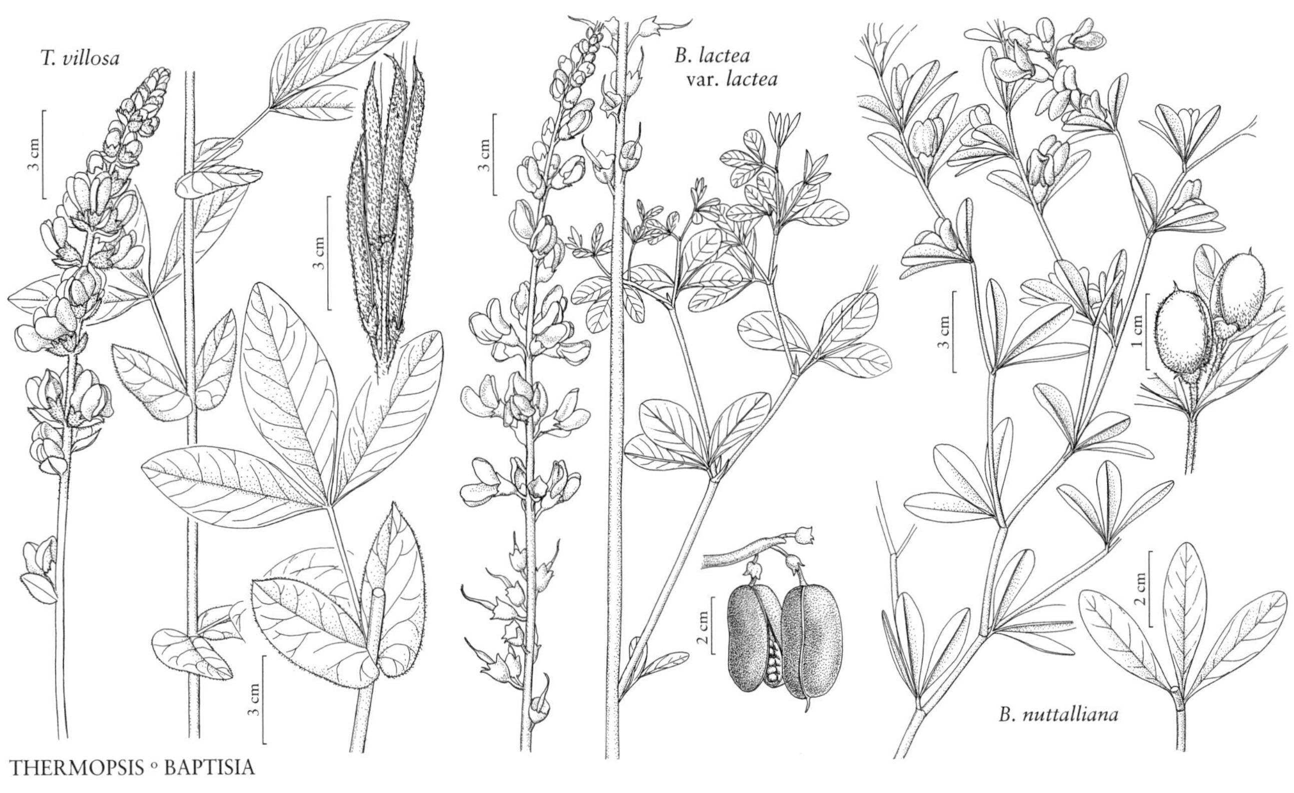

THERMOPSIS ◦ BAPTISIA

51. BAPTISIA Ventenat, Dec. Gen. Nov., 9. 1808 • Wild or false indigo [Greek *bapto*, to dip or dye, alluding to use of some species as substitutes for true indigo dyes] E

Billie L. Turner†

Herbs, perennial, bushy, unarmed; rootstock thick or rhizomatous. **Stems** stiffly erect or spreading, glabrous or pubescent. **Leaves** alternate, odd-pinnate; stipules present or absent; petiolate, sessile, or subsessile; leaflets usually 3, rarely 1 or 2, blade margins entire, surfaces glabrous or pubescent. **Inflorescences** 1–30+-flowered, axillary or terminal, racemes; bracts present or absent, 2, well developed when present; bracteoles usually absent, distal to middle of pedicel when present. **Flowers** papilionaceous; calyx campanulate, subactinomorphic, lobes 4; corolla white, yellow, violet, or blue, petals mostly distinct, keel petals slightly connate; stamens 10, distinct; anthers dorsifixed; ovary distinctly stipitate, glabrous or pubescent. **Fruits** legumes, stipitate, inflated, suborbicular, lanceoloid, ellipsoid, oblong, ovoid, or cylindric, indehiscent, leathery, glabrous or pubescent. **Seeds** 2–30+, obovoid to ovoid. $x = 9$.

Species 17 (17 in the flora): c, sc, e North America.

Baptisia is monophyletic and most closely related to the North American species of *Thermopsis* (B. L. Turner 1981; M. G. Mendenhall 1994; Wang H. C. et al. 2006). It is mostly confined to the eastern United States; *B. australis* var. *minor* and *B. tinctoria* barely extend into Canada. *Baptisia* is perhaps best known for having very distinct species that commonly hybridize, which confounded early botanists. For example, M. M. Larisey (1940) recognized 30 species in *Baptisia*, most of which are of hybrid origin. D. Isely (1981) provided an excellent account in which 15 species were recognized; in his account of 1998, 16 species were recognized, some with two or more varieties. Turner (2006c) provided detailed occurrence maps for the species and varieties treated here.

D. Isely (1981) provided a detailed summary of the hybridization problems in *Baptisia*. As documented by R. E. Alston and B. L. Turner (1962) and M. A. Kosnik et al. (1996), anywhere two species of *Baptisia* are found growing together or in proximity, hybrids and/or their derivatives can be expected.

SELECTED REFERENCES Larisey, M. M. 1940. A monograph of the genus *Baptisia*. Ann. Missouri Bot. Gard. 27: 119–244. Leebens-Mack, J. and B. G. Milligan. 1998. Pollination biology in hybridizing *Baptisia* (Fabaceae) populations. Amer. J. Bot. 85: 500–507. Mendenhall, M. G. 1994. Phylogeny of *Baptisia* and *Thermopsis* (Leguminosae) as Inferred from Chloroplast DNA and Nuclear Ribosomal DNA Sequences, Secondary Chemistry, and Morphology. Ph.D. dissertation. University of Texas. Turner, B. L. 2006c. Overview of the genus *Baptisia* (Leguminosae). Phytologia 88: 253–268.

1. Leaflets 1.
  2. Herbs pubescent; Brantley and Wayne counties, Georgia . . . . 6. *Baptisia arachnifera*
  2. Herbs glabrous; Alabama, Florida, Georgia, South Carolina.
    3. Leaves not perfoliate. . . . . 7. *Baptisia simplicifolia*
    3. Leaves perfoliate . . . . 8. *Baptisia perfoliata*
1. Leaflets usually 3 (1 or 2 distally in *B. sphaerocarpa*).
  4. Pedicels bracteolate.
    5. Flowers 10–15 mm; calyces 6–7 mm, lobes ± equal to tube . . . . 15. *Baptisia lecontei*
    5. Flowers 10–14 mm; calyces 8–13 mm, lobes much longer than tube.
      6. Herbs glabrous; ne Florida . . . . 16. *Baptisia calycosa*
      6. Herbs pubescent; easternmost Florida Panhandle. . . . . 17. *Baptisia hirsuta*
  4. Pedicels ebracteolate.
    7. Corollas dull violet to deep blue . . . . 4. *Baptisia australis*
    7. Corollas white, cream, or yellow.
      8. Corollas white, cream, or pale yellow.
        9. Legumes cylindric to oblong-lanceoloid, 7–10 mm wide; flowers 14–18 mm . . . . 1. *Baptisia alba*
        9. Legumes ellipsoid-cylindric or ellipsoid-lanceoloid to lanceoloid, 12–30 mm wide; flowers 18–25 mm.
          10. Racemes terminal, stiffly erect, not secund; corollas white. . . . . 2. *Baptisia lactea*
          10. Racemes axillary, ascending to horizontal, secund; corollas cream or pale yellow . . . . 13. *Baptisia bracteata* (in part)
      8. Corollas usually yellow (sometimes cream or pale yellow in *B. bracteata* and *B. megacarpa*).
        11. Legumes suborbicular, woody; leaflets 3 to mid stem, 1 or 2 distally . . . . 3. *Baptisia sphaerocarpa*
        11. Legumes ovoid, suborbicular, ellipsoid, lanceoloid, or ellipsoid-lanceoloid, leathery, brittle, papery, or woody; leaflets 3 throughout.
          12. Corollas 12–16 mm; legumes 8–15 mm. . . . . 9. *Baptisia tinctoria*
          12. Corollas (15–)18–28 mm; legumes 8–55 mm.
            13. Racemes secund, axillary, 8–30-flowered.
              14. Petioles 1–4 mm mid stem; c, n United States. . . . . 12. *Baptisia leucophaea*
              14. Petioles 5–14 mm mid stem; se United States.
                15. Bracts persistent. . . . . 13. *Baptisia bracteata* (in part)
                15. Bracts deciduous . . . . 14. *Baptisia cinerea*
            13. Racemes not secund, terminal or axillary, 1–10(–12)-flowered.
              16. Mid stem leaves sessile or subsessile; corollas 15–20 mm; sc United States . . . . 10. *Baptisia nuttalliana*
              16. Mid stem leaves subsessile or petiolate; corollas 18–25 mm; se United States.
                17. Petioles 15–20 mm mid stem; legumes 30–40 × 20–30 mm . . . . 5. *Baptisia megacarpa*
                17. Petioles 0.1–12 mm mid stem; legumes 10–25 × 10–12 mm . . . . 11. *Baptisia lanceolata*

1. Baptisia alba (Linnaeus) R. Brown in W. Aiton and W. T. Aiton, Hortus Kew. 3: 6. 1811 • Eastern white indigo [E]

Crotalaria alba Linnaeus, Sp. Pl. 2: 716. 1753; *Baptisia albescens* Small; *Sophora alba* (Linnaeus) Linnaeus

Herbs to 1.5 m, glabrous. **Leaves** petiolate; stipules deciduous, linear-lanceolate, 3–8 mm; petiole 5–20 mm; leaflets 3, blades obovate to elliptic-lanceolate. **Racemes** 8–20-flowered, terminal, bracteate. **Pedicels** 6–10 mm. **Flowers** 14–18 mm; calyx 4.5–6.5 mm, glabrous; corolla white, 12–16 mm. **Legumes** ascending, ± inflated, cylindric to oblong-lanceoloid, 20–30 × 7–10 mm, brittle. **Seeds** 20–30.

Flowering Mar–May. Pine or pine-oak woodlands in mostly sandy soils; 50–700 m; Ala., Fla., Ga., N.C., S.C., Tenn., Va.

D. Isely (1981) accepted *Baptisia alba* as containing *B. albescens*, as did R. L. Wilbur (1963c) and B. L. Turner (2006c); later, Isely (1998) recognized *B. alba* with two varieties and including *B. lactea* and *B. albescens*. M. Woods and A. R. Diamond (2014) accepted both *B. alba* and *B. albescens*. The taxonomy and nomenclature of these taxa were discussed in more detail by Turner.

Baptisia alba forms hybrids with *B. cinerea*, *B. lanceolata*, *B. perfoliata* (*B.* ×*fulva* Larisey), and *B. tinctoria* (*B.* ×*pinetorum* Larisey [= *B.* ×*serenae* M. A. Curtis]).

2. Baptisia lactea (Rafinesque) Thieret, Sida 3: 446. 1969 • Western white indigo [E] [F]

Dolichos lacteus Rafinesque, Fl. Ludov., 103. 1817

Herbs to 2 m, glabrous. **Leaves** petiolate; stipules caducous, lanceolate, 2–8 mm; petiole 5–15 mm; leaflets 3, blades obovate. **Racemes** 8–20-flowered, terminal, stiffly erect, ebracteate. **Pedicels** 3–10 mm. **Flowers** 18–25 mm; calyx 7–8 mm, glabrous; corolla white, 16–23 mm. **Legumes** black in age, ascending to spreading-pendent, plump, ellipsoid-cylindric, 23–50 × 10–30 mm, smooth. **Seeds** 20–30.

Varieties 2 (2 in the flora): c, se United States.

Baptisia lactea forms hybrids with *B. lanceolata*, *B. nuttalliana*, *B. sphaerocarpa* (*B.* ×*sulphurea* Engelmann), and *B. tinctoria* (*B.* ×*deamii* Larisey).

Peripheral intergradation between var. *lactea* and var. *pendula* occurs (hence their treatment as varieties); they are not known to co-occur at present.

1. Legumes 10–15 mm wide; mature stipes about as long as calyces; c United States . . . . 2a. *Baptisia lactea* var. *lactea*
1. Legumes 15–30 mm wide; mature stipes much longer than calyces; se United States . . . . .2b. *Baptisia lactea* var. *pendula*

2a. Baptisia lactea (Rafinesque) Thieret var. **lactea** [E] [F]

Baptisia leucantha Torrey & A. Gray

Legumes 10–15 mm wide; mature stipe about as long as calyx (4–8 mm). **2*n*** = 18.

Flowering Mar–May. Open forests and riverine glades, silty clay or sandy soils; 50–700 m; Ark., Ill., Ind., Iowa, Kans., Ky., La., Mich., Minn., Miss., Mo., Nebr., Ohio, Okla., Tenn., Tex., Wis.

2b. Baptisia lactea (Rafinesque) Thieret var. **pendula** (Larisey) B. L. Turner, Phytologia 88: 255. 2006 [E]

Baptisia pendula Larisey, Ann. Missouri Bot. Gard. 27: 170, plate 25. 1940; *B. lactea* var. *obovata* (Larisey) Isely

Legumes 15–30 mm wide; mature stipe much longer than calyx.

Flowering May–Jun. Grasslands, heavy soils; 50–700 m; Fla., Ga., N.C., S.C.

Variety *pendula* is closely related to var. *lactea*.

3. Baptisia sphaerocarpa Nuttall, J. Acad. Nat. Sci. Philadelphia 7: 97. 1834 [E]

Baptisia viridis Larisey

Herbs erect, to 1 m, glabrescent. **Leaves** petiolate; stipules deciduous, subulate, 4–16 mm; petiole 1–4 mm; leaflets 3 to mid stem, or 1 or 2 distally, blades obovate or elliptic to oblanceolate. **Racemes** 5+-flowered, terminal, stiffly erect, bracteate, bracts caducous. **Pedicels** 2–5 mm. **Flowers** 18–22 mm; calyx 7–9 mm, glabrous; corolla bright yellow, 16–20 mm. **Legumes** ascending to spreading, suborbicular, 7–11 × 7–11 mm, woody, glabrous. **Seeds** 2–4(–6). **2*n*** = 18.

Flowering Apr–May. Mostly clay or silty-clay soils; 10–200 m; La., Miss., Mo., Okla., Tex.

Baptisia sphaerocarpa forms hybrids with *B. lactea*, *B. leucophaea* (*B.* ×*intermedia* Larisey [= *B.* ×*bushii* Small and *B.* ×*stricta* Larisey]), and *B. nuttalliana*. *Baptisia* ×*bushii* was treated as a species by M. M. Larisey (1940). *Baptisia* ×*intermedia*, as described by Larisey, was said to be a hybrid of *B. leucophaea* var. *glabrescens* Larisey and *B. viridis*, which is treated here as synonymous with *B. sphaerocarpa*. Interestingly, these three hybrids (*B.* ×*bushii*, *B.* ×*intermedia*, and *B.* ×*stricta*) key out in adjacent couplets in the treatment by Larisey.

4. Baptisia australis (Linnaeus) R. Brown in W. Aiton and W. T. Aiton, Hortus Kew. 3: 6. 1811 • Blue wild indigo [E]

Sophora australis Linnaeus, Syst. Nat. ed. 12, 2: 287. 1767

Herbs robust, low-spreading, 0.5–1.5 m, glabrous. **Leaves** petiolate; stipules mostly persistent, lanceolate to ovate-lanceolate, 3–15 mm; petiole 4–12 mm; leaflets 3, blades obovate to oblanceolate. **Racemes** 8+-flowered, terminal, bracteate, bracts caducous. **Pedicels** 5–12 mm. **Flowers** 22–26 mm; calyx 8–12 mm, glabrous; corolla dull violet to deep blue, 20–24 mm. **Legumes** erect to ascending-divergent, ellipsoid-oblong to asymmetric-ovoid, 30–50 × 10–30 mm, leathery becoming brittle, glabrous. **Seeds** 20–30. **2*n*** = 18.

Varieties 2 (2 in the flora): c, e North America.

1. Legumes 10–20 mm wide; stipes 4–8 mm in fruit; ne United States . . . . 4a. *Baptisia australis* var. *australis*
1. Legumes much inflated, 20–30 mm wide; stipes 8–12 mm in fruit; Ontario and sc United States . . . . 4b. *Baptisia australis* var. *minor*

4a. Baptisia australis (Linnaeus) R. Brown var. **australis** [E]

Legumes 10–20 mm wide; stipe 4–8 mm in fruit. **2*n*** = 18.

Flowering May–Jun. Sandy or silty alluvial soils, grasslands, along streams in forests; 10–300 m; Ala., Conn., Ga., Ill., Ind., Md., Mass., N.H., N.J., N.Y., N.C., Ohio, Pa., Tenn., Vt., Va., W.Va., Wis.

Peripheral intergradation between the varieties of *Baptisia australis* occurs; they are not known to co-occur.

4b. Baptisia australis (Linnaeus) R. Brown var. **minor** (Lehmann) Fernald, Rhodora 39: 312. 1937 • Blue wild indigo [E]

Baptisia minor Lehmann, Index Seminum (Hamburg) 1827: 5, 16. 1827

Legumes much inflated, 2–3 cm wide; stipe 8–12 mm in fruit. **2*n*** = 18.

Flowering May–Jun. Sandy or silty alluvial soils, grasslands, along streams in forests; 10–300 m; Ont.; Ark., Iowa, Kans., Mo., Nebr., Okla., Tex.

Variety *minor* forms hybrids with *Baptisia sphaerocarpa* (*B.* ×*variicolor* Kosnik, Diggs, Redshaw & Lipscomb), and *B. lactea* (*B.* ×*bicolor* Greenman & Larisey), as documented by M. A. Kosnik et al. (1996). It is introduced in Ontario.

5. Baptisia megacarpa Chapman ex Torrey & A. Gray, Fl. N. Amer. 1: 386. 1840 [C] [E]

Herbs to 1.5 m, glabrous. **Leaves** petiolate; stipules caducous, lanceolate, very small; petiole 15–20 mm; leaflets 3, blades elliptic. **Racemes** 4–10 (–12)-flowered, terminal, not secund, ebracteate. **Pedicels** 8–15 mm. **Flowers** 20–24 mm; calyx 8–10 mm, glabrous; corolla yellow or pale yellow, 18–22 mm. **Legumes** mostly pendent, tan or brownish, inflated, broadly ellipsoid, 30–40 × 20–30 mm, leathery or brittle. **Seeds** 10–25.

Flowering Apr–May. Silty or silty clay, waterlogged soils along streams; of conservation concern; 10–50 m; Ala., Fla., Ga.

As noted by D. Isely (1981), *Baptisia megacarpa* is a relatively localized endemic superficially similar to the white-flowered *B. lactea* but readily distinguished by a number of characters, such as its yellow flowers and the thin walls and pale color of the fruits. In the DNA studies of M. G. Mendenhall (1994), *B. megacarpa* forms a clade with the *B. alba*-*B. australis*-*B. lactea*-*B. sphaerocarpa* complex.

6. Baptisia arachnifera W. H. Duncan, Rhodora 46: 29, figs. 1–5. 1944 [C] [E]

Herbs erect, 0.4–0.8 m, pubescent. **Leaves** sessile; stipules absent or appearing so; leaflet 1, blade broadly ovate, surfaces with cobwebby hairs. **Racemes** 8–12-flowered, terminal, bracteate. **Pedicels** 2 mm. **Flowers** 11–13 mm; calyx 4–5 mm, pubescent; corolla yellow, 9–11 mm. **Legumes** ascending, suborbicular to broadly lanceoloid, 8–12 × 6–9 mm, beaks attenuate, somewhat woody, tomentose. **Seeds** 2–4.

Flowering May–Jun. Sandy soils of pine or pine-palmetto woodlands; of conservation concern; 10–20 m; Ga.

Baptisia arachnifera is known only from Brantley and Wayne counties.

7. Baptisia simplicifolia Croom, Amer. J. Sci. Arts 25: 74. 1834 • Scare weed [E]

Herbs to 1 m, glabrous. **Leaves** sessile or subsessile; stipules absent or caducous; leaflet 1, blade ovate to broadly ovate. **Racemes** 15–25-flowered, terminal, bracteate, bracts persistent. **Pedicels** 3–4 mm. **Flowers** 14–17 mm; calyx 5–6 mm, glabrous; corolla pale yellow, 12–15 mm. **Legumes** ascending, lanceoloid, 10–12 × 6–8 mm, beaks attenuate, woody. **Seeds** 2–6. **2*n*** = 18.

Flowering Jun–Aug. Longleaf pine or palmetto-pine flatlands, heavy, silty-clay soils; 10–20 m; Fla.

Baptisia simplicifolia is known from the eastern region of the Florida panhandle.

8. Baptisia perfoliata (Linnaeus) R. Brown in W. Aiton and W. T. Aiton, Hortus Kew. 3: 5. 1811 • Cat-bells [E]

Crotalaria perfoliata Linnaeus, Sp. Pl. 2: 714. 1753

Herbs ascending or erect, much-branched, to 1 m, glabrous. **Leaves** sessile; stipules absent; leaflet 1, blade perfoliate, broadly ovate-elliptic. **Racemes** 1-flowered, axillary, ebracteate. **Pedicels** absent. **Flowers** 15–17 mm; calyx 5–7 mm, glabrous; corolla bright yellow, 13–15 mm. **Legumes** ascending, ovoid, 10–15 × 8–12 mm, abruptly beaked, woody. **Seeds** 2–4. **2*n*** = 18.

Flowering Apr–Jun. Open pine and pine-oak woodlands, sandy soils; 10–200 m; Ala., Fla., Ga., S.C.

Baptisia perfoliata forms hybrids with *B. alba*, *B. lanceolata*, and *B. tinctoria*; F_1 hybrids with the latter are called *B.* ×*microphylla* Nuttall.

9. Baptisia tinctoria (Linnaeus) R. Brown in W. Aiton and W. T. Aiton, Hortus Kew. 3: 6. 1811 [E] [W]

Sophora tinctoria Linnaeus, Sp. Pl. 1: 373. 1753; *Baptisia gibbesii* Small; *B. tinctoria* var. *crebra* Fernald; *B. tinctoria* var. *gibbesii* (Small) Fernald; *B. tinctoria* var. *projecta* Fernald

Herbs erect, to 1 m, glabrous. **Leaves** shortly petiolate or subsessile; stipules deciduous, minute; leaflets 3, blades obovate-cuneate to spatulate. **Racemes** 6+-flowered, terminal, long-exserted, bracteate, bracts caducous. **Pedicels** 3–5 mm. **Flowers** 14–18 mm; calyx 4–5 mm, glabrous or glabrate; corolla yellow, 12–16 mm. **Legumes** exserted-stipitate, erect, ovoid to ellipsoid, 8–15 × 5–9 mm, ± woody. **Seeds** 6–8. **2*n*** = 18.

Flowering May–Jul. Open, deciduous or pine woodlands; 10–700 m; Ont.; Conn., Del., Ga., Ind., Ky., Maine, Md., Mass., Mich., N.H., N.J., N.Y., N.C., Ohio, Pa., R.I., S.C., Tenn., Vt., Va., W.Va., Wis.

Baptisia tinctoria forms hybrids with *B. alba* (= *B.* ×*serenae* M. A. Curtis), *B. lactea* (*B.* ×*deamii* Larisey), and *B. perfoliata* (*B.* ×*fulva* Larisey [= *B.* ×*microphylla* Nuttall]). Within *Baptisia*, *B. tinctoria* and the unifoliolate-leaved species form an isolated clade (M. G. Mendenhall 1994).

10. Baptisia nuttalliana Small, Fl. S.E. U.S., 599. 1903 [E] [F]

Baptisia confusa Pollard & C. R. Ball, Proc. Biol. Soc. Wash. 13: 158. 1900 [not Sweet ex G. Don 1832], based on *B. lanceolata* (Walter) Elliott var. *texana* Holzinger, Contr. U.S. Natl. Herb. 1: 286. 1893, not *B. texana* Buckley 1862

Herbs compact, to 1 m, glabrate to puberulent. **Leaves** sessile or subsessile; stipules caducous, small; leaflets 3, blades elliptic to obovate. **Racemes** 1(–3)-flowered, solitary or clustered, axillary, ebracteate. **Pedicels** 2–5 mm. **Flowers** 17–22 mm; calyx 5–8 mm, pubescent; corolla yellow, 15–20 mm. **Legumes** ascending, ovoid, 8–14 × 8–12 mm, ± woody. **Seeds** 8–12. **2*n*** = 18.

Flowering Apr–May. Oak and pine-oak forests, dry sandy soils; 20–300 m; Ark., La., Miss., Okla., Tex.

Baptisia nuttalliana forms occasional hybrids with *B. lactea*, *B. leucophaea*, and *B. sphaerocarpa*, especially in eastern Texas where these taxa are sympatric.

11. Baptisia lanceolata (Walter) Elliott, Sketch Bot. S. Carolina 1: 467. 1817 • Gopher weed [E]

Sophora lanceolata Walter, Fl. Carol., 135. 1788

Herbs to 1 m, glabrous or pubescent. **Leaves** subsessile or petiolate; stipules caducous, small; petiole 0.1–12 mm mid stem; leaflets 3, blades obovate to oblanceolate. **Racemes** 1–5-flowered, terminal, bracteate. **Pedicels** 2–10 mm. **Flowers** 20–27 m; calyx 8–10 mm, pubescent; corolla yellow, 19–25 mm. **Legumes** ascending, suborbicular to lanceoloid, 10–25 × 10–12 mm, woody. **Seeds** 10–40. $2n = 18$.

Varieties 2 (2 in the flora): se United States.

Occasional plants in regions of contact between varieties of *Baptisia lanceolata* may be difficult to identify. D. Isely (1981) recognized isolated populations from central Florida as belonging to var. *elliptica*; these appear to belong to var. *lanceolata*, although they may be relics of ancestral hybridization and/or gene flow between the two.

Baptisia lanceolata hybridizes with *B. perfoliata*.

1. Leaflet blades to 15 mm wide; petioles 0.1–2 mm mid stem; ne Florida, Georgia, South Carolina .... 11a. *Baptisia lanceolata* var. *lanceolata*
1. Leaflet blades 16+ mm wide; petioles 4–12 mm mid stem; Alabama, westernmost Florida, Georgia......... 11b. *Baptisia lanceolata* var. *elliptica*

11a. Baptisia lanceolata (Walter) Elliott var. **lanceolata** [E]

Leaves: petiole 0.1–2 mm mid stem; blades to 15 mm wide.

Flowering Mar–May. Pine and pine-oak woodlands in sandy soils; 10–100 m; Fla., Ga., S.C.

11b. Baptisia lanceolata (Walter) Elliott var. **elliptica** (Small) B. L. Turner, Phytologia 88: 256. 2006 [E]

Baptisia elliptica Small, Fl. S.E. U.S., 559, 1331. 1903; *B. elliptica* var. *tomentosa* Larisey; *B. lanceolata* var. *tomentosa* (Larisey) Isely

Leaves: petiole 4–12 mm mid stem; blades 16+ mm wide.

Flowering Apr–May. Woodlands; 0–60 m; Ala., Fla., Ga.

D. Isely (1981, 1998), following Larisey, used the name var. *tomentosa* for this taxon; the present International Code of Nomenclature for Algae, Fungi, and Plants (Art. 11.6) mandates use of the autonym var. *elliptica* that resulted from publication of *Baptisia elliptica* var. *tomentosa* Larisey.

12. Baptisia leucophaea Nuttall, Gen. N. Amer. Pl. 1: 282. 1818 • Plains wild indigo [E] [F]

Baptisia alba (Linnaeus) Ventenat var. *macrophylla* (Larisey) Isely; *B. bracteata* Muhlenberg ex Elliott var. *glabrescens* (Larisey) Isely; *B. bracteata* var. *laevicaulis* (A. Gray ex Canby) Isely; *B. bracteata* var. *leucophaea* (Nuttall) Kartesz & Gandhi; *B. leucophaea* var. *glabrescens* Larisey; *B. leucophaea* var. *laevicaulis* A. Gray ex Canby

Herbs spreading, to 0.5 m, glabrous or pubescent. **Stems** deflexed in flower. **Leaves** petiolate; stipules persistent, ovate to triangular, 10–35 mm; petiole 1–4 mm mid stem; leaflets 3, blades elliptic to oblanceolate or broadly lanceolate to cuneate-obovate. **Racemes** 8–30-flowered, axillary, secund, bracteate, bracts persistent. **Pedicels** 25–40 mm. **Flowers** 18–25 mm; calyx 7–11 mm, glabrous or pubescent; corolla yellow, 17–23 mm. **Legumes** ascending or pendent, ellipsoid-lanceoloid to lanceoloid, 40–55 × 15–20 mm, ± papery, pubescent to glabrate. **Seeds** 20–30. $2n = 18$.

Flowering Mar–May. Grasslands, open areas, pine-oak woodlands, sandy soils; 10–3000 m; Ark., Ill., Ind., Iowa, Kans., Ky., La., Mich., Minn., Mo., Nebr., Okla., Tex., Wis.

Baptisia leucophaea is widespread and highly variable; the variation is compounded by hybridization with other taxa. M. M. Larisey (1940) treated *B. leucophaea* as having two varieties and treated *B. leucophaea* var. *laevicaulis* at specific rank. D. Isely (1981, 1998) included all of the Larisey taxa in the relatively isolated *B. bracteata*. There is little intergradation between *B. bracteata* and *B. leucophaea*.

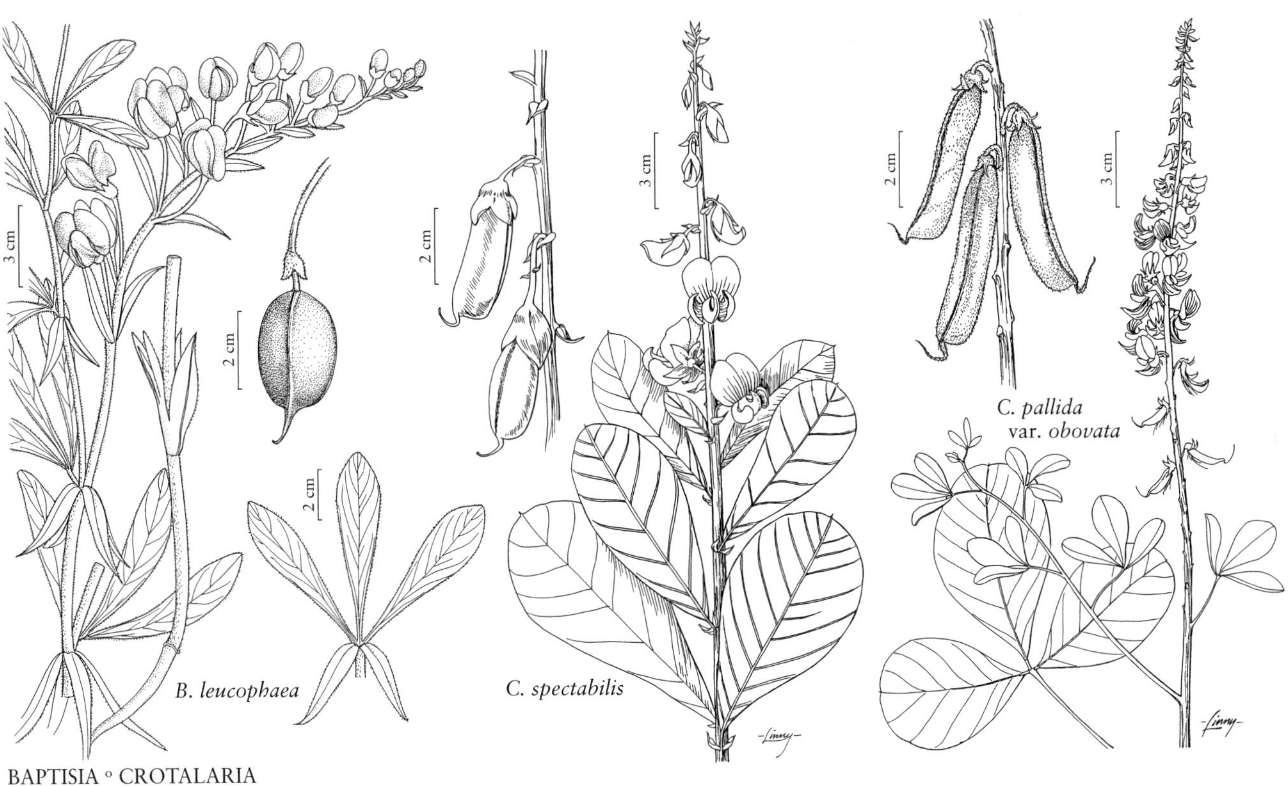

BAPTISIA ◦ CROTALARIA

Baptisia leucophaea is known to form F_1 hybrids and backcrosses with *B. australis* (*B.* ×*bicolor* Greenman & Larisey), *B. lactea*, *B. nuttalliana*, and *B. sphaerocarpa* (*B.* ×*intermedia* Larisey [= *B.* ×*stricta* Larisey and *B.* ×*bushii* Small]); see discussion under 3. *B. sphaerocarpa*.

13. Baptisia bracteata Muhlenberg ex Elliott, Sketch. Bot. S. Carolina 1: 469. 1817 [E]

Herbs to 0.5 m, glabrous or puberulent. **Stems** deflexed in flower. **Leaves** petiolate; stipules persistent, ovate to lanceolate, 10–30 mm; petiole 5–14 mm mid stem; leaflets 3, blades elliptic to oblanceolate or broadly lanceolate to cuneate-obovate. **Racemes** 8–30-flowered, axillary, ascending to horizontal, secund, bracteate, bracts persistent. **Pedicels** 10–18 mm. **Flowers** 20–25 mm; calyx 8–12 mm, glabrous or puberulent; corolla cream or pale yellow, 18–23 mm. **Legumes** ascending, ellipsoid-lanceoloid to lanceoloid, 30–45 × 15–20 mm, ± papery, puberulent to glabrate. **Seeds** 20–50. $2n = 18$.

Flowering Apr–May. Pine and pine-oak woodlands, sandy soils; 100–300 m; Ala., Ga., Mass., N.J., N.C., S.C.

Baptisia bracteata is very similar to *B. leucophaea*; it has mid stem leaves with longer petioles (5–14 versus 1–4 mm) and shorter flowering pedicels (10–18 versus 25–40 mm).

Baptisia bracteata forms hybrids and backcrosses with *B. lactea* and perhaps other species with which it might co-occur. No doubt such intermingling accounts for the exceptional variation found in *B. bracteata* (R. L. Wilbur 1963c).

14. Baptisia cinerea (Rafinesque) Fernald & B. G. Schubert, Rhodora 50: 201. 1948 [E]

Lasinia cinera Rafinesque, New Fl. 2: 50. 1837

Herbs erect, to 1 m, glabrous or pubescent. **Leaves** blackening upon drying, petiolate; stipules mostly deciduous, lanceolate, 10–30 mm; petiole 5–14 mm; leaflets 3, blades oval to broadly oblanceolate. **Racemes** 5–20-flowered, axillary, secund, bracteate, bracts deciduous. **Pedicels** 4–8 mm. **Flowers** 21–29 mm; calyx 6–8 mm, glabrous or puberulent; corolla yellow, 20–28 mm. **Legumes** ascending, ovoid, 20–30 × 6–10 mm, papery to ± woody. **Seeds** 2–4.

Flowering Apr–May. Pine and pine-oak woodlands, sandy soils; 0–100 m; N.C., S.C., Va.

Baptisia cinerea closely resembles *B. bracteata*; the floral bracts in *B. cinerea* are deciduous (versus persistent in *B. bracteata*), pedicels are shorter (4–8 versus 10–18 mm), legumes are smaller (2–3 versus 3–4 cm) with appressed (versus spreading) hairs, and leaflets are larger and readily blacken upon drying.

Baptisia cinerea and *B. bracteata* are essentially allopatric. Hybrids between *B. cinerea* and other species of *Baptisia* have not been reported; occasional hybrids between *B. cinerea* and others (for example, *B. lactea*) would not be surprising.

15. Baptisia lecontei Torrey & A. Gray, Fl. N. Amer. 1: 386. 1840 [E]

Herbs divaricate-branched, to 1 m, puberulent or glabrate. **Leaves** not blackening upon drying, petiolate; stipules mostly deciduous, lanceolate, 2–10 mm; petiole 2–10 mm; leaflets 3, blades spatulate to obovate. **Racemes** 3–10-flowered, flowers well spaced, terminal, bracteate, bracts persistent. **Pedicels** 10–20 mm, bracteolate. **Flowers** 10–15 mm; calyx 6–7 mm, lobes ± equal to tube, glabrous or pubescent; corolla lemon yellow, 9–14 mm. **Legumes** ascending, ovoid to suborbicular, 8–11 × 8–9 mm, abruptly short-beaked, somewhat woody. **Seeds** 2–4.

Flowering Apr–Jun. Pine and pine-oak woodlands, white, sandy soils; 0–30 m; Fla., Ga.

As noted by D. Isely (1981), *Baptisia lecontei* superficially resembles *B. tinctoria* in having relatively small flowers, yellow corollas, and somewhat similar legumes. *Baptisia tinctoria* does not have the persistent, foliaceous bracts and bracteolate pedicels of *B. lecontei*.

16. Baptisia calycosa Canby, Bot. Gaz. 3: 65. 1878 [E]

Herbs to 1 m, glabrous. **Leaves** petiolate; stipules persistent, lanceolate to elliptic, 10–20 mm; petiole 1–5 mm; leaflets 3, blades cuneate-ovate to spatulate, surfaces glabrate. **Racemes** 1-flowered, terminal, foliose, bracteate. **Pedicels** 10–40 mm, bracteolate. **Flowers** 12–14 mm; calyx 8–13 mm, lobes longer than tube, glabrate; corolla yellow, 10–12 mm. **Legumes** ascending, ellipsoid to suborbicular, 10–12 × 8–10 mm, ± woody. **Seeds** 2–4. **2*n*** = 18.

Flowering Apr–May. Pine and pine-oak woodlands, white, sandy soils; 0–10 m; Fla.

Baptisia calycosa is restricted to Clay and St. Johns counties.

17. Baptisia hirsuta Small, Fl. S.E. U.S., 598, 1331. 1903 [E]

Baptisia calycosa Canby var. *villosa* Canby, Bot. Gaz. 12: 39. 1887, not *B. villosa* (Walter) Elliott 1817

Herbs to 0.5 m, pubescent. **Leaves** petiolate; stipules persistent, elliptic to lanceolate, 10–20 mm; petiole 1–8 mm; leaflets 3, blades oblanceolate to obovate, surfaces hirsute. **Racemes** 1–5-flowered, terminal, bracteate. **Pedicels** 20–40 mm, bracteolate. **Flowers** 10–12 mm; calyx 8–10 mm, lobes longer than tube, pubescent; corolla yellow, 9–11 mm. **Legumes** ascending, broadly ovoid, 8–15 × 8–10 mm, ± woody. **Seeds** 2–4.

Flowering Apr–May. Pine and pine-oak woodlands, sandy soils; 0–10 m; Fla.

Baptisia hirsuta is known from the western Florida panhandle; within its range, it can be locally abundant and can invade secondary sites (D. Isely 1998). It differs from *B. calycosa* by its geography and vestiture. M. M. Larisey (1940) maintained *B. hirsuta*; Isely (1981, 1998) treated it as a variety of *B. calycosa*. M. G. Mendenhall (1994), using DNA data, treated these two taxa as species, noting that they formed a tight clade with *B. lecontei*.

52. CROTALARIA Linnaeus, Sp. Pl. 2: 714. 1753; Gen. Pl. ed. 5, 320. 1754, name conserved • Rattlebox, rattlepod, rabbitbells [Greek *krotalon* or Latin *Crotalum*, castanet or rattle, and *aria*, possession, alluding to rattling sound of seeds in mature pod]

Guy L. Nesom

Herbs [shrubs], annual or perennial, unarmed; taprooted. **Stems** erect, ascending, spreading, decumbent, or prostrate, glabrous or pubescent. **Leaves** alternate, palmately compound or unifoliolate; stipules present or absent, usually persistent, filiform to foliaceous; petiolate or subsessile; leaflets 1 or 3[–7], stipels absent, blades 5–150 mm, margins entire, surfaces glabrous or pubescent. **Inflorescences** (1 or)2–50-flowered, usually terminal or subterminal, leaf-opposed, rarely axillary, racemes [heads or flowers solitary or fascicled]; bracts present, persistent or caducous; bracteoles present, paired proximal to calyx. **Flowers** papilionaceous; calyx usually cylindrical, rarely campanulate or cupulate, lobes 5; corolla usually yellow, sometimes orangish, rarely white, blue, or lavender, glabrous or hairy outside; stamens 10, monadelphous; anthers alternately basifixed on long filaments and dorsifixed on small filaments, dehiscing longitudinally; style with 1 or 2 lines of hairs adaxially; stigma terminal, usually bilobed. **Fruits** legumes, subsessile to long-stipitate, usually inflated, globose, ovoid to ellipsoid, or cylindrical, dehiscent, often tardily so, glabrous or pubescent. **Seeds** 1–70, oblique-cordiform to oblong-reniform; hilar sinus obvious, aril sometimes conspicuous. x = 7, 8.

Species ca. 600 (15 in the flora): United States, Mexico, West Indies, Central America, South America, Europe, Asia, Africa, Indian Ocean Islands, Pacific Islands; tropics and subtropics, mostly eastern and southern tropical Africa; introduced in Australia.

Crotalaria biflora Linnaeus (native to India) was collected in 1959 as a waif on chrome ore piles in Newport News, Virginia (C. F. Reed 1964). The species is an annual, distinguished as hirsute-villous to subsericeous, stems prostrate, 5–12 cm, leaves sessile, unifoliolate, blades ovate to oblong or oblong-ovate, surfaces villous-hirsute, flowers one or two, on axillary peduncles, and hirsute, ovoid to cylindrical-ovoid legumes.

Crotalaria alata Buchanan-Hamilton ex D. Don (native to Himalayan Asia) was collected in 1939 as an escape in Gainesville, Florida (*W. A. Murrill s.n.*, MO); subsequently, it has not been recorded in the flora area. The species is perennial, distinguished as hirsute to strigose-hirsute, stems erect, 10–20 cm, leaves unifoliolate, blades lanceolate to elliptic-lanceolate or elliptic, stipules decurrent, forming wings on internodes, and apically bilobed, flowers in terminal and axillary racemes, 4–10 cm, and legumes glabrous.

SELECTED REFERENCES Miller, R. H. 1967. *Crotalaria* Seed Morphology, Anatomy, and Identification. Washington. [U.S.D.A. Agric. Res. Serv., Techn. Bull. 1373.]. Windler, D. R. 1973. Field and garden studies in *Crotalaria sagittalis* L. and related species. Phytologia 26: 289–354. Windler, D. R. 1974. A systematic treatment of the native unifoliolate crotalarias of North America (Leguminosae). Rhodora 76: 151–204.

1. Leaves 3-foliolate.
   2. Leaflet blades 5–15(–35) mm; legumes 7–20 mm.
      3. Stems mostly decumbent to prostrate, minutely and sparsely strigillose; legumes 12–20 mm . . . . 14. *Crotalaria pumila*
      3. Stems erect to decumbent, loosely strigose to strigose-hirsute; legumes 7–10 mm . . . . 15. *Crotalaria virgulata*
   2. Leaflet blades (10–)20–130(–180) mm; legumes (16–)18–70 mm.
      4. Leaflet blades linear to linear-lanceolate, elliptic-lanceolate, or lanceolate, lengths 5–10 times widths.
         5. Racemes 12–26(–40)-flowered; corollas 8–11 mm; legumes 4–6 mm diam. . . . . 9. *Crotalaria lanceolata*
         5. Racemes 4–12-flowered; corollas 18–20 mm; legumes (10–)15–20 mm diam. . . . . 10. *Crotalaria ochroleuca*
      4. Leaflet blades obovate, ovate, elliptic-obovate, elliptic-oblanceolate, elliptic, elliptic-lanceolate, or spatulate-obovate, lengths 1.3–4.5 times widths.
         6. Stipules absent; leaflet blades elliptic to elliptic-lanceolate, or elliptic-oblanceolate, 40–100(–140) mm, lengths 3–4.5 times widths; calyces basally truncate and deflexed against pedicels . . . . 11. *Crotalaria trichotoma*
         6. Stipules usually present (persistent or caducous); leaflet blades elliptic, ovate, obovate, elliptic-obovate, or spatulate-obovate, (10–)20–70 mm, lengths 1.3–2.5 times widths; calyces sometimes basally truncate, not deflexed against pedicels.
            7. Legumes 5–6 mm diam., slightly to conspicuously curved, minutely puberulent to glabrate; stems strigose; leaflet surfaces strigillose abaxially, glabrous adaxially . . . . 12. *Crotalaria pallida*
            7. Legumes 10–15 mm diam., straight, villous-hirsute to hispid-hirsute; stems hirsute-villous to strigose-hirsute; leaflet surfaces glabrous or hairy on abaxial midvein . . . . 13. *Crotalaria incana*
1. Leaves unifoliolate.
   8. Corollas usually blue to lavender, sometimes white or pale yellow tinged blue; stipules present, often encircling nodes . . . . 8. *Crotalaria verrucosa*
   8. Corollas bright yellow; stipules present and not encircling nodes, or absent.
      9. Stipules decurrent on mid and distal stems.
         10. Herbs annual; stems erect to decumbent, hirsute-pilose; leaflet blade lengths 4–8 times widths . . . . 1. *Crotalaria sagittalis*
         10. Herbs perennial; stems decumbent, prostrate, ascending, or erect, strigose or strigose-sericeous to hirsute-villous; leaflet blade lengths 1–12 times widths.
             11. Leaflet blades linear-lanceolate, linear-oblanceolate, linear, oblong, or elliptic (narrower distally), lengths (2–)4–10 times widths, surfaces glabrous adaxially; stems erect to ascending . . . . 2. *Crotalaria purshii*
             11. Leaflet blades broadly elliptic to elliptic-ovate, ovate, broadly lanceolate, linear, linear-lanceolate, or obovate-oblanceolate, lengths 1–12 times widths, surfaces strigose to strigose-hirsute adaxially; stems prostrate to decumbent or ascending. . . . . 3. *Crotalaria rotundifolia*
      9. Stipules, when present, not decurrent on stems.
         12. Herbs perennial; stipules absent; leaflet blades (5–)8–19 mm; stems 2–10 cm; corollas 8–9 mm. . . . . 4. *Crotalaria avonensis*
         12. Herbs annual; stipules usually present; leaflet blades 30–150 mm; stems 30–200(–400) cm; corollas 15–25 mm.
             13. Stipules ovate to ovate-lanceolate, 4–7 mm; floral bracts 5–8 mm, persistent; stems glabrous . . . . 5. *Crotalaria spectabilis*
             13. Stipules, when present, filiform or setaceous, 1–2 mm; floral bracts 2–5 mm, persistent or caducous; stems strigose or strigose-sericeous.
                 14. Leaflet blades obovate to spatulate or oblanceolate, 30–80 mm, lengths 2.2–3(–4) times widths; stems 30–90 cm . . . . 6. *Crotalaria retusa*
                 14. Leaflet blades linear-elliptic to oblong, 50–150 mm, lengths 2.5–4 times widths; stems 100–200(–400) cm. . . . . 7. *Crotalaria juncea*

1. Crotalaria sagittalis Linnaeus, Sp. Pl. 2: 714. 1753 • Arrowhead or common rattlebox [W]

Herbs annual. **Stems** erect to decumbent, 4–40 cm, hirsute-pilose. **Leaves** unifoliolate; stipules sometimes absent, decurrent on mid and distal stems, lanceolate-auriculate or triangular, with 2 distinct, persistent, triangular distal lobes, (3–)5–10 mm or absent (in var. *blumeriana*); subsessile; blade elliptic to oblong or linear-lanceolate, 10–80 mm, length 4–8 times width, surfaces strigose to sparsely rusty-pilose. **Racemes** (1 or)2–5-flowered, terminal, subterminal, or lateral, 2–6 cm; bracts persistent, linear-triangular. **Flowers:** calyx broadly cylindrical, 5–8 mm, lobes triangular-lanceolate, glabrous or slightly puberulous to rusty-pilose; corolla bright yellow, 9–11 mm. **Legumes** 7–27(–36) × 5–11 mm, glabrous.

Varieties 2 (2 in the flora): United States, Mexico, West Indies, Central America.

1. Stems 10–40 cm, erect; stipules prominent; legumes 10–27(–36) mm . . . . 1a. *Crotalaria sagittalis* var. *sagittalis*
1. Stems 4–10 cm, erect to decumbent; stipules reduced or absent; legumes 7–15 mm . . . . 1b. *Crotalaria sagittalis* var. *blumeriana*

1a. Crotalaria sagittalis Linnaeus var. **sagittalis** [W]

Crotalaria sagittalis var. *fruticosa* (Miller) Fawcett & Rendle; *C. sagittalis* var. *oblonga* Michaux

Stems erect, 10–40 cm. **Stipules** prominent. **Legumes** 10–27 (–36) mm. **2*n*** = 32.

Flowering Jun–Aug. Pastures, sandy fields, prairies, roadsides, disturbed sites, shale banks, rocky limestone hills, serpentine barrens, longleaf pine savannas, pine flatwoods, pine barrens, oak-hickory woods; 0–600 m; Ala., Ariz., Ark., Conn., Del., D.C., Ga., Ill., Ind., Iowa, Kans., Ky., La., Md., Mich., Minn., Miss., Mo., Nebr., N.H., N.J., N.Y., N.C., Ohio, Okla., Pa., R.I., S.C., S.Dak., Tenn., Tex., Vt., Va., W.Va., Wis.; Mexico; West Indies; Central America.

1b. Crotalaria sagittalis Linnaeus var. **blumeriana** H. Senn, Rhodora 41: 339. 1939

Crotalaria pringlei A. Gray

Stems erect to decumbent, 4–10 cm. **Stipules** reduced or absent. **Legumes** 7–15 mm. **2*n*** = 32.

Flowering Aug–Oct. Rocky ridges, sandy alluvium; 2000–2400 m; Ariz.; Mexico (Chihuahua, Sonora).

In Arizona, var. *blumeriana* is known from Cochise, Pima, and Santa Cruz counties.

Numerous varieties have been described among populations of the widespread and erratically variable *Crotalaria sagittalis*, but neither D. Isely (1998) nor D. R. Windler (1974) recognized varieties, noting that further study was necessary to understand the variation patterns, especially among the Mexican populations. However, Isely observed that isolated Arizona populations of var. *blumeriana* have small pods (7–15 mm), and the often tiny plants, which may be either erect or decumbent, are not the same as those found in the eastern United States. In contrast, garden plants grown from seeds of representative plants of var. *blumeriana* were as large as any of the plants grown from field seed of typical Mexican *C. sagittalis* (Windler 1973). The type specimen of *C. pringlei* is more like typical *C. sagittalis* and is unusual among the Arizona populations.

Variety *blumeriana* is treated formally here, recognizing that it is far out of range, geographically and ecologically, from typical *Crotalaria sagittalis* of the eastern United States. Its evolutionary affinities, perhaps, are with Mexican populations, but almost all of the species in Mexico occur in the southern half of the country, disjunct from both the Arizona and eastern North American plants.

2. Crotalaria purshii de Candolle in A. P. de Candolle and A. L. P. P. de Candolle, Prodr. 2: 124. 1825 • Pursh's or coastal plain rattlebox [E]

Crotalaria laevigata Pursh, Fl. Amer. Sept. 2: 469. 1813, not Lamarck 1786; *C. linearis* (Michaux) Rafinesque; *C. purshii* var. *bracteolifera* Fernald; *C. sagittalis* Linnaeus var. *linearis* Michaux

Herbs perennial. **Stems** erect to ascending, 15–50(–80) cm, sparsely, loosely strigose. **Leaves** unifoliolate; stipules lanceolate-auriculate or triangular, decurrent on mid and distal stems, with 2 distinct lobes, (3–)5–13 mm; blade linear, linear-lanceolate or -oblanceolate, oblong, or elliptic, narrower distally, 45–100 mm, length

(2.5–)4–10 times width, surfaces strigose abaxially, glabrous adaxially. **Racemes** (1 or)2–5(–12)-flowered, terminal, subterminal, or lateral, 6–25 cm; bracts persistent, subulate-triangular. **Flowers:** calyx broadly cylindrical, 6–9 mm, lobes triangular-lanceolate, glabrous or slightly puberulous; corolla bright yellow, 8–12 mm. **Legumes** 15–25(–30) × 7–10 mm, glabrous. **2*n*** = 32.

Flowering May–Jul. Roadsides, prairie swales, longleaf pine savannas, pine flatwoods; 0–200 m; Ala., Fla., Ga., La., Miss., N.C., S.C., Tenn., Tex., Va.

In Texas, *Crotalaria purshii* is known from Hunt County in the northeastern part of the state.

3. Crotalaria rotundifolia J. F. Gmelin, Syst. Nat. 2: 1095. 1792 • Rabbitbells [W]

Herbs perennial. Stems prostrate to decumbent or ascending, 10–70 cm, strigose or strigose-sericeous to hirsute-villous. **Leaves** unifoliolate; stipules lanceolate-auriculate or triangular, with 2 distinct lobes, decurrent on mid and distal stems, 2–10 mm; blade broadly elliptic, elliptic-ovate, ovate, broadly lanceolate, linear, linear-lanceolate, or obovate-oblanceolate, 9–50 mm, length 1–2.5(–12) times width, surfaces strigose to strigose-hirsute. **Racemes** (1 or)2–5-flowered, terminal, subterminal, or lateral, 4–20 cm; bracts persistent, linear-subulate to lanceolate. **Flowers:** calyx broadly cylindrical, 5–9 mm, lobes triangular-lanceolate, glabrous or slightly puberulous; corolla bright yellow, banner sometimes red-lined, 7–13 mm. **Legumes** 12–28 × 7–12 mm, glabrous.

Varieties 2 (2 in the flora): se United States, Mexico, Central America.

1. Leaves usually spreading, blades broadly elliptic to elliptic-ovate, ovate, or broadly lanceolate, 9–20 × 10–15 mm, lengths mostly 1–2.5 times widths..... 3a. *Crotalaria rotundifolia* var. *rotundifolia*
1. Leaves usually ascending-erect, blades linear to linear-lanceolate, or obovate-oblanceolate on proximal ⅓ of stems, linear distally, 10–50 × 1–4 mm, lengths 5–12 times widths .... 3b. *Crotalaria rotundifolia* var. *linaria*

3a. Crotalaria rotundifolia J. F. Gmelin var. **rotundifolia** [W]

Crotalaria maritima Chapman; *C. rotundifolia* var. *vulgaris* Windler; *C. sagittalis* Linnaeus var. *ovalis* Michaux

Leaves usually spreading; blades broadly elliptic to elliptic-ovate, ovate, or broadly lanceolate, 9–20 × 10–15 mm, length mostly 1–2.5 times width. **2*n*** = 32.

Flowering Apr–Oct. Roadsides, lawns, fields, dunes, beaches, sandhills, sandy openings, creek banks, rocky slopes, pine woods and savannas, pine-oak woods, live oak-laurel woods; 0–400 m; Ala., Ark., Fla., Ga., La., Miss., N.C., S.C., Va.; Mexico; Central America.

Plants have sometimes been identified as *Crotalaria angulata* Miller; that name is probably a synonym of *C. biflora* Linnaeus and does not refer to the plants in the flora area (D. Isely 1998).

3b. Crotalaria rotundifolia J. F. Gmelin var. **linaria** (Small) Fernald & B. G. Schubert, Rhodora 50: 203. 1948 [E]

Crotalaria linaria Small, Man. S.E. Fl., 679, 1505. 1933; *C. maritima* Chapman var. *linaria* (Small) H. Senn

Leaves usually ascending-erect; blade linear to linear-lanceolate, or obovate-oblanceolate on proximal ⅓ of stem, linear distally, 10–50 × 1–4 mm, length 5–12 times width. **2*n*** = 32.

Flowering Dec–May(–Aug). Beaches, disturbed sandy sites, pine-palmetto scrub, hammocks, pine woods; 0–30 m; Fla.

D. R. Windler (1974) recognized var. *vulgaris*, distinguished by spreading hairs on stems, from var. *rotundifolia* with appressed hairs on stems, but the difference is slight and sometimes subjectively interpreted. In contrast, var. *linaria* is a much more easily recognized variant, although it has recently been considered part of a polymorphic population system in Florida (Windler; D. Isely 1998).

Plants with all leaf blades linear, proximal to distal, are common on Big Pine Key and in the southern half of peninsular Florida with collections seen from Broward, Citrus, Dade, Hernando, Hillsboro, Lee, Manatee,

Marion, Martin, Monroe, Palm Beach, Pinellas, Polk, and Sarasota counties. Collections of plants with leaf blades elliptic to obovate on the proximal one-third of the stems, quickly becoming linear distally, are scattered through some of the same counties as well as slightly farther north (for example, Alachua and Lake counties). Typical *Crotalaria rotundifolia* also occurs in the southern counties (for example, Brevard, Collier, Miami-Dade, Martin, Polk, and Sarasota counties). Plants with linear leaf blades on the distal two-thirds of the stems are sharply restricted to the southern half of Florida and, in view of their striking morphological distinction, it seems useful to formally recognize them. By doing so, it is acknowledged that sympatry of vars. *linaria* and *rotundifolia* suggests that some degree of reproductive isolation may exist.

Forms of var. *linaria* and *Crotalaria purshii* may be similar in overall appearance (especially on herbarium sheets), but the two are allopatric, and *C. purshii* has erect to ascending-erect stems, leaves not densely overlapping with mid stem nodes 30–60 mm, and leaflet surfaces glabrous adaxially, compared to *C. rotundifolia* var. *linaria*, which usually has prostrate stems, leaves densely overlapping with mid stem nodes 4–15(–25) mm, and leaflet surfaces strigose.

4. Crotalaria avonensis DeLaney & Wunderlin, Sida 13: 315, figs. 1–5. 1989 • Avon Park rattlebox [C] [E]

Herbs perennial. Stems erect to slightly spreading, 2–10 cm, strigose to sericeous. **Leaves** unifoliolate; stipules absent; blade oblong, elliptic to ovate, or suborbiculate, (5–)8–19 mm, length 1.3–3.5 times width, surfaces loosely strigose-sericeous. **Racemes** (1 or)2–8-flowered, terminal, subterminal, or lateral, 2–6 cm; bracts persistent, linear-triangular. **Flowers:** calyx cylindrical, 7–8 mm, lobes triangular-lanceolate, loosely strigose; corolla bright yellow, 8–9 mm. **Legumes** 14–25 × 6–8 mm, glabrous or sparsely strigose on abaxial suture.

Flowering Mar–Jun. White sands, scrub dominated by Florida rosemary, oaks, and/or sand pine, disturbed areas along roads and trails; of conservation concern; 30–50 m; Fla.

Crotalaria avonensis is known only from northern Highlands and southern Polk counties on the Lake Wales Ridge; it is in the Center for Plant Conservation's National Collection of Endangered Plants.

5. Crotalaria spectabilis Roth, Nov. Pl. Sp., 341. 1821 • Showy rattlebox [F] [I] [W]

Crotalaria retzii Hitchcock

Herbs annual. Stems suffrutescent basally, erect, 50–150 cm, glabrous. **Leaves** unifoliolate; stipules ovate to ovate-lanceolate, not decurrent on stem, 4–7 mm; blade obovate to elliptic, 50–150 mm, length 1.5–2.5 times width, surfaces glaucous, strigose abaxially, glabrous-punctate adaxially. **Racemes** 12–22-flowered, terminal, subterminal, or lateral, 10–50 cm; bracts persistent, cordate-auriculate, 5–8 mm. **Flowers:** calyx broadly cylindrical, 10–15 mm, lobes triangular-lanceolate, glabrous; corolla bright yellow, faintly red-lined, 17–25 mm. **Legumes** 30–45 × 10–20 mm, glabrous. $2n = 16$.

Flowering (Jan–)Aug–Oct (year-round). Grassy or fallow fields, roadsides, ditches, borrow pits, lake edges, disturbed areas; 10–200 m; introduced; Ala., Ark., Fla., Ga., Ill., La., Md., Miss., Mo., N.C., S.C., Tenn., Tex., Va.; Asia; introduced also in Mexico, West Indies, Central America, South America, Indian Ocean Islands (Reúnion), Pacific Islands.

In Texas, *Crotalaria spectabilis* is known from Brazos, Cameron, Karnes, and Liberty counties.

6. Crotalaria retusa Linnaeus, Sp. Pl. 2: 715. 1753 • Rattleweed [I] [W]

Herbs annual. Stems erect, 30–90 cm, strigose to strigose-sericeous. **Leaves** unifoliolate; stipules sometimes absent, setaceous, not decurrent on stem, 1–2 mm; blade obovate to spatulate or oblanceolate, 30–80 mm, length 2.2–3(–4) times width, surfaces strigose abaxially, glabrous adaxially. **Racemes** 5–24-flowered, terminal, subterminal, or lateral, 10–20(–30) cm; bracts caducous, linear, 2–3 mm. **Flowers:** calyx broadly cylindrical, 12–15 mm, basally truncate, lobes triangular-lanceolate, glabrous or slightly puberulous; corolla bright yellow, with prominent reddish lines to strongly red-tinted, 20–25 mm. **Legumes** 25–40(–50) × 10–14 mm, glabrous. $2n = 16$.

Flowering Jul–Oct, Jan–Apr. Fallow fields, roadsides, sandy wastes; 0–100 m; introduced; Fla., Ga., Ky., La., Miss., N.C., S.C., Tex.; Africa; introduced also in Mexico, West Indies, Central America, South America, Asia, Indian Ocean Islands, Pacific Islands, Australia.

In the flora area, *Crotalaria retusa* is commonly found in subtropical Florida but much more rarely in temperate areas, where it does not persist.

7. Crotalaria juncea Linnaeus, Sp. Pl. 2: 714. 1753
• Sunn hemp [I]

Herbs annual. **Stems** erect, 100–200(–400) cm, densely, loosely strigose, hairs appressed-ascending, yellowish to golden brown. **Leaves** unifoliolate; stipules filiform, not decurrent on stem, 1–2 mm; blade linear-elliptic to oblong, 50–150 mm, length 2.5–4 times width, surfaces strigose, more densely so abaxially. **Racemes** 6–20-flowered, terminal, subterminal, or axillary, open, 10–50 cm; bracts persistent, narrowly ovate-lanceolate, 3–5 mm. **Flowers:** calyx broadly cylindrical, 1.5–2 mm, lobes triangular-lanceolate, glabrous or slightly puberulous; corolla deep, bright yellow, sometimes with faint reddish lines, 15–22 mm. **Legumes** 25–45 × 12–17 mm, densely hirsute-pilose, hairs yellow-brown.

Flowering Apr–Sep. Disturbed sites; 0–20 m; introduced; Ala., Fla., Ga.; Asia (India, Pakistan); introduced also in South America (Brazil, Colombia), Europe (Russia), Africa, Indian Ocean Islands (including Madagascar), Pacific Islands (Hawaii, Philippines), Australia.

The antiquity of the cultivation of *Crotalaria juncea* makes nativity difficult to interpret, but the species is now widely cultivated throughout India and Pakistan as well as other parts of the world, including Australia and Russia. The strong bast fiber of the bark has long been used in twine, rug yarn, cordage, cigarette and tissue papers, fish nets, sacking, and canvas. Plants of *C. juncea* are extremely fast-growing and are widely used throughout the tropics as so-called green manure to add nutrients and organic matter to the soil.

8. Crotalaria verrucosa Linnaeus, Sp. Pl. 2: 715. 1753
• Blue rattlebox, purple popbush [I]

Herbs annual. **Stems** erect, 30–80 cm, puberulent, hairs sharply upcurved, branches angled, slightly zigzag. **Leaves** unifoliolate; stipules ovate, orbiculate, or sickle-shaped, often encircling node, 7–20 mm; blade broadly obovate, elliptic, or broadly elliptic-lanceolate, 30–70(–120) mm, length 1–1.5(–2) times width, surfaces glabrous. **Racemes** 3–9(–15)-flowered, terminal, subterminal, or lateral, 3–6(–20) cm; bracts persistent or caducous, linear-triangular. **Flowers:** calyx broadly cylindrical, 2–3 mm, lobes ovate to lanceolate, glabrous or slightly puberulous; corolla blue to lavender, often variegated with white or blue- to purple-lined, or, sometimes, white or pale yellow tinged blue (drying yellowish), 12–15 mm. **Legumes** 30–40 × 9–12 mm, moderately hirsute-pilose, hairs spreading to ascending.

Flowering year-round. Sandy wastes along beaches, thickets, hammocks; 0–10 m; introduced; Fla.; Asia (India); introduced also in West Indies, Central America, South America, other regions of Asia, Indian Ocean Islands, Pacific Islands, Australia.

D. Isely (1998) noted that he had seen only two recent specimens, both from the Miami area, but that they were probably waifs; another collection has subsequently been observed from Martin County (*Reed 99184*, MO).

9. Crotalaria lanceolata E. Meyer in E. Meyer and J. F. Drège, Comm. Pl. Afr. Austr., 24. 1836
• Lanceleaf rattlebox [I] [W]

Subspecies 3–5 (1 in the flora): introduced; Africa.

Subspecies *exigua* Polhill and subsp. *prognatha* Polhill are known from Africa.

9a. Crotalaria lanceolata E. Meyer subsp. **lanceolata** [I] [W]

Herbs annual or short-lived perennial. **Stems** erect, 30–150 cm, strigillose to strigose-hirsute. **Leaves** 3-foliolate; stipules absent; leaflet blades linear to linear-lanceolate or lanceolate, 40–110(–150) mm, length 5–10 times width, surfaces sparsely strigose abaxially, glabrous adaxially. **Racemes** 12–26(–40)-flowered, terminal, subterminal, or lateral, 10–35 cm; bracts persistent, subulate or filiform, 0.5–3 mm, basally expanded. **Flowers:** calyx broadly cylindrical, truncate basally and deflexed against pedicel, 2.5–4 mm, lobes subulate to triangular-acuminate, usually shorter than tube, shiny-glabrous or glabrate; corolla yellow with faint reddish purple lines, often dark purple basally, 8–11 mm. **Legumes** (16–)18–38 × 4–6 mm, tip upcurved, strigose. $2n$ = 16.

Flowering Jul–Nov, Jan–Apr (year-round). Sandy fields, sandhills, roadsides, ditches, river and swamp edges, woodland edges, disturbed areas, pine flatwoods, palm-live oak woods; 0–20 m; introduced; Ala., Fla., Ga., La., N.C., S.C.; Africa; Indian Ocean Islands (Madagascar); introduced also in South America (Colombia), e Asia (Taiwan), Pacific Islands (Hawaii), Australia.

10. Crotalaria ochroleuca G. Don, Gen. Hist. 2: 138. 1832 • Slender leaf rattlebox [I] [W]

Herbs annual or short-lived perennial. **Stems** erect, 70–250 cm, strigose. **Leaves** 3-foliolate; stipules absent; leaflet blades linear to linear-lanceolate or elliptic-lanceolate, 50–130(–180) mm, length 7–10 times width, surfaces strigose abaxially, glabrous adaxially. **Racemes** 4–12-flowered, terminal or subterminal, 15–40 cm; bracts persistent, linear-triangular, minute. **Flowers:** calyx broadly cylindrical, truncate basally, 4–6 mm, lobes triangular, shiny-glabrous; corolla pale yellow with prominent reddish purple lines, 18–20 mm. **Legumes** straight, (40–)50–70 × (10–)15–20 mm, sparsely strigose or glabrescent. $2n = 16$.

Flowering Apr–Oct. Roadsides, ditches, prairie swales, sandy fields; 0–10 m; introduced; Ala., Fla., Ga., La., Miss., N.C., S.C.; Africa; introduced also in South America (Brazil), Asia (China), Pacific Islands (Papua New Guinea), Australia.

Crotalaria ochroleuca has often been identified in the United States as *C. intermedia* Kotschy or *C. brevidens* Bentham var. *intermedia* (Kotschy) Polhill.

11. Crotalaria trichotoma Bojer, Ann. Sci. Nat., Bot., sér. 2, 4: 265. 1835 • Zanzibar rattlebox, curara pea [I]

Crotalaria usaramoensis Baker f.; *C. zanzibarica* Bentham

Herbs annual or short-lived perennial. **Stems** suffrutescent basally, erect, 75–250 cm, strigose to strigillose, hairs tightly appressed. **Leaves** 3-foliolate; stipules absent; leaflet blades elliptic to elliptic-lanceolate or elliptic-oblanceolate, 40–100(–140) mm, length 3–4.5 times width, surfaces strigose abaxially, glabrous adaxially. **Racemes** 10–50-flowered, terminal, subterminal, or lateral, 10–40 cm; bracts persistent, linear-subulate. **Flowers:** calyx broadly cylindrical, basally truncate and deflexed against pedicel, 4–6 mm (length less than width), lobes triangular-lanceolate, glabrous or sparsely strigillose; corolla yellow with prominent reddish lines, each wing with a purple spot at base, 12–15 mm. **Legumes** 30–45 × 7–12 mm, sparsely to densely strigose to strigose-sericeous.

Flowering probably year-round. Roadsides; 0–10 m; introduced; Fla.; Africa; introduced also in Central America (Nicaragua), South America (Argentina, Peru), Asia (China, Java, Sri Lanka, Sumatra), Indian Ocean Islands, Pacific Islands, Australia.

In the flora area, *Crotalaria trichotoma* has been found only in Miami-Dade County.

R. M. Polhill (1982) stated that *Crotalaria trichotoma* does not belong in the genus *Crotalaria*, without stating its placement elsewhere. In contrast, D. Isely (1998) observed that *C. trichotoma* resembles the common *C. pallida* in flower but that the latter has wider leaflets and caducous bracts; the similarity of *C. trichotoma* to many other crotalarias is confirmed here.

12. Crotalaria pallida Aiton, Hort. Kew. 3: 20. 1789 [F] [I] [W]

Varieties 2 (1 in the flora): introduced; Africa.

12a. Crotalaria pallida Aiton var. **obovata** (G. Don) Polhill, Kew Bull. 22: 265. 1968 • Smooth rattlebox, streaked rattlepod [F] [I] [W]

Crotalaria obovata G. Don, Gen. Hist. 2: 138. 1832; *C. falcata* Vahl ex de Candolle

Herbs annual. **Stems** suffrutescent basally, erect, 60–200(–300) cm, moderately to densely strigose to sericeous or glabrescent. **Leaves** 3-foliolate; stipules sometimes absent, linear, 1–3 mm; leaflet blades broadly obovate to elliptic, elliptic-obovate, or spatulate-obovate, 20–50(–75) mm, length 1.5–2.5 times width, surfaces strigillose abaxially, glabrous adaxially. **Racemes** (8–)12–45-flowered, terminal, 10–30 cm; bracts caducous, filiform. **Flowers:** calyx broadly cylindrical, sometimes basally truncate, not deflexed against pedicels, 3–4 mm, lobes triangular-lanceolate, sparsely to densely strigose; corolla yellow to orangish, banner and keel strongly red- to reddish brown-lined, 11–15 mm. **Legumes** brown, slightly to conspicuously curved, 30–45 × 5–6 mm, minutely puberulent to glabrate, hairs ascending. $2n = 16$.

Flowering Jul–Oct, Dec–Apr (year-round). Roadsides, old or fallow fields, levees, lake edges, beach margins, disturbed sites, pine woods, dune scrub, palm-live oak edges; 0–200 m; introduced; Ala., Fla., Ga., Miss., N.C., S.C.; Africa; introduced also in Central America (El Salvador), South America (Colombia, Ecuador, Peru), Asia, Indian Ocean Islands, Pacific Islands, Australia.

Crotalaria pallida was collected in the flora area as early as 1886 as a ballast weed near Pensacola, Florida, by A. H. Curtis.

Crotalaria striata Schumacher & Thonning is an illegitimate name that pertains here.

13. Crotalaria incana Linnaeus, Sp. Pl. 2: 716. 1753 • Shake-shake [I]

Varieties 2 (1 in the flora): introduced; Africa; introduced widely.

Both subspecies of *Crotalaria incana* are native to southeast Africa, where they are partially sympatric. Subspecies *purpurascens* (Lamarck) Milne-Redhead occurs also in Madagascar. Plants of the latter are characterized as shrubs or creeping herbs, the stems with long, yellow-brown, spreading hairs (versus shorter, more appressed hairs in subsp. *incana*), inflorescence bracts usually 4–10 (versus 1–3) mm, and calyx lobes pilose (versus glabrate).

13a. Crotalaria incana Linnaeus var. **incana** [I]

Crotalaria cubensis de Candolle

Herbs annual or perennial. Stems sometimes suffrutescent basally, erect to ascending, 25–130 cm, hirsute-villous to strigose-hirsute, hairs mostly ascending. **Leaves** 3-foliolate; stipules sometimes caducous, triangular, 3–8 mm; leaflet blades elliptic, ovate, or obovate, (10–)30–70 mm, length 1.3–2 times width, surfaces glabrous, sometimes hairy on abaxial midvein. **Racemes** 5–30-flowered, terminal, subterminal, or lateral, 5–23 cm; bracts persistent or caducous, filiform. **Flowers:** calyx broadly cylindrical, sometimes basally truncate, not deflexed against pedicels, 1.5–3 mm, lobes narrowly triangular, glabrous or slightly puberulous; corolla yellow with prominent reddish lines near base, each wing with a reddish purple spot at base, 9–16 mm. **Legumes** straight, 25–35 × 10–15 mm, villous-hirsute to hispid-hirsute. **2*n*** = 14.

Flowering Feb–Oct (year-round). Roadsides, fields, riverbanks, coral wastes, beach ridges, pine woods; 0–10 m; introduced; Ala., Fla., Ga., S.C., Tex.; Africa; introduced also in Mexico, Central America, South America, Asia, Indian Ocean Islands, Pacific Islands, Australia.

14. Crotalaria pumila Ortega, Nov. Pl. Descr. Dec. 2: 23. 1797 • Low rattlebox

Herbs annual or perennial. Stems sometimes ligneous basally, mostly decumbent to prostrate, 15–100 cm, minutely and sparsely strigillose. **Leaves** 3-foliolate; stipules caducous, narrowly triangular, setaceous, 0.5–1 mm; leaflet blades narrowly obovate to oblong or elliptic-oblong, 7–15(–35) mm, length 1.5–3.5(–6) times width, surfaces strigose abaxially, glabrous adaxially. **Racemes** (1–)4–8-flowered, terminal, subterminal, or lateral, 1–6(–10) cm; bracts caducous, subulate. **Flowers:** calyx campanulate, 3–5.5 mm, lobes triangular, strigose; corolla yellow, often red- or orange-tinged or red-lined, 7–11 mm. **Legumes** yellowish, 12–20 × 4–8 mm, minutely strigillose. **2*n*** = 32.

Flowering Aug–Oct, Dec–May. Sandy waste areas, dunes, sand ridges, sandy pine woods, dune thickets, hammock margins, grassy hillsides, creek bottoms, alluvium; 0–10 m, 1100–1800 m; Ariz., Fla., N.Mex., Okla., Tex.; Mexico; West Indies; Central America; South America.

Plants of *Crotalaria pumila* in the south-central and southwestern United States tend to have more elongate leaflets than those from Florida and are often found on grassy hillsides, creek bottoms, and in alluvium, from 1100–1800 m; flowering is from August to October. In Florida, it is found in low elevation, mostly sandy habitats, and flowers from December to May. It was collected on chrome ore piles in Baltimore, Maryland, in the 1950s but did not become established there. A record cited by H. A. Senn (1939) attributed to Utah is doubtful, and no subsequent specimens have been reported from that state.

15. Crotalaria virgulata Klotzsch in W. C. H. Peters, Naturw. Reise Mossambique 6(1): 56. 1861 [I]

Varieties 6 (1 in the flora); introduced, Florida; Africa introduced also in South America, Australia.

15a. Crotalaria virgulata Klotzsch subsp. **grantiana** (Harvey) Polhill, Crotalaria Afr. Madag., 293. 1982 • Grant's rattlebox [I]

Crotalaria grantiana Harvey in W. H. Harvey et al., Fl. Cap. 2: 43. 1862

Herbs annual or short-lived perennial. Stems erect to decumbent, 50–150(–200) cm, loosely strigose to strigose-hirsute. **Leaves** 3-foliolate; stipules subulate to triangular, 1–2 mm; leaflet blades obovate to oblong-obovate, 5–15(–20) mm, length 2–3 times width, surfaces strigose abaxially, glabrous adaxially. **Racemes** 3–8-flowered, axillary or terminal, loose, 2–6 cm; bracts deciduous, linear, 2–4 mm. **Flowers:** calyx shallowly cupulate, 1 mm, lobes deltate-subulate to triangular-subulate, 4–5 mm, strigose; corolla yellow with red-lined banner, 6–9 mm. **Legumes** 7–10 × 6–7 mm, finely strigose to strigose-hirsute. **2*n*** = 16.

Flowering Apr–Nov. Open sandy areas; 0–50 m; introduced; Fla.; Africa; introduced also in South America, Australia.

In the flora area, var. *grantiana* has been found only in Highlands County.

53. LUPINUS Linnaeus, Sp. Pl. 2: 721. 1753; Gen. Pl. ed. 5, 322. 1754 • Lupine, bluebonnet [Derivation uncertain; Latin *lupinus*, wolf, or *lupe*, sadness, and *inus*, possession, perhaps alluding either to plants supposedly overrunning the ground as an animal might or to harsh taste of seeds causing facial contortion]

Teresa Sholars

Rhonda Riggins

Herbs, annual, biennial, or perennial, shrubs, or subshrubs, unarmed; usually from taproots or woody crowns, rarely rhizomes. **Cotyledons** usually deciduous, usually petiolate. **Stems** erect to decumbent or prostrate, branched or unbranched, usually pubescent, sometimes glabrous. **Leaves** alternate, usually palmately compound, rarely 3-foliolate or unifoliolate, usually cauline, sometimes crowded near base or basal; stipules present, setaceous, adnate to petiole; petiolate; leaflets (1 or 3)4–11(–17), stipels absent, blade margins entire, surfaces glabrous or pubescent. **Inflorescences** 3–100+-flowered, terminal, racemes, erect, rarely axillary and reduced to 1 or 2 flowers, flowers spirally arranged or whorled; bracts present, persistent or deciduous. **Flowers** papilionaceous, chasmogamous; calyx bilabiate, lobes connate, entire or toothed, usually with appendages (often inconspicuous) between lobes; corolla usually blue to purple, sometimes white, yellow, pink or rose; banner with central groove, sides reflexed; wings connivent at tips, corrugated; keel usually attenuate; stamens 10, monadelphous; anthers basifixed, dimorphic, alternately long on short filaments, short on long filaments; style brushy. **Fruits** legumes, sessile, straight, laterally compressed, usually oblong, splitting along both margins, valves usually twisted after dehiscence, usually pubescent, rarely glabrous. **Seeds** (1 or)2–12, usually smooth, rarely ridged or tuberculate, spheric, lentiform, or angulate. $x = 6$.

Species ca. 270 (88 in the flora): North America, Mexico, South America, Europe (Mediterranean), Africa; introduced in Asia (China), s Africa, Atlantic Islands (Iceland), Pacific Islands (New Zealand), Australia.

Most species of *Lupinus* occur in western North America and western South America. C. P. Smith (1944, 1938–1953) assigned North American lupines to subg. *Lupinus* and subg. *Platycarpos* S. Watson based on cotyledon structure (sessile versus petiolate) and 22 groups based on life span, flower arrangement, keel ciliation, and banner and wing pubescence, as well as some vegetative features.

The taxonomy of *Lupinus* is complicated. Thousands of names have been coined for lupines; circumscription is difficult, made problematic by the vast number of species recognized, then lumped and split in various ways by different taxonomists. Some authors (for example, D. B. Dunn 1955, 1959) discussed widespread hybridization in the genus. Some studies have indicated that gene flow and introgression through outcrossing in perennial species does occur (A. Liston et al. 1995). Perennial species have shown a preponderance of interbreeding groups that have resulted in gradients of characters.

Self-pollination is known to occur in annual species of *Lupinus*, which has resulted in the establishment of localized variants that have been recognized as distinct species. For example, *L. affinis*, *L. guadalupensis*, and *L. spectabilis* could easily be regarded as localized variants of *L. nanus*.

Phylogenetic analyses of molecular data for *Lupinus* included 50 North American species (C. S. Drummond et al. 2012). The species were assigned to three infrageneric lineages. One lineage included two species from Florida that have unifoliate leaves and $2n = 52$. The second lineage included two $2n = 36$ annual species from Texas that corresponds to group Subcarnosi sensu Smith. The third lineage included 44 species of western North American annuals and perennials having $2n = 48$. This lineage comprised two sister clades: one clade of seven species with sessile cotyledons that corresponds to subg. *Platycarpos*, and a second clade of 37 species with petiolate cotyledons. Within the second clade, annual species are sister to the derived perennials (24 species) which have colonized and diversified in montane habitats. While these studies provide insight into the evolution and biogeography of *Lupinus*, they have not resulted in a phylogenetic classification, and have not clarified relationships among the western North American taxa.

Many species of *Lupinus* contain alkaloids, especially in their seeds, fruits, and young leaves, that are toxic to livestock, especially sheep (G. Boschin and D. Resta 2013). These include *L. arboreus*, *L. latifolius*, and *L. leucophyllus* (M. Wink et al. 1995).

Lupinus albus Linnaeus and *L. luteus* Linnaeus, both European species that are sometimes cultivated, were each collected once as waifs in Florida. *Lupinus angustifolius* Linnaeus, another European species that is sometimes cultivated, has been collected as a waif in British Columbia, Florida, Georgia, Maine, and South Carolina.

1. Leaves appearing simple, unifoliolate.
    2. Stipules 9–15 mm (occurring only on very new growth, abortive or early deciduous) . . . . 88. *Lupinus westianus*
    2. Stipules 20–150 mm.
        3. Banner spot white to cream, corollas light to deep blue, limb centrally white at base . . . . 48. *Lupinus diffusus*
        3. Banner spot maroon, corollas lilac to reddish purple or pink . . . . 87. *Lupinus villosus*
1. Leaves palmately compound.
    4. Herbs annual.
        5. Cotyledons sessile, connate into a persistent disc or cup (if deciduous, leaving a circular scar); legumes usually ovoid, sometimes oblong; seeds 1 or 2(–6), usually tuberculate, ridged, or wrinkled, sometimes smooth.
            6. Flowers in crowded or widely spaced whorls; bracts reflexed; upper keel margins ciliate near claw.
                7. Stems hard, rigid; lower keel margins as densely ciliate as upper; leaflets usually pubescent adaxially, rarely glabrous; seeds dark brown, tuberculate . . . . 13. *Lupinus luteolus*
                7. Stems hollow at least near base; lower keel margins not as densely ciliate as upper or glabrous; leaflets glabrous adaxially; seeds usually mottled, ridged or smooth . . . . 15. *Lupinus microcarpus*
            6. Flowers usually spirally arranged or 1 or 2 (except *L. malacophyllus* crowded with proximal ones whorled becoming spirally arranged distally); bracts straight; keel margins glabrous.
                8. Leaves basal; herbage usually glabrous, sometimes sparsely pubescent when young, rarely at anthesis; pedicels 3–5 mm. . . . . 18. *Lupinus odoratus*
                8. Leaves cauline (often crowded near base); herbage sparsely pubescent to canescent or pilose; pedicles 0.5–3(–4) mm.
                    9. Racemes (1 or)2-flowered, axillary; free blades of stipules reduced, ca. 1 mm; leaflets 2–7 mm . . . . 29. *Lupinus uncialis*
                    9. Racemes several–many-flowered, terminal; free blades of stipules well developed; leaflets 7–30 mm.
                        10. Herbage canescent, hairs 0.6–1 mm; legumes undulate, sides with short inflated hairs becoming scaly when dry . . . . 21. *Lupinus shockleyi*
                        10. Herbage hairs appressed or spreading, more than 1 mm; legumes not obviously undulate, thinly pilose to coarsely hirsute.
                            11. Adaxial calyx lobe more than ½ as long as abaxial . . . . 12. *Lupinus kingii*
                            11. Adaxial calyx lobe less than ½ as long as abaxial.

12. Proximalmost flowers whorled, becoming spirally arranged distally; w Nevada . . . . 14. *Lupinus malacophyllus*
12. All flowers spirally arranged; Kansas westward to California (*L. pusillus* extending into Alberta and Saskatchewan).
    13. Pedicels 0.3–1.5 mm; racemes dense; seeds smooth. . . 5. *Lupinus brevicaulis*
    13. Pedicels to 3 mm; racemes usually elongate; seeds wrinkled or ridged.
        14. Leaves crowded near base; legumes ovoid, adaxial margin not constricted between seeds . . . . 8. *Lupinus flavoculatus*
        14. Leaves well distributed along stems; legumes oblong, adaxial margin constricted between seeds . . . . 20. *Lupinus pusillus*

[5. Shifted to left margin.—Ed.]

5. Cotyledons petiolate, usually withering and deciduous; legumes oblong; seeds usually more than 2, smooth.
    15. Lower (and often upper) keel margins ciliate near claw, glabrous near apex.
        16. Flowers distinctly whorled; corollas usually blue-purple, rarely white, lavender, or pink . . . . 26. *Lupinus succulentus* (in part)
        16. Flowers spirally arranged; corollas yellow, white, pink to magenta, or blue to purple.
            17. Racemes shorter than peduncles; banners yellow, wings usually pink, rarely white, keel petals white . . . . 24. *Lupinus stiversii*
            17. Racemes longer than peduncles; corollas usually yellow, white, dark pink, blue, or magenta, rarely pinkish.
                18. Corollas golden yellow or white; pedicels becoming recurved . . . . 6. *Lupinus citrinus*
                18. Corollas usually blue or dark pink to magenta, rarely pinkish; pedicels not recurved.
                    19. Herbage with appressed, stiff, stinging hairs; leaflets 10–20 mm wide . . . . 11. *Lupinus hirsutissimus*
                    19. Herbage without appressed, stiff, stinging hairs; leaflets 1.5–10 mm wide.
                        20. Petioles flat, leafletlike; keel stout, blunt, upper margins ciliate from claw to middle . . . . 28. *Lupinus truncatus*
                        20. Petioles not flat or leafletlike; keel pointed, upper margins usually glabrous (except *L. sparsiflorus* often ciliate near claw).
                            21. Pedicels 5–9 mm; bracts 10–15 mm, longer than buds . . . . 3. *Lupinus benthamii*
                            21. Pedicels 2–4 mm; bracts 3–8 mm, shorter than to slightly longer than buds.
                                22. Leaflets 5–10 mm wide, glabrous adaxially; corollas dark pink to magenta. . . . . 2. *Lupinus arizonicus*
                                22. Leaflets 2–4 mm wide, pubescent adaxially at least near margins; corollas usually blue, rarely pinkish. . . . . . 22. *Lupinus sparsiflorus*
    15. Lower and upper keel margins glabrous near claw, upper margins ciliate near apex, or glabrous.
        23. Flowers spirally arranged; keel margins glabrous.
            24. Primary peduncles and lateral branches decumbent; coastal dunes in San Luis Obispo County, California . . . . 17. *Lupinus nipomensis*
            24. Primary peduncles erect, lateral branches sometimes tufted or spreading; Arizona, California, Florida, Louisiana, Nevada, New Mexico, Oklahoma, Texas, Utah.
                25. Pubescence of stems and petioles spreading; leaflets pubescent; Arizona, California, Nevada, New Mexico, Texas, Utah . . . . 7. *Lupinus concinnus*
                25. Pubescence of stems and petioles mostly appressed or ascending; leaflets sparsely pubescent or glabrous adaxially; Florida, Louisiana, Oklahoma, Texas.
                    26. Racemes 18–45 cm; trans-Pecos Texas . . . . 10. *Lupinus havardii*
                    26. Racemes 2–12 cm; Florida, Louisiana, Oklahoma, c, e, s Texas.

27. Wing petals inflated; corollas pale blue-violet; calyx hairs becoming yellowish gray or brown on dried material; legumes yellowish gray- or brown-villous; Texas . . . . 25. *Lupinus subcarnosus*
27. Wing petals flat; corollas usually dark blue, rarely white; calyx hairs silvery; legumes white silky-villous; Florida, Louisiana, Oklahoma, Texas . . . . .27. *Lupinus texensis*

23. Flowers whorled at some or all nodes; upper keel margins usually ciliate near apex (except *L. pachylobus* glabrous).
28. Banners longer than wide; pedicels 1–3.5 mm.
29. Legumes usually less than 0.6 cm wide; upper keel margins usually ciliate near apex; Arizona, British Columbia, California, Oregon, Washington . . . . 4. *Lupinus bicolor*
29. Legumes 0.6–0.9 cm wide; upper keel margins glabrous; California, Washington . . . . 19. *Lupinus pachylobus*
28. Banners wider than or equaling length; pedicels 2.5–8 mm.
30. Upper keel margins with a tooth near middle . . . . 1. *Lupinus affinis*
30. Upper keel margins without a tooth.
31. Legumes less than 0.7 cm wide . . . . 16. *Lupinus nanus*
31. Legumes 0.8–1 cm wide.
32. Pedicels 4–5 mm; herbage sparsely pubescent; San Clemente Island, California . . . . .9. *Lupinus guadalupensis*
32. Pedicels 6–8 mm; herbage densely hairy; central Sierra Nevada foothills, California. . . . . .23. *Lupinus spectabilis*

[4. Shifted to left margin.—Ed.]

4. Herbs or shrubs, usually perennial, rarely biennial.
33. Rhizomes present, patch forming; east of Rocky Mountains . . . . 76. *Lupinus perennis*
33. Rhizomes usually not present, or if present (*L. formosus*) then west of Rocky Mountains.
34. Upper keel margins ciliate near claw or only from claw to middle (glabrous middle to tip).
35. Herbs annual, sometimes persisting, fleshy; racemes 15–25 cm; legumes 3.5–5 cm; plants of open or disturbed areas, roadbanks. . . . . . . 26. *Lupinus succulentus* (in part)
35. Herbs perennial, not fleshy; racemes 16–60 cm; legumes 2–4.5 cm; plants of moist areas, open woodlands . . . . 61. *Lupinus latifolius*
34. Upper keel margins usually glabrous or ciliate throughout, or ciliate from middle to tip.
36. Calyx spur 1–3 mm.
37. Wings with dense hair patch outside near tip; leaflets strigose adaxially . . . . 38. *Lupinus arbustus*
37. Wings glabrous; leaflets glabrous or hairy (but not strigose) adaxially. . . . . 40. *Lupinus argenteus* (in part)
36. Calyx not spurred or bulge or spur 0–1 mm.
38. Banners usually hairy abaxially (except usually glabrous in *L. pratensis* and *L. sulphureus*, best seen in bud).
39. Upper keel margins ± glabrous.
40. Subshrubs or shrubs, matted, 2–4 dm . . . . 32. *Lupinus albifrons* (in part)
40. Shrubs or herbs, not matted, (2–)4–20 dm.
41. Shrubs; plants of coastal strands, dunes . . . . 43. *Lupinus chamissonis*
41. Perennial herbs; plants of volcanic or dry soils, pine forests, Great Basin or riparian scrub, coniferous forests.
42. Adaxial surface of leaflets glabrous or pubescent and green.
43. Corollas usually pale yellow to orange-yellow, sometimes white; bracts ± persistent . . . . .34. *Lupinus angustiflorus*
43. Corollas usually purple, sometimes pink or white; bracts deciduous . . . . 36. *Lupinus apertus*

42. Adaxial surface of leaflets tomentose, pubescent, or villous, hairs silvery.
    44. Corollas usually yellow; herbs 2–5 dm . . . . .47. *Lupinus dalesiae*
    44. Corollas creamy yellow to pale yellow, or lavender to blue; herbs 5–9 dm.
        45. Corollas lavender to blue; stem hairs short-silky; elevation 1500–3000 m. . . . . 50. *Lupinus elatus* (in part)
        45. Corollas creamy yellow to pale yellow; stems long-villous; elevation 2500–4000 m . . . 74. *Lupinus padrecrowleyi*

[39. Shifted to left margin.—Ed.]

39. Upper keel margins usually ciliate.
    46. Subshrubs or shrubs.
        47. Raceme rachises deciduous, 8–30 cm; petioles 2–4 cm; chaparral, foothill woodlands, cismontane California; 0–1500 m. . . . . 32. *Lupinus albifrons* (in part)
        47. Raceme rachises persistent, 10–70 cm; petioles 4–10 cm; deserts, transmontane California; (700–)1200–2700 m . . . . 52. *Lupinus excubitus*
    46. Perennial herbs (sometimes subshrubs in *L. breweri*).
        48. Leaflets 10–30 mm wide.
            49. Corollas yellow; San Gabriel Mountains, California . . . . 75. *Lupinus peirsonii* (in part)
            49. Corollas usually ± purple to violet or light blue, rarely pink or pale yellow; British Columbia to San Luis Obispo County, California, eastward to Montana, Wyoming, and Colorado.
                50. Bracts persistent; British Columbia to Klamath Ranges and Modoc Plateau, California, eastward to Montana, Wyoming, and Colorado . . . . 63. *Lupinus leucophyllus* (in part)
                50. Bracts deciduous; Inner North Coast Ranges and Santa Lucia Mountains, California.
                    51. Peduncles 13–20 cm; leaflets long spreading-hairy; corollas light blue, pink, or pale yellow; Santa Lucia Mountains, California. . . 42. *Lupinus cervinus* (in part)
                    51. Peduncles 8–15 cm; leaflets densely silky; corollas purple to violet; Inner North Coast Ranges, California. . . . . 81. *Lupinus sericatus* (in part)
        48. Leaflets 2–10(–17) mm wide.
            52. Herbs to 2 dm.
                53. Flowers in dense, crowded whorls; elevation 2000–3500 m. . . . 41. *Lupinus breweri* (in part)
                53. Flowers in few, separated whorls; elevation 1500–3000 m. . . 60. *Lupinus lapidicola* (in part)
            52. Herbs or subshrubs 1–10(–15) dm.
                54. Basal and cauline leaves present at flowering.
                    55. Bracts persistent; leaflets 30–80(–130) mm, pubescent adaxially.
                        56. Leaflets silvery . . . . 63. *Lupinus leucophyllus* (in part)
                        56. Leaflets green . . . . 78. *Lupinus pratensis* (in part)
                    55. Bracts deciduous or tardily deciduous; leaflets 10–35(–60) mm, glabrous or pubescent adaxially.
                        57. Corollas pale sulfur yellow, blue, or white . . . . 84. *Lupinus sulphureus*
                        57. Corollas usually deep purple to light blue, sometimes violet, pink, or white, banner patch yellow to cream or absent.
                            58. Flowers (6–)9–12(–14) mm; herbs 2.5–4 dm; stems erect or ascending, clustered; proximal petioles (5–)7–9(–15) cm; leaflet hairs silky hairy, not tomentose or woolly. . . 40. *Lupinus argenteus* (in part)
                            58. Flowers 10–16 mm; herbs 2–3.5 dm; stems prostrate to matted; petioles 5–12 cm; leaflet hairs ± spreading, dense, tomentose to woolly. . . . . .56. *Lupinus grayi* (in part)

54. Basal leaves absent at flowering or, when present, then petioles less than 3 times as long as leaflets.
    59. Banners not much reflexed-recurved beyond midpoint, this less than 3 mm proximal to apex; pedicels 1–2.5 mm .... 40. *Lupinus argenteus* (in part)
    59. Banners well reflexed-recurved at or proximal to midpoint, this 3.5–6 mm proximal to apex; pedicels 2–8 mm.
        60. Herbs 1.5–3 dm; leaves cauline; leaflets 20–50 mm, silvery-silky adaxially.......................................71. *Lupinus obtusilobus*
        60. Herbs 2–10 dm; leaves cauline and sometimes clustered at base; leaflets 15–60(–90) mm, silky-villous or tomentose to woolly adaxially.
            61. Leaflets tomentose to woolly, hairs ± spreading, dense; flowers 10–15 mm; corollas bluish to purple; banner glabrous or hairy abaxially.....................66. *Lupinus ludovicianus* (in part)
            61. Leaflets usually silky; flowers 8–14(–18) mm; corollas pale purple to bright blue, sometimes yellowish or whitish; banner silky-hairy abaxially..............................82. *Lupinus sericeus*

[38. Shifted to left margin.—Ed.]

38. Banner usually glabrous abaxially (hairy in some varieties of *L. albifrons*, *L. argenteus*).
    62. Subshrubs or shrubs.
        63. Petioles greater than 3 cm; plants usually inland in California, Oregon.
            64. Subshrubs or shrubs; stems decumbent to prostrate-ascending.... 32. *Lupinus albifrons* (in part)
            64. Shrubs; stems erect... 65. *Lupinus longifolius*
        63. Petioles often 3 cm or less, rarely to 6 cm; plants of coastal bluffs, dunes, beaches in British Columbia, California, Oregon, Washington.
            65. Shrubs, usually 5–20 dm; stems ascending or erect; immediate coast and more inland..37. *Lupinus arboreus*
            65. Subshrubs, 2–5 dm; stems prostrate to decumbent; immediate coast .... 64. *Lupinus littoralis* (in part)
    62. Perennial herbs, rarely woody at base.
        66. Leaflets glabrous or sparsely hairy adaxially, appearing green.
            67. Upper keel margins glabrous.
                68. Corollas pale or bright yellow to orange-yellow; California.
                    69. Bracts 2–7 mm; herbs 4–6 dm; corollas bright yellow to orange-yellow ....46. *Lupinus croceus* (in part)
                    69. Bracts 7–14 mm; herbs 6–9 dm; corollas pale yellow ....51. *Lupinus elmeri*
                68. Corollas blue to purple, violet, lavender, pink, or white (may fade pale yellow to white in *L. tracyi*); widely distributed, including California.
                    70. Leaves basal and cauline.
                        71. Banners distinctly ruffled, markedly concave on lateral face; keel margins glabrous ....73. *Lupinus oreganus*
                        71. Banners smooth, not ruffled; keel margins ciliate ....77. *Lupinus polyphyllus* (in part)
                    70. Leaves cauline.
                        72. Flowers (11–)15–21 mm; Alaska, Canada, and Greenland..... ....70. *Lupinus nootkatensis* (in part)
                        72. Flowers 8–10(–12) mm; California and Oregon .... 86. *Lupinus tracyi*
            67. Upper keel margins ciliate (sometimes sparsely so in *L. onustus*).
                73. Herbs greater than 3.5 dm; leaves all cauline, no leaves clustered at base.
                    74. Leaflets long-villous abaxially, glabrous or glabrate adaxially; petioles 2–10 cm; flowers (11–)15–21 mm; Alaska, British Columbia, Newfoundland and Labrador (Newfoundland), Nova Scotia ....70. *Lupinus nootkatensis* (in part)
                    74. Leaflets glabrous or partly glabrate; petioles 3–5 cm; flowers 12–16 mm; California to British Columbia.................. 79. *Lupinus rivularis*

73. Herbs less than 3.5 dm; leaves basal and cauline, or cauline and clustered near base.
    75. Herbs rhizomatous (from slender, underground rootstock); flowers 8–11 mm, bracts 3–4 mm; leaflets silky-hairy abaxially; California, s Oregon . . . . 72. *Lupinus onustus*
    75. Herbs not rhizomatous; flowers 9–20 mm; bracts (3–)4–14 mm; leaflets hairy abaxially but not silky-hairy; Alaska to Nunavut, southward to California, eastward to New Mexico.
        76. Caudices subterranean; divisions rhizomelike; Colorado, n New Mexico, Utah . . . . 77. *Lupinus polyphyllus* (in part)
        76. Caudices superficial; divisions closely tufted; Alaska to Nunavut, southward to California, eastward to Colorado.
            77. Largest leaflets 35–110 mm . . . . 77. *Lupinus polyphyllus* (in part)
            77. Largest leaflets 10–40(–50) mm.
                78. Herbs 1–4 dm; Alaska and Canada . . . . 39. *Lupinus arcticus*
                78. Herbs (2–)3–6.5 dm; Colorado, Idaho, Nevada, Oregon, Utah, Washington . . . . 77. *Lupinus polyphyllus* (in part)

[66. Shifted to left margin.—Ed.]

66. Leaflets hairy, appearing greenish gray to silver adaxially.
    79. Bracts usually persistent; racemes usually dense (except *L. covillei* loose, spirally arranged, sometimes whorled).
        80. Leaflets 5–40 mm . . . . 62. *Lupinus lepidus*
        80. Leaflets (30–)40–110(–130) mm.
            81. Leaves all cauline, leaflets villous, hairs greater than 1 mm; racemes loose (flowers whorled or spirally arranged); corollas light blue . . . . 45. *Lupinus covillei* (in part)
            81. Leaves basal and cauline, leaflets strigose, hairs less than 1 mm; racemes dense; corollas violet to dark blue. . . . . 78. *Lupinus pratensis* (in part)
    79. Bracts usually ± deciduous (except *L. covillei* and *L. kuschei*); racemes ± open (spirally arranged or whorled).
        82. Upper keel margins usually glabrous, sometimes ciliate.
            83. Herbs or subshrubs, 0.5–2 dm; flowers 4–11 mm; keel ± straight.
                84. Petioles 1–3(–4) cm; stems prostrate, forming mats; stipules 2–5 mm; pedicels 1–3(–4) mm; plants of subalpine to alpine montane forests; California, Nevada, Oregon. . . . . 41. *Lupinus breweri* (in part)
                84. Petioles (2–)3–6(–8) cm; stems forming robust, dense tufts; stipules 6–11 mm; pedicels (2–)4–5 mm; plants of pumice gravel flats; California (Mono County) . . . . 49. *Lupinus duranii*
            83. Herbs, (1.5–)2–15 dm; flowers (8–)9–18 mm; keel usually upcurved.
                85. Stipules usually leaflike, lanceolate, green . . . . 54. *Lupinus fulcratus*
                85. Stipules not leaflike, setaceous, green to silvery.
                    86. Corollas usually yellow to orange-yellow, rarely lavender or violet.
                        87. Flowers 9–12 mm; corollas pale yellowish to lavender or violet; California, Oregon . . . . 30. *Lupinus adsurgens* (in part)
                        87. Flowers 12–15 mm; corollas bright yellow to orange-yellow; California . . . . 46. *Lupinus croceus* (in part)
                    86. Corollas usually blue, lavender, violet, purple, pink, rarely white or yellowish.
                        88. Leaves basal and cauline; plants of moist or wet places.
                            89. Flowers 10–13 mm; plants of sand dunes, roadsides, sandy woods; s Alaska to n British Columbia. . . . . 59. *Lupinus kuschei*
                            89. Flowers 9–15 mm; plants of moist to wet places; California . . . . 77. *Lupinus polyphyllus* (in part)
                        88. Leaves cauline; plants of dry places.
                            90. Banners narrow, wings narrow, not covering keel tip . . . . 31. *Lupinus albicaulis*
                            90. Banners ovate, wings wide, covering keel tip.

91. Leaflet blades green, sparsely to densely hairy.
   92. Flowers 9–12 mm; California, Nevada, Oregon . . . . .33. *Lupinus andersonii*
   92. Flowers 13–16 mm; California . . . . .58. *Lupinus hyacinthinus*
91. Leaflet blades gray-hairy to silvery-silky.
   93. Herbs rhizomatous; plants usually of valleys, grasslands; elevation 0–1500 m. . . . . 53. *Lupinus formosus*
   93. Herbs not rhizomatous; plants of mountains, forests; 500–3500 m.
      94. Corollas white with banner patch turning tawny; seeds 7–11 mm; California (Anthony Peak, Mendocino County) . . . . 35. *Lupinus antoninus*
      94. Corollas pale yellowish to lavender or violet and banner patch yellow to white, or lavender to blue and banner patch pale yellowish; seeds 4–6 mm; California, Oregon.
         95. Leaflet blade adaxial surfaces appressed hairy to ± silky to dull green; bracts 2–8 mm; flowers 9–12 mm; corollas pale yellow to lavender or violet; California, Oregon . . . . 30. *Lupinus adsurgens* (in part)
         95. Leaflets blade adaxial surfaces densely silver-silky to woolly; bracts 6–11 mm; flowers 10–14 mm; corollas lavender to blue; California . . . . 50. *Lupinus elatus* (in part)

[82. Shifted to left margin.—Ed.]

82. Upper keel margins ciliate.
   96. Herbs 0.1–3.5(–5) dm; stems usually ± prostrate to decumbent, rarely ascending.
      97. Corollas pink; California (Humboldt and Trinity counties) . . . . .44. *Lupinus constancei*
      97. Corollas purple, ± violet, lavender, rose, light blue, yellow, or white; Arizona, British Columbia, California.
         98. Leaves cauline.
            99. Leaflets 5–9; stems not weak; British Columbia to California . . .64. *Lupinus littoralis* (in part)
            99. Leaflets 3–5; stems weak; California (Marin, Monterey, Sonoma counties) . . . . 85. *Lupinus tidestromii*
         98. Leaves usually basal (if cauline, then clustered near base).
            100. Racemes 2–7 cm; banners ± pubescent adaxially . . . . 60. *Lupinus lapidicola* (in part)
            100. Racemes 10–23 cm; banners glabrous adaxially.
               101. Racemes 10–16 cm; flowers 10–16 mm; leaflets tomentose-woolly; California . . . . .56. *Lupinus grayi* (in part)
               101. Racemes 6–23 cm; flowers 7–13 mm; leaflets villous-hirsute with long, spreading hairs; Arizona. . . . . .57. *Lupinus huachucanus*
   96. Herbs (1–)2–15 dm; stems usually erect, ascending, or spreading, rarely decumbent.
      102. Leaflets densely tomentose or woolly.
         103. Stem hairs less than 1 mm, not sharp or stiff; petioles 5–12 cm; flowers 10–15 mm; California (San Luis Obispo County) . . . . 66. *Lupinus ludovicianus* (in part)
         103. Some stem hairs 1–3 mm, sharp, stiff; petioles 6–30 cm; flowers 10–18 mm; California. . . . . 67. *Lupinus magnificus*
      102. Leaflets sometimes densely hairy but not woolly.
         104. Leaves clustered at or near base.
            105. Corollas yellow . . . . 75. *Lupinus peirsonii* (in part)
            105. Corollas light blue, pink, pale yellow, purple, or violet.
               106. Peduncles 13–20 cm; corollas light blue, pink, or pale yellow (often drying straw-colored) . . . . 42. *Lupinus cervinus* (in part)
               106. Peduncles 8–15 cm; corollas purple to violet . . . . . . 81. *Lupinus sericatus* (in part)
         104. Some leaves cauline, spread along stems.

[107. Shifted to left margin.—Ed.]

107. Flowers 5–8 mm . . . . 40. *Lupinus argenteus* (in part)
107. Flowers 8–18 mm.
  108. Leaflets 10–50 mm.
    109. Herbs 1–4 dm; flowers 10–12 mm; California, Nevada, Oregon . . . . 69. *Lupinus nevadensis*
    109. Herbs 4–10 dm; flowers 12–15 mm; British Columbia to Alberta, southward to California, eastward to Utah and New Mexico.
      110. Legumes 2 cm wide; Arizona, New Mexico. . . . . .68. *Lupinus neomexicanus*
      110. Legumes 0.7–1 cm wide; British Columbia to Alberta, southward to California, ne Nevada, s Utah . . . . .77. *Lupinus polyphyllus* (in part)
  108. Leaflets 30–120(–150) mm.
    111. Corollas usually bright yellow, rarely pale purple. . . . . 80. *Lupinus sabineanus*
    111. Corollas blue.
      112. Herbs strigose to shaggy-pubescent; leaves yellow-green, leaflets 5–11 mm wide; proximal petioles 5–10 cm; bracts 7–15 mm, persistent; California . . . . 45. *Lupinus covillei* (in part)
      112. Herbs puberulent or hairy; leaves green; bracts 4–10 mm, semideciduous; California, New Mexico.
        113. Leaflets 2–5 mm wide; proximal petioles (3–)5–14 cm; California (Rock Creek to Yosemite National Park) . . . . 55. *Lupinus gracilentus*
        113. Leaflets 5–13 mm wide; proximal petioles 5–7 cm; New Mexico (Sacramento and White mountains) . . . . 83. *Lupinus sierrae-blancae*

1. Lupinus affinis J. Agardh, Syn. Lupini, 20. 1835 [E]

Lupinus affinis var. *carnosulus* (Greene) Jepson; *L. carnosulus* Greene; *L. nanus* Douglas ex Bentham var. *carnosulus* (Greene) C. P. Smith

Herbs, annual, 2–5 dm, pubescent. **Cotyledons** deciduous, petiolate. **Stems** ascending or erect, branched or unbranched. **Leaves** cauline; petiole 3–10 cm; leaflets 5–8, blades 20–50 × 4–11 mm, adaxial surface pubescent. **Peduncles** 5–18 cm; bracts deciduous, 5–7.5 mm. **Racemes** 10–40 cm; flowers whorled. **Pedicels** 3–6 mm. **Flowers** 8–12 mm; calyx 5–7 mm, lobes ± equal, entire; corolla blue, banner spot white, upper keel margins with a tooth near middle, ciliate from tooth to near apex, banner width equal to or greater than length. **Legumes** 3–5 cm, coarsely pubescent. **Seeds** 5–8.

Flowering late winter–spring. Uncommon in open areas; 0–800 m; Calif., Oreg.

Lupinus affinis is mostly a coastal species that occurs from the San Francisco Bay region northward to Lane County, Oregon.

Lupinus affinis intergrades with *L. nanus* and can be confused with *L. littoralis* var. *variicolor*, a perennial species with a toothed keel.

2. Lupinus arizonicus (S. Watson) S. Watson, Proc. Amer. Acad. Arts 12: 250. 1877 • Arizona lupine [F]

Lupinus concinnus J. Agardh var. *arizonicus* S. Watson, Proc. Amer. Acad. Arts 8: 537. 1873; *L. arizonicus* var. *barbatulus* (Thornberry ex C. P. Smith) I. M. Johnston; *L. brevior* (Jepson) J. A. Christian & D. B. Dunn; *L. concinnus* var. *brevior* (Jepson) D. B. Dunn; *L. sparsiflorus* Bentham var. *arizonicus* (S. Watson) C. P. Smith; *L. sparsiflorus* var. *barbatulus* Thornber ex C. P. Smith

Herbs, annual, 1–6 dm, with short-appressed and long, spreading hairs. **Cotyledons** deciduous, petiolate. **Stems** erect, usually branched, sometimes unbranched. **Leaves** cauline; petiole 2–8 cm; leaflets 5–10, blades 10–40 × 4–12 mm, adaxial surface glabrous. **Peduncles** 1–6 cm; bracts usually persistent, 4–8 mm. **Racemes** 6–30 cm; flowers spirally arranged or appearing ± whorled proximally. **Pedicels** 2–4 mm. **Flowers** 7–10 mm; calyx 3–6 mm, lobes ± equal, abaxial lobe entire, adaxial lobe deeply cleft; corolla banner and wings dark pink to magenta, drying blue-purple or whitish, banner spot yellowish, becoming darker magenta, lower keel margins ciliate near claw, upper margins glabrous. **Legumes** often secund, 1–2 cm, coarsely pubescent. **Seeds** 4–6. $2n = 48$.

Flowering spring. Sandy washes, open areas; 0–1100 m; Ariz., Calif., Nev.; Mexico (Baja California, Baja California Sur, Sonora).

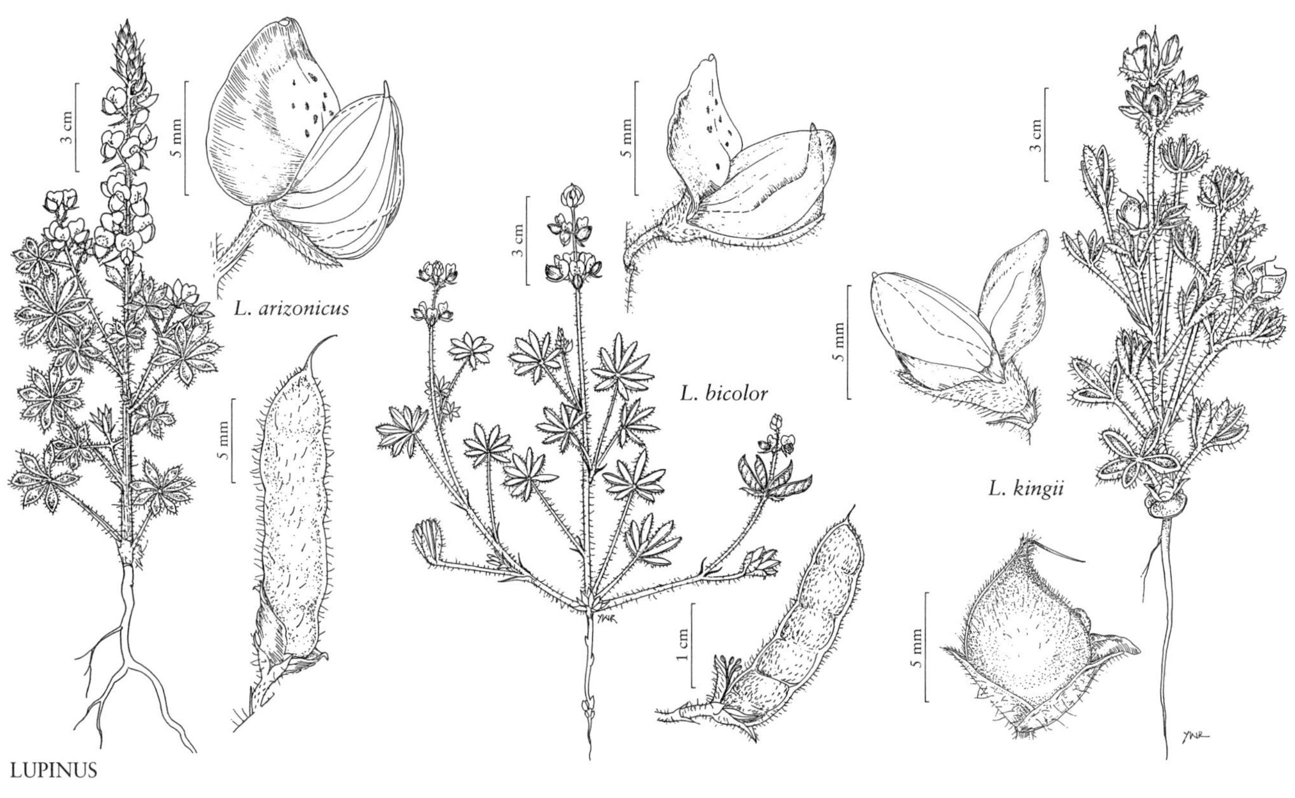

LUPINUS

Lupinus arizonicus occurs in the eastern Mojave and Sonora deserts of southeastern California, southwestern Arizona, and southern Nevada, plus adjacent areas in northern Mexico.

Robust plants have been named var. *barbatulus*.

3. Lupinus benthamii A. Heller, Muhlenbergia 2: 61. 1905 (as benthami) • Spider lupine [E]

Lupinus leptophyllus Bentham, Trans. Hort. Soc. London, ser. 2, 1: 411. 1835, not Chamisso & Schlechtendal 1830; *L. benthamii* var. *opimus* C. P. Smith

Herbs, annual, 2–7 dm, with short-appressed and long, spreading hairs. **Cotyledons** deciduous, petiolate. **Stems** erect, usually branched, sometimes unbranched. **Leaves** cauline; petiole 3–12 cm; leaflets 7–10, blades 20–50 × 1.5–3.5 mm, adaxial surface glabrous. **Peduncles** 4–7 cm; bracts deciduous, 10–15 mm, longer than buds. **Racemes** 10–40 cm; flowers spirally arranged, sometimes appearing ± whorled proximally. **Pedicels** 5–9 mm. **Flowers** 10–18 mm; calyx 5–6.5 mm, lobes ± equal, abaxial lobe entire, adaxial lobe deeply cleft; corolla bright blue, banner spot whitish, becoming magenta, lower keel margins ciliate near claw. **Legumes** 3 cm, coarsely pubescent. **Seeds** 5–8.

Flowering spring. Rocky slopes, open areas; 0–1500 m; Calif.

Lupinus benthamii occurs in the Sierra Nevada Foothills, Tehachapi Mountains, South Coastal Ranges, and parts of the delta region of the Great Central Valley.

4. Lupinus bicolor Lindley, Bot. Reg. 13: plate 1109. 1827 • Miniature lupine [F]

Lupinus bicolor subsp. *marginatus* D. B. Dunn; *L. bicolor* var. *micranthus* B. Boivin; *L. bicolor* subsp. *microphyllus* (S. Watson) D. B. Dunn; *L. bicolor* var. *microphyllus* (S. Watson) C. P. Smith; *L. bicolor* subsp. *pipersmithii* (A. Heller) D. B. Dunn; *L. bicolor* var. *pipersmithii* (A. Heller) C. P. Smith; *L. bicolor* var. *rostratus* (Eastwood) Jepson; *L. bicolor* subsp. *tridentatus* (Eastwood ex C. P. Smith) D. B. Dunn; *L. bicolor* var. *tridentatus* Eastwood ex C. P. Smith; *L. bicolor* var. *trifidus* (S. Watson) C. P. Smith; *L. bicolor* subsp. *umbellatus* (Greene) D. B. Dunn; *L. bicolor* var. *umbellatus* (Greene) C. P. Smith; *L. congdonii* (C. P. Smith) D. B. Dunn; *L. polycarpus* Greene

Herbs, annual, 0.5–4 dm, pubescent. **Cotyledons** deciduous, petiolate. **Stems** ascending or erect, branched or unbranched. **Leaves** cauline; petiole 1–7 cm; leaflets 5–8, blades 10–40 × 1–5 mm, adaxial surface glabrous or sparsely pubescent. **Peduncles** 3–10 cm; bracts deciduous, 4–6 mm. **Racemes** 4–20 cm; flowers usually in fewer than 5 whorls, sometimes spirally arranged. **Pedicels** 1–3.5 mm. **Flowers** 4–10 mm; calyx abaxial lobe entire, 4–6 mm, adaxial lobe deeply cleft, 2–4 mm; corolla usually blue, rarely light blue, pink, or white, banner spot white, becoming magenta, upper keel margins usually ciliate near apex, rarely glabrous, sometimes blunt, banner longer than wide. **Legumes** 1–3 × 0.3–0.6 cm, pubescent. **Seeds** 5–8. $2n = 48$.

Flowering late winter–spring (Mar–Jun). Open or disturbed areas; 0–1600 m; B.C.; Ariz., Calif., Oreg., Wash.; Mexico (Baja California, Baja California Sur, Sonora).

Lupinus bicolor is naturalized in Arizona. The named subspecies and varieties do not conform to consistently recognizable geographical or morphological entities (D. B. Dunn 1955). Vigorous plants with larger flowers may be confused with *L. nanus*. In California, plants on the Outer North Coast Ranges may persist for two growing seasons. *Lupinus bicolor* (as *L. polycarpus*) has been reported from Alabama (A. R. Diamond 2016) and Michigan (E. G. Voss and A. A. Reznicek 2012).

Lupinus micranthus Douglas (1829, not Gussone 1828) is an illegitimate name that pertains here.

5. Lupinus brevicaulis S. Watson, Botany (Fortieth Parallel), 53, plate 7, figs. 1–4. 1871 • Sand lupine

Herbs, annual, usually less than 1 dm, pubescent, hairs more than 1 mm. **Cotyledons** persistent, disclike, sessile. **Stems** very short, tufted, branched. **Leaves** cauline, crowded near base; stipules well developed; petiole 1–6 cm; leaflets (3 or)5–9, blades 8–20 × 2–9 mm, adaxial surface glabrous. **Peduncles** 1–8(–10) cm; bracts persistent, straight, 2–3 mm. **Racemes** dense, 3–16-flowered, 1–8 cm; flowers spirally arranged, crowded. **Pedicels** 0.3–1.5 mm. **Flowers** 6–8 mm; calyx abaxial lobe entire or shallowly cleft, ± 6 mm, adaxial lobe 2-toothed, 3 mm, less than 1/2 as long as abaxial; corolla bright blue, banner spot white or yellow, keel glabrous. **Legumes** not undulate, 1 cm, thinly pilose to coarsely hirsute. **Seeds** 1 or 2, smooth.

Flowering spring. Sandy washes, open areas, grasslands, pinyon pine-juniper forests, creosote bush scrub, mesquite; 300–2400 m; Ariz., Calif., Colo., Nev., N.Mex., Oreg., Utah, Wyo.; Mexico (Chihuahua, Sonora).

Lupinus brevicaulis resembles *L. flavoculatus* except that its flowers are smaller.

6. Lupinus citrinus Kellogg, Proc. Calif. Acad. Sci. 7: 93. 1877 [C] [E]

Herbs, annual, 1–6 dm, hairs soft, white, sometimes matted, to 2 mm. **Cotyledons** deciduous, petiolate. **Stems** ascending or erect, branched or unbranched. **Leaves** cauline; petiole 2–7 cm; leaflets 6–9, blades 15–35 × 3–10 mm, adaxial surface densely pubescent to tomentose. **Peduncles** 1–9 cm; bracts deciduous, 2.5–5 mm. **Racemes** 5–25 cm; flowers spirally arranged, sometimes appearing whorled proximally. **Pedicels** 2.5–5 mm, becoming recurved. **Flowers** 8.5–12 mm; calyx 3–5 mm, lobes ± equal, cleft; corolla golden yellow or white, lower keel margins short-ciliate near claw. **Legumes** 1–2 cm, glabrous or glabrate. **Seeds** 3–8, resembling bits of granite.

Varieties 2 (2 in the flora): California.

Lupinus citrinus is known from the central Sierra Nevada Foothills.

1. Corollas golden yellow . . . . 6a. *Lupinus citrinus* var. *citrinus*
1. Corollas white. . . . . . . 6b. *Lupinus citrinus* var. *deflexus*

6a. Lupinus citrinus Kellogg var. **citrinus** • Orange lupine [C] [E]

Corolla golden yellow, drying translucent, purplish.

Flowering spring–summer (Apr–Jul). Granitic soils; of conservation concern; 600–1700 m; Calif.

Variety *citrinus* is known from the central Sierra Nevada Foothills in Fresno and Madera counties.

6b. Lupinus citrinus Kellogg var. **deflexus** (Congdon) Jepson, Fl. Calif. 2: 277. 1936 • Mariposa lupine [C] [E]

Lupinus deflexus Congdon, Muhlenbergia 1: 38. 1904

Corolla white, pink- or lavender-tinged or not, banner sometimes drying translucent, yellow.

Flowering spring (Apr–May). Granitic soils; of conservation concern; 400–600 m; Calif.

Variety *deflexus*, like var. *citrinus*, is known from the central Sierra Nevada Foothills but in Mariposa County.

7. Lupinus concinnus J. Agardh, Syn. Lupini, 6, plate 1, fig. 1. 1835 • Bajada lupine

Lupinus agardhianus A. Heller; *L. concinnus* var. *agardhianus* (A. Heller) C. P. Smith; *L. concinnus* var. *desertorum* (A. Heller) C. P. Smith; *L. concinnus* subsp. *optatus* (C. P. Smith) D. B. Dunn; *L. concinnus* var. *optatus* C. P. Smith; *L. concinnus* subsp. *orcuttii* (S. Watson) D. B. Dunn; *L. concinnus* var. *orcuttii* (S. Watson) C. P. Smith; *L. concinnus* var. *pallidus* (Brandegee) C. P. Smith; *L. pallidus* Brandegee

Herbs, annual, 1–3 dm, spreading-pubescent. **Cotyledons** deciduous, petiolate. **Stems** ascending, tufted, or erect, branched or unbranched. **Leaves** cauline; petiole 2–7 cm, spreading-pubescent; leaflets 5–9, blades 10–30 × 1.5–8 mm, surfaces pubescent. **Peduncles** erect, 2–8 cm; bracts persistent, straight, 2.5–4 mm. **Racemes** 1–18 cm; flowers spirally arranged, solitary axillary flowers also sometimes present. **Pedicels** 0.7–2 mm. **Flowers** 5–12 mm; calyx 3–5 mm, lobes ± equal, abaxial lobe entire, adaxial lobe deeply cleft; corolla usually pink to purple, rarely white, banner spot white or yellowish, keel usually glabrous, rarely with few, minute cilia on lower margins. **Legumes** 1–1.5 cm, pubescent. **Seeds** 3–5. $2n = 48$.

Flowering spring. Open or disturbed areas, often following burns; 0–1600 m; Ariz., Calif., Nev., N.Mex., Tex., Utah; Mexico (Baja California, Baja California Sur, Sonora).

In Texas, *Lupinus concinnus* is known from the trans-Pecos region; in California it is more common in the central and southern areas.

Lupinus concinnus is a highly variable, predominantly self-pollinated complex and the named varieties cannot be consistently segregated. Desert plants with linear, coarsely hairy leaflets and few, minute cilia on lower keel margins (at times recognized as var. *desertorum*) may be confused with *L. sparsiflorus*.

8. Lupinus flavoculatus A. Heller, Muhlenbergia 5: 149, plate 5. 1909 [E]

Lupinus rubens Rydberg var. *flavoculatus* (A. Heller) C. P. Smith

Herbs, annual, 0.5–2 dm, pubescent, hairs more than 1 mm. **Cotyledons** persistent, disclike, sessile. **Stems** short, erect or spreading, branched or unbranched. **Leaves** cauline, crowded near base; stipules well developed; petiole 2–8 cm; leaflets 7–9, blades 10–20 × 5–8 mm, adaxial surface glabrous. **Peduncles** 3–5 (–10 in fruit) cm; bracts persistent, straight, 2–3 mm. **Racemes** elongate, dense, several–many-flowered, 2–12 cm, usually exceeding leaves; flowers spirally arranged. **Pedicels** 1–3 mm. **Flowers** 7–10 mm; calyx abaxial lobe shallowly cleft, 4–5 mm, adaxial lobe deeply cleft, 1–3 mm, less than 1/2 as long as abaxial; corolla bright blue, banner spot yellow, keel blunt, glabrous. **Legumes** not obviously undulate, ovoid, often secund, 0.5–1 cm, adaxial margin not constricted between seeds, thinly pilose to coarsely hirsute. **Seeds** 2–4, ridged.

Flowering spring. Sandy or gravelly desert areas; 600–2300 m; Ariz., Calif., Nev., Utah.

Lupinus flavoculatus is known from the Inyo and White mountains region of California, southern Nevada, Washington County, Utah, and Mohave County, Arizona. It resembles a hairy form of *L. odoratus*.

9. Lupinus guadalupensis Greene, Bull. Calif. Acad. Sci. 1: 184. 1885 • Guadalupe Island lupine [C]

Lupinus moranii Dunkle

Herbs, annual, 2–6 dm, sparsely pubescent. **Cotyledons** deciduous, petiolate. **Stems** erect, usually branched, sometimes unbranched. **Leaves** cauline; petiole 3–7 cm; leaflets 7–9, blades 20–50 × 3–5 mm, adaxial surface sparsely pubescent. **Peduncles** 5–8 cm; bracts deciduous, 8–10 mm. **Racemes** 10–25 cm; flowers usually whorled, sometimes spirally arranged. **Pedicels** 4–5 mm. **Flowers** 10–12 mm; calyx 6–10 mm, lobes ± equal, abaxial lobe entire, adaxial lobe deeply cleft; corolla blue, banner spot white, upper keel margins with few cilia near apex, banner as wide as long or wider. **Legumes** 3–6 × 0.8–1 cm, densely pubescent. **Seeds** 6–8.

Flowering spring. Sandy or gravelly areas; of conservation concern; 0–500 m; Calif.; Mexico (Baja California).

Lupinus guadalupensis is known from San Clemente Island in California and Guadalupe Island in Mexico. It intergrades with *L. nanus*.

10. Lupinus havardii S. Watson, Proc. Amer. Acad. Arts 17: 369. 1882 (as havardi)

Herbs, annual, 1–6 dm, ascending- or appressed-villous. **Cotyledons** usually persistent, usually inconspicuous, petiolate. **Stems** ascending or erect, usually branched, sometimes unbranched. **Leaves** cauline, often crowded near base; petiole 2–9 cm, ascending- or appressed-pubescent; leaflets (5 or)7, blades 10–20 × 5–10 mm, adaxial surface glabrate. **Peduncles** 5.5–

10 cm; bracts deciduous, 4–5 mm. **Racemes** 18–45 cm; flowers well spaced, usually spirally arranged. **Pedicels** 5–7 mm. **Flowers** 10–13(–15) mm; calyx 6–7 mm, abaxial lobe entire, 6 mm, adaxial lobe 3-cleft, 4 mm; corolla bright violet-blue, banner spot creamy or yellow, keel glabrous. **Legumes** 3.5–5 cm, villous. **Seeds** 6–8. **2*n*** = 36.

Flowering late winter–early spring. Limestone or igneous basins, flats, drainages, gravelly, sandy or silty soils, creosote-lechuguilla shrublands, roadsides; 600–1400 m; Tex.; Mexico (Chihuahua).

Lupinus havardii is known from the trans-Pecos region of Texas.

11. Lupinus hirsutissimus Bentham, Trans. Hort. Soc. London, ser. 2, 1: 411. 1835 • Stinging lupine

Herbs, annual, 2–10 dm, with short, appressed, stiff, pustulate, stinging hairs to 3.5 mm. **Cotyledons** deciduous, petiolate. **Stems** ascending or erect, branched or unbranched. **Leaves** cauline; petiole 4–9 cm; leaflets 5–8, blades 20–50 × 10–20 mm, adaxial surface hirsute. **Peduncles** 5–8 cm; bracts usually persistent, 4–5 mm. **Racemes** 15–40 cm; flowers spirally arranged. **Pedicels** 2–5 mm. **Flowers** 12–18 mm; calyx 6–10 mm, lobes ± equal, abaxial lobe entire, adaxial lobe deeply cleft; corolla deep pink to magenta, drying purplish, banner spot white becoming magenta, lower keel margins densely ciliate from middle to near claw. **Legumes** 2–4 cm, coarsely hairy. **Seeds** 3–6.

Flowering spring. Dry, rocky areas, burns; 0–1400 m; Calif.; Mexico (Baja California).

Lupinus hirsutissimus occurs in the central and southern coast regions into the adjacent mountains and Channel Islands.

Plants are often greater than one meter in height after fires.

12. Lupinus kingii S. Watson, Proc. Amer. Acad. Arts 8: 534. 1873 [E] [F]

Lupinus argillaceus Wooton & Standley; *L. capitatus* Greene; *L. kingii* var. *argillaceus* (Wooton & Standley) C. P. Smith; *L. sileri* S. Watson

Herbs, annual, 1–2.5(–4) dm, pilose, hairs soft, flexuous, more than 1 mm. **Cotyledons** persistent on young plants, becoming dry and deciduous, sessile. **Stems** ascending or erect, usually branched, sometimes unbranched. **Leaves** cauline; stipules well developed; petiole 1.3–3.3 cm; leaflets (3 or)4–7, blades 7–20(–24) × 3–5 mm, adaxial surface pubescent. **Peduncles** (1–)3–6 cm; bracts persistent, 3–4 mm. **Racemes** dense, several-flowered, 1–3 cm; flowers spirally arranged. **Pedicels** 0.8–2 mm. **Flowers** 5–9 mm; calyx 7–8 mm, adaxial lobe more than ½ as long as abaxial; corolla usually blue with pale banner patch, sometimes entirely white, keel glabrous. **Legumes** not obviously undulate, 0.9–1.3 cm, sparsely or densely pilose. **Seeds** 2.

Flowering late spring–summer (late May–Aug). Dry open places in ponderosa pine forests, pine-oak transition and upper edge of pinyon-juniper woodland; 1200–3000 m; Ariz., Colo., Nev., N.Mex., Utah, Wyo.

13. Lupinus luteolus Kellogg, Proc. Calif. Acad. Sci. 5: 38. 1873 • Butter lupine [E]

Lupinus luteolus var. *albiflorus* Eastwood; *L. milobakeri* C. P. Smith

Herbs, annual, 3–16(–20) dm, sparsely pubescent or glabrate, appearing glaucous. **Cotyledons** persistent or deciduous, disclike (leaving a circular scar), sessile. **Stems** ascending or erect, branched near middle or unbranched. **Leaves** cauline; petiole 2–5 cm; leaflets 7–9, blades 10–30 × 4–9 mm, adaxial surface usually pubescent. **Peduncles** 4–15 cm; bracts persistent, reflexed, 5–11 mm, pubescent. **Racemes** 9–35 cm; flowers in crowded whorls. **Pedicels** 1–3 mm. **Flowers** 10–16 mm; calyx appendages usually absent, abaxial lobe entire, 6–10 mm, adaxial lobe entire, 3–5 mm; corolla usually pale yellow, sometimes pinkish or bright blue, lower wing margins rarely ciliate, upper margins ciliate near claw, lower and upper keel margins densely ciliate near claw. **Legumes** 1–1.5 cm, pubescent. **Seeds** 2, dark brown, tuberculate.

Flowering spring–early summer. Clearings, open or disturbed areas; 0–1900 m; Calif., Oreg.

Lupinus luteolus is known primarily from the North Coast area in California, with isolated collections from the Diablo Range and Western Transverse Ranges. It is known from Oregon in Douglas, Jackson, and Klamath counties.

Lupinus luteolus from Siskiyou County in California to the Klamath Range of southern Oregon and northern California often (in about 50% of specimens) has leaflets that are glabrous adaxially. Plants from Round Valley, Mendocino County, are unusually tall and sometimes have flowers blue at anthesis; they are sometimes recognized as *L. milobakeri.*

14. Lupinus malacophyllus Greene, Pittonia 1: 215. 1888 [C] [E]

Herbs, annual, 0.7–1.6 dm, softly villous, with fine, spreading hairs, hairs more than 1 mm. **Cotyledons** persistent or deciduous, disclike, sessile, leaving a circular scar. **Stems** ascending or erect, branched or unbranched. **Leaves** basal and cauline; stipules well developed; petiole 1.5–4.5 cm; leaflets 5–7, blades 7–22 × 3–6 mm, adaxial surface softly villous. **Peduncles** 2–5.5 cm; bracts persistent, 5–7 mm. **Racemes** well exserted, several–many-flowered, 3–7 cm; flowers crowded, whorled proximally, becoming spirally arranged distally. **Pedicels** 2–4 mm. **Flowers** 8–10 mm; calyx 5–8 mm, lobes unequal, adaxial lobe less than 1/2 as long as abaxial; corolla blue or whitish and blue-tipped, keel glabrous. **Legumes** not obviously undulate, 1–1.3 cm, softly villous-pilose. **Seeds** 2.

Flowering spring–early summer (mid Apr–Jun). Colonial in openings among sagebrush on sandy or gravelly flats and foothill slopes; of conservation concern; 1400–1800 m; Nev.

Lupinus malacophyllus is known from Washoe and adjacent counties.

15. Lupinus microcarpus Sims, Bot. Mag. 50: plate 2413. 1823 • Chick lupine [F]

Herbs, annual, 1–8 dm, sparsely to densely pubescent. **Cotyledons** persistent or deciduous (leaving circular scar), disclike, sessile. **Stems** ascending or erect, branched near base or middle, or unbranched, hollow, at least near base. **Leaves** cauline; petiole 3–15 cm; leaflets 5–9(–11), blades 10–50 × 2–12 mm, adaxial surface glabrous. **Peduncles** 2–30 cm; bracts persistent, reflexed, 3.5–12 mm. **Racemes** 4–60 cm; flowers in crowded to widely spaced whorls. **Pedicels** 0.5–5 mm. **Flowers** 8–18 mm; calyx appendages usually absent, sometimes present, abaxial lobe 5–11 mm, adaxial lobe 2–6 mm; corolla white to dark yellow, pink to dark rose, or lavender to purple, lower wing margins sometimes ciliate, upper margins usually ciliate near claw, upper keel margins usually ciliate near claw, lower margins sometimes ciliate but not as densely. **Legumes** 1–1.8 cm, pubescent. **Seeds** 2, tan to brown, usually mottled, ridged or smooth.

Varieties 3 (3 in the flora): w North America, nw Mexico, South America.

Lupinus microcarpus is highly variable and with varieties intergrading.

1. Wings broadly elliptic, persistent and becoming translucent, upper and usually lower margins ciliate near claw; lower keel margins ciliate near claw; calyx appendages 1–2 mm . . . . 15c. *Lupinus microcarpus* var. *horizontalis*
1. Wings linear to oblanceolate, withering, not becoming translucent, upper margins usually ciliate near claw, lower rarely; lower keel margins sometimes ciliate near claw or sparsely so; calyx appendages usually absent.
   2. Calyx and flower bracts with long shaggy hairs; legumes usually erect or spreading . . . . 15a. *Lupinus microcarpus* var. *microcarpus*
   2. Calyx and flower bracts with few short and appressed, or long and spreading hairs; legumes usually secund, sometimes spreading . . . . 15b. *Lupinus microcarpus* var. *densiflorus*

15a. Lupinus microcarpus Sims var. **microcarpus** [F]

Lupinus densiflorus Bentham subsp. *austrocollium* (C. P. Smith) D. B. Dunn; *L. densiflorus* var. *austrocollium* C. P. Smith; *L. densiflorus* var. *crinitus* Eastwood ex C. P. Smith; *L. densiflorus* var. *palustris* (Kellogg) C. P. Smith; *L. densiflorus* var. *persecundus* C. P. Smith; *L. microcarpus* var. *ruber* (A. Heller) C. P. Smith; *L. microcarpus* var. *scopulorum* (C. P. Smith) C. P. Smith; *L. ruber* A. Heller; *L. subvexus* C. P. Smith; *L. subvexus* var. *albilanatus* C. P. Smith; *L. subvexus* var. *fluviatilis* C. P. Smith; *L. subvexus* var. *phoeniceus* C. P. Smith; *L. subvexus* var. *transmontanus* C. P. Smith

Bracts with long, shaggy hairs. **Calyces** with long, shaggy hairs; appendages usually absent. **Corolla** pink to rose, or lavender to purple, rarely yellowish or white; wings withering, linear to lanceolate, lower margins rarely ciliate, upper margins ciliate near claw; lower keel margins sometimes ciliate near claw. **Legumes** usually erect or spreading. $2n = 48$.

Flowering late spring–summer. Open or disturbed areas; 0–1600 m; B.C.; Ariz., Calif., Nev., Oreg., Wash.; Mexico (Baja California); South America (Argentina, Chile).

Variety *microcarpus* is introduced in Arizona (Gila County).

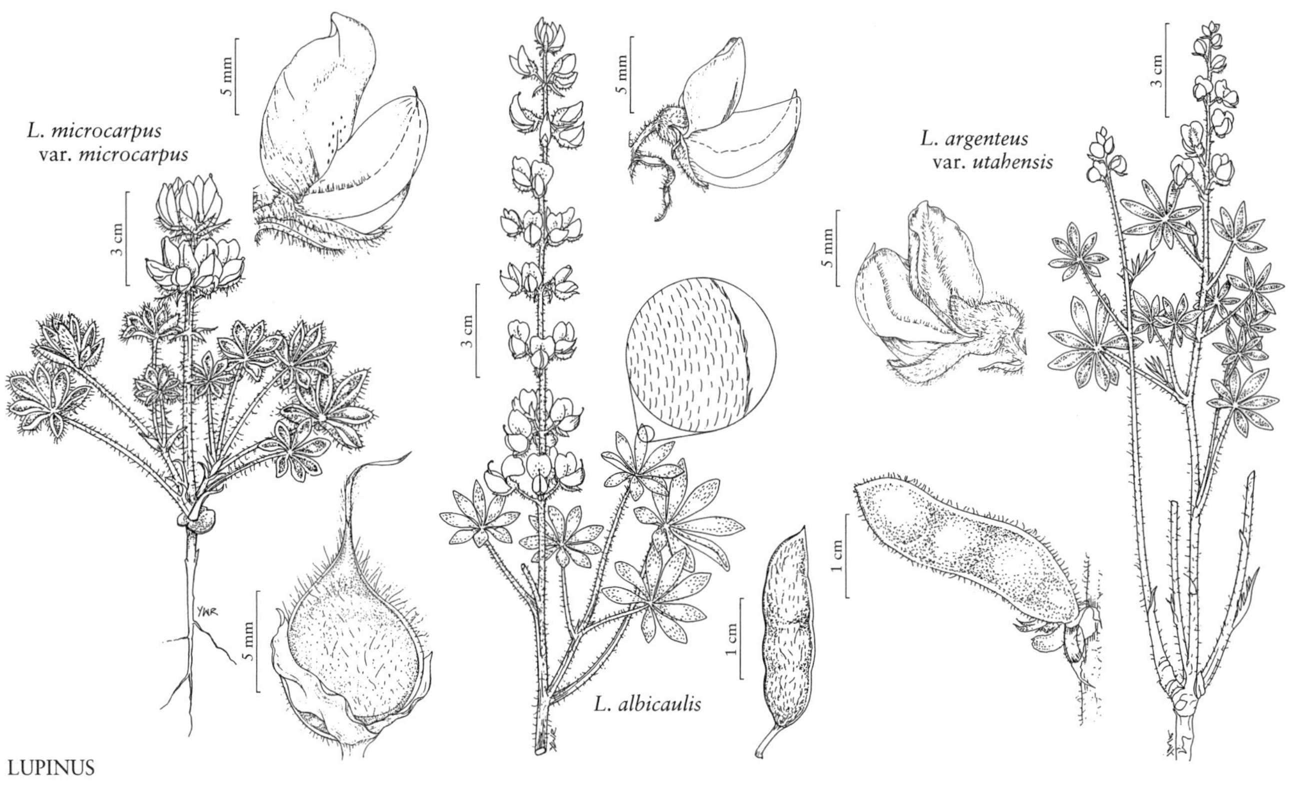

LUPINUS

15b. Lupinus microcarpus Sims var. **densiflorus** (Bentham) Jepson, Fl. Calif. 2: 279. 1936

Lupinus densiflorus Bentham, Trans. Hort. Soc. London, ser. 2, 1: 410. 1835; *L. densiflorus* var. *aureus* (Kellogg) Munz; *L. densiflorus* subsp. *lacteus* (Kellogg) R. M. Beauchamp; *L. densiflorus* var. *lacteus* (Kellogg) C. P. Smith; *L. densiflorus* var. *menziesii* (J. Agardh) C. P. Smith; *L. densiflorus* var. *versabilis* C. P. Smith

Bracts with short-appressed to long-spreading hairs. **Calyces** with sparsely appressed to spreading hairs; appendages usually absent. **Corolla** usually white to yellow, sometimes tinged pink or lavender, rarely rose or purple; wings withering, oblanceolate, lower margins rarely ciliate near claw, upper margins usually ciliate near claw; lower keel margins sometimes sparsely ciliate near claw. **Legumes** usually secund, sometimes spreading. **2*n*** = 48.

Flowering late spring. Open or disturbed areas, grasslands, roadbanks; 0–1600 m; Ariz., Calif.; Mexico (Baja California).

Variety *densiflorus* occurs widely in western and central California and is apparently localized in mountainous areas of Gila County, Arizona.

15c. Lupinus microcarpus Sims var. **horizontalis** (A. Heller) Jepson, Fl. Calif. 2: 280. 1936 [E]

Lupinus horizontalis A. Heller, Muhlenbergia 2: 74. 1905; *L. arenicola* A. Heller; *L. densiflorus* Bentham var. *glareosus* (Elmer) C. P. Smith; *L. horizontalis* var. *platypetalus* C. P. Smith

Bracts with short to long, spreading hairs. **Calyces** with appressed to spreading hairs; appendages usually purplish, 1–2 mm. **Corolla** lavender to purple, becoming translucent; wings persistent, broadly elliptic, lower and upper margins ciliate near claw; lower keel margins ciliate near claw. **Legumes** erect or spreading. **2*n*** = 48.

Flowering late spring. Desert washes, sandy or gravelly areas; 100–1700 m; Calif.

Variety *horizontalis* occurs in desert regions east of Inner South Coast Ranges (the western side of San Joaquin Valley) and the eastern Mojave Desert.

16. Lupinus nanus Douglas ex Bentham, Trans. Hort. Soc. London, ser. 2, 1: 409, plate 14, fig. 2. 1835 [E]

Lupinus blaisdellii Eastwood; *L. nanus* var. *apricus* (Greene) C. P. Smith; *L. nanus* subsp. *latifolius* (Bentham ex Torrey) D. B. Dunn; *L. nanus* var. *maritimus* Hoover; *L. nanus* subsp. *menkerae* (C. P. Smith) D. B. Dunn; *L. nanus* var. *menkerae* C. P. Smith; *L. nanus* var. *vallicola* (A. Heller) C. P. Smith; *L. vallicola* A. Heller; *L. vallicola* var. *apricus* (Greene) C. P. Smith

Herbs, annual, 1–6 dm, pubescent. **Cotyledons** deciduous, petiolate. **Stems** ascending or erect, branched or unbranched. **Leaves** cauline; petiole 2–8.5 cm; leaflets 5–7(–9), blades 10–40 × 1–12 mm, adaxial surface pubescent. **Peduncles** 2–15 cm; bracts deciduous, 4–12 mm. **Racemes** 4–40 cm; flowers usually whorled, sometimes spirally arranged distally. **Pedicels** 2.5–7 mm. **Flowers** 6–15 mm; calyx 4–8 mm, lobes ± equal, adaxial lobe deeply cleft; corolla usually blue, rarely light blue, lavender, pink, white, banner spot white, upper keel margins ciliate near apex, banner as wide as or wider than long. **Legumes** 2–4 × 0.4–0.7 cm, pubescent. **Seeds** 4–12. $2n = 48$.

Flowering late winter–spring. Open or disturbed areas; 0–1300 m; Calif., Oreg., Wash.

Lupinus nanus is a highly variable complex. Plants in northern California and southwestern Oregon, referred to as *L. vallicola*, have smaller flowers and may be confused with *L. bicolor*.

Lupinus nanus occurs throughout California except in the Great Basin and desert regions and northward to Washington.

17. Lupinus nipomensis Eastwood, Leafl. W. Bot. 2: 187. 1939 • Nipomo Mesa lupine [C] [E]

Herbs, annual, 1–2 dm, pubescent. **Cotyledons** deciduous, petiolate. **Stems** decumbent, branched. **Leaves** cauline; petiole 2–3 cm; leaflets 5–7, blades 10–15 × 5–6 mm, adaxial surface pubescent. **Peduncles:** primary peduncles and lateral branches decumbent, 2–3.5 cm; bracts usually persistent, 3–3.5 mm. **Racemes** dense, 3–9 cm; flowers spirally arranged, axillary flowers absent. **Pedicels** 1–1.5 mm. **Flowers** 6–7 mm; calyx 4–5.5 mm, lobes ± equal, adaxial lobe deeply cleft; corolla pink, banner spot white or yellowish, keel glabrous. **Legumes** 1.5–2 cm, pubescent or glabrate. **Seeds** 3 or 4.

Flowering winter–spring. Stabilized sand dunes; of conservation concern; 0–30 m; Calif.

Lupinus nipomensis is known only from the Guadalupe-Nipomo Dunes of southwestern San Luis Obispo County in the Central Coast, where it intergrades with *L. concinnus*.

Lupinus nipomensis is in the Center for Plant Conservation's National Collection of Endangered Plants.

18. Lupinus odoratus A. Heller, Muhlenbergia 2: 71. 1905 • Mohave lupine [E]

Lupinus odoratus var. *pilosellus* C. P. Smith

Herbs, annual, 1–3 dm, usually glabrous, sometimes sparsely pubescent when young, rarely at anthesis, hairs less than 0.5 mm. **Cotyledons** persistent, disclike, sessile. **Stems** basally branched or unbranched. **Leaves** basal; petiole 2–12 cm; leaflets 5–9, blades bright green, 8–24 × 3–10 mm, adaxial surface glabrous. **Peduncles** hollow, 6–15 cm; bracts persistent, straight, 2–4 mm, tips sparsely ciliate. **Racemes** 4–25 cm; flowers spirally arranged. **Pedicels** 3–7 mm. **Flowers** 7–10 mm; calyx lobes sometimes ciliate at tips, abaxial lobe entire, 4–5 mm, adaxial lobe rounded or shallowly 2-toothed, 3–3.5 mm; corolla deep blue-purple, banner spot white or yellow becoming magenta, keel glabrous. **Legumes** 1.5–2.5 cm, adaxial suture undulate and ciliate with long dense hairs, sides with a few short hairs becoming scaly on drying. **Seeds** 2–6, ridged.

Flowering spring. Creosote bush scrub, Joshua tree woodland, sandy desert flats, open areas; 500–1600 m; Ariz., Calif., Nev.

The fresh flowers of *Lupinus odoratus* smell like violets. Pilose plants can be confused with *L. flavoculatus*.

Lupinus odoratus occurs in the Mojave Desert region of California, northward to Inyo and Mono counties, and eastward into southern Nevada and Mohave County, Arizona.

The name *Lupinus odoratus* A. Heller is to be proposed for conservation against *L. odoratus* F. Dietrich (1836), a likely synonym of *L. nanus*.

19. Lupinus pachylobus Greene, Pittonia 1: 65. 1887 • Big pod lupine [E]

Herbs, annual, 1.5–4 dm, pubescent. **Cotyledons** deciduous, petiolate. **Stems** ascending or erect, branched or unbranched. **Leaves** cauline; petiole 4–8 cm; leaflets usually 7, blades 20–25 × 2–5 mm, adaxial surface pubescent. **Peduncles** 3–12 cm; bracts deciduous, 6 mm. **Racemes** 4–15 cm; flowers usually whorled, sometimes spirally arranged. **Pedicels** 1–2.5 mm. **Flowers** 7–9 mm; calyx 4.5–6 mm, lobes ± equal, abaxial lobe entire, adaxial lobe cleft; corolla blue, banner spot white, becoming dark magenta, keel blunt, glabrous, banner length greater than width. **Legumes** ± fleshy, 3 × 0.6–0.9 cm, densely pubescent. **Seeds** usually 5.

Flowering spring. Open or disturbed areas; 0–600 m; Calif., Wash.

In California, *Lupinus pachylobus* occurs from the foothills of the Cascade Range and Sierra Nevada to the outer North and South Coast ranges. In Washington, it is known from the San Juan Islands. It is uncommon and occurs and intergrades with *L. bicolor.*

20. Lupinus pusillus Pursh, Fl. Amer. Sept. 2: 468. 1814[1813] [E]

Herbs, annual, 0.5–2 dm, sparsely pubescent to pilose, hairs more than 1 mm. **Cotyledons** persistent, disclike, sessile. **Stems** short and tufted or erect, branched from base or near middle. **Leaves** cauline, often crowded near base; stipules well developed; petiole 1–9 cm; leaflets 5–9, blades 10–40 × 5–10 mm, adaxial surface glabrous. **Peduncles** 0–3.5 cm; bracts persistent, straight, 2–5 mm. **Racemes** 8–12-flowered, 2–11 cm, shorter than or slightly exceeding foliage; flowers spirally arranged. **Pedicels** 1–3.5 mm. **Flowers** 5–12 mm; calyx abaxial lobe entire, 5–6 mm, adaxial lobe cleft, 2.5–4 mm; corolla vivid blue, sometimes paler or white, sometimes bicolored, banner spot white or yellowish, keel glabrous. **Legumes** 1.5 cm, constricted between seeds, thinly pilose to coarsely hirsute. **Seeds** 2, wrinkled or ridged.

Varieties 3 (3 in the flora): c, w North America.

Lupinus pusillus is a highly variable species, with the varieties intergrading.

1. Peduncles 0–1 cm; racemes shorter than foliage; flowers 6–8 mm . . . . 20b. *Lupinus pusillus* var. *intermontanus*
1. Peduncles usually 1–3.5 cm; racemes equal to or longer than foliage; flowers 7–12 mm.
   2. Pedicels and calyx tubes strigose . . . . 20a. *Lupinus pusillus* var. *pusillus*
   2. Pedicels and calyx tubes glabrous . . . . 20c. *Lupinus pusillus* var. *rubens*

20a. Lupinus pusillus Pursh var. **pusillus** [E]

Peduncles usually 1–3.5 cm. **Racemes** 2–11 cm, equal to or longer than foliage. **Pedicels** strigose. **Flowers** 7–12 mm, relatively large; calyx tube strigose. **2*n*** = 48.

Flowering spring–early summer. Open, sandy areas; 800–2100 m; Alta., Sask.; Ariz., Colo., Kans., Mont., Nebr., N.Mex., Okla., Utah, Wyo.

In Arizona, var. *pusillus* is known across the northern part of the state where it may be locally common.

20b. Lupinus pusillus Pursh var. **intermontanus** (A. Heller) C. P. Smith, Bull. Torrey Bot. Club 46: 408. 1919 [E]

Lupinus intermontanus A. Heller, Muhlenbergia 8: 87, plate 12. 1912; *L. pusillus* var. *intermontanus* (A. Heller) C. P. Smith; *L. pusillus* subsp. *intermontanus* (A. Heller) D. B. Dunn

Peduncles 0–1 cm. **Racemes** 2–5 cm, usually shorter than foliage. **Pedicels** strigose. **Flowers** 6–8 mm; calyx tube strigose.

Flowering spring—early summer. Open sandy areas; 1100–1800 m; Calif., Idaho, Nev., Oreg., Wash., Wyo.

20c. Lupinus pusillus Pursh var. **rubens** (Rydberg) S. L. Welsh, Great Basin Naturalist 38: 331. 1978 [E]

Lupinus rubens Rydberg, Bull. Torrey Bot. Club 34: 45. 1907; *Lupinus odoratus* A. Heller var. *rubens* (Rydberg) Jepson; *L. pusillus* subsp. *rubens* (Rydberg) D. B. Dunn

Peduncles usually 1–3.5 cm. **Racemes** 2–11 cm, equal to or longer than foliage. **Pedicels** glabrous. **Flowers** 7–12 mm, relative large; calyx tube glabrous.

Flowering spring–early summer. Open, sandy areas; 700–1800 m; Ariz., Nev., Utah.

21. Lupinus shockleyi S. Watson, Proc. Amer. Acad. Arts 22: 470. 1887 • Desert lupine [E]

Herbs, annual, 0.4–3 dm, canescent, hairs 0.6–1 mm. **Cotyledons** persistent, disclike, sessile. **Stems** erect or ascending, very short, tufted or spreading, branched. **Leaves** cauline, crowded near base; stipules well developed; petiole 2–9 cm; leaflets 7–11, blades 10–30 × 4–10 mm, adaxial surface glabrous. **Peduncles** 1–10 cm; bracts persistent, straight, 2–4 mm. **Racemes** several–many-flowered, 3–14 cm; flowers spirally arranged. **Pedicels** 1–4 mm. **Flowers** 4.5–7 mm; calyx 3–6 mm, lobes ± equal, abaxial lobe entire, adaxial lobe cleft; corolla dark blue-purple or whitish with blue tip, banner spot white becoming yellow, keel blunt, glabrous. **Legumes** undulate, 1.5–2 cm, not constricted between seeds, ciliate with long, dense hairs, sides with short, inflated hairs becoming scaly on drying. **Seeds** 2, wrinkled.

Flowering spring (Apr–Jun). Dunes, sandy areas, washes, playas; 0–1500 m; Ariz., Calif., Nev.

Lupinus shockleyi occurs in the desert areas of southern California, adjacent areas of southern Nevada, and northwestern Arizona.

22. Lupinus sparsiflorus Bentham, Pl. Hartw., 303. 1849 • Coulter's lupine

Lupinus pondii Greene; *L. sparsiflorus* subsp. *inopinatus* (C. P. Smith) Dziekanowski & D. B. Dunn; *L. sparsiflorus* var. *inopinatus* C. P. Smith; *L. sparsiflorus* subsp. *mohavensis* Dziekanowski & D. B. Dunn; *L. sparsiflorus* var. *mohavensis* (Dziekanowski & D. B. Dunn) S. L. Welsh; *L. sparsiflorus* var. *pondii* (Greene) C. P. Smith

Herbs, annual, 1.5–4 dm, strigose, hairs short and appressed, also pilose, hairs long and spreading. **Cotyledons** deciduous, petiolate. **Stems** ascending or erect, branched or unbranched. **Leaves** cauline; petiole (1–)3–7 cm; leaflets (5–)7–11, blades (7–)15–30(–45) × 2–5 mm, adaxial surface glabrous or pubescent, at least marginally. **Peduncles** 2–4 cm; bracts usually deciduous, 3–5 mm, shorter than buds. **Racemes** 10–25 cm; flowers spirally arranged. **Pedicels** 2–5 mm. **Flowers** 10–12(–13) mm; calyx 3–6 mm, lobes ± equal, abaxial lobe entire, adaxial lobe deeply cleft; corolla usually blue, rarely pinkish, drying darker, banner spot whitish becoming magenta, lower keel margins ciliate near claw, upper margins often ciliate near claw. **Legumes** 1–2 cm, coarsely pubescent. **Seeds** 4 or 5.

Flowering spring (Mar–May). Washes, sandy areas, chaparral, grasslands, coastal sage scrub, Joshua tree/mesquite woodlands, creosote bush scrub; 0–1500 m; Ariz., Calif., Nev., Utah; Mexico (Baja California, Baja California Sur, Sonora).

Plants from the Mojave Desert often have smaller flowers and have been named subsp. *mohavensis*, and those from western San Diego County with pinkish flowers and truncate leaflets have been named var. *inopinatus*.

23. Lupinus spectabilis Hoover, Leafl. W. Bot. 2: 131. 1938 • Shaggyhair lupine [C] [E]

Lupinus nanus Douglas ex Bentham var. *perlasius* C. P. Smith

Herbs, annual, 2–6 dm, densely hairy, hairs to 3.5 mm. **Cotyledons** deciduous, petiolate. **Stems** erect, branched or unbranched. **Leaves** cauline; petiole 4–9 cm; leaflets usually 9, blades 10–40 × 4–9 mm, adaxial surface villous to pilose. **Peduncles** 5–12 cm; bracts usually deciduous, 8–9 mm. **Racemes** 10–40 cm; flowers whorled. **Pedicels** 6–8 mm. **Flowers** 11–17 mm; calyx 4–7 mm, lobes ± equal, abaxial lobe entire, adaxial lobe cleft; corolla usually blue, rarely white, banner spot white, upper keel margins ciliate near apex, banner as wide as or wider than long. **Legumes** 3–5 × 0.8–1 cm, densely pubescent. **Seeds** 5–10.

Flowering spring (Apr–May). Serpentine outcrops, chaparral, foothill woodlands; of conservation concern; 200–900 m; Calif.

Lupinus spectabilis is known from the central Sierra Nevada foothills in Mariposa and Tuolumne counties; it intergrades with *L. nanus*.

24. Lupinus stiversii Kellogg, Proc. Calif. Acad. Sci. 2: 192, fig. 58. 1863 (as stiverii) • Harlequin lupine [E]

Herbs, annual, 1–5 dm, sparsely pubescent. **Cotyledons** deciduous, petiolate. **Stems** ascending or erect, branched near middle. **Leaves** cauline; petioles 2–8 cm; leaflets usually 7, blades bright green, 20–50 × 5–15 mm, adaxial surface sparsely pubescent. **Peduncles** 8–18 cm; bracts tardily deciduous, 3–5 mm. **Racemes** dense, 5–10 cm; flowers spirally arranged. **Pedicels** 1.5–4 mm. **Flowers** 13–18 mm; calyx abaxial lobe entire, 5–7 mm, adaxial lobe deeply cleft, 4–6 mm; corolla banner yellow, wings usually pink, rarely white, keel white, lower and upper margins ciliate from claw to middle. **Legumes** 2 cm, glabrous or glabrate. **Seeds** usually 5.

Flowering late spring (Apr–Jul). Clearings, open areas, chaparral, oak woodlands, yellow pine forest; 100–2200 m; Calif.

Lupinus stiversii is found in the Sierra Nevada, the northern portion of Southern Coast Ranges (Monterey County), the San Gabriel Mountains, and the San Bernardino Mountains.

25. Lupinus subcarnosus Hooker, Bot. Mag. 63: plate 3467. 1836 • Texas bluebonnet

Herbs, annual, 1.5–4 dm, pubescent, hairs appressed or ascending. **Cotyledons** usually persistent, petiolate. **Stems** ascending or erect, branched. **Leaves** cauline, often crowded near base; petiole 1–6 cm; leaflets 5 or 6, blades 10–25 × 4–15 mm, adaxial surface glabrate. **Peduncles** 3–8 cm; bracts deciduous, 2.5–3 mm. **Racemes** 6–12 cm; flowers crowded or spaced, spirally arranged, crowded on young growth. **Pedicels** 3–7 mm. **Flowers** 9–12 mm; calyx 5–6 mm, abaxial lobe 3-lobed, 3–4 mm, adaxial lobe cleft, 2–2.5 mm, hairs becoming yellowish gray or brown on dried material; corolla pale blue-violet, banner spot white, keel glabrous, wings inflated. **Legumes** 2.5–3.5 cm, yellowish gray- or brown-villous. **Seeds** 4 or 5. $2n = 36$.

Flowering spring. Sandy soils, roadsides, open woodlands, coastal plains; 0–300 m; Tex.; Mexico (Coahuila, Nuevo Léon).

Lupinus subcarnosus is abundant and conspicuous in the coastal plain of southeastern Texas and extends into northern Mexico.

26. Lupinus succulentus Douglas ex K. Koch, Wochenschr. Vereines Beford. Gartenbaues Konigl. Preuss. Staaten 4: 277. 1861 • Arroyo lupine

Lupinus succulentus var. *brandegeei* C. P. Smith; *L. succulentus* var. *layneae* C. P. Smith

Herbs, annual, sometimes persisting more than one season, (1–)2–10 dm, fleshy, sparsely pubescent. **Cotyledons** deciduous, petiolate. **Stems** ascending or erect, branched or unbranched, usually succulent. **Leaves** cauline, may be crowded at base on new growth; petiole 6–15 cm; leaflets 7–9, blades 20–60 × 7–20 mm, adaxial surface glabrous. **Peduncles** 5–9 cm; bracts deciduous, 3–5 mm. **Racemes** 15–25 cm; flowers whorled. **Pedicels** 3–7 mm. **Flowers** 12–18 mm; calyx 4–7 mm, lobes ± equal, abaxial lobe entire, adaxial lobe cleft; corolla usually blue-purple, rarely white, lavender, or pink, banner spot white, becoming magenta, upper wing margins ciliate near claw, lower and upper keel margins ciliate near claw. **Legumes** 3.5–5 cm, coarsely pubescent to tomentose. **Seeds** 6–9. $2n = 48$.

Flowering late winter–late spring (Feb–May). Open or disturbed areas, roadbanks; 0–1300 m; Ariz., Calif.; Mexico (Baja California, Baja California Sur).

Lupinus succulentus occurs widely throughout California except in the Great Basin and desert regions and extends into northern Mexico; it is introduced in Arizona. It may occasionally persist more than one season in Californian North Coast locations.

27. Lupinus texensis Hooker, Bot. Mag. 63: plate 3492. 1836 • Texas bluebonnet

Herbs, annual, 1.5–4 dm, pubescent, hair appressed or ascending. **Cotyledons** deciduous, petiolate. **Stems** ascending or erect, branched. **Leaves** cauline, crowded near base; petiole 2–6 cm; leaflets 5 or 6 (or 7), blades 10–25 × 6–12 mm, adaxial surface glabrous. **Peduncles** 3–6 cm; bracts deciduous, 2–3 mm. **Racemes** 2–12 cm; flowers spirally arranged. **Pedicels** 4–6 mm. **Flowers** 10–13 mm; calyx 6–8 mm, abaxial lobe entire or cleft, 4–5 mm, adaxial lobe cleft, 2–3 mm, hairs silvery; corolla usually dark blue, rarely white, banner spot bright white, keel glabrous, wings flat. **Legumes** 2.5–3.5 cm, white silky-villous. **Seeds** 4 or 5. $2n = 36$.

Flowering spring–summer. Prairies, open fields, pastures, roadsides; 0–600 m; Fla., La., Okla., Tex.; Mexico (Coahuila, Nuevo Léon, Tamaulipas).

Lupinus texensis is introduced in Florida in Alachua and Pinellas counties. In Texas, it is widespread in the southern two-thirds of the state.

28. Lupinus truncatus Nuttall ex Hooker & Arnott, Bot. Beechey Voy., 336. 1838

Herbs, annual, 2–5(–8) dm, finely pubescent, appearing glabrous. **Cotyledons** deciduous, petiolate. **Stems** ascending or erect, branched or unbranched. **Leaves** cauline; petiole flattened and leafletlike, 3–10 cm; leaflets 5–8, blades 20–40 × 2–5 mm, apex usually truncate, adaxial surface glabrous. **Peduncles** 3–10 cm; bracts persistent, 2–5 mm. **Racemes** 6–35 cm; flowers loosely spirally arranged. **Pedicels** 2–4 mm. **Flowers** 8–13 mm; calyx 3–4 mm, lobes ± equal, abaxial lobe entire or shallowly cleft, 2.5–3 mm, adaxial lobe deeply cleft, 1.5–2 mm; corolla banner and wings magenta, banner spot white or yellowish, becoming dark magenta, keel stout, blunt, lower and upper margins ciliate from claw to middle. **Legumes** ±3 cm, pubescent. **Seeds** 6–8.

Flowering spring (Mar–May). Openings in coastal sage scrub, chaparral, oak woodlands, burned areas; 0–1200 m; Calif.; Mexico (Baja California).

Lupinus truncatus is known in the flora area from San Cruz County southward in the Central and South Coast regions; the South Coast, Transverse, and Peninsular ranges; and the Channel Islands.

29. Lupinus uncialis S. Watson, Botany (Fortieth Parallel), 54, plate 7, figs. 5–10. 1871 [E]

Lupinus uncialis var. *cryptanthus* Eastwood

Herbs, annual, 0.1–0.2 dm, pilose. **Cotyledons** persistent, disclike, sessile. **Stems** very short, densely tufted, branched. **Leaves** cauline, densely tufted or crowded near base; free blades of stipules reduced, 1 mm; petiole 0.4–1.5 cm; leaflets (3 or)5, blades 2–7 × 1–1.5 mm, adaxial surface villous. **Peduncles** 1.5–4 mm; bracts persistent, 1 mm. **Racemes:** flowers solitary or paired, axillary. **Pedicels** 1 mm. **Flowers** 4–5 mm; calyx 2.5–3 mm, abaxial lobe shallowly cleft, 2–2.5 mm, adaxial lobe 2-toothed, 0.5–1 mm; corolla banner white, wings and keel purplish, keel glabrous. **Legumes** 0.6–1 cm, pilose. **Seeds** 1 or 2.

Flowering spring (May–Jun). Open areas, barrens, talus in sagebrush and pinyon-juniper woodlands, on limestone, rhyolite, volcanic ash and sinter around hot springs; 1400–2400 m; Calif., Idaho, Nev., Oreg.

Lupinus uncialis occurs in the Great Basin of Nevada and extends into California, Idaho, and Oregon.

30. Lupinus adsurgens Drew, Bull. Torrey Bot. Club 16: 150. 1889 [E]

Lupinus adsurgens var. *lilacinus* A. Heller ex C. P. Smith; *L. adsurgens* var. *undulatus* C. P. Smith; *L. alcis-montis* C. P. Smith; *L. aliceae* C. P. Smith; *L. arvensiplasketti* C. P. Smith; *L. brandegeei* Eastwood; *L. debilis* Eastwood; *L. klamathensis* Eastwood; *L. lilacinus* A. Heller; *L. pendeltonii* A. Heller

Herbs, perennial, 2–6 dm, hairy, silver to dull green. **Cotyledons** deciduous, petiolate. **Stems** decumbent, ascending, or erect, unbranched or branched. **Leaves** cauline; stipules not leaflike, green to silvery, 5–17 mm; petiole 2–6 cm; leaflets 6–9, blades 20–50 × 3–7 mm, widest above middle, adaxial surface pubescent, appressed-hairy to ± silky or dull green. **Peduncles** 2–8 cm; bracts deciduous, 2–8 mm. **Racemes** 2–23 cm; flowers spirally arranged to subwhorled. **Pedicels** 2–6 mm. **Flowers** 9–12 mm; calyx bulge or spur 0–1 mm, abaxial lobe entire or minutely 3-toothed, 3–7 mm, adaxial lobe 2-toothed, 4–6.5 mm; corolla pale yellowish to lavender or violet, banner patch yellow to white, banner glabrous abaxially, keel upcurved, glabrous, banner ovate, wings wide, covering keel tip. **Legumes** 2–4 cm, silky. **Seeds** 3–6, mottled brown, 4–6 mm. **2*n*** = 48.

Flowering May–Jul. Dry slopes, montane forests; 500–3500 m; Calif., Oreg.

Lupinus adsurgens is found in the San Francisco Bay region and North Coast Ranges of California, north to southern Oregon (Josephine County), and throughout the Sierra Nevada.

All parts of *Lupinus adsurgens* are toxic, causing crooked neck disease in cattle (A. M. Davis 1982).

31. Lupinus albicaulis Douglas in W. J. Hooker, Fl. Bor.-Amer. 1: 165. 1832 [E] [F]

Lupinus albicaulis var. *bridgesii* S. Watson; *L. albicaulis* var. *shastensis* (A. Heller) C. P. Smith; *L. formosus* Greene var. *bridgesii* (S. Watson) Greene; *L. gormanii* Piper; *L. ochroleucus* Eastwood; *L. pumicola* A. Heller; *L. purpurascens* A. Heller; *L. shastensis* A. Heller; *L. whiltoniae* Eastwood; *L. wolfianus* C. P. Smith

Herbs, perennial, 3–12 dm, puberulent to silky-appressed. **Cotyledons** deciduous, petiolate. **Stems** ascending-erect, clustered, branched. **Leaves** cauline; stipules not leaflike, green to silvery, 5–18 mm; petiole 2–7 cm; leaflets 5–10, blades 20–70 × 5–14 mm, adaxial surface pubescent. **Peduncles** 2–12 cm; bracts deciduous, 6–16 mm. **Racemes** open, 10–44 cm; flowers usually whorled. **Pedicels** 2–7 mm. **Flowers** (8–)12–16 mm; calyx bulge or spur 0–1 mm, abaxial lobe entire or 3-toothed, 7–13 mm, adaxial lobe 2-toothed, 6–12 mm; corolla usually purple, rarely yellowish white, banner patch indistinct, banner glabrous abaxially, keel strongly upcurved, glabrous, banner and wings narrow, not covering tip. **Legumes** 2–5 cm, silky. **Seeds** 3–7, gray to tan, mottled tan, 4–7 mm. **2*n*** = 48.

Flowering May–Jul. Dry slopes, sandy prairies, openings of mixed conifer forests, ± montane; 500–3000 m; Calif., Oreg., Wash.

Lupinus albicaulis ranges from the Cascades in western Oregon and Washington, and in California from the northern North Coast Ranges to the western slope of the Sierra Nevada and southward into the Western Transverse Ranges. Plants with flowers 8–11 mm have been called var. *shastensis*.

32. Lupinus albifrons Bentham, Edwards's Bot. Reg. 19: plate 1642. 1834

Subshrubs or shrubs, rarely perennial herbs, (1–)2–50 dm, usually silvery, sometimes greenish. **Cotyledons** deciduous, petiolate. **Stems** decumbent to erect, clustered, branched or unbranched. **Leaves** cauline, clustered near base or not; stipules 6–20 mm; petiole 1–8(–12) cm; leaflets 6–10, blades 10–45 × 4–18 mm, surfaces hairy. **Peduncles** 5–13 cm; bracts deciduous, 4–24 mm. **Racemes** 4–40 cm, rachis usually deciduous or semi-deciduous; flowers usually spirally arranged or loosely whorled. **Pedicels** 3–10 mm. **Flowers** 10–18 mm; calyx bulge or spur 0–1 mm, abaxial lobe entire or 3-toothed, 6–10 mm, adaxial lobe deeply divided, 6–8 mm; corolla violet to lavender, patch usually yellow, rarely white, turning purple, banner usually hairy abaxially, rarely glabrous, keel usually unlobed proximally, adaxial margin usually ciliate middle to tip, abaxial margins glabrous. **Legumes** 3–5 cm, hairy. **Seeds** 4–9, mottled tan, 4–6 mm.

Varieties 8 (8 in the flora): w United States, n Mexico.

Lupinus albifrons is the most common shrubby lupine in western North America. The combination of silver-pubescent leaves, banners that are pubescent abaxially, and keels that are usually ciliate will separate it from the coastal *L. arboreus* and the dune loving *L. chamissonis*. The desert *L. excubitus* is separated by petiole length, raceme rachis persistence and size, elevation, and distribution. Some of the varieties (*austromontanus*, *collinus*, and *medius*) are woody at base but can appear herbaceous.

1. Shrubs, 5–50 dm.
    2. Flowers 14–18 mm; leaves greenish hairy . . . . 32f. *Lupinus albifrons* var. *hallii*
    2. Flowers 10–14 mm; leaves silver-silky.
        3. Inflorescence bracts 4–8 mm; coastal California, s Oregon . . . . 32a. *Lupinus albifrons* var. *albifrons*
        3. Inflorescence bracts 10–24 mm; San Francisco Bay region, Central Coast, n Channel Islands, California . . . . 32e. *Lupinus albifrons* var. *douglasii*
1. Subshrubs (occasionally semi-herbaceous and woody at base), 1–7(–10) dm.
    4. Flowers 14–18 mm.
        5. Plants herbaceous toward base; racemes 14–40 cm; Tehachapi Mountains, California, southward. . . . . 32c. *Lupinus albifrons* var. *austromontanus*
        5. Plants woody toward base; racemes 6–12 cm; San Bernardino and San Gabriel mountains, California. . . . . 32g. *Lupinus albifrons* var. *johnstonii*

[4. Shifted to left margin.—Ed.]

4. Flowers 10–16 mm.
    6. Petioles to 12 cm; Sonora Desert, California . . . . 32h. *Lupinus albifrons* var. *medius*
    6. Petioles 3–8 cm; cismontane California.
        7. Pubescence woolly to shaggy; shrubs or subshrubs 2–10 dm; Santa Lucia Mountains, Monterey County, California . . . . 32b. *Lupinus albifrons* var. *abramsii*
        7. Pubescence appressed-silvery, not woolly or shaggy; subshrubs 2–4 dm; n, s Coast Ranges, n Sierra Nevada Foothills, California, Oregon . . . . 32d. *Lupinus albifrons* var. *collinus*

32a. Lupinus albifrons Bentham var. **albifrons** [E]

Lupinus albifrons var. *eminens* (Greene) C. P. Smith; *L. albifrons* var. *fissicalyx* (A. Heller) C. P. Smith; *L. brittonii* Abrams; *L. eminens* Greene; *L. fissicalyx* A. Heller; *L. fragrans* A. Heller

Shrubs, 5–50 dm, usually with distinct trunk, green to silvery. **Leaves** silver-silky; petiole 2–5 cm. **Inflorescence bracts** 4–8 mm. **Racemes** 8–30 cm. **Flowers** 10–14 mm.

Flowering Mar–Jun. Chaparral, foothill woodlands; 0–1500 m; Calif., Oreg.

Variety *albifrons* is known from much of coastal California, the Sierra Nevada Foothills, and southern Oregon (cismontane).

32b. Lupinus albifrons Bentham var. **abramsii** (C. P. Smith) Hoover, Leafl. W. Bot. 10: 348. 1966 • Abrams's lupine [C] [E]

Lupinus abramsii C. P. Smith, Bull. Torrey Bot. Club 51: 308. 1924 (as abramsi)

Subshrubs or shrubs, 2–10 dm, woolly to shaggy. **Leaves** silver-hairy; petiole 3–5 cm. **Inflorescence bracts** 10–15 mm. **Racemes** 15–25 cm. **Flowers** 11–16 mm.

Flowering May–Jun. Open woodlands; of conservation concern; 600–2000 m; Calif.

Variety *abramsii* is known only from the Santa Lucia Mountains of Monterey County.

32c. Lupinus albifrons Bentham var. **austromontanus** Jepson, Fl. Calif. 2: 252. 1936

Lupinus austromontanus A. Heller, Muhlenbergia 2: 69. 1905; *L. excubitus* M. E. Jones subsp. *austromontanus* (A. Heller) R. M. Beauchamp; *L. excubitus* var. *austromontanus* (A. Heller) C. P. Smith

Herbs or subshrubs, herbaceous toward base, 2–5 dm, usually silver-hairy. **Leaves** silver-hairy; petiole 4–15 cm. **Inflorescence bracts** 8–9 mm. **Racemes** 14–40 cm. **Flowers** 14–18 mm.

Flowering May–Jul. Dry slopes, upper chaparral and yellow pine forests; 1000–3000 m; Calif.; Mexico (n Baja California).

Variety *austromontanus* is known from the Tehachapi Mountains southward to northern Baja California.

32d. Lupinus albifrons Bentham var. **collinus** Greene, Fl. Francisc., 46. 1891 [E]

Lupinus albifrons var. *flumineus* C. P. Smith; *L. collinus* (Greene) A. Heller; *L. isabelianus* Eastwood

Subshrubs, 2–4 dm, appressed-silvery. **Leaves** clustered near base, appressed-silvery; petiole 3–8 cm. **Inflorescence bracts** 7–9 mm. **Racemes** 4–14 cm. **Flowers** 10–15 mm.

Flowering Mar–Jun. Cliffs, openings in forests; 0–2000 m; Calif., Oreg.

Variety *collinus* is known from the northern part of the Sierra Nevada Foothills and extends into adjacent southern Oregon and the North and South Coast ranges of California.

Variety *collinus* is one of the host plants for the endangered Mission Blue butterfly.

32e. Lupinus albifrons Bentham var. **douglasii** (J. Agardh) C. P. Smith in W. L. Jepson, Man. Fl. Pl. Calif., 531. 1925 [E]

Lupinus douglasii J. Agardh, Syn. Lupini, 34. 1835; *L. fallax* Greene

Shrubs, 10–20 dm, usually silver-silky. **Leaves** silver-silky; petiole 1–4 cm. **Inflorescence bracts** 10–24 mm. **Racemes** 10–15 cm. **Flowers** 10–14 mm.

Flowering Mar–Jun. Coastal scrub, chaparral, open woodland; 0–500 m; Calif.

Variety *douglasii* is known from the San Francisco Bay region, the Central Coast, and the northern Channel Islands.

32f. Lupinus albifrons Bentham var. **hallii** (Abrams) Jepson, Fl. Calif. 2: 252. 1936

Lupinus hallii Abrams, Bull. Torrey Bot. Club 37: 151, fig. 2. 1910; *L. excubitus* M. E. Jones var. *hallii* (Abrams) C. P. Smith; *L. hallii* Abrams; *L. paynei* Davidson

Shrubs, 5–16 dm, greenish hairy. **Leaves** silky-pubescent; petiole 2.5–4.5 cm. **Inflorescence bracts** 6.5–8 mm. **Racemes** to 40 cm. **Flowers** 14–18 mm.

Flowering Apr–Jun. Gravelly and sandy washes, coastal sagebrush scrub, chaparral; 0–1500 m; Calif.; Mexico (Baja California).

Variety *hallii* is known from San Bernardino and Ventura counties southward to northern Baja California. *Lupinus paynei* is considered distinct by D. I. Huang and E. A. Friar (2011) based on molecular data.

32g. Lupinus albifrons Bentham var. **johnstonii** (C. P. Smith) Jepson, Fl. Calif. 2: 252. 1936 [E]

Lupinus excubitus M. E. Jones var. *johnstonii* C. P. Smith in W. L. Jepson, Man. Fl. Pl. Calif., 532. 1925

Subshrubs, woody toward base, 1–2(–3) dm, silver-hairy. **Leaves** silvery-hairy; petiole 5–12 cm. **Inflorescence bracts** 8–9 mm. **Racemes** 6–12 cm. **Flowers** 14–18 mm.

Flowering May–Jul. Dry slopes under pines; 1500–2500 m; Calif.

Variety *johnstonii* is known from the San Bernardino and San Gabriel mountains.

32h. Lupinus albifrons Bentham var. **medius** Jepson, Fl. Calif. 2: 252. 1936 • Mountain springs bush lupine [C]

Lupinus excubitus M. E. Jones subsp. *medius* (Jepson) R. M. Beauchamp; *L. excubitus* var. *medius* (Jepson) Munz; *L. grayi* S. Watson var. *medius* (Jepson) C. P. Smith

Subshrubs, 3–7 dm, silver-tomentose. **Leaves** silver-tomentose; petiole to 12 cm. **Inflorescence bracts** 8–9 mm. **Racemes** 3–14 cm. **Flowers** (10–)11–13 mm.

Flowering Mar–Apr. Creosote bush scrub, washes; of conservation concern; 200–2000 m; Calif.; Mexico (Baja California).

Variety *medius* is known from the Sonoran Desert in eastern San Diego and western Imperial counties southward to northern Baja California.

33. Lupinus andersonii S. Watson, Botany (Fortieth Parallel), 58. 1871 (as andersoni) [E]

Lupinus indigoticus Eastwood; *L. lingulae* C. P. Smith; *L. louisegrisetiae* C. P. Smith; *L. mariposanus* Eastwood; *L. rimae* Eastwood

Herbs, perennial, 2–10+ dm, green, densely hairy. **Cotyledons** deciduous, petiolate. **Stems** erect or ascending, branched. **Leaves** cauline; stipules not leaflike, green to silvery, 3–15 mm; petiole 2–6 cm; leaflets 6–9, blades 20–60 × 5–10 mm, adaxial surface pubescent. **Peduncles** 1–8.5 cm; bracts deciduous, 2–10 mm. **Racemes** open, 2–23 cm; flowers ± whorled. **Pedicels** 1.5–5 mm. **Flowers** 9–12 mm; calyx bulge or spur 0–1 mm, abaxial lobe 2 or 3-toothed, 3–8 mm, adaxial lobe 2-toothed, 5–7 mm; corolla usually light blue or lavender to purple, rarely white, banner patch white turning purple, banner glabrous abaxially, keel upcurved, glabrous, banner ovate, wings wide, covering keel tip. **Legumes** 2–4.5 cm, silky. **Seeds** 4–6, brown, mottled tan, 4–6 mm.

Flowering Jun–Sep. Dry slopes, yellow pine, lodgepole pine, and white and red fir forests; 1500–3000 m; Calif., Nev., Oreg.

Lupinus andersonii is found widely in regions of the Sierra Nevada in California and western Nevada plus adjacent areas of southern Oregon. The erect branching with puberulent leaflets and a banner that is glabrous abaxially distinguish it from *L. angustiflorus*, *L. apertus*, and *L. padrecrowleyi*, which have pubescence at least on the abaxial crest of the banner. According to P. A. Munz (1959), *L. egressus* C. P. Smith may be of hybrid origin (*L. fulcratus* × *L. andersonii*).

34. Lupinus angustiflorus Eastwood, Leafl. W. Bot. 2: 226. 1940 [E]

Lupinus andersonii S. Watson var. *christinae* (A. Heller) Munz; *L. christinae* A. Heller

Herbs, perennial, 5–12 dm, green, glabrous or sparsely hairy. **Cotyledons** deciduous, petiolate. **Stems** ascending-erect, branched. **Leaves** cauline; stipules 5–13 mm; petiole 1–5 cm; leaflets 6–9, blades 20–60 × 4–8 mm, adaxial surface glabrous or with scattered hairs. **Peduncles** 1–8 cm; bracts ± persistent, 3–7 mm. **Racemes** open, 6–34 cm; flowers spirally arranged. **Pedicels** 2–4 mm. **Flowers** 8–10(–12) mm; calyx bulge or spur 0–1 mm, abaxial lobe entire or 3-toothed, 4–9 mm, adaxial lobe 2-toothed, 4–8 mm; corolla usually pale yellow to orange-yellow, sometimes white, banner patch orange to yellow, keel tip pale lavender, banner usually hairy abaxially, keel glabrous. **Legumes** 2.5–4 cm, hairy. **Seeds** 1–4, speckled tan and brown, 4.5–5.5 mm.

Flowering Jun–Sep. Volcanic soils; 1000–3500 m; Calif.

Lupinus angustiflorus is known from the High Cascade Range, the northern and central High Sierra Nevada, and the Great Basin region of northeastern California. It is usually found on volcanic soils associated with yellow pine, red fir, lodgepole pine, and mountain hemlock forests. In Mono County, it is more commonly associated with sagebrush, bitterbrush, rabbitbrush, and wax currant. The persistent bracts, yellow flowers, and abaxial pubescence on the banner clearly separate this taxon from other species.

35. Lupinus antoninus Eastwood, Leafl. W. Bot. 3: 202. 1943 • Anthony Peak lupine [C] [E]

Lupinus adsurgens Drew var. *lilacinus* A. Heller ex C. P. Smith

Herbs, perennial, 2–5 dm, gray- to silvery-hairy. **Cotyledons** deciduous, petiolate. **Stems** decumbent-erect, branched. **Leaves** cauline; stipules not leaflike, green to silvery, 10–12 mm; petiole 1–2 cm; leaflets 6 or 7, blades 15–25 × 3–7 mm, adaxial surface pubescent. **Peduncles** 1–4 cm; bracts semideciduous, 7–8 mm. **Racemes** open, 4–20 cm; flowers spirally arranged. **Pedicels** 3–4 mm. **Flowers** 12–14 mm; calyx bulge or spur 0–1 mm, abaxial lobe 3-toothed, 6–8 mm, adaxial lobe 2-toothed, 6–8 mm; corolla white, banner patch turning tawny, banner glabrous abaxially, keel upcurved, glabrous, banner ovate, wings wide, covering keel tip. **Legumes** 2.5–3.5 cm, silky. **Seeds** 4 or 5, mottled brown, 7–11 mm.

Flowering Jun–Jul. Open fir forests; of conservation concern; ca. 2000 m; Calif.

Lupinus antoninus is known only from the type locality on the southwestern slope of Anthony Peak in Mendocino County. The habit and pubescence resemble those of *L. adsurgens*, but the larger white flowers, the large seeds, and thick stems differentiate it morphologically. According to M. Conrad (1980), it also has different alkaloids. This taxon has not been seen since 1995 and may be extirpated.

36. Lupinus apertus A. Heller, Muhlenbergia 8: 103, fig. 15. 1912 [E]

Lupinus andersonii S. Watson var. *apertus* (A. Heller) C. P. Smith

Herbs, perennial, 2–6 dm, green, puberulent to sparsely appressed-hairy. **Cotyledons** deciduous, petiolate. **Stems** erect, branched. **Leaves** cauline; stipules 5–10 mm; petiole 2–5 cm; leaflets 7–9, blades 25–55 × 4–12 mm, adaxial surface pubescent. **Peduncles** 1–8 cm; bracts deciduous, 3.5–5 mm. **Racemes** 8–11 cm; flowers spirally arranged to whorled. **Pedicels** 3–6 mm. **Flowers** 10–12 mm; calyx bulge or spur 0–1 mm, abaxial lobe entire or 3-toothed, 4.5–7 mm, adaxial lobe 2-toothed, 3.5–6 mm; corolla usually purple, sometimes pink or white, banner patch usually white, banner hairy abaxially, keel glabrous. **Legumes** 2–3 cm, hairy. **Seeds** 3 or 4, 5–6 mm.

Flowering Jun–Jul. Dry, rocky soils; 1500–3000 m; Calif., Nev.

Lupinus apertus is found in the northern High Sierra Nevada from Plumas to El Dorado counties in California and eastward to southwestern Washoe County, Nevada.

Lupinus apertus can be differentiated from *L. andersonii* by its abaxial banner pubescence and from *L. angustiflorus* by its pale yellow to orange-yellow flowers. *Lupinus apertus* is reportedly toxic.

37. Lupinus arboreus Sims, Bot. Mag. 18: plate 682. 1803 • Yellow bush lupine

Lupinus arboreus var. *eximius* (Burtt Davy) C. P. Smith; *L. propinquus* Greene

Shrubs, usually 5–20 dm, green-glabrous or silver-hairy. **Cotyledons** deciduous, petiolate. **Stems** ascending or erect, branched, woody. **Leaves** cauline; stipules 8–12 mm; petiole 2–3(–6) cm; leaflets 5–12, blades 20–60 × 3–10 mm, adaxial surface glabrous. **Peduncles** 4–10 cm; bracts deciduous, 8–10 mm. **Racemes** 10–30 cm; flowers whorled or not. **Pedicels** 4–10 mm. **Flowers** 14–18 mm; calyx bulge or spur 0–1 mm, abaxial lobe entire, 5–7 mm, adaxial lobe 2-toothed, 5–9 mm; corolla usually yellow, rarely lilac to purple, banner patch darker or not or white, banner glabrous abaxially, lower keel margins glabrous, adaxial margin ciliate from claw to tip. **Legumes** 4–7 cm, hairy. **Seeds** 8–12, black to tan, often striped lighter, 4–5 mm. $2n = 48$.

Flowering Apr–Jul. Coastal bluffs, dunes, disturbed sand; 0–100 m; B.C.; Calif., Oreg., Wash.; Mexico (Baja California); introduced in South America (Argentina, Chile), Europe, Pacific Islands (New Zealand), Australia (including Tasmania).

Lupinus arboreus is known from the central California coast southward to northern Baja California; it was introduced as a sand binder and has become naturalized in northern California, Oregon, Washington, and southern British Columbia.

Lupinus arboreus grades into *L. rivularis* in the North Coast of California. Plants with yellow petals and sweet-smelling flowers are widely cultivated as a sand binder. Hairier plants from the western San Francisco Bay area with yellow banners and blue wings have been called var. *eximius*; plants with glabrous leaflets and purple petals have been called *L. propinquus*. *Lupinus arboreus* hybridizes with *L. littoralis* and probably other species. Seeds of *L. arboreus* species are toxic.

38. Lupinus arbustus Douglas, Edwards's Bot. Reg. 15: plate 1230. 1829 • Spur lupine [E]

Lupinus arbustus subsp. *calcaratus* (Kellogg) D. B. Dunn; *L. arbustus* var. *montanus* (Howell) D. B. Dunn; *L. arbustus* subsp. *neolaxiflorus* D. B. Dunn; *L. arbustus* subsp. *pseudoparviflorus* (Rydberg) D. B. Dunn; *L. arbustus* subsp. *silvicola* (A. Heller) D. B. Dunn; *L. caesius* Eastwood; *L. caudatus* Kellogg var. *submanens* C. P. Smith; *L. caudatus* Kellogg var. *subtenellus* C. P. Smith; *L. elegantulus* Eastwood; *L. inyoensis* A. Heller var. *demissus* C. P. Smith; *L. laxiflorus* Douglas ex Lindley var. *calcaratus* (Kellogg) C. P. Smith; *L. laxiflorus* var. *cognatus* C. P. Smith; *L. laxiflorus* var. *elmerianus* C. P. Smith; *L. laxiflorus* var. *lyleianus* C. P. Smith; *L. laxiflorus* var. *pseudoparviflorus* (Rydberg) C. P. Smith & H. St. John; *L. laxiflorus* var. *silvicola* (A. Heller) C. P. Smith; *L. laxiflorus* var. *villosulus* C. P. Smith; *L. lyleianus* C. P. Smith; *L. mucronulatus* Howell var. *umatillensis* C. P. Smith; *L. multitinctus* A. Nelson; *L. noldekeae* Eastwood; *L. proteanus* Eastwood; *L. pseudoparviflorus* Rydberg; *L. silvicola* A. Heller; *L. wenatchensis* Eastwood; *L. yakimensis* C. P. Smith

Herbs, perennial, 2–7 dm, green or gray-silky. **Cotyledons** deciduous, petiolate. **Stems** erect, ascending, or decumbent, branched. **Leaves** cauline and basal; stipules 4–9 mm; petiole 2–16 cm; leaflets 7–10(–13), blades 20–70 × 3–15 mm, adaxial surface strigose. **Peduncles** 2–5 cm; bracts deciduous, 3–6 mm. **Racemes** open, 3–18 cm; flowers whorled. **Pedicels** 1–7 mm. **Flowers** 8–14 mm; calyx spur distinct, 1–3 mm, abaxial lobe 3-toothed, 2.5–5 mm, 1–3 mm, adaxial lobe 2-toothed, 2–4 mm; corolla blue, purple, pink, white, or yellowish, banner patch white, yellowish, or absent, banner hairy abaxially, wings with dense hair patch outside near tip, lower keel margins glabrous, adaxial margin ciliate. **Legumes** 2–3 cm, silky. **Seeds** 3–6, tan, 5–6 mm.

Flowering May–Jul. Open sagebrush scrub or mixed-conifer forests; 1500–3000 m; B.C.; Calif., Idaho, Mont., Oreg., Utah, Wash.

Lupinus arbustus is known from the Cascade and Klamath ranges, San Gabriel Mountains, Sierra Nevada, and the Great Basin area in California; Owyhee Desert in Idaho and Oregon; eastern Washington and western Montana; and western Juab and Tooele counties, Utah.

Lupinus arbustus is separated from the *argenteus* group by the presence of hairs on the corolla wings. Recognition of subspecies and varieties of this already complex species leads to precarious separation among taxa.

Lupinus variegatus A. Heller (1912, not Poiret 1814) is an illegitimate name that pertains here.

39. Lupinus arcticus S. Watson, Proc. Amer. Acad. Arts 8: 526. 1873 • Arctic lupine [E]

Lupinus borealis A. Heller; *L. donnellyensis* C. P. Smith; *L. gakonensis* C. P. Smith; *L. multicaulis* C. P. Smith; *L. multifolius* C. P. Smith; *L. nootkatensis* Donn ex Sims var. *kjellmannii* Ostenfeld; *L. polyphyllus* Lindley subsp. *arcticus* (S. Watson) L. Ll. Phillips; *L. toklatensis* A. Nelson; *L. yukonensis* Greene

Herbs, perennial, 1–4 dm, hairs thinly appressed silky-sericeous, or few to many and spreading; caudex superficial, divisions closely tufted. **Cotyledons** deciduous, petiolate. **Stems** ascending to erect, hollow, tufted, branched at crown. **Leaves** mostly basal with a few cauline proximal to inflorescences; stipules 8–10 mm; petiole 5–19 cm; leaflets 6–10, blades 13–90 × 10–15 mm, abaxial surface thinly strigose, adaxial surface glabrous. **Peduncles** 4–8.5 cm; bracts caducous to tardily deciduous, 8–14 mm. **Racemes** 5–8(–15 in fruit) cm; flowers spirally arranged or in 3–7 whorls. **Pedicels** 4–6 mm. **Flowers** 14–19(–21) mm; calyx bulge or spur 0–1 mm, abaxial lobe 6–11 mm, entire or faintly notched at tip, adaxial lobe ± gibbous basally, adaxial lobe teeth with slight notch at tip, 4–8 mm; corolla usually blue to purplish, sometimes pink, rarely white, banner spot white or yellow, sometimes becoming purple, banner glabrous abaxially, lower keel margins densely ciliate near claw or glabrous or sparsely ciliate towards tip, adaxial margin glabrous or sparsely ciliate towards tips. **Legumes** 2–4.3 cm, silky-pilose. **Seeds** 5–8, mottled. $2n = 48$.

Flowering Jun–Aug. Well-drained hummocks of alpine and arctic tundra, moist to mesic meadows, gravel bars, clearings, roadsides, thickets, open forests; 0–2000 m; B.C., N.W.T., Nunavut, Yukon; Alaska.

The relationship between *Lupinus arcticus* and *L. latifolius* is unclear. They may be distinguished by the presence of proximal keel ciliation in *L. latifolius*, and basal rather than cauline leaves dominating in *L. arcticus*.

40. Lupinus argenteus Pursh, Fl. Amer. Sept. 2: 468. 1814 [E] [F]

Herbs, perennial, 1–15 dm, green and glabrous or silvery-hairy; from superficial or shallowly buried root crown. **Cotyledons** deciduous, petiolate. **Stems** erect or ascending, green or purplish, clustered, branched or unbranched. **Leaves** basal and/or cauline; stipules 2–12 mm; petiole 1–15 cm; leaflets (5 or)6–10, blades 10–60 × 4–10 mm, abaxial surface hairy, adaxial surface glabrous or hairy (but not strigose). **Peduncles** (1–)4–25(–30) cm; bracts usually deciduous, 3–4 mm. **Racemes** loose, 5–16(–25) cm; flowers whorled or not. **Pedicels** (1–)2–5(–7) mm. **Flowers** 5–15 mm; calyx 4–8 mm, bulge or spur 0–3 mm (may be variable on plant), abaxial lobe entire or 3-toothed, adaxial lobe entire or 2-toothed; corolla usually blue, sometimes purple, violet, pink, lilac, or white, banner patch yellowish to whitish, blue, brown, or absent, banner not much reflexed-recurved beyond midpoint, this less than 3 mm proximal to apex, banner glabrous or pubescent abaxially, wings glabrous, lower keel margins glabrous, upper margins ciliate. **Legumes** (1–)2–3 cm, hairy or silky. **Seeds** (2 or)3–5(or 6), tan, brown, or red.

Varieties 14 (14 in the flora): w North America.

1. Calyx spur 1–3 mm.
   2. Flowers in profile appearing open, spur pronounced . . . . 40e. *Lupinus argenteus* var. *heteranthus*
   2. Flowers in profile appearing closed; spur less pronounced.
      3. Petioles of proximal cauline leaves 1.5–3 cm . . . . 40c. *Lupinus argenteus* var. *argophyllus*
      3. Petioles of proximal cauline leaves 3–12 cm . . . . 40n. *Lupinus argenteus* var. *utahensis*
1. Calyx bulge 0–1 mm, but not elongated into a spur.
   4. Leaflets oblanceolate, flat, green, surfaces glabrous or adaxially pubescent; plants of cool, moist mountain meadows, stream banks, lakeshores.

5. Corollas pale blue with brown banner patch; pedicels 1–2.5 mm . . . . 40d. *Lupinus argenteus* var. *fulvomaculatus*
5. Corollas usually blue with yellow banner spot or none; pedicels usually 3–4 mm.
    6. Stems unbranched and racemes solitary, terminal . . . . 40m. *Lupinus argenteus* var. *rubricaulis*
    6. Stems branched, giving rise to several racemes.
        7. Corolla wings (7.5–)8–10 mm . . . . 40b. *Lupinus argenteus* var. *argentatus*
        7. Corolla wings 5–7.5 mm . . . . 40l. *Lupinus argenteus* var. *parviflorus*

[4. Shifted to left margin.—Ed.]

4. Leaflets oblanceolate or elliptic-oblanceolate, narrow and often folded, surfaces gray or silver-pubescent; plants of dry open areas, foothills to mountains.
    8. Stem hairs descending in backward direction or widely spreading . . . . 40k. *Lupinus argenteus* var. *palmeri*
    8. Stem hairs forwardly appressed.
        9. Flowers large, (7–)8–15 mm.
            10. Basal and cauline leaves present at flowering . . . . 40j. *Lupinus argenteus* var. *montigenus*
            10. Basal leaves absent at flowering.
                11. Flowers (7–)8–12 mm . . . . .40a. *Lupinus argenteus* var. *argenteus*
                11. Flowers 12–15 mm . . . . 40i. *Lupinus argenteus* var. *moabensis*
        9. Flowers small, 5–7(–9) mm.
            12. Banners densely pubescent. . . . . 40g.*Lupinus argenteus* var. *holosericeus*
            12. Banner glabrous or thinly strigulose abaxially.
                13. Wings 5.5–7 mm; banner usually thinly strigulose abaxially; Kaibab Plateau, Arizona, Colorado, Nevada, New Mexico, Utah; elevation 2000–2800 m. . . . . .40f. *Lupinus argenteus* var. *hillii*
                13. Wings 5–6 mm; banner glabrous abaxially; Sierra Nevada, California, adjacent Nevada; elevation 1500–3500 m. . . . . 40h. *Lupinus argenteus* var. *meionanthus*

40a. Lupinus argenteus Pursh var. **argenteus** E

Lupinus abiesicola C. P. Smith; *L. acclivatatis* C. P. Smith; *L. alexanderae* C. P. Smith; *L. amniculi-putorii* C. P. Smith; *L. annieae* C. P. Smith; *L. argenteus* var. *decumbens* (Torrey) S. Watson; *L. argenteus* var. *laxiflorus* (Douglas ex Lindley) Dorn; *L. argenteus* var. *lemmonii* (C. P. Smith) Isely; *L. argenteus* var. *stenophyllus* (Rydberg) P. H. Davis; *L. argenteus* var. *tenellus* (Douglas ex G. Don) D. B. Dunn; *L. calcicola* C. P. Smith; *L. cariciformis* C. P. Smith; *L. charlestonensis* C. P. Smith; *L. clarkensis* C. P. Smith; *L. corymbosus* A. Heller; *L. edwardpalmeri* C. P. Smith; *L. flavopinuum* C. P. Smith; *L. fremontensis* C. P. Smith; *L. funstonianus* C. P. Smith; *L. garrettianus* C. P. Smith; *L. johannis-howellii* C. P. Smith; *L. lanatocarinus* C. P. Smith; *L. laxiflorus* Douglas ex Lindley; *L. laxiflorus* var. *foliosus* Torrey & A. Gray; *L. lemmonii* C. P. Smith; *L. lucidulus* Rydberg; *L. lutescens* C. P. Smith; *L. merrillianus* C. P. Smith; *L. munzii* Eastwood; *L. patulipes* C. P. Smith; *L. populorum* C. P. Smith; *L. pulcher* Eastwood; *L. siccosilvae* C. P. Smith; *L. sitgreavesii* S. Watson; *L. stenophyllus* Rydberg; *L. sublanatus* Eastwood; *L. tenellus* Douglas ex G. Don; *L. trainianus* C. P. Smith

Herbs 2–15 dm, hairs forwardly appressed. **Stems** branched. **Leaves** cauline; petiole 1–5 cm; leaflet blades narrow and often folded, oblanceolate or elliptic-oblanceolate, surfaces gray or silver-pubescent. **Pedicels** (1–)2–5(–6) mm. **Flowers** (7–)8–12 mm; calyx bulge less than 1 mm; corolla blue, purple, pink, or white, banner ± hairy abaxially. $2n = 48$.

Flowering Jun–Oct. Dry sagebrush scrub, meadows, openings in conifer forests; 1000–2000 m; Alta., Sask.; Ariz., Calif., Colo., Idaho, Mont., Nev., N.Mex., N.Dak., Oreg., S.Dak., Utah, Wyo.

Variety *argenteus* is known from the Panamint Mountains in eastern California to southern Canada, western North Dakota, western South Dakota, Colorado, and central New Mexico. It is widespread in the intermountain region in Arizona, southern Idaho, Nevada, eastern Oregon, Utah, and southwestern Wyoming.

Lupinus lemmonii C. P. Smith belongs here since D. Isely (1998) and T. H. Kearney and R. H. Peebles (1960) stated that the only diagnostic character that differentiates this from var. *argenteus* is its southern location.

40b. Lupinus argenteus Pursh var. **argentatus** (Rydberg) Barneby in A. Cronquist et al., Intermount. Fl. 3(B): 246. 1989 [E]

Lupinus decumbens Torrey var. *argentatus* Rydberg, Fl. Colorado, 197. 1906; *Lupinus argenteus* var. *boreus* (C. P. Smith) S. L. Welsh; *L. spathulatus* Rydberg; *L. spathulatus* var. *boreus* C. P. Smith

Herbs 2–5.5 dm, glabrous or sparsely pubescent. **Stems** normally branched. **Leaves** mostly cauline, basal usually absent at flowering; leaflet blades flat, oblanceolate, surfaces glabrous or adaxially pubescent. **Racemes** several. **Pedicels** 3–4 mm. **Flowers:** (7.5–)8–10 mm; calyx often distinctly gibbous abaxially at base; corolla blue, large, wings (7.5–)8–10 mm, banner spot blue or yellow, banner usually hairy abaxially. $2n = 48$.

Flowering Jun–Sep. Cool, moist mountain meadows, stream banks, lakeshores, high mountain elevations, sometimes to or above timberline; 1700–3400 m; Ariz., Colo., Idaho, Mont., N.Mex., Utah, Wyo.

Variety *argentatus* is known from the Rocky Mountains in Colorado to Idaho, Montana, and Wyoming, southward to Arizona and New Mexico, and in the Wasatch and Utah plateaus, from Salt Lake to eastern Iron County, Utah. In Arizona, it is apparently restricted to the Kaibab Plateau, where it is rare.

Variety *argentatus* can be separated from the other varieties by the absence of a spur and its abaxially gibbous calyx. The herbs are mesomorphic plants of cool, moist or wet mountain meadows, the leaflets are green, flowers are relatively large, wings are 7.5–10 mm, and the stems are branched.

40c. Lupinus argenteus Pursh var. **argophyllus** (A. Gray) S. Watson, Proc. Amer. Acad. Arts 8: 541. 1873 [E]

Lupinus decumbens Torrey var. *argophyllus* A. Gray, Mem. Amer. Acad. Arts, n. s. 4: 37. 1849; *L. aduncus* Greene; *L. argophyllus* (A. Gray) Cockerell; *L. caudatus* Kellogg subsp. *argophyllus* (A. Gray) L. Ll. Phillips; *L. caudatus* var. *argophyllus* (A. Gray) S. L. Welsh; *L. helleri* Greene; *L. laxiflorus* Douglas ex Lindley var. *argophyllus* (A. Gray) M. E. Jones; *L. ornatus* Douglas var. *glabratus* S. Watson; *L. plattensis* S. Watson

Herbs 2–8 dm, pubescent. **Stems** branched. **Leaves** cauline; petiole of proximal cauline leaves 1.5–3 cm; leaflet blade surfaces silvery-pubescent. **Pedicels** 2–4 mm in flower, to 8 mm in fruit. **Flowers** 8–12 mm, in profile appearing closed; calyx spur 1–3 mm (less pronounced); corolla light blue, banner usually hairy abaxially. $2n = 48$.

Flowering Jun–Aug. Pinyon-juniper woodlands, grasslands; 1200–2200 m; Ariz., Colo., Mont., Nebr., N.Mex., Okla., S.Dak., Tex., Wyo.

Variety *argophyllus* is known from the foothills of the Rocky Mountains from Montana and South Dakota southward to northern Arizona, New Mexico, and the San Juan Basin in southwestern Colorado, and eastward into Nebraska, Oklahoma, Texas, and Wyoming.

Variety *argophyllus* can be separated by the spurred calyx, flowers in profile appearing closed or shallowly gaping, and petioles of the lowest or largest cauline leaves 1.5–3 cm.

40d. Lupinus argenteus Pursh var. **fulvomaculatus** (Payson) Barneby, Great Basin Naturalist 46: 257. 1986 [E]

Lupinus fulvomaculatus Payson, Bot. Gaz. 60: 376. 1915; *L. ingratus* Greene

Herbs 1–10 dm, glabrous or pubescent. **Stems** branched. **Leaves** usually cauline, basal leaves usually absent at flowering, if present then petioles less than 3 times as long as leaflets; leaflet blades flat, oblanceolate, surfaces glabrous or pubescent adaxially. **Pedicels** 1–2.5 mm. **Flowers** 6–8 mm; calyx bulge 0–1 mm; corolla pale blue with brown banner patch, banner glabrous or hairy abaxially. $2n = 48$.

Flowering Jun–Aug. Cool, moist mountain meadows, stream banks, lakeshores, forests; 2000–3600 m; Ariz., Colo., N.Mex., Utah.

Variety *fulvomaculatus* is known from the Abajo and La Sal mountains in southeastern Utah, mountainous Colorado, in the Santa Fe National Forest and vicinity in New Mexico, and in northeastern Apache County, Arizona, where it is rare.

40e. Lupinus argenteus Pursh var. **heteranthus** (S. Watson) Barneby in A. Cronquist et al., Intermount. Fl. 3(B): 246. 1989 [E]

Lupinus meionanthus A. Gray var. *heteranthus* S. Watson, Botany (Fortieth Parallel), 56. 1871; *L. argentinus* Rydberg; *L. caudatus* Kellogg; *L. caudatus* subsp. *cutleri* (Eastwood) L. W. Hess & D. B. Dunn; *L. caudatus* var. *cutleri* (Eastwood) S. L. Welsh; *L. cutleri* Eastwood; *L. hendersonii* Eastwood; *L. inyoensis* A. Heller; *L. laxiflorus* Douglas ex Lindley var. *inyoensis* (A. Heller) Jepson; *L. rosei* Eastwood

Herbs 2–8 dm, densely silky throughout. **Stems** branched or unbranched. **Leaves** basal, sometimes also cauline; leaflet blade surfaces densely silver-silky. **Pedicels** (1–)2–5(–6) mm. **Flowers** 8–14 mm, in profile appearing open; calyx spur 1–2 mm (pronounced); corolla violet or blue to white, banner silky abaxially, wings glabrous. **2*n*** = 48.

Flowering May–Sep. Dry, open slopes, sagebrush scrub, pinyon-juniper woodlands; 1000–3000 m; Calif., Idaho, Nev., Oreg.

Variety *heteranthus* ranges from the Cascades in Oregon southward through the Sierra Nevada and eastward to Mono County, and disjunctly in the San Gabriel Mountains, in California, and is widespread over the western one-fourth of the intermountain region from Steens Mountain and eastern Lake County in Oregon eastward to Humboldt, Pershing, and Nye counties in Nevada. It grades in the northeast into var. *utahensis* and in the southeast into var. *palmeri* and var. *argenteus* in Idaho.

Variety *heteranthus* differs from var. *utahensis* by the more pronounced calyx spur and the more widely gaping flowers.

40f. Lupinus argenteus Pursh var. **hillii** (Greene) Barneby in A. Cronquist et al., Intermount. Fl. 3(B): 246. 1989 [E]

Lupinus hillii Greene, Leafl. Bot. Observ. Crit. 2: 236. 1912; *L. hillii* var. *osterhoutianus* (C. P. Smith) Harmon; *L. ingratus* Greene var. *arizonicus* C. P. Smith; *L. marcusianus* C. P. Smith; *L. osterhoutianus* C. P. Smith

Herbs to 3 dm, hairs inconspicuous and forwardly appressed to spreading. **Stems** branched. **Leaves** usually cauline, basal leaves usually absent at flowering, if present then petioles less than 3 times as long as leaflets; leaflet blades narrow and folded, oblanceolate or elliptic-oblanceolate, surfaces gray or silvery-pubescent. **Pedicels** (1–)2–5(–6) mm. **Flowers** 6–8 mm; calyx bulge 0–1 mm; corolla blue-purple, wings 5.5–7 mm, banner equaling wings, usually thinly strigulose abaxially. **2*n*** = 48.

Flowering Jun–Sep. Ponderosa pine forest, upper edge of pinyon-juniper woodlands; 2000–2800 m; Ariz., Colo., Nev., N.Mex., Utah.

Variety *hillii* is the small-flowered form that occurs in the Southwest in which the flowers are budlike and scarcely gaping.

40g. Lupinus argenteus Pursh var. **holosericeus** (Nuttall) Barneby in A. Cronquist et al., Intermount. Fl. 3(B): 245. 1989 [E]

Lupinus holosericeus Nuttall in J. Torrey and A. Gray, Fl. N. Amer. 1: 380. 1840; *L. evermannii* Rydberg; *L. stockii* C. P. Smith; *L. summae* C. P. Smith

Herbs 2–7 dm, densely silky throughout, hairs forwardly appressed. **Stems** branched or unbranched. **Leaves** usually cauline, basal leaves usually absent at flowering, if present then petioles less than 3 times as long as leaflets; leaflet blades narrow and folded, oblanceolate or elliptic-oblanceolate, surfaces densely silky. **Pedicels** (1–)2–5 (–6) mm. **Flowers** 5–9 mm; calyx bulge 0–1 mm; corolla purplish blue, wings 5–7.5 mm, banner densely hairy abaxially, to middle or distally. **2*n*** = 48.

Flowering Jun–Aug. Dry, open places, sagebrush plains, low hills in the intermountain region, slopes and ridges of the Rocky Mountains; 1500–3500 m; Colo., Idaho, Nev., Oreg., Utah.

Variety *holosericeus* is known from the Ruby Mountains of northeastern Nevada through the middle and lower Snake River plains and Owyhee Desert in southern Idaho and adjacent Oregon, northern Nevada, western Colorado, and northeastern Utah.

This variety is close to var. *utahensis,* but the flowers are smaller, and the calyx is not spurred.

40h. Lupinus argenteus Pursh var. **meionanthus** (A. Gray) Barneby in A. Cronquist et al., Intermount. Fl. 3(B): 246. 1989 [E]

Lupinus meionanthus A. Gray, Proc. Amer. Acad. Arts 6: 522. 1865

Herbs 2–5(–9) dm, hairs forwardly appressed, silvery. **Stems** branched. **Leaves** cauline; leaflet blades narrow and folded, oblanceolate or elliptic-oblanceolate, surfaces appressed-silvery to gray-green. **Pedicels** 2–3 mm. **Flowers** 5–6(–7) mm; calyx bulge 0–1 mm, but not elongated into a spur; corolla dull blue to lilac, banner patch yellow, wings 5–6 mm, banner glabrous abaxially. **2*n*** = 48.

Flowering Jul–Aug. Dry banks, red fir and lodgepole pine forests, sagebrush scrub; 1500–3500 m; Calif., Nev.

Variety *meionanthus* is known from the Sierra Nevada in California to adjacent western Nevada.

40i. Lupinus argenteus Pursh var. **moabensis** S. L. Welsh, Great Basin Naturalist 46: 262. 1986 E

Herbs 2–9 dm, hairs forwardly appressed. **Stems** branched. **Leaves** usually cauline, basal usually absent at flowering, if present then petioles less than 3 times as long as leaflets; leaflet blades narrow and folded, oblanceolate or elliptic-oblanceolate, surfaces gray or silvery-pubescent with appressed hairs. **Pedicels** 5–7 mm. **Flowers** 12–15 mm; calyx bulge 0–1 mm; corolla purple, wings 12–14 mm, banner ± hairy abaxially. **2*n*** = 48.

Flowering Apr–Jul. Sandy washes, pinyon-juniper woodlands, ponderosa pine forests, badlands; 1500–2500 m; Ariz., Colo., Utah.

Variety *moabensis* is known from the badlands of the Colorado Plateau in Utah and adjacent Arizona and Colorado. It is known for its very large, showy flowers.

40j. Lupinus argenteus Pursh var. **montigenus** (A. Heller) Barneby in A. Cronquist et al., Intermount. Fl. 3(B): 246. 1989 E

Lupinus montigenus A. Heller, Muhlenbergia 6: 109, fig. 18. 1910; *L. caudatus* Kellogg subsp. *montigenus* (A. Heller) L. W. Hess & D. B. Dunn; *L. olivebrowniae* C. P. Smith; *L. olivenortoniae* C. P. Smith; *L. stinchfieldiae* C. P. Smith

Herbs 2.5–4 dm, densely silvery-hairy, hairs forwardly appressed. **Stems** branched or unbranched. **Leaves** basal and cauline; proximal petioles usually (5–)7–9(–15) cm; leaflet blades narrow and folded, oblanceolate or elliptic-oblanceolate, surfaces gray or silvery-pubescent with silky hairs. **Pedicels** 4–5(–6) mm. **Flowers** 9–12(–14) mm; calyx bulge less than 1 mm; corolla blue to violet, banner patch yellow to cream, hairy abaxially. **2*n*** = 48.

Flowering Jul–Aug. Dry, open montane forests, sagebrush scrub; 2400–3500 m; Calif., Nev.

Variety *montigenus* is found along the eastern face of the Sierra Nevada from the Rock Creek Basin in Inyo County, California, to Washoe County, Nevada.

Variety *montigenus* can be differentiated by its long-petioled basal leaves at flowering, absence of a calyx spur, and open large flowers with banners that are hairy abaxially.

40k. Lupinus argenteus Pursh var. **palmeri** (S. Watson) Barneby, Great Basin Naturalist 46: 257. 1986 E

Lupinus palmeri S. Watson, Proc. Amer. Acad. Arts 8: 530. 1873; *L. candidissimus* Eastwood; *L. clokeyanus* C. P. Smith; *L. fontis-batchelderi* C. P. Smith; *L. inyoensis* A. Heller var. *eriocalyx* C. P. Smith; *L. jaegerianus* C. P. Smith; *L. junipericola* C. P. Smith; *L. keckianus* C. P. Smith; *L. portae-westgardiae* C. P. Smith

Herbs 3–6 dm, hairs descending in backward direction or widely spreading. **Stems** branched. **Leaves** cauline; petiole 4–10 cm; leaflet blades narrow and folded, oblanceolate or elliptic-oblanceolate, surfaces densely gray spreading-hairy and silvery-silky. **Pedicels** 2–7 mm. **Flowers** 8–10(–12) mm; calyx bulge or spur less than 1 mm; corolla blue, banner hairy abaxially. **2*n*** = 48.

Flowering May–Jun. Dry, open montane forests, ponderosa pine and pinyon-juniper woodlands; (1400–) 1700–3100 m; Ariz., Calif., Nev., N.Mex., Utah, Wash.

Variety *palmeri* is widespread over central and northwestern Arizona and adjacent New Mexico, and through high elevations in California, Nevada, Utah, and Washington.

It is similar to variety *argenteus* except stem pubescence is of mixed long-spreading and short hairs.

40l. Lupinus argenteus Pursh var. **parviflorus** (Nuttall) C. L. Hitchcock in C. L. Hitchcock et al., Vasc. Pl. Pacif. N.W. 3: 302. 1961 E

Lupinus parviflorus Nuttall in W. J. Hooker and G. A. W. Arnott, Bot. Beechey Voy., 336. 1838; *L. argenteus* var. *myrianthus* (Greene) Isely; *L. argenteus* subsp. *parviflorus* (Nuttall) L. Ll. Phillips; *L. floribundus* Greene; *L. myrianthus* Greene; *L. parviflorus* subsp. *myrianthus* (Greene) Harmon

Herbs 2–5(–8) dm, mostly glabrous. **Stems** branched. **Leaves** cauline; leaflet blades green, flat, oblanceolate, surfaces glabrous or glabrate. **Racemes** several. **Pedicels** 3–4 mm. **Flowers** 5–7.5 mm, wings 5–7.5 mm; calyx bulge 0–1 mm, but not elongated into a spur; corolla blue, banner spot yellow, glabrous or hairy abaxially. **2*n*** = 48.

Flowering Jun–Sep. Wet places in spruce-aspen or lodgepole pine forests or ponderosa pine-sagebrush woodlands; 1500–2800 m; Ariz., Idaho, Mont., S.Dak., Wyo.

Variety *parviflorus* is known from southwestern Idaho, western Montana, northern Wasatch Mountains and mountainous Owyhee County in Idaho, the Black

Hills in South Dakota, western Wyoming, and disjunctly on the Shivwits Plateau in northwestern Arizona (Mohave County).

The combination of small flowers, villous pedicels, and broad, green, glabrous (or nearly so) adaxial leaflet surfaces separates this variety from others of the species.

40m. Lupinus argenteus Pursh var. **rubricaulis** (Greene) S. L. Welsh, Great Basin Naturalist 38: 326. 1978 E

Lupinus rubricaulis Greene, Pl. Baker. 3: 35. 1901; *L. alpestris* A. Nelson; *L. alsophilus* Greene; *L. argenteus* var. *depressus* (Rydberg) C. L. Hitchcock; *L. caudatus* Kellogg var. *rubricaulis* (Greene) C. P. Smith; *L. depressus* Rydberg; *L. maculatus* Rydberg; *L. monticola* Rydberg; *L. pulcherrimus* Rydberg

Herbs 2–5.5 dm, glabrous or pubescent. **Stems** unbranched. **Leaves** cauline; leaflet blades green, flat, oblanceolate, surfaces glabrous or adaxially pubescent. **Racemes** solitary, terminal. **Pedicels** 3–4 mm. **Flowers** 8–11 mm; calyx bulge 0–1 mm, but not elongated into a spur; corolla blue, banner spot yellow, glabrous or hairy abaxially. **2*n*** = 48.

Flowering Jun–Sep. Moist places in forests; (2200–) 2400–3400 m; B.C.; Ariz., Colo., Idaho, Mont., Nev., Utah, Wyo.

Variety *rubricaulis* ranges from British Columbia to Montana, southward into northeastern Nevada, the Uinta and Wasatch mountains in Utah, Apache and Coconino counties in Arizona, and western Colorado. It is very similar to var. *argenteus* but found in more moist or mesic habitats.

40n. Lupinus argenteus Pursh var. **utahensis** (S. Watson) Barneby in A. Cronquist et al., Intermount. Fl. 3(B): 246. 1989 E F

Lupinus holosericeus Nuttall var. *utahensis* S. Watson, Proc. Amer. Acad. Arts 8: 533. 1873; *L. caudatus* Kellogg var. *utahensis* (S. Watson) S. L. Welsh; *L. henrysmithii* C. P. Smith; *L. montis-liberatis* C. P. Smith; *L. standingii* C. P. Smith

Herbs 2–7 dm, hairs densely white-silky throughout. **Stems** branched or unbranched. **Leaves** basal and cauline; petiole of proximal cauline leaves 3–12 cm; leaflet blade surfaces silky-pubescent. **Pedicels** 2–5 mm. **Flowers** 8–11 mm, in profile appearing closed; calyx spur 1–3 mm, less pronounced; corolla lavender or blue-purple, banner densely hairy abaxially. **2*n*** = 48.

Flowering May–Sep. Plains and foothills, in sagebrush, open ponderosa pine; 1300–2800 m; Colo., Idaho, Mont., Nev., Oreg., Utah.

Variety *utahensis* is widespread within Bonneville Basin in southeastern Idaho, Nevada, and Utah. It extends into the Owyhee Desert and lake sections in southwestern Idaho and southeastern Oregon, westward in Nevada to Pershing and northern Nye counties and eastward in Utah to the periphery of the Colorado Basin in Colorado and Montana. The variety is silky and spurred, with basal leaves at flowering.

41. Lupinus breweri A. Gray, Proc. Amer. Acad. Arts 7: 334. 1868 E

Herbs or subshrubs, perennial, to 2 dm, matted or tufted, silvery-silky. **Cotyledons** deciduous, petiolate. **Stems** prostrate, branched, base ± woody. **Leaves** cauline, clustered near base; stipules 2–5 mm; petiole 1–5 (–6) cm; leaflets 5–10, blades 3–20 × 2–6 mm, adaxial surface pubescent. **Peduncles** 1–3(–8) cm; bracts deciduous, 3–5 mm. **Racemes** dense, 1–10 cm; flowers whorled. **Pedicels** 1–3(–4) mm. **Flowers** 4–11 mm; calyx bulge or spur 0–1 mm, abaxial lobe entire or 3-toothed, 4–6 mm, adaxial lobe 2-toothed, 4–7 mm; corolla blue to violet, banner patch white or yellow, banner glabrous or densely hairy abaxially, keel straight, abaxial margins glabrous, adaxial margin glabrous or ciliate. **Legumes** 1–2 cm, silky. **Seeds** 3 or 4, mottled tan, brown, 3–4 mm.

Varieties 3 (3 in the flora): w United States.

1. Banner silky abaxially, keel strongly ciliate . . . . 41c. *Lupinus breweri* var. *grandiflorus*
1. Banner glabrous abaxially, keel glabrous.
    2. Flowers 6–9 mm; leaflet blades 6–20 mm . . . . .41a. *Lupinus breweri* var. *breweri*
    2. Flowers 4–6(–7) mm; leaflet blades 3–5 mm . . . . 41b. *Lupinus breweri* var. *bryoides*

41a. Lupinus breweri A. Gray var. **breweri** E

Lupinus breweri var. *parvulus* C. P. Smith

Herbs or subshrubs with caudex usually below ground, forming a mat. **Leaflet blades** 6–20 mm. **Peduncles** 1–3 cm. **Racemes** 1–2 cm. **Flowers** 6–9 mm; banner glabrous abaxially, keel ± glabrous.

Flowering Jun–Aug. Dry, stony slopes and benches, open subalpine to alpine montane forests; 1000–4000 m; Calif., Nev., Oreg.

Variety *breweri* is known from Mount Pinos through the Sierra Nevada and Siskiyou Mountains in California, to southern Oregon (Mt. Ashland, Jackson County), and western Nevada in Washoe County.

41b. Lupinus breweri A. Gray var. **bryoides** C. P. Smith in W. L. Jepson, Man. Fl. Pl. Calif., 526. 1925 [E]

Lupinus tegeticulatus Eastwood

Herbs or subshrubs with caudex usually above ground, forming a dense tuft. **Leaflet blades** 3–5 mm. **Peduncles** 1–2 cm. **Racemes** 2–3 cm. **Flowers** 4–6(–7) mm; banner and keel ± glabrous.

Flowering Jul–Aug. Open subalpine to alpine montane forests; 2500–4000 m; Calif., Nev.

Variety *bryoides* is known from the western Transverse Ranges in Ventura County and the central and southern Sierra Nevada (Inyo to Tulare counties) to the White Mountains in California, and Mineral County to the Sweetwater, Wassuk, and White ranges in Nevada.

41c. Lupinus breweri A. Gray var. **grandiflorus** C. P. Smith in W. L. Jepson, Man. Fl. Pl. Calif., 526. 1925 [E]

Lupinus breweri var. *clokeyanus* C. P. Smith; *L. campbelliae* Eastwood; *L. campbelliae* var. *bernardinus* Eastwood; *L. monensis* Eastwood; *L. tegeticulatus* Eastwood var. *grandiflorus* (C. P. Smith) Barneby

Herbs or subshrubs with caudex above ground, matted. **Leaflet blades** 6–11 mm. **Peduncles** 2–8 cm. **Racemes** 2–10 cm. **Flowers** (6–)9–11 mm; banner ± silky abaxially, keel strongly ciliate.

Flowering Jun–Aug. Volcanic sand; 2000–3500 m; Calif.

Variety *grandiflorus* is known from throughout the Sierra Nevada and in the San Bernardino and White mountains.

42. Lupinus cervinus Kellogg, Proc. Calif. Acad. Sci. 2: 229, fig. 73. 1863 • Santa Lucia lupine [E]

Herbs, perennial, 1.5–3 dm, gray-green, spreading-hairy. **Cotyledons** deciduous, petiolate. **Stems** erect, clustered, unbranched. **Leaves** cauline, clustered near base; stipules 5–6 mm; petiole 13–15 cm; leaflets 4–8, blades 40–80 × 10–30 mm, adaxial surface long spreading-hairy. **Peduncles** 13–20 cm; bracts deciduous, 3–4 mm. **Racemes** open, to 20 cm; flowers whorled or spirally arranged. **Pedicels** 3–6 mm. **Flowers** 14–16 mm; calyx bulge or spur 0–1 mm, abaxial lobe entire or 2-toothed, 8–10 mm, adaxial lobe entire or 2-toothed, 6–7 mm; corolla light blue, pink, or pale yellow, often drying straw-colored, banner patch yellow, banner ± hairy abaxially, lower keel margins ciliate near claw, adaxial margin ciliate throughout. **Legumes** 3–6 cm, silky. **Seeds** 4–8, light brown with brown line or mottled tan, 2–4 mm.

Flowering May–Jun. Dry sites in forests, broad-leaved upland forests, chaparral, lower montane coniferous forests; 300–1500 m; Calif.

Lupinus cervinus is known from the Santa Lucia Mountains in Monterey and San Luis Obispo counties.

43. Lupinus chamissonis Eschscholtz, Mém. Acad. Imp. Sci. St. Pétersbourg Hist. Acad. 10(2): 288. 1826 • Dune bush lupine [E]

Shrubs, 5–20 dm, silver, densely appressed-hairy. **Cotyledons** deciduous, petiolate. **Stems** erect or ascending, branched. **Leaves** cauline; stipules 8–10 mm; petiole 1–3.5 cm; leaflets 5–9, blades 10–25 × 3–6 mm, adaxial surface pubescent. **Peduncles** 2–6 cm; bracts deciduous, 7–10 mm. **Racemes** 5–20 cm; flowers ± whorled. **Pedicels** 4–8 mm. **Flowers** 8–16 mm; calyx bulge or spur 0–1 mm, abaxial lobe entire, 7–9 mm, adaxial lip deeply lobed, 5–7 mm; corolla light violet to blue, banner patch persistently yellow, banner densely hairy abaxially, lower keel margins ± ciliate, adaxial margins glabrous. **Legumes** 2.5–3.5 cm, hairy. **Seeds** 4–8, mottled brown, 4–5 mm.

Flowering Mar–Jul. Coastal strands, dunes; 0–10 m; Calif.

Lupinus chamissonis is known along the immediate coast from Los Angeles to Sonoma counties.

44. Lupinus constancei T. W. Nelson & J. P. Nelson, Brittonia 35: 180, fig. 1. 1983 • Lassics lupine [C] [E]

Lupinus lepidus Douglas ex Lindley var. *constancei* (T. W. Nelson & J. P. Nelson) Isely

Herbs, perennial, less than 1.5 dm, matted, long-shaggy-hairy. **Cotyledons** deciduous, petiolate. **Stems** ± prostrate, branched. **Leaves** cauline, clustered near base; stipules less than 6 mm; petiole 6–8(–14) cm; leaflets 6 or 7, blades 10–20 × 8–10 mm, adaxial surface pubescent. **Peduncles** 1.5–4 cm; bracts deciduous, 2.5–3 mm. **Racemes** dense, 3–5 cm, usually exceeding leaves; flowers whorled. **Pedicels** 1–4 mm. **Flowers** 8–12 mm, in 5–12 whorls; calyx bulge or spur 0–1 mm, abaxial lobe entire, 4–5 mm, adaxial lobe notched, 4–5 mm; corolla pink, banner patch light yellow, keel dark rose, white at claw, banner glabrous abaxially, strongly reflexed, lower keel margins glabrous, adaxial margin ciliate. **Legumes** 1.5–2.5 cm, shaggy. **Seeds** 3–5, tan.

Flowering Jul. Serpentine barrens in openings of lower montane conifer forests; of conservation concern; 1500–2000 m; Calif.

Lupinus constancei is known from only two populations in the Lassics Range (Inner North Coast Range) in southeastern Humboldt and northwestern Trinity counties.

45. Lupinus covillei Greene, Proc. Acad. Nat. Sci. Philadelphia 44: 365. 1893 [E]

Lupinus dasyphyllus Greene; *L. gracilentus* Greene var. *covillei* (Greene) D. W. Taylor

Herbs, perennial, 2–9 dm, strigose to shaggy-pubescent. **Cotyledons** deciduous, petiolate. **Stems** erect, clustered, unbranched or branched. **Leaves** cauline, yellow-green; stipules 12–30 mm; proximal petioles 5–10 cm, distal ones 2 cm; leaflets 4–9, blades 30–110 × 5–11 mm, adaxial surface villous, hairs greater than 1 mm. **Peduncles** 2–6 cm; bracts persistent, 7–15 mm. **Racemes** 2–6 cm, usually exceeding leaves; flowers spirally arranged or whorled. **Pedicels** 2–5 mm. **Flowers** 10–14 mm; calyx bulge or spur 0–1 mm, abaxial lobe entire or 3-toothed, 6–11 mm, adaxial lobe 2-toothed, 6–8 mm; corolla light blue, banner patch yellow, banner glabrous abaxially, lower keel margins glabrous, adaxial margin sparsely ciliate ± middle to tip. **Legumes** 2.5–4 cm, woolly. **Seeds** 4–6, beige, mottled dark, 3–4 mm.

Flowering Jul–Sep. Depressions, meadow edges, moist, rocky slopes, subalpine forests; 2500–3500 m; Calif.

Lupinus covillei is known from Tuolumne County southward to Tulare County and eastward into Mono County.

46. Lupinus croceus Eastwood, Leafl. W. Bot. 2: 126. 1938 • Saffron-flowered lupine [E]

Lupinus croceus var. *pilosellus* (Eastwood) Munz; *L. pilosellus* Eastwood

Herbs, perennial, 4–6 dm, green, hairy. **Cotyledons** deciduous, petiolate. **Stems** erect or ascending, clustered, unbranched or branched. **Leaves** cauline; stipules not leaflike, green to silvery, 4–10 mm; petiole 2–8 cm; leaflets 5–9, blades 30–60 × 3–10 mm, adaxial surface pubescent or glabrous. **Peduncles** 2–6 cm; bracts tardily deciduous, 2–7 mm. **Racemes** 6–28 cm; flowers whorled or not. **Pedicels** 3–6 mm. **Flowers** 12–15 mm; calyx bulge or spur 0–1 mm, abaxial lobe 2 or 3-toothed, 6–7 mm, adaxial lobe 2-toothed, 4–6 mm; corolla bright yellow to orange-yellow, banner usually glabrous abaxially, sparsely hairy on ridge, keel upcurved, glabrous. **Legumes** 2–3.5 cm, hairy. **Seeds** 3–5, mottled tan, 6–8 mm.

Flowering May–Aug. Dry, rocky places, yellow pine and fir forests, montane chaparral; 900–2700 m; Calif.

Lupinus croceus is known from the Cascade and Klamath ranges.

Herbs with spreading hairs and subequal calyx lobes have been called var. *pilosellus*.

47. Lupinus dalesiae Eastwood, Leafl. W. Bot. 2: 266. 1940 (as dalesae) • Quincy lupine [E]

Lupinus formosus Greene var. *clemensiae* C. P. Smith

Herbs, perennial, 2–5 dm, long-white-spreading-hairy. **Cotyledons** deciduous, petiolate. **Stems** ascending or erect, branched. **Leaves** cauline; stipules 6–16 mm; petiole 1–3 cm; leaflets 6–9, blades 20–45 × 3–8 mm, adaxial surface tomentose, hairs silvery. **Peduncles** 2–5 cm; bracts deciduous, 5–9 mm. **Racemes** 5–16 cm; flowers ± whorled. **Pedicels** 2–5.5 mm. **Flowers** 9–12 mm; calyx bulge or spur 0–1 mm, abaxial lobe 3-toothed, 3–7 mm, adaxial lobe 2-toothed, 4–7 mm; corolla usually yellow, banner hairy abaxially, keel ± glabrous. **Legumes** 2–3 cm, strigose. **Seeds** 3–5, tan, 3–5 mm.

Flowering May–Aug. Open, dry areas in pine forests; (800–)1000–2500 m; Calif.

Lupinus dalesiae is known only from the high Sierra Nevada in Plumas County. It is distinctive with its white pubescence, yellow flowers, and banner that is hairy abaxially.

P. A. Munz (1959) treated *Lupinus dalesiae* as a synonym of *L. adsurgens* var. *undulatus* C. P. Smith, but *L. adsurgens* has a banner that is glabrous abaxially.

48. Lupinus diffusus Nuttall, Gen. N. Amer. Pl. 2: 93. 1818 • Oak Ridge lupine E F

Lupinus cumulicola Small

Herbs, usually perennial, sometimes annual or biennial, 2–8 dm, densely silky-pubescent, silvery becoming rusty or tawny. **Cotyledons** deciduous, petiolate. **Stems** decumbent, spreading, many branched. **Leaves** basal, clustered; stipules 20–150 mm; petiole 2.5–10 cm; leaflet 1, blades 40–120 × 18–33 mm, adaxial surface densely sericeous or strigulose. **Peduncles** 3–4 cm; bracts deciduous, 4–8 mm. **Racemes** 8–30 cm; flowers whorled. **Pedicels** 1–4 mm. **Flowers** 11–15 mm; calyx abaxial lobe entire, 5–10 mm, adaxial lobe 3-fid with 2 linear laterals, 4–8 mm; corolla light to deep blue, limb centrally white at base, banner spot white to cream, glabrous abaxially, keel glabrous. **Legumes** 3–5 cm, appressed villous to sericeous. **Seeds** 4–7, gray mottled black, 4 mm.

Flowering Mar–May (year-round). Sandhills, sand pine scrub, open woodlands; 0–50 m; Ala., Fla., Ga., Miss., N.C., S.C.

Lupinus diffusus differs from the other unifoliolate species in its much shorter pubescence and banners with a white eyespot. *Lupinus cumulicola* represents peninsular Florida forms that have strongly ascending foliose stems and sometimes broader leaves than usual. Some plants of *L. diffusus* from southern Florida have a vesture of hairs that approach those of *L. villosus* in length.

Lupinus diffusus seeds are known to be toxic (D. J. Wagstaff 2008).

49. Lupinus duranii Eastwood, Leafl. W. Bot. 2: 251. 1940 (as durani) • Mono Lake lupine C E

Lupinus tegeticulatus Eastwood var. *duranii* (Eastwood) Barneby

Herbs, perennial, 0.5–1.2 dm, robust, tufted, shaggy. **Cotyledons** deciduous, petiolate. **Stems** erect, branched. **Leaves** basal; stipules 6–11 mm; petiole (2–) 3–6(–8) cm; leaflets 5–8, blades 5–20 × 5–8 mm, adaxial surface pubescent. **Peduncles** 3–7 cm; bracts ± deciduous, 4–5 mm. **Racemes** crowded, 2–6 cm; flowers whorled. **Pedicels** (2–)4–5 mm. **Flowers** 8–11 mm; calyx bulge or spur 0–1 mm, abaxial lobe ± entire, 6–7 mm, adaxial lobe deeply 2-toothed, 5–7 mm; corolla violet, banner patch cream or white, keel ± straight, banner glabrous abaxially, lower keel margins glabrous, adaxial margin usually glabrous. **Legumes** 1–2 cm, appressed-villous. **Seeds** 3–5, white.

Flowering May–Aug. Dry volcanic pumice, gravel, Great Basin scrub, subalpine and montane coniferous forests; of conservation concern; 2000–3000 m; Calif.

Lupinus duranii is known only from the eastern Sierra Nevada in Mono County. Reports of it from Madera County are questionable.

50. Lupinus elatus I. M. Johnston, Bull. S. Calif. Acad. Sci. 17: 63. 1918 • Silky lupine E

Lupinus albicaulis Douglas var. *elatus* (I. M. Johnston) Jepson; *L. formosus* Greene var. *elatus* (Johnston) C. P. Smith

Herbs, perennial, 5–9 dm, silvery-woolly to -silky. **Cotyledons** deciduous, petiolate. **Stems** ascending or erect, clustered, branched, short-silky. **Leaves** cauline; stipules not leaflike, green to silvery, 5–17 mm; petiole 2–5 cm; leaflets 6–8, blades 20–80 × 2–7 mm, widest below middle, adaxial surface pubescent, hairs densely silver-silky to woolly. **Peduncles** 2–8 cm; bracts deciduous, 6–11 mm. **Racemes** 5–40 cm; flowers ± whorled. **Pedicels** 2–4 mm. **Flowers** 10–14 mm; calyx bulge or spur 0–1 mm, abaxial lobe 3-toothed, 6–8 mm, adaxial lobe notched, 5–7 mm; corolla lavender to blue, banner patch pale yellowish, banner usually glabrous abaxially, keel upcurved, glabrous, banner ovate, wings wide, covering keel tip. **Legumes** 2–3 cm, pubescent. **Seeds** 4–6, mottled olive brown, 5–6 mm.

Flowering Jun–Aug. Dry conifer forests; 1500–3000 m; Calif.

Lupinus elatus is found at high elevations in the southern Sierra Nevada and Transverse Ranges. It closely resembles *L. adsurgens* and *L. andersonii*.

51. Lupinus elmeri Greene, Pittonia 3: 159. 1897 [C] [E]

Lupinus sylvestris Drew, Bull. Torrey Bot. Club 16: 150. 1889, not Lamarck 1778; *L. albicaulis* Douglas var. *sylvestris* Greene

Herbs, perennial, 6–9 dm, green, hairy. **Cotyledons** deciduous, petiolate. **Stems** erect, branched distally, emerging from ground stout, red. **Leaves** cauline; stipules 6–20 mm; petiole 1–7 cm; leaflets 6–8(–10), blades (15–)38–61 × 8–13 mm, adaxial surface green, ± puberulent to short-villous. **Peduncles** 3–9 cm; bracts ± persistent, 7–14 mm (conspicuously longer than buds). **Racemes** 15–20 cm; flowers not whorled. **Pedicels** 2–6 mm. **Flowers** 8–14 mm; calyx bulge or spur 0–1 mm, abaxial lobe 3-toothed, 6–10 mm, adaxial lobe notched, 7–9 mm; corolla pale yellow, banner glabrous abaxially, keel upcurved, glabrous. **Legumes** 2.5–5 cm, hairy. **Seeds** 3–6.

Flowering Jun–Jul. Open areas in red fir forests; of conservation concern; (1300–)1500–2000 m; Calif.

Lupinus elmeri is known from South Fork Mountain in Humboldt and Trinity counties.

52. Lupinus excubitus M. E. Jones, Contr. W. Bot. 8: 26. 1898 • Guard lupine

Shrubs, 10–20 dm, densely silver appressed-hairy. **Cotyledons** deciduous, petiolate. **Stems** erect, branched. **Leaves** cauline; stipules 5–20 mm; petiole 4–10 cm; leaflets 7–9, blades 5–50 × 4–7 mm, adaxial surface densely pubescent, silver-hairy. **Peduncles** 7–20 cm; bracts deciduous, 8–9 mm. **Racemes** 10–70 cm, rachis persistent; flowers whorled or not. **Pedicels** 4–6 mm. **Flowers** with distinctive sweet smell, 10–13 mm; calyx 6–8 mm, bulge or spur 0–1 mm, abaxial lobe entire or 3-toothed, adaxial lobe deeply notched; corolla violet to lavender, banner patch bright yellow, turning purple, banner usually hairy abaxially, keel usually ± lobed proximally, abaxial margins glabrous, adaxial margin ciliate middle to tip. **Legumes** 3–5 cm, silky. **Seeds** 5–8, mottled yellow-brown with lateral lines.

Flowering Apr–Jun. Desert slopes, washes; (700–)1200–2700 m; Calif.; Mexico (Baja California).

Lupinus excubitus is known from Inyo to San Bernardino counties in the Mojave Desert, desert mountains, and southern Sierra Nevada east of the crest (transmontane).

Circumscriptions of *Lupinus excubitus* have been diverse. See discussion under 32. *L. albifrons*, under which many varieties now have been treated as synonyms.

53. Lupinus formosus Greene, Fl. Francisc., 42. 1891

Herbs, perennial, 12–8 dm, densely hairy to tomentose, gray to silver; rhizomes 3–7 mm diam. **Cotyledons** deciduous, petiolate. **Stems** ascending, spreading, or erect, branched. **Leaves** cauline; stipules not leaf-like, green to silvery, 4–15 mm; petiole 2–7 cm; leaflets 7–9, blades 25–70 × 6–14 mm, adaxial surface pubescent. **Peduncles** 3–7 cm; bracts deciduous, 4–14 mm. **Racemes** 10–30 cm; flowers ± whorled. **Pedicels** 3–7 mm. **Flowers** 10–18 mm; calyx bulge or spur 0–1 mm, abaxial lobe entire or 3-toothed, 8–12 mm, adaxial lobe 2-toothed, 7–11 mm; corolla purple, banner patch white or not, banner glabrous abaxially, keel upcurved, glabrous, banner ovate, wings wide, covering keel tip. **Legumes** 3–4.5 cm, hairy. **Seeds** 5–7, mottled brown, 4–7 mm.

Varieties 2 (2 in the flora): California, nw Mexico.

1. Flowers 10–14 mm; stems 3–4 mm diam. . . . . 53a. *Lupinus formosus* var. *formosus*
1. Flowers 16–18 mm; stems 5–7 mm diam. . . . . 53b. *Lupinus formosus* var. *robustus*

53a. Lupinus formosus Greene var. **formosus**

Lupinus albicaulis Douglas var. *proximus* (A. Heller) Jepson; *L. lelandsmithii* Eastwood; *L. lutosus* A. Heller; *L. marinensis* Eastwood; *L. pasadenensis* Eastwood; *L. proximus* A. Heller; *L. puntoreyesensis* C. P. Smith; *L. salticola* Eastwood

Stems 3–4 mm diam. **Flowers** 10–14 mm.

Flowering Apr–Sep. Dry clay soils, grasslands, open areas under pines, valleys; 0–1000(–3000) m; Calif.; Mexico (Baja California).

Variety *formosus* is found throughout California and into northern Baja California (Sierra Juárez Mountains).

53b. Lupinus formosus Greene var. **robustus** C. P. Smith in W. L. Jepson, Man. Fl. Pl. Calif., 529. 1925 [E]

Lupinus albopilosus A. Heller; *L. caeruleus* A. Heller; *L. greenei* A. Nelson; *L. navicularius* A. Heller; *L. sonomensis* A. Heller

Stems 5–7 mm diam. **Flowers** 16–18 mm.

Flowering Apr–Jun. Valley grasslands; 0–1500 m; Calif.

Variety *robustus* is most commonly found in the Central Valley grasslands but can grow in the foothills of the western slope of the Sierra Nevada and the Central, Southern Coast, and Transverse ranges.

54. Lupinus fulcratus Greene, Pittonia 3: 159. 1897 [E]

Lupinus albicaulis Douglas var. *fulcratus* (Greene) Jepson; *L. andersonii* S. Watson var. *fulcratus* (Greene) C. P. Smith; *L. beaneanus* C. P. Smith; *L. finitus* C. P. Smith; *L. fraxinetorum* Greene

Herbs, perennial, 3–8 dm, green, spreading-hairy. **Cotyledons** deciduous, petiolate. **Stems** erect, unbranched or branched. **Leaves** cauline; stipules green, leaflike, lanceolate, 6–30 mm; petiole 3–6 cm; leaflets 6–9, blades 20–60 × 4–8 mm, adaxial surface pubescent. **Peduncles** 1–11 cm; bracts deciduous, 4–10 mm. **Racemes** 3–20 cm; flowers ± whorled. **Pedicels** 2–7 mm. **Flowers** 10–14 mm; calyx bulge or spur 0–1 mm, abaxial lobe entire or 3-toothed, 5–12 mm, adaxial lobe 2-toothed, 5–10 mm; corolla blue, banner patch white, banner glabrous abaxially, keel upcurved, usually glabrous, sparsely hairy near middle of adaxial margin. **Legumes** 2–4 cm, silky. **Seeds** 2–6, beige, mottled brown, 4–5 mm.

Flowering May–Sep. In mixed conifer forests, on granitic soils; 1500–3000 m; Calif.

Lupinus fulcratus is found at higher elevations in the Sierra Nevada. It closely resembles *L. andersonii* except for the leaflike stipules.

Lupinus ionewalkerae C. P. Smith, *L. lingulae* C. P. Smith, and *L. cymbaegressus* C. P. Smith may be hybrids with *L. andersonii* (P. A. Munz 1959).

55. Lupinus gracilentus Greene, Proc. Acad. Nat. Sci. Philadelphia 44: 365. 1893 • Slender lupine [C] [E]

Herbs, perennial, 2–8 dm, green, puberulent to hairy. **Cotyledons** deciduous, petiolate. **Stems** erect or slightly spreading, clustered, unbranched or branched distally. **Leaves** cauline; stipules 10–15 mm; proximal petioles (3–)5–14 cm, distal ones (1–)2–4 cm; leaflets 5–8, blades 35–80 × 2–5 mm, adaxial surface pubescent. **Peduncles** 6–12 cm; bracts semideciduous, 4–10 mm. **Racemes** 6–20 cm; flowers in 4–8 distinct whorls. **Pedicels** 2–4 mm. **Flowers** 8–18 mm; calyx bulge or spur 0–1 mm, abaxial lobe 2 or 3-toothed or entire, 5–7 mm, adaxial lobe 2-toothed, 7 mm; corolla blue, banner patch white to yellowish, banner glabrous abaxially, lower keel margins glabrous, adaxial keel sparsely ciliate. **Legumes** 2–3 cm, densely hairy. **Seeds** 6–8.

Flowering Jul–Sep. Open moist sites, subalpine forests; of conservation concern; 2500–3500 m; Calif.

Lupinus gracilentus is known from the southern Sierra Nevada (Rock Creek) in Inyo and Mono counties northward to Yosemite National Park.

56. Lupinus grayi (S. Watson) S. Watson, Proc. Amer. Acad. Arts 11: 126. 1876

Lupinus andersonii S. Watson var. *grayi* S. Watson, Proc. Amer. Acad. Arts 8: 531. 1873 (as andersoni); *L. ionegristiae* C. P. Smith; *L. louisebucariae* C. P. Smith

Herbs, perennial, 2–3.5 dm, spreading-tomentose to -woolly. **Cotyledons** deciduous, petiolate. **Stems** prostrate to matted, clustered, usually unbranched. **Leaves** usually basal; stipules 4–10 mm; petiole 5–12 cm; leaflets 5–11, blades 10–35 × 4–7 mm, adaxial surface hairs ± spreading, dense, tomentose to woolly. **Peduncles** 3–15 cm; bracts deciduous, 4–5(–10) mm. **Racemes** 10–16 cm; flowers ± whorled. **Pedicels** 2–4 mm. **Flowers** fragrant, 10–16 mm; calyx bulge or spur 0–1 mm, abaxial lobe entire or 3-toothed, 7–12 mm, adaxial lobe deeply 2-toothed, 5–10 mm; corolla deep purple to light blue, banner patch yellow turning reddish, banner glabrous or hairy abaxially, lower keel margins usually ciliate near base, adaxial margin densely hairy. **Legumes** 2–3.5 cm, hairy. **Seeds** 4–6, mottled gray-brown with dark lateral line, 3–4 mm.

Flowering May–Jul. Openings in yellow pine and red fir forests; 500–2500 m; Calif.; Mexico (Baja California).

Lupinus grayi is known from the Sierra Nevada from Kern County northward to Plumas County.

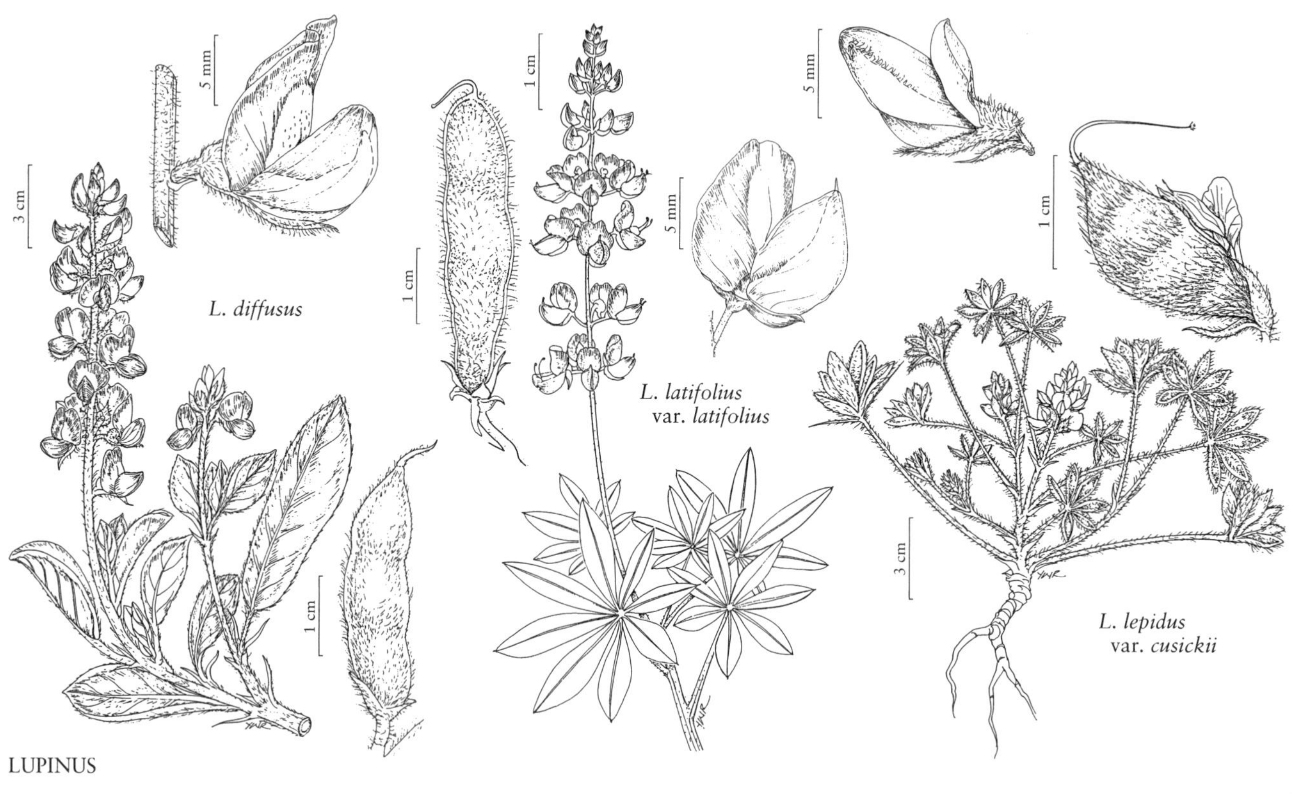

LUPINUS

57. **Lupinus huachucanus** M. E. Jones, Contr. W. Bot. 12: 10. 1908 • Huachuca Mountain lupine [C]

Lupinus platanophilus M. E. Jones

Herbs, perennial (often with annual aspect), 0.1–2 dm, conspicuously pilose, from taproot. **Cotyledons** deciduous, petiolate. **Stems** prostrate to decumbent, clustered, acaulescent or short-spreading and unbranched. **Leaves** mostly near base, in a rosette; stipules 4–10 mm; petiole 1–9 cm; leaflets 5–7(or 8), blades 10–55 × 4–12 mm, adaxial surface greenish, surfaces copiously villous-hirsute with long, spreading hairs, abaxially more dense. **Peduncles** 3–4.5 cm; bracts deciduous, 4–8 mm. **Racemes** 6–23 cm; flowers spirally arranged. **Pedicels** 1–4 mm. **Flowers** 7–13 mm; calyx bulge or spur 0–1 mm, lobes entire, 5–7.5 mm; corolla violet-blue, banner yellow toward center, tip of keel purple, wings yellow toward center, banner glabrous abaxially, upper keel margins ciliate to densely ciliate. **Legumes** 1.5–2 cm, hispid. **Seeds** 3–5, dark with light spots.

Flowering Mar–May. Desert mountains, pine woodlands, canyons along trails; of conservation concern; 1500–2000(–2100) m; Ariz.; Mexico (Chihuahua, Durango, Sonora).

Lupinus huachucanus occurs in the Santa Rita Mountains in Santa Cruz County, Chiricahua and Huachuca mountains in Cochise County, and in Pima County.

Lupinus huachucanus somewhat resembles *L. concinnus* but is readily distinguished by its spreading habit, racemes surpassing the foliage, violet-blue corollas, and ciliate keel. *Lupinus concinnus* is an annual with a more erect habit, pink corollas, and a non-ciliate keel.

58. **Lupinus hyacinthinus** Greene, Leafl. Bot. Observ. Crit. 2: 85. 1910

Lupinus albicaulis Douglas var. *hyacinthinus* (Greene) Jepson; *L. andersonii* S. Watson var. *sublinearis* C. P. Smith; *L. formosus* Greene var. *hyacinthinus* (Greene) C. P. Smith

Herbs, perennial, 4–10 dm, gray becoming green, sparsely hairy. **Cotyledons** deciduous, petiolate. **Stems** erect, unbranched or branched distally. **Leaves** cauline; stipules not leaflike, green to silvery, 5–16 mm; petiole 3–6 cm; leaflets 7–12, blades 30–80 × 4–8 mm, adaxial surface sparsely pubescent. **Peduncles** 3–12 cm; bracts deciduous, 5–9 mm. **Racemes** 4–22 cm; flowers ± whorled. **Pedicels** 2–6 mm. **Flowers** 13–16 mm; calyx bulge or spur 0–1 mm, abaxial lobe entire or 3-toothed, 7–11 mm, adaxial lobe 2-toothed, 6–10 mm; corolla light blue to purple, banner patch yellowish to white, banner glabrous abaxially, keel upcurved, glabrous, banner ovate, wings wide, covering keel tip. **Legumes** 3–4 cm, silky. **Seeds** 3–7, beige, speckled brown, 4–6 mm.

Flowering Jun–Aug. Dry slopes, under yellow pines and white fir; 2000–3500 m; Calif.; Mexico (Baja California).

Lupinus hyacinthinus is found in southern California in the San Gabriel, San Jacinto, and Santa Rosa mountains and on the Sierra San Pedro Mártir in Baja California. It is distinguished from its close relatives by its larger flowers in combination with green (versus gray or dull green) leaves.

59. Lupinus kuschei Eastwood, Leafl. W. Bot. 3: 170. 1942 • Yukon lupine [E]

Lupinus jacobandersonii C. P. Smith; *L. porsildianus* C. P. Smith; *L. sericeus* Pursh var. *kuschei* (Eastwood) B. Boivin

Herbs, perennial, 1.5–5(–6) dm, densely silky-sericeous. **Cotyledons** deciduous, petiolate. **Stems** decumbent to erect, few to several-tufted, unbranched or branched. **Leaves** mostly basal with 3 or 4 cauline; stipules not leaflike, green to silvery, 8–12 mm; basal petioles 4–7 cm, proximal cauline petioles 3.5–15 cm, distal ones 2–3.5 cm; leaflets 5–9, blades 15–70 × 3–8 mm, surfaces densely pubescent, adaxially less pubescent and greener. **Peduncles** 2.5–7(–13) cm; bracts subpersistent, 4–10 mm. **Racemes** 3–10(–12) cm; flowers in 3–6 whorls. **Pedicels** 2–5(–7) mm. **Flowers** 10–13 mm; calyx slightly gibbous adaxially near base, bulge or spur 0–1 mm, abaxial lobe 3-lobed, 5–7 mm, adaxial lobe 2-lobed, 4–6 mm; corolla blue to purple, banner spot light yellow, banner with inconspicuous hairs abaxially, adaxial keel glabrous or with a few cilia along adaxial edges towards tip, keel upcurved. **Legumes** 1.5–3 cm, silky-pilose. **Seeds** 4–6.

Flowering Jun–Sep. Mesic to dry, sandy, gravelly, or rocky openings, lodgepole pine forests, alpine pumice fields; 80–2600 m; B.C., Yukon; Alaska.

Lupinus kuschei is of conservation concern in Alaska; it is known from southern Alaska to northern British Columbia and the Yukon Territory.

Lupinus kuschei may prove to be a hybrid between *L. arcticus* and *L. sericeus.*

60. Lupinus lapidicola A. Heller, Bull. Torrey Bot. Club 51: 306. 1924 • Mount Eddy lupine [E]

Herbs, perennial, less than 1 dm, silver-silky. **Cotyledons** deciduous, petiolate. **Stems** ± prostrate or ascending, branched. **Leaves** basal (clustered near base); stipules 4–5 mm; petiole 2–4.5 cm; leaflets 6–8, blades 10–20 × 2–4 mm, adaxial surface pubescent. **Peduncles** 5–10 cm; bracts usually deciduous, 4–5 mm. **Racemes** 2–7 cm; flowers in few whorls, widely separated. **Pedicels** 2–4 mm. **Flowers** 9–12 mm; calyx bulge or spur 0–1 mm, abaxial lobe obscurely 3-toothed, 5–6 mm, adaxial lobe notched, 4–5 mm; corolla ± violet, banner patch yellow, banner usually hairy abaxially, lower keel margins glabrous, adaxial margin ciliate. **Legumes** 2–3 cm, pilose. **Seeds** 1 or 2.

Flowering Jul. Dry, granite gravel, yellow pine and subalpine forests, granitic or serpentine soils; 1500–3000 m; Calif.

Lupinus lapidicola is relatively rare and is known only from the Klamath Ranges in northwestern California.

61. Lupinus latifolius J. Agardh, Syn. Lupini, 18. 1835 [F]

Lupinus rivularis Douglas ex Lindley var. *latifolius* (J. Agardh) S. Watson

Herbs, perennial, 3–24 dm, not fleshy, green, glabrous or hairy. **Cotyledons** deciduous, petiolate. **Stems** erect or spreading, branched or unbranched. **Leaves** cauline, basal when present withered by anthesis; stipules 5–10 mm; petiole 4–20 cm; leaflets 5–11, blades 40–100 × 6–24 mm, abaxial surface ± hairy, adaxial surface glabrous or hairy. **Peduncles** 8–20 cm; bracts deciduous, 8–12 mm. **Racemes** 16–60 cm; flowers whorled or spirally arranged. **Pedicels** 2–12 mm. **Flowers** 8–18 mm; calyx abaxial lobe entire or notched, 4–8 mm, adaxial lobe entire or 2-toothed, 5–10 mm; corolla blue or purple to white, banner patch usually white to yellowish turning purple, banner glabrous abaxially, lower keel margins usually ciliate, adaxial margin ciliate from claw to middle. **Legumes** 2–4.5 cm, ± densely hairy. **Seeds** 6–10, mottled dark brown, 3–4 mm.

Varieties 5 (5 in the flora): w North America, nw Mexico.

Various authors have differed in their circumscriptions of *Lupinus latifolius.* For example, P. K. Vaughn and D. B. Dunn (1977) recognized three varieties, D. Isely (1998) recognized six varieties, and C. L. Hitchcock et al. (1955–1969, vol. 3) recognized three varieties. The most conservative approach has been taken here by recognizing taxa that have the clearest characteristics, but that approach might not reflect phylogeny. Research is needed to clarify the varieties and particularly the relationships among *L. latifolius* and *L. arcticus*, *L. perennis*, and *L. polyphyllus*.

Lupinus latifolius is known to cause birth defects in livestock (R. F. Keeler et al. 1977).

1. Flowers 8–14 mm.
   2. Flowers 10–14(–16) mm . . . . 61a. *Lupinus latifolius* var. *latifolius*
   2. Flowers 8–10(–12) mm . . . . 61e. *Lupinus latifolius* var. *viridifolius*
1. Flowers 12–18 mm.
   3. Stems densely hairy, not hollow; San Francisco Bay area, California . . . . 61b. *Lupinus latifolius* var. *dudleyi*
   3. Stems glabrate or sparsely strigose, hollow; sw California or n Oregon to British Columbia.
      4. Herbs 5–20 dm, caudex often unbranched; Arizona, California . . . . 61c. *Lupinus latifolius* var. *parishii*
      4. Herbs 2.5–6 dm, caudex branched; n Oregon to British Columbia . . . . 61d. *Lupinus latifolius* var. *subalpinus*

61a. Lupinus latifolius J. Agardh var. **latifolius** F

Lupinus arcticus S. Watson subsp. *canadensis* (C. P. Smith) D. B. Dunn; *L. caudicifer* Eastwood; *L. columbianus* A. Heller; *L. columbianus* var. *simplex* C. P. Smith; *L. lasiotropis* Greene ex Eastwood; *L. latifolius* var. *canadensis* C. P. Smith; *L. latifolius* var. *columbianus* (A. Heller) C. P. Smith; *L. latifolius* var. *leucanthus* (Rydberg) Isely; *L. latifolius* var. *ligulatus* (Greene) C. P. Smith; *L. latifolius* subsp. *longipes* (Greene) Kenney & D. B. Dunn; *L. latifolius* var. *longipes* (Greene) C. P. Smith; *L. latifolius* var. *simplex* (C. P. Smith) Isely; *L. latifolius* var. *thompsonianus* (C. P. Smith) C. L. Hitchcock; *L. leucanthus* Rydberg; *L. ligulatus* Greene; *L. longipes* Greene; *L. sericeus* Pursh var. *thompsonianus* C. P. Smith; *L. suksdorfii* B. L. Robinson ex Piper

Herbs to 10(–15) dm. **Stems** not hollow, glabrous or puberulent. **Flowers** 10–14(–16) mm.

Flowering Apr–Sep. Mesic areas, streamsides, open woodlands; 0–3500 m; B.C., Yukon; Ariz., Calif., Oreg., Wash.; Mexico (Baja California).

Variety *latifolius* is known from throughout coastal and montane areas of cismontane California northward through western Oregon and Washington into British Columbia and Yukon, and in Mohave and Yavapai counties, Arizona.

61b. Lupinus latifolius J. Agardh var. **dudleyi** C. P. Smith in W. L. Jepson, Man. Fl. Pl. Calif., 530. 1925 E

Lupinus dudleyi (C. P. Smith) Eastwood; *L. latifolius* subsp. *dudleyi* (C. P. Smith) Kenney & D. B. Dunn

Herbs 0.9–11 dm, caudex usually branched. **Stems** not hollow, densely hairy. **Flowers** 13–16 mm.

Flowering Apr–May. Chaparral; 0–1000 m; Calif.

Variety *dudleyi* is known from the San Francisco Bay area.

61c. Lupinus latifolius J. Agardh var. **parishii** C. P. Smith in W. L. Jepson, Man. Fl. Pl. Calif., 530. 1925 (as parishi)

Lupinus latifolius subsp. *parishii* (C. P. Smith) Kenney & D. B. Dunn; *L. parishii* Eastwood

Herbs 5–20 dm, caudex often unbranched. **Stems** hollow, glabrate to sparsely strigose. **Flowers** 14–18 mm.

Flowering May–Aug. Moist areas; 50–3500 m; Ariz., Calif.; Mexico (Baja California).

Variety *parishii* is known from central and southern California, from Santa Barbara and Tulare counties to San Diego County, and eastward to Apache, Coconino, and Yavapai counties in Arizona. It is found at higher elevations in the central and southern Sierra Nevada and at lower elevations along the south coast and inland ranges.

61d. Lupinus latifolius J. Agardh var. **subalpinus** (Piper & B. L. Robinson) C. P. Smith, Bull. Torrey Bot. Club 51: 308. 1924 E

Lupinus subalpinus Piper & B. L. Robinson, Contr. U.S. Natl. Herb. 11: 356. 1906; *L. arcticus* subsp. *subalpinus* (Piper & B. L. Robinson) D. B. Dunn; *L. arcticus* var. *subalpinus* (Piper & B. L. Robinson) C. P. Smith; *L. glacialis* C. P. Smith; *L. volcanicus* Greene; *L. volcanicus* var. *rupestricola* C. P. Smith

Herbs (1–)2–3(–6) dm, caudex branched at base. **Stems** hollow, soft-shaggy to glabrate (appearing whitish to reddish from hair). **Flowers** 12–18 mm.

Flowering (Jun–)Jul–Aug. Volcanic sand, alpine or subalpine ridges and meadows; (500–)1000–2500 m; B.C.; Oreg., Wash.

Variety *subalpinus* is known from the Coast Mountains and Cascade Range in British Columbia southward through Washington to the volcanic cones of northern Oregon. It is also reported from western Yukon [*Beamish et al. 681151* (UBC), *Beamish et al. s.n.* (UBC)] but the specimens have not been examined; it is absent from Haida Gwaii (Queen Charlotte Islands).

There is some evidence that var. *subalpinus* hybridizes with *Lupinus nootkatensis* (D. B. Dunn and J. M. Gillett 1966). Circumscription of var. *subalpinus* is not clear. It is sometimes placed as a variety of *L. latifolius* and sometimes as a variety of *L. arcticus*. Variety *subalpinus* can be differentiated from *L. arcticus* by the leaves being mostly cauline versus mostly basal.

61e. Lupinus latifolius J. Agardh var. **viridifolius** (A. Heller) C. P. Smith, Contr. Dudley Herb. 1: 50. 1927 [E]

Lupinus viridifolius A. Heller, Muhlenbergia 2: 64. 1905; *L. latifolius* var. *barbatus* (L. F. Henderson) Munz; *L. ligulatus* Greene var. *barbatus* L. F. Henderson

Herbs 4–6 dm. **Stems** not hollow, usually strigose, rarely glabrous. **Flowers** 8–10(–12) mm.

Flowering Jun–Aug. Moist areas; 1000–2000 m; Calif., Oreg.

Variety *viridifolius* is known from the Cascade and Klamath ranges in Oregon and the Modoc Plateau in northern California.

62. Lupinus lepidus Douglas ex Lindley, Bot. Reg. 14: plate 1149. 1828 • Dwarf lupine [E] [F]

Herbs, perennial, less than 6 dm, matted, hairy. **Cotyledons** deciduous, petiolate. **Stems** acaulescent or prostrate to ± erect, unbranched or branched. **Leaves** usually basal, sometimes cauline present; stipules 3–25 mm; petiole 2–13 cm; leaflets 5–8, blades 5–40 × 3–7 mm, surfaces pubescent. **Peduncles** 2–13 cm; bracts usually persistent, 4–15 mm. **Racemes** dense, 3–20 cm, not exceeding to exserted beyond leaves; flowers whorled, usually crowded. **Pedicels** 0.4–3 mm. **Flowers** 6–13 mm; calyx bulge or spur 0–1 mm, abaxial lobe entire or 3-toothed, 4–7 mm, adaxial lobe entire or 2-toothed, 3–7 mm; corolla pink, violet, or blue, banner glabrous abaxially, lower keel margins glabrous, adaxial margin ciliate. **Legumes** 1–2 cm, hairy. **Seeds** 2–6, ± mottled tan or green to brown, 2–4 mm.

Varieties 10 (10 in the flora): w North America.

Dwarf perennial lupines are usually characterized by a cespitose habit, persistent inflorescence bracts, banners that are glabrous abaxially, and ciliate keel petals. The history of the taxonomy of this group was discussed in detail by B. J. Cox (1972), R. C. Barneby (1989), and K. A. Weitemier (2010). Barneby gave justification for his conservative treatment of this taxon, which is generally followed here. Genetic analysis in lupines has shown little separation, according to Weitemier, but he suggested that there is good evidence to retain these variations as varieties, following Barneby, rather than elevating them to species level.

1. Racemes not exceeding leaves, or only partially so.
    2. Banner recurved, reflexed, 3+ mm wide . . . . 62b. *Lupinus lepidus* var. *aridus*
    2. Banner not or scarcely recurved, overhanging wings, 2.5–3 mm wide.
        3. Stems present and branched; leaves basal and cauline; racemes loose; pedicels 2.5–4 mm . . . . 62f. *Lupinus lepidus* var. *cusickii*
        3. Stems very short or absent, densely tufted; leaves basal; racemes dense; pedicels 0.4–1.5 mm. . . . . . 62j. *Lupinus lepidus* var. *utahensis*
1. Racemes entirely exserted beyond leaves.
    4. Leaves clustered near base (appearing ± basal); herbs appearing acaulescent or shortly caulescent.
        5. Flowers 9–12 mm; leaflet blades 10–20 mm; rare, only from Mt. Ashland, Oregon . . . . .62c. *Lupinus lepidus var ashlandensis*
        5. Flowers 6–9(–10) mm; leaflet blades 5–30 mm; British Columbia southward to California, eastward to Idaho, Nevada.
            6. Racemes ± dense, 2–8 cm; herbs to 1 dm; leaflet blades 5–10 mm; elevation (1600–)2000–3500 m . . . . 62g. *Lupinus lepidus* var. *lobbii*
            6. Racemes elongate, (2–)4.5–11(–15) cm; herbs 1.2–3.5 dm; leaflet blades 10–30 mm; elevation 1000–2500 m . . . . .62i. *Lupinus lepidus* var. *sellulus*
    4. Leaves usually spread along stems or at least with some tufts of cauline leaves; herbs usually strongly caulescent (except stems short or absent in var. *culbertsonii*).
        7. Flowers 10–14 mm; Alberta, British Columbia, Alaska, Oregon, Washington. . . . . 62a. *Lupinus lepidus* var. *lepidus*
        7. Flowers 7–11.5(–12) mm; California, Nevada.
            8. Racemes dense, (5–)12–30 cm; flowers in 9–12 whorls, dense; leaves cauline; elevation (300–)1500–2500(–3200 m). . . . . .62d. *Lupinus lepidus* var. *confertus*
            8. Racemes usually open, 2–10(–12) cm; flowers in (2 or)3–7 whorls, ± well spaced; leaves basal and cauline; elevation 1900–4000 m.

[9. Shifted to left margin.—Ed.]

9. Leaflet blades usually 10–30 mm; flowers (9–)10–11.5 mm; elevation 1900–3600 m. . . . . 62e. *Lupinus lepidus* var. *culbertsonii*
9. Leaflet blades usually 5–15(–30) mm; flowers usually 7–9(–12) mm; elevation 2300–4000 m . . . . 62h. *Lupinus lepidus* var. *ramosus*

62a. Lupinus lepidus Douglas ex Lindley var. **lepidus** • Pacific or dwarf lupine [E]

Lupinus minimus Douglas

Herbs 20–40 cm, sericeous. **Stems** erect. **Leaves** usually basal; leaflet blades 5–40 × 3–7 mm, adaxial surface pubescent. **Peduncles** (2–)4.5–13 cm; bracts persistent, 4–15 mm. **Racemes** 8–13 cm, exserted beyond leaves, ± dense, flowers whorled. **Pedicels** 1–3 mm. **Flowers** in 9–11 whorls, 10–14 mm; corolla blue. **Seeds** 3–6, 2–3 mm.

Flowering Apr–Jul. Open prairies, in sandy, gravelly soils; 30–500 m; Alta., B.C.; Alaska, Oreg., Wash.

Variety *lepidus* was historically present throughout much of the Willamette Valley; it has been extirpated from much of its range and is probably now only present in Oregon at a few sites (K. A. Weitemier 2010).

62b. Lupinus lepidus Douglas ex Lindley var. **aridus** (Douglas) Jepson, Fl. Calif. 2: 268. 1936 [E]

Lupinus aridus Douglas, Edwards's Bot. Reg. 15: plate 1242. 1829; *L. abortivus* Greene; *L. aridus* var. *abortivus* (Greene) C. P. Smith; *L. brachypodus* Piper; *L. hellerae* A. Heller; *L. lepidus* subsp. *medius* Detling; *L. lepidus* var. *medius* (Detling) H. St. John; *L. minimus* Douglas var. *hellerae* (A. Heller) C. P. Smith & H. St. John; *L. sellulus* Kellogg var. *medius* (Detling) B. J. Cox; *L. volutans* Greene

Herbs (7–)10–15(–35) cm, pilose to ± hirsute-bristly. **Stems** loosely tufted, subacaulescent or shortly caulescent, rarely branched. **Leaves** appearing basal; leaflet blades (13–)15–28(–35) mm. **Peduncles** 0–4(–8) cm; bracts 6–9 mm. **Racemes** 3.5–20(–25) cm, usually partially exserted from leaves. **Pedicels** stout, 1–2.5(–3) mm. **Flowers** in 6–14 whorls, 7–12.5 mm; corolla pale blue or blue to blue-purple, banner recurved, reflexed, 3+ mm wide, wings (7–)8–12.5 mm. **2*n*** = 48.

Flowering (Apr–)May–Jun(–Jul). Bluffs, barrens, sandy or gravelly hillsides among sagebrush, pinyon-juniper woodlands; 200–2200 m; Ariz., Calif., Idaho, Nev., Oreg., Utah, Wash.

Variety *aridus* is found widely scattered over southeastern Oregon, southwestern Idaho, southward in Nevada to Washoe, Nye, and Lincoln counties, eastward into adjacent Iron and Washington counties in Utah, and northward in the Columbia Basin in Oregon and Washington; it is reported in northwestern Arizona and is rarely found in eastern California in Mono County.

62c. Lupinus lepidus Douglas ex Lindley var. **ashlandensis** (B. J. Cox) Isely, Native Natural. Legum. U.S., 705. 1998 [C] [E]

Lupinus aridus Douglas subsp. *ashlandensis* B. J. Cox, Canad. J. Bot. 52: 655, figs. 1B, 3B. 1974

Herbs 7–12 cm, hairs long-dense, appressed, silvery. **Stems** absent. **Leaves** basal; leaflet blades 10–20 mm, surfaces with long, dense, silvery-appressed hairs. **Peduncles** (3–)5–7.5 cm; bracts 5 mm. **Racemes** 3–8 cm (not including peduncle), slightly exceeding leaves, dense. **Pedicels** 1 mm. **Flowers** in 9–13 whorls, 9–12 mm; calyx abaxial lobe 2–3 mm, adaxial lobe 5 mm; corolla blue-violet. **Legumes** 7–11 mm, pubescent. **Seeds** 2–4. **2*n*** = 48.

Flowering Jun–Aug. Alpine slopes; of conservation concern; 2100–2300 m; Oreg.

Variety *ashlandensis* is known only from Mount Ashland in the Siskiyou Mountains of Jackson County.

62d. Lupinus lepidus Douglas ex Lindley var. **confertus** (Kellogg) C. P. Smith, Bull. Torrey Bot. Club 51: 304. 1924 [E]

Lupinus confertus Kellogg, Proc. Calif. Acad. Sci. 2: 192, fig. 59. 1863; *L. aridus* Douglas var. *torreyi* (A. Gray ex S. Watson) C. P. Smith; *L. confertus* var. *wrightii* Greene; *L. lepidus* var. *torreyi* (A. Gray ex S. Watson) Jepson; *L. torreyi* A. Gray ex S. Watson

Herbs 25–60 cm, hairy. **Stems** decumbent to erect. **Leaves** cauline; leaflet blade 15–30 mm, surfaces hairy. **Peduncles** 3–13 cm; bracts 5–14 mm. **Racemes** (5–)12–30 cm, exserted beyond leaves, dense. **Pedicels** stout, ± 1–1.5 mm. **Flowers** in 9–15 whorls, 7–9 mm, dense; corolla blue or pink to lavender, banner patch yellowish fading brown to red. **2*n*** = 48.

Flowering Jun–Aug. Meadows, vernally moist areas in pine forests and sagebrush; (300–)1500–2500(–3200) m; Calif., Nev.

Variety *confertus* is found in Douglas, Esmeralda, Lyon, Mineral, Ormsby, and Washoe counties in Nevada, and in the high Cascades, high Sierra Nevada, Transverse Ranges, Great Basin province, and into the desert mountains in California.

62e. Lupinus lepidus Douglas ex Lindley var. **culbertsonii** (Greene) C. P. Smith, Bull. Torrey Bot. Club 51: 304. 1924 (as culbertsoni) • Hockett Meadows lupine [C] [E]

Lupinus culbertsonii Greene, Leafl. Bot. Observ. Crit. 1: 73. 1904

Herbs 15–40 cm, greenish, sparsely pilose or villous. **Stems** absent or short, decumbent. **Leaves** greenish, basal, also with a few cauline tufts; leaflet blades usually 10–30 mm, surface sparsely pilose. **Peduncles** 8.5–16 cm; bracts 4–5 mm. **Racemes** 4–9(–12) cm, exserted beyond leaves, usually open. **Pedicels** 2–3 mm. **Flowers** in 3–7 whorls, well spaced, (9–)10–11.5 mm; corolla blue, banner patch white to light yellow. **2*n*** = 48.

Flowering Jun–Aug. Mesic sites beneath lodgepole pine, meadows and seeps on granitic and limestone rocky sites; of conservation concern; 1900–3600 m; Calif.

Variety *culbertsonii* is found in the southern Sierra Nevada (Kaweah River, Fresno and Tulare counties, and Kings Canyon and Sequoia national parks).

62f. Lupinus lepidus Douglas ex Lindley var. **cusickii** (S. Watson) C. L. Hitchcock in C. L. Hitchcock et al., Vasc. Pl. Pacif. N.W. 3: 315. 1961 [C] [E] [F]

Lupinus cusickii S. Watson, Proc. Amer. Acad. Arts 22: 469. 1887; *L. aridus* Douglas var. *cusickii* (S. Watson) C. P. Smith; *L. lepidus* subsp. *cusickii* (S. Watson) Detling; *L. longivallis* C. P. Smith

Herbs 5(–10) cm, canescent, taprooted. **Stems** ascending-erect, several from taproot, profusely branched at base, elongated stem internode 1–3 cm. **Leaves** basal and cauline; leaflet blades 10–25 mm, surfaces hairy. **Peduncles** 1–6 cm (together with racemes 2–10 cm); bract 2–3.5 mm. **Racemes** 2–10 cm, not exserted beyond leaves, or only partially so, loose. **Pedicels** 2.5–4 mm. **Flowers** in 6–9 whorls, 7–10 mm; corolla bluish, banner not or scarcely recurved, 2.5–3 mm wide. **2*n*** = 48.

Flowering Jul. Barren tuffaceous or gravelly clay bluffs and gullied riverbanks, usually associated with junipers, sagebrush, and *Eriogonum*; of conservation concern; 1300–1500 m; Idaho, Oreg.

Variety *cusickii* is known from a few populations near Unity in Baker County, Oregon (K. A. Weitemier 2010) and near Donnelly and McCall in Valley County, Idaho.

62g. Lupinus lepidus Douglas ex Lindley var. **lobbii** (S. Watson) C. L. Hitchcock in C. L. Hitchcock et al., Vasc. Pl. Pacif. N.W. 3: 315. 1961 [E]

Lupinus aridus Douglas var. *lobbii* S. Watson, Proc. Amer. Acad. Arts 8: 533. 1873; *L. alpinus* A. Heller; *L. aridus* var. *washoensis* (A. Heller) C. P. Smith; *L. fruticulosus* Greene; *L. lobbii* (S. Watson) A. Gray ex Greene; *L. lyallii* A. Gray; *L. lyallii* var. *danaus* (A. Gray) S. Watson; *L. lyallii* var. *fruticulosus* (Greene) C. P. Smith; *L. lyallii* var. *lobbii* (S. Watson) C. P. Smith; *L. lyallii* subsp. *washoensis* (A. Heller) B. J. Cox; *L. minutifolius* Eastwood; *L. paulinius* Greene; *L. perditorum* Greene; *L. rubro-soli* Eastwood; *L. sellulus* Kellogg var. *lobbii* (S. Watson) B. J. Cox; *L. washoensis* A. Heller

Herbs to 13 cm, hairy to shaggy. **Stems** absent or shortly caulescent, then prostrate and matted. **Leaves** usually basal; leaflet blades 5–10 mm, surfaces hairy to shaggy abaxially, greenish and sometimes glabrate adaxially. **Peduncles** 5–8(–13) cm; bracts 5–6 mm. **Racemes** 2–8 cm, exserted beyond leaves, ± dense. **Pedicels** 1–2 mm. **Flowers** in 4–7 whorls, 6–10 mm; corolla usually violet, rarely white, banner patch white. **2*n*** = 48.

Flowering Jun–Sep. Dry rocks, gravelly ridges, meadows, montane and subalpine; (1600–)2000–3500 m; B.C.; Calif., Idaho, Nev., Oreg., Wash.

Variety *lobbii* is found in British Columbia and southward through the Cascades of Washington and Oregon to the high mountains of the North Coast Ranges, Sierra Nevada, and White Mountains in California. It is known also from the Basin and Range peaks in Idaho and Nevada.

Lupinus pinetorum A. Heller (1910, not M. E. Jones 1898) is an illegitimate name that pertains here.

62h. Lupinus lepidus Douglas ex Lindley var. **ramosus** Jepson, Fl. Calif. 2: 268. 1936 [E]

Lupinus brunneomaculatus Eastwood; *L. crassulus* Greene; *L. culbertsonii* Greene subsp. *hypolasius* (Greene) B. J. Cox; *L. danaus* A. Gray var. *bicolor* Eastwood; *L. hypolasius* Greene

Herbs 13–30 cm, shaggy. **Stems** decumbent to erect. **Leaves** some basal, mostly cauline; leaflet blades usually 5–15(–30) mm, surfaces hairy to shaggy. **Peduncles** 3–5 cm; bracts 4–9 mm. **Racemes** 2–10 cm, exserted beyond leaves, open. **Pedicels** slender, 1.5–3 mm. **Flowers** fragrant, in (2 or)3–7 whorls, ± well spaced, 7–9(–12) mm; corolla blue, banner patch white to yellow. **2*n*** = 48.

Flowering Jul–Aug. Open stony crests, gravelly hillsides, subalpine; 2300–4000 m; Calif.

Variety *ramosus* is known from the central and southern Sierra Nevada and in the Sweetwater and White mountains.

62i. Lupinus lepidus Douglas ex Lindley var. **sellulus** (Kellogg) Barneby in A. Cronquist et al., Intermount. Fl. 3(B): 256. 1989 [E]

Lupinus sellulus Kellogg, Proc. Calif. Acad. Sci. 5: 36. 1873; *L. sellulus* var. *artulus* (Jepson) Eastwood; *L. sellulus* subsp. *ursinus* (Eastwood) Munz

Herbs 12–35 cm, silvery-silky-pubescent. **Stems** short, prostrate to ± erect. **Leaves** sub-basal; leaflet blades 10–30 mm, surfaces gray-green to silvery-hairy. **Peduncles** 1–3, 4–14 cm; bracts 4–8 mm. **Racemes** (2–)4.5–11(–15) cm, exserted beyond leaves, elongate. **Pedicels** 1–1.5 mm. **Flowers** in 12–17 whorls, 8–9 mm; corolla lavender or purple, banner patch yellow to white turning red. $2n = 48$.

Flowering Jun–Aug. Dry rocks, open conifer forests, especially Jeffrey and ponderosa pine forests; 1000–2500 m; Calif., Idaho, Nev., Oreg.

Variety *sellulus* is known from the southern Cascade Ranges and Sierra Nevada westward to the North Coast Ranges in northern California and southern Oregon, and eastward through the Owyhee Desert to the lower Snake River Plains in Idaho and the headwaters of the Humboldt River in Nevada.

62j. Lupinus lepidus Douglas ex Lindley var. **utahensis** (S. Watson) C. L. Hitchcock in C. L. Hitchcock et al., Vasc. Pl. Pacif. N.W. 3: 315. 1961 [E]

Lupinus aridus Douglas var. *utahensis* S. Watson, Proc. Amer. Acad. Arts 8: 534. 1873; *L. amniculi-cervi* C. P. Smith; *L. caespitosus* Nuttall; *L. longivallis* C. P. Smith; *L. psoraleoides* Pollard

Herbs short-lived, 10–25 cm, matted, densely hairy. **Stems** very short or absent, densely tufted. **Leaves** basal; leaflet blades 8–20 mm, surfaces densely hairy. **Peduncles** 0–1.4(–2) cm; bracts 8–15 mm. **Racemes** (2–)3–6 cm, not exceeding leaves, dense. **Pedicels** 0.4–1.5 mm. **Flowers** in 2 or 3 whorls, 7–10 mm; corolla purple or violet, banner patch white, banner not or scarcely recurved, 2.5–3 mm wide, upper keel margins ciliate near tip. $2n = 48$.

Flowering Jun–Aug. Mountain meadows, gravel bars, streambeds, lakeshores, sand or rocks, with sagebrush, lodgepole pine forests and above timberline; 1500–3500 m; Ariz., Calif., Colo., Idaho, Mont., Nev., N.Mex., Oreg., Utah, Wyo.

Variety *utahensis* is widespread in the Rocky and Great Basin mountains from central Idaho and western Montana southward to northwestern New Mexico and northeastern Arizona (Chuska Mountains in Apache County), westward to eastern Oregon, northern Nevada, and eastern Lassen County, California, and disjunct in the White Mountains on the California-Nevada border.

63. Lupinus leucophyllus Douglas ex Lindley, Bot. Reg. 13: plate 1124. 1828 • White-leaved poison or velvet lupine [E] [F]

Lupinus canescens Howell; *L. canescens* subsp. *amblyophyllus* B. L. Robinson ex Piper; *L. cyaneus* Rydberg; *L. eatonianus* C. P. Smith; *L. enodatus* C. P. Smith; *L. erectus* L. F. Henderson; *L. falsoerectus* C. P. Smith; *L. forslingii* C. P. Smith; *L. holosericeus* Nuttall var. *amblyophyllus* (B. L. Robinson ex Piper) C. P. Smith; *L. leucophyllus* var. *belliae* C. P. Smith; *L. leucophyllus* var. *canescens* (Howell) C. P. Smith; *L. leucophyllus* subsp. *erectus* (L. F. Henderson) Harmon; *L. leucophyllus* var. *plumosus* (Douglas) B. L. Robinson; *L. leucophyllus* var. *retrorsus* (L. F. Henderson) C. P. Smith; *L. leucophyllus* var. *tenuispicus* (A. Nelson) C. P. Smith; *L. macrostachys* Rydberg; *L. plumosus* Douglas; *L. retrorsus* L. F. Henderson; *L. tenuispicus* A. Nelson

Herbs, perennial, 4–9 dm, white-woolly and long-stiff-hairy. **Cotyledons** deciduous, petiolate. **Stems** erect, clustered, unbranched or branched. **Leaves** cauline, some clustered at base; stipules 6–15 mm; petiole 3–20 cm; leaflets 6–11, blades 30–90 × 6–19 mm, adaxial surface pubescent. **Peduncles** 2–8 cm; bracts usually persistent, 3–12 mm. **Racemes** 8–30 cm; flowers dense, spiciform. **Pedicels** stout, 1–2 mm. **Flowers** 10–13 mm; calyx bulge or spur 0–1 mm, abaxial lobe entire, 3–8 mm, adaxial lobe 2-toothed, 3–6 mm; corolla lavender or purple to yellowish, often turning brown, banner patch yellow to brown, banner not much reflexed-recurved beyond midpoint, this less than 3 mm proximal to apex, banner densely hairy abaxially, lower keel margins glabrous, adaxial margin ciliate throughout. **Legumes** 2–3.6 cm, hairy. **Seeds** 3–6, mottled gray-tan. $2n = 24, 48$.

Flowering May–Aug. Grassy hillsides, sagebrush flats, glades and meadows; 500–2000 m; B.C.; Calif., Colo., Idaho, Mont., Nev., Oreg., Utah, Wash., Wyo.

Lupinus leucophyllus is known from southern British Columbia southward to northern California and eastward to western Montana, western Wyoming, and northwestern Colorado. It is considered toxic, and can form very dense stands.

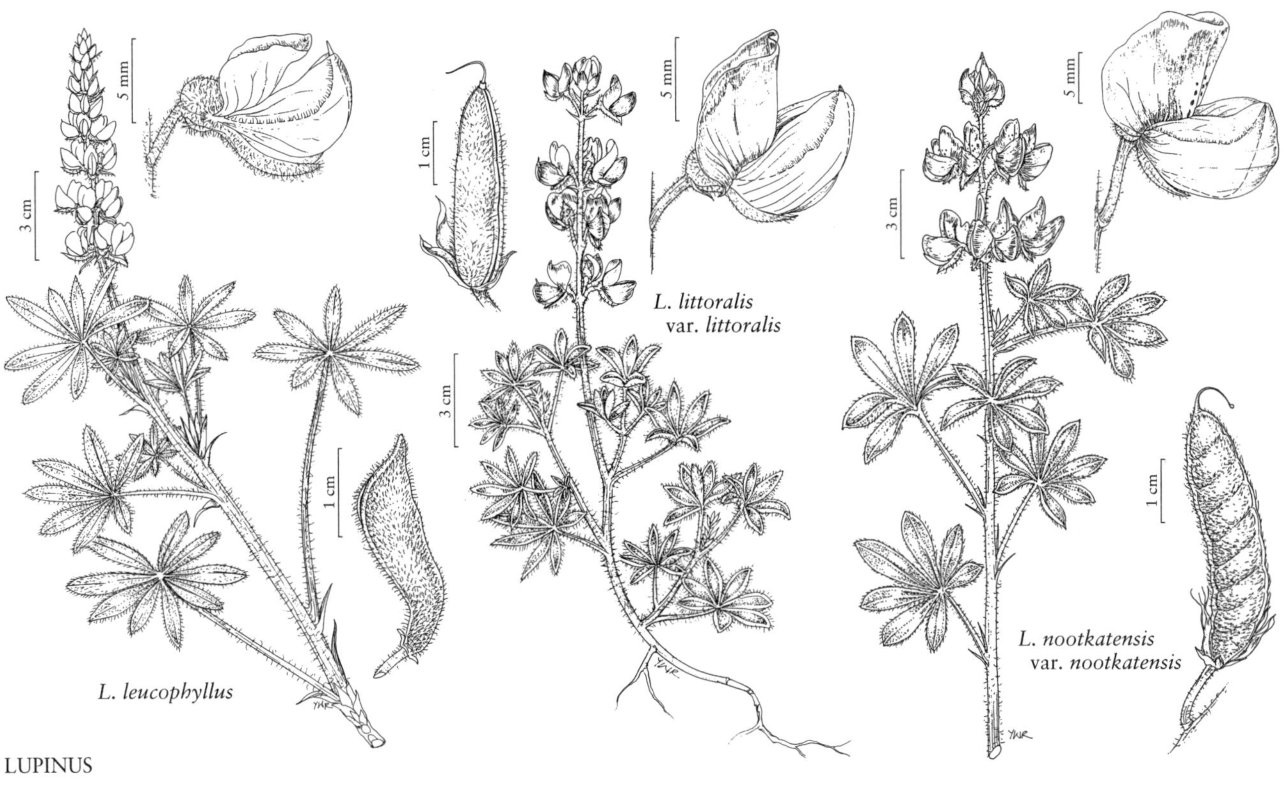

LUPINUS

64. Lupinus littoralis Douglas, Bot. Reg. 14: plate 1198. 1828 • Seashore lupine E F

Herbs or subshrubs, perennial, to 2–5 dm, greenish to silver, spreading-villous, especially at nodes, or densely appressed- or spreading-silver-hairy. **Cotyledons** deciduous, petiolate. **Stems** prostrate to decumbent, branched, not weak, from woody base. **Leaves** cauline, often appearing clustered near base first year; stipules 7–16 mm; petiole 2–10 cm; leaflets 5–9, blades 15–35 × 3–9 mm, adaxial surface pubescent. **Peduncles** 4–12 cm; bracts deciduous, 4–7 mm. **Racemes** ± open, 6–16 cm; flowers whorled or not. **Pedicels** 4–12 mm. **Flowers** 10–16 mm; calyx bulge or spur 0–1 mm, abaxial lobe 3-toothed or entire, 8–9 mm, adaxial lobe 2-toothed, 7–8 mm; corolla blue to lilac, white, yellow, rose, or purple (sometimes on same plant), banner patch whitish or yellow, or absent, banner glabrous abaxially, lower keel margins glabrous, adaxial margin ciliate. **Legumes** 3–4 cm, hairy. **Seeds** 7–12.

Varieties 2 (2 in the flora): w North America.

Lupinus littoralis is a prostrate perennial that grows on the ocean bluffs and dunes of western North America. It hybridizes with *L. arboreus* (K. S. Wear 1998) and probably *L. rivularis*. It can be distinguished from *L. tidestromii* by the latter having three leaflets on some leaves and weak stems.

1. Flowers 10–13 mm; corollas blue to lilac, except banner patch whitish; roots bright yellow; petioles less than 2 times as long as leaflet blades, 3–5 cm; British Columbia to Mendocino County, California . . . . 64a. *Lupinus littoralis* var. *littoralis*
1. Flowers 11–16 mm; corollas white, yellow, rose, or purple (often on same plant); roots not yellow; petioles 2 times as long as leaflet blades, 4–10 cm; Sonoma to San Luis Obispo counties, California . . . . 64b. *Lupinus littoralis* var. *variicolor*

64a. Lupinus littoralis Douglas var. **littoralis** E F

Herbs or subshrubs spreading-villous, especially at nodes; roots bright yellow. **Stems** to 3 dm. **Leaves:** stipules 8–16 mm; petiole 3–5 cm, petiole less than 2 times as long as leaflet blades; leaflets 5–9. **Flowers** 10–13 mm; corolla blue to lilac, banner patch whitish. **Legumes** 3–4 cm. **Seeds** 9–14. **2*n*** = 48.

Flowering May–Aug. Coastal terraces, dunes, beaches; 0–100 m; B.C.; Calif., Oreg., Wash.

Variety *littoralis* is known from British Columbia to Mendocino County in northern California.

64b. Lupinus littoralis Douglas var. **variicolor** (Steudel) Isely, Native Natural. Legum. U.S., 711. 1998 [E]

Lupinus variicolor Steudel, Nomencl. Bot. ed. 2, 2: 78. 1841, based on *L. versicolor* Lindley, Edwards's Bot. Reg. 23: plate 1979. 1837, not Sweet 1823; *L. franciscanus* Greene; *L. micheneri* Greene

Herbs or subshrubs usually densely appressed- or spreading-silver-hairy; roots not yellow. **Stems** 2–5 dm. **Leaves:** stipules 7–8 mm; petiole 4–10 cm, 2 times as long as leaflet blades; leaflets 6–9. **Flowers** 11–16 mm; corolla white, yellow, rose, or purple (often on same plant), banner patch absent. **Legumes** 3–4 cm. **Seeds** 7–9. $2n = 48$.

Flowering Apr–Jul. Coastal terraces, beaches; 0–400 m; Calif.

Variety *variicolor* ranges from Sonoma County southward to San Luis Obispo County; it is one of the host plants to the endangered Mission Blue butterfly.

65. Lupinus longifolius (S. Watson) Abrams, Fl. Los Angeles, 209. 1904

Lupinus chamissonis Eschscholtz var. *longifolius* S. Watson in W. H. Brewer et al., Bot. California 1: 117. 1876; *L. albifrons* Bentham var. *longifolius* (S. Watson) Isely; *L. mollisifolius* Davidson

Shrubs, 10–15 dm, usually greenish, soft-short-hairy. **Cotyledons** deciduous, petiolate. **Stems** erect, clustered, branched. **Leaves** cauline; stipules 5–14 mm; petiole 4–7(–10) cm; leaflets 5–10, blades 30–60 × 6–12 mm, adaxial surface pubescent. **Peduncles** 5–12 cm; bracts deciduous, 4–11 mm. **Racemes** 20–45 cm; flowers ± whorled or not. **Pedicels** 5–10 mm. **Flowers** 12–18 mm; calyx bulge or spur 0–1 mm, abaxial lobe entire, 10–15 mm, adaxial lobe 2-toothed, 8–10 mm; corolla violet to blue, banner patch yellowish to white or absent, banner glabrous abaxially, lower keel margins glabrous, adaxial margin ciliate middle to tip. **Legumes** dark, 4–6 cm, hairy. **Seeds** 6–8, brownish to gray, 5–6 mm.

Flowering Apr–Jun. Coastal sage scrub, chaparral, coastal bluffs, inland canyons; 0–500 m; Calif.; Mexico (Baja California).

Lupinus longifolius occurs in southwestern California and adjacent Baja California.

66. Lupinus ludovicianus Greene, Bull. Calif. Acad. Sci. 1: 184. 1885 • San Luis Obispo County lupine [C] [E]

Herbs, perennial, 3–6 dm, woolly-tomentose. **Cotyledons** deciduous, petiolate. **Stems** decumbent or erect, branched just above ground, hairs less than 1 mm, not sharp or stiff. **Leaves** cauline, clustered at base; stipules 7–12 mm; petiole 5–12 cm; leaflets 5–9, blades 15–40 × 5–12 mm, adaxial surface densely tomentose to woolly, hairs ± spreading. **Peduncles** stout, 6–10 cm; bracts deciduous, 7–8 mm. **Racemes** 10–40 cm; flowers ± whorled or not. **Pedicels** 2–5 mm. **Flowers** 10–15 mm; calyx bulge or spur 0–1 mm, abaxial lobe 3-toothed, 6–8 mm, adaxial lobe deeply notched, 6–7 mm; corolla bluish to purple, banner patch yellow turning purple to white, banner well reflexed-recurved at or proximal to midpoint, this 3.5–6 mm proximal to apex, banner glabrous or ± hairy abaxially, lower keel margins glabrous, adaxial margin ciliate middle to tip. **Legumes** 2–3 cm, hairy. **Seeds** 3 or 4, mottled grayish, 4–7 mm.

Flowering Apr–Jul. Open, grassy areas, on limestone and sandstone, oak woodlands; of conservation concern; 50–600 m; Calif.

Lupinus ludovicianus is known only from San Luis Obispo County.

67. Lupinus magnificus M. E. Jones, Contr. W. Bot. 8: 26. 1898 [E]

Herbs, perennial, 6–12 dm, white-woolly. **Cotyledons** deciduous, petiolate. **Stems** erect, branched at base, hairs 1–3 mm, sharp, stiff. **Leaves** usually basal; stipules 10–24 mm; petiole 6–30 cm; leaflets 5–9, blades 20–55 × 6–15 mm, adaxial surface densely woolly. **Peduncles** 10–50 cm; bracts deciduous, 4–5 mm. **Racemes** 10–45 cm; flowers whorled or not. **Pedicels** 2–8 mm. **Flowers** fragrant, 10–18 mm; calyx bulge or spur 0–1 mm, abaxial lobe entire, 5–11 mm, adaxial lobe, 2-toothed, 5–9 mm; corolla lavender to rose, banner patch yellow turning purple, banner glabrous abaxially, lower keel margins glabrous, adaxial margin ciliate middle to tip. **Legumes** 3–7 cm, densely hairy. **Seeds** 5–8, tan, 3–4 mm.

Varieties 3 (3 in the flora): California.

1. Flowers (13–)16–18 mm . . . . 67a. *Lupinus magnificus* var. *magnificus*
1. Flowers 10–13 mm.
   2. Keel petals curved; racemes 20–40 cm . . . . 67b. *Lupinus magnificus* var. *glarecola*
   2. Keel petals straight; racemes 10 cm . . . . 67c. *Lupinus magnificus* var. *hesperius*

67a. Lupinus magnificus M. E. Jones var. **magnificus** • Panamint Mountains lupine C E

Racemes 30–45 cm. **Pedicels** stout, 4 mm. **Flowers** (13–)16–18 mm. **Keel petals** slightly curved.

Flowering May–Jun(–Jul). Desert scrub, pinyon and juniper woodlands, upper montane coniferous forests; of conservation concern; 1000–2600 m; Calif.

Variety *magnificus* is known from the Great Basin and Mojave desert ranges in Inyo County.

67b. Lupinus magnificus M. E. Jones var. **glarecola** M. E. Jones, Contr. W. Bot. 8: 26. 1898 • Coso Mountains lupine E

Lupinus kerrii Eastwood

Racemes 20–40 cm. **Pedicels** slender, 8 mm. **Flowers** 10–13 mm. **Keel petals** curved.

Flowering Apr–Jun. Granitic soils, often talus and scree, desert scrub, Joshua tree woodland; 1100–2500 m; Calif.

Variety *glarecola* is known from the Mojave Desert ranges in Inyo County.

67c. Lupinus magnificus M. E. Jones var. **hesperius** (A. Heller) C. P. Smith in W. L. Jepson, Man. Fl. Pl. Calif., 533. 1925 • McGee Meadow lupine C E

Lupinus hesperius A. Heller, Muhlenbergia 2: 212. 1906

Racemes 10 cm. **Pedicels** stout, 4 mm. **Flowers** 10–13 mm. **Keel petals** straight.

Flowering Apr–Jun. Sandy soils, desert scrub, upper montane coniferous forests; of conservation concern; 1200–1900 m; Calif.

Variety *hesperius* is known from the eastern slopes of the Sierra Nevada in Inyo County.

68. Lupinus neomexicanus Greene, Pittonia 4: 133. 1900 (as neo-mexicanus) • New Mexico lupine

Lupinus blumeri Greene

Herbs, perennial, (3–)4–10 dm, hirsutulous or shortly pilose (green and inconspicuously hairy). **Cotyledons** deciduous, petiolate. **Stems** erect or ascending, few-clustered, unbranched or branched. **Leaves** cauline (basal not present at anthesis); stipules 4–13 mm; petiole 2.5–6 cm; leaflets 5–8, blades broadly oblanceolate, 20–40(–50) × 4–11 mm, abaxial surface appressed-hairy, adaxial surface glabrate. **Peduncles** 5–12 cm; bracts deciduous, 4–6 mm. **Racemes** 4–15 cm; flowers spirally arranged or ± whorled. **Pedicels** 5–8 mm. **Flowers** (10–)12–14 mm; calyx lobes entire, 6 mm; corolla pale lavender to reddish purple, banner spot yellow or white, banner glabrous abaxially, keel distally ciliolate. **Legumes** 4 × 2 cm, villous. **Seeds** 3–6.

Flowering May–Sep. Mountain meadows, canyons, oak, aspen, conifer woodlands; 1500–2500 m; Ariz., N.Mex.; Mexico (Chihuahua, Durango, Oaxaca, Sonora).

Lupinus neomexicanus is known in the flora area from southeastern Arizona to Rio Arriba County in New Mexico.

69. Lupinus nevadensis A. Heller, Muhlenbergia 6: 107, fig. 17. 1910 E

Herbs, perennial, 1–4 dm, long-hairy. **Cotyledons** deciduous, petiolate. **Stems** erect, tufted, unbranched. **Leaves** basal and cauline; stipules 8–10 mm; basal petioles to 14 cm, cauline to 4 cm; leaflets 6–10, blades 20–50 × 4–6 mm, adaxial surface pubescent. **Peduncles** 3–6 cm; bracts deciduous, 4–5 mm. **Racemes** 5–17 cm; flowers spirally arranged. **Pedicels** 4–8 mm. **Flowers** 10–12 mm; calyx bulge or spur 0–1 mm, abaxial lobe 3-toothed, 4–5 mm, adaxial lobe 2-toothed, 3–4 mm; corolla blue, banner patch white to yellowish, banner glabrous abaxially, keel strongly upcurved, lower keel margins glabrous, adaxial margin ciliate. **Legumes** 2.5–4 cm, densely hairy. **Seeds** 3–4.

Flowering Apr–Aug. Hillsides, valleys, with sagebrush, Great Basin scrub, pinyon-juniper woodlands; 1000–3000 m; Calif., Nev., Oreg.

Lupinus nevadensis is found in Lassen, Mono, and northern Inyo counties in eastern California, Washoe County southward to Mineral County in western Nevada, and Harney County in southern Oregon.

70. Lupinus nootkatensis Donn ex Sims, Bot. Mag. 32: plate 1311. 1810 • Nootka lupine [E] [F]

L. perennis Linnaeus var. *nootkatensis* (Donn ex Sims) L. Ll. Phillips

Herbs, perennial, (1–)4–10(–12) dm, hairs appressed to spreading, sparse to dense; caudex subterranean, woody. **Cotyledons** deciduous, petiolate. **Stems** ascending to erect, clustered, unbranched or branched, sometimes thick, hollow. **Leaves** cauline; stipules 1–8 cm; proximal petioles 3–8.5 cm, distal ones 2–7 cm; leaflets 5–8(–15), blades (10–)20–50(–70) × 5–15 mm, abaxial surface long-villous, adaxial surface usually glabrous or glabrate. **Peduncles** (1–)4–9.5 cm; bracts deciduous, 1–5 mm. **Racemes** 1.8–30 cm; flowers in 1–15 whorls. **Pedicels** 1–8 cm. **Flowers** 11–21 mm; calyx bulge or spur 0–1 mm, abaxial lobe entire or deeply lobed, 6–12 mm, adaxial lobe 2-lobed or cleft less than 1/3 length, 6–8 mm; corolla usually bluish purple, sometimes pink, rarely white, banner glabrous abaxially, adaxial keel glabrous or densely ciliate along most of adaxial edge. **Legumes** 3–6 cm, silky. **Seeds** 7–11.

Varieties 2 (2 in the flora): n North America, Europe, Atlantic Islands (Iceland).

1. Hairs spreading, long and shaggy; stems 10–15 mm diam.; bracts 16–19 mm . . . . 70a. *Lupinus nootkatensis* var. *nootkatensis*
1. Hairs finely silky-sericeous; stems 6–7(–9) mm diam.; bracts 7–13 mm . . . . 70b. *Lupinus nootkatensis* var. *fruticosus*

70a. Lupinus nootkatensis Donn ex Sims var. **nootkatensis** [F]

Lupinus albertensis C. P. Smith; *L. kiskensis* C. P. Smith; *L. nootkatensis* var. *ethel-looffiae* C. P. Smith; *L. nootkatensis* var. *henrylooffii* C. P. Smith; *L. nootkatensis* var. *perlanatus* C. P. Smith; *L. trifurcatus* C. P. Smith

Stems 10–15 mm diam, hairs spreading, long and shaggy. **Bracts** 16–19 mm. $2n = 48$.

Flowering Jun–Sep. Mesic to moist meadows, riverbars, stream banks, shorelines, clearings, roadsides, thickets, forest openings in lowland to lower alpine zones; 0–2000 m; Greenland; Alta., B.C., Nfld. and Labr. (Nfld.), N.S., Yukon; Alaska; Europe (Finland, Sweden, Norway); Atlantic Islands (Iceland).

Variety *nootkatensis* is common along the coast from southern Alaska, including the Aleutian Islands, southward to Vancouver Island, and is frequent in the coastal mountains. It is found occasionally inland to the Rocky Mountains, northward to Alaska and Yukon, but is rare in interior southern British Columbia. Variety *nootkatensis* is introduced in Newfoundland and Nova Scotia for restoration and is a garden escape in Greenland.

70b. Lupinus nootkatensis Donn ex Sims var. **fruticosus** Sims, Bot. Mag. 47: plate 2136. 1820 [E].

Lupinus arboreus Sims var. *fruticosus* (Sims) S. Watson; *L. nootkatensis* var. *unalaskensis* S. Watson

Stems 6–7(–9) mm diam., hairs finely appressed silky-sericeous (short and soft-wavy) throughout. **Bracts** 7–13 mm.

Flowering Jun–Sep. Mountain meadows, stream banks; 1000–2000 m; Alta., B.C., Yukon; Alaska.

71. Lupinus obtusilobus A. Heller, Muhlenbergia 8: 115, fig. 22. 1912 [E]

Lupinus ornatus Douglas var. *obtusilobus* (A. Heller) C. P. Smith

Herbs, perennial, 1.5–3 dm, appressed-silvery-silky; with woody, branching root crown. **Cotyledons** deciduous, petiolate. **Stems** decumbent, ascending, or erect, clustered, usually unbranched. **Leaves** cauline; stipules 7–14 mm; petiole 2–5 cm; leaflets 6 or 7, blades 20–50 × 4–8 mm, adaxial surface hairs silvery-silky. **Peduncles** (1–)2–4(–5) cm; bracts 3–4 mm. **Racemes** dense, 3–7 cm; flowers ± whorled. **Pedicels** 2–5 mm. **Flowers** 11–13 mm; calyx 6–7 mm, bulge or spur 0–1 mm, abaxial lobe 3-toothed, adaxial lobe 2-toothed; corolla blue to lilac, banner patch yellow, banner well reflexed-recurved at or proximal to midpoint, this 3.5–6 mm proximal to apex, banner broader than long, hairy abaxially, lower keel margins glabrous, adaxial margin ciliate. **Legumes** 2.5–4 cm, silky. **Seeds** 4–5, mottled brown, 3–4 mm.

Flowering Jun–Sep. Gravelly summits, red fir, subalpine forests; 1500–3500 m; Calif., Nev.

Lupinus obtusilobus is known in California from the North Coast Ranges, Klamath Ranges, Cascade Ranges, and northern Sierra Nevada (south to Nevada County), and in the Carson Range in eastern California and western Nevada.

72. Lupinus onustus S. Watson, Proc. Amer. Acad. Arts 11: 127. 1876 [E]

Lupinus alilatissimus C. P. Smith; *L. mucronulatus* Howell; *L. oreganus* A. Heller var. *pusillulus* C. P. Smith; *L. pinetorum* M. E. Jones; *L. sulphureus* Douglas subsp. *delnortensis* (Eastwood) L. Ll. Phillips; *L. thompsonianus* C. P. Smith; *L. violaceus* A. Heller

Herbs, perennial, 2–3 dm, green, silky; rhizomatous, from slender underground rootstock. **Cotyledons** deciduous, petiolate. **Stems** short-decumbent, clustered, unbranched. **Leaves** cauline, clustered near base; stipules 8–10 mm; petiole (5–)8–13 cm; leaflets 5–9, blades oblanceolate, 15–50 × 4–10 mm, abaxial surface silky-hairy, adaxial surface glabrous. **Peduncles** 4–8 cm; bracts deciduous, 3–4 mm. **Racemes** 5–15 cm; flowers not whorled. **Pedicels** 3–5 mm. **Flowers** 8–11 mm; calyx bulge or spur 0–1 mm, abaxial lobe entire, 3.5–6 mm, adaxial lobe 2-toothed, 2–5 mm; corolla violet, banner glabrous abaxially, lower keel margins glabrous, adaxial margin ciliate. **Legumes** 3–4.5 cm, hairy. **Seeds** 5 or 6, brown, 6–7 mm.

Flowering Apr–Sep. Dry banks, yellow pine forests, serpentine soils; 500–2000 m; Calif., Oreg.

Lupinus onustus is known in California from the southern Cascade Range, Klamath Ranges, and northern Sierra Nevada, to the Siskiyou Mountains of southwestern Oregon.

73. Lupinus oreganus A. Heller, Muhlenbergia 7: 89, fig. 14. 1911 • Kincaid's lupine [C] [E]

Lupinus oreganus var. *kincaidii* C. P. Smith; *L. sulphureus* Douglas var. *kincaidii* (C. P. Smith) C. L. Hitchcock

Herbs, perennial, 3–10 dm, appressed-silky, green but sometimes hair is tawny; rhizomatous. **Cotyledons** deciduous, petiolate. **Stems** erect, usually unbranched. **Leaves** cauline (few and large) and basal (persistent until after anthesis); stipules 11 mm; petiole 5–20 cm; leaflets (7–)9–11(or 12), blades 20–50(–80) × 5–12 mm, abaxial surface with long, appressed hairs, especially on margins and veins, adaxial surface usually glabrous. **Peduncles** 11–18 cm; bracts deciduous, 5 mm. **Racemes** loose, 11–40 cm; flowers spirally arranged or whorled. **Pedicels** 5–12 mm. **Flowers** fragrant, 8–13 mm; calyx bulge or spur 0–1 mm, abaxial lobe entire, 6 mm, adaxial lobe notched, 4–6 mm; corolla blue to purple, yellowish, or creamy white, banner distinctly ruffled, markedly concave on lateral face, banner glabrous or sparsely pubescent abaxially, wings glabrous, keel curved upward, lower keel margins glabrous, adaxial margin glabrous. **Legumes** 2–3 cm, glabrous. **Seeds** 4 or 5. $2n = 48$.

Flowering Apr–Jun. Dry hills, open ground, rocky, well-drained soils, sometimes serpentine, upland prairies, ecotones between grasslands and forests; of conservation concern; 70–900 m; Oreg., Wash.

Lupinus oreganus is known from west of the Cascades from Douglas County, Oregon, northward to Lewis County in Washington. Historically, it was found in British Columbia in Victoria on Vancouver Island but has not been seen there since the 1920s and is now considered extirpated there.

Lupinus oreganus is a food plant for Fender's Blue Butterfly, listed by ESA as endangered. *Lupinus oreganus* (as var. *kincaidii*) is listed as endangered in Washington. It is also listed as extirpated by the Committee on the Status of Endangered Wildlife in Canada and the Species at Risk Act.

74. Lupinus padrecrowleyi C. P. Smith, Sp. Lupinorum, 510. 1945 • Father Crowley's lupine [C] [E]

Lupinus dedeckerae Munz & D. B. Dunn

Herbs, perennial, 5–7.5 dm, silver- to white-woolly. **Cotyledons** deciduous, petiolate. **Stems** erect, clustered, branched or unbranched, long-villous. **Leaves** basal and cauline; stipules 5–11 mm; petiole 2–3 cm; leaflets 6–9, blades 25–75 × 4–6 mm, adaxial surface villous, hairs silvery. **Peduncles** 2–5.5 cm; bracts deciduous or persistent, 4–9 mm. **Racemes** 7–21 cm; flowers ± whorled. **Pedicels** 2–3.5 mm. **Flowers** 10–14 mm; calyx bulge or spur 0–1 mm, abaxial lobe 3-toothed, 5.5–8 mm, adaxial lobe, 2-toothed, 5–7 mm; corolla cream to pale yellow, banner usually hairy abaxially, keel glabrous. **Legumes** 2–3 cm, silky. **Seeds** 2 or 3, white, mottled black, 4–5 mm.

Flowering Jun–Sep. Great Basin scrub, riparian scrub, upper montane coniferous forests, in decomposed granite; of conservation concern; 2500–4000 m; Calif.

Lupinus padrecrowleyi is known from the southern Sierra Nevada, mostly on the east slope, in Inyo, Mono, and Tulare counties.

Lupinus padrecrowleyi can easily be distinguished from other *Lupinus* species by its usually white-woolly leaves, both clustered at base and along the stem, banners that are hairy abaxially, glabrous keels, and cream to yellow flowers.

75. Lupinus peirsonii H. Mason, Madroño 1: 187. 1928 (as peirsoni) • Peirson's lupine [C] [E]

Herbs, perennial, 3–6 dm, silver-silky. **Cotyledons** deciduous, petiolate. **Stems** erect, branched from just above ground. **Leaves** cauline, clustered at base, ± fleshy; stipules 15–20 mm; petiole 2–15 cm; leaflets 5–8, blades widely oblanceolate, 25–70 × 10–30 mm, surfaces silver-silky. **Peduncles** 1–2.5 cm; bracts deciduous, 5–7 mm. **Racemes** 1–1.5 cm; flowers ± whorled. **Pedicels** 1–2 mm. **Flowers** 10–12 mm; calyx bulge or spur 0–1 mm, abaxial lobe entire, 5–7 mm, adaxial lobe obscurely 2-toothed, 4–6 mm; corolla yellow, banner usually hairy abaxially, lower keel margins glabrous, adaxial margin ciliate middle to tip. **Legumes** 3–4 cm, silky. **Seeds** 3–5.

Flowering Apr–Jun. Gravelly or rocky areas, Joshua tree woodland, montane coniferous forests, pinyon and juniper woodlands; of conservation concern; 1000–2500 m; Calif.

Lupinus peirsonii is known only from the San Gabriel Mountains in Los Angeles County.

76. Lupinus perennis Linnaeus, Sp. Pl. 2: 721. 1753 • Sundial lupine [E] [F]

Lupinus nuttallii S. Watson; *L. perennis* subsp. *gracilis* (Chapman) D. B. Dunn; *L. perennis* var. *gracilis* Chapman; *L. perennis* var. *occidentalis* S. Watson

Herbs, perennial, 2–8 dm, glabrous or densely shaggy; rhizomatous, patch-forming. **Cotyledons** deciduous, petiolate. **Stems** erect, unbranched or sparsely branched distally, usually hollow. **Leaves** cauline; stipules 4–12 mm, longer proximally becoming smaller distally; petiole (2–)5–10(–15) cm; leaflets 7–11, blades (15–)20–45(–50) × 4–15 mm, abaxial surface appressed to spreading hairy, strigose, adaxial surface green, glabrous. **Peduncles** (2.5–)4–9 cm; bracts tardily deciduous, 3–6 mm. **Racemes** 8–20(–30) cm; flowers spirally arranged or whorled. **Pedicels** (3–)5–7(–10) mm. **Flowers** (8–)12–16 mm; calyx abaxial lobe slightly 3-dentate, 5–6 mm, adaxial lobe notched, 4–5 mm; corolla usually blue, sometimes pink or white, banner glabrous abaxially, upper keel margins ciliate. **Legumes** 3–5 cm, villous. **Seeds** 5 or 6. $2n$ = 48, 96.

Flowering (Mar–)Apr–Jul(–Oct). Sandy soils in dry areas, pine barrens, openings in oak or conifer forests, bluffs, meadows, roadsides; 0–500 m; Ont.; Ala., Conn., Del., D.C., Fla., Ga., Ill., Ind., Iowa, Ky., La., Mass., Mich., Minn., Miss., Ohio, Maine, Md., N.H., N.J., N.Y., N.C., Pa., R.I., S.C., Tex., Vt., Va., W.Va., Wis.; introduced in Asia (China).

Shorter plants with more basal leaves have been recognized as subsp. *gracilis*; intermediates between the named varieties are abundant. Variety *occidentalis* was described from Michigan and Wisconsin as differing by its dense pubescence, which is a variable trait.

In the northern part of its range, *Lupinus perennis* is sympatric with *L. polyphyllus* and can be differentiated because the latter has more leaflets and a glabrous keel. *Lupinus perennis* is of conservation concern in some states and is an important host plant for lepidopterans; the federally endangered Karner Blue butterfly relies on *L. perennis* as a larval host plant and sundial lupine also is a larval host plant for Frosted Elfin (*Callophrys irus*) and Wild Indigo Duskywing (*Erynnis baptisiae*) butterflies and several species of moths.

Lupinus perennis is toxic and potentially fatal to livestock, due to the alkaloid D-lupaine (M. Wink et al. 1995).

Lupinus gracilis Nuttall (1834, not Kunth 1824) is an illegitimate name that pertains here.

77. Lupinus polyphyllus Lindley, Bot. Reg. 13: plate 1096. 1827 [E] [F]

Herbs, perennial, 1–15 dm, green, glabrous or hairy; caudex subterranean and divisions rhizomelike, or superficial and divisions closely tufted. **Cotyledons** deciduous, petiolate. **Stems** erect, tufted, unbranched, stout, usually hollow. **Leaves** basal and cauline; stipules not leaflike, green to silvery, 5–40 mm; petiole 3–45 cm, basal long-petiolate and forming a basal tuft, cauline petioles shorter distally; leaflets (5 or)6–12(–17), blades (10–)30–150 × 5–25 mm, adaxial surface hairy or glabrous. **Peduncles** 3–13 cm; bracts deciduous, 7–11 mm. **Racemes** open, 6–40 cm; flowers ± whorled. **Pedicels** (2–)3–15 mm. **Flowers** 9–15 mm; calyx 4–8 mm, bulge or spur 0–1 mm, lobes entire; corolla violet to lavender, pink, or white, banner patch yellow to white, sometimes turning red-purple, banner glabrous abaxially, keel upcurved, glabrous, ciliate, or ciliolate. **Legumes** 2.5–5 × 0.7–1 cm, hairy. **Seeds** 3–9.

Varieties 6 (6 in the flora): w North America; introduced in South America (Argentina, Chile), Eurasia, Pacific Islands (New Zealand), Australia.

Lupinus polyphyllus was hybridized with *L. arboreus* and other species to create the Russell Lupine garden hybrid, which is invasive and occurs in New Zealand and the United Kingdom.

1. Adaxial surfaces of leaves silky strigulose, gray or silver . . . . 77d. *Lupinus polyphyllus* var. *humicola*
1. Adaxial surfaces of leaves glabrous or ± puberulent, green.
   2. Herbs 5.5–12 dm; adaxial keel glabrous; plants of meadows, streams, or shores.
      3. Leaflets 9–17, blades 60–150 mm; widely distributed, Alaska and British Columbia southward to California, eastward to Montana, introduced in Ontario and Michigan, eastward to Prince Edward Island, and southward to Massachusetts and Maryland . . . . 77a. *Lupinus polyphyllus* var. *polyphyllus*
      3. Leaflets 5–11, blades 35–100 mm; British Columbia, California, Idaho, Nevada, Oregon, Washington, Wyoming . . . . 77c. *Lupinus polyphyllus* var. *burkei*
   2. Herbs (1–)1.5–6.5 dm; adaxial keel ciliolate; plants of dry or vernally moist sites.
      4. Caudices subterranean, divisions rhizomelike; plants of barren clay sites in oak chaparral and sagebrush, 1200–3000 m . . . . . . 77b. *Lupinus polyphyllus* var. *ammophilus*
      4. Caudices above ground, divisions closely tufted, not rhizomelike; plants of valleys, foothill canyons, sagebrush scrub, arid microhabitats, 600–3000 m.
         5. Herbs (2–)3–6.5 dm; longest leaflet blades 35–110 mm; plants widespread in valleys and foothill canyons at 600–3000 m; Colorado, Idaho, Nevada, New Mexico, Oregon, Utah, Washington, Wyoming . . . . 77e. *Lupinus polyphyllus* var. *prunophilus*
         5. Herbs (1–)1.5–4 dm; longest leaflet blades 20–45 mm; plants of sagebrush scrub and arid microhabitats at 1000–2500 m; California, Idaho, Nevada, Oregon, Washington . . . . 77f. *Lupinus polyphyllus* var. *saxosus*

77a. Lupinus polyphyllus Lindley var. **polyphyllus** [E]

Lupinus grandifolius Lindley ex J. Agardh; *L. pallidipes* A. Heller; *L. polyphyllus* var. *grandifolius* (Lindley ex J. Agardh) Torrey & A. Gray; *L. polyphyllus* var. *pallidipes* (A. Heller) C. P. Smith; *L. pseudopolyphyllus* C. P. Smith

Herbs 5.5–12(–15) dm, caudex subterranean. **Stems** hollow at base. **Leaflets** 9–17, blades 60–150 mm, surfaces abaxially ± strigose, adaxially glabrous or puberulent. **Flowers:** upper keel margins glabrous. $2n$ = 48, 96.

Flowering May–Aug. Moist to mesic meadows, riverbars, stream banks, seashores, clearings, roadsides, glades, open forests; 0–3000 m; Alta., B.C., N.B., Nfld. and Labr. (Nfld.), N.S., Ont., P.E.I., Que.; Alaska, Calif., Conn., Idaho, Maine, Md., Mass., Mich., Mont., N.H., N.Y., Oreg., Vt., Wash.; introduced in Europe, Pacific Islands (New Zealand), Australia.

Populations of var. *polyphyllus* in eastern North America (Ontario and eastward in Canada, and Minnesota and eastward in the United States) have resulted from horticultural introductions.

77b. Lupinus polyphyllus Lindley var. **ammophilus** (Greene) Barneby, Great Basin Naturalist 46: 257. 1986 [E]

Lupinus ammophilus Greene, Pittonia 4: 136. 1900; *L. ammophilus* Greene var. *crassus* (Payson) Isely; *L. crassus* Payson

Herbs 1.5–5.5 dm, hirsute, caudex subterranean, divisions rhizomelike. **Stems** diffuse, subhollow. **Leaflets** 6–9(or 10), largest blade (25–)30–60 mm, abaxial surface hirsute. **Flowers:** upper keel margins ciliate. $2n$ = 48.

Flowering Apr–Jul. Barren clay, seeps, oak-pinyon-juniper chaparral, sagebrush scrub; 1200–3000 m; Ariz., Colo., N.Mex., Utah.

Variety *ammophilusis* is rare in Arizona and is known only from Apache County.

77c. Lupinus polyphyllus Lindley var. **burkei** (S. Watson) C. L. Hitchcock in C. L. Hitchcock et al., Vasc. Pl. Pacif. N.W. 3: 321. 1961 [E] [F]

Lupinus burkei S. Watson, Proc. Amer. Acad. Arts 8: 525. 1873; *L. bernardinus* (Abrams ex C. P. Smith) Abrams; *L. burkei* var. *caerulemontanus* D. B. Dunn & B. J. Cox; *L. elongatus* Greene ex A. Heller; *L. perglaber* Eastwood; *L. piperitus* Davidson; *L. piperitus* var. *sparsipilosus* Eastwood; *L. polyphyllus* subsp. *bernardinus* (Abrams ex C. P. Smith) Munz; *L. polyphyllus* subsp. *superbus* (A. Heller) Munz; *L. procerus* Greene ex A. Heller; *L. superbus* A. Heller var. *bernardinus* Abrams ex C. P. Smith; *L. superbus* var. *elongatus* (Greene ex A. Heller) C. P. Smith

Herbs 5.5–12 dm, caudex branched, subterranean. **Stems** erect, often hollow, coarse. **Leaflets** (5–)7–11, largest blade 35–100 mm, surfaces abaxially sometimes sparsely hairy, adaxially glabrous. **Flowers:** upper keel margins glabrous, rarely ciliolate. $2n$ = 48.

Flowering May–Aug. Wet places in mountains; 900–3000 m; B.C.; Calif., Idaho, Nev., Oreg., Wash., Wyo.

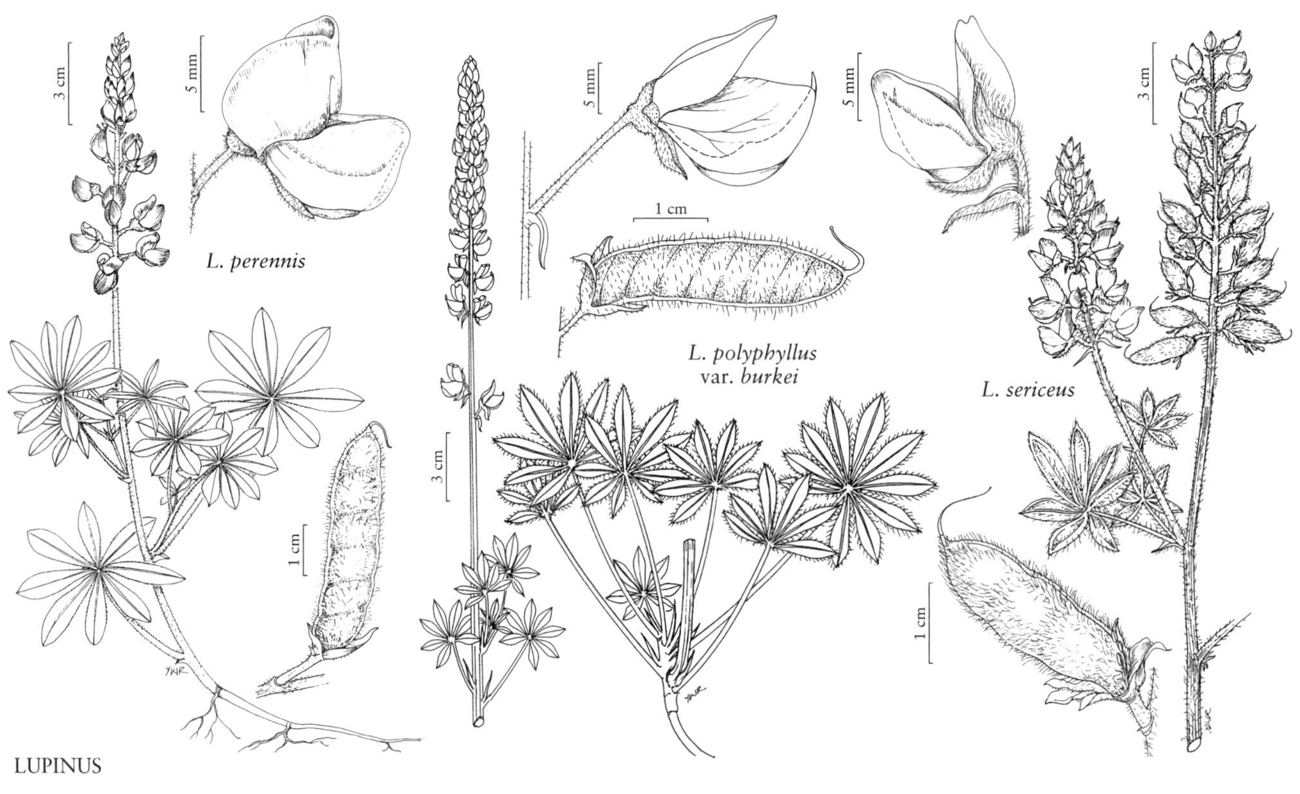

LUPINUS

Variety *burkei* is known from southern British Columbia southward to the Transverse Ranges in southern California and eastward to western Montana and northwestern Wyoming.

77d. Lupinus polyphyllus Lindley var. **humicola** (A. Nelson) Barneby, Great Basin Naturalist 46: 257. 1986 [E]

Lupinus humicola A. Nelson, Bull. Torrey Bot. Club 25: 204. 1898; *L. arcticus* S. Watson var. *cottonii* (C. P. Smith) C. P. Smith; *L. arcticus* var. *humicola* (A. Nelson) C. P. Smith; *L. arcticus* var. *tetonensis* (E. E. Nelson) C. P. Smith; *L. cottonii* C. P. Smith; *L. diversalpicola* C. P. Smith; *L. flavescens* Rydberg; *L. holmgrenianus* C. P. Smith; *L. humicola* var. *tetonensis* E. E. Nelson; *L. rydbergii* Blankinship; *L. wyethii* S. Watson; *L. wyethii* subsp. *tetonensis* (E. E. Nelson) B. J. Cox & D. B. Dunn

Herbs 2–4.5(–7) dm, caudex above ground. **Stems** ascending, not hollow. **Leaflets** (5–)7–12, blades 30–55(–70) mm, surfaces silky-strigulose, gray or silver, often folded, appearing linear. **Flowers:** upper keel margins usually ciliate. **2*n*** = 48.

Flowering (Apr–)May–Jun(–Sep). Dry desert slopes, dry washes, pinyon-juniper woodlands, grassy sites, thinly wooded sites; 1400–2500 m; Alta., B.C.; Ariz., Calif., Colo., Idaho, Mont., Nev., Oreg., Utah, Wash., Wyo.

Variety *humicola* is of conservation concern in California, where it is known only from Inyo County. In Arizona, it is known only from Navajo County, south of Lake Powell.

77e. Lupinus polyphyllus Lindley var. **prunophilus** (M. E. Jones) L. Ll. Phillips, Res. Stud. State Coll. Wash. 23: 180. 1955 [E]

Lupinus prunophilus M. E. Jones, Contr. W. Bot. 13: 7. 1910; *L. arcticus* S. Watson var. *prunophilus* (M. E. Jones) C. P. Smith; *L. biddlei* L. F. Henderson ex C. P. Smith; *L. tooelensis* C. P. Smith; *L. wyethii* S. Watson var. *prunophilus* (M. E. Jones) C. P. Smith

Herbs (2–)3–6.5 dm, pilose, caudex above ground, divisions closely tufted, not rhizomelike. **Stems** not or scarcely hollow. **Leaflets** 7–10, blades (30–)35–90 (–110) mm, surfaces abaxially pilose, adaxially glabrous. **Flowers:** upper keel margins usually ciliate, rarely glabrous. **2*n*** = 48.

Flowering Apr–Jul. Valleys, foothill canyons; 600–3000 m; Colo., Idaho, Nev., N.Mex., Oreg., Utah, Wash., Wyo.

Variety *prunophilus* is known in northern New Mexico, western Colorado, Idaho, eastern and southern Nevada, eastern Oregon, northern Utah, and into the Columbia Basin in Washington.

77f. Lupinus polyphyllus Lindley var. **saxosus** (Howell) Barneby in A. Cronquist et al., Intermount. Fl. 3(B): 240. 1989 [E]

Lupinus saxosus Howell, Erythea 1: 110. 1893; *L. saxosus* var. *subsericeus* (B. L. Robinson ex Piper) C. P. Smith; *L. subsericeus* B. L. Robinson ex Piper

Herbs (1–)1.5–4 dm; caudex superficial, divisions closely tufted, not rhizomelike. **Stems** incurved-ascending, not hollow. **Leaflets** 6–9(–12), blades 10–40(–45) mm, surfaces abaxially with spreading hairs, adaxially glabrous or marginally hairy. **Flowers:** upper keel margins ± sparsely ciliate. **2*n*** = 48.

Flowering (Apr–)May–Jun(–Jul). Sagebrush scrub, arid microhabitats; 1000–2500 m; Calif., Idaho, Nev., Oreg., Wash.

Variety *saxosus* is known from the Modoc Plateau in northeastern California, eastern and northern Nevada, eastern Oregon, eastern Washington, and southwestern Idaho.

78. Lupinus pratensis A. Heller, Muhlenbergia 2: 210. 1906 [E]

Lupinus pratensis var. *eriostachyus* C. P. Smith; *L. sellulus* Kellogg var. *elatus* Eastwood

Herbs, perennial, 3–7 dm, green, hairy. **Cotyledons** deciduous, petiolate. **Stems** erect, unbranched or branched distally, hollow. **Leaves** basal and cauline, green; stipules 5–20 mm; basal petioles 10–25 cm, cauline 1–4 cm; leaflets 5–10, blades 30–80(–130) × 5–8 mm, adaxial surface strigose, hairs less than 1 mm. **Peduncles** 4–17 cm; bracts persistent, 5–10 mm. **Racemes** 5–28 cm, usually exceeding leaves; flowers dense. **Pedicels** 1–3 mm. **Flowers** 10–12 mm; calyx bulge or spur 0–1 mm, abaxial lobe entire, 5–6 mm, adaxial lobe 2-toothed, 4–7 mm; corolla violet to dark blue, banner patch orange to red, banner usually glabrous abaxially, rarely hairy, lower keel margins glabrous, adaxial margin densely ciliate. **Legumes** 1.5–2 cm, hairy to woolly. **Seeds** 4–6, brown, mottled tan, 3–4 mm.

Flowering May–Sep. Meadows, stream banks, sagebrush scrub to subalpine forests; 2000–3500 m; Calif.

Lupinus pratensis is known from the southern Sierra Nevada in Fresno, Inyo, Mono, and Tulare counties. Plants from Big Pine Creek in Inyo County with banners that are hairy abaxially have been called var. *eriostachyus*.

79. Lupinus rivularis Douglas ex Lindley, Edwards's Bot. Reg. 19: plate 1595. 1833 • Riverbank lupine [E]

Lupinus amphibius Suksdorf; *L. lignipes* A. Heller

Herbs, perennial, 3.5–10 dm, green, ± glabrous. **Cotyledons** deciduous, petiolate. **Stems** decumbent, ascending, or erect, branched, dark brown to red, usually hollow. **Leaves** cauline; stipules 7–15 mm; petiole 3–5 cm; leaflets 5–9, blades 20–40 × 4–9 mm, adaxial surface glabrous. **Peduncles** 3–15 cm; bracts deciduous, 8–10 mm. **Racemes** open, 15–50 cm; flowers ± whorled or not. **Pedicels** 5–10 mm. **Flowers** 12–16 mm; calyx bulge or spur 0–1 mm, abaxial lobe entire or ± 3-toothed, 7–9 mm, adaxial lobe 2-toothed, 7–8 mm; corolla violet, banner glabrous abaxially, lower keel margins glabrous, adaxial margin ciliate claw to tip. **Legumes** dark, 3–7 cm, sparsely hairy. **Seeds** 7 or 8, mottled brown with black line, 3–4 mm.

Flowering Mar–Jun. Gravelly prairies, open woods, riverbanks; 0–500 m; B.C.; Calif., Oreg., Wash.

Lupinus rivularis ranges from Mendocino County in California northward through Oregon and Washington. It has been confirmed in British Columbia (where it is of conservation concern) in the extreme southwestern corner of the province, with a single population on southern Vancouver Island and five populations in the lower Fraser Valley.

Lupinus rivularis is distinguished by its absence of wood, banners that are glabrous abaxially, ciliate keels, glabrous leaf surfaces, and violet flowers. It grades into blue-flowered *L. arboreus* but blooms earlier (late winter, spring) and is not sweet-smelling. L. L. Phillips (1955) considered *L. rivularis* as synonymous with *L. albicaulis*.

Lupinus rivularis is widely planted for erosion control in western Oregon; it is of conservation concern in Canada.

80. Lupinus sabineanus Douglas ex Lindley, Edwards's Bot. Reg. 17: plate 1435. 1831 (as sabinianus) • Sabine's lupine [E]

Lupinus sabinei Douglas

Herbs, perennial, (5–)6–12 dm, woody, hairs stiff to short-silky-appressed. **Cotyledons** deciduous, petiolate. **Stems** erect or ascending, clustered, unbranched or branched distally, stout. **Leaves** cauline; stipules 10–15 mm; petiole 2–25 cm; leaflets 8–11, blades (30–)60–120(–150) × 3–15 mm, abaxial surface silky, slightly less so abaxially. **Peduncles** 4–10 cm; bracts early deciduous to persistent, 10–18 mm. **Racemes** 12–40 cm, loose to dense; flowers whorled. **Pedicels** 4–12 mm. **Flowers** (13–)15–18 mm; calyx sometimes somewhat bulged and asymmetrical, abaxial lobe entire or notched, 7–8 mm, adaxial lobe shallowly notched, 6–7 mm; corolla bright yellow, rarely pale purple, keel falcate, banner glabrous or hairy abaxially, upper keel margins densely ciliate. **Legumes** 3–4.5 cm, tomentose. **Seeds** 4–7, pinkish brown to dull reddish brown, 6–7 mm.

Flowering May–early Jun. Open ponderosa pine forests, dry hillsides, open woods; 500–1200 m; Oreg., Wash.

Lupinus sabineanus is known only from the Blue Mountains of northeastern Oregon and southeastern Washington (where it is of conservation concern).

81. Lupinus sericatus Kellogg, Proc. Calif. Acad. Sci. 7: 92. 1877 • Cobb Mountain lupine [C] [E]

Herbs, perennial, 1.5–5 dm, silver to gray-green, short-appressed-hairy. **Cotyledons** deciduous, petiolate. **Stems** erect, ascending, or decumbent, branched. **Leaves** cauline, clustered near base; stipules 2–7 mm; petiole 5–15 cm; leaflets 4–7, blades widely spoon-shaped, 30–40(–50) × 10–20 mm, surfaces densely silky. **Peduncles** 8–15 cm; bracts deciduous, 3–4 mm. **Racemes** open to dense, 10–30 cm; flowers ± whorled. **Pedicels** 4–6 mm. **Flowers** 12–16 mm; calyx bulge or spur 0–1 mm, abaxial lobe 3-toothed, 7–10 mm, adaxial lobe 2-toothed, 6–10 mm; corolla purple to violet, banner ± hairy abaxially, lower keel margins usually ± glabrous, adaxial margin ciliate claw to tip. **Legumes** 2–3 cm, hairy. **Seeds** 3–7, light brown, 3–5 mm.

Flowering Mar–Jun. Open wooded slopes; of conservation concern; 200–1600 m; Calif.

Lupinus sericatus is known from the southern Inner North Coast Ranges in Colusa, Lake, Napa, and Sonoma counties.

82. Lupinus sericeus Pursh, Fl. Amer. Sept. 2: 468. 1813 • Silky lupine [E] [F]

Lupinus aeger-ovium C. P. Smith; *L. aliumbellatus* C. P. Smith; *L. alpicola* L. F. Henderson ex Piper; *L. amniculi-salicis* C. P. Smith; *L. amplus* Greene; *L. arceuthinus* Greene; *L. bakeri* Greene; *L. bakeri* subsp. *amplus* (Greene) Fleak & D. B. Dunn; *L. barbiger* S. Watson; *L. blankinshipii* A. Heller; *L. buckinghamii* C. P. Smith; *L. comatus* Rydberg; *L. diaboli-septem* C. P. Smith; *L. dichrous* Greene; *L. falsocomatus* C. P. Smith; *L. fikerianus* C. P. Smith; *L. flavicaulis* Rydberg; *L. flexuosus* Lindley ex J. Agardh; *L. garfieldensis* C. P. Smith; *L. habrocomus* Greene; *L. hermanworkii* C. P. Smith; *L. hiulcoflorus* C. P. Smith; *L. huffmannii* C. P. Smith; *L. jonesii* Rydberg; *L. larsonianus* C. P. Smith; *L. leucopsis* J. Agardh; *L. marianus* Rydberg; *L. ornatus* Douglas; *L. puroviridus* C. P. Smith; *L. quercus-jugi* C. P. Smith; *L. ramosus* E. E. Nelson; *L. rickeri* C. P. Smith; *L. sericeus* subsp. *asotinensis* L. Ll. Phillips; *L. sericeus* var. *asotinensis* (L. Ll. Phillips) C. L. Hitchcock; *L. sericeus* var. *barbiger* (S. Watson) S. L. Welsh; *L. sericeus* var. *fikerianus* (C. P. Smith) C. L. Hitchcock; *L. sericeus* var. *flexuosus* (Lindley ex J. Agardh) C. P. Smith; *L. sericeus* subsp. *huffmannii* (C. P. Smith) Fleak & D. B. Dunn; *L. sericeus* var. *jonesii* (Rydberg) Isely; *L. sericeus* var. *wallowensis* C. P. Smith; *L. spiraeaphilus* C. P. Smith; *L. subulatus* Rydberg; *L. tuckerianus* C. P. Smith

Herbs, perennial, (2–)4–14 dm, silky-strigose to finely hirsute (with both short and long hairs). **Cotyledons** deciduous, petiolate. **Stems** erect, ascending, or decumbent, branched distally. **Leaves** mostly cauline, basal normally absent; stipules 5–7 mm; petiole 2–14 cm (longer proximally becoming shorter distally); leaflets 5–13, blades 10–60(–90) × 3–11(–19) mm, surfaces usually silky, rarely thinly silky appearing glabrous abaxially. **Peduncles** 2–4 cm; bracts subdeciduous, 5–8 mm. **Racemes** 12–25(–42) cm; flowers whorled or spirally arranged. **Pedicels** 2–5(–6) mm. **Flowers** 8–14 (–18) mm; calyx sometimes slightly saccate, abaxial lobe subentire or entire, 5 mm, adaxial lobe 2-fid, 6 mm; corolla pale purple to bright blue, sometimes yellowish or whitish, banner spot white to yellow turning brown, banner well reflexed-recurved at or proximal to midpoint, this 3.5–6 mm proximal to apex, keel moderately curved, banner silky-hairy abaxially, adaxial keel ciliate almost full length, not reaching tip. **Legumes** 2–3.7 cm, densely pilosulous. **Seeds** (2 or) 3–5(–7).

Flowering May–Aug. Meadows, dry banks, bunchgrass prairies, sagebrush scrub, openings in conifer forests; 200–3100 m; Alta., B.C.; Ariz., Colo., Idaho, Mont., Nev., N.Mex., Oreg., Utah, Wash., Wyo.

Lupinus sericeus is widespread and common from the southern interior mountains in British Columbia and southwestern Alberta southward to eastern Washington and eastern Oregon to northern New Mexico and northwestern Arizona, northeastern Nevada through Idaho and Wyoming to the Black Hills in South Dakota.

Plants with creamy or white flowers in southeastern Washington are known as subsp. *asotinensis*. D. Isely (1998) recognized this taxon based on petal color and distribution, but since white and yellow flowers occur throughout the range of *Lupinus sericeus*, it is not formally recognized here.

Lupinus pureriae C. P. Smith may be a hybrid derived in part from *L. sericeus*, according to an annotation by D. B. Dunn on the holotype (CAS0008254).

83. Lupinus sierrae-blancae Wooten & Standley, Contr. U.S. Natl. Herb. 16: 138. 1913 • Sierra Blanca lupine [E]

Lupinus aquilinus Wooton & Standley; *L. laetus* Wooton & Standley; *L. sierrae-blancae* subsp. *aquilinus* (Wooton & Standley) Fleak & D. B. Dunn

Herbs, perennial, 6.5–15.2 dm, appearing green and glabrous but finely and inconspicuously pubescent. **Cotyledons** deciduous, petiolate. **Stems** erect, solitary, branched, robust, succulent, hirsutulous. **Leaves** cauline; stipules 6–9 mm; proximal petioles 5–7 cm, withering, distal ones 3.5–6.5 cm; leaflets 7–10, blades 30–95 × 5–13 mm, abaxial surface finely strigulose, adaxial surface glabrate, yellow-green or gray-green. **Peduncles** 4–5 cm; bracts semi-deciduous, 5–7 mm. **Racemes** 5–34 cm; flowers whorled or spirally arranged. **Pedicels** 2–8(–10) mm. **Flowers** 10–14 mm; calyx abaxial lobe ± slightly gibbous, 9–15 mm, adaxial lobe slightly notched, 7–11 mm; corolla pale blue and whitish, banner with conspicuous darker spot, banner glabrous or hairy abaxially, keel falcate, often ± ciliolate distally. **Legumes** 3.5 × 0.8–1 cm, hirsute. **Seeds** 5–7. $2n$ = 48.

Flowering Jun–Aug. Meadows in pine or fir forests, roadsides; 1800–3100 m; N.Mex.

Lupinus sierrae-blancae is known only from the Sierra Blanca and Sacramento Mountains in Lincoln and Otero counties.

84. Lupinus sulphureus Douglas in W. J. Hooker, Fl. Bor.-Amer. 1: 166. 1832 • Sulfur lupine [E] [F]

Herbs, perennial, (3–)4–8(–10) dm, hairs stiff to silky-appressed, whitish, grayish, or brownish. **Cotyledons** deciduous, petiolate. **Stems** erect, densely tufted, unbranched distally. **Leaves** basal and cauline, persisting until after flowering; stipules 4–8 mm; proximal petioles 4–20 cm, distal ones 1.5–5 cm; leaflets 6–15, blades white to greenish, (20–)25–70 × 4–10 mm, abaxial surface hairy-strigulose or sericeous, adaxial surface strigulose-silky to sparsely hairy or glabrous. **Peduncles** 2.5–6 cm; bracts tardily deciduous, 5–9 mm. **Racemes** 6–20 cm; flowers whorled or spirally arranged. **Pedicels** (2–)4–10 mm. **Flowers** 8–12 mm; calyx asymmetrical but not spurred, silky, abaxial lobe entire, 4–7 mm, adaxial lobe 2-fid, 3–5 mm; corolla pale sulfur yellow, blue, or white, banner glabrous or sparsely hairy abaxially (pubescence extending above calyx as a line), upper keel margins usually ciliate most of length, sometimes glabrous. **Legumes** 2–3 cm, pilose to silky. **Seeds** 4 or 5, pinkish brown.

Varieties 2 (2 in the flora): w North America.

1. Racemes (5–)12–20 cm; flowers usually sulfur yellow (ranging from white to occasionally blue); leaflet blade adaxial surface strigose-silky to sparsely hairy or glabrous, abaxial surface hairy strigulose. . . . . .84a. *Lupinus sulphureus* var. *sulphureus*
1. Racemes 7–10(–11) cm; flowers blue to white; leaflet blade surfaces ± equally strigulose or sericeous . . . . . 84b. *Lupinus sulphureus* var. *bingenensis*

84a. Lupinus sulphureus Douglas var. **sulphureus** [E] [F]

Lupinus sulphureus var. *applegateianus* C. P. Smith; *L. sulphureus* var. *echlerianus* C. P. Smith

Leaves: leaflet blade surfaces abaxially hairy-strigulose, adaxially strigose-silky to sparsely hairy or glabrous. **Peduncles** 3–5 cm. **Racemes** (5–)12–20 cm. **Corollas** usually pale sulfur yellow, sometimes white to bluish. $2n$ = 48.

Flowers Apr–Aug. Prairies, sagebrush scrub, open conifer forests; 50–3000 m; B.C.; Idaho, Mont., Oreg., Wash.

Variety *sulphureus* is known from British Columbia southward along the eastern edge of the Cascades in Washington and northeastern Oregon, eastward to Idaho and Montana. It may be found along the Columbia River to the Willamette River Valley and into southwestern Washington.

84b. Lupinus sulphureus Douglas var. **bingenensis** (Suksdorf) Gandhi & Vincent, Phytoneuron 2019-41: 2. 2019 • Bingen lupine [E]

Lupinus bingenensis Suksdorf, Werdenda 1: 12. 1923; *L. bingenensis* var. *albus* Suksdorf; *L. bingenensis* var. *dubius* C. P. Smith; *L. bingenensis* var. *roseus* Suksdorf; *L. bingenensis* var. *subsaccatus* Suksdorf; *L. leucopsis* J. Agardh var. *bingenensis* (Suksdorf) C. P. Smith; *L. leucopsis* var. *dubius* C. P. Smith; *L. leucopsis* var. *hendersonianus* C. P. Smith; *L. leucopsis* var. *mollis* (A. Heller) C. P. Smith; *L. leucopsis* var. *shermanensis* C. P. Smith; *L. mollis* A. Heller; *L. ostiofluminis* C. P. Smith; *L. sericeus* Pursh var. *egglestonianus* C. P. Smith; *L. sulphureus* subsp. *subsaccatus* (Suksdorf) L. Ll. Phillips; *L. sulphureus* var. *subsaccatus* (Suksdorf) C. L. Hitchcock

Leaves: leaflet blade surfaces ± equally strigulose or sericeous. **Racemes** 7–10(–11) cm. **Corollas** usually blue or purplish, rarely white, banner patch none or white. **2*n*** = 48.

Flowering Apr–Aug. Prairies, sagebrush scrub, open conifer forests; 50–3000 m; B.C.; Idaho, Mont., Oreg., Wash.

Variety *bingenensis* is known from east of the Cascades in Oregon (along the Columbia River and in the Blue Mountains) and Washington, in south-central British Columbia from north of Obsidian and slightly eastward to the Webber Creek area (Olalla to Quilenchena), and eastward to Idaho and Montana. It is of conservation concern in British Columbia.

85. Lupinus tidestromii Greene, Erythea 3: 17. 1895 • Tidestrom's lupine [C] [E]

Lupinus layneae Eastwood; *L. littoralis* Douglas var. *layneae* (Eastwood) Isely; *L. tidestromii* var. *layneae* (Eastwood) Munz

Herbs, perennial, 1–3 dm, white-shaggy-hairy; sometimes weakly rhizomatous. **Cotyledons** deciduous, petiolate. **Stems** ± prostrate, branched, weak. **Leaves** cauline; stipules 8–12 mm; petiole 1–3 cm; leaflets 3–5, blades 5–20 × 2–5 mm, adaxial surface sericeous. **Peduncles** 4–8 cm; bracts deciduous, 4–5 mm. **Racemes** open, 2–10 cm; flowers whorled. **Pedicels** 3–5 mm. **Flowers** 11–13 mm; calyx 5–6 mm, bulge or spur 0–1 mm, abaxial lobe entire or notched, adaxial lobe deeply notched; corolla light blue to lavender, banner patch white to yellow turning violet, banner glabrous abaxially, lower keel margins glabrous, adaxial margin ciliate claw to tip. **Legumes** 2–3 cm, shaggy. **Seeds** 5–8, tan, mottled brown, 3–4 mm.

Flowering Apr–Jun. Dunes, beaches; of conservation concern; 0–100 m; Calif.

Lupinus tidestromii is known from coastal areas of Marin, Monterey, and Sonoma counties.

Shaggier plants from the northern North Coast geographic region of California have been called var. *layneae*, commonly known as the Point Reyes lupine.

86. Lupinus tracyi Eastwood, Leafl. W. Bot. 2: 268. 1940 • Tracy's lupine [C] [E]

Herbs, perennial, 4–7 dm, glabrous, glaucous. **Cotyledons** deciduous, petiolate. **Stems** solitary, erect, slender, usually unbranched. **Leaves** cauline; stipules 7–9 mm; petiole to 1 cm; leaflets 6 or 7, blades 10–40 × 4–10 mm, adaxial surface glabrous. **Peduncles** 2–6 cm; bracts deciduous, 8–10 mm. **Racemes** 4–16 cm; flowers ± whorled or not. **Pedicels** 5–6 mm. **Flowers** 8–10(–12) mm; calyx bulge or spur 0–1 mm, abaxial lobe 3-toothed, 3–5 mm, adaxial lobe 2-toothed, 3–8 mm; corolla whitish to dull blue (at least in bud), often fading to pale yellow, banner glabrous abaxially, keel glabrous, tip sometimes exserted. **Legumes** 1.5–2.5 cm, white-hairy, dark when dry. **Seeds** 3 or 4, 4–5 mm.

Flowering (May–)Jun–Jul. Dry, open montane forests; of conservation concern; 800–2500 m; Calif., Oreg.

Lupinus tracyi is known from the Klamath Ranges of northern California and adjacent areas in southern Oregon.

87. Lupinus villosus Willdenow, Sp. Pl. 3: 1029. 1802 • Lady lupine [E]

Herbs, usually annual, sometimes biennial, robust, 2–6 dm, spreading, hairs long, shaggy, silver or tawny. **Cotyledons** deciduous, petiolate. **Stems** sprawling or ascending, clustered, branched. **Leaves** basal; stipules conspicuous, 20–30 mm; petiole 3.5–9.5 cm; leaflet 1, blades 150–270 × 12–33 mm, surfaces sericeous or abaxially thinly pubescent. **Peduncles** 7–9 cm; bracts

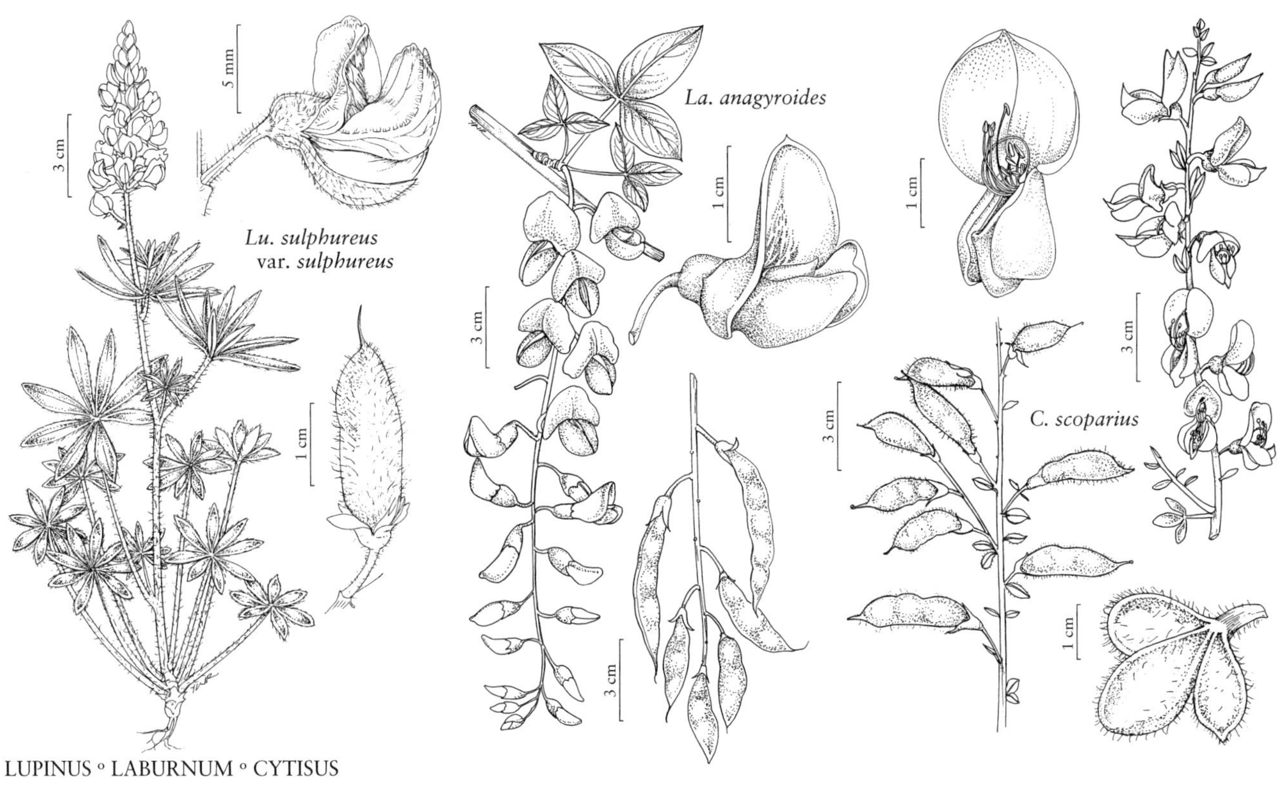

LUPINUS ◦ LABURNUM ◦ CYTISUS

deciduous, 6–15 mm. **Racemes** 11–25 cm; flowers whorled or spirally arranged. **Pedicels** 2–4 mm. **Flowers** 10–14 mm; calyx abaxial lobe entire, 10–11 mm, adaxial lobe entire, 7–9 mm; corolla lilac to reddish purple or pink, banner spot maroon, glabrous. **Legumes** (1.5–)2.5–4 cm, shaggy-villous. **Seeds** 2–4. **2*n*** = 52.

Flowering Mar–Apr. Sandhills, open woods; 0–50 m; Ala., Fla., Ga., La., Miss., N.C., S.C.

In Florida, *Lupinus villosus* reaches as far south as Polk County.

Lupinus villosus is of conservation concern in North Carolina.

88. Lupinus westianus Small, Torreya 26: 91. 1926 • Gulf Coast lupine [E]

Herbs, biennial or perennial, 3–5 dm, hairs short-appressed, velvety to shaggy. **Cotyledons** deciduous, petiolate. **Stems** spreading-ascending, clustered, robust, branched or unbranched. **Leaves** cauline; stipules abortive or early deciduous (occurring only on very new growth), 9–15 mm; petiole 2–3.5 cm; leaflet 1, blades 30–70 × 15–25 mm, surfaces short-appressed, velvety to satiny sericeous. **Peduncles** 2.5–6.5 cm; bracts deciduous, 4–7 mm. **Racemes** 4–25 cm; flowers whorled. **Pedicels** 4–6 mm. **Flowers** 11–14 mm; calyx abaxial lobe ovate, 2-lobed, 8–12 mm, adaxial lobe lanceolate, entire or obscurely 3-lobed, 5–10 mm; corolla pink or rose to blue, banner spot maroon to dark blue, banner glabrous abaxially, keel glabrous. **Legumes** 1.5–2.5 cm, villous. **Seeds** 2–4.

Varieties 2 (2 in the flora): Florida.

1. Corollas blue to pale lavender-blue, banner spots dark blue. . . . . . . 88a. *Lupinus westianus* var. *westianus*
1. Corollas pink, banner spots deep reddish purple . . . . 88b. *Lupinus westianus* var. *aridorum*

88a. Lupinus westianus Small var. **westianus** [E]

Perennials, 3+ dm, woody. **Leaves** cauline, 3–9.5 cm; petiole 1–5.5 cm; leaflet surfaces velvety. **Peduncles** 2.5–5 cm; bracts 4–7 mm. **Racemes** 4–25 cm. **Pedicels** 1–4 mm. **Flowers** 12–14 mm; calyx abaxial lobe 9–12 mm, adaxial lobe 5–10 mm; corolla blue to pale lavender-blue, banner spot dark blue. **Legumes** 2.5–3 cm, long-shaggy hairy.

Flowering Mar–May. Coastal sands, adjacent pine or oak scrub, sandhills, roadbanks; 0–50 m; Fla.

Variety *westianus* is found in the western peninsula from Bay, Escambia, Franklin, Gulf, and Okaloosa counties.

88b. Lupinus westianus Small var. **aridorum** (McFarlin ex Beckner) Isely, Brittonia 38: 356. 1986 C E

Lupinus aridorum McFarlin ex Beckner, Phytologia 50: 209. 1982

Biennials, to 5 dm, woody, short-appressed hairy, velvety. **Leaves** cauline, 3.5–7 cm; petiole 1–4.5 cm; leaflet surfaces short-appressed hairy. **Peduncles** 3–3.5 cm; bracts 5 mm. **Racemes** 8–10.5 cm. **Pedicels** 2–4 mm. **Flowers** 12–14 mm; calyx abaxial lobe 10 mm, adaxial lobe 8–10 mm; corolla pink, banner spot deep reddish purple. **Legumes** to 2 cm.

Flowering Mar–May. Pine, pine-palmetto, oak-palmetto scrub, dry sand ridges; of conservation concern; 0–50 m; Fla.

Variety *aridorum* is known in the middle peninsula from Orange, Osceola, and Polk counties.

Variety *aridorum* is in the Center for Plant Conservation's National Collection of Endangered Plants as *L. aridorum.*

54. LABURNUM Fabricius, Enum., 228. 1759 • Golden-chain tree [Ancient Latin name applied by Pliny to some species of *Cytisus*] I

Gordon C. Tucker

Zachary E. Guthrie

Trees or shrubs, unarmed. **Stems** erect, young growth appressed-pubescent, glabrescent, or glabrous. **Leaves** alternate, palmate; stipules present, minute; petiolate; leaflets 3, subsessile, stipels absent, blade margins entire, surfaces glabrous or pubescent abaxially, glabrous adaxially. **Inflorescences** 20–50-flowered, axillary, racemes, pendulous [erect]; bracts present; bracteoles near midpoint of pedicel, subopposite. **Flowers** papilionaceous; calyx zygomorphic, campanulate, bilabiate, lobes 5; corolla yellow, glabrous, banner ovate or orbiculate, keel shorter than wings; stamens 10, monadelphous; anthers dimorphic, shorter ones versatile, alternate, longer ones basifixed, dehiscing apically; ovary stipitate; style glabrous; stigma terminal. **Fruits** legumes, stipitate, pendulous, subterete, weakly torulose, narrowly ellipsoid to oblong [oblong-linear], indehiscent, constricted between seeds, fleshy, pubescent. **Seeds** [1]2–4(–8), reniform-compressed; hilum lateral. $x = 10$.

Species ca. 3 (2, including 1 hybrid, in the flora): introduced; s Europe, w Asia, n Africa; introduced also nearly worldwide in temperate areas.

Laburnum includes three Old World species and one hybrid. *Laburnum alpinum* (Miller) Berchtold & J. Presl, a native of southern Europe (leaves and fruits glabrous), is cultivated in North America and is not reported to escape; it forms a hybrid with *L. anagyroides* called *L.* ×*watereri.* The remaining species sometimes placed in *Laburnum*, *L. caramanicum* (Boissier & Heldrich) Bentham & Hooker f., is a shrub native to Greece and southwest Asia that has been infrequently cultivated in the southern United States. It is readily distinguished from other *Laburnum* by having upright versus pendulous racemes and usually is treated in a distinct genus, *Podocytisus* Boissier & Heldreich, allied to *Cytisus*, *Hesperolaburnum* Maire, and *Laburnum.*

In *Laburnum,* all parts of the plants are toxic and can be lethal if consumed in excess (D. Frohne and H. J. Pfander 2004). The main toxins are a series of quinolizidine alkaloids of the cytisine type.

1. Leaflet blades appressed silky-pubescent abaxially; young growth appressed-pubescent; pedicels (4–)8–15 mm; legumes densely appressed-pubescent . . . . 1. *Laburnum anagyroides*
1. Leaflet blades glabrous or glabrescent abaxially; young growth glabrescent or glabrous; pedicels 4–9 mm; legumes sparsely appressed-pubescent . . . . 2. *Laburnum* ×*watereri*

1. Laburnum anagyroides Medikus, Vorles. Churpfälz. Phys.-Öcon. Ges. 2: 363. 1787 (as anagyroidis) [F] [I]

Cytisus laburnum Linnaeus, Sp. Pl. 2: 739. 1753; *Laburnum vulgare* J. Presl

Trees or shrubs 2–7 m, young growth appressed-pubescent. **Leaves:** petiole (1–)2–6(–10) cm; leaflet blades elliptic, oblong-elliptic, or elliptic-obovate, 2–6.5 × 1.2–2.5 cm, surfaces appressed silky-pubescent abaxially. **Racemes** 15–40 cm; axis silky appressed-pubescent; bracts caducous, obovate, 2 × 0.5–1 mm, apex truncate or obtuse; bracteoles caducous, elliptic, 2 × 1 mm, apex subacute. **Pedicels** (4–)8–15 mm. **Flowers:** calyx 5 mm, puberulent, abaxial lobes 2 mm longer than lateral, adaxial lobes rounded and connate nearly to apex; corolla 18(–23) mm. **Legumes** yellowish green, 4–7 × 0.7–0.9 cm, base acute, apex rounded, dull, densely appressed-pubescent, sutures ± winged. **Seeds** 2–4(–8), black, slightly lunate, 4.5–5 mm. $2n = 20$.

Flowering late spring–summer. Forest edges, coastal thickets, roadsides; 0–1500 m; introduced; B.C.; Calif., Mass., Oreg., Utah, Wash.; s Europe; introduced also nearly worldwide in temperate areas.

A valued and attractive cultivated plant, *Laburnum anagyroides* was introduced to the flora area in the early nineteenth century. Named forms exist, varying in leaflet shape, indument, and inflorescence compactness. Some cultivars have erect racemes similar to those of *L. caramanicum*.

2. Laburnum ×watereri (A. C. Rosenthal & Bermann) Dippel, Handb. Laubholzk. 3: 673. 1893 • Voss's golden-chain tree [I]

Laburnum vulgare J. Presl var. *watereri* A. C. Rosenthal & Bermann, Wiener Ill. Gart.-Zeitung 9: 469. 1884

Trees or shrubs 5–7 m, young growth glabrescent or glabrous. **Leaves:** petiole (2–)3–5(–6) cm; leaflet blades elliptic, oblong-elliptic, or elliptic-obovate, 2–6.5(–8) × 2–6.5 cm, surfaces glabrous or glabrescent abaxially. **Racemes** 15–40 cm; axis silky appressed-pubescent; bracts caducous, obovate, 2 × 0.5–1 mm, apex truncate or obtuse; bracteoles caducous, elliptic, 2 × 1 mm, apex subacute. **Pedicels** 4–9 mm. **Flowers:** calyx 5 mm, puberulent, abaxial lobes 2 mm longer than lateral, adaxial lobes rounded and connate nearly to apex; corolla 8–10 mm. **Legumes** (often not developing) yellowish green, 4–7 × 0.7–0.9 cm, base acute, apex rounded, dull, sparsely appressed-pubescent, sutures narrowly winged. **Seeds** (often not formed) 2 or 3, black, slightly lunate, 5 mm.

Flowering summer. Roadsides, woodland edges; 0–150 m; introduced; Maine; s Europe; introduced also nearly worldwide in temperate areas.

This hybrid of *Laburnum alpinum* and *L. anagyroides* is documented as a naturalized plant in North America only in a limited area of Acadia National Park and vicinity.

55. CYTISUS Desfontaines, Fl. Atlant. 2: 139. 1798, name conserved • Broom, escobón [Greek *kytisos*, wood clover, presumably alluding to resemblance to *Medicago arborea*] [I]

Gordon C. Tucker

Debra K. Trock

Jenna M. Annis

Chamaecytisus Link

Shrubs [subshrubs or trees], unarmed [armed]. **Stems** green, gray-green, or brownish green, usually ascending or erect, sometimes becoming pendent [prostrate], angled or terete [grooved], pubescent or glabrescent. **Leaves** alternate, odd-pinnate, sometimes reduced or absent in *C. multiflorus*; stipules present, caducous, lanceolate; petiolate; leaflets 1–5, stipels absent, blade margins entire, surfaces pubescent or glabrous. **Inflorescences** 1–7(or 8)-flowered, axillary and terminal, racemes or glomerules; bracts present, subpersistent or caducous, usually small, leaflike, 1–3-foliolate; bracteoles paired proximal to calyx. **Flowers** papilionaceous; calyx cylindric or campanulate, 8–9 mm, lobes 5, connate most of their length, shallowly lobed; corolla yellow or white [pink, purple], usually glabrous, banner reflexed or not; stamens 9 or 10, monadelphous [diadelphous]; anthers basifixed; ovary usually sessile, rarely stipitate; style abruptly incurved near middle or gently curved ± throughout, glabrous; stigma terminal. **Fruits** legumes, sessile or short-stipitate, laterally compressed or inflated, oblong or linear-oblong, base acuminate to acute, apex acute to rounded, explosively dehiscent, not constricted between seeds, pubescent or glabrous. **Seeds** 3–12, reniform, ovoid, or rounded, with callous appendage. $x = 12$.

Species ca. 50 (4 in the flora): introduced; s, w Europe, nw Africa, n Atlantic Islands; introduced also in s South America, Pacific Islands (New Zealand), Australia.

Chamaecytisus has been treated as distinct (for example, D. Isely 1998); molecular phylogenies have indicated that its species are embedded within the evolutionary structure of *Cytisus* (E. Käss and M. Wink 1995; P. Cubas et al. 2002).

Cytisus villosus Pourret, a native of southwestern Europe, has been reported as a waif in New York State (R. S. Mitchell and G. C. Tucker 1997). It also occurs in a small population in Victoria, British Columbia (*Lomer 8672*, UBC).

1. Twigs terete, grayish or brownish green, becoming pendent; leaflet blades 10–30 mm; inflorescences pendent, (1–)3–7(or 8)-flowered; calyces cylindric, 8–9 mm, abaxial lips 3-lobed; seeds black, ovoid or rounded . . . . . 4. *Cytisus proliferus*
1. Twigs 5–10-angled, green, erect or ascending; leaflet blades 2–7(–9) mm; inflorescences erect, 1(–3)-flowered; calyces campanulate, 5–7 mm, lips barely lobed; seeds olivaceous to dark brown, reniform.
    2. Twigs 8–10-angled; calyces appressed-pubescent; legumes inflated, densely white-hairy . . . . . 3. *Cytisus striatus*
    2. Twigs 5-angled; calyces glabrous, puberulent, or villous; legumes laterally compressed, glabrous or margins villous.
        3. Calyces glabrous or puberulent; corollas usually yellow, rarely white (then unmarked), wings sometimes reddish; legumes narrowly oblong, 3.1–4(–5.5) cm . . . . . 1. *Cytisus scoparius*
        3. Calyces villous; corollas white, banner with medial dark line; legumes linear-oblong, 2.5–3 cm . . . . . 2. *Cytisus multiflorus*

1. Cytisus scoparius (Linnaeus) Link, Enum. Hort. Berol. Alt. 2: 241. 1822 • Scotch broom [F] [I] [W]

Spartium scoparium Linnaeus, Sp. Pl. 2: 709. 1753; *Cytisus scoparius* var. *andreanus* (Puissant) Dippel

Shrubs (0.7–)1.5–3 m; twigs erect or ascending, green, strongly 5-angled, pubescent or glabrescent. **Leaves** 12–15 mm; petiole (2–)6–10 mm, densely pilose, appressed-villous, or glabrate; leaflets (1 or)3 or 5 (often unifoliolate in new growth), blades obovate or oblong, 5–6.5(–9) × (1.5–)2–4 mm, base rounded, apex abruptly acuminate or cuspidate, surfaces lustrous with age, puberulent or glabrous. **Inflorescences** erect, 1 (2 or 3)-flowered. **Pedicels** (3–)6–10(–12) mm, glabrous. **Flowers:** calyx campanulate, 5–7 mm, lips barely lobed, puberulent or glabrous; corolla usually yellow, rarely white throughout, wings sometimes reddish, 16–20 (–25) mm, banner reflexed or not. **Legumes** laterally compressed, narrowly oblong, 3.1–4(–5.5) cm, surfaces glabrous, margins villous. **Seeds** 4–12, brown, reniform, 2–3 mm. **2*n*** = 24, 46, 48.

Flowering Mar–Jun(–Oct). Thickets, roadsides; 0–1000 m; introduced; B.C., N.S., P.E.I.; Ala., Alaska, Calif., Conn., Del., D.C., Ga., Idaho, Ky., Maine, Md., Mass., Mich., Mont., N.H., N.J., N.Y., N.C., Ohio, Oreg., Pa., S.C., Tenn., Va., Wash., W.Va.; s, w Europe; nw Africa; n Atlantic Islands; introduced also in s South America (Argentina, Chile), Pacific Islands (New Zealand).

Cytisus scoparius is a problem exotic (C. C. Bossard 1991, 1993, 1996), especially in the coastal regions of Oregon, Washington, and southern British Columbia, where infestations cover nearly one million hectares. It has long been in cultivation and was introduced to North America in 1850. Plants with reddish wing petals have been distinguished as var. *andreanus*. Forms with white petals, double-petaled flowers, and dwarf, compact, or procumbent growth forms are known.

Cytisus ×*dallimorei* Rolfe, the hybrid of *C. scoparius* and *C. multiflorus*, has been recorded from California.

SELECTED REFERENCES Bossard, C. C. 1991. The role of habitat disturbance, seed predation, and ant dispersal on establishment of the exotic shrub *Cytisus scoparius* in California. Amer. Midl. Naturalist 126: 1–13. Bossard, C. C. 1993. Seed germination in the exotic shrub *Cytisus scoparius* (Scotch broom) in California. Madroño 40: 47–61. Bossard, C. C. 1996. *Cytisus scoparius*. In: J. M. Randall and J. Marinelli, eds. 1996. Invasive Plants: Weeds of the Global Garden. Brooklyn. P. 52.

2. Cytisus multiflorus (L'Héritier) Sweet, Hort. Brit., 112. 1826 • Spanish or Portuguese broom [I]

Spartium multiflorum L'Héritier in W. Aiton, Hort. Kew 3: 11. 1789

Shrubs 1–3(–4) m; twigs erect or ascending, green, strongly 5-angled, pubescent or glabrescent. **Leaves** 15 mm; petiole (2–)3–6 mm, densely pilose, appressed-villous, or glabrate; leaflets (1 or)3 or 5 (leaves often unifoliolate in new growth or distal parts of shoots), blades lanceolate-linear or oblong, 3–7 × 2–5 mm, base rounded, apex abruptly acuminate or cuspidate, surfaces dull, densely pilose, appressed-villous, or glabrate. **Inflorescences** erect, 1–3-flowered, usually precocious. **Pedicels** 3–7 mm, glabrous. **Flowers:** calyx campanulate, 5 mm, lips barely lobed, villous; corolla white, banner proximally with medial dark line, 20 mm, banner 5–10 mm, reflexed or not. **Legumes** beige, laterally compressed, linear-oblong, 2.5–3 cm, surfaces glabrous. **Seeds** 4–6, olivaceous to dull brown, reniform, 2.5(–3) mm. **2*n*** = 48, 96.

Flowering Mar–May. Roadsides; 40–600 m; introduced; B.C.; Calif., Oreg., Wash.; sw Europe; introduced also in Pacific Islands (New Zealand).

Cytisus multiflorus is easily distinguished from *C. proliferus*, which also has white petals, by its strongly angled green stems; shorter leaflets; smaller, erect inflorescences; shorter, campanulate calyces with scarcely lobed lips; and shorter, glabrous legumes.

Cytisus multiflorus hybridizes with *C. scoparius* (*C.* ×*dallimorei*).

3. Cytisus striatus (Hill) Rothmaler, Feddes Repert. Spec. Nov. Regni Veg. 53: 149. 1944 [I] [W]

Genista striata Hill, Veg. Syst. 13(app.): 63, plate 13 [as Genister]. 1768

Shrubs 2–3 m; twigs erect or ascending, green, strongly 8–10-angled, villous or glabrescent. **Leaves** 15 mm; petiole (2–)3–6 mm, densely pilose, appressed-villous, or glabrate; leaflets 1 or 3 (often unifoliate in new growth), blades obovate or oblong, 2–6.5 × 2–6.5 mm, base rounded, apex abruptly acuminate or cuspidate, surfaces lustrous with age, puberulent or glabrous. **Inflorescences** erect, 1 or 2-flowered. **Pedicels** 5–10 mm, glabrous. **Flowers:** calyx campanulate, 5 mm, lips barely lobed, appressed-pubescent; corolla yellow, 20–25 mm, banner not reflexed. **Legumes** inflated (not laterally compressed), narrowly oblong, 1.5–4 cm, surfaces densely white-hairy. **Seeds** 3–6, dark brown, reniform, 2–3 mm. **2*n*** = 46, 48.

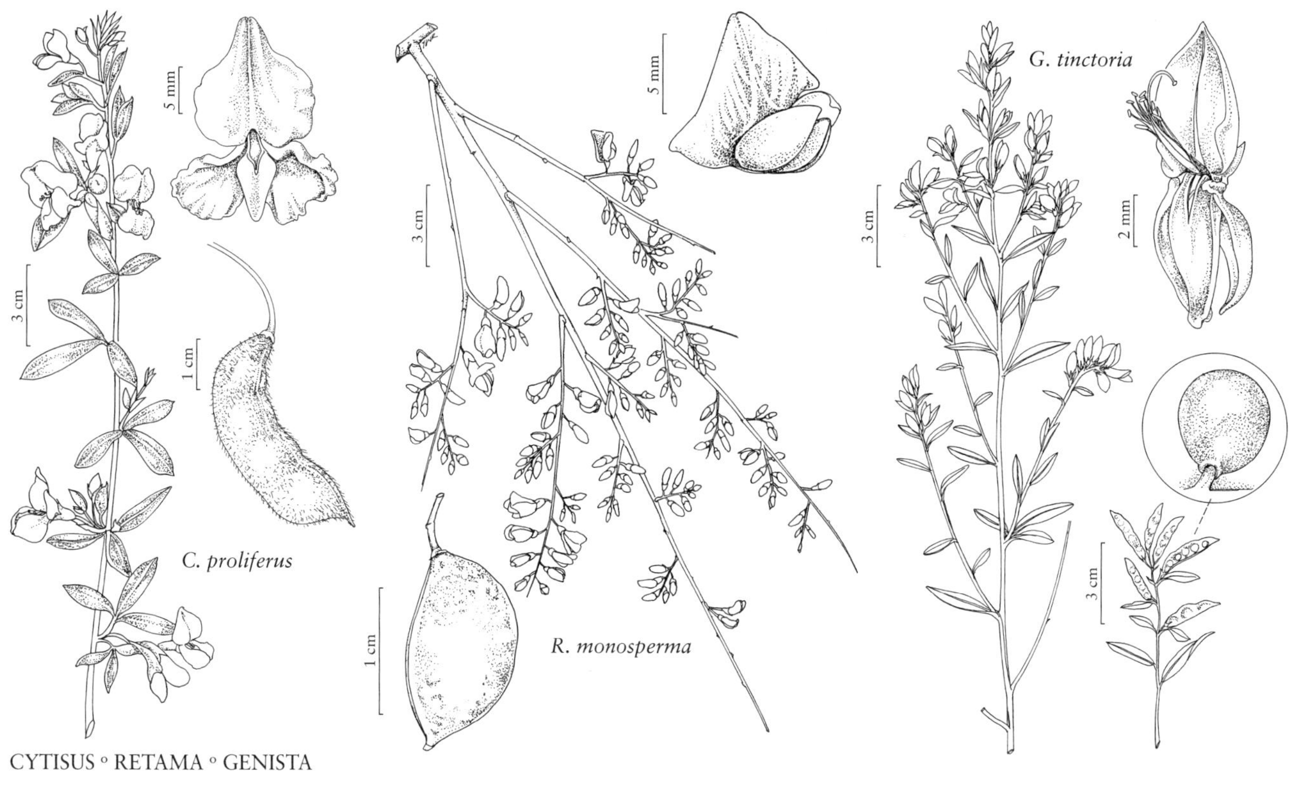

CYTISUS ◦ RETAMA ◦ GENISTA

Flowering May–Aug. Disturbed areas, roadsides; 0–300 m; introduced; B.C.; Calif., Oreg.; sw Europe; introduced also in s South America (Chile).

Cytisus striatus is extensively naturalized in California, from the San Francisco Bay area to the Peninsular Ranges; in Oregon, it is known from Douglas and Lane counties.

4. **Cytisus proliferus** Linnaeus f., Suppl. Pl., 328. 1782 F I

Chamaecytisus proliferus (Linnaeus f.) Link

Shrubs to 1–4(–5) m; twigs becoming pendent, grayish or brownish green, terete, canescent. **Leaves** 20–50 mm; petiole 5–10(–12) mm, densely sericeous; leaflets 3, blades lanceolate to ovate, 10–30 × 2–6 mm, base cuneate, apex acute, abruptly acuminate, surfaces dull in age, densely appressed-pilose. **Inflorescences** pendent, (1–)3–7(or 8)-flowered. **Pedicels** 10–15 mm, sericeous. **Flowers:** calyx light green, cylindric, 8–9 mm, tube 5–6 mm, abaxial lip shallowly 3-lobed, adaxial lip widely 2-lobed, densely pubescent; corolla white, petals clawed, 10–15 mm, banner with purple lines or spots adaxially, reflexed or not, wings equaling banner, sparsely pubescent, keel oblong, shorter than banner. **Legumes** black, flattened, oblong, 3.5–5 cm, with short, straight mucro, surfaces sericeous. **Seeds** (3–)6–10, black, ovoid to rounded, 5–7 mm, strophiolate. $2n = 48$.

Flowering Feb–Jun. Coastal sage scrub, disturbed annual grasslands, alluvial fans on well-drained granitic sandy-loam soils; 0–100 m; introduced; Calif.; Atlantic Islands (Canary Islands); introduced also in w South America (Ecuador), Europe (Italy), Australia (Tasmania).

Cytisus proliferus is escaped from cultivation with populations established in Los Angeles, Marin, Santa Barbara, and Santa Clara counties. The California Invasive Plants Council lists it as an alert species. Each plant produces thousands of seeds, which are dispersed by ants and birds.

56. RETAMA Rafinesque, Sylva Tellur., 22. 1838, name conserved • Bridal veil broom [Arabic *rotem*, *retem*, or *retama*, broom bush] [I]

Debra K. Trock

Shrubs [trees], unarmed. **Stems** erect, ascending, or pendent, branched from base, slender, persistently gray-green, canescent, nearly leafless. **Leaves** alternate [subopposite], unifoliolate; stipules present; petiolate; blade margins entire, surfaces sericeous. **Inflorescences** 10–50(–80+)-flowered, axillary, racemes [clustered on short axillary shoots]; bracts present, caducous. **Flowers** papilionaceous, short-pedicellate; calyx campanulate [turbinate or urceolate], 3–5 mm, bilabiate, lobes 5, glabrous or pubescent; corolla white [yellow], glabrous or pubescent; wings longer or shorter than keel; stamens 10, monadelphous; anthers basifixed, dimorphic; ovary sessile; style incurved, white to greenish yellow, glabrous. **Fruits** legumes, short-stipitate, obovoid, indehiscent or incompletely dehiscent along adaxial suture, not constricted between seeds, glabrous or glabrate. **Seeds** 1[–3], ovoid to rounded. $x = 24$.

Species 3 (1 in the flora): introduced, California; sw Europe, n Africa, Atlantic Islands (Canary Islands); introduced also in w South America, se Europe, Australia.

1. Retama monosperma (Linnaeus) Boissier, Voy. Bot. Espagne 2(5): 144. 1840 [F] [I]

Spartium monospermum Linnaeus, Sp. Pl. 2: 708. 1753; *Genista monosperma* (Linnaeus) Lamarck

Shrubs to 1–4 m. **Leaves:** stipules inconspicuous or caducous, 3–4 mm; leaflet blade linear-lanceolate to linear-subspatulate. **Racemes** pendent, short. **Flowers:** calyx deep red, broadly campanulate, abaxial lip 3-lobed, middle lobe minutely fringed, adaxial lip 2-lobed; petals clawed, banner rhombic-ovate or obovate, 10–12 mm, wings longer than banner, sparsely pubescent, keel narrowly oblong, shorter than banner. **Legumes** 12–18 × 8–10 mm, with short, curved mucro. **Seeds** black, strophiolate. $2n = 48$.

Flowering Feb–Jun. Coastal sage scrub, disturbed annual grasslands, alluvial fans on well drained granitic sandy-loam soils; 0–200 m; introduced; Calif.; Europe (Portugal, Spain); n Africa; introduced also in South America (Ecuador), Europe (Italy), Australia (Tasmania).

Retama monosperma is an invasive escape with populations established in Amador, Los Angeles, Riverside, and San Diego counties. The California Invasive Plants Council lists it as an alert species because it is invasive in other regions with similar climates. *Retama monosperma* is also an official State of California Noxious Weed (sect. 4500 Agricultural Code), not legal to be sold in the state (although planting is determined by each county). Each plant produces large numbers of seeds, which are dispersed by ants and birds.

SELECTED REFERENCE Jacobsen, E. 2000. *Retama monosperma.* In: C. M. Bossard et al., eds. 2000. Invasive Plants of California's Wildlands. Berkeley. Pp. 266–268.

57. GENISTA Linnaeus, Sp. Pl. 2: 709. 1753; Gen. Pl. ed. 5, 318. 1754 • Broom [Latin *genu*, knee, alluding to flexuous twigs used as common broom] [I]

Debra K. Trock

Shrubs [small trees], armed or unarmed, 1–6 m. **Stems** erect, branched from base, slender, striate, persistently greenish, sericeous to glabrescent. **Leaves** often caducous, alternate or opposite, unifoliolate or odd-pinnate; stipules present [absent], inconspicuous, adnate to leaf bases; sessile or petiolate; leaflets 1 or 3, blade margins entire, surfaces glabrous or pubescent. **Inflorescences** 1–20[–30]-flowered, terminal or axillary, clusters or racemes [panicles], or flowers solitary; bracts present. **Flowers** papilionaceous; calyx tubular-campanulate, bilabiate, abaxial lip 3-lobed, adaxial lip 2-lobed; corolla yellow, petals clawed; stamens 10, monadelphous;

anthers basifixed, dimorphic; ovary sessile, style abruptly incurved distally, glabrous. **Fruits** legumes, stipitate, compressed, narrowly oblong [falcate-rhomboid and inflated], dehiscent, not constricted between seeds, usually pubescent, rarely glabrous. **Seeds** 3–10, ovoid, cordate, ellipsoid, rhombic, or orbicular, strophiolate. x = 24.

Species ca. 90 (5 in the flora): introduced; w Europe, n Africa; introduced widely.

A. Kleist et al. (2014) found evidence suggesting multiple horticultural introductions of *Genista monspessulana* (French broom) in California. They also indicated that inter-taxon hybridization may also be occurring among the *Genista* populations in the state, possibly contributing to the invasive success of the species.

A small population of *Genista pilosa* Linnaeus was recently found on Vancouver Island, British Columbia (*F. Lomer 7732*, UBC V236493, Sep. 7, 2011).

SELECTED REFERENCE Gibbs, P. E. 1966. A revision of the genus *Genista* L. Notes Roy. Bot. Gard. Edinburgh 27: 11–99.

1. Leaflets 1 . . . . 5. *Genista tinctoria*
1. Leaflets 3.
   2. Leaflet blades linear to narrowly elliptic, margins revolute . . . . 2. *Genista linifolia*
   2. Leaflet blades elliptic to oblanceolate, obovate, or elliptic, margins entire, sometimes ciliolate.
      3. Leaflet blades 5–10 mm; banners with V-shaped patch of pubescence from base to apex; wings and keel longer than banner . . . . 1. *Genista canariensis*
      3. Leaflet blades (5–)10–25 mm; banners glabrous; wings and keel slightly shorter than banner.
         4. Inflorescences terminal racemes; bracts 1–2.5 mm; seeds orbicular, 2.5–3 mm, olive to brownish or black, hilum red-orange. . . . . 3. *Genista maderensis*
         4. Inflorescences dense, axillary clusters on short shoots; bracts 2–3 mm; seeds ovoid, 1–1.3 mm, tan to dark brown, hilum greenish yellow . . . . 4. *Genista monspessulana*

1. Genista canariensis Linnaeus, Sp. Pl. 2: 709. 1753 (as canariensi) • Canary broom [I] [W]

Cytisus canariensis (Linnaeus) Kuntze; *Teline canariensis* (Linnaeus) Webb & Berthelot

Shrubs (1–)2–4 m. **Stems** sericeous, hairs yellow-brown. **Leaves** petiolate; stipules 0.5–2 mm; petiole 2–6 mm; leaflets 3, blades obovate or rounded, 5–10 mm, base tapering to cuneate, apex rounded to mucronate, surfaces densely sericeous abaxially, sparsely pilose to pannose adaxially. **Inflorescences** 5–20-flowered, terminal or axillary, racemes, 10–60 mm; bracts 3–4 mm. **Pedicels** 1–2.5 mm. **Flowers**: calyx 4–6 mm, densely floccose; banner ovate, 10–12 mm, ± V-shaped patch of pubescence from base to apex; wings and keel longer than banner, wings glabrous, keel pubescent abaxially. **Legumes** narrowly oblong, 15–30 mm, puberulent. **Seeds** 5–8, dark brown, rhombic-ovoid, 2–2.5 mm. $2n$ = 48.

Flowering Feb–Apr. Disturbed areas; 0–1000 m; introduced; Calif., Wash.; Europe; Atlantic Islands (Canary Islands).

Genista canariensis is known from Alameda, Los Angeles, Monterey, Orange, San Diego, San Luis Obispo, and Santa Barbara counties in California, and Klickitat County in Washington.

2. Genista linifolia Linnaeus, Sp. Pl. ed. 2, 2: 997. 1763 • Mediterranean broom [I]

Cytisus linifolius (Linnaeus) Lamarck; *Teline linifolia* (Linnaeus) Webb & Berthelot

Shrubs 1–2.5 m. **Stems** densely sericeous, hairs yellow-brown. **Leaves** petiolate; stipules 1–6 (–10) mm; petiole 1–5 mm; leaflets 3, blades linear to narrowly elliptic, 15–60 mm, base attenuate, margins revolute, apex acuminate, surfaces densely pubescent abaxially, sparsely white-pannose adaxially. **Inflorescences** 5–20-flowered, terminal, racemes, dense, 15–30 mm; bracts 1–2 mm. **Pedicels** 2–7 mm. **Flowers**: calyx 5–15 mm, densely floccose; banner narrowly ovate, 10–15(–18) mm, apex notched, densely pubescent; wings and keel equaling banner, pubescent abaxially. **Legumes** narrowly oblong, 15–35 mm, sericeous. **Seeds** 6–8, yellow-tan to brown, widely ellipsoid to rounded, 2 mm.

Flowering Feb–Aug. Disturbed areas; 0–700 m; introduced; Calif.; sw Europe; n Africa; Atlantic Islands (Canary Islands); introduced also in Australia.

Genista linifolia is known from Humboldt, Los Angeles, San Diego, and Santa Barbara counties.

3. Genista maderensis (Webb & Berthelot) Webb ex Lowe, Man. Fl. Madeira 1: 123. 1862 • Madeira dyer's greenweed [I]

Teline maderensis Webb & Berthelot, Hist. Nat. Îles Canaries 3(2,2): 37. 1842

Shrubs 1–6 m. **Stems** densely sericeous, hairs whitish to yellow-brown. **Leaves** petiolate; stipules persistent, 1.5–6 mm; petiole 5–10 mm; leaflets 3, blades obovate to oblanceolate or elliptic, 5–25 mm, base tapering to cuneate, apex obtuse to rounded, often mucronate, surfaces densely pubescent abaxially, sparsely lanate adaxially. **Inflorescences** 3–20-flowered, terminal, racemes, 15–70 mm; bracts 1–2.5 mm. **Pedicels** 2–4 mm. **Flowers:** calyx 4–8 mm, densely sericeous; banner widely ovate, 9–16 mm, glabrous; wings and keel slightly shorter than banner, wings glabrous, keel pubescent abaxially. **Legumes** narrowly oblong, 20–40 mm, sericeous. **Seeds** 3–6(–10), olive to brownish or black, orbicular, 2.5–3 mm; hilum red-orange.

Flowering Apr–Aug. Disturbed areas; 0–700 m; introduced; Calif.; Atlantic Islands (Madeira).

Genista maderensis is known from Butte, El Dorado, Los Angeles, Monterey, and San Mateo counties.

4. Genista monspessulana (Linnaeus) L. A. S. Johnson, Contr. New South Wales Natl. Herb. 3: 98. 1962 • French broom [I] [W]

Cytisus monspessulanus Linnaeus, Sp. Pl. 2: 740. 1753; *Teline monspessulana* (Linnaeus) K. Koch

Shrubs 1.5–3 m. **Stems** sericeous, hairs silvery. **Leaves** petiolate; stipules deciduous, 0.5–2 mm; petiole 1–5 mm; leaflets 3, blades oblanceolate to obovate, 10–15 mm, base cuneate, margins ciliolate, apex obtuse and mucronate, surfaces sericeous abaxially, glabrous adaxially. **Inflorescences** 4–10-flowered, axillary, clustered on short shoots, dense, 15–60 mm; bracts caducous, narrowly linear, 2–3 mm. **Pedicels** 1–3 mm. **Flowers:** calyx 5–7 mm, sericeous; banner ovate, 10–15 mm, glabrous; wings and keel slightly shorter than banner, wings glabrous, keel tomentose abaxially and distally. **Legumes** oblong, 15–25 mm, densely sericeous. **Seeds** (3–)5–7(–10), tan to dark brown, ovoid, 1–1.3 mm; hilum greenish yellow. **2*n*** = 44, 46, 48.

Flowering Feb–Aug. Grasslands, oak woodlands, coastal scrub, chaparral, conifer and mixed evergreen forests, mostly in disturbed areas; 0–900 m; introduced; B.C.; Calif., Oreg.; s Europe; w Asia; n Africa; Atlantic Islands (Azores, Canary Islands); introduced also in South America (Argentina, Chile, Uruguay).

The flowers and possibly other parts of *Genista monspessulana* have been reported as toxic. The species apparently hybridizes with *G. canariensis* and *G. stenopetala* Webb & Berthelot. *Genista stenopetala* was previously reported from California; it now appears that the only known specimens of the species were cultivated and that many specimens previously annotated to this name were hybrids with *G. monspessulana*. The hybrid is found in Oregon.

5. Genista tinctoria Linnaeus, Sp. Pl. 2: 710. 1753 • Dyer's greenweed, genêt des tinturiers [F] [I] [W]

Shrubs prostrate to erect, 0.5–2 m. **Stems** much branched from base, glabrous or sparsely and irregularly hairy. **Leaves** sessile or subsessile; stipules 0.8–1.5 mm; petiole less than 1 mm; leaflet 1, blade broadly elliptic, lanceolate, or oblanceolate to obovate, 5–50 mm, base rounded, margins sparsely ciliolate, apex aristulate, surfaces glabrous or sparsely pubescent along margins and midvein. **Inflorescences** 1–6-flowered, terminal, simple or compound racemes (30–)40–60(–80) mm; bracts foliaceous, 6–9 mm. **Pedicels** 1–2 mm. **Flowers:** calyx 3–7 mm, glabrous or glabrate to densely pubescent; banner broadly ovate, 8–12 mm, glabrous; wings and keel equaling banner, glabrous. **Legumes** narrowly oblong, 15–25 mm, glabrous. **Seeds** 4–10, yellow-tan, cordate, 1–1.3 mm. **2*n*** = 48, 96.

Flowering Mar–Aug. Recently disturbed areas; 0–1500 m; introduced; B.C., N.S., Ont., Que.; Conn., D.C., Idaho, Maine, Md., Mass., Mich., Miss., N.J., N.Y., Ohio, R.I., Vt., Va., Wash., Wis.; Europe; introduced also in South America (Argentina), Asia (China).

Genista tinctoria is the most widely distributed and variable taxon in the genus. Two characters that seem to show the most variation are the presence or absence of indument on the leaves, calyx, and fruit and the growth form, with prostrate plants having inflorescences consisting of few-flowered racemes and more erect plants having compound or paniculate racemes. Local and regional floras in the areas to which these plants are endemic often recognize varieties; however, there seems to be no good geographic or genetic basis for doing so.

58. SPARTIUM Linnaeus, Sp. Pl. 2: 708. 1753; Gen. Pl. ed. 5, 317. 1754 • Spanish broom [Greek *sparton*, cordage, probably alluding to ancient use for making rope and brooms] [I]

Debra K. Trock

Shrubs or trees, unarmed. **Stems** evergreen, erect, rushlike, glabrous. **Leaves** alternate to subopposite, unifoliolate or obsolescent; stipules present; petiolate; blade margins entire, surfaces appressed-hairy abaxially, glabrous adaxially. **Inflorescences** 5–20-flowered, terminal, racemes; bracts and bracteoles present. **Flowers** papilionaceous, showy, pedicellate; calyx campanulate, lobes 5; corolla yellow; stamens 10, monadelphous; anthers dimorphic, 9 basifixed, 1 dorsifixed; style incurved, indument dense, silky proximally. **Fruits** legumes, sessile, flattened, linear-oblong, dehiscent, sericeous or glabrous. **Seeds** 6–18, transversely oblong. $x = 12$.

Species 1: introduced; s Europe, sw Asia, nw Africa; introduced also in South America, Pacific Islands (Hawaii), Australia.

1. Spartium junceum Linnaeus, Sp. Pl. 2: 708. 1753 [F] [I] [W]

Shrubs or trees 2–4(–5) m. **Stems** evergreen, longitudinally striate, flexible, glaucous, sparsely branched distally, becoming woody; pith spongy. **Leaves** early deciduous, blade bright green adaxially, oblong-linear to lanceolate, 1–2 × 0.2–0.5 cm. **Inflorescences** to 46 cm, lax; bracts deciduous, proximal, small; bracteoles 2, distal. **Flowers** sweet-scented; calyx tube broadly ovate, 8–10 mm, irregularly unilabiate or, rarely, bilabiate, lobes distinct almost to base; banner broadly obovate to rounded, 2–2.5 cm; wings oblong, slightly shorter than banner, apex obtuse; keel oblong, apex beaked. **Legumes** dark brown to black, 5–10(–12) × 0.5+ cm, compressed between seeds; valves twisted to eject seeds. **Seeds** yellow-brown; without appendage near hilum. $2n = 48+$.

Flowering Mar–Nov. Poor, rocky soils, riverbanks, post-burn chaparral, disturbed areas; 0–1500 m; introduced; Calif., Oreg., Tex., Wash.; s Europe, sw Asia, nw Africa; introduced also in South America, Pacific Islands (Hawaii), Australia.

Spartium junceum was introduced to California in 1858 as an ornamental; it quickly colonized disturbed habitats in Mediterranean/chaparral climates and can become a fire hazard. All parts of the plant are poisonous. In Europe, flowers have been used to make dye, and fibers are used as cordage. *Spartium junceum* is considered an invasive plant or noxious weed in the four states in which it occurs.

59. ULEX Linnaeus, Sp. Pl. 2: 741. 1753; Gen. Pl. ed. 5, 329. 1754 • Gorse [Latin *ulicis*, ancient name for prickly rosemary-like shrub used for arresting gold pieces carried by running water, applied to present taxon] [I]

Debra K. Trock

Shrubs, heavily armed. **Stems** erect, extensively branched from base, striate, shoots modified to thorns, 1–3 cm, new growth glaucous, older stems hirsute to tomentose, hairs gray to red-brown. **Leaves** persistent, alternate, unifoliolate or odd-pinnate (3-foliolate in seedlings), leaflets gradually reduced to phyllodes; stipules absent; petiolate; phyllodes spinelike, surfaces pubescent. **Inflorescences** 1–5-flowered, axillary, usually clusters, rarely short racemes; bracts absent; bracteoles 2, immediately subtending calyx. **Flowers** papilionaceous; calyx bilabiate, lobes 5, abaxial lip 3-lobed, adaxial lip 2-lobed; corolla yellow; stamens 10, monadelphous;

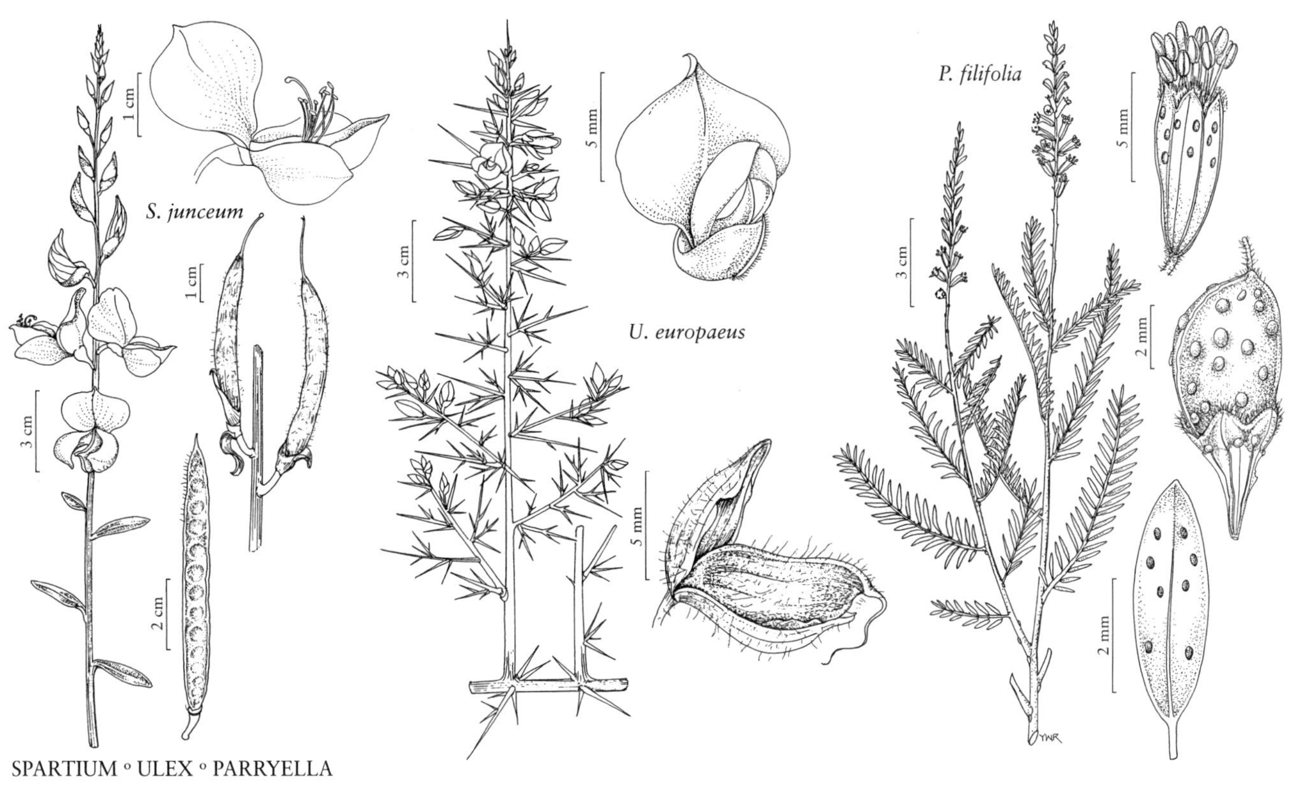

SPARTIUM ◦ ULEX ◦ PARRYELLA

anthers dorsifixed; ovary sessile; style incurved, glabrous. **Fruits** legumes, partly enclosed by calyx, pedicellate, slightly compressed, ovoid, oblong, or linear, dehiscent, densely villous. **Seeds** 1–6, reniform. $x = 16$.

Species ca. 20 (1 in the flora): introduced; w Europe, n Africa; introduced also in South America, c, n Europe, Asia, Africa, Pacific Islands (Hawaii, New Zealand), Australia.

SELECTED REFERENCE Clements, D. R. et al. 2001. The biology of Canadian weeds. 112. *Ulex europaeus* L. Canad. J. Pl. Sci. 81: 325–337.

1. Ulex europaeus Linnaeus, Sp. Pl. 2: 741. 1753

• Common gorse [F] [I]

Shrubs 2–3 m. **Stems** extensively intertwined, branchlets leafy; older plants with dead mass at center. **Phyllodes** 4–14 mm. **Bracteoles** 1.5–7 mm wide. **Flowers:** calyx ± yellow, membranous, lobes concave, 12–15 mm, hairs ± spreading; corolla persistent; banner ovate, to 20 mm; wings and keel oblong, slightly shorter than banner, obtuse; wings slightly longer than keel. **Legumes** dark purplish brown, 1.5–2.5 × 6–8 mm, explosively dehiscent. **Seeds** brownish green; hilar appendages relatively small. $2n = 32, 64, 96$.

Flowering Jan–Nov. Roadsides, pastures, open forests, coastal bluffs, floodplains, disturbed areas in well-drained soils, particularly in coastal regions; 0–400 m; introduced; B.C.; Calif., Mass., N.Y., Oreg., Pa., Va., Wash., W.Va.; w Europe; introduced also in South America, c, n Europe, Asia, Africa, Pacific Islands (Hawaii, New Zealand), Australia.

Ulex europaeus is cultivated for fodder, bedding, and hedges; the flowers are used to produce a dye. An extract from the seeds is used for tissue typing, due to its ability to selectively bind with certain types of lipids and proteins.

In Massachusetts, the species was last collected in 1931 and is likely extirpated there.

60. PARRYELLA Torrey & A. Gray, Proc. Amer. Acad. Arts 7: 397. 1868 • [For Charles C. Parry, 1823–1890, pioneer botanist in western North America, and Latin *-ella*, commemorative] [E]

Leila M. Shultz

Shrubs, unarmed, aromatic, dotted with conspicuous oil glands. **Stems** erect, glandular. **Leaves** alternate, odd-pinnate; stipules present, caducous; sessile; leaflets 17–41, blades linear-filiform or oblong-elliptic, margins entire, surfaces puberulent. **Inflorescences** 10–50(–90)-flowered, terminal, racemes; bracts absent. **Pedicels** relatively short, hairy. **Flowers** non-papilionaceous; calyx narrowly campanulate, lobes 5; corolla absent; stamens 10, monomorphic, distinct; anthers versatile; ovary 2-loculed; style sinuous; stigma punctiform. **Fruits** legumes, sessile, slightly compressed laterally, obovoid, indehiscent, prominently gland-dotted. **Seeds** 1 or 2, obovoid. $x = 10$.

Species 1: sw United States.

Parryella is part of the amorphoid group of legumes (*Amorpha*, *Eysenhardtia*, etc.), characterized by non-papilionaceous flowers (M. McMahon and L. Hufford 2004). The relationships of *Parryella* within this group are discussed under 61. *Amorpha*.

1. Parryella filifolia Torrey & A. Gray, Proc. Amer. Acad. Arts 7: 397. 1868 • Parryella [E] [F]

Shrubs lemon-scented, 5–16 dm. **Stems** pliant, purplish, turning gray with age, widely branched. **Leaves** narrowly lanceolate, 30–170 × 8–40 mm; leaflet blades 4–16(–20) × 0.3–1.5 mm, margins revolute, plane, or concave. **Flowers:** calyx shallowly lobed, 2–3.8 × 1–2 mm, glandular-punctate, lobes green with yellow glands, rounded or acute; stamens conspicuously exserted beyond hypanthium, unequal. **Legumes** 4–8 × 1.5–3 mm, beaked, style-base persistent, prominently dotted with red or orange glands. $2n = 20$.

Flowering early–late summer. Sand dunes, bluffs, talus, rock ledges; 1400–2000 m; Ariz., Colo., N.Mex., Utah.

Parryella filifolia, a broomlike shrub, is restricted to the Colorado Plateau of the western United States. The foliage varies in morphology from the southern to the northern part of its range. Plants in Colorado, New Mexico, and Utah are microphyllous with revolute leaves; in Arizona, the leaflets are larger and concavely folded. No attempt has been made to separate these groups taxonomically.

61. AMORPHA Linnaeus, Sp. Pl. 2: 713. 1753; Gen. Pl. ed. 5, 319. 1754 • False indigo [Greek *a-*, without, and *morphos*, shape, misshapen, alluding to the simplified, non-papilionaceous flowers]

Shannon C. K. Straub

James L. Reveal†

Alan S. Weakley

Shrubs, rarely subshrubs, unarmed, often gland-dotted; sometimes rhizomatous, pungently fragrant when bruised. **Stems** usually erect, sometimes spreading, glabrous or pubescent. **Leaves** alternate, odd-pinnate; stipules present; petiolate; leaflets (7–)9–45(–63), opposite or subopposite, stipels present, petiolulate, blade margins entire or crenulate, veins usually obscured abaxially, midvein mucronate, surfaces gland-dotted or eglandular, pubescent or glabrous. **Inflorescences**

50–120+-flowered, terminal, racemes, usually solitary or clustered, rarely paniculiform (*A. paniculata*); bracts present, caducous, entire or crenulate, often gland-dotted; bracteoles caducous, entire. **Pedicels** spreading to ascending, sometimes obscure, articulate to hypanthium. **Flowers** non-papilionaceous, reduced to a single banner petal enveloping androecium and gynoecium; calyx persistent, slightly zygomorphic, greenish to reddish or purplish, sometimes drying blackish, cylindric, funnelform, campanulate, turbinate, conic, or obconic, lobes 5, obscure or distinct, not accrescent; banner petal purple, reddish purple, purplish, blue, lavender, violet, violet-blue, or white, glabrous; stamens 10, monadelphous basally, at least at early anthesis, or distinct, exserted; anthers dorsifixed, relatively small, dehiscing longitudinally; ovary slightly compressed, ovoid; styles slender, often exserted; stigma terminal, capitate. **Fruits** legumes, often persistent through next growing season, sessile or shortly stipitate, straight, curved, or bent, falcate or D-shaped, slightly compressed and asymmetrical, oblong to obovoid or claviform, indehiscent, dispersed with calyx, glabrous or pubescent. **Seeds** 1(or 2), laterally compressed, ovoid to oblong. $x = 10$.

Species 16 (15 in the flora): North America, nw Mexico; introduced in Europe, Asia, Africa.

Amorpha is notable among papilionoid legumes for having a non-papilionaceous corolla consisting solely of a banner petal, although deviation from the normal papilionoid floral form is common throughout Amorpheae. Even though recognition of the genus has never been in question, due to its easily distinguished floral characters, delimitation of species within the genus has long caused consternation among taxonomists. The range and intergradation of morphological variation have resulted in a prodigious list of recognized species, varieties, and forms, most often associated with the *A. fruticosa* complex. Early taxonomic treatments failed to result in a satisfactory circumscription of the genus (C. K. Schneider 1907; P. A. Rydberg 1919–1920; E. J. Palmer 1931), but the insightful and thorough work of R. L. Wilbur (1975), closely followed by D. Isely (1998) and here, was a marked improvement.

The "amorphoid" clade of Amorpheae, to which *Amorpha* belongs, has been strongly supported as monophyletic in molecular analyses (M. McMahon and L. Hufford 2004), although most relationships among genera in the clade remain unclear. Analyses of chloroplast, ribosomal DNA, and low-copy nuclear gene sequence data indicated that *Amorpha* may not be monophyletic because either *Errazurizia rotundata* or *Parryella filifolia*, or both, are nested within it (McMahon and Hufford 2004, 2005; McMahon 2005). Some of these analyses have indicated that *E. rotundata* and *P. filifolia* are sister species (combined analyses of chloroplast *trn*K, *mat*K, ITS/5.8S rDNA, nuclear *CNGC4*), which may or may not be nested in *Amorpha*; other analyses indicated that *E. rotundata* is nested among *Amorpha* species while *P. filifolia* may or may not be (*trn*K, *mat*K analyzed alone, *CNGC4* analyzed alone). These conflicting outcomes leave the relationship of these two species to each other and to *Amorpha* unclear. Preliminary analyses of additional nuclear gene data sets have also indicated that *E. rotundata* and *P. filifolia* are nested in *Amorpha* but have not clarified whether or not they are sister species (S. C. K. Straub and J. J. Doyle 2014). Morphological evidence also supports the close association of *E. rotundata* (originally described as *P. rotundata* Wooton), *P. filifolia*, and *Amorpha*. *Parryella filifolia* lacks a corolla, and the corolla of *E. rotundata* is either absent or consists of a single petal, which suggests a closer association in terms of floral evolution to *Amorpha* than to the other 5-petaled genera of Amorpheae, an observation supported by developmental studies (McMahon and Hufford 2005). W. F. Mahler (1965) hypothesized a close relationship of *Amorpha*, *E. rotundata*, and *P. filifolia* based on shared pollen characteristics.

The phylogenetic relationships among *Amorpha* species remain unclear due to lack of molecular variation in non-coding chloroplast, nuclear rDNA spacer regions, and nuclear gene intron sequence data. Preliminary results from phylogenetic analyses, including DNA sequence data from most species of the genus, indicate that *A. californica* is the earliest diverging species in the genus and that *A. georgiana* and *A. nana* are closely related; however, the relationships among the other species of the genus are thus far unresolved (S. C. K. Straub and J. J. Doyle 2014). The lack of molecular variation may be indicative of a rapid radiation in the genus or of continued gene flow and partial genetic homogenization through hybridization and introgression, possibly mediated by widespread species. Ongoing genetic work has suggested that polyploidy is more common in *Amorpha* than previously recognized. *Amorpha fruticosa* has long been known to be a tetraploid, and new information from nuclear gene DNA sequences and microsatellites now indicates that *A. confusa*, *A. crenulata*, and *A. roemeriana* may also be tetraploids, although this is yet to be confirmed by chromosome counts (Straub et al. 2009; Straub and Doyle). Clearly, further work is needed to resolve species relationships within *Amorpha*, to update species concepts within the genus, and to determine whether or not *Amorpha* is monophyletic as circumscribed or if *Errazurizia rotundata* and *P. filifolia* should be added to *Amorpha*.

Amorpha has been a group of interest for many years in the search for biologically active compounds. In the area of medicinal biochemistry, anti-tumor and anti-inflammatory compounds have been isolated from *A. fruticosa* (L. Li et al. 1993; J. Y. Cho et al. 2000). Antimicrobial agents have been identified in both *A. fruticosa* and *A. nana* (L. A. Mitscher et al. 1981, 1985). *Amorpha fruticosa* has also been investigated for its insecticidal and insect repellant properties (R. C. Roark 1947). The glands on the fruits of this species have been shown to contain compounds that poison numerous types of insects through ingestion or contact (for example, chinch bug, cotton aphid, pea aphid, spotted cucumber beetle, mosquito larvae) and also insect repellant properties (for example, striped cucumber beetle, flour beetles, dog fleas, and houseflies; C. H. Brett 1946, 1946b).

Native Americans of the Great Plains employed several of the more common *Amorpha* species for a variety of uses. *Amorpha fruticosa* was used for bedding, horse feed, and arrow shafts, and stems were arranged on the ground to create a clean place to put butchered meat (M. R. Gilmore 1919; P. A. Vestal and R. E. Schultes 1939; D. J. Rogers 1980). *Amorpha canescens* was used to treat stomach pain, intestinal worms, eczema, neuralgia, and rheumatism, and powdered leaves were applied to wounds (W. J. Hoffman 1891; Gilmore 1909, 1919; Hu. H. Smith 1928). The leaves were also mixed with buffalo fat and smoked or used to make tea (Gilmore 1919). The dried leaves of *A. nana* were used to treat catarrh (F. H. Elmore 1944).

A few *Amorpha* species are found regularly in cultivation, the most common being *A. fruticosa* and *A. canescens*, while *A. californica*, *A. herbacea*, and *A. nana* are less commonly part of the horticultural trade. *Amorpha fruticosa* has also been used in the United States and abroad for soil stabilization, erosion control, and in windbreaks, and has been investigated as a potential forage and biomass production crop (S. Karrenberg et al. 2003; L. R. DeHaan et al. 2006; K. Török et al. 2003). Cultivation of *A. fruticosa* has led to its escape and naturalization in many parts of Europe and Asia.

Amorpha apiculata Wiggins is known from Baja California, Mexico.

SELECTED REFERENCES Palmer, E. J. 1931. Conspectus of the genus *Amorpha*. J. Arnold Arbor. 12: 157–197. Schneider, C. K. 1907. Conspectus generis Amorphae. Bot. Gaz. 43: 297–307. Wilbur, R. L. 1964b. A revision of the dwarf species of *Amorpha* (Leguminosae). J. Elisha Mitchell Sci. Soc. 80: 51–65. Wilbur, R. L. 1975. A revision of the North American genus *Amorpha* (Leguminosae-Psoraleae). Rhodora 77: 337–409.

1. Petioles and rachises with spinelike glands; Arizona, California, Oregon. . . . . 1. *Amorpha californica*
1. Petioles and rachises without spinelike glands; widespread in United States, southernmost Canada.
    2. Subshrubs or shrubs, rarely perennial herbs, (0.1–)0.3–1.4(–3) m; petioles 0.5–15 (–20) mm; leaflet margins usually slightly to conspicuously revolute.
        3. Shrubs mostly canescent, rarely glabrous; eglandular or sparsely gland-dotted; c United States, s, c Canada . . . . 7. *Amorpha canescens*
        3. Shrubs not canescent; usually densely gland-dotted; widespread in n, c, se United States, s, c Canada.
            4. Leaflet midveins terminated by a swollen mucro; shrubs mostly densely puberulent to pubescent, when glabrous, then plants of Florida.
                5. Leaflet blades (6–)8–18(–24) cm, margins entire or inconspicuously crenulate; petioles (0.5–)1–10(–13) mm. . . . . .5. *Amorpha herbacea*
                5. Leaflet blades (8–)15–25(–30) cm, margins crenulate; petioles (3–)8–15 (–18) mm. . . . . 6. *Amorpha crenulata*
            4. Leaflet midveins terminated by a slender mucro; shrubs usually glabrous or sparsely pubescent and not of Florida.
                6. Petioles (6–)8–15(–20) mm; racemes branched, 10–20(–30) cm; banners bright blue . . . . .4. *Amorpha confusa*
                6. Petioles 1–8(–10) mm; racemes usually unbranched, (2–)3–20(–30) cm; banners reddish purple, rarely lavender.
                    7. Leaflet blades (3–)6–15(–18) cm; petioles 1–3(–5) mm; filaments distinct; anthers yellow; ovaries pubescent; se United States . . . . . 2. *Amorpha georgiana*
                    7. Leaflet blades (1.5–)3–7(–10) cm; petioles (2–)4–8(–10) mm; filaments connate basally; anthers purplish; ovaries glabrous; n, c United States, sc Canada . . . . .3. *Amorpha nana*
    2. Shrubs or suffrutescent herbs, 1–3(–4) m; petioles (5–)10–60(–90) mm; leaflet margins flat or slightly revolute.
        8. Calyx lobes as long as or longer than tubes, adaxial calyx lobes usually not rounded . . . . .10. *Amorpha schwerinii*
        8. Calyx lobes as long as or distinctly shorter than tubes, adaxial calyx lobes usually rounded or leaflets with conspicuous raised venation and paniculiform inflorescence if calyx lobes not rounded.
            9. Leaflet veins conspicuous, distinctly raised abaxially; racemes paniculiform . . . . .9. *Amorpha paniculata*
            9. Leaflet veins obscure, not raised abaxially; racemes 1–8(–12)-branched.
                10. Leaflet midveins terminated by a swollen mucro.
                    11. Leaflets (9–)13–19(or 21), blades 4–10(–12) mm wide, mucro 0.1–0.2 mm, petiolules distinctly warty-glandular; banners bright blue to deep violet-blue; legumes 4.5–6 mm . . . . .12. *Amorpha laevigata*
                    11. Leaflets (7 or)9–13(–17), blades (7–)15–25(–38) mm wide, mucro 0.2–0.8 mm, petiolules gland-dotted, rarely eglandular; banners purple; legumes 6–9 mm.
                        12. Racemes (4–)6–12(–20) cm; calyx obviously gland-dotted on distal ⅓; Texas . . . . .8. *Amorpha roemeriana*
                        12. Racemes (8–)10–20 cm; calyx not obviously gland-dotted on distal ¼; Arkansas, Oklahoma . . . . 13. *Amorpha ouachitensis*
                10. Leaflet midveins terminated by a slender or slightly swollen mucro.
                    13. Calyx lobes 0–0.6(–0.8) mm. . . . . .11. *Amorpha glabra*
                    13. Calyx lobes 0.2–1.4 mm.
                        14. Foliage and calyx drying blackish; leaflet blades distinctly shiny adaxially. . . . . 14. *Amorpha nitens*
                        14. Foliage and calyx not drying blackish; leaflet blades not shiny adaxially. . . . . .15. *Amorpha fruticosa*

1. Amorpha californica Nuttall in J. Torrey and A. Gray, Fl. N. Amer. 1: 306. 1838

Shrubs, (0.7–)1–3(–4) m; arising from compact, woody root. **Stems** smooth, often with spinelike glands, mostly short-pilose to puberulent, glabrate, or glabrous. **Leaves** (5–)10–20 cm; stipules linear to narrowly oblong, (2–)4–6 mm; petiole (7–)10–15(–25) mm, glands spinelike, scattered, puberulent or glabrous; rachis glands spinelike, puberulent to short-pilose; leaflets (11–)13–19(–25), stipels acicular, 1–1.5 mm, petiolule 0.7–1.5(–1.8) mm, gland-dotted, pilosulous or glabrous, blade mostly oblong, (8–)15–25(–42) × (6–)10–15(–20) mm, base round to subcordate, margins not revolute, entire or finely crenulate, apex round to obtuse or emarginate, surfaces puberulent to short-pilose or glabrous; midveins terminated by a swollen, globose mucro, 0.2–0.5 mm. **Racemes** unbranched, (5–)10–18(–25) cm; rachis often with spinelike glands, pilose; bracteoles linear to lanceolate, 1.5–4 mm, usually gland-dotted, sometimes eglandular, short-pilose. **Pedicels** 0.3–1.2 mm, eglandular, mostly puberulent to short-pilose. **Flowers:** calyx tube narrowly cylindric to funnelform, 2–2.8 mm, distal ½ sometimes gland-dotted, puberulent, short-pilose, or glabrous; lobes triangular to narrowly lanceolate, 0.4–2(–2.5) mm; banner reddish purple, broadly obovate, 5–7 × 2.5–4 mm, indistinctly clawed, margins entire; filaments 6–7 mm, connate basally 2–3.2 mm; anthers pale yellow; ovary mostly densely short-pilose. **Legumes** sessile, 6–8 × 2.5–3.5 mm, margins curved outward abaxially, straight adaxially, at least distal ½ gland-dotted, mostly short-pilose. **Seeds** olive brown or reddish brown, 3–4 × 1.5–2 mm, smooth.

Varieties 2 (2 in the flora): w United States, nw Mexico.

1. Shrubs mostly short-pilose or puberulent; calyx tubes puberulent to short-pilose, lobes (0.8–)1–2(–2.5) mm . . . . 1a. *Amorpha californica* var. *californica*
1. Shrubs glabrous or glabrate; calyx tubes glabrous or sparsely short-pilose, lobes 0.4–0.8(–1) mm . . . . 1b. *Amorpha californica* var. *napensis*

1a. Amorpha californica Nuttall var. **californica** • California false indigo or indigo-bush

Shrubs mostly puberulent or short-pilose. **Leaflets:** blade surfaces puberulent to short-pilose. **Calyces:** tube puberulent to short-pilose; lobes (0.8–)1–2(–2.5) mm. **2*n*** = 20.

Flowering May–Jul. Wooded or chaparral slopes; 200–2300 m; Ariz., Calif., Oreg.; Mexico (Baja California).

1b. Amorpha californica Nuttall var. **napensis** Jepson, Man. Fl. Pl. Calif., 556. 1925 • Napa false indigo or indigo-bush [C] [E]

Shrubs glabrous or glabrate. **Leaflets:** blade surfaces glabrous, except midveins adaxially pubescent. **Calyces:** tube glabrous or sparsely short-pilose; lobes 0.4–0.8(–1) mm.

Flowering May–Jul. Wooded or chaparral slopes; of conservation concern; 100–600 m; Calif.

Of all taxa of *Amorpha* in the flora area, *A. californica* is one of the most distinctive, due to the presence of spinelike glands. Of the two varieties, var. *californica* is the more widespread and common, with var. *napensis* a localized endemic in a small portion of northern California (Marin, Napa, and Sonoma counties). At this time, var. *napensis* is not listed by the state of California or any federal agency.

2. Amorpha georgiana Wilbur, Rhodora 56: 261, figs. 1–6. 1954 • Georgia false indigo or indigo-bush [E]

Shrubs, 0.3–1.2 m; arising from compact, woody root. **Stems** finely longitudinally grooved and ridged, gland-dotted, sparsely puberulent or glabrous. **Leaves** (3–)6–15(–18) cm; stipules sometimes persistent, linear or setaceous, (1–)1.5–2(–2.5) mm; petiole 1–3(–5) mm, gland-dotted, puberulent or glabrous; rachis sparsely gland-dotted, puberulent or glabrous; leaflets (11–)15–43(–47), stipels acicular or setaceous, 0.8–1.8 mm, petiolule 0.7–1.5(–1.8) mm, gland-dotted, mostly puberulent or glabrous, blade elliptic to oblong or, at least terminal leaflet, ovate to suborbiculate, (3–)6–10(–21) × (2–)3–6(–12) mm, base truncate or round to subcordate, margins usually revolute, entire or inconspicuously crenulate, apex round to obtuse or emarginate, surfaces usually glabrous or glabrate, sometimes sparsely pubescent; midvein terminated by a slender mucro, (0.2–)0.4–1 mm. **Racemes** usually unbranched, (2–)5–20(–30) cm, rarely with 2–4 lateral branches, these (2–)3–5(–6) cm; rachis sparsely gland-dotted, often glabrous, sometimes puberulent; bracteoles linear to narrowly subulate, 1.5–2.5(–3) mm, usually eglandular, glabrous or sparsely pubescent, margins often ciliate. **Pedicels** 0.4–1 mm, eglandular, glabrous or glabrate. **Flowers**: calyx tube turbinate to narrowly campanulate or cylindric, 1.7–2.2 mm, distal ⅓–⅔ rarely gland-dotted, glabrous; lobes triangular to acuminate, 0.4–1.2(–1.5) mm, densely ciliate; banner usually reddish purple, rarely lavender, broadly obovate to obcordate, (4–)5–6 × 3–3.5(–4) mm, distinctly clawed, margins entire or finely erose; filaments 5–8 mm, distinct; anthers yellow; ovary pubescent. **Legumes** stipitate, 4–5.5 × 2–2.5 mm, margins curved outward abaxially, straight adaxially, at least distal ½–⅔ gland-dotted, glabrous. **Seeds** usually olive green, sometimes olive-tan, 2–2.3 × 1–1.3 mm, smooth, lustrous.

Flowering Apr–May. Sandy river terraces in woods, sometimes bordering moist thickets on the middle and inner Atlantic Coastal Plain; 0–100 m; Ga., N.C., S.C.

Amorpha georgiana is a Federal species of concern and is listed as endangered by the states of Georgia and North Carolina, and as a species of concern by South Carolina. Only about 900 individuals are known, most in and around the Fort Bragg Military Reservation in North Carolina (B. A. Sorrie 1995; V. M. Miller 2004). *Amorpha georgiana* is distributed from south-central and southeastern North Carolina to central Georgia; reports from southern Georgia (Echols County) are erroneous, based on misidentification of material of *A. herbacea* var. *floridana*.

3. Amorpha nana Nuttall, Cat. Pl. Upper Louisiana, no. 5. 1813 • Dwarf false indigo, fragrant indigo-bush [E]

Amorpha microphylla Pursh

Shrubs, (0.1–)0.3–0.6(–1) m; usually rhizomatous. **Stems** finely longitudinally grooved and ridged, gland-dotted, strigulose to glabrate. **Leaves** (1.5–)3–7(–10) cm; stipules linear or setaceous, (2–)3–5(–6.5) mm; petiole (2–)4–8(–10) mm, usually gland-dotted, mostly strigulose, sometimes glabrous; rachis gland-dotted, puberulent or glabrous; leaflets (7–)13–27(–41), stipels acicular, (1–)1.5–2.5(–3) mm, petiolule 0.7–1 mm, gland-dotted, especially abaxially, mostly pubescent to glabrate, blade usually elliptic to oblong or ovate, rarely obovate to suborbiculate, (2–)6–13(–18) × (2–)3–6(–8) mm, base mostly round, margins usually somewhat revolute, entire or inconspicuously crenulate, apex round to truncate or emarginate, surfaces glabrous, margins puberulent; midvein usually terminated by a slender mucro, (0.6–)0.8–1.2(–1.5) mm. **Racemes** unbranched, (2–)3–7(–9) cm; rachis eglandular, usually puberulent; bracteoles linear to narrowly spatulate, (2.5–)3–4(–5) mm, eglandular, puberulent. **Pedicels** 1–2(–2.5) mm, eglandular, usually puberulent. **Flowers**: calyx tube turbinate, (1.5–)1.8–2(–2.2) mm, at least distal ½ gland-dotted, glabrous; lobes triangular to narrowly lanceolate, (0.8–)1–2(–2.2) mm; banner dark reddish purple, broadly obcordate, 4.5–6 × 3.5–4.5 mm, distinctly clawed, margins finely erose, apex emarginate; filaments 6–8 mm, connate basally 0.5–1 mm; anthers purplish; ovary glabrous. **Legumes** sessile, 4.5–5.5 × 2–2.8 mm, margins curved outward abaxially, straight adaxially, at least distal ⅔ gland-dotted, glabrous. **Seeds** olive brown, 2.5–3 × 1–1.5 mm, reticulate. **2*n*** = 20.

Flowering May–Jul. Prairies, hillsides, buttes, sandy soils, clay soils if well-drained, in prairies, prairies on shale slopes, usually calcareous soils; 200–2200 m; Man.; Colo., Iowa, Kans., Minn., Nebr., N.Mex., N.Dak., Okla., S.Dak.

Amorpha nana is listed as threatened by the state of Iowa; it is encountered more commonly in the northern and western parts of its range.

4. Amorpha confusa (Wilbur) S. C. K. Straub, Sorrie & Weakley, J. Bot. Res. Inst. Texas 3: 154. 2009 • Savanna false indigo or indigo-bush [E]

Amorpha georgiana Wilbur var. *confusa* Wilbur, J. Elisha Mitchell Sci. Soc. 80: 58. 1964

Shrubs, 0.3–1.4 m; arising from compact, woody root. **Stems** finely longitudinally grooved and ridged, gland-dotted, strigulose to glabrate. **Leaves** (8–)12–20(–26) cm; stipules sometimes persistent, linear or setaceous, (1–)1.5–2(–2.5) mm; petiole (6–)8–15(–20) mm, gland-dotted, puberulent or glabrous; rachis sparsely gland-dotted, puberulent or glabrous; leaflets (11–)15–31(–35), stipels acicular or setaceous, 0.8–1.8 mm, petiolule 0.7–1.5(–1.8) mm, gland-dotted, mostly puberulent or glabrous, blade elliptic to oblong or ovate to suborbiculate, (10–)15–25(–35) × (7–)9–15(–18) mm, base truncate or round to subcordate, margins usually revolute, entire or inconspicuously crenulate, apex round to obtuse or emarginate, surfaces sparsely to conspicuously gland-dotted, usually glabrous or glabrate, sometimes sparsely pubescent abaxially; midvein terminated by a slender mucro, (0.2–)0.4–1 mm. **Racemes** (1–)3–5(–8)-branched, 10–20(–30) cm; rachis sparsely gland-dotted, puberulent; bracteoles linear to narrowly subulate,

1.5–2.5(–3) mm, usually eglandular, sparsely pubescent or sparsely ciliate. **Pedicels** 0.4–1 mm, eglandular, sparsely pubescent. **Flowers:** calyx tube turbinate to narrowly campanulate or cylindric, 1.7–2.2 mm, distal ⅓–⅔ rarely gland-dotted, glabrous; lobes: abaxial lobe acuminate, slightly longer, adaxial lobes triangular to acuminate, 0.4–1.2(–1.5) mm, margins densely ciliate; banner bright blue, broadly obovate to obcordate, (4–)5–6 × 3–3.5(–4) mm, distinctly clawed, margins entire or finely erose; filaments 5–8 mm, distinct; anthers yellow; ovary pubescent. **Legumes** sessile or stipitate, 4–5.5 × 2–2.5 mm, margins curved outward abaxially, straight adaxially, at least distal ½–⅔ gland-dotted, glabrous. **Seeds** olive brown or brown, 2–2.3 × 1–1.5 mm, smooth, lustrous.

Flowering (May–)Jun–Jul. Pine woodlands, savannas, and road banks in outer Atlantic Coastal Plain; 0–50 m; N.C.

Amorpha confusa is known presently only from Brunswick and Columbus counties; it is believed to be extirpated in adjacent South Carolina. The taxon is a Federal species of concern and is listed as threatened in North Carolina. It is usually encountered growing in loamy soils, most often of the Foreston soil series.

5. Amorpha herbacea Walter, Fl. Carol., 179. 1788 E

Shrubs, (0.3–)0.6–1.2(–1.5) m; arising from thick, horizontal rootstock. **Stems** finely longitudinally grooved and ridged, often obscurely gland-dotted, sparsely to densely puberulent, glabrate, or glabrous. **Leaves** (6–)8–18(–24) cm; stipules sometimes persistent, mostly acicular, (1–)1.2–2.5(–3) mm; petiole (0.5–)1–10(–13) mm, gland-dotted, usually puberulent or strigulose, rarely glabrous; rachis sparsely gland-dotted, often puberulent, sometimes glabrous; leaflets (15–)23–45 (–63), stipels acicular to setaceous, (0.4–)0.8–2 mm, petiolule (0.7–)1–2 mm, gland-dotted, usually puberulent, rarely glabrous, blade elliptic to oblong or ovate to suborbiculate, (7–)10–25(–32) × (3–)4–10(–5) mm, base obtuse to round or truncate to subcordate, margins often revolute, entire or inconspicuously crenulate, apex obtuse to round or emarginate, surfaces densely pubescent or glabrous; midvein terminated by a swollen mucro, 0.2–0.8 mm, mucro sessile or short-stalked, glandlike. **Racemes** (1–)4–12(–20)-branched, (3–)10–18(–40) cm; rachis sparsely gland-dotted, puberulent; bracteoles mostly linear, (1.2–)1.8–2.5(–3) mm, gland-dotted, sparsely hairy. **Pedicels** (0.2–)0.4–1.2(–1.8) mm, sparsely gland-dotted, puberulent or, sometimes, glabrous. **Flowers:** calyx tube turbinate to narrowly campanulate or cylindric, 1.5–2.5(–3) mm, distal ½–⅔ often gland-dotted, puberulent, short-pilose, strigulose, glabrate, or glabrous; lobes: abaxial lobe narrowly triangular, slightly longer, adaxial lobes triangular or obtuse, (0.4–)0.5–1.2(–1.5) mm; banner white, lavender, or violet, broadly obcordate, (4–)5–6(–7) × (2–)2.5–3.5 mm, distinctly clawed, margins entire or finely erose; filaments 6–8 mm, distinct; anthers yellow to yellowish orange; ovary puberulent or glabrous. **Legumes** sessile, 4–6 × 1.8–2.5 mm, margins strongly curved outward abaxially, straight to slightly arched adaxially, distal ½–⅔ gland-dotted, puberulent or glabrous. **Seeds** not seen.

Varieties 2 (2 in the flora): se United States.

1. Shrubs usually densely short-pubescent or puberulent at least distally, sometimes sparsely pubescent or glabrate; calyx tubes densely puberulent or short-pilose; legumes often densely to sparsely puberulent, sometimes proximal ⅓–½ glabrous, sometimes glabrous throughout. . . . . .5a. *Amorpha herbacea* var. *herbacea*
1. Shrubs usually glabrous or glabrate distally, sometimes sparsely pubescent; calyx tubes often glabrous or glabrate, sometimes strigulose; legumes usually glabrous. . . . . 5b. *Amorpha herbacea* var. *floridana*

5a. Amorpha herbacea Walter var. **herbacea** • Clusterspike false indigo, dwarf indigo-bush E

Amorpha cyanostachya M. A. Curtis

Shrubs usually densely short-pubescent or puberulent at least distally, sometimes sparsely pubescent or glabrate. **Leaves:** rachis usually puberulent. **Racemes** usually densely puberulent. **Calyces:** tube densely puberulent or short-pilose. **Legumes** often densely to sparsely puberulent, sometimes proximal ⅓–½ glabrous, sometime glabrous throughout.

Flowering May–Jul(–Sep). Open woods, sandhills, and savannas of the Atlantic Coastal Plain, Piedmont, and a single specimen from North Carolina mountains; 0–500 m; Ala., Fla., Ga., N.C., S.C.

5b. Amorpha herbacea Walter var. **floridana** (Rydberg) Wilbur, J. Elisha Mitchell Sci. Soc. 80: 55. 1964 • Florida false indigo or indigo-bush [E]

Amorpha floridana Rydberg in N. L. Britton et al., N. Amer. Fl. 24: 31. 1919

Shrubs usually glabrous or glabrate distally, sometimes sparsely pubescent. **Leaves:** rachis usually glabrous, sometimes puberulent. **Racemes** sparsely puberulent. **Calyces:** tube usually glabrous or glabrate, sometimes strigulose. **Legumes** usually glabrous.

Flowering May–Sep. Pine woodlands on the Atlantic Coastal Plain; 0–50 m; Fla., Ga.

Variety *floridana* is a species of special concern in the state of Georgia.

6. Amorpha crenulata Rydberg in N. L. Britton et al., N. Amer. Fl. 24: 30. 1919 • Crenulate false indigo, crenulate lead plant [C] [E]

Amorpha herbacea Walter var. *crenulata* (Rydberg) Isely

Shrubs, 0.4–1(–3) m; arising from thick, horizontal rootstock. **Stems** finely longitudinally grooved and ridged, often obscurely gland-dotted, sparsely puberulent or glabrous. **Leaves** (8–)15–25(–30) cm; stipules mostly acicular, 1.2–2.2 mm; petiole (3–)8–15(–18) mm, gland-dotted, sparsely puberulent or glabrous; rachis sparsely gland-dotted, often glabrous; leaflets (19–)23–33(–41), stipels acicular, 0.4–1.5 mm, petiolule (1–)1.5–2(–3) mm, gland-dotted, usually glabrous, blade elliptic to oblong or ovate to suborbiculate, (7–)12–25(–42) × (2.5–)5–9(–11) mm, base obtuse to round or truncate to subcordate, margins usually conspicuously revolute, crenulate, apex obtuse to round or emarginate, surfaces gland-dotted abaxially, glabrous or glabrate; midvein terminated by a swollen mucro, 0.2–0.5 mm. **Racemes** (1–)4–10-branched, (5–)10–25(–30) cm; rachis sparsely gland-dotted, sparsely puberulent; bracteoles linear to narrowly spatulate, 1.2–2.5 mm, gland-dotted, sparsely hairy. **Pedicels** (0.5–)1–1.8(–2.2) mm, gland-dotted, sparsely puberulent. **Flowers:** calyx tube turbinate to narrowly campanulate, (2–)2.2–3.2(–3.5) mm, distal 1/2 often gland-dotted, glabrous or glabrate; lobes: abaxial lobe narrowly triangular, slightly longer, adaxial lobes triangular or obtuse, 0.8–1.8(–2) mm; banner violet or white, broadly obcordate, (4.5–)5–6(–7) × 3–4.5 mm, distinctly clawed, margins entire or finely erose; filaments 6–9 mm, distinct; anthers yellowish; ovary glabrous. **Legumes** sessile, 4–6.5 × 1.8–2.5 mm, margins strongly curved outward abaxially, straight to slightly arched adaxially, distal 2/3 gland-dotted, glabrous. **Seeds** not seen.

Flowering Feb–Aug(–Nov). Rocky margins of pine woodlands and coastal prairies of the Miami Rock Ridge; of conservation concern; 0–10 m; Fla.

Amorpha crenulata is restricted to the Miami Rock Ridge of southeastern Florida, where about 350 individuals remain in four populations confined to Miami-Dade County. Conservation measures for this species, including an *ex situ* collection, restored populations, and seed bank, are overseen by Fairchild Tropical Garden in Coral Gables (for example, J. Roncal et al. 2006; K. S. Wendelberger et al. 2007).

Amorpha crenulata is in the Center for Plant Conservation's National Collection of Endangered Plants; as *A. herbacea* var. *crenulata*, it is listed in NatureServe as a plant of concern.

7. Amorpha canescens Pursh, Fl. Amer. Sept. 2: 467. 1813 • Leadplant [E] [F]

Shrubs, rarely perennial herbs, (0.3–)0.5–0.8(–1.2) m; usually rhizomatous. **Stems** finely striate longitudinally, sparsely gland-dotted or eglandular, usually canescent becoming glabrate, rarely glabrous. **Leaves** (3–)6–12(–15) cm; stipules linear to linear-lanceolate or setaceous, (1.2–)2–3(–3.5) mm, eglandular, canescent abaxially, glabrous adaxially; petiole 0.5–3(–5) mm, eglandular, tomentose to canescent; rachis eglandular, tomentose to canescent or puberulent; leaflets (11–)27–41(–49), stipels acicular, (0.5–)0.8–1.2 mm, petiolule 0.5–1(–1.8) mm, usually eglandular, usually canescent to pilose, blade usually elliptic to oblong or ovate, rarely ovate to suborbiculate, (3–)10–18(–25) × (2–)4–7(–12) mm, base truncate or round to subcordate, margins sometimes slightly revolute, entire, apex round to obtuse or emarginate, surfaces usually canescent to velutinous, rarely glabrous; midvein terminated by a slender mucro, (0.2–)0.4–0.8(–1.2) mm. **Racemes** (1–)5–20(–30+)-branched, (2–)7–15(–25) cm; rachis sparsely gland-dotted, sparsely pilose to pubescent; bracteoles linear to narrowly lanceolate, (2.5–)3–4(–4.5) mm, eglandular, pilose abaxially, glabrous adaxially. **Pedicels** (0.4–)0.5–1.2(–1.5) mm, eglandular, sparsely pilose to pubescent. **Flowers:** calyx tube turbinate to somewhat campanulate, (1.5–)1.8–2(–2.5) mm, inconspicuously gland-dotted, usually densely pubescent, rarely glabrous or glabrate; lobes triangular to narrowly lanceolate, (0.6–)1–1.5(–1.8) mm; banner bright violet, broadly obcordate, 4.5–6 × 2.5–4 mm,

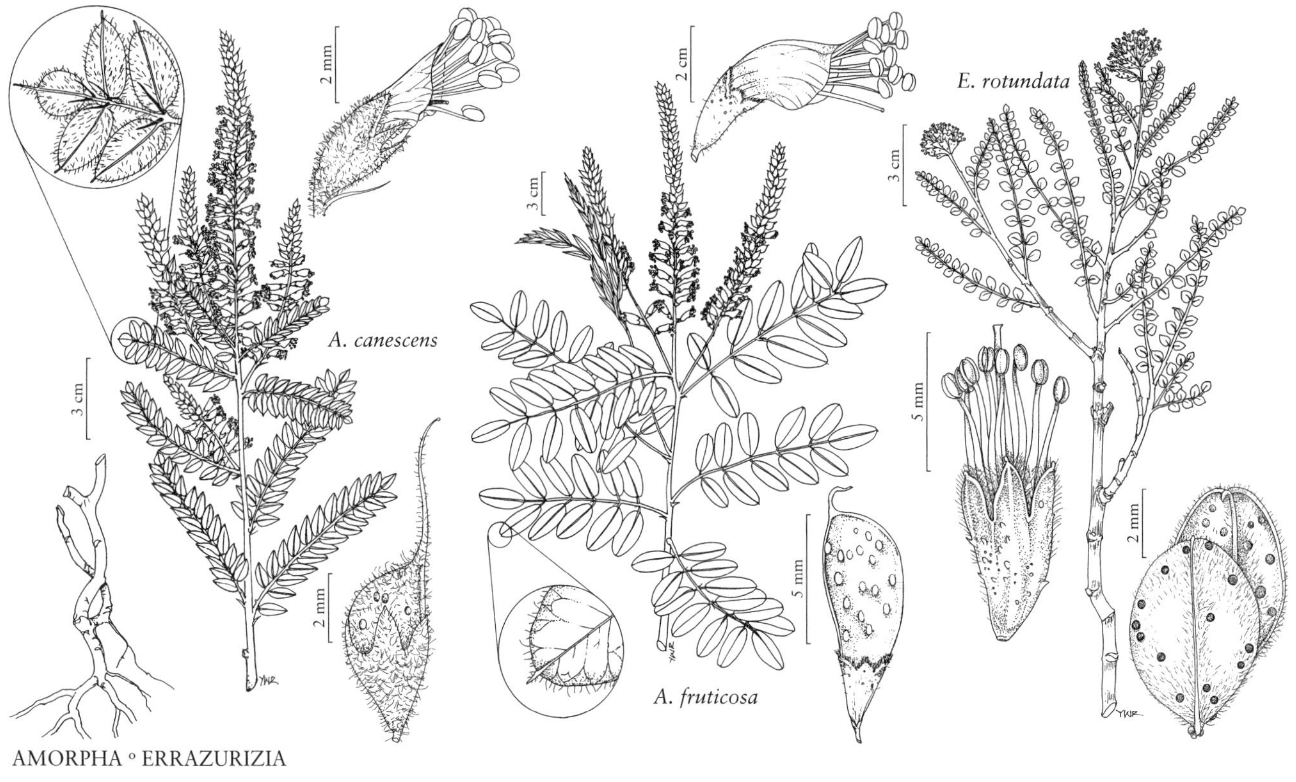

AMORPHA ◦ ERRAZURIZIA

distinctly clawed, margins entire or finely erose; filaments 6–8 mm, connate basally 1.5–2 mm; anthers yellowish to golden brown; ovary densely pilose. **Legumes** stipitate, (3–)3.5–4.5(–5) × 2–3.5 mm, margins curved outward abaxially, straight adaxially, at least distal ½–⅔ gland-dotted, usually villous, rarely glabrous. **Seeds** olive brown, 2–2.8 × 1–1.4 mm, smooth. **2*n*** = 20.

Flowering May–Aug(–Sep). Prairies, hillsides, open woodlands, sometimes in fields, along roadsides, mainly on the Great Plains; 200–1800 m; Man., Ont.; Ark., Colo., Ill., Ind., Iowa, Kans., La., Mich., Minn., Mo., Mont., Nebr., N.Mex., N.Dak., Okla., S.Dak., Tex., Wis., Wyo.

The common name of *Amorpha canescens* stems from a historical, misguided belief that its occurrence indicated the presence of lead. It is a palatable range plant and thus subject to intensive grazing pressure; in some mowed fields, meadows, and pastures, the plant often appears as an herbaceous perennial. The Bureau of Land Management considers *A. canescens* to be a sensitive species in Montana, where it is presumed to be extirpated. Hybrids between *A. canescens* and *A. fruticosa*, named *A.* ×*notha* E. J. Palmer, are rare. *Amorpha canescens* is a species of concern in Arkansas, where it is at the edge of its range; it is not rare, in general, being one of the most often cultivated species of *Amorpha*.

8. **Amorpha roemeriana** Scheele, Linnaea 21: 461. 1848 • Roemer's false indigo, Texas indigo-bush

Amorpha texana Buckley

Shrubs, 1–3 m; arising from compact, woody root. **Stems** smooth, gland-dotted, puberulent or glabrous. **Leaves** (5–)10–15(–20) cm; stipules linear, 1.5–2 mm, eglandular, puberulent; petiole (5–)15–30 mm, gland-dotted, usually puberulent; rachis eglandular, usually puberulent; leaflets (7–)9–11(–15), stipels acicular, 1.2–2 mm, petiolule 2–5(–7) mm, usually gland-dotted, puberulent or glabrous, blade usually narrowly elliptic to oblong, rarely obovate to suborbiculate, (10–)25–40(–50) × (7–)15–25(–38) mm, base round, margins flat, entire or conspicuously crenulate, apex round or emarginate, surfaces puberulent abaxially, glabrate or glabrous adaxially; midvein terminated by a slightly swollen mucro, 0.4–0.8 mm. **Racemes** 1–3(–6)-branched, (4–)6–12(–20) cm; rachis sparsely gland-dotted, puberulent; bracteoles linear to narrowly lanceolate, 1.2–2.2 mm, eglandular, puberulent to short-pilose. **Pedicels** 1–1.5 mm, eglandular, puberulent. **Flowers:** calyx tube funnelform, 2.5–3.8 mm, distal ⅓ gland-dotted, short-pilose or glabrous; lobes usually narrowly lanceolate, (0.2–)0.4–1.2(–1.4) mm; banner purple, broadly obcordate, 5–7 × 5–6 mm, indistinctly clawed, margins entire or slightly erose; filaments 6–10 mm, connate basally 4–6 mm; anthers yellow; ovary glabrous. **Legumes** sessile, 6–7 × 2.5–3.5 mm, margins curved outward abaxially, straight or bent inward adaxially, at least distal ½ gland-dotted, glabrous or slightly hairy. **Seeds** brown, reddish brown, or greenish brown, 2.5–4.5 × 1.5–2 mm, smooth, not lustrous.

Flowering Apr–Jun. Grasslands and open woodlands on limestone soils; 400–800 m; Tex.; Mexico (Coahuila).

In the flora area, *Amorpha roemeriana* is confined to the Edwards Plateau area of central Texas, where it occurs in Bandera, Bexar, Blanco, Comal, Gillespie, Hays, Kendall, Kerr, Kinney, Medina, Travis, and Uvalde counties.

9. Amorpha paniculata Torrey & A. Gray, Fl. N. Amer. 1: 306. 1838 • Panicled false indigo or indigo-bush [C] [E]

Shrubs or suffrutescent herbs, 1–3 m; arising from compact, woody root. **Stems** longitudinally grooved and ridged, eglandular, mostly puberulent, canescent, or tomentose, sometimes glabrate. **Leaves** (10–)20–40 cm; stipules linear, 2–3 mm, eglandular, pubescent; petiole (20–)30–60(–90) mm, eglandular, puberulent, canescent, or tomentose; rachis eglandular, puberulent or canescent; leaflets (9–)11–19, stipels acicular, 1–2 mm, petiolule (2–)4–10 mm, sparsely gland-dotted, usually pilosulous proximally, glabrous distally, blade narrowly elliptic to oblong or ovate, 15–30(–50) × (14–)18–22(–26) mm, base round, margins flat, entire, apex round, surfaces sparsely gland-dotted abaxially, canescent to tomentose or glabrate abaxially, usually puberulent to glabrate or glabrous adaxially; veins conspicuous, distinctly raised abaxially; midvein terminated by a slender mucro, 0.5–1.8 mm. **Racemes** (1–)5–12-branched, paniculiform, (5–)15–30(–40) cm; rachis eglandular, short-pilose; bracteoles linear, 1–2 mm, eglandular, short-pilose. **Pedicels** 1–2 mm, eglandular, short-pilose. **Flowers:** calyx tube funnelform, 1.8–2.2 mm, distal ⅓ gland-dotted, usually short-pilose, rarely glabrate; lobes: abaxial lobe linear to narrowly lanceolate, adaxial lobes usually triangular to ovate, (1–)1.2–2 mm; banner purple, broadly obcordate, 5–7 × 3–4 mm, indistinctly clawed, margins entire or slightly erose; filaments 5–6 mm, connate basally 2.5–3 mm; anthers orange; ovary glabrous. **Legumes** sessile, 4–6(–8) × 2–2.5 mm, margins curved outward abaxially, bent outward adaxially, gland-dotted, glabrous. **Seeds** reddish brown, 3–3.5 × 1.5–1.8 mm, smooth.

Flowering May–Jun. Moist, acid thickets, bogs, and swamps; of conservation concern; 10–300 m; Ark., La., Okla., Tex.

Amorpha paniculata is listed as threatened in Arkansas and as a species of concern in Oklahoma.

10. Amorpha schwerinii C. K. Schneider, Ill. Handb. Laubholzk. 2: 71, figs. 42l,m, 44a. 1907 (as schwerini) • Schwerin's false indigo, Piedmont indigo-bush [E]

Shrubs, (1–)1.5–2.5 m; arising from compact, woody root. **Stems** finely grooved, gland-dotted, puberulent. **Leaves** (5–)8–12(–22) cm; stipules linear to narrowly lanceolate, 3–4.5 mm, eglandular, pubescent abaxially, glabrous adaxially; petiole (7–)10–18(–25) mm, usually eglandular, pubescent; rachis usually eglandular, puberulent; leaflets (7–)19–27(–29), stipels acicular, 1–2.2 mm, petiolule (0.5–)1–2 mm, gland-dotted, pilosulous to puberulent, blade usually elliptic to narrowly oblong, rarely ovate to suborbiculate, (5–)15–30(–40) × (4–)8–15(–20) mm, base truncate to subcordate, margins slightly revolute, entire or slightly crenulate, apex obtuse to round or emarginate, surfaces gland-dotted, pilose to pubescent; midvein terminated by a swollen mucro, 0.2–0.5(–0.8) mm. **Racemes** 1(or 2)-branched, (2–)4–8(–12) cm; rachis usually eglandular, puberulent to pubescent; bracteoles linear to narrowly lanceolate, 2–3.5 mm, pilosulous abaxially, glabrous adaxially. **Pedicels** (0.8–)1–1.5(–2) mm, eglandular, puberulent to pubescent. **Flowers:** calyx tube turbinate to cylindric, 1.8–2.5 mm, distal ⅓ or less gland-dotted, pilosulous; lobes linear to narrowly lanceolate, (1.2–)2–3.5 mm; banner purplish, broadly obovate to obcordate, 4.5–6.5 × 3–4.2 mm, distinctly clawed, margins entire or erose; filaments 6–8 mm, connate basally 1.5–2 mm; anthers golden yellow; ovary usually pubescent. **Legumes** sessile, 5–6.5 × 1.8–2.2 mm, margins curved outward abaxially, straight adaxially, at least distal ½ gland-dotted, usually glabrous. **Seeds** not seen.

Flowering Apr–Jun. Dry to moist open woodlands and forests; 100–600 m; Ala., Ga., N.C., S.C.

Amorpha schwerinii is listed as a species of special concern in Georgia and South Carolina, and as significantly rare in North Carolina.

11. Amorpha glabra Desfontaines ex Persoon, Syn. Pl. 2: 295. 1807 • Mountain false indigo, Appalachian indigo-bush [E]

Shrubs, 1–2 m; arising from compact, woody root. **Stems** smooth, sparsely gland-dotted or eglandular, usually glabrous, sometimes glabrate. **Leaves** (10–)14–22(–30) cm; stipules linear to linear-lanceolate, 2.5–4.5 mm, eglandular, slightly hairy or margins ciliate; petiole (16–)20–40(–60) mm, sparsely gland-dotted or eglandular, glabrous or sparsely puberulent; rachis sparsely gland-dotted, glabrous or, rarely, sparsely puberulent; leaflets (9–)11–15(–19), stipels acicular to setaceous, 1.2–2 mm, petiolule 2–4(–5.5) mm, sparsely gland-dotted, usually glabrous, blade often elliptic to oblong, sometimes ovate to, rarely, orbiculate, (14–)20–45(–75) × (10–)14–28(–36) mm, base round to truncate or subcordate, margins slightly revolute, entire or slightly crenulate, apex obtuse to broadly round or emarginate, surfaces gland-dotted, mostly glabrous; midvein terminated by a slightly swollen mucro, 0.2–0.4 mm. **Racemes** 1–3(or 4)-branched, (5–)10–18(–28) cm; rachis gland-dotted, usually glabrous; bracteoles usually narrowly lanceolate, (0.5–)0.8–1.5(–2) mm, eglandular, puberulent, often ciliate. **Pedicels** (0.8–)1–2.5(–3) mm, eglandular, usually glabrous. **Flowers:** calyx tube broadly turbinate to campanulate, 2–3(–3.2) mm, eglandular, glabrous except rim ciliate; lobes obscure or developed, then rounded to broadly triangular-dentate, 0–0.6(–0.8) mm; banner purplish, broadly obcordate, (4.5–)6–8(–8.5) × 4–6 mm, clawed, margins entire or erose; filaments 8–11 mm, connate basally 3–4.5 mm; anthers golden yellow to orange; ovary glabrous. **Legumes** sessile, (6.5–)7.5–9(–10) × (2.5–)3–4(–4.5) mm, margins distinctly curved outward abaxially, straight or nearly so adaxially, at least distal ⅔ gland-dotted, glabrous. **Seeds** not seen.

Flowering May–Jul. Dry to moist thickets and woods, pine-oak heath ridges; (30–)400–1200 m; Ala., Ga., N.C., S.C., Tenn.

Amorpha glabra is listed as a species of concern in South Carolina.

12. Amorpha laevigata Nuttall in J. Torrey and A. Gray, Fl. N. Amer. 1: 306. 1838 • Smooth false indigo or indigo-bush [E]

Shrubs, 1–2(–3) m; arising from compact, woody root. **Stems** smooth, gland-dotted, usually glabrous, sometimes strigulose to glabrate. **Leaves** (5–)8–20 (–25) cm; stipules linear to setaceous, 2–3 mm, eglandular, glabrous; petiole 10–25(–30) mm, gland-dotted, usually glabrous; rachis gland-dotted, usually glabrous; leaflets (9–)13–19(–21), stipels acicular, 1–2 mm, petiolule 2–5 mm, glands distinctly warty, usually strigulose, sometimes glabrous, blade elliptic to narrowly oblong, (10–)15–35(–40) × 4–10(–12) mm, base round, margins flat, entire or slightly crenulate, apex often emarginate, sometimes round, surfaces gland-dotted abaxially, eglandular adaxially, glabrous or sparsely strigulose abaxially, glabrous adaxially; midvein terminated by a swollen mucro, 0.1–0.2 mm. **Racemes** (1 or)2 or 3(–8)-branched, 10–20(–25) cm; rachis sparsely gland-dotted or eglandular, sparsely strigulose; bracteoles linear to narrowly lanceolate, 1.5–3 mm, gland-dotted, strigulose. **Pedicels** 0.6–1.2 mm, eglandular, strigulose. **Flowers:** calyx tube funnelform to campanulate, 1.5–3 mm, distal ⅔ gland-dotted, usually glabrous, sometimes strigulose; lobes: abaxial lobe narrowly lanceolate, adaxial lobes round to triangular, 0.2–1.2 mm; banner bright blue to deep violet-blue, broadly obcordate, 4–6 × 4–4.5 mm, indistinctly clawed, margins entire or finely erose; filaments 6–9 mm, connate basally 3–5 mm; anthers orange; ovary glabrous. **Legumes** sessile, 4.5–6 × 2–2.5 mm, margins curved outward abaxially, straight or slightly curved inward adaxially, at least distal ¾ gland-dotted, usually glabrous, rarely sparsely strigulose. **Seeds** not seen.

Flowering May–Jun. Prairies and open woods, often in moist places; 10–500 m; La., Okla., Tex.

Amorpha laevigata is an under-collected, ill-defined taxon with characters that overlap with those of several other species. Further study may show that it does not warrant recognition or, alternatively, that it is an extremely rare endemic in need of conservation concern.

13. Amorpha ouachitensis Wilbur, Rhodora 77: 394. 1975 • Ouachita false indigo or indigo-bush [E]

Shrubs, 1–2 m; arising from compact, woody root. **Stems** smooth, sparsely gland-dotted, pilosulous or glabrous. **Leaves** 7–23 cm; stipules lanceolate, 3–4 mm, eglandular, glabrous except with villous tuft apically; petiole 10–17 mm, gland-dotted, sparsely pubescent to glabrate or glabrous; rachis sparsely gland-dotted, sparsely puberulent or glabrous; leaflets (7–)9–13(–17), stipels acicular, 1.2–2.2 mm, petiolule 2–3(–4) mm, usually sparsely gland-dotted, rarely eglandular, pilosulous to glabrate or glabrous, blade broadly elliptic to broadly oblong, (12–)25–40(–70) × (9–)15–25 (–35) mm, base round, margins flat, entire or slightly crenulate, apex often emarginate, sometimes round to truncate, surfaces gland-dotted, puberulent to glabrate or glabrous; midvein terminated by a swollen mucro, 0.2–0.6 mm. **Racemes** 1–4-branched, (8–)10–20 cm; rachis sparsely gland-dotted or eglandular, puberulent or glabrous; bracteoles narrowly oblong, 1–1.5 mm, glabrous except margin stiffly hairy. **Pedicels** 1–1.5 mm, eglandular, puberulent to glabrate or glabrous. **Flowers:** calyx tube narrowly conical to funnelform, 2.8–3.2 mm, distal 1/4 not obviously gland-dotted, puberulent to glabrate or glabrous; lobes mostly round, 0.4–0.9 (–1.2) mm; banner purple, obcordate, 5–7.5 × 4.5–6 mm, not clawed, margins entire, apex emarginate; filaments 8–10 mm, connate basally 3–6 mm; anthers yellow; ovary usually glabrous. **Legumes** sessile, 7–9 × 3–4 mm, margins curved outward abaxially, straight or sharply bent adaxially, at least distal 1/2 gland-dotted, usually glabrous. **Seeds** dark brownish to blackish, 4–5 × 2.5–3 mm, smooth.

Flowering Apr–Jun. Moist thickets and woods; 100–600 m; Ark., Okla.

Amorpha ouachitensis is listed as a species of concern by the states of Arkansas and Oklahoma; it is in the Center for Plant Conservation's National Collection of Endangered Plants.

14. Amorpha nitens F. E. Boynton, Biltmore Bot. Stud. 1: 139. 1902 • Shining false indigo, dark indigo-bush [E]

Shrubs, 1–2(–3) m; arising from compact, woody root. **Stems** smooth, usually eglandular, mostly glabrous or puberulent. **Leaves** 10–18(–22) cm; stipules linear to narrowly setaceous, 3–5 mm, sometimes sparsely gland-dotted, short-pilose; petiole (15–)20–35(–50) mm, eglandular, usually glabrous; rachis eglandular, usually glabrous; leaflets (7–)9–15(–19), stipels not seen, petiolule 2–5(–7) mm, eglandular, glabrous or pilosulous, blade drying blackish, usually elliptic to oblong, sometimes ovate, 20–40(–70) × (10–)15–35(–45) mm, base round, margins flat, entire, apex usually emarginate, sometimes round, surfaces distinctly shiny adaxially, usually glabrous and eglandular, rarely sparsely puberulent and sparsely gland-dotted abaxially; midvein terminated by a slender mucro, 0.1–0.2 mm. **Racemes** 1–3(–8)-branched, (5–)8–15(–25) cm; rachis usually eglandular, usually glabrous, sometimes puberulent; bracteoles drying blackish, linear to setaceous, 1.5–3 (–4) mm, usually eglandular, glabrous or short-pilose. **Pedicels** drying blackish, 1–2.2 mm, eglandular, glabrous or short-pilose. **Flowers:** calyx drying blackish, tube usually funnelform to obconic, rarely campanulate, 2–2.5 mm, usually eglandular, glabrous or short-pilose; lobes: abaxial lobe triangular, slightly longer, adaxial lobes round to triangular, 0.2–1.4 mm; banner reddish purple, broadly obovate, 4.5–6 × 3–4.8 mm, obscurely clawed, margins entire or irregularly erose; filaments 5–7 mm, connate basally 2–2.5 mm; anthers yellow; ovary glabrous. **Legumes** short-stipitate, 6–8 × 2.5–3.5 mm, margins curved outward abaxially, straight or slightly curved inward adaxially, rarely at least distal 1/3 gland-dotted, glabrous. **Seeds** not seen.

Flowering Apr–Jun. Moist thickets and woods; 50–600 m; Ala., Ark., Ga., Ill., Ky., La., Okla., S.C., Tenn.

Amorpha nitens is listed as endangered by the state of Illinois and as a species of special concern in Georgia; it is considered to be a sensitive species in the Shawnee National Forest by the United States Forest Service. *Amorpha nitens* and *A. fruticosa* share most of their characters and differ most distinctively by the tendency to blacken upon drying ascribed to *A. nitens*, although some *A. fruticosa* individuals can blacken upon drying as well.

15. Amorpha fruticosa Linnaeus, Sp. Pl. 2: 713. 1753 • Bastard or desert false indigo, faux indigo commun, tall indigo-bush F W

Amorpha angustifolia (Pursh) F. E. Boynton; *A. bushii* Rydberg; *A. croceolanata* P. Watson; *A. curtisii* Rydberg; *A. dewinkeleri* Small; *A. fruticosa* var. *angustifolia* Pursh; *A. fruticosa* var. *croceolanata* (P. Watson) Mouillefert; *A. fruticosa* var. *occidentalis* (Abrams) Kearney & Peebles; *A. occidentalis* Abrams; *A. tennessensis* Shuttleworth; *A. virgata* Small

Shrubs, (1–)2–3(–4) m; arising from compact, woody root. **Stems** smooth, eglandular or, sometimes, sparsely gland-dotted, usually puberulent to glabrate, rarely glabrous. **Leaves** 10–25(–28) cm; stipules linear, 2–4 mm, usually eglandular, pilosulous; petiole (8–)10–40 mm, usually eglandular, sometimes sparsely gland-dotted, usually puberulent to glabrate, rarely glabrous; rachis usually eglandular, sometimes sparsely gland-dotted, puberulent to glabrate; leaflets [5–]9–21(–31), stipels setaceous, 2–4 mm, petiolule (1.5–)2–4 mm, often eglandular, sometimes sparsely gland-dotted, usually pilosulous to puberulent or glabrate, rarely glabrous, blade usually elliptic to oblong, rarely ovate, (10–)20–40(–50) × (5–)10–20(–25) mm, base acute to rounded, margins flat, entire or nearly so, apex acute to round or, rarely, emarginate, surfaces usually pilosulous to puberulent or glabrate, sometimes glabrous at least adaxially; midvein terminated by a slender mucro, 0.5–1.5 mm. **Racemes** (1 or)2–8(–12)-branched, (5–)10–20(–25) cm; rachis usually eglandular, mostly puberulent to pilosulous, sometimes glabrate; bracteoles linear to setaceous, 1.5–3 mm, pilosulous abaxially, glabrous adaxially. **Pedicels** 1–2.2 mm, usually eglandular, puberulent to pilosulous. **Flowers:** calyx tube obconic to funnelform or campanulate, 2–3(–4) mm, distal ⅓ gland-dotted or, infrequently, eglandular, puberulent to pilosulous or glabrous; lobes triangular-dentate, 0.2–1.2 mm, margins ciliate; banner reddish purple, broadly obovate to obcordate, 5–6 × 3.5–4.2 mm, indistinctly clawed, margins entire, apex slightly emarginate or erose; filaments 6–8 mm, connate basally 1–2(–3) mm; anthers yellow; ovary glabrous or, rarely, pubescent. **Legumes** sessile, 5–9 × (2–)3–4.5 mm, margins curved outward abaxially, straight to curved adaxially, more often gland-dotted nearly throughout, sometimes eglandular, usually glabrous or pubescent. **Seeds** reddish brown, 3.5–4.5 × 1.5–1.8 mm, smooth, lustrous. **2*n*** = (38) 40.

Flowering Apr–Jun(–Jul). Dry or moist grasslands, scrublands, woodlands, river and stream banks, tidal marshes, roadsides, fields, or waste places; 0–2400 m; Man., N.B., Ont., Que.; Ala., Ariz., Ark., Calif., Colo., Conn., Del., D.C., Fla., Ga., Idaho, Ill., Ind., Iowa, Kans., Ky., La., Maine, Md., Mass. Mich., Minn., Miss., Mo., Nebr., N.H., N.J., N.Mex., N.Y., N.C., N.Dak., Ohio, Okla., Oreg., Pa., R.I., S.C., S.Dak., Tenn., Tex., Utah, Vt., Va., Wash., W.Va., Wis., Wyo.; Mexico (Baja California, Chihuahua); introduced in Europe, Asia, Africa.

Amorpha fruticosa is frequently planted as an ornamental and is locally naturalized in Europe, Asia, Africa.

Following R. L. Wilbur (1975) and D. Isely (1998), we maintain *Amorpha fruticosa* here in a broad circumscription, as the numerous varieties, forms, and regional species delimited from the larger taxon appear to have little taxonomic value due to overlapping morphological variation and widespread plasticity. This species is commonly available in the horticultural trade and is cultivated worldwide. Plants in cultivation can be especially robust, rising to six meters tall with far fewer leaflets than usual. *Amorpha fruticosa* spreads easily in riparian habitats and is often weedy. Although the native range of *A. fruticosa* encompasses much of North America, it has only relatively recently become established in the Pacific Northwest, perhaps due to its use for erosion control, and has only been recorded from Idaho, Oregon, and Washington since the 1980s (J. B. Glad and R. R. Halse 1993). This species is considered to be introduced also in Ontario and Quebec.

62. ERRAZURIZIA Philippi, Anales Univ. Chile, I, Mem. Ci. Lit. 41: 688. 1872 • [For Federico Errázuriz Zañartu, 1825–1877, President of Chile]

David M. Sutherland

Shrubs, unarmed, gland-dotted almost throughout. **Stems** gnarled, highly branched, pubescent. **Leaves** alternate, odd-pinnate; stipules present; petiolate; leaflets [5–]29–61, mostly opposite, stipels absent, blades suborbiculate to oblong-ovate, margins entire, surfaces pubescent. **Inflorescences** 6–15-flowered, terminal, spikes; bracts present; bracteoles absent, often represented by 2 sessile glands. **Flowers** usually papilionaceous, sometimes apetalous or only banner present;

calyx campanulate, tube 10-ribbed, lobes 5; corolla absent or vestigial banner present [petals 5], yellow; stamens [9]10, monadelphous; anthers dorsifixed. **Fruits** legumes, sessile, somewhat compressed, obovoid-ellipsoid, indehiscent, scattered glands present, strigulose. **Seed** 1, slightly compressed, ellipsoid.

Species 4 (1 in the flora): Arizona, Mexico, South America (Chile).

SELECTED REFERENCE Barneby, R. C. 1977. *Errazurizia.* Mem. New York Bot. Gard. 27: 13–21.

1. Errazurizia rotundata (Wooton) Barneby, Leafl. W. Bot. 9: 210. 1962 C E

Parryella rotundata Wooton, Bull. Torrey Bot. Club 25: 457. 1898

Shrubs to 3.5 dm. **Stems** repeatedly branched, gnarled at maturity, bearing numerous raised, orange or brownish glands when young, strigulose or cinereous. **Leaves** 3–14 cm; stipules caducous or persistent, subulate, linear, or triangular; leaflet blade 1–8 mm, diminishing distally, apex emarginate, surfaces with scattered, raised glands abaxially. **Peduncles** 0–1 cm. **Spikes** relatively dense; axes 4–15 mm; bracts caducous, lanceolate-acuminate or subulate, 1.6–2.5 mm. **Flowers:** calyx subactinomorphic, 5–6.5 mm, thinly pilose, tube 3.5–4.2 mm, 10-ribbed, not anastomosing into arches distally, regions between ribs each with a row of 2–5 raised glands, lobes oblong-obovate, apex obtuse or gland-apiculate; banner, when present, erect, pale yellow, fading reddish, oblanceolate, 5–5.4 × 1.5–2.1 mm; stamens strongly exserted, (7–)8.5–12 mm; filaments distinct to 8 mm (from basal tube); anthers 1–1.3 mm; style usually glabrous. **Legumes** mostly tan, 9–12 mm; valves becoming papery. **Seeds** chestnut, somewhat compressed, (4.6–)5–7 mm.

Flowering early spring. On sandstone, in sand; of conservation concern; 300–1500 m; Ariz.

Errazurizia rotundata is known only from two limited areas near Tuba City, Coconino County, and Winslow, Navaho County, in northeast Arizona; it differs from congeners by its reduced or absent corolla, its exserted, 10-merous androecium, and its larger leaflet number. The species was described initially in the genus *Parryella*; R. C. Barneby (1977) noted that it combines characteristics of that genus and *Psorothamnus*. Molecular and morphological studies by M. McMahon (2005) and S. C. K. Straub and J. J. Doyle (2014) have shown it to be closer to *Parryella filifolia* and *Amorpha* species than to other species of *Errazurizia* but have not resolved its placement; see the discussion under 61. *Amorpha*.

63. EYSENHARDTIA Kunth in A. von Humboldt et al., Nov. Gen. Sp. 6(fol.): 382; 6(qto.): 489, plate 592. 1824, name conserved • Kidneywood [For Carl Wilhelm Eysenhardt, 1794–1825, German physician, botanist, and zoologist, professor at Königsberg (Kaliningrad)]

Douglas H. Goldman

Shrubs or trees, unarmed, mostly glandular-punctate throughout newer growth and reproductive material. **Stems** erect, eglandular or glandular-punctate, brown- to gray-pubescent, often becoming glabrescent. **Leaves** alternate, odd-pinnate, scented when crushed; stipules present, subulate, relatively small; petiolate; leaflets (5 or)7–47[–61], stipels usually present, subulate, blade margins entire, surfaces pubescent abaxially, brown glands sometimes present, glabrous or pubescent adaxially. **Inflorescences** (5–)30–100(–150)-flowered, usually terminal, rarely axillary, racemes (spikelike); bracts present, early-deciduous to persistent, minute, usually lanceolate; bracteoles minute or absent. **Flowers** fragrant, not typically papilionaceous; calyx funnel-shaped, pubescent, lobes 5; corolla white [yellow-white or pink], sometimes becoming purple, slightly irregular, petals scarcely differentiated, subequal, eglandular, glabrous; stamens 10, visible, diadelphous, filaments connate ca. ½ their lengths; anthers basifixed; style bent apically, often with gland at bend or near tip; stigma capitate. **Fruits** legumes, subsessile to short-stalked, laterally compressed, ovoid-ellipsoid, oblong, or oblong-lanceolate, indehiscent, glabrous. **Seeds** 1(or 2), obovoid, oblanceolate, or oblong-subreniform to falcate-ellipsoid. $x = 10$.

Species 10–15 (3 in the flora): sw, sc United States, Mexico, Central America (El Salvador, Guatemala).

Eysenhardtia is a complicated genus with unclear species boundaries, especially in Mexico. It is closely related to *Amorpha*, *Apoplanesia*, *Errazurizia*, and *Parryella*, all members of the papilionoid tribe Amorpheae (M. McMahon and L. Hufford 2004).

The Mexican *Eysenhardtia polystachya* is reputed to be a New World source of lignum nephriticum, which was used to treat kidney ailments (J. M. Lang and D. Isely 1982). Wood chips from this plant, placed in water, produce a solution that fluoresces blue in bright light. The tropical Asian *Pterocarpus indicus* Willdenow also has been a source of lignum nephriticum. The chemical properties of these fluorescent solutions were described by M. Muyskens (2006).

SELECTED REFERENCE Lang, J. M. and D. Isely. 1982. *Eysenhardtia* (Leguminosae: Papilionoideae). Iowa State J. Res. 56: 393–417.

1. Shrubs, to 1 m; styles eglandular; racemes 1–3.5 cm; legumes ascending, straight, ovoid-ellipsoid, lengths less than or equal to 2 times widths, not flattened; seeds completely filling fruit, slightly compressed, edges blunt; leaves (0.5–)1–2.5(–3) cm, leaflets (5 or)7–15(or 17), blades 1–4(–5) mm, abaxial surfaces with glands of similar size; w Texas . . . . . . 1. *Eysenhardtia spinosa*
1. Shrubs or trees, 1.5–5 m; styles with glands near tip; racemes 3–11(–16) cm; legumes ascending or reflexed, straight or falcate, oblong or oblong-lanceoloid, lengths more than or equal to 3 times widths, flattened throughout or near base; seeds filling ½ or ⅔ of fruit, slightly or strongly compressed, edges blunt or sharp; leaves (1–)2–10(–14) cm, leaflets (7–)13–35(–47), blades 3–20 mm, abaxial surfaces with some glands much larger than others; Arizona, New Mexico, Texas.
    2. Leaflet blades with largest abaxial glands along midvein and margins; legumes ascending, flattened near base; seeds filling ca. ⅔ of fruit, slightly compressed, edges blunt; Texas. . . . . .2. *Eysenhardtia texana*
    2. Leaflet blades with largest abaxial glands randomly scattered; legumes reflexed, entire fruit appearing flattened; seeds filling ca. ½ of fruit, strongly compressed, edges sharp; Arizona, New Mexico . . . . 3. *Eysenhardtia orthocarpa*

1. Eysenhardtia spinosa Engelmann, Boston J. Nat. Hist. 6: 174. 1850 • Spiny kidneywood [C]

Shrubs, to 1 m. **Leaves** (0.5–)1–2.5(–3) cm; leaflets (5 or)7–15(or 17), blades suborbiculate to oblong-ovate, 1–4(–5) mm, surfaces pubescent abaxially, with glands of similar size, glabrous adaxially. **Racemes** 1–3.5 cm. **Flowers:** calyx tube 2–3 mm, lobes acute to acuminate, 0.5–0.9 mm; corolla white, turning purple, 4–6(–7.5) mm; style eglandular. **Legumes** ascending, straight, ovoid-ellipsoid, 4.5–6 × 2.5–3 mm, length less than or equal to 2 times width, not flattened. **Seeds** completely filling legume, slightly compressed, obovoid, edges blunt. $2n = 20$.

Flowering Jul–Oct. Dry, semi-desert grassland and shrubland; of conservation concern; 1200–1700 [–2000] m; Tex.; Mexico (Chihuahua, Durango).

Eysenhardtia spinosa can appear spiny due to the persistent, dead inflorescence rachises that are short and erect. By far the rarest species of the genus in the flora area, it has been collected in Presidio County.

2. Eysenhardtia texana Scheele, Linnaea 21: 462. 1848 • Texas kidneywood, vara dulce [F]

Shrubs, 1–3(–5) m. **Leaves** (1–)2–7(–10) cm; leaflets (7–)13–35(–47), blades elliptic to oblong, 3–13 mm, surfaces sparsely to moderately pubescent, abaxially with some glands much larger than others, largest along midvein and margins. **Racemes** 3–11(–15) cm. **Flowers:** calyx tube 2–4 mm, lobes obtuse to acute, 0.3–0.7 mm; corolla 5–8 mm; style with gland near tip.

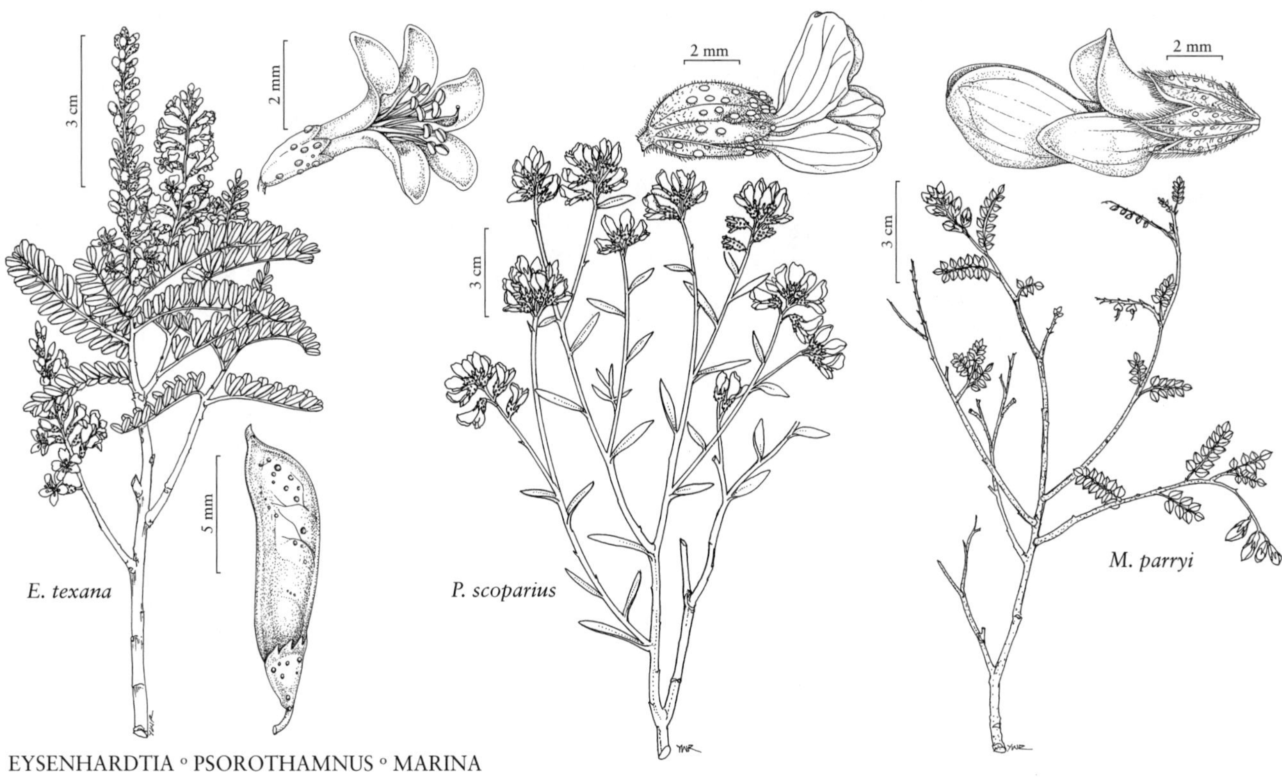

EYSENHARDTIA ∘ PSOROTHAMNUS ∘ MARINA

Legumes ascending, usually falcate, rarely straight, oblong, 6–13 × 2–3 mm, length more than or equal to 3 times width, flattened near base. **Seeds** filling ca. ⅔ of legume, slightly compressed, oblong-subreniform to falcate-ellipsoid, edges blunt. **2*n*** = 20.

Flowering Mar–Nov. Grasslands, open woodlands, shrublands, semi-desert, mildly disturbed areas; 10–1600[–2500] m; Tex.; Mexico (Chihuahua, Coahuila, Durango, Guerrero, Hidalgo, México, Nuevo León, Puebla, San Luis Potosí, Tamaulipas, Veracruz).

Eysenhardtia texana is widespread and common in parts of central, southern, and western Texas, particularly in calcareous soils. Stems and leaves of this species apparently have antibacterial and antifungal chemical properties (G. A. Wächter et al. 1999).

3. Eysenhardtia orthocarpa (A. Gray) S. Watson, Proc. Amer. Acad. Arts 17: 339. 1882

Varieties 2 (1 in the flora): sw United States, n Mexico.

In the United States, only the widespread, typical variety of *Eysenhardtia orthocarpa* is native; var. *tenuifolia* Lang is found only in Mexico (J. M. Lang and D. Isely 1982; R. McVaugh 1987; F. Shreve and I. L. Wiggins 1964 [treated as *E. reticulata* Pennell]).

3a. Eysenhardtia orthocarpa (A. Gray) S. Watson var. **orthocarpa**

Eysenhardtia amorphoides Kunth var. *orthocarpa* A. Gray, Smithsonian Contr. Knowl. 5 (6): 37. 1853

Shrubs, 1.5–5 m. **Leaves** (3–)5–14 cm; leaflets (13–)17–35(–47), blades oblong to narrowly oblong, 5–20 mm, surfaces pubescent, abaxially with some glands much larger than others, largest randomly scattered. **Racemes** (3–)5–10(–16) cm. **Flowers:** calyx tube 2–3.5 mm, lobes acute, 0.3–0.8 mm; corolla 6–10 mm; style with gland near tip. **Legumes** reflexed, falcate to straight, oblong-lanceoloid, 10–16 × 2.5–4 mm, length more than or equal to 3 times width, entire fruit appearing flattened. **Seeds** filling ca. ½ of legume, strongly compressed, obovoid to oblanceolate, edges sharp.

Flowering May–Aug. Semi-desert grasslands, shrublands, open pine-oak-juniper woodlands or savannas, rocky soils; [100–]1100–1800[–2000] m; Ariz., N.Mex.; Mexico (Chihuahua, Jalisco, Sinaloa, Sonora).

Plants of *Eysenhardtia orthocarpa* in the United States have been called *E. polystachya* (T. H. Kearney and R. H. Peebles 1960; W. C. Martin and C. R. Hutchins 1980); that species is native only to central and southern Mexico (J. M. Lang and D. Isely 1982; R. McVaugh 1987).

64. PSOROTHAMNUS Rydberg in N. L. Britton et al., N. Amer. Fl. 24: 45. 1919 • [Greek *psora*, scab, and *thamnos*, shrub, alluding to glandular-pustulate branches]

David M. Sutherland

Psorodendron Rydberg

Shrubs, subshrubs, or trees, armed or unarmed, sterile shoots sometimes sharp-tipped. **Stems** erect, usually pubescent, rarely glabrate or glabrous, glandular nearly throughout, gland-dotted when young. **Leaves** alternate, odd-pinnate or unifoliolate; stipules present, caducous, usually triangular to subulate or linear, rarely obovate; petiolate; leaflets 1–17(or 19), stipels absent, blade margins entire or gland-crenulate, surfaces usually glandular-punctate abaxially, pubescent. **Inflorescences** 1–20+-flowered, terminal and axillary (sometimes leaf-opposed), usually racemes, rarely spikes; bracts present, caducous; bracteoles 0 or 2, at apex of pedicel or base of calyx. **Flowers** papilionaceous; calyx campanulate, lobes 5, unequal; ribs 10, not anastomosing into closed arches distally; corolla usually blue, blue-purple, pink-purple, magenta-purple, violet-purple, violet, or bicolored, sometimes with yellow eye, rarely white; banner blade differentiated from claw, reflexed less than 90°, claw shorter; wings not adnate to keel, blades oblique basally, claws shorter, linear; keel not strongly twisted, blades narrowly overlapping and adherent, oblique basally, blunt-tipped, claws linear; stamens 10, monadelphous, equal or alternately short and long; anthers dorsifixed; style glabrous or pilosulous. **Fruits** legumes, sessile, mostly tan, plump to compressed, obovoid, ovoid-ellipsoid, obovoid-ellipsoid, or obliquely obovoid or ellipsoid, indehiscent, often membranous proximally, thickened distally, gland-dotted, glabrous or pubescent. **Seeds** usually 1, rarely 2, chestnut to brownish or greenish, sometimes with brown or purple spots, somewhat compressed, oblong. $x = 10$.

Species 9 (9 in the flora): sw United States, nw Mexico.

Psorothamnus and *Psorodendron* have equal priority. R. C. Barneby (1977d) was the first to accept *Psorothamnus* and cite *Psorodendron* as a synonym. Members of *Psorothamnus* often have been placed in *Dalea*. They differ from *Dalea* in the placement of the wing and keel petals, which are attached to the hypanthium rim and are not adnate to the stamen tube. R. C. Barneby (1977d) placed the nine species into four sections: *Capnodendron* Barneby (*P. spinosus*), *Winnemucca* Barneby (*P. kingii*), *Xylodalea* (S. Watson) Barneby (*P. arborescens*, *P. fremontii*, *P. schottii*), and *Psorothamnus* (*P. emoryi*, *P. polydenius*, *P. scoparius*, *P. thompsoniae*).

Asagraea Baillon 1870, not Lindley 1839, is an illegitimate name that pertains here.

SELECTED REFERENCE Barneby, R. C. 1977d. *Psorothamnus*. Mem. New York Bot. Gard. 27: 21–54.

1. Bracteoles absent.
   2. Leaves unifoliolate or pinnate, leaflets 1 or 3; branches broomlike . . . . 7. *Psorothamnus scoparius*
   2. Leaves mostly pinnate, leaflets 3–17(or 19), sometimes unifoliolate distally; branches divaricate.
      3. Leaves mostly pinnate, sometimes unifoliolate distally; terminal leaflets each longer than laterals; stems with antrorse-spreading hairs (when present). . . . . 6. *Psorothamnus emoryi*
      3. Leaves all pinnate; terminal leaflets each shorter than laterals; stems with retrorse hairs.
         4. Calyces with longer abaxial lobes; racemes dense to relatively loose, rachises 0.3–3 cm . . . . 8. *Psorothamnus polydenius*
         4. Calyces with shorter abaxial lobes; racemes loose and open, rachises (1–)2–9 cm. . . . . 9. *Psorothamnus thompsoniae*

1. Bracteoles present.
   5. Inflorescences with thornlike tips at anthesis.
      6. Trees (shrublike when young); anthers with gland-tipped connectives . . . . 1. *Psorothamnus spinosus*
      6. Subshrubs (stems at intervals from creeping rootstocks); anthers without gland-tipped connectives. . . . . 2. *Psorothamnus kingii*
   5. Inflorescences without thornlike tips at anthesis.
      7. Leaves unifoliolate or pinnate; leaflet blades linear . . . . 3. *Psorothamnus schottii*
      7. Leaves usually pinnate (leaflets 3–13), sometimes unifoliolate distally; leaflet blades often lanceolate, ovate, obovate, elliptic, rhombic-elliptic, rhombic-ovate, linear, linear-elliptic, or linear-oblanceolate.
         8. Legumes with scattered blister-glands (glands not confluent); leaflet blades silky-strigulose, villous-tomentulose to glabrate, loosely hairy, or glabrous . . . . .4. *Psorothamnus arborescens*
         8. Legumes with numerous blister-glands (glands confluent into vertical ridges); leaflet blades strigulose, more strongly so adaxially . . . . .5. *Psorothamnus fremontii*

1. Psorothamnus spinosus (A. Gray) Barneby, Mem. New York Bot. Gard. 27: 25. 1977 • Smoke tree

Dalea spinosa A. Gray, Pl. Nov. Thurb., 315. 1854

Trees, small, rounded, appearing shrublike when young. **Branches** divergent; sterile shoots sharp-tipped or thornlike. **Stems** 70(–100) dm, gland-dotted distally when young, glands orange, silvery-silky to glabrate. **Leaves** unifoliolate, 0.2–2.2 cm, leaflet 1, blade oblanceolate or cuneate-oblanceolate, surfaces gland-tipped abaxially, strigulose. **Racemes** loose; rachis with thornlike tip in anthesis, 1–4 cm; bracts ovate, 0.5–8 mm; bracteoles present. **Flowers:** calyx 4.5–5.2 mm, silky-strigulose, tube 3–3.8 mm, ribs not prominent, intervals each with (0 or)1(or 2) large glands, lobes ovate, abaxial lobe shorter; corolla indigo-blue; banner obcordate, 6.4–7.5 mm, base auriculate, claw linear to cuneate; wings broadly oblanceolate, 5.5–6.8 × (2.4–)3–4.5 mm; keel obovate, 6.6–8.2 × 4.2–5.4 mm; stamens 9.5–11.5 mm; filaments distinct to 4.1–4.9 mm; anthers 0.7–1.1 mm, connective gland-tipped. **Legumes** obovoid, 3–4 mm, with several glands proximally, pilosulous distally. **Seeds** rarely 2, 3 mm.

Flowering late spring–mid summer (fall). Rocky or sandy deserts, wetter areas; -70–400 m; Ariz., Calif., Nev.; Mexico (Baja California, Sonora).

Leaves of *Psorothamnus spinosus* are not retained for long; most of the time, the tree crown consists of a rounded mass of silvery branches. In California, *P. spinosus* is known from the desert areas in the southeastern part of the state.

2. Psorothamnus kingii (S. Watson) Barneby, Mem. New York Bot. Gard. 27: 27. 1977 [E]

Dalea kingii S. Watson, Botany (Fortieth Parallel), 64, plate 10, figs. 1–3. 1871

Subshrubs. Branches diffuse; sterile shoots sharp-tipped. **Stems** at intervals from creeping rootstocks, 1–3.5 dm, gland-dotted when young, ± pilose to appressed-pubescent and nearly sericeous. **Leaves** pinnate, 1–4.5 cm; leaflets 3–9, blades ovate to oblong-elliptic, (3–)5–12(–15) mm, terminal leaflet slightly longer than or ± equal to laterals, surfaces irregularly gland-dotted abaxially, densely hairy, especially adaxially, to glabrate. **Racemes** loose; rachis with thornlike tip in anthesis, 1–4 cm; bracts subulate, 1.5–2.5 mm; bracteoles present. **Flowers:** calyx 7–8.2 mm, thinly strigulose, tube 3.8–4.2 mm, ribs not prominent, intervals each with 2–7 glands, lobes ovate to lanceolate, abaxial lobe shorter; corolla blue; banner obovate, 7–9.2 mm, claw cuneate; wings oblong, 5–6.6 × 3.2–3.9 mm; keel broadly obovate, 5.2–6.5 × 3.4–4 mm; stamens 8–9.5 mm; filaments distinct to 3.3–4.4 mm; anthers 0.8–1.5 mm, connective not gland-tipped. **Legumes** obliquely obovoid, (3.5–)4–5.5 mm, gland-dotted distally, pubescent. **Seeds** 1 or 2, 3.1–2.8 mm. $2n = 20$.

Flowering summer. Dune-sand, flat areas around dunes; 1200–1600 m; Nev.

Psorothamnus kingii is known from near Winnemucca and from Carson Sink in Churchill and Humboldt counties.

3. Psorothamnus schottii (Torrey) Barneby, Mem. New York Bot. Gard. 27: 31. 1977 • Indigo bush

Dalea schottii Torrey in W. H. Emory, Rep. U.S. Mex. Bound. 2(1): 53. 1859

Shrubs. Branches divaricate; sterile shoots on shorter lateral branches sharp-tipped. **Stems** 1–2.5 dm, eglandular and usually glabrous or sparsely strigulose when young, rarely canescent. **Leaves** unifoliolate or pinnate, (0.7–)1–3 cm; leaflets 1 (or 3), blades linear, 6–30 mm, terminal leaflet longer than laterals, surfaces usually glabrous with glandular margins abaxially, densely silvery-pubescent adaxially. **Racemes** loose; rachis without thornlike tip in anthesis, 1–9 cm; bracts triangular-subulate, 0.5–1.3 mm; bracteoles present. **Flowers:** calyx (4–) 4.6–5.7(–6.5) mm, glabrous or strigulose externally, tube (2.8–)3.3–4.3(–4.6) mm, ribs prominent, narrow abaxial intervals each with 1–5 glands in 1 row, broader adaxial intervals each with 1–17 glands in 2 rows, lobes ovate-deltate to triangular, abaxial lobe slightly shorter and narrower; corolla deep blue, banner with yellow eye; banner flabellate, (6.4–)7.1–10.5 mm, tapered to cuneate claw, apex retuse; wings broadly oblong, (6–)7–8.6 × 3–4.2 mm; keel broadly oblong, (6.1–)6.5–8(–8.8) × 3.7–4.7 mm; stamens 7–11 mm; filaments distinct to 3.5–6.5 mm; anthers 0.9–1.3 mm, connective not gland-tipped. **Legumes** obovoid, 7–10 mm, with large, separate glands, puberulent distally. **Seeds** 6–8 mm. $2n = 20$.

Flowering (fall–)late winter–early spring(–late spring). Rocky and sandy desert flats, slopes, washes; 5–800 m; Ariz., Calif.; Mexico (Baja California).

In California, *Psorothamnus schottii* is known from the Sonoran Desert regions in the very southeastern parts of the state.

4. Psorothamnus arborescens (Torrey ex A. Gray) Barneby, Mem. New York Bot. Gard. 27: 33. 1977

Dalea arborescens Torrey ex A. Gray, Pl. Nov. Thurb., 316. 1854

Shrubs. Branches irregular, stiff; sterile shoots often sharp-tipped. **Stems** 3–10 dm, gland-dotted distally when young, glands prickle-shaped, hairy to glabrate. **Leaves** usually pinnate, sometimes unifoliolate distally, (0.3–)1–3.5(–5.5) cm; leaflets (1 or 3)5–11, blades ovate, obovate, lanceolate, linear, elliptic, rhombic-elliptic, rhombic-ovate, or linear-oblanceolate, 2–14 (–17) mm, terminal leaflet seldom longer than laterals, surfaces gland-dotted abaxially, silky-strigulose, villous-tomentulose to glabrate, loosely hairy, or glabrous. **Racemes** loose; rachis without thornlike tip in anthesis, (1–)1.5–12 cm; bracts subulate to linear, 2.5–4 mm; bracteoles present. **Flowers:** calyx 5–9 mm, pilosulous to minutely puberulent, strigulose, silky-canescent, or glabrate, tube 3–4.5 mm, ribs prominent, broader adaxial intervals with 2 rows, narrower one with 1 row of 3–5 glands, lobes broadly lanceolate, triangular, or lanceolate, abaxial lobe often shorter; corolla indigo-blue to violet; banner flabellate to flabellate-ovate, 6.3–10 mm, base cuneate to auriculate, claw cuneate; wings oblong to oblong-ovate, 5.4–8.2 × 2.2–3.5 mm; keel obliquely obovate, 5.8–8.4 × 3.3–4.9 mm; stamens (5.5–)6.5–9.8 mm; filaments distinct to (3–)3.5–5.6 mm; anthers (0.8–)0.9–1.3 mm, connective not gland-tipped. **Legumes** ovoid-ellipsoid or obliquely ellipsoid, 8–10 mm, with scattered blister-glands, glands not confluent, glabrous or sparsely villosulous. **Seeds** (4.7–)5–6 mm.

Varieties 4 (4 in the flora): sw United States, nw Mexico.

1. Calyces 7–9 mm, lobes to 3–5.4 mm.
   2. Leaflets (3 or)5 or 7, blades ovate to obovate, elliptic, or broadly lanceolate. . . . . 4a. *Psorothamnus arborescens* var. *arborescens*
   2. Leaflets (5 or)7–11, blades linear to linear-oblanceolate. . . . . 4d. *Psorothamnus arborescens* var. *pubescens*
1. Calyces 5–6.9 mm, lobes to 1.8–3.7 mm.
   3. Calyx tube glabrate or puberulent; leaflet blades lanceolate to rhombic-ovate or -elliptic, surfaces loosely hairy or glabrous . . . . 4b. *Psorothamnus arborescens* var. *minutifolius*
   3. Calyx tube silky-canescent externally; leaflet blades linear-oblanceolate to narrowly elliptic, surfaces silky-strigulose . . . . 4c. *Psorothamnus arborescens* var. *californicus*

4a. Psorothamnus arborescens (Torrey ex A. Gray) Barneby var. **arborescens**

Dalea fremontii Torrey ex A. Gray var. *saundersii* (Parish) Munz

Leaves 1–3.5 cm; leaflets (3 or) 5 or 7, blades ovate to obovate or elliptic, or broadly lanceolate, (3–)5–10 mm, surfaces villous-tomentulose to glabrate. **Flowers:** calyx 7–9 mm, tube 3.6–4.5 mm, pilosulous to glabrate; corolla indigo blue; banner 9–10 mm; keel 8.2–8.4 mm.

Flowering spring. Rocky areas; 300–800 m; Calif.; Mexico (Sonora).

Variety *arborescens* is restricted to the southwestern deserts.

4b. Psorothamnus arborescens (Torrey ex A. Gray) Barneby var. **minutifolius** (Parish) Barneby, Mem. New York Bot. Gard. 27: 35. 1977 [E]

Parosela johnsonii (S. Watson) Vail var. *minutifolia* Parish, Bot. Gaz. 55: 308. 1913

Leaves 1–3.5(–5.5) cm; leaflets (3 or)5 or 7, blades lanceolate to rhombic-ovate or -elliptic, 3–13(–17) mm, surfaces loosely hairy or glabrous. **Flowers:** calyx 5–6.8 mm, tube 3–4.2 mm, glabrate or minutely puberulent; corolla indigo blue to violet; banner 7.6–9 mm; keel 6.3–8.2 mm. **2*n*** = 10, 40.

Flowering spring. Stony and gravelly slopes and washes; 150–1900 m; Calif., Nev.

Variety *minutifolius* is restricted to the west-central and northern Mojave Desert.

4c. Psorothamnus arborescens (Torrey ex A. Gray) Barneby var. **californicus** (S. Watson) Sutherland, Gandhi & Vincent, J. Bot. Res. Inst. Texas 14: 188. 2020 [C] [E]

Dalea californica S. Watson, Proc. Amer. Acad. Arts 11: 132. 1876; *Parosela californica* (S. Watson) Vail; *Parosela californica* var. *simplicifolia* Parish; *Psorothamnus arborescens* var. *simplicifolius* (Parish) Barneby

Leaves 0.3–3.5 cm; leaflets (1 or)5 or 7(or 9), blades linear-oblanceolate to narrowly elliptic, 2–12 mm, surfaces silky-strigulose. **Flowers:** calyx 5.2–6.9 mm, tube 3–4.2 mm, silky-canescent externally; corolla indigo blue; banner 6.3–7.8 mm; keel 5.8–6.4 mm. **2*n*** = 10.

Flowering late winter–spring. Stony, rocky, or sandy ground in creosote-bush scrub, regions transitional to oak-juniper-manzanita associations; of conservation concern; 100–1100 m; Calif.

Variety *californicus* is known from the San Bernardino Mountains and adjacent desert regions.

4d. Psorothamnus arborescens (Torrey ex A. Gray) Barneby var. **pubescens** (Parish) Barneby, Mem. New York Bot. Gard. 27: 38. 1977 [C] [E]

Parosela johnsonii (S. Watson) Vail var. *pubescens* Parish, Bot. Gaz. 55: 308. 1913

Leaves 1.5–3.5 cm; leaflets (5 or)7–11, blades linear to linear-oblanceolate, 3–14 mm, surfaces silky-strigulose. **Flowers:** calyx 7.3–9 mm, tube 3.6–4.4 mm, pilosulous to loosely strigulose; corolla indigo blue; banner 7 mm; keel 6–6.4 mm.

Flowering spring–early summer. Rocky slopes, clay barrens; of conservation concern; 1000–1500 m; Ariz., Utah.

Variety *pubescens* is known from areas near the Colorado River.

5. Psorothamnus fremontii (Torrey ex A. Gray) Barneby, Mem. New York Bot. Gard. 27: 40. 1977 [E]

Dalea fremontii Torrey ex A. Gray, Pl. Nov. Thurb., 316. 1854

Shrubs. Branches irregular; sterile shoots not or faintly sharp-tipped. **Stems** 3–10 dm, ± eglandular when young, strigulose. **Leaves** pinnate, 1–4 cm; leaflets 3–7(or 9), blades obovate to linear-elliptic, linear-oblanceolate, or linear, (2–)3–25 mm, terminal leaflet seldom longer than laterals, surfaces gland-dotted abaxially, strigulose, more strongly so adaxially. **Racemes** loose; rachis without thornlike tip in anthesis, 2–9(–11) cm; bracts subulate, 1.2–2 mm; bracteoles present. **Flowers:** calyx (5–)5.4–7.7 mm, glabrous or strigulose externally, tube (5–)5.4–7.7 mm, ribs prominent, intervals each with 1 row of 2–5 glands, adaxial ones with 4–7 scattered glands, lobes lanceolate or triangular-lanceolate, abaxial lobe becoming reflexed, nearly equal but narrower; corolla magenta-purple; banner flabellate to flabellate-ovate, 7.3–9.3 mm, base cuneate or auriculate, claw cuneate; wings oblong to oblong-ovate, 6.1–7.3 × (2.6–)2.8–3.8 mm; keel obliquely obovate, (6–)6.4–7.5 × (3.6–)4–4.7 mm; stamens 6.6–9.1 mm; filaments distinct to 3.2–4.4 mm; anthers (0.7–)0.9–1.2 mm, connective not gland-tipped. **Legumes** obliquely obovoid, 7–10 mm, with numerous blister-glands, glands confluent into vertical ridges, glabrous or glabrate. **Seeds** 4.4–5.8 mm.

Varieties 2 (2 in the flora): sw United States.

Psorothamnus fremontii is often separated from *P. arborescens* with difficulty because the critical distinction requires mature fruit. Most other features are too variable or overlapping to be of much use. Flowering specimens can usually be identified if the location of the collection is considered, since the two species are largely allopatric. *Psorothamnus fremontii* is confined to southeastern California, southern Nevada, northern and western Arizona, and south-central Utah; *P. arborescens* is found mainly west and north of *P. fremontii* in California, Nevada, and northwestern Mexico, except for var. *pubescens*, which occurs with *P. fremontii* in north-central Arizona and south-central Utah.

1. Leaflet blades obovate to linear-elliptic or linear-oblanceolate, (2–)3–15(–20) × 1.5–2(–4) mm . . . . 5a. *Psorothamnus fremontii* var. *fremontii*
1. Leaflet blades linear, (3–)5–25 × 0.7–1(–1.2) mm . . . . 5b. *Psorothamnus fremontii* var. *attenuatus*

5a. Psorothamnus fremontii (Torrey ex A. Gray) Barneby var. **fremontii** E

Dalea fremontii Torrey ex A. Gray var. *johnsonii* (S. Watson) Munz

Leaflet blades obovate to linear-elliptic or linear-oblanceolate, (2–)3–15(–20) × 1.5–2(–4) mm. $2n = 20$.

Flowering spring–early summer. Rocky, gravelly, or sandy deserts; 200–1600 m; Ariz., Calif., Nev., Utah.

5b. Psorothamnus fremontii (Torrey ex A. Gray) Barneby var. **attenuatus** Barneby, Mem. New York Bot. Gard. 27: 41, plate 4. 1977 E

Leaflet blades linear, (3–)5–25 × 0.7–1(–1.2) mm.

Flowering spring–early summer. Rocky desert slopes and flats; 150–1000 m; Ariz., Calif., Nev.

Variety *attenuatus* is known from the lower Colorado River and is rather weakly differentiated from var. *fremontii*. Some specimens of var. *fremontii* from southern Utah, although far out of the range of var. *attenuatus*, approach it in leaflet shape and width.

6. Psorothamnus emoryi (A. Gray) Rydberg in N. L. Britton et al., N. Amer. Fl. 24: 47. 1919

Dalea emoryi A. Gray, Pl. Nov. Thurb., 315. 1854

Varieties 2 (1 in the flora): sw United States, nw Mexico.

A small-flowered plant, var. *arenarius* (Brandegee) Barneby is known from the Baja California peninsula.

6a. Psorothamnus emoryi (A. Gray) Rydberg var. **emoryi**

Subshrubs. Branches divaricate; sterile shoots not sharp-tipped. **Stems** 3–10 dm, gland-dotted when young, glands sometimes concealed by pubescence, usually tomentulose, hairs antrorse-spreading, rarely glabrous. **Leaves** usually pinnate, sometimes unifoliolate distally, 0.8–3.2(–4) cm; leaflets (1 or)3–9(–13), blades suborbiculate to oblong-oblanceolate, or (terminal leaflet) obovate to oblanceolate or linear-oblanceolate, 2–16(–20) mm, terminal leaflet much longer than laterals, surfaces glandular, glands often concealed by pubescence, tomentulose. **Spikes** dense, capitate; rachis not spine-tipped in anthesis, (0.1–)0.3–1.1 cm; bracts subulate to lanceolate-elliptic, 1.5–3 mm; bracteoles absent. **Flowers:** calyx (4.1–)4.3–7.2 mm, pilosulous, tube (2.2–)2.4–3.4 mm, ribs prominent, intervals each with 1 or 2 rows of small glands, lobes lanceolate to ovate-triangular, abaxial lobe usually slightly longer; corolla bicolored, banner whitish, purple- or violet-margined, wings and keel whitish, banded purple or white; banner ovate, 5.3–6.3 mm, base cordate, claw linear; wings oblong or oblong-lanceolate, (3.5–)3.8–5.2 × 1.3–1.8 mm; keel obliquely oblong-ovate to obovate, 4.2–6.2 × (2–)2.2–2.9 mm; stamens 6.3–7.8 mm; filaments distinct to 0.5–0.9 mm; anthers 0.5–0.9 mm, connective gland-tipped. **Legumes** obovoid-ellipsoid, 2.3–2.8 mm, gland-dotted distally, pilosulous. **Seeds** 1.5 mm. $2n = 10$.

Flowering spring–early summer (fall–winter). Sandy or gravelly desert flats or dunes; -30–800 m; Ariz., Calif.; Mexico (Baja California, Baja California Sur, Sonora).

In California, var. *emoryi* is known from the Mojave and Sonoran desert regions in the southeastern part of the state.

7. Psorothamnus scoparius (A. Gray) Rydberg in N. L. Britton et al., N. Amer. Fl. 24: 48. 1919 F

Dalea scoparia A. Gray, Mem. Amer. Acad. Arts, n. s. 4: 32. 1849

Shrubs or subshrubs. Branches broomlike; sterile shoots not sharp-tipped. **Stems** to 10 dm, gland-dotted when young, often gray-strigulose, hairs antrorse. **Leaves** unifoliolate or pinnate, (0.2–)0.4–2 cm; leaflets 1 or 3, blades linear-oblanceolate, 2–15 mm, terminal leaflet longer than laterals, surfaces gland-dotted abaxially, strigulose. **Racemes** relatively loose; rachis not spine-tipped in anthesis, (0.1–)0.3–1.8 cm; bracts ovate to oblanceolate, 1.5–2.5 mm; bracteoles absent. **Flowers:** calyx 3.5–4.5 mm, densely pilosulous, tube 2.2–3 mm, ribs fairly prominent, intervals each with 1 row of (1 or)2–5 glands, lobes ovate, abaxial lobe shorter; corolla usually bright blue or blue-purple with pale yellow eye, rarely white; banner 6.4–9 mm, oblong-obovate, base cordate; wings oblong-lanceolate, 5–6.7 × 1.7–2.1 mm; keel obliquely obovate, (4.2–)4.6–5.8 × 1.7–2.1 mm; stamens 5.5–8.5 mm; filaments distinct to 2.3–2.6 mm; anthers 0.6–0.9 mm, connective gland-tipped. **Legumes** obliquely obovate, 4 mm, with large glands distally, glabrous proximally, pilosulous distally. **Seeds** 2.1–2.7 mm. **2*n*** = 20.

Flowering fall (late spring–early summer). Sandy desert flats or dunes; 1100–1600 m; Ariz., N.Mex., Tex.; Mexico (Chihuahua, Coahuila).

Psorothamnus scoparius, a distinctive broomlike plant, is usually nearly leafless by flowering time. In Texas, *P. scoparius* is known only from El Paso and Hudspeth counties in the trans-Pecos region.

8. Psorothamnus polydenius (Torrey) Rydberg in N. L. Britton et al., N. Amer. Fl. 24: 46. 1919 (as polyadenius) [E]

Dalea polydenia Torrey in S. Watson, Botany (Fortieth Parallel), 64, plate 9. 1871

Shrubs. Branches divaricate; sterile shoots almost sharp-tipped. **Stems** 4–10(–15) dm, densely gland-dotted when young, silky-pilosulous, hairs retrorse. **Leaves** pinnate, 0.7–2.7 cm; leaflets 7–13, blades obovate to suborbiculate, 1–4.5 mm, terminal leaflet shorter than laterals, surfaces with submarginal and apical glands abaxially, glands visible, pubescent. **Racemes** dense to relatively loose; rachis not spine-tipped in anthesis, 0.3–3 cm; bracts lanceolate or linear-lanceolate, 1.6–6.5 mm; bracteoles absent. **Flowers:** calyx 3.9–5.3(–8.3) mm, pilosulous throughout or tube glabrous, tube 1.9–2.8(–3) mm, ribs prominent, intervals each with 1 row of 2–6 glands, lobes triangular-lanceolate to lanceolate, abaxial lobe longer; corolla pink-purple, banner with yellow eye; banner 4.6–6.1(–6.6) mm, ovate-cordate, ovate, base cordate, apex emarginate, claw linear; wings oblong, 4–5(–5.4) × 1.5–2.1 mm; keel obovate, (3.7–)4–5.3 × 2.4–3.7 mm; stamens 5.2–6.8 mm; filaments distinct to (1.5–)2–3 mm; anthers (0.5–)0.6–0.8(–1) mm, connective gland-tipped. **Legumes** obliquely obovoid, 2.5 mm, with large glands distally, glabrous proximally, sparsely pilosulous distally. **Seeds** 2–2.5 mm.

Varieties 2 (2 in the flora): sw United States.

1. Calyx lobes 1.8–2.5 mm . . . . 8a. *Psorothamnus polydenius* var. *polydenius*
1. Calyx lobes 3.6–5.2 mm . . . . 8b. *Psorothamnus polydenius* var. *jonesii*

8a. Psorothamnus polydenius (Torrey) Rydberg var. **polydenius** [E]

Leaves 0.7–1.5 cm; leaflets 7–13, blades obovate to suborbiculate, 1–3 mm. **Racemes** relatively dense; rachis 0.3–1.2(–1.8) cm; bracts lanceolate, 1.6–2.5 mm, margins entire, gland-spurred. **Calyces** pilosulous throughout or tube glabrous, lobes 1.8–2.5 mm. **2*n*** = 10.

Flowering spring–early summer (fall). Sandy or gravelly slopes and flats, dunes; 800–2300 m; Calif., Nev., Utah.

In California, var. *polydenius* is known from the southeastern part of the state, east of the Sierra Nevada and in the Mojave and Sonoran desert regions.

8b. Psorothamnus polydenius (Torrey) Rydberg var. **jonesii** Barneby, Mem. New York Bot. Gard. 27: 52. 1977 [C] [E]

Dalea nummularia M. E. Jones, Contr. W. Bot. 18: 41. 1933; *Psorothamnus nummularius* (M. E. Jones) S. L. Welsh

Leaves 1–2.7 cm; leaflets 9–11, blades obovate, 1.5–4.5 mm. **Racemes** relatively loose; rachis 2–3 cm; bracts linear-lanceolate (sometimes apex caudate), 4–6.5 mm, margins toothed, eglandular. **Calyces** pilosulous throughout, lobes 3.6–5.2 mm.

Flowering late spring–early summer. Salt desert scrub communities; of conservation concern; 1200–1500 m; Utah.

Variety *jonesii* is known only from salt desert shrub communities near the Green River in central Utah.

S. L. Welsh et al. (2003) treated *Psorothamnus nummularius* as endemic to eastern Emory County.

9. Psorothamnus thompsoniae (Vail) S. L. Welsh & N. D. Atwood, Great Basin Naturalist 35: 354. 1976 (as thompsonae) E

Parosela thompsoniae Vail, Bull. Torrey Bot. Club 24: 18. 1897 (as thompsonae)

Shrubs. Branches divaricate; sterile shoots sharp-tipped. **Stems** 4–9(–15) dm, gland-dotted when young, silky-pilosulous, hairs retrorse. **Leaves** pinnate, (1–)1.4–3 cm; leaflets 7–17(or 19), blades obovate, oblanceolate, linear-oblanceolate, or linear-oblong, 2–7 mm, terminal leaflet shorter than laterals, surfaces sparsely gland-dotted abaxially, strigulose, more strongly so adaxially. **Racemes** loose and open; rachis not spine-tipped in anthesis, (1–)2–9 cm; bracts ovate-elliptic, 0.6–1.5 mm; bracteoles absent. **Flowers:** calyx 3.7–5 mm, pilosulous throughout, or tube glabrous, lobes pilosulous, tube 2.4–3.3 mm, ribs prominent, intervals each with 1–4 large glands, lobes ovate to oblong-ovate, abaxial lobe shorter; corolla pink- to violet-purple; banner (5.5–)6–8.4 mm, ovate to suborbiculate, base cuneate or cordate, claw linear; wings oblong, 5.8–6.6 × 2.6–3.2 mm; keel obovate, 5.6–6.7 × 3.4–3.8 mm; stamens 6–7.7 mm; filaments distinct to 2.5–3.5 mm; anthers 0.8–0.9 mm, connective gland-tipped. **Legumes** obliquely obovoid, 4–4.5 mm, with large glands distally, glabrous proximally, sparsely pilosulous distally. **Seeds** 2.1–2.6 mm.

Varieties 2 (2 in the flora): sw United States.

1. Leaflet blades obovate or broadly oblanceolate, 2–4(–5) mm; calyx tube usually glabrous, lobes pilosulous, sometimes pilosulous throughout . . . . .9a. *Psorothamnus thompsoniae* var. *thompsoniae*
1. Leaflet blades linear-oblanceolate or linear-oblong, 3–7 mm; calyx usually pilosulous throughout . . . . .9b. *Psorothamnus thompsoniae* var. *whitingii*

9a. Psorothamnus thompsoniae (Vail) S. L. Welsh & N. D. Atwood var. **thompsoniae** E

Leaflets 7–13, blades obovate or broadly oblanceolate, 2–4(–5) mm. **Calyces:** tube usually glabrous, lobes pilosulous, sometimes pilosulous throughout.

Flowering late spring–early summer. Open, gravelly slopes, sandstone outcrops, salt and mixed desert shrub communities; 1100–2300 m; Utah.

Variety *thompsoniae* is known from Emery, Garfield, Kane, San Juan, and Wayne counties.

9b. Psorothamnus thompsoniae (Vail) S. L. Welsh & N. D. Atwood var. **whitingii** (Kearney & Peebles) Barneby, Mem. New York Bot. Gard. 27: 54. 1977 (as thompsonae var. whitingi) C E

Dalea whitingii Kearney & Peebles, J. Wash. Acad. Sci. 29: 484. 1939 (as whitingi)

Leaflets 7–17(or 19), blades linear-oblanceolate or linear-oblong, 3–7 mm. **Calyces** usually pubescent throughout.

Flowering late spring–early summer. Clay or sandy soils, talus in canyons, mixed desert shrub communities; of conservation concern; 1100–1600 m; Ariz., Utah.

Variety *whitingii* is known from San Juan County, Utah, from near Monument Valley westward to Navajo Mountain, and disjunctly in Wupatki National Monument, Coconino County, Arizona.

65. MARINA Liebmann, Vidensk. Meddel. Naturhist. Foren. Kjøbenhavn 1853: 103. 1854 • [For Doña Marina (La Malinche), ca. 1500–ca. 1529, Nahua interpreter for Hernán Cortés in Mexico]

David M. Sutherland

Herbs or shrubs, perennial [**annual**], unarmed. **Stems** erect or decumbent, glabrous or pubescent (trichomes stiff, short, not spirally twisted). **Leaves** alternate, usually odd-pinnate, rarely unifoliolate; stipules present, caducous or persistent, deltate, ovate, or subulate; petiolate; leaflets 1–25(–29)[–45], stipels absent, blades with pale sinuous lines and single gland between petiolules, margins entire or glandular-crenulate, surfaces lineolate, with pale, sinuous, ascending lines, usually glandular-punctate abaxially, usually pubescent, sometimes glabrous.

Inflorescences (1–)5–75-flowered, terminal or leaf-opposed, racemes; bracts present, caducous [persistent]; bracteoles absent. **Pedicels** glandular basally, sometimes also apically. **Flowers** papilionaceous; calyx campanulate, lobes 5, ribs 10, not anastomosing distally into closed arches, intervals between ribs membranous, glandular; corolla white, lilac, blue, blue-violet, or purple, often bicolored; banner claw reflexed to 90°; wings and keel epistemonous, arising from apex of stamen tube or laterally from it; wings not adnate to keel; keel blades usually narrowly overlapping and adherent; stamens [5 or 9]10, monadelphous, ± equal; anthers dorsifixed; ovule 1. **Fruits** loments, mostly tan, stipitate, compressed [plump], obovoid, obliquely obovoid, or harp-shaped [obliquely obdeltoid], indehiscent, pericarp membranous or papery, glandular, glabrous or pilosulous. **Seed** 1, tan to purplish or greenish, somewhat compressed, reniform. x = 10.

Species 38 (4 in the flora): sw United States, Mexico, Central America (Guatemala).

Marina is close to *Dalea* and is separated primarily on differences in the calyces, whose ribs do not form closed arches in *Marina* as they do in *Dalea*, and the leaves, whose leaflets have pale, sinuous lines in *Marina* but not in *Dalea* and whose axes bear single adaxial glands between the petiolules in *Marina* and usually two in *Dalea*. R. C. Barneby (1977b) placed the four species in the flora area into sect. *Carroa* (C. Presl) Barneby (*M. diffusa*) and sect. *Marina* (*M. calycosa*, *M. orcuttii*, and *M. parryi*).

SELECTED REFERENCE Barneby, R. C. 1977b. *Marina*. Mem. New York Bot. Gard. 27: 55–135.

1. Shrubs (sometimes flowering precociously); calyces glabrous. . . . . 4. *Marina diffusa*
1. Herbs (becoming suffrutescent in *M. parryi*); calyces strigulose to hirsute, hirtellous, or hirsutulous.
    2. Stems densely glandular-verruculose; racemes sparsely flowered distally; flowers not nodding, usually separated by distinct intervals. . . . . 1. *Marina parryi*
    2. Stems eglandular or nearly so; racemes moderately densely flowered; flowers nodding.
        3. Calyces 5.2–7 mm; keel petals 4.3–5.8 mm; leaflet blades not gland-dotted abaxially. . . . . 2. *Marina calycosa*
        3. Calyces 4.2–5 mm; keel petals 3.6–4.1 mm; leaflet blades gland-dotted abaxially. . . 3. *Marina orcuttii*

1. Marina parryi (Torrey & A. Gray) Barneby, Mem. New York Bot Gard. 27: 68. 1977 [F]

Dalea parryi Torrey & A. Gray, Proc. Amer. Acad. Arts 7: 397. 1868, based on *D. divaricata* Bentham var. *cinerea* A. Gray, Proc. Amer. Acad. Arts 7: 335. 1868

Herbs (becoming suffrutescent), erect, 1.5–7 dm. **Stems** usually branched, densely glandular-verruculose, strigulose. **Leaves** 1.4–4.5(–6) cm; leaflets (9 or)11–23(–29), blades orbiculate-obcordate to oblong-ovate, 0.5–5(–7) mm, surfaces pubescent, gland-dotted abaxially. **Peduncles** (0.5–)1–5(–9.5) cm. **Racemes** sparsely flowered distally; axis 2–10 cm; bracts 1.5–3(–5.5) mm. **Pedicels** 0.3–0.5 mm. **Flowers** not nodding, usually separated by distinct intervals; calyx (2.8–)3–4.3(–4.5) mm, loosely strigulose to hirsute, tube 1.6–2(–2.1) mm, rib intervals each with 5 or 6 glands, lobes ovate, unequal; corolla usually bicolored; banner whitish with yellowish eye, blue or bluish near margin, deltate-cordate to reniform, 2.8–4 mm; epistemonous petals blue proximally and pale distally, or blue-violet throughout; wings ovate to oblong-ovate, 2.6–3.8 × 1.4–2 mm; keel elliptic-obovate, 3.6–4.8 × 2.4–3.2 mm; stamens (5–)5.5–7 mm; filaments distinct to 2 mm; anthers 0.5–0.8 mm. **Loments** harp-shaped, 1.8–2.4 mm, puberulent, with arcs of glands distally. **Seeds** 1.6–2 mm. $2n$ = 20.

Flowering late winter–spring (fall). Rocky or sandy desert washes, alluvial fans; 10–1000 m; Ariz., Calif., Nev.; Mexico (Baja California, Baja California Sur, Sonora).

2. Marina calycosa (A. Gray) Barneby, Mem. New York Bot. Gard. 27: 83. 1977

Dalea calycosa A. Gray, Smithsonian Contr. Knowl. 5(6): 40. 1853

Herbs, decumbent, 0.5–2 dm. **Stems** branched or simple, eglandular or nearly so, strigulose. **Leaves** 1–3 cm; leaflets (9 or)11–25, blades obovate to oblong-obovate, 1.5–7 mm, surfaces pubescent, not gland-dotted abaxially. **Peduncles** 0.3–3 cm. **Racemes** moderately densely flowered; axis (1–)1.5–6.5 cm; bracts 2.5–4 mm. **Pedicels** 0.3–0.6 mm. **Flowers** nodding; calyx 5.2–7 mm, hirtellous, tube 1.8–2.5 mm, rib intervals each with ± 5 glands, lobes lanceolate-elliptic, slightly unequal; corolla bicolored; banner whitish or pinkish tan, blue or purplish near margin, deltate-cordate to reniform, 3.7–5 mm; epistemonous petals whitish, blue or purplish on margins; wings obliquely ovate, 3.3–4.2 × 2.1–2.8 mm; keel broadly ovate or obovate, 4.3–5.8 × 3–3.7 mm; stamens 7–8 mm; filaments distinct to 2.5–3 mm; anthers 0.7–1 mm. **Loments** obliquely obovoid, 2.6–3 mm, puberulent, with arcs of glands distally. **Seeds** 2 mm.

Flowering spring–early summer (late summer–fall). Rocky or sandy hillsides in oak woodlands, dry grassland; 1200–2500 m; Ariz., N.Mex.; Mexico (Chihuahua, Nuevo León, Sonora).

Marina calycosa is similar in habit and overall appearance to *Dalea neomexicana*, which it overlaps in range and with which it has, sometimes, been confused.

3. Marina orcuttii (S. Watson) Barneby, Mem. New York Bot. Gard. 27: 85. 1977

Dalea orcuttii S. Watson, Proc. Amer. Acad. Arts 20: 359. 1885

Varieties 2 (1 in the flora): California, nw Mexico.

Marina orcuttii is similar to *M. calycosa*, differing principally in the smaller flowers. Variety *orcuttii* is confined to the Santa Rosa Mountains of south-central California and northern Baja California. Variety *campanea* Barneby is distributed in southern Baja California and northern Baja California Sur.

3a. Marina orcuttii (S. Watson) Barneby var. **orcuttii** C

Herbs, decumbent, 1–1.5(–2.5) dm. **Stems** simple or few-branched, eglandular, strigulose. **Leaves** 0.8–3 cm; leaflets 11–17, blades obovate to oblanceolate, (1.5–)2–5 mm, surfaces pubescent abaxially, glabrous adaxially, gland-dotted abaxially. **Peduncles** (1–)1.5–3.5 cm. **Racemes** moderately densely flowered; axis (0.5–)1–2.7 cm; bracts 1.8–2.5 mm. **Pedicels** 0.2–0.4 mm. **Flowers** nodding; calyx 4.2–5 mm, hirsutulous, tube 1.7–2.2 mm, rib intervals each with 4 or 5 glands, lobes lanceolate-elliptic, ± unequal; corolla bicolored; banner pale, lilac near margin, oblong-cordate to reniform, 2.6–3.3 mm; epistemonous petals lilac-striped proximally, whitish distally; wings obliquely ovate, 2.6–3 × 1.3–1.8 mm; keel ovate or obovate, 3.6–4.1 × 2.4–2.7 mm; stamens 4.5–5.2 mm; filaments distinct to 1.6–1.9 mm; anthers 0.5–0.8 mm. **Loments** obliquely obovoid, ca. 3 mm, puberulent, with arcs of glands distally. **Seeds** 2 mm.

Flowering spring–fall. Gravelly hillsides in chaparral or pine forests; of conservation concern; 1000–1200 m; Calif.; Mexico (Baja California).

4. Marina diffusa (Moricand) Barneby, Mem. New York Bot. Gard. 27: 126. 1977

Dalea diffusa Moricand, Pl. Nouv. Amér., 8, plate 6. 1834

Varieties 2 (1 in the flora): Arizona, Mexico, Central America (Guatemala).

Marina diffusa is known from the Patagonia Mountains of southeastern Arizona and in western Mexico south to Guatemala. Variety *radiolata* Barneby occurs in Nayarit, Mexico. *Marina diffusa* is unlike other species of *Marina* and *Dalea* in the flora area by having its racemes grouped into diffuse panicles. R. C. Barneby (1977b) assigned Guatemalan material to var. *diffusa* and said it needs study.

4a. Marina diffusa (Moricand) Barneby var. **diffusa**

Shrubs (sometimes flowering precociously), erect, 10–25 dm. **Stems** several-branched (broom-like), sparsely or obscurely glandular, glabrous. **Leaves** 1.5–3.5(–4) cm; leaflets 1–5, blades oblong to oblong-oblanceolate, 0.7–5 mm, surfaces glabrous, minutely glandular-punctate abaxially. **Peduncles** 0.5–3(–4) cm. **Racemes** usually loosely or remotely flowered, sometimes flowers solitary; axis (0–)0.1–0.5 cm; bracts to 1 mm. **Pedicels**

(0.6–)0.8–1.5 mm. **Flowers** not nodding; calyx 2.5–3.6 mm, glabrous, tube (1.5–)1.8–2.2 mm, rib intervals each with 2–5 distinct or confluent glands, lobes ovate-triangular to semiorbiculate, ± unequal; corolla bicolored; banner whitish or white and purple striped, lobes blue or purple, ovate-deltate, tubular at top of claw, 2.5–3.5 mm; epistemonous petals rose to purple or violet; wings obovate, 3.5–4.6 × 2.2–3 mm; keel broadly obovate, 4.2–5.3 × 2.8–3.5 mm; stamens (5.5–)6–8 mm; filaments distinct to 1.5–2 mm; anthers 0.5–0.7 mm. **Loments** obovoid, not strongly compressed, 2.7–2.9 mm, glabrous, glands scattered, not forming arcs. **Seeds** 2.1–2.5 mm. **2*n*** = 20 (Mexico).

Flowering late summer–early spring. Brushy hillsides, openings in oak woodlands; 1300–1500 m; Ariz.; Mexico; Central America (Guatemala).

66. DALEA Linnaeus, Opera Var., 244. 1758, name conserved • [For Samuel Dale, 1659–1739, English botanist]

David M. Sutherland

Kuhnistera Lamarck; *Parosela* Cavanilles; *Petalostemon* Michaux; *Thornbera* Rydberg

Herbs, annual or perennial, shrubs, or subshrubs, usually unarmed, rarely thorns present, usually glandular nearly throughout, rarely sparsely so. **Stems** erect, spreading, ascending, decumbent, prostrate, matted, or tufted, branched, glandular or eglandular, glabrous or pubescent, trichomes spirally twisted. **Leaves** alternate, usually odd-pinnate, rarely 3-foliolate; stipules present, caducous or persistent, deltate, ovate, or subulate; petiolate; leaflets 3–43 (–49), stipels absent, blades with 2 adaxial intrapetiolular glands and 2 abaxial postpetiolular glands often present between opposing leaflets, not lineolate, margins usually entire, rarely undulate-crenate or crenulate, surfaces usually glandular-punctate abaxially, often pubescent, sometimes glabrous. **Inflorescences** 10–500+-flowered, loosely to densely flowered, terminal, leaf-opposed, or axillary, usually spikes (sometimes headlike), rarely racemes; bracts present, caducous or persistent; bracteoles absent or glandlike, spiculiform. **Flowers** papilionaceous or not conventionally so (abaxial petals not connate or forming a keel); calyx campanulate, lobes 5, unequal or ± equal; ribs 10, usually anastomosing distally, forming closed arches, intervals between ribs usually glandular, rarely eglandular; petals (3 or)5, corollas white, pale to dark blue, lavender, pink, rose, blue-violet, magenta-purple, or bicolored; banner reflexed, sometimes as much as 90°, claw slender, shorter to longer than blade; other petals epistemonous, attached to stamen tube at varying levels, petals usually similar, sometimes differentiated into wings and keel; wings, if differentiated, not adnate to keel petals; keel, if differentiated, distinct, connate by overlapping margins, or valvately coherent to form conventional keel, blunt-tipped; stamens usually 5, 9, or 10, rarely 4 or 6–8, monadelphous, ± uniform, rarely only 3–6 fertile; anthers dorsifixed; style glabrous or pilosulous; ovules 2. **Fruits** legumes, sessile, mostly tan, usually ± compressed, obliquely ovoid or semiorbicular, usually indehiscent, sometimes tardily dehiscent, pericarp often membranaceous proximally, thickened distally, usually gland-dotted, usually glabrous or pilosulous, sometimes glabrate, villosulous, pilose, or glabrescent. **Seed** 1, brownish, tan, chestnut, or greenish, somewhat compressed, asymmetrically reniform. x = 7, 8.

Species ca. 170 (58 in the flora): North America, Mexico, West Indies, Central America, South America.

Dalea is found from south-central Canada throughout much of the United States; it does not occur west of the Sierra Nevada and Cascade mountains. This treatment follows closely the treatment by R. C. Barneby (1977c). Barneby placed the 58 species in the flora area in three subgenera and nine sections: subg. *Theodora* Barneby was divided into two sections, *Theodora* (spp. 1–3) and *Lachnostachyae* (Rydberg) Barneby (spp. 4); subg. *Dalea* contained three sections,

Thornbera (Rydberg) Barneby (spp. 5 and 6), *Dalea* (spp. 7–14), and *Kuhnistera* (Lamarck) Barneby (spp. 15–37); and subg. *Parosela* (Cavanilles) Barneby included three sections, sect. *Parosela* (Cavanilles) Barneby (spp. 39–49), sect. *Psoropogon* Barneby (spp. 50–52), and sect. *Cylipogon* (Rafinesque) Barneby (spp. 53–58).

Species that R. C. Barneby (1977c) assigned to sect. *Kuhnistera* had been monographed by D. K. Wemple (1970) as the genus *Petalostemon.* Barneby followed Wemple closely in the delimitation of taxa, although he recognized some of the species treated by Wemple only at the varietal level and felt unable to continue recognition of *Petalostemon* as a separate genus. The characteristics that define *Petalostemon* all occur separately or in combination in other species of *Dalea.* If *Petalostemon* is recognized, some species, such as *D. obovata* and several species related to *D. exigua*, become controversial in their placement.

Dalea shares with *Marina* a unique placement of the inner two pairs of petals, which have migrated out on a tubular disc and appear to perch on the stamen tubes. The two genera are separated morphologically by well-correlated features including ovule number (two in *Dalea*, one in *Marina*, both developing one seed), the basic chromosome number (seven in *Dalea*, ten in *Marina*), the structure of the trichomes (flexuous, spirally twisted when long and changing color in drying in *Dalea*, stiff, short, and unchanged by drying in *Marina*), the presence (in *Marina*) or absence (in *Dalea*) of sinuous lines (lineoles) on the leaflets, and the calyx rib architecture (anastomosing in the lobes in *Dalea* but not in *Marina*).

In the key and descriptions, leaflet numbers are for leaflets of principal leaves, diameters of inflorescences exclude corollas, indument of calyx is external unless otherwise indicated, and glands on calyx tubes "between ribs" refers to pairs of adjacent ribs.

SELECTED REFERENCES Barneby, R. C. 1977c. *Dalea.* Mem. New York Bot. Gard. 27: 135–592. Wemple, D. K. 1970. Revision of the genus *Petalostemon* (Leguminosae). Iowa State J. Sci. 45: 1–102.

1. Corollas papilionaceous (2 abaxial petals connate into a conventional keel enclosing stamens).
    2. Keel petals connate by overlapping margins; inflorescences densely flowered racemes.
        3. Banners 5.7–7.6 mm; corollas dark blue or blue-violet . . . . 4. *Dalea lachnostachys*
        3. Banners 2.8–5.6 mm; corollas whitish, often lilac- or violet-tinged.
            4. Perennial herbs; keel petals persistent, remaining attached to stamen column . . . . 1. *Dalea neomexicana*
            4. Annual herbs, sometimes appearing perennial; keel petals detaching from stamen column after anthesis.
                5. Calyx tube 1.6–2.5 mm, lobes shorter than exserted keel; leaflet blade margins ± entire to obscurely undulate . . . . 2. *Dalea mollis*
                5. Calyx tube 2.5–3.3 mm, lobes exceeding keel; leaflet blade margins undulate-crenate . . . . 3. *Dalea mollissima*
    2. Keel petals connate valvately; inflorescences loosely or densely flowered spikes.
        6. Corollas opening yellow, sometimes brownish, purplish, pinkish, reddish, or orangish in age.
            7. Annual herbs; leaves and stems glabrous . . . . 48. *Dalea brachystachys*
            7. Perennial herbs; leaves and stems pubescent.
                8. Leaflets usually 5.
                    9. Bracts 6–12 mm; calyces (8.5–)9–12.3 mm . . . . 55. *Dalea wrightii*
                    9. Bracts 2.5–5.5 mm; calyces 4.5–7.4(–7.5) mm.
                        10. Banners (4–)4.4–5.5 mm; keel blades 2.9–4.8 mm; spikes 7–13 (–15) mm diam. . . . . 53. *Dalea nana*
                        10. Banners 6.3–8.6 mm; keel blades (4.7–)5–7 mm; spike (12–)14–21 mm diam. . . . . 54. *Dalea aurea*

8. Leaflets usually 3.
 11. Keel blades 3.2–4 mm; spikes densely flowered; axis not visible at anthesis . . . . 58. *Dalea laniceps*
 11. Keel blades 5.2–6.4 mm; spikes densely to loosely flowered; axis sometimes partially visible at anthesis.
  12. Calyces (5.1–)5.5–7.8 mm; leaflet blades linear-elliptic to linear; c, nc Texas . . . . 56. *Dalea hallii*
  12. Calyces (8.3–)8.5–12(–13.3) mm; leaflet blades obovate to broadly oblanceolate; w Texas to Arizona, Colorado, Kansas, New Mexico, Oklahoma . . . . 57. *Dalea jamesii*

[6. Shifted to left margin.—Ed.]

6. Corollas not predominantly yellow, sometimes banner yellowish or with yellow center.
 13. Annual herbs; leaflets 3 or 5, blades linear-filiform . . . . 49. *Dalea filiformis*
 13. Perennial herbs, shrubs, or subshrubs; leaflets usually 5–35, rarely 3 (in *D. enneandra*, *D. lasiathera*, and *D. pogonathera*), blades usually obovate to oblanceolate, oblong to elliptic, or ovate, rarely linear-oblanceolate.
  14. Corollas, including banner, opening white to cream or greenish, sometimes becoming brownish or maroon in age.
   15. Perennial herbs; stamens 9; spikes remotely flowered, axes (1–)2.5–12 cm. . . . . 52. *Dalea enneandra*
   15. Shrubs or subshrubs; stamens 10; spikes loosely flowered (but flowers not remote), axes 0.2–2(–3) cm.
    16. Leaflets 15–23 (or 25); stamens (6.2–)6.5–8.5 mm; calyx lobes triangular-aristate and abaxial not uncinate . . . . 46. *Dalea carthagenensis*
    16. Leaflets 7–11; stamens 4.3–5.5 mm; calyx lobes triangular-aristate and abaxial becoming uncinate. . . . . 47. *Dalea scandens*
  14. Corollas usually opening pink to magenta or purple to violet, rarely all white (in *D. frutescens*), banner often white to yellowish or marked with a pale, yellowish, or greenish center, sometimes reddish in age.
   17. Corollas not opening bicolored, banner sometimes with yellowish or greenish center; herbs.
    18. Calyx tube 2.6–3.4 mm, lobes triangular-aristate, becoming plumose; leaflets (3 or)5 or 7 . . . . 50. *Dalea pogonathera*
    18. Calyx tube 3.3–3.9 mm, lobes triangular-subulate, pilosulous, not plumose; leaflets (3–)7–11. . . . . 51. *Dalea lasiathera*
   17. Corollas usually opening bicolored, rarely white (in *D. frutescens*), banner whitish to yellowish, epistemonous petals pink, rose, magenta, purple, or violet; shrubs or subshrubs.
    19. Calyces glabrous . . . . 39. *Dalea frutescens*
    19. Calyces sparsely to densely pubescent.
     20. Calyx tube with inconspicuous glands (0–2), when present, then minute in intervals between calyx ribs), lobes each with several elongated, pricklelike glands . . . . 43. *Dalea tentaculoides*
     20. Calyx tube with obvious blister glands between ribs, lobes without gland spurs, or with a few inconspicuous blister glands.
      21. Subshrubs, mat-forming, stems procumbent or arching (often rooting along stems); bracts persistent . . . . 40. *Dalea greggii*
      21. Shrubs or subshrubs, not mat-forming, stems relatively erect; bracts early or tardily deciduous or persistent.
       22. Calyces (7.5–)8.5–13.5(–16.2) mm. . . . . 45. *Dalea formosa*
       22. Calyces (3.5–)3.8–7.2 mm.
        23. Spikes involucrate; leaflets 5 or 7(or 9) . . . . 41. *Dalea pulchra*
        23. Spikes not involucrate; leaflets (5 or)7–19.

24. Stems prominently tuberculate or verrucose distally; calyx tube length greater than ½ of overall calyx; sc New Mexico to w Texas . . . . 42. *Dalea bicolor*
24. Stems eglandular to glandular-verruculose distally; calyx tube length ½ or less of overall calyx; se Arizona to sw New Mexico . . . . 44. *Dalea versicolor*

1. Corollas not conventionally papilionaceous (2 abaxial petals usually distinct, rarely weakly adherent, not connate into a conventional keel enclosing stamens).
    25. Annual herbs.
        26. Bracts persistent through anthesis; fertile stamens 3–6.
            27. Calyx tube with 4–7 blister glands between ribs; spikes 8.5–10.5(–11) mm diam.; leaflets (5–)11–17 . . . . 10. *Dalea emarginata* (in part)
            27. Calyx tube with 0 or 1 (or 2) blister glands between ribs; spikes 5–8(–9) mm diam.; leaflets 3–7 (or 9).
                28. Calyx tube eglandular; leaflets usually 3 or 5. . . . . 9. *Dalea exigua*
                28. Calyx tube with 1 (or 2) blister glands between ribs; leaflets usually 5 or 7 . . . . 11. *Dalea polygonoides*
        26. Bracts deciduous by anthesis; fertile stamens 7–10.
            29. Stamens (7.5–)8–11 mm; blades of epistemonous petals (2–)3–5 mm; rare in extreme se Arizona. . . . . 13. *Dalea exserta*
            29. Stamens 4.2–6.8 mm; blades of epistemonous petals 1.3–2.4(–2.6) mm; widespread or restricted to ec Arizona, adjacent New Mexico.
                30. Calyx pilose or pilosulous, tube (1.7–)2–2.5(–2.8) mm; epistemonous petals 4; widespread. . . . . 12. *Dalea leporina*
                30. Calyx glabrous, except lobes, tube (2.4–)2.6–3.4(–4.5) mm; epistemonous petals 2; restricted to a small region of ec Arizona, adjacent New Mexico . . . . 14. *Dalea urceolata*
    25. Perrenial herbs (sometimes short-lived), subshrubs, or shrubs.
        31. Stamens (8–)10.
            32. Banners: blade ± peltate, ± cucullate; stamens 8–10 (sometimes only 5 functional); herbs prostrate, always growing in sand . . . . .38. *Dalea lanata*
            32. Banners plane, blade not peltate; stamens 10; herbs erect, often growing on rocky hillsides, canyons, woodlands, not always in sand.
                33. Herbs silky-villosulous or pilosulous to puberulent throughout (especially near base).
                    34. Calyces pilosulous; epistemonous petals attached near tip of stamen tube; corollas white. . . . . 5. *Dalea albiflora*
                    34. Calyces glabrate or pubescent distally; epistemonous petals attached near middle of stamen tube; corollas white or epistemonous petals blue or bluish . . . . .6. *Dalea lumholtzii*
                33. Herbs glabrous proximal to inflorescences.
                    35. Corollas white or whitish, banner reddish or purplish in age; spikes 7–9 mm diam.. . . . . .7. *Dalea grayi*
                    35. Corollas bright purple or banner whitish (lilac-tinged); spikes 8–12 mm diam.. . . . . .8. *Dalea pringlei*
        31. Stamens 5.
            36. Spikes (12–)14–20 mm diam.; corollas white . . . . 15. *Dalea obovata*
            36. Spikes mostly 5.5–14(–16) mm diam.; corollas magenta-, rose-, lavender-, or lilac-purple, rose-lilac, lavender, pink, pinkish tan, or white (if spikes greater than 14 mm diam., corollas rose-lilac or rose-purple).
                37. Stamens 3.8–4.6 mm, filaments distinct to 0.9–1.2 mm . . . . . . 10. *Dalea emarginata* (in part)
                37. Stamens 5–12(–12.7) mm, filaments distinct to 2.2–7.6(–8.7) mm.

38. Spikes conspicuously involucrate (subtended by sterile bracts, some transitional to leaves proximally), appearing capitate; calyx tube eglandular, pilose. . . . . .37. *Dalea pinnata*
38. Spikes not involucrate or not obviously so (when involucrate, bracts not transitional to leaves proximally), not appearing capitate; calyx tube glandular or eglandular, glabrous or pubescent.
[39. Shifted to left margin.—Ed.]

39. Leaflets (7 or) 9–41(–49).
    40. Corollas white; calyx tube with 1–7 blister glands between ribs.
        41. Spike axis (1.5–)2.5–9(–13) cm; leaflets 13–41(–49) . . . . 23. *Dalea phleoides*
        41. Spikes appearing nearly globose, axis 0.4–1(–1.2) cm; leaflets (7 or)9 or 11(or 13) . . . . .26. *Dalea multiflora* (in part)
    40. Corollas usually pink, rose, rose-purple, lavender or lavender-purple, rarely white; calyx tube eglandular between ribs.
        42. Calyx tube densely pilosulous, including lobes . . . . 29. *Dalea villosa*
        42. Calyx tube glabrous, lobes sometimes pilosulous.
            43. Spike axis partially visible at anthesis, 4–9 cm; leaflets 11–17; rare in Bandera, Uvalde, and Val Verde counties, Texas . . . . .22. *Dalea sabinalis*
            43. Spike axis not visible at anthesis, 1.5–4.5 cm; leaflets 19–29(or 31); rare in Alabama, Illinois, Tennessee. . . . . 24. *Dalea foliosa*

39. Leaflets 3–9.
    44. Calyx tube without blister glands between ribs; leaflet blades linear to linear-oblanceolate, linear-oblong, or linear-elliptic.
        45. Spikes densely flowered, axis not visible; bracts persistent through anthesis.
            46. Calyces (4.4–)5–6.2 mm, pilosulous, with lines of antrorse, subappressed hairs proximal to sinuses and on margins of lobes . . . . .31. *Dalea compacta*
            46. Calyces 3–5(–5.2) mm, pubescence not restricted to lines, or, if partly restricted, then hairs near base of calyx retrorse.
                47. Calyces with antrorse hairs at base . . . . 30. *Dalea purpurea*
                47. Calyces with retrorse or tangled hairs at base.
                    48. Calyx base with retrorse hairs; legumes glabrous or apically ± pilosulous; c, n Texas, adjacent Oklahoma. . . . . .32. *Dalea tenuis*
                    48. Calyx base with intertangled hairs; legumes tomentulose on distal ⅔; Bibb County, Alabama . . . . 33. *Dalea cahaba*
        45. Spikes loosely to moderately densely flowered, axis partially visible, at least at anthesis; bracts usually deciduous by anthesis, sometimes held between calyces (proximals persistent in *D. gattingeri*).
            49. Leaflets 7 or 9; calyx with ribs leading to sinuses stronger than those leading to lobes so that calyx tube bluntly 5-angled in cross section. . . . . .34. *Dalea reverchonii*
            49. Leaflets usually 3–7, rarely 9 (in *D. gattingeri*); calyx prominently to indistinctly 10-ribbed, tube ± circular in cross section.
                50. Leaflets 5 or 7 (or 9); stems proximally glabrous or glabrescent, distally usually sparsely pilosulous; Alabama, Arkansas, Georgia, Missouri, Tennessee. . . . . 35. *Dalea gattingeri*
                50. Leaflets 3 or 5; stems pilosulous proximally, distally usually glabrescent; Colorado, Kansas, New Mexico, Oklahoma, Texas. . . . . 36. *Dalea tenuifolia*
    44. Calyx tube usually with 1–several blister glands between ribs; leaflet blades oblanceolate to oblong-elliptic, obovate, oblong-obovate, obovate-cuneate, elliptic, or linear, sometimes glands absent or inconspicuous, then leaflet blades elliptic, oblanceolate, obovate, or oblong-elliptic.
        51. Calyx usually pilose to pilosulous, sometimes glabrous (in *D. searlsiae*).
            52. Spikes 13–16 mm diam. . . . . 17. *Dalea ornata*
            52. Spikes 6–12(–13) mm diam.

53. Calyces subsymmetric, not recessed opposite banner; spike axis (1–) 1.5–5.5(–7.5) cm . . . . 25. *Dalea candida* (in part)
53. Calyces asymmetric, slightly to deeply recessed opposite banner; spike axis (1–)2–18 cm (when calyx slightly recessed, then spike axis, at least those terminating main stems, 9–18 cm).
    54. Calyces slightly recessed opposite banners; axis of longest terminal spikes often 9–18 cm. . . . . 16. *Dalea cylindriceps*
    54. Calyces deeply recessed opposite banners; axis of spikes mostly 2–9 cm.
        55. Corollas white, ochroleucous when dry; spike axis not visible at anthesis; ne, e Arizona, s, c Utah. . . . . 18. *Dalea flavescens*
        55. Corollas usually rose-purple, rarely white; spike axis partially visible at anthesis; nw Arizona, w California, Nevada, w Utah . . . . 19. *Dalea searlsiae* (in part)

[51. Shifted to left margin.—Ed.]

51. Calyx glabrous, sometimes lobes ciliolate, or, sometimes, pilosulous (in *D. candida*).
    56. Calyx with 3+ blister glands between ribs and glands scattered or in more than 1 row in spaces between adaxial ribs.
        57. Corollas pale pink to rose-purple; spike axis 1.5–9(–13) cm, usually partially visible at anthesis; from near Albuquerque and Belen, New Mexico . . . . 20. *Dalea scariosa*
        57. Corollas white; spike axis 0.3–1.4 cm, not visible at anthesis; from a small region in w Texas . . . . 21. *Dalea bartonii*
    56. Calyx usually with (0 or) 1–4 blister glands between ribs.
        58. Calyx not deeply recessed opposite banner (opening not oblique); corollas white.
            59. Leaflets 5–9; spikes cylindric, axis (1–)1.5–5.5(–7.5) cm . . . . 25. *Dalea candida* (in part)
            59. Leaflets (7 or)9 or 11(or 13); spikes nearly globose, axis 0.4–1(–1.2) cm . . . . 26. *Dalea multiflora* (in part)
        58. Calyx deeply recessed opposite banner (opening oblique); corollas pink, lavender, rose-purple, pinkish tan, or white.
            60. Leaflet blades linear, involute . . . . 28. *Dalea feayi*
            60. Leaflet blades elliptic to oblanceolate or obovate, flat or folded.
                61. Spikes (8–)9–11 mm diam., axis partially visible at anthesis, (1.5–)2–9 (–14) cm; nw Arizona, w California, Nevada to w Utah . . . . 19. *Dalea searlsiae* (in part)
                61. Spikes 7–10 mm diam., axis not visible at anthesis, 0.5–3(–3.5) cm; Alabama, Florida, Georgia, w Louisiana to Mississippi . . . . 27. *Dalea carnea*

1. Dalea neomexicana (A. Gray) Cory, Rhodora 38: 406. 1936

Dalea mollis Bentham var. *neomexicana* A. Gray, Smithsonian Contr. Knowl. 3(5): 47. 1852 (as neo-mexicana)

Perennial herbs, matted or tufted, gray-silky pubescent. **Stems** 0.3–3.5 dm, sparsely to densely glandular-pustulate. **Principal leaves** 0.8–4.5 cm; leaflets 7–15, blades cuneate-obcordate to obovate or elliptic-ovate, 2.5–8 mm, margins entire or undulate-crenate. **Peduncles** 0.3–0.4 cm. **Inflorescences** racemes, spikelike, densely flowered, not involucrate, 1.3–1.6 mm diam.; axis not visible, 1–6 cm; bracts soon deciduous, 2–6 mm. **Calyces** ± symmetric, 4.2–8 mm, densely pilose; tube 2.1–3.1 mm, with 5–7(–9) glands between ribs, lobes triangular-aristate or plumose. **Corollas** bicolored, banner whitish, violet-tinged, other petals white or whitish; papilionaceous; banner 4–5.6 mm, blades ± cordate, (2.8–)3–3.7 × 2.3–3.4 mm; epistemonous petals attached proximal to middle of stamen tube; wings 2.4–3.3 × 1.3–1.8 mm; keel persistent, remaining attached to stamen column, connate by overlapping margins, blades 2.4–3.5 × 1.8–2.2 mm. **Stamens** 10, 5–6.7 mm, filaments distinct to 2.4 mm, anthers 0.5–0.7(–1) mm. **Legumes** 1.2–3 mm, pilose distally, eglandular. **Seeds** 1.7–2.4 mm.

Varieties 3 (2 in the flora): sw United States, n Mexico.

Dalea neomexicana somewhat resembles *Marina calycosa* in habit and overall appearance. It is sometimes confused also with *D. mollis* and *D. mollissima*, since the annual nature of those species is not always apparent in well-developed plants.

Variety *megaladenia* Barneby is known from northern Mexico in the states of Chihuahua, Coahuila, and Durango.

1. Leaflet blades cuneate-obcordate, margins usually undulate-crenulate . . . . 1a. *Dalea neomexicana* var. *neomexicana*
1. Leaflet blades obovate or elliptic-ovate, margins usually entire. . . . . 1b. *Dalea neomexicana* var. *longipila*

1a. Dalea neomexicana (A. Gray) Cory var. **neomexicana**

Leaflet blades cuneate-obcordate, margins usually undulate-crenulate, submarginal glands to 0.2–0.3 mm wide. **2*n*** = 16.

Flowering spring–early summer (fall). Rocky hills and washes in arid grasslands; 700–1800 m; Ariz., N.Mex., Tex.; Mexico (Chihuahua, Coahuila, Sonora).

In Texas, var. *neomexicana* is known from the trans-Pecos and Big Bend regions.

1b. Dalea neomexicana (A. Gray) Cory var. **longipila** (Rydberg) Barneby, Mem. New York Bot. Gard. 27: 159. 1977 (as neo-mexicana)

Parosela longipila Rydberg in N. L. Britton et al., N. Amer. Fl. 24: 64. 1919; *Dalea longipila* (Rydberg) Cory

Leaflet blades obovate or elliptic-ovate, margins usually entire, submarginal glands to 0.1–0.2 mm wide.

Flowering spring (fall). Stony hills, limestone soils; 300–1800 m; Tex.; Mexico (Coahuila, Nuevo León, Tamaulipas).

In Texas, var. *longipila* is known from the trans-Pecos and Big Bend regions.

2. Dalea mollis Bentham, Pl. Hartw., 306. 1849

Annual herbs, prostrate or decumbent, ± pilose or pilosulous. **Stems** 1–3.5(–6.5) dm, glandular-tuberculate. **Principal leaves** (0.5–)1–3.5 cm; leaflets (7 or) 9–13 (or 15), blades obovate to obcordate, (2–)3–8 mm, margins ± entire or obscurely undulate. **Peduncles** 0.2–2.5(–4.5) cm. **Inflorescences** racemes, ± densely flowered, pedicels with black, prickleshaped glands at base and toward apex, not involucrate, 8–14 mm diam.; axis not visible, (0.5–)1–3.5 cm; bracts deciduous, (3–)4.5–8 mm. **Calyces** ± symmetric, 3.3–6.6 mm, pilose; tube 1.6–2.5 mm, with (1 or)2–6 glands between ribs, lobes triangular or triangular-aristate. **Corollas** whitish, banner and keel sometimes lilac-tinged; papilionaceous; banner 3–4.2 mm, blades broadly triangular to suborbiculate-cordate, (1.5–)1.7–2.9 × 2.2–3.2 mm; epistemonous petals attached near or proximal to middle of stamen tube; wings 2.1–3 × 1.1–1.4 mm; keel detaching from stamen tube after anthesis, connate by overlapping margins, blades 2.3–3.4 × 1.4–2 mm. **Stamens** 10, 3.5–5.7 mm, filaments distinct to 2 mm, anthers 0.4–0.6 mm. **Legumes** 2.2–2.7 mm, pilosulous distally and dotted with small glands. **Seeds** 1.8–2.2 mm. **2*n*** = 16 [Mexico].

Flowering late winter–mid spring (fall–early winter). Sandy or rocky desert slopes, flats, roadsides; -50–700 m; Ariz., Calif., Nev.; Mexico (Baja California, Baja California Sur, Coahuila, Sonora).

Some collectors assume that *Dalea mollis* is perennial; the season of bloom can be long in a good year, and individual plants can be robust. Most of the fall and early-winter plants are collected in early bloom; an occasional plant from that time-period is taken in late bloom. *Dalea mollis* is similar to *D. mollissima* and mixed collections are relatively common. In California, *D. mollis* is known from the desert regions in the southeastern part of the state.

3. Dalea mollissima (Rydberg) Munz, Aliso 4: 93. 1958

Parosela mollissima Rydberg in N. L. Britton et al., N. Amer. Fl. 24: 64. 1919

Annual herbs, prostrate or decumbent, ± pilose or pilosulous. **Stems** 0.5–3.5 dm, glandular-tuberculate. **Principal leaves** 2–4 cm; leaflets 9–15, blades cuneate-obovate, 3–9(–10) mm, margins undulate-crenate. **Peduncles** 0.2–2.5(–4.5) cm. **Inflorescences** racemes, spikelike, densely flowered, not involucrate, (12–)13–16(–17) mm diam.; axis not visible, 1.5–7.5 cm; bracts deciduous, 4.5–7 mm. **Calyces** ± symmetric, (5.8–)6.1–8.2 mm, pilose; tube (2.5–)2.7–3.3 mm, with (3 or)4–7 glands between ribs, lobes triangular or triangular-aristate. **Corollas** whitish, banner sometimes lilac-tinged, keel tip sometimes lilac-tinged; papilionaceous; banner 2.8–3.7 mm, blade broadly triangular to suborbiculate-cordate, (1.6–)1.8–2.2 × (1.4–)1.7–2.2 mm; epistemonous petals attached proximal to middle of stamen tube; wings 1.8–2.1 × 1.1–1.3 mm; keel detaching from stamen column after anthesis, connate by overlapping margins, blades 2.6–2.9 × 1.5–1.8 mm. **Stamens** 10, 4.3–5 mm, filaments distinct to 1 mm, anthers 0.4–0.5 mm. **Legumes** 2.4–3 mm, pilosulous distally and dotted with small glands. **Seeds** 1.8–2.2 mm. **2*n*** = 16.

Flowering early spring(–fall, winter). Sandy or rocky desert slopes, flats, roadsides; 0–900 m; Ariz., Calif., Nev., Tex.; Mexico (Baja California).

Although *Dalea mollissima* normally blooms early in the spring, with adequate summer moisture it germinates in fall and winters over, so that individual plants can be large and may be mistaken as perennial. It resembles *D. mollis*, with which it overlaps in range, and may be collected with that species. Cuneate-obovate and undulate-margined leaves of *D. mollissima* resemble those of *D. neomexicana*, leading to further confusion among herbarium specimens. In California, *D. mollissima* is known only from the desert regions in the southeastern part of the state.

4. **Dalea lachnostachys** A. Gray, Smithsonian Contr. Knowl. 3(5): 46. 1852

Perennial herbs, erect, ± pilosulous. **Stems** 1.5–4 dm, black-warty. **Principal leaves** 3–8 (–9.5) cm; leaflets (5 or) 7 or 9 (or 11), blades obovate, (5–)7–17 mm, margins entire or ± crenulate, surfaces glandular-pustulate around margins abaxially. **Peduncles** 1–8(–11) cm. **Inflorescences** racemes, spikelike, relatively densely flowered, not involucrate, (15–)16–19(–20) mm diam.; axis usually not visible, 2.5–5 cm; bracts deciduous, 7–11 mm. **Calyces** ± symmetric, (4.3–)5.8–7.7 mm, pilose; tube 2.6–3.1 mm, with 3 or 4 small glands between ribs, lobes triangular-aristate. **Corollas** dark blue or blue-violet; papilionaceous; banner 5.7–7.6 mm, blade shallowly cordate, (3.5–)3.8–4.8 × 2.2–3.8 mm; epistemonous petals attached well proximal to middle of stamen tube; wings 3.7–5 × 1.3–1.8 mm; keel connate by overlapping margins, blades (3.8–)4–4.7 × 1.7–2.2 mm. **Stamens** 10, 6.6–8.7 mm, filaments distinct to 2.3–2.9 mm, anthers (0.5–)0.6–0.8 mm. **Legumes** (3–) 3.3–4 mm, pilosulous distally, eglandular. **Seeds** 1.8–2.4 mm. $2n = 14$.

Flowering late summer–fall. Open deserts, dry grasslands, open woodlands, sometimes on limestone; 1000–1800 m; Ariz., N.Mex., Tex.; Mexico (Chihuahua, Coahuila, Sonora).

Dalea lachnostachys occurs in southern Arizona, southwestern New Mexico, and trans-Pecos Texas.

5. **Dalea albiflora** A. Gray, Smithsonian Contr. Knowl. 5(6): 38. 1853 [F]

Dalea ordiae A. Gray

Perennial herbs, erect, ± silky-villosulous. **Stems** (2–)2.5–5 (–7) dm, sparsely gland-dotted distally. **Principal leaves** 1–4 cm; leaflets (13–)17–35(–41), blades oblanceolate to linear-elliptic, (1.5–)2–7(–10) mm. **Peduncles** 0.5–8.5 cm. **Inflorescences** spikes, densely flowered, not involucrate, 7–10 mm diam.; axis not visible, (1–)1.5–6(–7) cm; bracts early deciduous to persistent, 1.5–3.2 mm. **Calyces** asymmetric, recessed opposite banner, (2.8–) 3.2–5.1 mm, pilosulous; tube (1.9–)2–3(–3.3) mm, with 3–6 glands between ribs, lobes triangular. **Corollas** white; not conventionally papilionaceous; banner plane, (4.4–)5–6.4 mm, blade oblong-ovate, not peltate, proximally cordate to cuneate, (2.6–)3–4 × (2–)2.2–3.4 mm; epistemonous petals attached high on stamen tube, just proximal to separation of filaments, blades (2.7–)3.1–4.4 × (0.8–)1.3–1.9(–2.2) mm. **Stamens** 10, (5–)6–8 mm, filaments distinct to 3.5–4.5 mm, anthers 0.4–0.6 mm. **Legumes** 2.2–2.9 mm, villosulous distally and gland-dotted. **Seeds** 1.6–2 mm. $2n = 14, 24$.

Flowering fall (spring–summer). Open woodlands, grasslands, roadsides; 1000–2300 m; Ariz., N.Mex.; Mexico (Chihuahua, Durango, Sinaloa, Sonora).

Dalea albiflora is a complex and variable species that could use further morphological and cytological studies. While herbarium specimens cannot be sorted into varieties in any consistent way, in the field, delicate plants with slender, creeping rootstocks may grow with, and appear quite distinct from, plants with a stout caudex; such plants have been called *D. ordiae*. There are few chromosome counts available; preliminary study suggests that the former plants are tetraploid and the latter diploid (D. E. Ward et al. 1993).

6. **Dalea lumholtzii** B. L. Robinson & Fernald, Proc. Amer. Acad. Arts 30: 115. 1894

Perennial herbs, erect, pilosulous to puberulent. **Stems** 1.5–5 (–6) dm, glandular-verruculose. **Principal leaves** (2–)2.5–5 cm; leaflets (9–)21–35, blades linear, linear-oblanceolate, or linear-elliptic, (1.5–)2–9(–10) mm. **Peduncles** (1.5–)2.5–10 cm. **Inflorescences** spikes, densely flowered, not obviously involucrate, 6–8.5 mm diam.; axis not visible, 0.4–1.4(–3) cm; bracts persistent, (1.5–) 2–4 mm. **Calyces** strongly asymmetric, deeply recessed

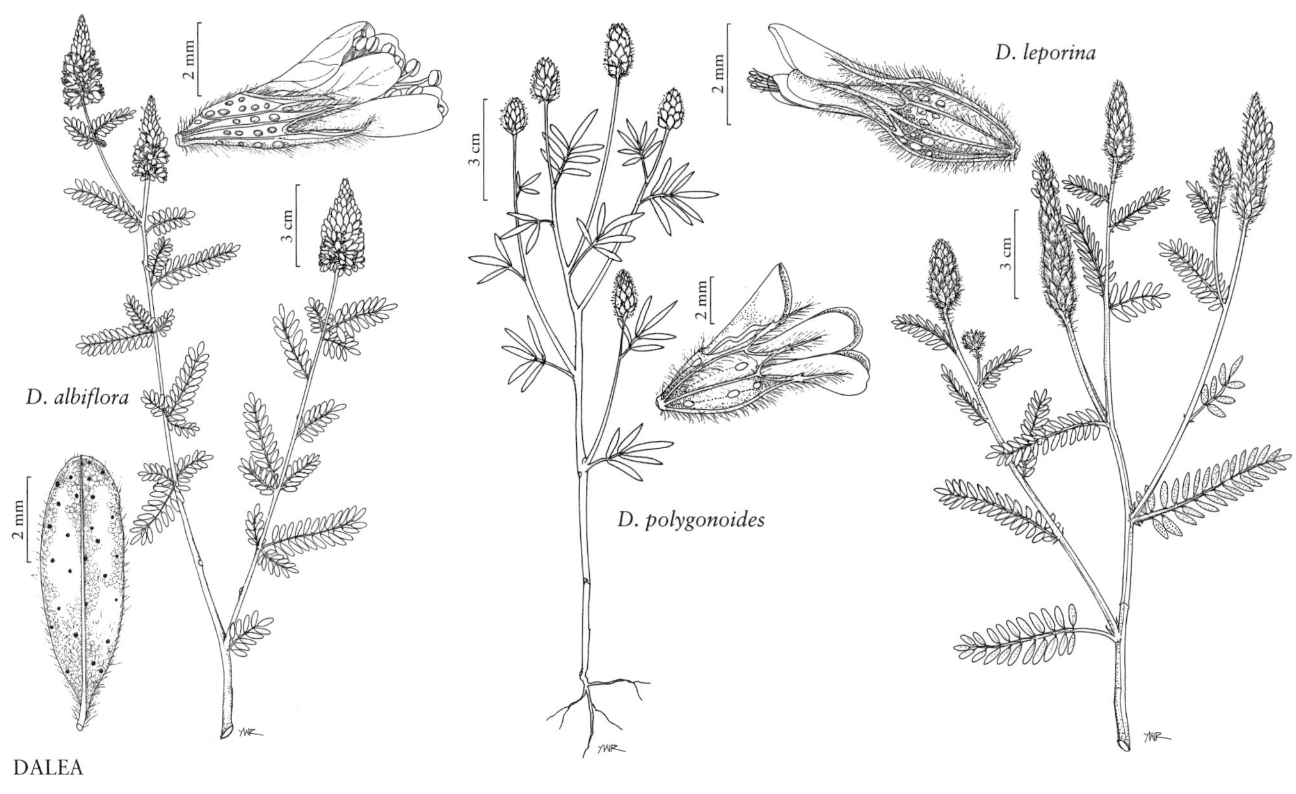

DALEA

opposite banner, 2.7–4(–4.3) mm, glabrate or pubescent distally; tube 2.1–2.8(–3) mm, with (0 or)3–6 minute glands between ribs, lobes subulate. **Corollas** white, or epistemonous petals blue or bluish; not conventionally papilionaceous; banner plane, 3–5.2 mm, blade ovate-elliptic to suborbiculate, not peltate, 2–2.4 × 2–2.4 mm; epistemonous petals attached near middle of stamen tube, blades 2.3–4 × 1.1–1.3 mm. **Stamens** 10, 5–7.7 mm, filaments distinct to 2.6–3.7 mm, anthers 0.6–0.7 mm. **Legumes** 2.2–2.6 mm, puberulent distally, eglandular. **Seeds** 1.6–1.8 mm.

Flowering fall. Open rocky hillsides and canyons, open pine or oak woodlands; 1400–1900 m; Ariz.; Mexico (Chihuahua, Sonora).

Some herbarium labels comment on the lemon odor of *Dalea lumholtzii.* Although the epistemonous petals are generally blue or bluish, white-petaled plants are not uncommon in the flora area.

7. **Dalea grayi** (Vail) L. O. Williams, Ann. Missouri Bot. Gard. 23: 450. 1936

Parosela grayi Vail, Bull. Torrey Bot. Club 24: 14. 1897, based on *Dalea laevigata* A. Gray, Smithsonian Contr. Knowl. 5(6): 38. 1853, not Sessé & Mociño ex G. Don 1832

Perennial herbs, erect, glabrous proximal to inflorescences. **Stems** (3–)3.5–7(–9) dm, eglandular or sparsely gland-dotted. **Principal leaves** 1–5 cm; leaflets (11–)17–43, blades elliptic-oblanceolate to narrowly obovate, 1–4.5(–5.5) mm. **Peduncles** 0.5–5(–10) cm. **Inflorescences** spikes, densely flowered, not involucrate, 7–9 mm diam.; axis not visible, (0.4–)0.7–5.5(–7) cm; bracts persistent, (2.2–)2.5–4.5 mm. **Calyces** subsymmetric, 3.6–4.8(–5.2) mm, silky-pilosulous; tube 2–2.7 mm, with 3–6 glands between ribs, lobes triangular-acuminate to -aristate. **Corollas** white or whitish, banner reddish or purplish in age; not conventionally papilionaceous; banner plane, 4–5.7 mm, blade triangular-cordate to rhombic-ovate, not peltate, 1.6–2.5 × 2–2.4 mm; epistemonous petals attached high on stamen tube, just proximal to separation of filaments, blades 2.2–3.1 × 0.8–1.4 mm. **Stamens** 10, 5.5–7 mm, filaments distinct to 2.7–4 mm, anthers 0.5–0.7 mm. **Legumes** 2.2–2.5 mm, villosulous distally and dotted with small glands. **Seeds** 1.6 mm. **2*n*** = 14.

Flowering fall (spring–summer). Rocky slopes, washes, canyons, open pine or oak woodlands; 700–2200 m; Ariz., N.Mex.; Mexico (Chihuahua, Durango, Sinaloa, Sonora).

Dalea grayi occurs in southeastern Arizona as far northwest as Gila County and far southwestern New Mexico (Grant and Hidalgo counties).

8. Dalea pringlei A. Gray, Proc. Amer. Acad. Arts 17: 201. 1882

Varieties 3 (1 in the flora): sw United States, n Mexico.

Two varieties of *Dalea pringlei* occur in Mexico. Variety *multijuga* Barneby is found in Chihuahua, Sinaloa, and Sonora, while var. *oxyphyllidia* Barneby is restricted to the Río Mayo area of Sonora.

8a. Dalea pringlei A. Gray var. **pringlei**

Perennial herbs, erect, glabrous proximal to inflorescences. **Stems** (1.5–)2–6(–8) dm, minutely gland-dotted. **Principal leaves** 1.5–4.5(–5.5) cm; leaflets 13–29, blades ovate to elliptic, 1–15 mm. **Peduncles** 1–6 cm. **Inflorescences** spikes, somewhat loosely flowered, not involucrate, 8–12 mm diam.; axis partially visible, (1–)1.5–6.5(–9) cm; bracts persistent, 2–2.5 mm. **Calyces** subsymmetric, (3.5–)4.3–6.1(–6.5) mm, silky-pilose; tube 1.7–2.5(–2.7) mm, with 3–6(or 7) glands between ribs, lobes triangular-acuminate. **Corollas** purple, banner sometimes whitish (lilac-tinged); not conventionally papilionaceous; banner plane, 2–5.1 mm, blade cordate to rhombic, not peltate, 1.2–2 × 1.2–2.4 mm; epistemonous petals attached high on stamen tube, at or just proximal to separation of filaments, blades 1.7–2.6 × 0.8–1.5 mm. **Stamens** 10, 5.5–7 mm, filaments distinct to 2.2–3.2 mm, anthers 0.5–0.6 mm. **Legumes** 2.5–3 mm, villosulous distally and dotted with small glands. **Seeds** 1.7–2.2 mm. **2*n*** = 14.

Flowering spring, fall. Rocky slopes, canyons, desert scrub; 800–1200 m; Ariz.; Mexico (Sonora).

Variety *pringlei* occurs in southeastern Arizona in Cochise, Pima, and Santa Cruz counties.

9. Dalea exigua Barneby, Mem. New York Bot. Gard. 27: 200. 1977

Petalostemon exilis A. Gray, Smithsonian Contr. Knowl. 5(6): 41. 1853, not *Dalea exilis* de Candolle 1825

Annual herbs, erect, glabrate. **Stems** 1–4(–4.5) dm, eglandular or weakly gland-dotted. **Principal leaves** 1.5–5.5 cm; leaflets 3 or 5, blades linear-oblanceolate to -elliptic, (0.5–)1–3.7(–4) cm. **Peduncles** (2.5–)4–16 cm. **Inflorescences** spikes, densely flowered, not involucrate, 5–8 mm diam.; axis not visible, (0.8–)1.3–4.5(–6) cm; bracts persistent through anthesis, 2.5–3.3 mm. **Calyces** asymmetric, recessed opposite banner, 3.8–4.3 mm, silky-pilose; tube 1.9–2.2 mm, with 0 glands between ribs, lobes triangular-aristate. **Corollas** lavender or pink-purple; not conventionally papilionaceous; banner 3.4–4.2 mm, blade ovate, 1.3–1.6 × 1–1.2 mm; epistemonous petals attached high on stamen tube, just proximal to separation of filaments, blades 1.7–2.3 × 0.9–1.1 mm. **Stamens** 4–7, 3–6 fertile, 3.2–4 mm, filaments distinct to 1 mm, anthers 0.2–0.3 mm. **Legumes** 2.5 mm, pilosulous distally, eglandular. **Seeds** 1.9–2.3 mm.

Flowering fall. Grassy slopes, roadsides, open oak, juniper, or pine woodlands; 1500–2400 m; Ariz., N.Mex.; Mexico (Chihuahua, Sonora).

Dalea exigua occurs in southeastern Arizona (Cochise, Pima, and Santa Cruz counties) and adjacent southwestern New Mexico. A disjunct population occurs in McKinley County, New Mexico.

10. Dalea emarginata (Torrey & A. Gray) Shinners, Field & Lab. 17: 84. 1949

Petalostemon emarginatus Torrey & A. Gray, Fl. N. Amer. 1: 311. 1838 (as emarginatum)

Annual herbs (sometimes overwintering), erect, ± glabrous proximal to inflorescence. **Stems** (1.5–)2–6 dm, with scattered, small, raised glands distally. **Principal leaves** (1–)1.5–3.5 cm; leaflets (5–)11–17, blades oblong-oblanceolate or obovate, 4–9 mm. **Peduncles** (6–)10–35(–40) cm. **Inflorescences** spikes, densely flowered, inconspicuously involucrate (lowest bracts not subtending flowers), 8.5–10.5(–11) mm diam.; axis not visible, 1–4(–4.5) cm; bracts persistent through anthesis, 1–2.5 mm. **Calyces** asymmetric, recessed opposite banner, 3–4.2 mm, densely pilosulous; tube 1.8–2.2 mm, with 4–7 blister glands between ribs, lobes ovate. **Corollas** magenta-purple; not conventionally papilionaceous; banner 3.8–4.4 mm, blade ovate, 1.8 × 1.2 mm; epistemonous petals attached at or abaxial pair just proximal to filament separation, blades 1.6–2 × 0.5–0.9 mm. **Stamens** 5, sometimes with vestiges of alternate filaments, 3.8–4.6 mm, filaments distinct to 0.9–1.2 mm, anthers 0.5 mm. **Legumes** 2.4–2.8 mm, pilosulous distally and gland-dotted. **Seeds** 1.6–1.9 mm.

Flowering fall–winter. Beaches, dunes, sandy soils; 0–200 m; La., Tex.; Mexico (Tamaulipas, Veracruz).

Dalea emarginata was first described under *Petalostemon* but was rejected from that genus by D. K. Wemple (1970) because of its annual habit. R. C. Barneby (1977c) considered it to be taxonomically isolated within *Dalea*. Adaxial surfaces of the leaflets often become a remarkable blue-green in drying, a trait observed also in several other daleas that were placed in *Petalostemon* and in the evidently distantly related yellow-petaled *D. nana*. In Texas, *D. emarginata* is known from the southern half of the state, east of the Big Bend region.

11. Dalea polygonoides A. Gray, Smithsonian Contr. Knowl. 5(6): 39. 1853 [F]

Annual herbs, erect, glabrous proximal to inflorescences. **Stems** 0.5–3 dm, sparsely glandular-verruculose distally. **Principal leaves** (0.7–)1–3 cm; leaflets (3 or) 5 or 7 (or 9), blades oblong-oblanceolate, 5–12(–15) mm. **Peduncles** 1.5–7 (–15) cm. **Inflorescences** spikes, relatively densely flowered, not obviously involucrate, 5.5–8(–9) mm diam.; axis usually not visible, (0.5–)0.8–2.5(–3) cm; bracts persistent through anthesis, 2–4 mm. **Calyces** asymmetric, recessed opposite banner, 2.8–4 mm, sparsely pilose or glabrous proximally; tube 1.6–2.1 mm, with 1(or 2) large blister glands between ribs, lobes triangular-aristate. **Corollas** usually rose-purple to lavender, rarely white; not conventionally papilionaceous; banner 2.7–3.8 mm, blade flabellate, 1.4–2.3 × 1.2–1.5 mm; epistemonous petals attached near middle of stamen tube, blades somewhat unequal, laterals 1.3–1.6 × 0.3–0.6 mm, abaxials 1.3–1.9 × 0.7–1 mm. **Stamens** (6 or)7–9, usually 5 fertile, 2.2–3.5 mm, filaments distinct to 0.4–0.7 mm, anthers 0.1–0.2 mm. **Legumes** 2.5–3 mm, pilosulous distally, eglandular. **Seeds** 1.5–1.9 mm. $2n = 14$.

Flowering late summer–fall. Rocky slopes, flats, roadsides, openings in pine or juniper forests; 1900–2800 m; Ariz., N.Mex., Tex.; Mexico (Chihuahua, Durango).

Dalea polygonoides occurs at higher elevations throughout much of Arizona, New Mexico, and trans-Pecos Texas.

12. Dalea leporina (Aiton) Bullock, Bull. Misc. Inform. Kew 1939: 196. 1939 • Hare's-foot dalea [F]

Psoralea leporina Aiton, Hort. Kew. 3: 81. 1789; *Dalea alopecuroides* Willdenow; *Parosela alopecuroides* (Willdenow) Rydberg

Annual herbs, erect, glabrous proximal to inflorescences. **Stems** (1.5–)2.5–10(–15) dm, ± sparsely glandular-verruculose distally. **Principal leaves** 2–9.5 cm; leaflets (17–)21–35(–49), blades oblanceolate to obovate, (2–)3–12 mm. **Peduncles** (1.5–)3–12(–15) cm. **Inflorescences** spikes, relatively densely flowered, not involucrate, 8–12(–15) mm diam.; axis usually not visible, (0.8–)1.5–7(–10) cm; bracts deciduous by anthesis, 2.5–7 mm. **Calyces** asymmetric, recessed opposite banner, 3–5.2 mm, sparsely to densely pilose or pilosulous; tube (1.7–)2–2.5(–2.8) mm, with (1 or)2 irregular rows of 2–6 small glands between ribs, sometimes merging into fewer, larger glands, lobes ovate-triangular to lanceolate-acuminate. **Corollas** white to purple or blue; not conventionally papilionaceous; banner (3.4–)4.4–6 mm, blade ovate to oblong-elliptic, (1.7–)2–3.7 × 1.2–2.4 mm; epistemonous petals attached near or distal to middle of stamen tube, blades (1.3–)1.6–2.4 × (0.4–)0.5–1 mm, laterals often slightly narrower than abaxials. **Stamens** 9 or 10, 5–6.8 mm, filaments distinct to 0.6–1 mm, anthers 0.2–0.4 mm. **Legumes** 1.4–3 mm, pilosulous distally and, sometimes, glandular-punctate. **Seeds** 1.7–2.4 mm. $2n = 14$.

Flowering late summer–early winter. Disturbed, open, moist to dry ground; 200–2600 m; Ala., Ariz., Colo., Ill., Ind., Iowa, Kans., Mass., Mich., Minn., Mo., Nebr., N.Mex., N.Dak., Ohio, Pa., S.Dak., Tenn., Tex., Va., Wis.; Mexico; Central America; South America.

Dalea leporina has the broadest range of any member of *Dalea*, from the interior of the United States and Mexico to Costa Rica, and is disjunct in the Andes Mountains of South America. It varies in some characters, most of which were regarded by R. C. Barneby (1977c) as trivial or not taxonomically useful. It has been found on occasion as a weed far east of its range, for example, in Massachusetts (D. E. Snyder 1950).

13. Dalea exserta (Rydberg) Gentry, Publ. Carnegie Inst. Wash. 527: 138. 1942

Parosela exserta Rydberg in N. L. Britton et al., N. Amer. Fl. 24: 73. 1920

Annual herbs, erect, glabrous proximal to inflorescences. **Stems** ribbed, (1.5–)5–10(–12) dm, glandular-verrucose distally. **Principal leaves** 3–10 cm; leaflets 19–37, blades oblong-elliptic to oblanceolate, 2–9 mm. **Peduncles** (1–)2.5–14 cm. **Inflorescences** spikes, relatively densely flowered, not involucrate, 13–16 mm diam.; axis usually not visible, (1.5–)2–8 cm; bracts deciduous by anthesis, (3–)4–8 mm. **Calyces** asymmetric, recessed opposite banner, 4.8–7 mm, glabrous; tube (2.5–)2.7–3.8 mm, with 2–4(–8) large glands between ribs, lobes triangular-aristate. **Corollas** white, sometimes banner purplish in age; not conventionally papilionaceous; banner 4.9–7.3 mm, blade lanceolate-oblong to oblong-elliptic, 3–4.8 × 2.2–2.3 mm; epistemonous petals attached near or proximal to middle of stamen tube, blades somewhat unequal, laterals (2–)3.4–5 × 1–1.8 mm, abaxials 3–3.7 × 1.1–1.6 mm. **Stamens** 8–10, (7.5–)8–11 mm, filaments distinct to 0.1–1.6 mm, anthers 0.4–0.5 mm. **Legumes** 2.2–2.8 mm, pilosulous distally and dotted with small glands. **Seeds** 1.6–1.8(–2) mm. $2n$ = 14 (Mexico).

Flowering fall–spring. Openings in woods, disturbed ground; 1000–1200 m; Ariz.; Mexico; Central America.

The existence of *Dalea exserta* in the flora area rests on specimens collected in 1939 by Goodding in Sycamore Canyon, near Ruby in Santa Cruz County. Because it is an annual that often grows in disturbed ground, it may be found again there or at some other locality in southern Arizona.

14. Dalea urceolata Greene, Leafl. Bot. Observ. Crit. 1: 199. 1906

Varieties 3 (1 in the flora): sw United States, Mexico.

Dalea urceolata is remarkable for its reduced corolla with two epistemonous petals and is rare throughout most of its range.

Variety *tripetala* (Paul G. Wilson) Barneby occurs in south-central Mexico (Michoacán to Morelos) and has fewer stamens (5–7) than var. *urceolata* (7–10). Variety *lucida* (Rose ex Rydberg) Barneby occurs in Durango and lacks the epistemonous petals; the banner is the only petal.

14a. Dalea urceolata Greene var. **urceolata**

Annual herbs, erect, glabrous proximal to inflorescences. **Stems** 0.5–3 dm, sparsely gland-dotted distally. **Principal leaves** 1.5–7 cm; leaflets (7–)11–29, blades oblong-oblanceolate, 2.5–9.5 mm. **Peduncles** 0.5–7.5 (–12) cm. **Inflorescences** spikes, relatively densely flowered, not obviously involucrate, 9–10.5 mm diam.; axis usually not visible, 0.8–4(–5) cm; bracts deciduous by anthesis, 2–5(–6) mm. **Calyces** asymmetric, deeply recessed opposite banner, 3.5–6 mm, glabrous, except lobes; tube (2.4–)2.6–3.4(–4.5) mm, with 3–7 large glands between ribs, lobes triangular to triangular-acuminate. **Corollas** pale blue to white; not conventionally papilionaceous; banner 3.8–5.5 mm, blade ovate-elliptic to subcordate, 2.2–2.8 × 1.4–2.2 mm; epistemonous petals 2, attached near middle of stamen tube, blades 1.4–2.2(–2.6) × 0.5–0.9 mm. **Stamens** 7–10, 4.2–6 mm, filaments distinct to 0.8–1.2 mm, anthers 0.3 mm. **Legumes** 2.5 mm, pilosulous distally and dotted with small glands. **Seeds** 1.5 mm.

Flowering late summer–fall. Grassy areas, open conifer woodlands; 2000–2600 m; Ariz., N.Mex.; Mexico (Chihuahua).

In the flora area, var. *urceolata* is restricted to a small region of east-central Arizona and adjacent New Mexico.

15. Dalea obovata (Torrey & A. Gray) Shinners, Field & Lab. 17: 84. 1949 [E]

Petalostemon obovatus Torrey & A. Gray, Fl. N. Amer. 1: 310. 1838 (as obovatum)

Perennial herbs, short-lived, erect, ± lanate-pilose. **Stems** to 5.5 dm, sparsely dotted with small, raised glands. **Principal leaves** (2–)2.5–5 cm; leaflets 7–11, blades obovate, (8–)10–16 mm, surfaces eglandular. **Peduncles** 0–3 (–10) cm. **Inflorescences** spikes, densely flowered, not involucrate, (12–)14–20 mm diam.; axis not visible, 3.5–11 cm; bracts early deciduous, interfloral ones often held in place by crowded flowers, 5.5–11 mm. **Calyces**± asymmetric, slightly recessed opposite banner, 3.3–5.8 mm, pilose; tube (1.3–)1.4–2.1 mm, with 1 or 2 small glands between ribs, lobes triangular-aristate. **Corollas** white, ochroleucous in drying; not conventionally papilionaceous; banner (3.5–)4–7 mm, blade ovate-oblong, (2–)2.2–2.9(–3.1) × 1.2–2 mm; epistemonous petals attached at or just proximal to separation of filaments, blades 2–3.2 × 0.5–0.9 mm.

Stamens 5, (4.5–)5–6.6 mm, filaments distinct to 1–2.2 mm, anthers 0.6–0.8 mm. **Legumes** 2.7–3 mm, pilosulous distally, eglandular. **Seeds** 1.7 mm.

Flowering spring (fall–early winter). Sandy, open ground on and near Gulf Coastal Plain; 0–400 m; Tex.

Dalea obovata occurs in the southern coastal plain of Texas as far north and west as Frio, Medina, and Travis counties.

16. Dalea cylindriceps Barneby, Mem. New York Bot. Gard. 27: 228. 1977 [E]

Petalostemon macrostachyus Torrey, Ann. Lyceum Nat. Hist. New York 2: 176. 1827, not *Dalea macrostachya* Moricand 1833

Perennial herbs, short-lived, erect, glabrous proximal to inflorescences. **Stems** (1–)3–6(–8) dm, dotted with small raised glands distally. **Principal leaves** 3–7 cm; leaflets 7 or 9, blades oblanceolate to oblong-elliptic, (12–)15–25 mm. **Peduncles** (3–)6–20 cm. **Inflorescences** spikes, densely flowered, not obviously involucrate, 9–12 mm diam.; axis not visible, (1.5–)2.5–18 cm; bracts early deciduous, interfloral ones often held in place by crowded flowers, 4–6.5 mm. **Calyces** ± asymmetric, slightly recessed opposite banner, 3.4–4.3 mm, pilose; tube 1.9–2.3 mm, with 2–5 small, pale blister glands between ribs, lobes lanceolate to ovate. **Corollas** whitish, ochroleucous, faintly greenish, or pink; not conventionally papilionaceous; banner 4.7–6.2 mm, blade broadly triangular to ovate-cordate, 1.4–2.7 × 1.6–2.1 mm; epistemonous petals attached at separation of filaments, blades 1.5–4 × 0.3–0.8 mm. **Stamens** 5, 5.3–7.7 mm, filaments distinct to 2.2–4.3 mm, anthers 0.7–0.9 mm. **Legumes** 2.5–3 mm, pilosulous distally and gland-dotted. **Seeds** 1.7–2.1 mm. $2n = 14$.

Flowering summer. Sandy soils or gravelly places near streams, sandsage shrublands in dunes; 900–1600 m; Colo., Kans., Nebr., N.Mex., Okla., S.Dak., Tex., Wyo.

Dalea cylindriceps is wide-ranging; its distribution is discontinuous and it is seldom common. Although many of the specimens show a strong perennial root, others look more like sturdy annuals, having perhaps flowered during the first year of growth. In Texas, the species is known from the trans-Pecos and west-central part of the state.

The name *Dalea compacta* has been misapplied to the species now known as *D. cylindriceps* (R. C. Barneby 1977c).

17. Dalea ornata (Douglas) Eaton & Wright, Man. Bot. ed. 8, 219. 1840 (as ornatum) [E]

Petalostemon ornatus Douglas in W. J. Hooker, Fl. Bor.-Amer. 1: 138. 1831 (as Petalostemum ornatum)

Perennial herbs, erect, glabrous proximal to inflorescence. **Stems** (2–)2.5–6(–7) dm, dotted with small, raised glands. **Principal leaves** 2.5–5.5(–6.5) cm; leaflets 5 or 7 (or 9), blades oblanceolate to obovate, 7–22 mm. **Peduncles** 1–11 cm. **Inflorescences** spikes, densely flowered, not involucrate, 13–16 mm diam.; axis not visible, (1–)1.5–5 cm; bracts deciduous, interfloral ones often held in place by crowded flowers, (3–)4–7.5(–8.5) mm. **Calyces** subsymmetric, (3.6–)3.9–6.3(–6.7) mm, pilose throughout or distally; tube (2.4–)2.7–3.6(–3.8) mm, with 2–9 small glands between ribs, lobes lanceolate to ovate. **Corollas** usually rose-purple to lilac, rarely white; not conventionally papilionaceous; banner 7–9 mm, blade ovate to oblong-ovate, 3.3–4.5 × (2–)2.3–4 mm; epistemonous petals attached at separation of filaments, blades (3.3–)3.5–5 × 1.4–2 mm. **Stamens** 5, (7.3–)7.7–12 mm, filaments distinct to (3.6–)4.7–7.6 mm, anthers 1–1.4 mm. **Legumes** 3–3.5 mm, pilosulous distally and gland-dotted. **Seeds** 2–2.4 mm. $2n = 14$.

Flowering spring–early summer. Rocky, sandy, or clay soils in dry areas, often among sagebrush; 100–2000 m; Calif., Idaho, Nev., Oreg., Wash.

Dalea ornata is nearly endemic to the Columbia-Snake river basin. In California, the species is known only from the Shaffer Mountain region in Lassen County.

18. Dalea flavescens (S. Watson) S. L. Welsh ex Barneby, Mem. New York Bot. Gard. 27: 231. 1977 [E]

Petalostemon flavescens S. Watson, Amer. Naturalist 7: 299. 1873; *Dalea epica* S. L. Welsh

Perennial herbs, erect, pilosulous except stems glabrous. **Stems** (2.5–)3–4.5 dm, glandular-tuberculate. **Principal leaves** (2–)2.5–4(–4.5) cm; leaflets 5 or 7, blades oblong-obovate to narrowly oblong-elliptic, 7–17(–19) mm, surfaces glandular-punctate to glandular-verruculose abaxially. **Peduncles** (4–)7–20(–25) cm. **Inflorescences** spikes, densely flowered, not involucrate, 8.5–12(–13) mm diam.; axis not visible, (1–)1.5–7(–10) cm; bracts deciduous, interfloral ones often held in place by crowded flowers, 2.5–5.5(–6.5) mm. **Calyces** asymmetric, deeply recessed opposite banner, (3–)3.3–4.7(–5.2) mm, pilosulous, especially distally; tube (2–)2.2–2.8 mm, with 0–3 small, pale blister glands between ribs, lobes lanceolate. **Corollas** white, ochroleucous in drying; not conventionally papilionaceous; banner 5–7.4 (–8.4) mm, blade broadly triangular to ovate, 2.6–4.2 × 2.2–3.9(–4.5) mm; epistemonous petals attached at separation of filaments, blades 3–3.9(–4.5) × 0.9–1.6 (–1.9) mm. **Stamens** 5, (5.5–)6.2–10(–12.7) mm, filaments distinct to 3.4–6.2(–8.7) mm, anthers 0.9–1.6 mm. **Legumes** 3.1–3.7 mm, pilosulous distally and dotted with small glands. **Seeds** 2.1–2.4 mm.

Flowering late spring–summer. Dry hills, sandy or rocky places, desert shrub communities, sometimes on limestone; 900–1600 m; Ariz., Utah.

The distributions of *Dalea flavescens* and *D. searlsiae* are nearly discrete.

19. Dalea searlsiae (A. Gray) Barneby, Mem. New York Bot. Gard. 27: 234. 1977 E

Petalostemon searlsiae A. Gray, Proc. Amer. Acad. Arts 8: 380. 1872

Perennial herbs, erect, pilosulous throughout or glabrous proximal to inflorescence. **Stems** (2.5–)3–5.5 dm, glandular-tuberculate. **Principal leaves** 2–5.5 cm; leaflets 5 or 7(or 9), blades flat or folded, oblanceolate to obovate, 7–20 mm, surfaces glandular-tuberculate abaxially. **Peduncles** (2.5–)4–16(–20) cm. **Inflorescences** spikes, relatively densely flowered, not obviously involucrate, (8–)9–11 mm diam.; axis partially visible at anthesis, (1.5–) 2–9(–14) cm; bracts deciduous, 3–5(–6) mm. **Calyces** asymmetric, deeply recessed opposite banner, opening oblique, (3.2–)3.5–4.6(–4.8) mm, glabrous or pilosulous proximally, pilosulous distally; tube 2–2.8 mm, with (0 or)2–4 small, pale blister glands between ribs, lobes lanceolate-subulate or adaxial pair triangular-ovate. **Corollas** usually rose-purple, rarely white; not conventionally papilionaceous; banner 5.3–7.2 mm, blade ovate to ovate-triangular or -oblong, 2.8–3.7 × 2.2–3.4 mm; epistemonous petals attached at separation of filaments, blades (2.7–)3–4.1 × (0.9–)1.1–1.6 mm. **Stamens** 5, 5.5–8.5 mm, filaments distinct to 3–5.1 mm, anthers 1.1–1.5 mm. **Legumes** 3.2–4 mm, pilosulous to ± glabrous distally and gland-dotted. **Seeds** 2–2.8 mm.

Flowering spring–summer. Rocky or sandy slopes or washes, among pine, juniper, or oak, sometimes in desert scrub; 1100–2000 m; Ariz., Calif., Nev., Utah.

The ranges of *Dalea searlsiae* and *D. flavescens* overlap only in a small area of south-central Utah and north-central Arizona. In California, *D. searlsiae* is known from the Inyo and White mountains and other desert mountains in the southeastern part of the state.

20. Dalea scariosa S. Watson, Proc. Amer. Acad. Arts 17: 369. 1882 E

Perennial herbs, erect, glabrous proximal to inflorescences. **Stems** 2–7 dm, glandular-tuberculate. **Principal leaves** 1–2.5 cm; leaflets (5 or) 7 or 9, blades obovate-cuneate, 3–8 mm. **Peduncles** 0.5–5 cm. **Inflorescences** spikes, relatively loosely flowered, not involucrate, 9–11 mm diam.; axis often partially visible at anthesis, 1.5–9(–13) cm; bracts early deciduous, 2.5–5 mm. **Calyces** asymmetric, recessed opposite banner, 4–5.8 mm, glabrous; tube 3–3.8 mm, green intervals each with a single row (or adaxial pair with 2 or 3 rows) of 3–5 blister glands, lobes subulate or adaxial pair triangular to triangular-apiculate. **Corollas** pale pink to rose-purple; not conventionally papilionaceous; banner 7.2–8 mm, blade suborbiculate-cordate, 4–4.5 × 1–4.5 mm; epistemonous petals attached at separation of filaments, blades 3.7–4 × 1.8–2.2 mm, laterals often wider than abaxials. **Stamens** 5, 8.5–9.8 mm, filaments distinct to 5–5.4 mm, anthers 0.7–1.1 mm. **Legumes** 3.2–4 mm, glabrate, slightly ciliate distally and at proximal end of style, gland-dotted. **Seeds** 2.3–3 mm. $2n = 14$.

Flowering summer(–early fall). Sandy or limey soils, grasslands, sometimes with mesquite or juniper; 1400–1600 m; N.Mex.

Dalea scariosa is a geographically restricted and beautiful plant that is known only from locations near Alburquerque and Belen. It appears to be related to two other rare taxa, *D. bartonii* and *D. sabinalis*.

21. Dalea bartonii Barneby, Mem. New York Bot. Gard. 27: 239, plate 54. 1977 (as bartoni) C E

Perennial herbs, erect, glabrous proximal to inflorescences. **Stems** 1.2–2.5 dm, gland-dotted. **Principal leaves** 0.8–2(–2.3) cm; leaflets 5–9, blades obovate-cuneate, 2.5–7.5 mm. **Peduncles** 0.1–0.6 cm. **Inflorescences** spikes, ± densely flowered, not involucrate, 8 mm diam.; axis not visible, 0.3–1.4 cm; bracts early deciduous or proximal ones persistent, 2–3 mm. **Calyces** somewhat asymmetric, slightly recessed opposite banner, 3.8–4.3 mm, glabrous; tube 2.8–3.5 mm, with 3–8+ blister glands between ribs, lobes triangular-subulate or adaxial pair triangular-acuminate. **Corollas** white; not conventionally papilionaceous; banner 5.4 mm, blade deltate-obcordate, 2.5 × 3 mm; epistemonous petals attached at separation of filaments, blades 3 × 1.5 mm.

Stamens 5, 9.5 mm, filaments distinct to 4.5 mm, anthers unknown. **Legumes** 2.8 mm, sparsely pubescent along abaxial side, densely so at base of style, gland-dotted. **Seeds** 2 mm.

Flowering summer. Limestone soils; of conservation concern; 1000–1100 m; Tex.

Dalea bartonii is known only from the type locality in Brewster County, although a vegetative specimen from adjacent Terrell County was annotated as *D. bartonii* by B. L. Turner.

Dalea bartonii was assigned by D. K. Wemple (1970) to *D. sabinalis* (as *Petalostemon sabinalis*), but R. C. Barneby (1977c) considered it closer to *D. scariosa* and could not readily accommodate it in his concept or either *D. scariosa* or *D. sabinalis*. The known specimens were collected in July but were in late flower and early fruit, indicating that the peak of bloom was earlier.

22. Dalea sabinalis (S. Watson) Shinners, Field & Lab. 17: 83. 1949 [C] [E]

Petalostemon sabinalis S. Watson, Proc. Amer. Acad. Arts 21: 448. 1886

Perennial herbs, erect, glabrous proximal to inflorescences. **Stems** 2.5–5(–6) dm, sparsely gland-dotted. **Principal leaves** 2–4 cm; leaflets 11–17, blades linear-oblanceolate, 7–15 mm. **Peduncles** 6–12 cm. **Inflorescences** spikes, relatively loosely flowered, not involucrate, 6.5–8 mm diam.; axis usually partially visible at anthesis, 4–9 cm; bracts early deciduous, 3 mm. **Calyces** asymmetric, recessed opposite banner, 3–3.3 mm, glabrous, lobes sometimes pilosulous; tube 2.3–2.5 mm, greenish intervals between ribs eglandular, lobes subulate or adaxial pair triangular-ovate. **Corollas** pink to rose; not conventionally papilionaceous; banner 5.4 mm, blade deltate-obcordate, 2.5 × 3 mm; epistemonous petals attached at separation of filaments, blades 3 × 1.5 mm. **Stamens** 5, 5–6 mm, filaments distinct to 2.5–3 mm, anthers 0.6 mm. **Legumes** 3 mm, glabrate, margins ± short-ciliate distally, minutely gland-dotted. **Seeds** 1.5–2.1 mm.

Flowering spring. Open slopes, limestone soils; of conservation concern; 500–600 m; Tex.

Dalea sabinalis was first found at the entrance to Sabinal Canyon in Bandera County, but collections are known also from nearby Uvalde and Val Verde counties; it has not been collected since the 1950s, and no extant populations are known.

23. Dalea phleoides (Torrey & A. Gray) Shinners, Field & Lab. 17: 83. 1949 [E]

Petalostemon phleoides Torrey & A. Gray, Fl. N. Amer. 1: 310. 1838

Perennial herbs, erect, pilosulous throughout or in part. **Stems** (2.5–)3–7 dm, glandular-tuberculate. **Principal leaves** 2.5–5.5(–6.5) cm; leaflets 13–41 (–49), blades oblong to oblanceolate or oblong-elliptic, 2–14 mm, surfaces glandular-verruculose abaxially. **Peduncles** (1–)2–20(–25) cm. **Inflorescences** spikes, densely flowered, not obviously involucrate, 5.5–7.5 mm diam.; axis not visible, (1.5–) 2.5–9(–13) cm; bracts early deciduous or proximals persistent, interfloral ones held in place by crowded flowers, 2.5–4.5 mm. **Calyces** asymmetric, deeply recessed opposite banner, 2.5–3.8 mm, glabrous or pilosulous; tube 1.7–2.5(–2.8) mm, with 1 or 2 blister glands between ribs, adaxial with 3–7, lobes triangular-subulate or adaxial pair broadly triangular. **Corollas** white; not conventionally papilionaceous; banner 5.3–6.8 mm, blade deltate-obcordate, 2.8–3.5(–4) × 2.6–3.6 (–5.2) mm; epistemonous petals attached at or near separation of filaments, blades 3–3.9 × 0.5–0.9 mm. **Stamens** 5, 5.2–7.4 mm, filaments distinct to 3–4.3 mm, anthers 0.6–0.9 mm. **Legumes** 2.5–2.9 mm, pilosulous distally, sometimes also gland-dotted. **Seeds** apparently unknown.

Varieties 2 (2 in the flora): sc United States.

B. L. Turner (2013) divided *Dalea phleoides* into three species: *D. phleoides*, distinguished from *D. drummondiana* by longer leaf blades and calyces, and *D. carrizoana*, based on the absence of indument and an allopatric distribution (from DeWitt to Maverick counties) south of the range of the other two species; the latter two are treated here as synonyms of *D. phleoides* var. *microphylla*.

1. Leaflets 13–21(–25), blades 5–14 mm . . . . 23a. *Dalea phleoides* var. *phleoides*
1. Leaflets 25–41(–49), blades 2–7 mm . . . . 23b. *Dalea phleoides* var. *microphylla*

23a. Dalea phleoides (Torrey & A. Gray) Shinners var. **phleoides** [E]

Petalostemon glandulosus J. M. Coulter & Fisher

Leaflets 13–21(–25), blades 5–14 mm. **Spike axis** not pilosulous. **Calyces** glabrous or glabrate. **2*n*** = 14.

Flowering spring–early summer. Sandy soils, oak and pine woodlands, roadsides; 0–300 m; La., Okla., Tex.

In Texas, var. *phleoides* is known from the eastern portion of the state.

23b. Dalea phleoides (Torrey & A. Gray) Shinners var. **microphylla** (Torrey & A. Gray) Barneby, Mem. New York Bot. Gard. 27: 244. 1977 [E]

Petalostemon phleoides Torrey & A. Gray var. *microphyllus* Torrey & A. Gray, Fl. N. Amer. 1: 310. 1838 (as microphyllum); *Dalea carrizoana* B. L. Turner; *D. drummondiana* Shinners; *P. microphyllus* (Torrey & A. Gray) A. Heller

Leaflets 25–41(–49), blades 2–7 mm. **Spike axis** usually pilosulous, rarely glabrous. **Calyces** pilosulous, at least basally.

Flowering spring–early summer. Sandy soils, open woods, dunes, beaches; 0–600 m; Ark., Okla., Tex.

In Texas, var. *microphylla* is known from the eastern half of the state.

24. Dalea foliosa (A. Gray) Barneby, Mem. New York Bot. Gard. 27: 245. 1977 • Leafy prairie-clover [C] [E]

Petalostemon foliosus A. Gray, Proc. Amer. Acad. Arts 7: 336. 1868

Perennial herbs, erect, glabrous proximal to inflorescences. **Stems** 3–8 dm, eglandular. **Principal leaves** 3–5.5 cm; leaflets 19–29(or 31), blades oblong-oblanceolate to -elliptic, 5–10 mm. **Peduncles** 0–2 cm. **Inflorescences** spikes, densely flowered, not involucrate, 8–10 mm diam.; axis not visible, 1.5–4.5 cm; bracts persistent through anthesis, 4.8–5.4 mm. **Calyces** subsymmetric, 3.8–4.4 mm, glabrous or lobes sometimes pilosulous; tube 2.4–2.7 mm, with 0 glands between ribs, lobes triangular-lanceolate or adaxial pair ovate-triangular. **Corollas** lavender-purple; not conventionally papilionaceous; banner 5.2–6 mm, blade ovate to suborbiculate, 2.1–2.5 × 2.6–3.2 mm; epistemonous petals attached at separation of filaments, blades 2.7–3 × 0.8–1 mm. **Stamens** 5, 5.4–7.2 mm, filaments distinct to 2.7–3.7 mm, anthers 0.6–0.9 mm. **Legumes** 2.5–3 mm, glabrous, dotted with small glands distally. **Seeds** 1.8–2 mm. **2*n*** = 14.

Flowering late summer–fall. Limestone glades, prairie remnants; of conservation concern; 100–300 m; Ala., Ill., Tenn.

Dalea foliosa is rare and in 1991 was designated federally as endangered. At that time, there were 14 known populations, only four of which had state or Nature Conservancy protection. The species is in the Center for Plant Conservation's National Collection of Endangered Plants.

25. Dalea candida Willdenow, Sp. Pl. 3: 1337. 1802 • White prairie-clover

Petalostemon candidus (Willdenow) Michaux

Perennial herbs, erect to diffusely spreading, glabrous throughout or proximal to inflorescence. **Stems** 2.5–10 dm, minutely gland-dotted or eglandular. **Principal leaves** (1.5–)2–6 cm; leaflets 5–9, blades oblong to obovate or narrowly elliptic-oblanceolate, (6–)9–35 mm. **Peduncles** 0–5.5(–7.5) cm. **Inflorescences** spikes, densely to somewhat loosely flowered, cylindric, not involucrate, 6–9.5(–10) mm diam.; axis visible or not, especially in fruit, (1–)1.5–5.5(–7.5) cm; bracts early deciduous or proximals persistent, interfloral ones held in place by crowded flowers, 2.5–5.5 mm. **Calyces** subsymmetric, (2.9–)3–4.2(–4.4) mm, pilosulous or tube glabrous; tube 1.9–2.7 mm, not deeply recessed opposite banner, with 1 (or 2) glands between ribs, lobes lanceolate to triangular, ± unequal, abaxial pair longest. **Corollas** white; not conventionally papilionaceous; banner (4–)4.2–5.7 mm, blade deltate-obovate, 2.3–3.4 × 2.4–3.7(–4.2) mm; epistemonous petals attached at separation of filaments, blades 2–3.1 × 1.1–2.6 mm. **Stamens** 5, (5–)5.2–7.6 mm, filaments distinct to 2.5–4.5 mm, anthers 0.7–1.2 mm. **Legumes** (2.6–)2.8–4(–4.5) mm, glabrate or distally pilose, with ± prominent, elongated to circular glands on sides. **Seeds** 1.7–2.3 mm.

Varieties 2 (2 in the flora): North America, n Mexico.

Varieties *candida* and *oligophylla* were treated as separate species by D. K. Wemple (1970) and are fairly well defined. In regions of overlap, var. *oligophylla* normally occupies higher, drier sites than var. *candida*.

1. Spike axis not visible; calyx tube glabrous . . . . 25a. *Dalea candida* var. *candida*
1. Spike axis partially visible, especially in fruit; calyx tube usually pubescent, sometimes glabrous . . . . 25b. *Dalea candida* var. *oligophylla*

25a. Dalea candida Willdenow var. **candida** [E]

Stems erect, 5–10 dm. **Principal leaves** 3–6 cm; leaflets (5 or)7 (or 9), blades (12–)15–35 mm. **Spikes** densely flowered, (6–)6.5–9.5(–10) mm diam.; axis not visible, (1–)1.5–5.5(–7) cm; bracts 3–5.5 mm. **Calyces:** tube glabrous, with 1 small gland between ribs. **Epistemonous petals:** blades 2–2.9 × 1.3–1.7 mm. **2*n*** = 14.

Flowering late spring–summer(–fall). Prairies, roadsides; 0–1100 m; Man., Ont., Sask.; Ala., Ark., Ga., Ill., Ind., Iowa, Kans., Ky., La., Minn., Miss., Mo., Nebr., N.Dak., Okla., S.C., S.Dak., Tenn., Tex., W.Va., Wis.

In Texas, var. *candida* is known from the eastern half of the state.

25b. Dalea candida Willdenow var. **oligophylla** (Torrey) Shinners, Spring Fl. Dallas-Fort Worth, 409. 1958

Petalostemon gracilis Nuttall var. *oligophyllus* Torrey in W. H. Emory, Not. Milit. Reconn., 139. 1848 (as gracile var. oligophyllum); *P. candidus* (Willdenow) Michaux var. *oligophyllus* (Torrey) F. J. Hermann

Stems erect or diffusely spreading, 2.5–7 dm. **Principal leaves** (1.5–)2–5 cm; leaflets 5 or 7, blades (6–)9–20(–24) mm. **Spikes** ± loosely flowered, 6–8 mm diam.; axis becoming partially visible, 1–5(–7.5) cm; bracts 2.5–4 mm. **Calyces:** tube usually pubescent, sometimes glabrous, with 1 or 2 small glands between ribs. **Epistemonous petals:** blades 2.3–3.1 × 1.1–2.6 mm. **2*n*** = 14.

Flowering late spring–fall. Prairies, roadsides; 400–1300 m; Alta., Man., Ont., Sask.; Ariz., Colo., Iowa, Kans., Minn., Mont., Nebr., N.Mex., N.Dak., Okla., S.Dak., Tex., Utah, Wyo.; Mexico (Chihuahua, Durango, Sonora).

In Texas, var. *oligophylla* is known from the northwestern half of the state, including the trans-Pecos region.

26. Dalea multiflora (Nuttall) Shinners, Field & Lab. 17: 82. 1949 [E]

Petalostemon multiflorus Nuttall, J. Acad. Nat. Sci. Philadelphia 7: 92. 1834 (as multiflorum); *Kuhnistera multiflora* (Nuttall) A. Heller

Perennial herbs, erect to spreading, glabrous. **Stems** 3–8 dm, glandular-punctate. **Principal leaves** 2–3 cm; leaflets (7 or) 9 or 11(or 13), blades oblong to elliptic-oblanceolate, or linear-oblong, 7–13 mm. **Peduncles** (0–)0.5–3(–7) cm. **Inflorescences** spikes, densely flowered, nearly globose, inconspicuously involucrate (lowest bracts not subtending flowers), 7–9 mm diam.; axis not visible, 0.4–1(–1.2) cm; bracts early deciduous or proximals persistent, interfloral ones held in place by crowded flowers, 2–2.4 mm. **Calyces** subsymmetric, (2.9–)3–4.2(–4.4) mm, glabrous, lobes ciliolate; tube 1.6–2.6 mm, not deeply recessed opposite banner, with 1(–3) small blister glands between ribs, lobes lanceolate to triangular, ± unequal, abaxial pair longest. **Corollas** white; not conventionally papilionaceous; banner (4–)4.2–5.7 mm, blade deltate-obovate, 2.3–3.4 × 2.4–3.7(–4.2) mm; epistemonous petals attached at separation of filaments, blades 2.3–3.5 × 1.5–2.1 mm. **Stamens** 5, (5–)5.2–7.6 mm, filaments distinct to 2.5–4.5 mm, anthers 0.7–1.2 mm. **Legumes** 2.5–3 mm, glabrate, with ± prominent elongated glands on sides. **Seeds** 1.6–2 mm.

Flowering late spring–early fall. Prairies, rocky hills; 0–700 m; Colo., Kans., Mo., Nebr., Okla., Tex.

Dalea multiflora shows considerable geographic variation in stature. Its floral structure is similar to that of *D. candida* var. *candida*, and individuals intermediate between the two species occur (R. C. Barneby 1977c). In Texas, *D. multiflora* is known from the eastern two-thirds of the state.

27. Dalea carnea (Michaux) Poiret in F. Cuvier, Dict. Sci. Nat. ed. 2, 12: 462. 1818 [E]

Petalostemon carneus Michaux, Fl. Bor.-Amer. 2: 49. 1803 (as Petalostemum carneum)

Perennial herbs, erect to ascending or diffusely spreading to procumbent, glabrous proximal to inflorescences. **Stems** 3–8(–10) dm, gland-dotted distally. **Principal leaves** 1.5–4 cm; leaflets 5–9, blades flat or folded, elliptic to oblanceolate, (5–)6–17 mm. **Peduncles** 0–8 cm. **Inflorescences** spikes, densely flowered, not involucrate, 7–10 mm diam.;

axis not visible, 0.5–3(–3.5) cm; bracts deciduous with fruit, 2–5.5 mm. **Calyces** asymmetric, deeply recessed opposite banner, opening oblique, 2.7–4.3 mm, glabrous except lobes ciliolate; tube 2–3.5 mm, with (0 or)1–3 small blister glands between ribs, lobes subulate or adaxial pair ovate. **Corollas** usually white, sometimes pink to pinkish tan; not conventionally papilionaceous; banner 3.8–5.7 mm, blade ovate, 1.8–3 × 1.4–2.4 mm; epistemonous petals attached at separation of filaments, blades 1.7–3.3 × 0.7–1.11 mm. **Stamens** 5, 5–9.5 mm, filaments distinct to 2.7–6 mm, anthers 0.6–0.9 mm. **Legumes** 2.5–3 mm, glabrous or distally pilosulous, ± glandular. **Seeds** 1.4–1.8 mm.

Varieties 3 (3 in the flora): se United States.

The varieties of *Dalea carnea* are fairly distinctive, and two are largely allopatric. Variety *gracilis* occurs in the Florida panhandle and west while var. *carnea* is found farther east and throughout peninsular Florida. Variety *albida* overlaps the ranges of the other varieties and extends north into Georgia.

1. Calyces 3.2–4.3 mm, lobes 0.9–1.5 mm; petals usually pink to pinkish tan, rarely white . . . . 27a. *Dalea carnea* var. *carnea*
1. Calyces 2.7–3.5 mm, lobes 0.6–1.1 mm; petals white.
    2. Leaflets mostly 5; stamens 6–9.5 mm; stems erect to ascending . . . . 27b. *Dalea carnea* var. *albida*
    2. Leaflets mostly 7; stamens 5–6 mm; stems diffusely spreading to procumbent . . . . .27c. *Dalea carnea* var. *gracilis*

27a. Dalea carnea (Michaux) Poiret var. **carnea** E

Stems erect to ascending, 3–8 (–10) dm. **Principal leaves** 1.5–3.5 cm; leaflets (5 or)7 or 9. **Spike** 8–10 mm diam., axis 1–3(–3.5) cm. **Calyces** 3.2–4.3 mm; tube 2–3.2 mm, lobes 0.9–1.5 mm. **Petals** usually pink to pinkish tan, rarely white. **Stamens** (5.5–)6–9.5 mm. $2n = 14$.

Flowering summer–early winter. Relatively low, moist ground, often with palmettos; 0–20 m; Fla., Ga.

In Florida, var. *carnea* is known from the eastern panhandle southward throughout the peninsula.

27b. Dalea carnea (Michaux) Poiret var. **albida** (Torrey & A. Gray) Barneby, Mem. New York Bot. Gard. 27: 255. 1977 E

Petalostemon carneus Michaux var. *albidus* Torrey & A. Gray, Fl. N. Amer. 1: 311. 1838 (as carneum var. albidum); *Dalea albida* (Torrey & A. Gray) D. B. Ward; *P. albidus* (Torrey & A. Gray) Small

Stems erect to ascending, 4–8 (–10) dm. **Principal leaves** 1.5–4 cm; leaflets mostly 5. **Spike** 7–9 mm diam., axis 0.7–2 cm. **Calyces** 2.9–3.5 mm; tube 2.1–3.5 mm, lobes 0.6–1.1 mm. **Petals** white. **Stamens** 6–9.5 mm. $2n = 14$.

Flowering summer–fall. Relatively dry areas, open oak or pine woods, roadsides; 0–150 m; Ala., Fla., Ga.

In Florida, var. *albida* is known from the northern peninsula south to Polk County and westward to the central panhandle.

27c. Dalea carnea (Michaux) Poiret var. **gracilis** (Nuttall) Barneby, Mem. New York Bot. Gard. 27: 256. 1977 E

Petalostemon gracilis Nuttall, J. Acad. Nat. Sci. Philadelphia 7: 92. 1834 (as gracile); *Dalea mountjoyae* M. Woods

Stems diffusely spreading to procumbent, 3–7 dm. **Principal leaves** 2–3.5 cm; leaflets mostly 7. **Spike** 7–8 mm diam., axis 0.5–1.5 cm. **Calyces** 2.7–3.3 mm; tube 2–2.5 mm, lobes 0.6–0.9(–1.1) mm. **Petals** white. **Stamens** 5–6 mm. $2n = 14$.

Flowering late summer–fall. Grassy areas, pine woods; 0–70 m; Ala., Fla., Ga., La., Miss.

In Florida, var. *gracilis* is known from Jefferson County, plus the central and western panhandle regions.

28. Dalea feayi (Chapman) Barneby, Mem. New York Bot. Gard. 27: 257. 1977 E

Petalostemon feayi Chapman, Fl. South. U.S. ed. 2, 615. 1883

Perennial herbs, erect, becoming somewhat shrubby, glabrous proximal to inflorescences. **Stems** 3–7 dm, with scattered, small glands. **Principal leaves** 1.5–3.5 cm; leaflets 7 or 9, blades involute, linear, (6–)7–12(–14) mm. **Peduncles** 0–8 cm. **Inflorescences** spikes, densely flowered, not involucrate, 7–9 mm diam.; axis not visible, 0.6–1.1 cm; bracts deciduous with fruit or proximal ones persistent, 0.8–2 mm. **Calyces** asymmetric, deeply recessed opposite banner, opening oblique, 3.2–4.4 mm, glabrous; tube 2.5–3.4 mm, with 1–3 blister glands between ribs, lobes subulate or adaxial pair ovate-subulate. **Corollas** usually pink to lavender, rarely white; not conventionally papilionaceous; banner 4.4–5.2 mm, blade broadly ovate, 2.1–2.6 × 1.8–2.5 mm; epistemonous petals attached at separation of filaments, blades 2.6–3.5 × 0.9–1.2 mm. **Stamens** 5, 6.5–9.2 mm, filaments distinct to 3.5–5 mm, anthers 0.8 mm. **Legumes** 3–3.3 mm, glabrous, ± glandular. **Seeds** (1.5–)2–2.2 mm. **2*n*** = 14.

Flowering summer–fall (year-round). Sandy pine woods, on white sand; 0–30 m; Fla., Ga.

Dalea feayi occurs in xeric soils and generally does not grow in the same habitats as *D. carnea*. In Florida, the species is frequent in the peninsula and central panhandle regions.

29. Dalea villosa (Nuttall) Sprengel, Syst. Veg. 3: 326. 1826 [E]

Petalostemon villosus Nuttall, Gen. N. Amer. Pl. 2: 85. 1818 (as villosum)

Perennial herbs, erect or ascending to spreading, sometimes trailing, sparsely pubescent or densely villosulous. **Stems** 2.5–8(–9) dm, ± eglandular. **Principal leaves** 2–4(–4.5) cm; leaflets (9 or) 11–17(–21), blades elliptic to elliptic-oblanceolate, 8.5–15 mm. **Peduncles** 0–1(–2.5) cm. **Inflorescences** spikes, moderately densely flowered, not involucrate, 7–10 mm diam.; axis eventually visible, 3–12(–14) cm; bracts deciduous, (1.5–)2–5.5 mm. **Calyces** asymmetric, recessed opposite banner, 2.8–3.8 mm, densely pilosulous; tube 1.9–2.7 mm, with 0 glands between ribs, lobes lanceolate or subulate or adaxial pair triangular to ovate. **Corollas** usually rose-purple to pale pink or lavender, rarely white; not conventionally papilionaceous; banner 4.4–5.6 mm, blade ovate to elliptic, 2.3–3 × 2–2.6 mm; epistemonous petals attached at separation of filaments, blades 2.1–3.8 × 0.9–1.3 mm. **Stamens** 5, (5–)5.4–7 mm, filaments distinct to 2.5–4.4 mm, anthers 0.6–0.9(–1) mm. **Legumes** 2.5–3.2 mm, distally villosulous, ± eglandular. **Seeds** 2–2.4 mm.

Varieties 2 (2 in the flora): North America.

1. Stems usually 2.5–5 dm, rarely longer, densely villosulous; leaflet blades 8.5–10(–11) mm, surfaces densely villosulous . . . . 29a. *Dalea villosa* var. *villosa*
1. Stems 5–8(–9) dm, sparsely pubescent; leaflet blades 10–15 mm, surfaces sparsely pubescent . . . . .29b. *Dalea villosa* var. *grisea*

29a. Dalea villosa (Nuttall) Sprengel var. **villosa** [E]

Stems ascending to spreading or, sometimes, trailing, usually 2.5–5 dm, rarely longer, densely villosulous. **Leaflet blades** 8.5–10(–11) mm, surfaces densely villosulous. **2*n*** = 14.

Flowering mid–late summer. Sandy prairies, open, sandy woodlands, blowouts and semi-stabilized ground in inland sand dunes; 0–1500 m; Man., Sask.; Colo., Iowa, Kans., Mich., Minn., Mo., Mont., Nebr., N.Mex., N.Dak., Okla., S.Dak., Tex., Wis., Wyo.

In Texas, var. *villosa* is known from the northwestern part of the state, and its range does not overlap with var. *grisea*. Variety *villosa* is listed by the Committee on the Status of Endangered Wildlife in Canada as being threatened in Canada.

29b. Dalea villosa (Nuttall) Sprengel var. **grisea** (Torrey & A. Gray) Barneby, Mem. New York Bot. Gard. 27: 262. 1977 [E]

Petalostemon griseus Torrey & A. Gray, Fl. N. Amer. 1: 310. 1838 (as griseum)

Stems erect, 5–8(–9) dm, sparsely pubescent. **Leaflet blades** 10–15 mm, surfaces sparsely pubescent. **2*n*** = 14.

Flowering spring–early summer. Sandy, open woods; 50–150 m; Ark., La., Tex.

While both varieties occur in Texas, the ranges do not overlap. Over 100 km separate the westernmost occurrence of var. *grisea* in Falls and Milam counties from the easternmost occurrence of var. *villosa* in Eastland County.

30. Dalea purpurea Ventenat, Descr. Pl. Nouv., plate 40. 1801 • Purple prairie-clover [E] [F]

Petalostemon purpureus (Ventenat) Ryberg

Perennial herbs, erect to spreading, glabrous, puberulent, pilose, or tomentulose. **Stems** 2–9 dm, eglandular or with few scattered glands. **Principal leaves** 1.7–4(–4.5) cm; leaflets 3 or 5(or 7), blades linear to linear-elliptic, (7–)10–24(–28) mm. **Peduncles** (0–)3–15 cm. **Inflorescences** spikes, densely flowered, not involucrate, 7–12 mm diam.; axis not visible, (1–)1.5–7 cm; bracts persistent through anthesis, (2.3–)2.7–5.8(–7) mm.

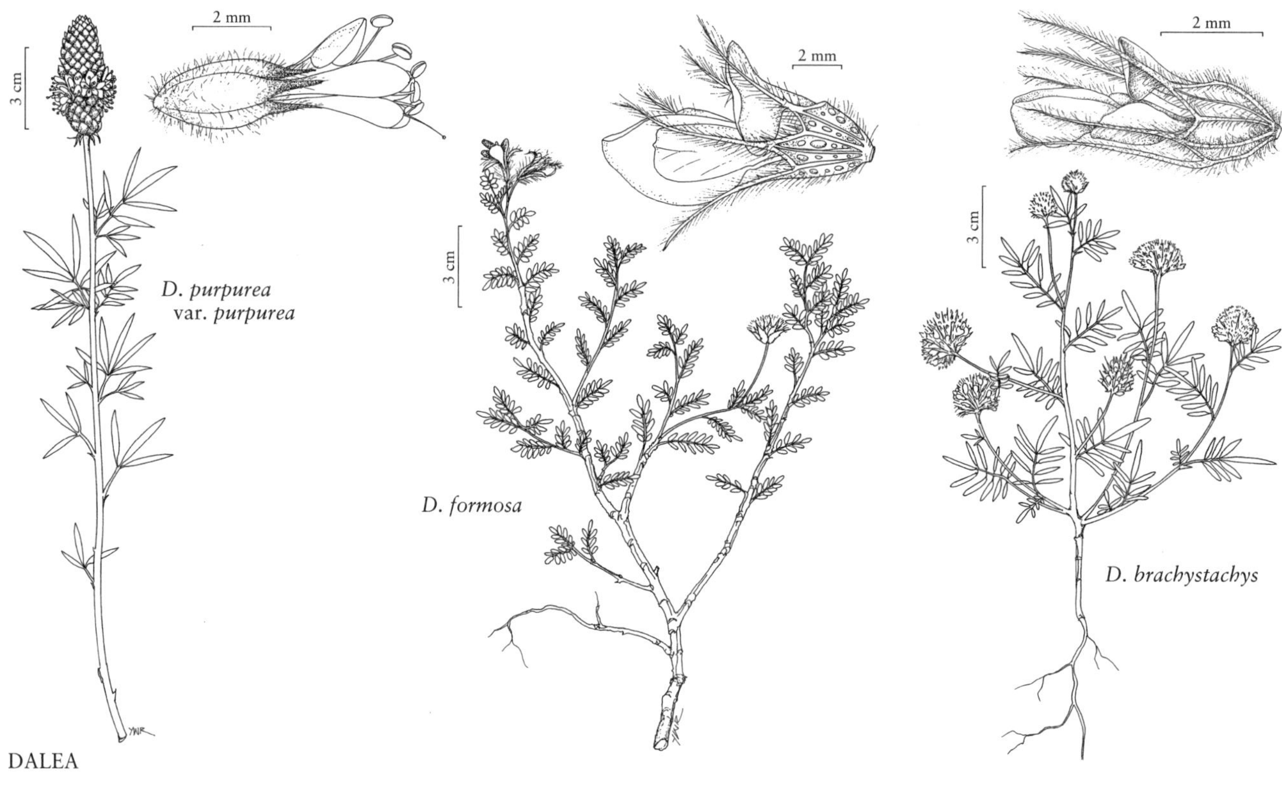

DALEA

Calyces subsymmetric, 3.2–4.5 mm, pilosulous, base with antrorse hairs; tube (1.7–)2–2.8(–2.9) mm, with 0 glands between ribs, lobes lanceolate to ovate, adaxial pair broadest. **Corollas** rose, magenta, pale purple, lilac, or pink; not conventionally papilionaceous; banner (4.3–)4.7–6.7(–7.2) mm, blade ovate to suborbiculate, 1.7–2.6(–2.8) × 1.7–2.8(–3.2) mm; epistemonous petals attached at separation of filaments, blades 2.5–3.8 (–4) × 0.8–1.3(–1.5)mm. **Stamens** 5, 5.6–8.5(–9) mm, filaments distinct to 3–5.2(–5.5) mm, anthers (0.7–) 0.8–1.3(–1.4) mm. **Legumes** 2.1–2.6 mm, distally pilosulous and gland-dotted. **Seeds** 1.6–2.1 mm.

Varieties 2 (2 in the flora): North America.

Dalea purpurea is characteristic of prairies and has a wide geographical distribution. It is sometimes cultivated for its showy purple flowers and drought tolerance. Livestock find it palatable; it decreases with grazing.

1. Spikes (8–)9.5–12 mm diam.; peduncles 0–10 cm (often absent or very short on side shoots) . . . . 30a. *Dalea purpurea* var. *purpurea*
1. Spikes 7–9 mm diam.; peduncles 3–15 cm . . . . 30b. *Dalea purpurea* var. *arenicola*

30a. Dalea purpurea Ventenat var. **purpurea** [E] [F]

Herbs usually puberulent, pilose, or tomentulose, sometimes glabrous proximal to inflorescences. **Stems** 2–9 dm. **Peduncles** 0–10 cm, often absent or very short on side shoots. **Spikes** (8–)9.5–12 mm diam. $2n = 14$.

Flowering summer. Prairies, open woods; 10–2300 m; Alta., Man., Ont., Sask.; Ala., Ariz., Ark., Colo., Ga., Ill., Ind., Iowa, Kans., Ky., La., Mich., Minn., Miss., Mo., Mont., Nebr., N.Mex., N.Y., N.Dak., Ohio, Okla., S.Dak., Tenn., Tex., Wis., Wyo.

In Texas, var. *purpurea* is known from scattered localities across the northern part of the state with a range that does not overlap with var. *arenicola*. Variety *purpurea* is introduced in Arizona and probably elsewhere.

30b. Dalea purpurea Ventenat var. **arenicola** (Wemple) Barneby, Mem. New York Bot. Gard. 27: 267. 1977 E

Petalostemon arenicola Wemple, Iowa State J. Sci. 45: 94, figs. 8, 11I, 12D. 1970; *Dalea arenicola* (Wemple) B. L. Turner

Herbs glabrous proximal to inflorescences. **Stems** 2–4(–5) dm. **Peduncles** 3–15 cm. **Spikes** 7–9 mm diam. **2*n*** = 14.

Flowering late spring–summer. Sandy or rocky areas, often in alluvium; 500–1300 m; Colo., Kans., Nebr., N.Mex., Okla., Tex.

In Texas, var. *arenicola* is known from the northwestern quarter of the state. Variety *arenicola* occurs in areas of loose sand, while var. *purpurea* occurs in more compacted soil. The varieties are generally fairly distinctive except in areas where the two types of soils are in close proximity.

31. Dalea compacta Sprengel, Syst. Veg. 3: 327. 1826 E

Petalostemon compactus (Sprengel) Swezey

Perennial herbs, erect to ascending or decumbent, glabrous or sparsely pilosulous. **Stems** 3–6(–7) dm, sparsely glandular-punctate. **Principal leaves** (2–)2.5–5.5 cm; leaflets (3 or)5 or 7(or 9), blades linear-oblanceolate to -elliptic, (10–)12–25 mm. **Peduncles** 0–15 cm. **Inflorescences** spikes, densely flowered, not involucrate, 10.5–14(–15) mm diam.; axis not visible, (0.5–)1–3 cm; bracts persistent through anthesis, 2–7.5 mm. **Calyces** subsymmetric, (4.4–)5–6.2 mm, pilosulous, with lines of antrorse, subappressed hairs proximal to sinuses and on margins of lobes; tube 3–3.8 mm, with 0 glands between ribs, lobes subulate or adaxial pair triangular-ovate. **Corollas** rose-lilac or rose-purple; not conventionally papilionaceous; banner 5.4–9 mm, blade ovate-oblong or -deltate, 2.2–3.5 × 2.4–3.6 mm; epistemonous petals attached at separation of filaments, blades 2.8–4 × 1.1–1.8 mm. **Stamens** 5, 8–10.5 mm, filaments distinct to 3.3–5(–5.4) mm, anthers 1–1.5 mm. **Legumes** 3–3.5 mm, glabrous except apex, eglandular. **Seeds** 1.5 mm.

Varieties 2 (2 in the flora): sc United States.

Dalea compacta is most abundant in east Texas, where it is found in habitats similar to those occupied by *D. purpurea* in prairies of the mid United States.

1. Principal interfloral bracts exceeding subtended calyces, 4.5–7.5 mm . . . . 31a. *Dalea compacta* var. *compacta*
1. Principal interfloral bracts equaling or shorter than subtended calyces, 2–5 mm. . . . . 31b. *Dalea compacta* var. *pubescens*

31a. Dalea compacta Sprengel var. **compacta** E

Petalostemon decumbens Nuttall

Peduncles 0(–2.5) cm. **Principal interfloral bracts** exceeding subtended calyces, 4.5–7.5 mm.

Flowering spring–early summer. Open grasslands, heavy clay or calcareous soils; 0–200 m; Ark., Okla., Tex.

In Texas, var. *compacta* is known from the eastern half of the state. The name *Dalea compacta* has been misapplied to the species now known as *D. cylindriceps* (R. C. Barneby 1977c).

31b. Dalea compacta Sprengel var. **pubescens** (A. Gray) Barneby, Mem. New York Bot. Gard. 27: 270. 1977 E

Petalostemon violaceus Michaux var. *pubescens* A. Gray, Smithsonian Contr. Knowl. 3(5): 46. 1852 (as violaceum); *P. pulcherrimus* (A. Heller) A. Heller

Peduncles (1.5–)2–15 cm. **Principal interfloral bracts** equaling or shorter than subtended calyces, 2–5 mm. **2*n*** = 14.

Flowering spring–early summer(–fall). Grasslands, calcareous soils; 10–500 m; Ark., La., Okla., Tex.

In Texas, var. *pubescens* is known from the eastern coastal part of the state.

32. Dalea tenuis (J. M. Coulter) Shinners, Field & Lab. 17: 84. 1949 E

Petalostemon violaceus Michaux var. *tenuis* J. M. Coulter, Contr. U.S. Natl. Herb. 1: 34. 1890; *P. tenuis* (J. M. Coulter) A. Heller

Perennial herbs, erect, glabrous or sparsely pilosulous. **Stems** 1.5–4(–5) dm, sparsely glandular-punctate. **Principal leaves** 1.5–3.5 cm; leaflets 3 or 5, blades linear, 6–15 mm. **Peduncles** 2.5–18 cm. **Inflorescences** spikes, densely flowered, not involucrate, 7–12 mm diam.; axis not visible, 0.5–2.5 cm; bracts persistent through anthesis, 1.5–4.5 mm. **Calyces** subsymmetric, 3–5.2 mm, silky-pilosulous, base with subappressed and retrorse hairs; tube 2–3.1 mm, with 0 glands between ribs, lobes subulate or adaxial pair triangular-ovate. **Corollas** pink; not conventionally papilionaceous; banner 4.6–5.8 mm, blade ovate, 2.2–2.5 × 1.5–2.8 mm; epistemonous petals attached at separation of filaments, blades 2.7–3.1 × 1–1.3 mm. **Stamens** 5, 6–8.5 mm, filaments distinct to 2.5–4.8 mm, anthers 0.8–1 mm. **Legumes** 3.6 mm, glabrous or apically pilosulous, eglandular. **Seeds** apparently unknown.

Flowering late spring–early summer (fall). Rocky limestone soils; 200–600 m; Okla., Tex.

Dalea tenuis is largely a species of central Texas occurring as far east as McLennan County and south to Bandera County.

33. Dalea cahaba J. R. Allison, Castanea 66: 166, fig. 5. 2001 [C] [E]

Perennial herbs, decumbent to weakly ascending, glabrate to pilosulous. **Stems** ribbed, simple or proximally branched, 1.7–6.5(–7) dm, eglandular. **Principal leaves** 1.5–3.7 cm; leaflets 3 or 5, blades inrolled to involute, linear to linear-lanceolate, 5–20 mm. **Peduncles** (0.5–)2–8.5 cm. **Inflorescences** spikes, densely flowered, not involucrate, (7–)9–12 mm diam.; axis not visible, 0.5–2.2(–2.8) cm; bracts persistent through anthesis, proximals 4–7 mm, median 3.3–5 mm. **Calyces** subsymmetric, 4–5 mm, tomentulose, base with intertangled hairs; tube 2.5 mm, with 0 glands between ribs, lobes lanceolate-acuminate or adaxial pair lanceolate-ovate-acuminate to ovate-acuminate. **Corollas** rose-purple; not conventionally papilionaceous; banner 3.5–5.3 mm, blade ovate, 2–2.5 × 1.7–1.8 mm; epistemonous petals attached at separation of filaments, blades 2.5–3 × 1.1–1.8 mm. **Stamens** 5, 6–7 mm, filaments distinct for 4–4.5 mm, anthers (0.7–)0.9–1.2 mm. **Legumes** 3.2–4.4 mm, glabrous at base, tomentulose on distal ⅔, eglandular. **Seeds** 1.9–2.2 mm.

Flowering late spring–early summer. Open glades, dolomite soils; of conservation concern; 70–200 m; Ala.

Dalea cahaba is apparently restricted to open glades in the Ketona dolomite formation in Bibb County. Because it is distinguished from similar species only by its sprawling habit and indument, genetic and transplant studies are needed to verify its status as a distinct species.

34. Dalea reverchonii (S. Watson) Shinners, Field & Lab. 17: 84. 1949 (as reverchoni) [C] [E]

Petalostemon reverchonii S. Watson, Proc. Amer. Acad. Arts 21: 449. 1886 (as reverchoni)

Perennial herbs, decumbent, pilosulous. **Stems** 1.5–2 dm, eglandular. **Principal leaves** 2–3 cm; leaflets 7 or 9, blades linear-oblong or -oblanceolate, 5–12 mm. **Peduncles** 0–1 cm. **Inflorescences** spikes, loosely flowered, not involucrate, 8–10 mm diam.; axis visible, 1.5–5 cm; bracts deciduous, 2.5 mm. **Calyces** subsymmetric, 4.2–4.6 mm, silky-pilosulous to -tomentulose, hairs subappressed; tube 1.9–2.1 mm, with ribs leading to sinuses stronger than those leading to lobes, tube appearing bluntly 5-angled, with 0 glands between ribs, lobes lanceolate-acuminate or adaxial pair triangular-acuminate. **Corollas** magenta-purple; not conventionally papilionaceous; banner 4.3–4.6 mm, blade ovate to elliptic, 2.1–2.3 × 1.8–2 mm; epistemonous petals attached at separation of filaments, blades 2.6–3 × 1.1–1.3 mm. **Stamens** 5, 6.1–7.2 mm, filaments distinct to 3.3–4 mm, anthers 0.7–0.9 mm. **Legumes** 3.1–3.5 mm, pilosulous and gland-dotted distally. **Seeds** 1.3 mm.

Flowering spring–early summer (fall). Rocky limestone soils; of conservation concern; ca. 400 m; Tex.

Dalea reverchonii occurs in Hood, Parker, and Wise counties in north-central Texas. It is in the Center for Plant Conservation's National Collection of Endangered Plants.

35. Dalea gattingeri (A. Heller) Barneby, Mem. New York Bot. Gard. 27: 274. 1977 [E]

Kuhnistera gattingeri A. Heller, Bull. Torrey Bot. Club 23: 121, plate 262. 1896; *Petalostemon gattingeri* (A. Heller) A. Heller

Perennial herbs, diffusely spreading, distally pilosulous on stems. **Stems** 1.5–3.5 dm, usually glabrous or glabrescent at base, pilosulous distally, eglandular or with scattered small glands. **Principal leaves** 2–3.5 cm; leaflets 5 or 7(or 9), blades linear to linear-oblanceolate or linear-elliptic, 8–18 mm. **Peduncles** 0.5–2.5 cm. **Inflorescences** spikes, moderately densely flowered, not involucrate, (8–)9–10 mm diam.; axis becoming partially visible, 1.5–7.5 cm; bracts early deciduous or proximals persistent, interfloral ones held in place by crowded flowers, 3–5(–6) mm. **Calyces** subsymmetric, 4–5 mm, pilose-tomentulose; tube

2–2.5(–2.7) mm, prominently to indistinctly 10-ribbed, ± circular in cross section, with 0 glands between ribs, lobes lanceolate or adaxial pair ovate. **Corollas** rose-purple; not conventionally papilionaceous; banner 5.2–6.2 mm, blade ovate, 2.1–2.6 × (1.6–)2–2.8 mm; epistemonous petals attached at separation of filaments, blades 2.6–3.2 × 0.9–1.3 mm. **Stamens** 5, 6.3–7.8 mm, filaments distinct to 3.8–5.4 mm, anthers 0.8–1 mm. **Legumes** 2.8–3.3 mm, pilosulous distally and dotted with small glands. **Seeds** 2.2 mm. **2*n*** = 14.

Flowering late spring–summer. Cedar glades and barrens, on rocky, calcareous soils; 150–500 m; Ala., Ark., Ga., Mo., Tenn.

Dalea gattingeri is a narrow habitat specialist that can be locally common in suitable habitat.

36. Dalea tenuifolia (A. Gray) Shinners, Field & Lab. 17: 84. 1949 [E]

Petalostemon tenuifolius A. Gray, Proc. Amer. Acad. Arts 11: 73. 1876

Perennial herbs, diffusely spreading to decumbent, mostly pilosulous ± throughout. **Stems** (1.5–)2–5(–5.5) dm, usually pilosulous at base, glabrescent distally, eglandular. **Principal leaves** 2–4 cm; leaflets 3 or 5, blades linear-oblanceolate, 10–22 mm. **Peduncles** (0.9–)1.5–8(–12.5) cm. **Inflorescences** spikes, moderately densely flowered, not involucrate, 8–10 mm diam.; axis becoming partially visible, (0.5–)1–7(–9) cm; bracts deciduous by anthesis, 2.5–4.5 (–5.5) mm. **Calyces** subsymmetric, (3.1–)3.4–4.5 mm, densely pilose; tube (1.6–)1.9–2.4 mm, prominently to indistinctly 10-ribbed, ± circular in cross section, with 0 glands between ribs, lobes lanceolate or adaxial pair ovate-lanceolate to ovate. **Corollas** rose-purple; not conventionally papilionaceous; banner 5.5–6.5 mm, blade cordate, 2.3–3.1 × 2.6–3.1 mm; epistemonous petals attached at separation of filaments, blades 2.7–3.4 × 1.2–1.5 mm. **Stamens** 5, 6–8.3 mm, filaments distinct to 3.5–5 mm, anthers 0.9–1.5 mm. **Legumes** 2.8–3.5 mm, pilosulous and often gland-dotted distally. **Seeds** 2 mm. **2*n*** = 14.

Flowering late spring–summer (fall). Rocky places, limestone soils; 800–1400 m; Colo., Kans., N.Mex., Okla., Tex.

Dalea tenuifolia is known from the southern high plains. In Texas, the species is found in the northern panhandle and extreme north-central part of the state.

37. Dalea pinnata (J. F. Gmelin) Barneby, Mem. New York Bot. Gard. 27: 278. 1977 • Summer-farewell [E]

Kuhnia pinnata J. F. Gmelin, Syst. Nat. 2: 375. 1791; *Kuhnistera pinnata* (J. F. Gmelin) Kuntze; *Petalostemon pinnatus* (J. F. Gmelin) S. F. Blake

Perennial herbs, erect, glabrous proximal to inflorescences. **Stems** (3–)4.5–9(–10) dm, finely to coarsely glandular-tuberculate proximal to inflorescences. **Principal leaves** 1–2.5 cm; leaflets 3–11(or 13), blades linear or elliptic-oblanceolate, 5–11 mm. **Peduncles** absent. **Inflorescences** spikes, densely flowered, appearing capitate, conspicuously involucrate, with several whorls of clearly differentiated sterile bracts proximal to spike, 6–13 mm diam.; axis not visible, 0.6–1.2 cm; bracts deciduous, basal involucral bracts persistent, becoming transitional to foliage leaves, 5–8 mm. **Calyces** subsymmetric, slightly recessed opposite banner, 4.5–7.8(–8.2) mm, pilose; tube (1.5–)1.7–2.3(–2.7) mm, with 0 glands between ribs, lobes linear, becoming plumose. **Corollas** white; not conventionally papilionaceous; banner (5–)5.4–8.6 mm, blade lanceolate to oblong-elliptic, proximally cuneate (subhastate), 2.7–4.3 × 0.6–1.4 mm; epistemonous petals attached at separation of filaments, blades 3–5 × 0.5–1.4 mm. **Stamens** 5, 8.8–10.8 mm, filaments distinct to 4.2–5.5 mm, anthers 0.6–0.9 mm. **Legumes** 2.5–3 mm, pilosulous distally, eglandular. **Seeds** 1.7 mm.

Varieties 3 (3 in the flora): se United States.

Dalea pinnata, with its headlike spikes and conspicuous involucres, resembles a member of the Asteraceae. This resemblance is heightened after the petals drop because the slender, plumose calyx-lobes begin to resemble a pappus.

The varieties of *Dalea pinnata* have limited geographical overlap and var. *pinnata* is the most widespread.

1. Leaflets 3. . . . . 37b. *Dalea pinnata* var. *trifoliata*
1. Leaflets 5–11(or 13).
    2. Involucres: 6–9 mm wide; stems finely glandular-tuberculate proximal to spikes . . . . 37a. *Dalea pinnata* var. *pinnata*
    2. Involucres 10–13 mm wide; stems coarsely glandular-tuberculate proximal to spikes . . . . 37c. *Dalea pinnata* var. *adenopoda*

37a. Dalea pinnata (J. F. Gmelin) Barneby var. **pinnata** E

Stems finely glandular-tuberculate proximal to spikes. **Leaflets** 5–11(or 13), blades usually involute, ± linear. **Involucres** 6–9 mm wide. **Epistemonous petals** (including claw) 3.7–4.5 mm. **2*n*** = 14.

Flowering fall–early winter. Open, sandy pine and oak woods; 0–150 m; Ala., Fla., Ga., N.C., S.C.

In Florida, var. *pinnata* is frequent in the northern counties of the central peninsula.

37b. Dalea pinnata (J. F. Gmelin) Barneby var. **trifoliata** (Chapman) Barneby, Mem. New York Bot. Gard. 27: 279. 1977 E

Petalostemon corymbosus Michaux var. *trifoliatus* Chapman, Fl. South. U.S. ed. 3, 101. 1897

Stems finely glandular-tuberculate proximal to spikes. **Leaflets** 3, blades involute, linear. **Involucres** 6–9 mm wide. **Epistemonous petals** (including claw) 4.8–6.8 mm. **2*n*** = 14.

Flowering fall–early winter. Sandy pine or oak woods; 0–150 m; Ala., Fla., Ga., La., Miss.

Variety *trifoliata* occurs primarily in the Gulf coastal plain.

37c. Dalea pinnata (J. F. Gmelin) Barneby var. **adenopoda** (Rydberg) Barneby, Mem. New York Bot. Gard. 27: 279. 1977 E

Kuhnistera adenopoda Rydberg in N. L. Britton et al., N. Amer. Fl. 24: 136. 1920; *Dalea adenopoda* (Rydberg) Isely; *K. truncata* Small

Stems coarsely glandular-tuberculate proximal to spikes. **Leaflets** 5–11 (or 13), blades not involute, elliptic-oblanceolate. **Involucres** 10–13 mm wide. **Epistemonous petals** (including claw) 4.3–6 mm.

Flowering fall–winter(–early spring). Sandy openings in pine and oak woodlands, often on white sand; 0–20 m; Fla.

Variety *adenopoda* is known from peninsular Florida as far north as Seminole County.

38. Dalea lanata Sprengel, Syst. Veg. 3: 327. 1826

Perennial herbs, prostrate, densely to sparsely pilosulous or glabrous. **Stems** (2.5–)3–7 dm, eglandular or sparsely glandular-punctate or -verruculose. **Principal leaves** 1–3 cm; leaflets 9–15, blades obovate to broadly oblanceolate, 3–10(–12) mm. **Peduncles** 0.4–4 cm. **Inflorescences** spikes, loosely flowered, not involucrate, 6–8 mm diam.; axis visible, (1–)1.5–7.5(–9) cm; bracts persistent, 2.6–4 mm. **Calyces** subsymmetric, 3.3–4.5 (–4.8) mm, villosulous throughout or on lobes; tube 1.8–2.5 mm, with 1–4 glands between ribs, lobes triangular to lanceolate, ovate-acuminate, or -apiculate. **Corollas** red-violet to magenta or purple; not conventionally papilionaceous; banner 2.8–4.3 mm, blade ovate-cordate, ± peltate, ± cucullate, 1.8–3.1 × 1.8–2.8 mm; epistemonous petals attached near middle of stamen tube, blades 2–3.8 × 1.5–2.2 mm. **Stamens** (5–)8–10 (sometimes only 5 functional), 6.5–8.5 mm, filaments distinct to 1.9–2.9 mm, anthers 0.4–0.6 mm. **Legumes** 2.5–3.1 mm, pilosulous distally and dotted with small glands. **Seeds** 1.8–1.3 mm.

Varieties 2 (2 in the flora): sw United States, n Mexico.

The geographical ranges of the two varieties show little overlap, with a separation at roughly the Pecos River.

1. Calyces: tube and lobes villosulous . . . . 38a. *Dalea lanata* var. *lanata*
1. Calyces: tube glabrous, lobes usually villosulous . . . . 38b. *Dalea lanata* var. *terminalis*

38a. Dalea lanata Sprengel var. **lanata** E

Dalea austrotexana B. L. Turner

Herbs densely pilosulous. **Calyces:** tube 2.2–2.5 mm, villosulous; lobes triangular to lanceolate, villosulous. **Epistemonous petal blades** 2.8–3.8 mm. **2*n*** = 14.

Flowering late spring–fall. Loose sand; 0–1300 m; Ark., Colo., Kans., N.Mex., Okla., Tex.

Variety *lanata* is found mostly from 1200–1300 m and is disjunct on the Texas coastal plain from 0–300 m.

It has been argued that the southeast Texas populations of *Dalea lanata* should be recognized as a distinct species, *D. austrotexana*, due to genetic isolation from the remainder of *D. lanata* and a difference in leaflet length (B. L. Turner 2006b).

38b. Dalea lanata Sprengel var. **terminalis** (M. E. Jones) Barneby, Mem. New York Bot. Gard. 27: 283. 1977

Dalea terminalis M. E. Jones, Contr. W. Bot. 12: 8. 1908; *D. glaberrima* S. Watson

Herbs densely to sparsely pilosulous or glabrous. **Calyces:** tube 1.8–2.5 mm, glabrous; lobes deltate- to ovate-acuminate or -apiculate, usually villosulous. **Epistemonous petal blades** 2–3.4 mm. **2*n*** = 14.

Flowering summer–fall. Loose sand, often on dunes; 900–1900 m; Ariz., Colo., Nev., N.Mex., Tex., Utah; Mexico (Chihuahua, Coahuila).

39. Dalea frutescens A. Gray, Boston J. Nat. Hist. 6: 175. 1850

Shrubs, highly branched, glabrous proximal to inflorescences. **Stems** 3–8(–12) dm, glandular-tuberculate distally. **Principal leaves** 1–2 cm; leaflets 9–19 (or 21), blades obovate to broadly oblanceolate, 1.5–3.5 (–5) mm. **Peduncles** 0.2–4.5 (–5) cm. **Inflorescences** spikes, densely or loosely flowered, not involucrate, 8–11 mm diam.; axis usually not visible, 0.2–2.5 cm; bracts deciduous, 2.2–3.4(–4.5) mm. **Calyces** subsymmetric, 3.8–4.2 mm, glabrous; tube 2.6–3.2(–3.5) mm, usually with 3–5(–7) glands between ribs, lobes broadly triangular to triangular-acuminate, unequal, abaxial longest. **Corollas** usually bicolored, rarely all white, banner whitish with yellowish eye, reddish in age, epistemonous petals vivid pink-purple; papilionaceous; banner 5.1–6.2 mm, blade ovate-cordate, 3.2–4.2 × 3.4–4.6 mm, proximal lobes connate, forming obconic pit; epistemonous petals attached near or proximal to middle of stamen tube; wings 4.3–5.2 × 2.7–3 mm; keel connate valvately, blades (5–)5.3–6.5 × 3.3–3.9 mm. **Stamens** 10, 6.8–8.2 mm, filaments distinct to 1.8–2.7 mm, anthers 0.5–0.8 mm. **Legumes** 2.8–3.5 mm, glabrous or distally pilosulous, dotted with small glands distally. **Seeds** 1.7–2.3 mm. **2*n*** = 14.

Flowering late summer–fall (spring). Rocky ground, desert grasslands, scrub, open juniper or oak woodlands, often on limestone; 200–2300 m; N.Mex., Okla., Tex.; Mexico (Chihuahua, Coahuila, Nuevo León, Tamaulipas, Zacatecas).

Dalea frutescens is reported to be palatable for livestock and to decline under grazing pressure. In Texas, the species is widespread away from the coastal areas and generally from the Edwards Plateau westward to the trans-Pecos region.

40. Dalea greggii A. Gray, Pl. Nov. Thurb., 314. 1854

Subshrubs, horizontal-spreading, mat-forming, at least young foliage silky-pilosulous. **Stems** procumbent or arching, often rooting along stems, 3–5 (–20+) dm, eglandular or glandular-verruculose distally. **Principal leaves** 0.6–2.5(–3) cm; leaflets 5–9, blades obovate to oblanceolate, 2–7(–9) mm. **Peduncles** 0–4(–6) cm. **Inflorescences** spikes, relatively densely flowered, not involucrate, 8–11 mm diam.; axis usually not visible, 0.4–3(–5.5) cm; bracts persistent, 2–4 mm. **Calyces** subsymmetric, (4–)4.2–6 mm, silky-pilosulous; tube (2–)2.2–2.8(–3) mm, usually with 3–8(–10) blister glands between ribs (scattered or in a row), lobes triangular-acuminate to lanceolate or aristate, unequal, abaxial longest. **Corollas** bicolored, banner cream to pale yellow, reddish in age, epistemonous petals pink to pink-purple; papilionaceous; banner 4.4–6.2 mm, blade deltate-cordate, 2.6–3.5 × 3.2–4.3 mm, proximal lobes connate, forming obconic pit; epistemonous petals attached proximal to middle of stamen tube; wings 3.2–4.6 × 1.6–2.4 mm; keel connate valvately, blades 4–4.8(–5.3) × 2.2–3.3 mm. **Stamens** 10, 5.5–7.5 mm, filaments distinct to 1.7–2.4 mm, anthers 0.5–0.7 mm. **Legumes** 2.1–2.8 mm, pilosulous and gland-dotted distally. **Seeds** 1.6–2 mm. **2*n*** = 14 (Mexico).

Flowering spring, fall, (year-round). Rocky slopes, deserts, open woodlands, limestone soils; 600–1400 m; Ariz., N.Mex., Tex.; Mexico (Chihuahua, Coahuila, Durango, Nuevo León, San Luis Potosí, Tamaulipas, Zacatecas, south as far as Oaxaca).

Dalea greggii is cultivated as a ground cover and for erosion control in xeriscaping. In Texas, the species is known from the eastern trans-Pecos and Big Bend regions.

41. Dalea pulchra Gentry, Madroño 10: 227, plate 14. 1950

Shrubs, relatively erect, stiffly-branching, silky- or velvety-pubescent distally. **Stems** 5–10 dm, verruculose distally. **Principal leaves** 0.5–1.5 cm; leaflets 5 or 7(or 9), blades obovate to oblanceolate, 1.5–5 mm. **Peduncles** 0–1 cm. **Inflorescences** spikes, densely flowered, obviously involucrate (proximalmost several whorls of bracts subtending rudimentary buds), 11.5–16 mm diam.; axis not visible, 0.4–0.7 cm; bracts deciduous, interfloral ones sometimes held in place by crowded flowers, 2–6.5 mm. **Calyces** asymmetric, recessed opposite banner, (4.5–)4.8–7.2 mm, densely pilose; tube 2.4–3.4 mm, hyaline intervals usually with row of inconspicuous blister glands between ribs (or eglandular), lobes triangular-aristate, spurred laterally near proximal end, unequal, abaxial longest. **Corollas** bicolored, banner cream, reddish in age, epistemonous petals pink-purple; papilionaceous; banner 6–7.5 mm, blade ovate- or deltate-cordate, 2.8–4.2 × 3.4–4.4 mm; epistemonous petals attached proximal to middle of stamen tube; wings 4.1–5 × 2–2.6 mm; keel connate valvately, blades 5.2–6.8 × 3–3.5 mm. **Stamens** 10, 7.5–9 mm, filaments distinct to 1.8–2.8 mm, anthers 0.6–0.7 mm. **Legumes** 2.5–3 mm, densely pubescent distally, eglandular. **Seeds** 1.5–1.8 mm. **2*n*** = 14.

Flowering spring. Sandy to gravelly or rocky grasslands, open oak, juniper, or pine woodlands, desert scrub; 900–1400 m; Ariz., N.Mex.; Mexico (Chihuahua, Sonora).

Plants of *Dalea pulchra* are attractive in flower. The spikes shatter quickly at anthesis; legumes and seeds are seldom seen.

42. Dalea bicolor Humboldt & Bonpland ex Willdenow, Hort. Berol. 2: plate 89. 1809; Enum. Pl., 787. 1809

Varieties 5 (1 in the flora): sw United States, Mexico.

Only var. *argyrea* enters the flora area; the other varieties are confined to Mexico. Variety *orcuttiana* Barneby occurs in Baja California, var. *naviculifolia* (Hemsley) Barneby in Oaxaca, var. *canescens* (M. Martens & Galeotti) Barneby in Oaxaca and Puebla, and var. *bicolor* is widely distributed in central and northern Mexico.

42a. Dalea bicolor Humboldt & Bonpland ex Willdenow var. **argyrea** (A. Gray) Barneby, Mem. New York Bot. Gard. 27: 427. 1977

Dalea argyrea A. Gray, Smithsonian Contr. Knowl. 3(5): 47. 1852 (as argyraea)

Shrubs, relatively erect, low and rounded, pilosulous distally. **Stems** (2–)4–9 dm, glandular-tuberculate or -verrucose distally. **Principal leaves** 1–3.5 cm; leaflets (5 or)7–13, blades obovate to obovate-oblong, (2–)3–9 mm. **Peduncles** 0–4(–5) cm. **Inflorescences** spikes, relatively densely flowered, not involucrate, 8–10 mm diam.; axis not to partially visible, 0.5–4 cm; bracts persistent or deciduous, 1–5.5(–6) mm. **Calyces** subsymmetric, (3.5–)3.8–5 mm, densely short-pubescent; tube 2.6–3.2 mm, with 2–4 blister glands between ribs, lobes broadly triangular-apiculate, unequal, abaxial longest. **Corollas** bicolored, banner yellowish or white, reddish in age, epistemonous petals rose-purple to pink or violet; papilionaceous; banner 3.2–7.5(–8) mm, blade deltate-cordate to orbiculate, (2.2–)2.8–4.8(–5.8) × 2.4–5.2 mm; epistemonous petals attached near or proximal to middle of stamen tube; wings 3.6–5.5 × 1.8–3 mm; keel connate valvately, blades 4.6–7 × 2.1–4.4 mm. **Stamens** 10, 5.6–10.5(–12) mm, filaments distinct to (1.7–)2–4 mm, anthers 0.6–1 mm. **Legumes** 2.2–2.7 mm, usually pilosulous distally, rarely glabrous, and dotted with small glands. **Seeds** apparently unknown.

Flowering (summer–)fall(–winter). Rocky slopes, open and brushy areas, often on limestone soils; 400–2100 m; N.Mex., Tex.; Mexico (Coahuila, Nuevo León, Tamaulipas).

Variety *argyrea* occurs in trans-Pecos Texas and Val Verde County, and in southeastern New Mexico in Chaves, Eddy, and Lincoln counties.

43. Dalea tentaculoides Gentry, Madroño 10: 238, plates 18, 19. 1950 [C]

Shrubs or subshrubs, relatively erect, sparsely pilosulous or glabrous proximal to inflorescences. **Stems** 3–6(–12) dm, glandular-tuberculate distally. **Principal leaves** 3–6 cm; leaflets 19–35, blades oblong-elliptic to obovate, 2.5–8 mm. **Peduncles** (0–)0.2–2.2 cm. **Inflorescences** spikes, relatively densely flowered, not involucrate, 11–15 mm diam.; axis not to partially visible, 1–2(–2.5) cm; bracts persistent or deciduous, (2.5–)3–5.5 mm. **Calyces** asymmetric, recessed opposite banner, 5.2–7.8 mm, sparsely pilosulous; tube 2.5–3.1 mm, with 0–2 glands between ribs, lobes lanceolate-acuminate, each with several elongated, pricklelike glands (gland spurs). **Corollas** bicolored, banner whitish, reddish in age, epistemonous petals rose-purple; papilionaceous; banner 6.2–6.7 mm, blade flabellate, 3–3.5 × 3.9–4.2 mm; epistemonous petals attached proximal to middle of stamen tube; wings 4.9–5.8 × 2.2–3 mm; keel connate valvately, blades 5–6.2 × 3.2–4.4 mm. **Stamens** 10, 8–9.5 mm, filaments distinct to 2.6–3.5 mm, anthers 0.7–1 mm. **Legumes** 3 mm, pilosulous distally, eglandular. **Seeds** 1.5 mm.

Flowering spring (fall). Rocks in canyons, rocky volcanic slopes in desert mountains; of conservation concern; 900–2200 m; Ariz.; Mexico (Sonora).

Dalea tentaculoides occurs in Santa Cruz and Pima counties. It is in the Center for Plant Conservation's National Collection of Endangered Plants.

44. Dalea versicolor Zuccarini, Abh. Math.-Phys. Cl. Königl. Bayer. Akad. Wiss. 1: 342. 1832

Varieties 7 (1 in the flora): sw United States, Mexico, Central America (Guatemala)

R. C. Barneby (1977c) used a hierarchical classification for this large, mainly Mexican species. Variety *sessilis* is one of four varieties in subsp. *versicolor*; three other varieties are recognized in subsp. *argyrostachys* (Hooker & Arnott) Barneby. The complex variation in this group is further complicated by seasonal dimorphism. In fall-blooming plants, relatively elongated spikes terminate long shoots; in spring-blooming plants, shorter and more numerous spikes are borne on short shoots from the axils of fallen leaves.

Variety *versicolor* occurs in southern Mexico and Guatemala.

44a. Dalea versicolor Zuccarini var. **sessilis** (A. Gray) Barneby, Phytologia 26: 1. 1973

Dalea wislizeni A. Gray var. *sessilis* A. Gray, Proc. Amer. Acad. Arts 16: 105. 1880

Shrubs or subshrubs, relatively erect, glabrous or pilosulous. **Stems** 2–7 dm, eglandular or glandular-verruculose distally. **Principal leaves** 1–4 cm; leaflets 9–19, blades oblanceolate to elliptic or obovate, 1–7.7(–9) mm. **Peduncles** 0–7(–10) cm. **Inflorescences** spikes, relatively densely flowered, not involucrate, 12–15 mm diam.; axis usually not visible, 0.5–2 cm; bracts deciduous, (2.5–)3–7.5 mm. **Calyces** somewhat asymmetric, sometimes slightly recessed opposite banner, 5.7–7 mm, densely pilose; tube 2.4–2.8(–3) mm, with 3–6 blister glands between ribs, lobes triangular-aristate, spurred laterally near base, unequal, abaxial longest. **Corollas** bicolored, banner cream to pale yellow, reddish in age, epistemonous petals rose-pink to -purple or magenta; papilionaceous; banner (4.8–)5–8.2 mm, blade deltate-cordate, (2.4–)2.8–4.6 × 2–5.2 mm; epistemonous petals attached proximal to middle of stamen tube; wings (3.7–)4–6.5 × 1.7–3.3 mm; keel connate valvately, blades (4–)4.4–7(–7.5) × 2.7–4.2 mm. **Stamens** 10, 7–10.5(–12) mm, filaments distinct to 1.8–3.2 mm, anthers 0.5–0.9 mm. **Legumes** 2.4–2.9 mm, pilosulous and gland-dotted distally. **Seeds** 1.6–2 mm. **2*n*** = 14.

Flowering spring, fall. Rocky slopes, canyons, oak or pine woodlands, desert grasslands; 900–2100 m; Ariz., N.Mex.; Mexico (Chihuahua, Sinaloa, Sonora).

Variety *sessilis* occurs primarily in the southeastern quarter of Arizona and into southwestern New Mexico. An outlier population occurs in Mohave County in northwestern Arizona.

45. Dalea formosa Torrey, Ann. Lyceum Nat. Hist. New York 2: 177. 1827 • Feather-plume [F]

Shrubs, relatively erect, often gnarled, glabrous or glabrate proximal to inflorescences. **Stems** 1.5–9 dm, eglandular or sparsely glandular-tuberculate distally. **Principal leaves** 0.3–1.1 cm; leaflets (5 or)7–13 (or 15), blades obovate-cuneate to oblanceolate, 1–6(–7) mm. **Peduncles** 0–1(–1.8) cm. **Inflorescences** spikes, loosely flowered, 2–9-flowered, not involucrate, 8 mm diam.; axis usually visible, 0.2–0.8(–3.5) cm; bracts early deciduous or ± persistent, brown, 2–6 mm, glandular. **Calyces** asymmetric, not recessed opposite banner, opening oblique, (7.5–)8.5–13.5(–16.2) mm, long-pilose; tube (3–)3.5–5(–5.2) mm, with 3 or 4(or 5) prominent blister glands between ribs, lobes lanceolate-acuminate, becoming aristate, plumose, with pointed projecting glands laterally. **Corollas** bicolored, banner cream to pale yellow, reddish in age, epistemonous petals rose- or magenta-purple; papilionaceous; banner (6.6–)7–8.8 mm, blade deltate-obcordate, (4–)4.3–5.5 × (3.4–)4–6.4 mm; epistemonous petals attached proximal to middle of stamen tube; wings 5.2–7.4 × 2.4–3.7 mm; keel connate valvately, blades (6–)6.3–7.6 × 3.2–4.5 mm. **Stamens** 10, 9–12.5 mm, filaments distinct to 2.4–4.5 mm, anthers 0.8–1.2 mm. **Legumes** 3–3.5 mm, pilosulous and gland-dotted distally. **Seeds** 2.8–3 mm. **2*n*** = 14, 21, 42.

Flowering spring (fall). Rocky desert, grasslands, open woodlands; 500–2100 m; Ariz., Colo., N.Mex., Okla., Tex.; Mexico (Chihuahua, Coahuila, Sonora).

As R. C. Barneby (1977c) pointed out, *Dalea formosa* is distinctive in appearance. It is complex cytologically, with diploid plants known from Arizona, New Mexico, Texas, and Mexico; tetraploid plants from Texas and Mexico; and hexaploid plants from New Mexico, Texas, and Mexico (R. Spellenberg 1981). In Texas, the species is known from widespread areas of the western half of the state.

46. Dalea carthagenensis (Jacquin) J. F. Macbride, Publ. Field Mus. Nat. Hist., Bot. Ser. 13(3): 375. 1943 (as carthaginensis)

Psoralea carthagenensis Jacquin, Enum. Syst. Pl., 27. 1760

Varieties 9 (1 in the flora): Florida, Mexico, West Indies, Central America, South America.

R. C. Barneby (1977c) recognized nine varieties in *Dalea carthagenensis*, a complex and polymorphic species. The eight varieties found outside the flora area occur in Mexico, West Indies, Central America, and South America. The calyces of *D. carthagenensis* sometimes have slightly hooked lobes when mature, a feature used to distinguish *D. scandens*; the two species are allopatric.

46a. Dalea carthagenensis (Jacquin) J. F. Macbride var. **floridana** (Rydberg) Barneby, Mem. New York Bot. Gard. 27: 519. 1977 [C] [E]

Parosela floridana Rydberg in N. L. Britton et al., N. Amer. Fl. 24: 114. 1920; *Dalea floridana* (Rydberg) Diggs & Weakley

Shrubs or subshrubs, villosulous throughout to ± glabrescent. **Stems** 6–20 dm, sparsely glandular-verruculose distally. **Principal leaves** 3–5.5(–7) cm; leaflets 15–23(or 25), blades obovate to oblong-elliptic, 4–18(–20) mm. **Peduncles** 0–2.5 cm. **Inflorescences** spikes, loosely flowered, not involucrate, 10–15 mm diam.; axis visible, (0.2–)0.4–1.5(–2) cm; bracts deciduous near anthesis, (2.5–)3–5 mm. **Calyces** asymmetric, not recessed opposite banner, opening oblique, (5.2–)5.5–7 mm, villosulous throughout or tube glabrescent; tube (2.4–)2.6–3.2 mm, with 2–8 small glands between ribs, sometimes obscure, lobes triangular-aristate, abaxial not uncinate. **Corollas** greenish white or cream, brownish or maroon in age; papilionaceous; banner 4.2–5.2 mm, blade deltate-cordate, 2.5–3.4 × 2.6–3.4 mm; epistemonous petals attached proximal to middle of stamen tube; wings 2.3–4.2 × 1.2–2 mm; keel connate valvately, blades 4–5.4 × (2–)2.2–3 mm. **Stamens** 10, (6.2–)6.5–8.5 mm, filaments distinct to 0.9–2 mm, anthers 0.6–0.7 mm. **Legumes** 2.3–2.7 mm, villosulous and gland-dotted distally. **Seeds** 1.7–1.8 mm.

Flowering fall–spring. Open pine woods and hammocks, roadsides, along canals; of conservation concern; 0–20 m; Fla.

Variety *floridana* occurs in southern Florida as far north as Palm Beach County.

47. Dalea scandens (Miller) R. T. Clausen, Bull. Torrey Bot. Club 73: 83. 1946

Psoralea scandens Miller, Gard. Dict. ed. 8, Psoralea no. 4. 1768

Varieties 5 (1 in the flora): Texas, Mexico, West Indies, Central America.

In addition to var. *paucifolia*, R. C. Barneby (1977c) recognized four varieties from Mexico to the Caribbean region and Central America.

47a. Dalea scandens (Miller) R. T. Clausen var. **paucifolia** (J. M. Coulter) Barneby, Mem. New York Bot. Gard. 27: 527. 1977

Dalea domingensis de Candolle var. *paucifolia* J. M. Coulter, Contr. U.S. Natl. Herb. 1: 34. 1890; *D. thyrsiflora* A. Gray

Shrubs or subshrubs, villosulous. **Stems** 5–12 dm, sparsely glandular-verruculose distally. **Principal leaves** 2–4.5 cm; leaflets 7–11, blades obovate to ovate, (4–)5–13(–16) mm. **Peduncles** absent or less than 0.1 cm, except terminal one for each major branch sometimes to 0.25 cm. **Inflorescences** spikes, loosely flowered, not involucrate, 10–13 mm diam.; axis often visible, 0.2–2(–3) cm; bracts deciduous, 2–6.5 mm. **Calyces** asymmetric, not recessed opposite banner, opening oblique, 4.2–6 mm, villous throughout or proximally glabrous; tube (1.6–)1.8–2.8(–3.1) mm, with 2 or 3 prominent glands between ribs, lobes triangular-aristate, abaxial becoming uncinate, all becoming plumose, laterally gland-spurred. **Corollas** greenish cream, brownish purple in age; papilionaceous; banner 2.5–3.7 mm, blade ovate to nearly orbiculate, 1.9–3 × 1.9–3 mm; epistemonous petals attached proximal to middle of stamen tube; wings 2–3 × 1–1.7 mm; keel connate valvately, blades 2.5–3.5(–3.7) × 1.4–1.9 (–2.1) mm. **Stamens** 10, 4.3–5.5 mm, filaments distinct to 0.6–0.8 mm, anthers 0.6 mm. **Legumes** 2.3–2.7 mm, villosulous and gland-dotted distally. **Seeds** unknown. $2n = 14$.

Flowering fall–early spring. Brushy hillsides, thickets; 0–150[–1600] m; Tex.; Mexico (Chiapas, Nuevo León, San Luis Potosí, Tamaulipas, Yucatan); West Indies (w Cuba).

Similar in appearance to *Dalea carthagenensis*, *D. scandens* var. *paucifolia* is widespread and variable. It occurs in the southern Texas coastal plain as far north as Nueces County.

48. Dalea brachystachys A. Gray, Smithsonian Contr. Knowl. 5(6): 39. 1853 F

Dalea lemmonii Parry ex A. Gray

Annual herbs (monocarpic), erect or diffuse, glabrous proximal to inflorescences. **Stems** (0.5–)1–3.5(–4) dm, eglandular or sparsely glandular-verruculose. **Principal leaves** 0.8–2.5(–3) cm; leaflets (3 or) 5–11, blades oblanceolate to linear-oblanceolate, 2–14(–16) mm. **Peduncles** 1–7 cm. **Inflorescences** spikes, densely flowered, not obviously involucrate, 8–11 mm diam.; axis not to partially visible, 0.3–1.6 cm; bracts deciduous near anthesis, 2.5–6 mm. **Calyces** subsymmetric, (3.5–)4.4–5.8(–6) mm, pilose; tube 1.5–2.1 mm, with (0–)3 glands between ribs, lobes triangular-aristate. **Corollas** clear yellow, pinkish or brownish in age; papilionaceous; banner 2–3.4 (–6) mm, blade deltate-ovate or cordate, 1–2 × 1–2 mm; epistemonous petals attached proximal to middle of stamen tube; wings 1–2(–2.9) × 0.7–1.1(–1.8) mm; keel connate valvately, blades 1.8–2.8(–3.8) × 1.3–2 (–2.4) mm. **Stamens** (9 or)10, 3.5–5.5 mm, filaments distinct to 1–1.4(–2) mm, anthers 0.3–0.5(–0.6) mm. **Legumes** 2.3–2.6 mm, pilosulous and, sometimes, gland-dotted distally. **Seeds** 1.4–1.7 mm. $2n = 14$.

Flowering late summer–fall (spring). Dry, open habitats in deserts, desert grasslands, open oak, juniper, or pine woodlands; 1300–2500 m; Ariz., N.Mex., Tex.; Mexico (Chihuahua, Coahuila, Durango, Puebla, San Luis Potosí, Sonora, Tamaulipas, Zacatecas).

Dalea brachystachys is found as far south as southeastern Puebla. In the flora area, it is most common in extreme southeastern Arizona and adjacent southwestern New Mexico, with scattered populations through much of both states. Unlike most annual *Dalea* species, it is rarely weedy.

49. Dalea filiformis A. Gray, Smithsonian Contr. Knowl. 5(6): 39. 1853

Annual herbs, erect, glabrous or glabrate proximal to inflorescences. **Stems** (0.4–)0.7–3 (–3.5) dm, eglandular. **Principal leaves** 1–3.5 cm; leaflets 3 or 5, blades linear-filiform, 5–23 mm. **Peduncles** (1.3–)2–8 cm. **Inflorescences** spikes, relatively densely flowered, not involucrate, 5–7 mm diam.; axis not to partially visible, (0.2–)0.3–1.5(–2) cm; bracts early deciduous, 1.5–2.8 mm. **Calyces** ± asymmetric, not strongly recessed opposite banner, opening oblique, (2.5–)2.8–3.5 mm, pilosulous; tube (1.3–)2.8–3.5 mm, with 0 or 1(or 2) small glands between ribs, lobes triangular-acuminate or -aristate. **Corollas** all pinkish or reddish, or banner paler; papilionaceous; banner 2.6–3.5 mm, blade ovate or deltate-ovate, 1.4–1.8 × 0.9–1.6 mm; epistemonous petals attached proximal to middle of stamen tube; wings 1.2–1.8(–2) × 0.8–1.1 mm; keel connate valvately, blades 1.4–1.9 × 0.8–1.1 mm. **Stamens** 10, 2.5–3.5 mm, filaments distinct to 0.6–0.9 mm, anthers 0.2–0.3 mm. **Legumes** 2–2.4 mm, pilosulous and, sometimes, gland-dotted distally. **Seeds** 1.5–1.9 mm. $2n = 14$.

Flowering late summer–fall (spring). Open oak, juniper, or pine woodlands, grasslands, rocky soils along roads, disturbed places; 1600–2400 m; Ariz., N.Mex.; Mexico (Chihuahua, Durango, Sonora).

Dalea filiformis is distinctive in its relatively few, narrow leaflets. Its range is primarily southeastern and central Arizona and southwestern New Mexico, but it does occur in northern Arizona to nearly the Utah border, and there is one report for northern New Mexico in Sandoval County.

50. Dalea pogonathera A. Gray, Mem. Amer. Acad. Arts, n. s. 4: 31. 1849

Perennial herbs, decumbent to ascending, glabrous proximal to inflorescences. **Stems** (0.4–)0.7–3.5 dm, sparsely glandular-punctate. **Principal leaves** (0.4–) 0.8–2(–2.5) cm; leaflets (3 or)5 or 7, blades oblanceolate to oblong-elliptic, (1.5–)2–10 mm. **Peduncles** 0.5–4 cm. **Inflorescences** spikes, loosely flowered, not involucrate, 9–18 (–20) mm diam.; axis visible, 1–8 cm; bracts persistent, 3–6 mm. **Calyces** ± asymmetric, opening oblique, 5.2–10.5 mm, densely villosulous; tube 2.6–3.4 mm, with 4–7 small glands between ribs, lobes triangular-aristate, becoming plumose. **Corollas** violet-purple, banner with whitish or greenish center; papilionaceous; banner (4.5–)4.8–7.8 mm, blade broadly ovate, proximally cordate, 2–3.6 × 2.4–4 mm; epistemonous petals attached near middle of stamen tube; wings 2.3–3.9 × 1.2–2.1 mm; keel connate valvately, blades 3.4–5.8 × 1.9–3.1 mm. **Stamens** 9 or 10, (6.5–)7.5–10.5 mm, filaments distinct to 1.7–3 mm, anthers (0.4–)0.5–0.7 mm. **Legumes** 2.8–3.5 mm, densely pilosulous distally, eglandular. **Seeds** 1.9–2.4 mm.

Varieties 2 (2 in the flora): sw United States, n Mexico.

The varieties of *Dalea pogonathera* are geographically mostly separated with a broad transitional zone where intermediate individuals occur. Variety *pogonathera* is the more westerly distributed and upland form; var. *walkerae* has a more easterly range and occurs in more lowland situations. The region of intermediacy occurs in the Rio Grande valley from roughly Val Verde County to Zapata County.

1. Spike diam. 13–18(–20) mm; calyx: longest lobe 4+ mm . . . . . .50a. *Dalea pogonathera* var. *pogonathera*
1. Spike diam. 9–12(–13) mm; calyx: longest lobe to 4 mm . . . . 50b. *Dalea pogonathera* var. *walkerae*

50a. Dalea pogonathera A. Gray var. **pogonathera**

Stems 1–3.5 dm. **Principal leaves** 1–2(–2.5) cm. **Spikes** 13–18(–20) mm diam.; axis (1–) 1.5–8 cm; bracts 4–6 mm. **Calyces:** longest lobe 4+ mm. **Keel blades** 4.3–5.8 × 2.3–3.1 mm. $2n$ = 14.

Flowering nearly year-round. Rocky deserts, desert grasslands, often on limestone; 600–1800 m; Ariz., N.Mex., Tex.; Mexico (Chihuahua, Coahuila, Durango, Nuevo León, San Luis Potosí, Zacatecas).

50b. Dalea pogonathera A. Gray var. **walkerae** (Tharp & F. A. Barkley) B. L. Turner, Field & Lab. 24: 16. 1956

Parosela walkerae Tharp & F. A. Barkley, Bull. Torrey Bot. Club 73: 133. 1946

Stems (0.4–)0.7–2(–2.5) dm. **Principal leaves** (0.4–)0.8–1.8 cm. **Spikes** 9–12(–13) mm diam.; axis 1–4(–5) cm; bracts 3–4.5 mm. **Calyces:** longest lobe to 4 mm. **Keel blades** 3.4–4.8 × 1.9–2.7 mm. $2n$ = 14.

Flowering nearly year-round. Plains, hills, beaches, often sandy, clay soils; 0–200 m; Tex.; Mexico (Coahuila, Nuevo León, San Luis Potosí, Tamaulipas).

51. Dalea lasiathera A. Gray, Smithsonian Contr. Knowl. 3(5): 48. 1852

Perennial herbs, decumbent to ascending, glabrous proximal to inflorescences. **Stems** 1–3(–3.5) dm, sparsely gland-dotted. **Principal leaves** (1–)1.5–3 cm; leaflets (3–)7–11, blades linear-oblanceolate to elliptic, 5–12 mm. **Peduncles** 1.5–5(–6) cm. **Inflorescences** spikes, relatively densely flowered, not involucrate, 11–13 mm diam.; axis not to partially visible, 2–6 cm; bracts persistent, (3–)3.5–5.5 mm. **Calyces** ± asymmetric, opening oblique, 5.3–6.9 mm, silky-pilosulous; tube 3.3–3.9 mm, with 3–5(–16) glands between ribs, lobes triangular-subulate, not plumose. **Corollas** violet-purple, banner with yellowish center; papilionaceous; banner 6.2–7.5 mm, blade broadly ovate, 3.8–4.6 × 4.2–5 mm, proximal lobes connate, forming obconic pit; epistemonous petals attached near or proximal to middle of stamen tube; wings 3.7–4.7 × 2.2–3 mm; keel connate valvately, blades 5.3–6.5 × 2.3–3.7 mm. **Stamens** 10, 8.5–12 mm, filaments distinct to 3.4–4.7 mm, anthers 0.8–1.2 mm. **Legumes** 3–3.5 mm, pilosulous distally, eglandular. **Seeds** 2.3 mm.

Flowering spring (fall). Rocky hillsides, open oak woods, with mesquite; 150–1600 m; Tex.; Mexico (Coahuila, Nuevo León, Tamaulipas).

Dalea lasiathera is most abundant on the Edwards Plateau with outlying populations in the trans-Pecos region and Wichita County in the Red River valley.

52. Dalea enneandra Nuttall, Cat. Pl. Upper Louisiana, no. 30. 1813 [E] [F]

Parosela enneandra (Nuttall) Britton

Perennial herbs, erect, glabrous proximal to inflorescences. **Stems** (5–)6–12 dm, eglandular or sparsely glandular-punctate. **Principal leaves** 1.3–2.6 cm; leaflets (3–)7–11(or 13), blades narrowly oblanceolate or elliptic, 4–11(–12) mm. **Peduncles** 0.5–3.5(–5.5) cm. **Inflorescences** spikes, remotely flowered, most flowers separated by distinct intervals, not involucrate, 7–10 mm diam.; axis visible, (1–)2.5–12 cm; bracts persistent, enfolding and falling with fruit, 3–4.2 mm. **Calyces** ± asymmetric, opening oblique, 6.2–7.6 mm, silky-pilosulous; tube 3–3.5(–3.7) mm, with 3 or 4 inconspicuous glands between ribs, lobes triangular-aristate, becoming plumose. **Corollas** white; papilionaceous; banner 5.7–7 mm, blade broadly ovate, 3.6–4 × 3.2–4.2 mm, proximal lobes connate, forming obconic pit; epistemonous petals attached near or proximal to middle of stamen tube; wings 2.7–3.4 × 1.4–2 mm; keel connate valvately, blades (4.5–)4.8–5.8 × 2.6–3 mm. **Stamens** 9, 6.3–9.4 mm, filaments distinct to 2.2–3.5 mm, anthers 0.8–1.2 mm. **Legumes** 3–3.7 mm, pilosulous and, sometimes, gland-dotted distally. **Seeds** 2.4–2.8 mm. $2n$ = 14.

Flowering summer–early fall. Plains, prairies, many substrates; 30–1400 m; Colo., Ill., Iowa, Kans., Mo., Mont., Nebr., N.Mex., N.Dak., Okla., S.Dak., Tex., Wyo.

Dalea enneandra is native to the Great Plains and as far east as the Texas coast and the loess hill prairies of western Iowa and northwestern Missouri. It is naturalized in DuPage County, Illinois. Its persistent calyx aids in wind dispersal of fruit.

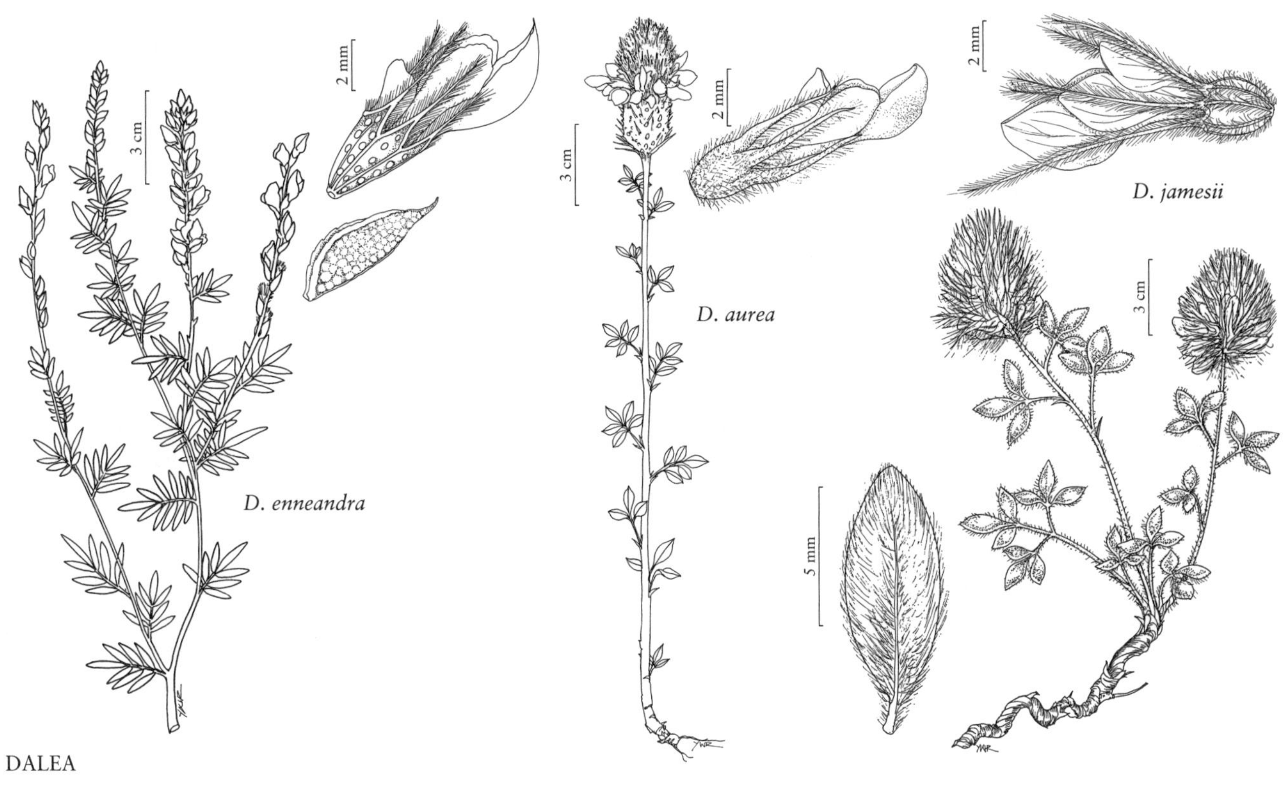

DALEA

53. Dalea nana Torrey ex A. Gray, Mem. Amer. Acad. Arts, n. s. 4: 31. 1849

Perennial herbs, prostrate, diffusely spreading, or erect, silky-pilosulous. **Stems** (0.5–)1–3.5 dm, nearly eglandular. **Principal leaves** 1–2.5(–3) cm; leaflets (3 or)5(or 7), blades obovate to olanceolate, 3–15 mm, surfaces inconspicuously glandular-punctate abaxially. **Peduncles** 0–3.5 cm. **Inflorescences** spikes, densely to loosely flowered, not involucrate, 7–13(–15) mm diam.; axis not to partially visible, 0.5–4(–5) cm; bracts deciduous at anthesis or later, 2.5–5.5 mm. **Calyces** subsymmetric, 4.5–6.5(–7.5) mm, densely pilose; tube 1.9–2.7 mm, with 3 or 4 small glands between ribs, lobes triangular-aristate, becoming plumose. **Corollas** clear yellow, purplish or brownish in age; papilionaceous; banner (4–)4.4–5.5 mm, blade suborbiculate-cordate to reniform, 1.5–3.2 × (1.5–)2–3.6 mm; epistemonous petals attached near or distal to middle of stamen tube; wings 2.1–3.7 × 0.9–1.8 mm; keel connate valvately, blades 2.9–4.8 × 1.6–2.8 mm. **Stamens** 10, (6–)6.4–10 mm, filaments distinct to 1.1–2.3 mm, anthers 0.4–0.7 mm. **Legumes** 2.5–3 mm, distally with 2 rows of ascending hairs on either side of a glabrescent row, eglandular. **Seeds** 1.8–2.2 mm.

Varieties 2 (2 in the flora): sw United States, n Mexico.

Dalea nana shows extensive variability in a number of features, including habit, height, and bract shape.

1. Bracts 2–4 mm wide; spikes loosely flowered, axis partially visible . . . . .53a. *Dalea nana* var. *nana*
1. Bracts 1.2–2 mm wide; spikes densely flowered, axis not visible . . . . 53b. *Dalea nana* var. *carnescens*

53a. Dalea nana Torrey ex A. Gray var. **nana**

Herbs diffusely spreading to prostrate. **Spikes** loosely flowered, 7–13 mm diam.; axis partially visible, 0.5–4(–5) cm; bracts broadly ovate- to obovate-acuminate, 2.5–5.5 × 2–4 mm. **2*n*** = 14.

Flowering spring–early fall. Grasslands, open pine or juniper woodlands, sandy and gravelly soils, seldom on limestone soils; 10–1500 m; Ariz., Colo., Kans., N.Mex., Okla., Tex.; Mexico (Chihuahua, Nuevo León, Tamaulipas).

Variety *nana* occurs as far north as southeastern Colorado and southwestern Kansas and is generally found on neutral or acidic substrates.

53b. Dalea nana Torrey ex A. Gray var. **carnescens** (Rydberg) Kearney & Peebles, J. Wash. Acad. Sci. 29: 483. 1939

Parosela carnescens Rydberg, Fl. Rocky Mts., 1063. 1917

Herbs diffuse to erect. **Spikes** densely flowered, 10–13(–15) mm diam.; axis not visible, 0.5–5 cm; bracts narrowly ovate- to lanceolate-acuminate, 3.5–5.5 × 1.2–2 mm. **2*n*** = 14.

Flowering spring, late summer–fall. Rocky soils, open grasslands, open oak or juniper woodlands, mostly on limestone; 300–1200 m; Ariz., N.Mex., Tex.; Mexico (Chihuahua, Coahuila, Durango, Nuevo León, Sonora, Tamaulipas).

Variety *carnescens* most often grows in alkaline soils and is found in southeastern and central Arizona, southern New Mexico, and Texas, especially in the trans-Pecos, Edwards Plateau, and Rio Grande valley regions.

54. Dalea aurea Nuttall ex Pursh, Fl. Amer. Sept. 2: 740. 1813 [F]

Dalea ceciliana B. L. Turner

Perennial herbs, erect, pilose to pilosulous. **Stems** (2–)3–7.5 dm, nearly eglandular. **Principal leaves** 1–3.5(–4) cm; leaflets (3 or)5(or 7), blades obovate to oblong-oblanceolate, (3–)4–16 (–20) mm. **Peduncles** absent or very short, sometimes appearing relatively long due to small size of distalmost leaves. **Inflorescences** spikes, densely flowered, not involucrate, (12–)14–21 mm diam.; axis not visible, (1–)1.5–6 cm; bracts persistent to anthesis, 2.5–5.5 mm. **Calyces** subsymmetric, 6.1–7.4 mm, silky-pilose; tube 2.2–2.8 mm, with 3 or 4 small glands between ribs, lobes lanceolate-aristate, becoming plumose. **Corollas** clear yellow; papilionaceous; banner 6.3–8.6 mm, blade deltate-cordate, 3–4.2 × 3.2–4.4 mm; epistemonous petals attached near middle of stamen tube; wings 4.7–5.6 × 2–2.4 mm; keel connate valvately, blades (4.7–)5–7 × 2.6–3.2 mm. **Stamens** 10, 10–12.5 mm, filaments distinct to 2.5–3 mm, anthers 0.6–0.9 mm. **Legumes** 3–3.5 mm, distally with 2 rows of ascending hairs on either side of a glabrescent row, eglandular. **Seeds** 2–2.4 mm. **2*n*** = 14, 24.

Flowering summer–early fall. Open prairies, dry slopes, rocky or sandy areas, on limestone; 10–1800 m; Ariz., Colo., Kans., Nebr., N.Mex., Okla., S.Dak., Tex., Wyo.; Mexico (Chihuahua, Coahuila).

Dalea aurea is sometimes cultivated in rock gardens or dry soil for its showy flowers with yellow petals. In Texas, the species is quite widespread.

55. Dalea wrightii A. Gray, Smithsonian Contr. Knowl. 3(5): 49. 1852

Dalea wrightii var. *warnockii* (Tharp & F. A. Barkley) B. L. Turner

Perennial herbs, erect to decumbent or ascending, silky-pilose. **Stems** 0.4–2.6(–3.6) dm, eglandular. **Principal leaves** 1–3.5 cm; leaflets 5, blades rhombic-ovate to lanceolate, 4–15(–20) mm, surfaces apparently eglandular. **Peduncles** absent or very short. **Inflorescences** spikes, relatively densely flowered, not involucrate, 17–23 mm diam.; axis not to partially visible, (1.5–)2–6 cm; bracts deciduous near anthesis, 6–12 mm. **Calyces** somewhat asymmetric, slightly recessed opposite banner, (8.5–)9–12.3 mm, densely pilose; tube (2.5–)2.7–3.5 mm, with 4 glands between ribs, lobes triangular-aristate, becoming plumose. **Corollas** clear yellow, pinkish or orangish brown in age; papilionaceous; banner 7.8–9.5 mm, blade cordate, 2–3 × 2.4–3.4 mm; epistemonous petals attached distal to middle of stamen tube; wings 2.6–3.4 × 1.8–2.3 mm; keel connate valvately, blades (2.6–)3–4(–4.2) × 1.6–2.2 mm. **Stamens** 10, 10–13 mm, filaments distinct to 1.5 mm, anthers 0.5–0.7 mm. **Legumes** 2.8–3.5 mm, distally with 2 rows of ascending hairs on either side of a glabrescent row, eglandular. **Seeds** 2–2.8 mm. **2*n*** = 14.

Flowering early spring–fall. Rocky grasslands, desert slopes, on limestone; 500–1800 m; Ariz., N.Mex., Tex.; Mexico (Chihuahua, Coahuila, Sonora).

Dalea wrightii occurs in southeastern Arizona, southern New Mexico, and trans-Pecos Texas.

56. Dalea hallii A. Gray, Proc. Amer. Acad. Arts 8: 625. 1873 [E]

Perennial herbs, decumbent to ascending, strigulose. **Stems** 1.3–3(–4) dm, eglandular or with scattered small glands. **Principal leaves** 1.5–4.5 cm; leaflets 3, blades linear-elliptic to linear, 8–30(–35) mm. **Peduncles** usually absent, rarely to 1 cm. **Inflorescences** spikes, relatively loosely flowered, not involucrate, 14–17 mm diam.; axis partially visible, 1–5 cm; bracts deciduous near anthesis, 4–6.5 mm. **Calyces** asymmetric, recessed opposite banner, (5.1–)5.5–7.8 mm, pilosulous to pilose; tube 2.4–3 mm, with 2 or 3 small glands between ribs, lobes lanceolate-aristate. **Corollas** yellow, rarely brownish in age; papilionaceous; banner 5–6.2 mm, blade deltate-cordate, 2.8–3.3 × 3–3.8 mm; epistemonous petals attached near middle of stamen tube; wings 3.6–5 × 2.2–2.8 mm; keel connate valvately, blades 5.2–6.4 × 3.6–4 mm. **Stamens** 10, 9.5–11.5 mm, filaments distinct to 2.5–3 mm, anthers (0.7–)0.8–1 mm. **Legumes** 3 mm, distally with 2 rows of ascending hairs on either side of a glabrescent row, eglandular. **Seeds** 2.2 mm.

Flowering spring (fall). Rocky outcrops in grasslands, usually on limestone; 100–600 m; Tex.

Dalea hallii is endemic to central and north-central Texas from the edge of the Edwards Plateau from as far south as Bandera County northward to Fannin County along the Red River.

57. Dalea jamesii (Torrey) Torrey & A. Gray, Fl. N. Amer. 1: 308. 1838 [F]

Psoralea jamesii Torrey, Ann. Lyceum Nat. Hist. New York 2: 175. 1827

Perennial herbs, erect to ascending, silky-pilose to -pilosulous. **Stems** 0.4–1.7(–2) dm, eglandular. **Principal leaves** (0.6–)1–3(–4) cm; leaflets 3, blades obovate to broadly oblanceolate, (3–)5–18 mm, surfaces apparently eglandular. **Peduncles** absent or very short. **Inflorescences** spikes, relatively densely flowered, not obviously involucrate, (16–)18–23(–25) mm diam.; axis not to partially visible, 1.5–6.5(–8) cm; bracts deciduous at anthesis, (4–)5–8(–9) mm. **Calyces** somewhat asymmetric, slightly recessed opposite banner, (8.3–)8.5–12(–13.3) mm, pilose; tube (2.4–)2.8–3.5 mm, with 3 or 4 small glands between ribs, lobes triangular-aristate. **Corollas** clear yellow, orangish brown in age; papilionaceous; banner 5.2–6.2 mm, blade deltate-cordate, 3.2–4.2 × 3.2–4.4 mm, proximal lobes connate, forming obconic pit; epistemonous petals attached proximal to middle of stamen tube; wings 3.9–5.1 × 2.3–3.2 mm; keel connate valvately, blades 5.3–6.3 × 3.2–3.8 mm. **Stamens** 10, (9.5–)10–11.7 mm, filaments distinct to 1.7–3 mm, anthers (0.8–)0.9–1.2 mm. **Legumes** 3.5–4 mm, distally with 2 rows of ascending hairs on either side of a glabrescent row, eglandular. **Seeds** 2.3–3 mm. **2*n*** = 14.

Flowering spring–early summer (fall). Rocky grasslands, deserts, open pine or juniper woodlands; 900–2100 m; Ariz., Colo., Kans., N.Mex., Okla., Tex.; Mexico (Chihuahua).

Dalea jamesii occurs from far southwestern Kansas to southeastern Arizona. In Texas, the species occurs in the northern panhandle and trans-Pecos regions.

58. Dalea laniceps Barneby, SouthW. Naturalist 15: 390. 1971

Perennial herbs, erect to ascending, silvery-pilose. **Stems** 0.3–0.8 dm, eglandular. **Principal leaves** (1–)1.5–3.5 cm; leaflets 3, blades rhombic-ovate to elliptic-oblanceolate, 5–18 mm, surfaces apparently eglandular. **Peduncles** absent. **Inflorescences** spikes, densely flowered, not obviously involucrate, 15–20 mm diam.; axis not visible, 0.7–3(–3.5) cm; bracts persistent through anthesis, 6–9 mm. **Calyces** somewhat asymmetric, slightly recessed opposite banner, 7.8–8.7 mm, densely pilose; tube 2.5–2.9 mm, with 2 or 3 small glands between ribs, lobes triangular-aristate, becoming plumose. **Corollas** clear yellow, reddish brown in age; papilionaceous; banner 7–8.2 mm, blade reniform, 1.8–2.4 × 1.9–2.8 mm; epistemonous petals attached distal to middle of stamen tube; wings 2.4–2.7 × 1.2–1.4 mm; keel connate valvately, blades 3.2–4 × 1.6–2 mm. **Stamens** 10, 10–11 mm, filaments distinct to 1.2–1.6 mm, anthers 0.5–0.6 mm. **Legumes** ± 2.5 mm, distally with 2 rows of ascending hairs on either side of a glabrescent row, eglandular. **Seeds** 2.3–3 mm. **2*n*** = 14.

Flowering summer–fall. Rocky slopes and hills, deserts, grasslands, open pine woods; 900–2500 m; Tex.; Mexico (Chihuahua, Coahuila, Durango, Nuevo León, San Luis Potosí, Zacatecas).

In the flora area, *Dalea laniceps* is limited to the southeastern area of trans-Pecos Texas.

67. ANDIRA Lamarck, Encycl. 1: 171. 1783, name conserved • [Sanskrit/Tamal/ Malayalam *anjali* or Portuguese *angelyn*, cavity formed by hollowing palms, probably alluding to wood's use to make canoes and boats] [I]

Velva E. Rudd†

Michael A. Vincent

Trees, unarmed. **Stems** puberulent or glabrescent; peduncles and pedicels eglandular. **Leaves** alternate, odd-pinnate; stipules present; petiolate; leaflets [3–](7 or)9–13(or 15), blade margins entire, surfaces glabrous or glabrate. **Inflorescences** 25–75-flowered, terminal and axillary, racemes and panicles; bracts present. **Flowers** papilionaceous; calyx campanulate, lobes 5; corolla pink to reddish purple; stamens 10, diadelphous; anthers dorsifixed, uniform. **Fruits** legumes (drupaceous), stipitate, pendent, plump, ovoid or subglobose, indehiscent, glabrous. **Seed** 1, ellipsoid to subglobose or ovoid. $x = 10$.

Species 29 (1 in the flora): introduced, Florida; Mexico, West Indies, Central America, South America, Africa.

Attribution of the generic name to Lamarck, instead of Jussieu, was clarified by R. T. Pennington (2002) and R. K. Brummitt (2004).

SELECTED REFERENCE Pennington, R. T. 2003. Monograph of *Andira* (Leguminosae-Papilionoideae). Syst. Bot. Monogr. 64: 1–143.

1. **Andira inermis** (W. Wright) Kunth ex de Candolle in A. P. de Candolle and A. L. P. P. de Candolle, Prodr. 2: 475. 1825 • Cabbage-bark tree [F] [I]

Geoffroea inermis W. Wright, London Med. J. 8: 256. 1787

Subspecies 3 (1 in the flora): introduced, Florida; Mexico, West Indies, Central America, South America, Africa.

1a. **Andira inermis** (W. Wright) Kunth ex de Candolle subsp. **inermis** [F] [I]

Andira jamaicensis (W. Wright) Urban

Trees to 35 m. **Leaves:** stipules caducous, linear-subulate, 2–3 mm; leaflets: stipels caducous, subulate, blades elliptic to oblong, 35–135 × 14–60 mm, base rounded or subacute, cuneate, apex acute to acuminate. **Racemes:** axis brown-tomentose; bracts lanceolate, 4–5 × 1 mm; bracteoles setaceous or subulate, 1 mm. **Pedicels** 0.2–1 mm. **Flowers:** calyx slightly zygomorphic, 3–4 mm, tomentose, lobes deltate, 0.3–0.7 mm; corolla 10 mm, banner glabrous, keel petals distinct; style incurved, relatively short; stigma capitate, relatively small. **Legumes** 25–40 × 20–25 mm. $2n = 20$.

Flowering summer. Disturbed areas; 1–10 m; introduced; Fla.; Mexico; West Indies; Central America; South America; Africa.

Subspecies *inermis* was collected as living plants on Bahia Honda Key, and transplanted to Buena Vista, where they were grown in cultivation (J. K. Small 1933; R. W. Long and O. Lakela 1971).

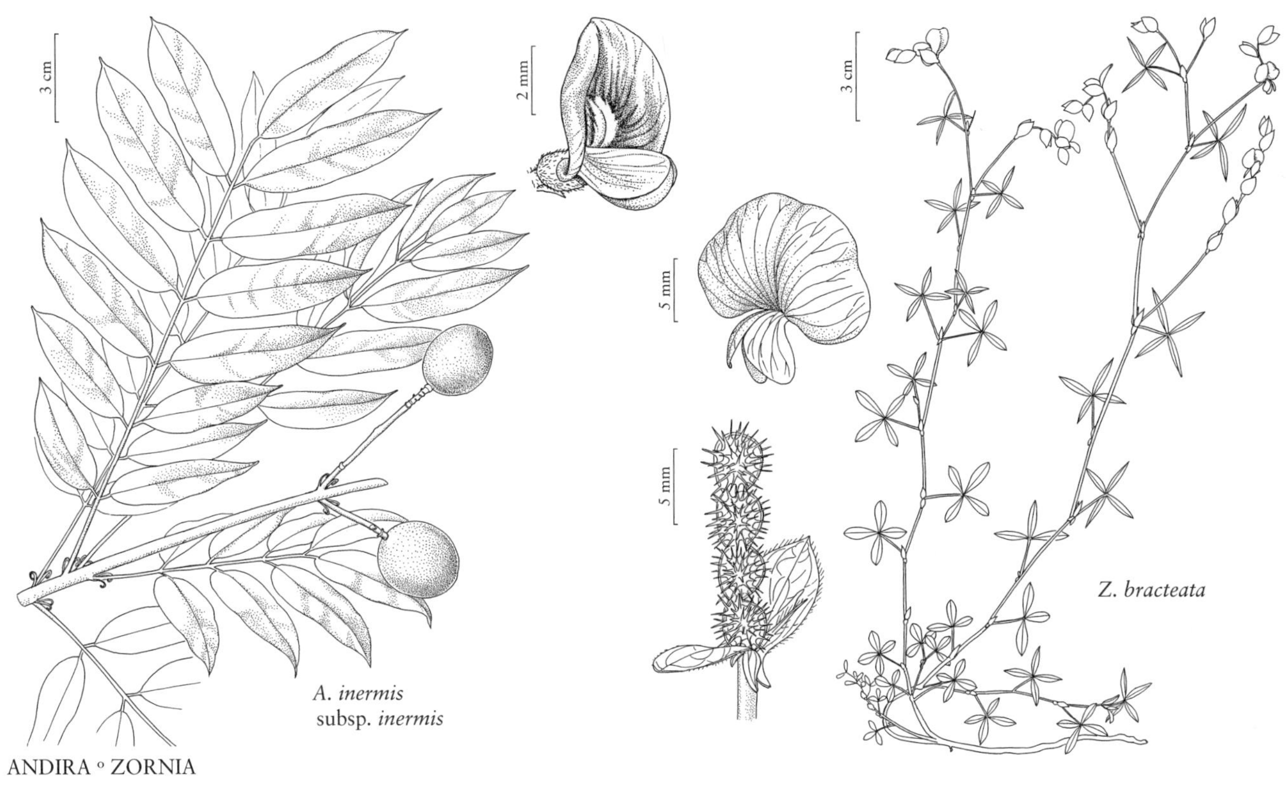

68. ZORNIA J. F. Gmelin, Syst. Nat. 2: 1076, 1096. 1792 • Viperina [For Johannes Zorn, 1739–1799, German pharmacist]

Robert H. Mohlenbrock

Herbs [subshrubs], perennial [annual], unarmed; roots slender. **Stems** prostrate or erect, glabrous or pubescent, sometimes glandular-pubescent. **Leaves** alternate, even-pinnate; stipules present, paired, peltate; petiolate; leaflets 2 or 4, stipels absent, blade margins entire, surfaces sometimes punctate, glabrous or pubescent. **Inflorescences** 1–15-flowered, terminal or axillary, spikes, erect; bracts present, paired, peltate, auriculate, margins ciliate; bracteoles absent. **Flowers** papilionaceous, chasmogamous; calyx short-tubular, lobes 5, apex usually acute; corolla yellow or orange-yellow; banner longer, wider than wings; wings not adnate to keel, auriculate; keel subprostrate, incurved; stamens 10, monadelphous, filaments equal; anthers alternately dorsifixed and versatile, and sub-basifixed; style curved, glabrous or pubescent. **Fruits** loments, stipitate [sessile], brown or tan, flattened, straight or curved, linear to oblong, indehiscent, glabrous or pubescent; segments 2–15, breaking apart at maturity, margins ciliate, surfaces sometimes reticulate, often bristly with retrorse hairs. **Seeds** 2–15, black [dark brown], compressed, ovoid. $x = 10$.

Species 75 (3 in the flora): s United States, Mexico, West Indies, Central America, South America, Asia, Africa, Indian Ocean Islands (Madagascar), Australia.

Zornia has traditionally been considered closely related to *Stylosanthes*, differing by its even-pinnate leaves without stipels and its loments with usually more than two segments. Molecular studies place *Zornia* closer to *Adesmia* de Candolle and *Poiretia* Ventenat in the *Adesmia* clade and rather distantly related to *Stylosanthes* (M. Lavin et al. 2001). The North American species of *Zornia* fall into three sections: sect. *Zornia* has four leaflets; sect. *Isophylla* Mohlenbrock has two leaflets, and the leaflets of proximal and distal leaves are essentially the same shape; sect. *Anisophylla* Mohlenbrock has two leaflets, and the leaflets of proximal and distal leaves differ in shape, with proximal ones usually broader and shorter, distal ones lanceolate to linear.

SELECTED REFERENCE Mohlenbrock, R. H. 1961. A monograph of the leguminous genus *Zornia*. Webbia 16: 1–141.

1. Leaflets 4 . . . . 1. *Zornia bracteata*
1. Leaflets 2.
    2. Bracts (excluding auricles) 12+ mm, crowded; loments included within bracts or exserted by 1 or 2 segments. . . . . 2. *Zornia reticulata*
    2. Bracts (excluding auricles) less than 12 mm, much interrupted proximally becoming crowded distally; loments exserted beyond bracts by 3–8 segments. . . . . 3. *Zornia gemella*

1. Zornia bracteata J. F. Gmelin, Syst. Nat. 2: 1096. 1792 • Viperina [E] [F]

Stems erect, to 80 cm, glabrous or strigulose. **Leaves:** stipules to 15 mm, epunctate, glabrous; petiole ⅔ to as long as leaflets, glabrous or sparsely hairy; leaflets 4, blades linear to narrowly elliptic, 25 × 8 mm, ± similar throughout or distalmost smaller, base cuneate, apex acute, surfaces epunctate, glabrous, abaxial midvein strigose. **Spikes** 1–10-flowered, crowded or ± lax, 2–17 cm; bracts 5–7-veined, lanceolate-ovate to ovate, 10 × 7 mm, apex acute, surfaces epunctate, glabrous; auricles 1–2.2 mm. **Flowers:** calyx tube 7–10-veined, 3–4 mm, ± strigose; corolla yellow; banner 10–14 mm, longer than wings. **Loments** exserted beyond bracts; segments 2–6, 2.7–3.5 × 2.5–3.3 mm, not reticulate, eglandular, glabrous; bristles to 1 mm. **Seeds** 1.5–1.8 mm.

Flowering summer. Sandy or gravelly soils; 0–500 m; Ala., Fla., Ga., La., Miss., N.C., S.C., Tex., Va.

For his *Zornia bracteata*, Gmelin referred to *Anonymos bracteata* by T. Walter (1788), an invalid name that is the basis for the epithet by Gmelin. Reports of *Z. bracteata* from Mexico appear to be based on a Berlandier collection (P), labeled only as "Mexico", and is excluded from the range of the species as a doubtful record. The name *Z. tetraphylla* Michaux is an illegitimate later homonym and pertains here.

2. Zornia reticulata Smith in A. Rees, Cycl. 39: Zornia no. 2. 1818 • Reticulate viperina

Stems to 75 cm, glabrous or pilose. **Leaves:** stipules 4–11 mm, punctate or epunctate, glabrous or villous; petiole ½ to as long as leaflets, glabrous or pilose; leaflets 2, blades broadly lanceolate to ovate-lanceolate proximally, or lanceolate to linear distally, 24 × 12 mm proximally, 30 × 5–7(–13) mm distally, base cuneate or rounded proximally, or cuneate distally, apex acute proximally or acute to acuminate distally, surfaces punctate or epunctate, glabrous or strigose to villous. **Spikes** (2–)5–15-flowered, usually crowded, to 10 cm; bracts 5–9-veined, lanceolate to lanceolate-ovate, 12(–14) × 8 mm, apex acute to acuminate, surfaces punctate or epunctate, glabrous or villous; auricles frequently notched basally, often falcate, to 3.5 mm. **Flowers:** calyx tube 7–10-veined, to 4 mm, strigose distally; corolla yellow or orange-yellow; banner 13–15 mm, longer than wings and keel. **Loments** concealed by bracts or distalmost segment exserted; segments usually 4–7 segments concealed by bracts, sometimes with 1 or 2 segments exserted beyond bracts, 2–2.4 × 1.9–2.2 mm, reticulate, eglandular, pilose to villosulous; bristles 0.2–0.4(–1) mm. **Seeds** 1.1–1.4 mm. **2*n*** = 20.

Flowering summer. Sandy soils; 0–200 m; Ariz., Tex.; Mexico; West Indies; Central America; South America.

Some specimens from Texas identified as *Zornia gemella* and those from Arizona identified and annotated as either *Z. gemella* or *Z. leptophylla* (Bentham) Pittier are actually *Z. reticulata*.

3. Zornia gemella Vogel, Linnaea 12: 61. 1838

Stems erect, to 50 cm, glabrous or pilose. **Leaves:** stipules 3–12 mm, punctate, glabrous or puberulent; petiole ⅓–½ as long as leaflet, glabrous or pilose; leaflets 2, blades lanceolate, 25 × 4 mm, proximal larger than distal, base cuneate, apex acute, surfaces punctate, often glabrous, sometimes pilose. **Spikes** 2–7-flowered, much interrupted proximally becoming crowded distally, to 60 cm; bracts 7-veined, oblong-lanceolate or broadly lanceolate, 7 × 5 mm, apex acute to acuminate, surfaces usually punctate, glabrous or pilose; auricles 1 mm. **Flowers:** calyx tube 7–10-veined, to 4 mm, usually ± strigose; corolla orange-yellow or yellow; banner 13–15 mm, longer than wings. **Loments** exserted beyond bracts by 3–8 segments; segments 4–8, 2–2.4 × 1.9–2.2 mm, reticulate, eglandular, pilose to villous; bristles 0.2–0.4 mm. **Seeds** 1.2–1.4 mm. **2*n*** = 20.

Flowering summer. Sandy or rocky soils; 100–1200 m; Fla., Tex.; Mexico; West Indies; Central America; South America.

Zornia gemella is known from Hillsborough County, Florida, and from several counties in Texas, ranging from Lavaca County southward to Willacy County, and westward to Jim Hogg County.

69. NISSOLIA Jacquin, Enum. Syst. Pl., 7, 27. 1760, name conserved • [For Guillaume Nissole, 1647–1735, French botanist]

Velva E. Rudd†

Michael A. Vincent

Chaetocalyx de Candolle; *Pseudomachaerium* Hassler

Vines, perennial, herbaceous or ± woody, unarmed. **Stems** climbing, twining, or prostrate, pubescent to glabrate. **Leaves** alternate, odd-pinnate; stipules present, usually caducous; petiolate; leaflets 5(or 7), stipels absent, blade margins entire, surfaces puberulent, glabrate, or glabrous. **Inflorescences** 1–8-flowered, axillary, fascicles or racemes [panicles]; bracts present, stipulelike; bracteoles usually absent. **Flowers** papilionaceous; calyx nearly actinomorphic, campanulate, lobes 5; corolla yellow [white or purplish]; stamens 10, monadelphous, filament tube splitting adaxially at maturity; anthers dorsifixed. **Fruits** loments, stipitate, flattened, lanceoloid, segments breaking apart, individual ones indehiscent, pubescent, glabrate, or glabrescent; segments 2–4, proximal 1–4 segments fertile, distal segment sterile, flat, winglike. **Seeds** 1–4, reddish brown, laterally compressed, reniform, sublustrous; hilum relatively small, circular.

Species 14 (3 in the flora): sw United States, Mexico, Central America, South America; warm-temperate and tropical regions.

SELECTED REFERENCES de Moura, T. M. et al. 2018. A new circumscription of *Nissolia* (Leguminosae-Papilionoideae-Dalbergieae), with *Chaetocalyx* as a new generic synonym. Novon 26: 193–213. Rudd, V. E. 1956. A revision of the genus *Nissolia*. Contr. U.S. Natl. Herb. 32: 173–206.

1. Fruits with sterile segment 6–11 mm, fertile segments 7–10 mm; stems prostrate; leaf axis recurved; leaflets usually folded when dry .... 1. *Nissolia wislizeni*
1. Fruits with sterile segment 10–30 mm, fertile segments 4–7 mm; stems climbing or twining; leaf axis ± straight; leaflets usually not folded when dry.
    2. Corollas 14–20 mm; pedicels 9–11 mm; calyx tube 4.5–6 × 4–5 mm, lobes 1.5–4.5 mm; leaflets 5 or 7...2. *Nissolia platycalyx*
    2. Corollas (8–)10–12 mm; pedicels 5–7 mm; calyx tube (2–)3–4 × 2–3 mm, lobes 2–4 mm; leaflets 5 .... 3. *Nissolia schottii*

1. Nissolia wislizeni (A. Gray) A. Gray, J. Proc. Linn. Soc., Bot. 5: 25. 1861

Chaetocalyx wislizeni A. Gray, Smithsonian Contr. Knowl. 3(5): 51. 1852

Stems prostrate, to 1.2 m, moderately white-pubescent and glandular-setose. **Leaves** 0.5–6 cm; stipules deltate-ovate, 5–7 × 1–2.5 mm; leaflets 5, usually folded when dry, axis recurved, blades orbiculate to elliptic, 4–20 × 4–22 mm, base obtuse to subcordate, apex obtuse to emarginate, mucronulate, surfaces puberulent to glabrate abaxially, glabrous adaxially. **Inflorescences** 1–5-flowered, fasciculate. **Pedicels** 3–20 mm. **Flowers:** calyx (3–)4–5 mm, puberulent and setose; tube (2–)3–4 mm × 3 mm; lobes deltate-subulate, 1 mm; corolla (8–)10–15 mm. **Loments** 2–5-segmented, 20–40 mm, pubescent to glabrate; fertile segments 7–10 × 3–7 mm, sterile segment 6–11 × 3–7 mm; stipe 1–2 mm. **Seeds** 5 × 3 mm.

Flowering Jul–Aug. Open grasslands, mesas, slopes; 1500–1600 m; Ariz.; Mexico (Aguascalientes, Chihuahua, Durango, Guanajuato, Hidalgo, Jalisco, Oaxaca, Querétaro, San Luis Potosí, Sonora, Zacatecas).

Nissolia wislizeni is known from Coconino County in the flora area.

2. Nissolia platycalyx S. Watson, Proc. Amer. Acad. Arts 17: 344. 1882

Stems climbing, to 1.5 m, moderately crisp-pubescent or glabrescent. **Leaves** 4–7 cm; stipules lanceolate, 3–5 × 0.5–1 mm; leaflets 5 or 7, usually not folded when dry, axis ± straight, blades elliptic to oblong, 5–25 × 4–15 mm, base obtuse, apex obtuse, mucronulate, surfaces glabrous. **Inflorescences** 1–4-flowered, racemes. **Pedicels** 9–11 mm. **Flowers:** calyx 6.5–10 mm, pubescent to glabrate; tube 4.5–6 × 4–5 mm; lobes subulate, 1.5–4.5 mm; corolla 14–20 mm. **Loments** 2–4-segmented, 30–50 mm, pubescent to glabrate; fertile segments 5–7 × 5 mm, sterile segment 20–30 × 6–10(–15) mm; stipe 4 mm. **Seeds** 5 × 3 mm.

Flowering May–Sep. Chaparral slopes; 1700 m; Tex.; Mexico (Chihuahua, Coahuila, Durango, Nuevo León, San Luis Potosí, Tamaulipas, Veracruz).

Nissolia platycalyx is known from Brewster County in the flora area.

3. Nissolia schottii (Torrey) A. Gray, J. Proc. Linn. Soc., Bot. 5: 26. 1861 [F]

Chaetocalyx schottii Torrey in W. H. Emory, Rep. U.S. Mex. Bound. 2(1): 56, plate 18. 1859

Stems twining, to 1 m, moderately crisp-pubescent to glabrate, sometimes glandular-setose. **Leaves** 3–8 cm; stipules lanceolate, 3–5 × 0.5–1 mm; leaflets 5, usually not folded when dry, axis ± straight, blades elliptic to rhombic, 5–40 × 3–25 mm, base obtuse, apex acute to obtuse, mucronulate, surfaces glabrate. **Inflorescences** 1–8-flowered, racemes or fascicles. **Pedicels** 5–7 mm. **Flowers:** calyx 5–7 mm, glabrous or glabrate, margins pubescent; tube (2–)3–4 × 2–3 mm; lobes subulate, 2–4 mm; corolla (8–)10–12 mm. **Loments** 2–4-segmented, 20–30 mm, pubescent to glabrate; fertile segments 4–6 × 4–5 mm, sterile segment 10–15 × 6–10 mm; stipe 1–2 mm. **Seeds** 3 × 2–2.5 mm.

Flowering Jul–Aug. Mountain slopes, canyons; 700–1200 m; Ariz.; Mexico (Baja California, Baja California Sur, Chihuahua, Durango, Sinaloa, Sonora).

Nissolia schottii is known from Pima County in the flora area.

70. CHAPMANNIA Torrey & A. Gray, Fl. N. Amer. 1: 355. 1838 • Alicia [For Alvan Wentworth Chapman, 1809–1899, American physician and botanist in Florida]

Robert H. Mohlenbrock

Herbs, perennial, [shrubs or trees], unarmed. **Stems** erect, villous. **Leaves** alternate, odd-pinnate; stipules present; petiolate; leaflets 3–9, blade margins entire, surfaces pubescent. **Inflorescences** 2–4-flowered, terminal and axillary, panicles; bracts absent; bracteoles present.

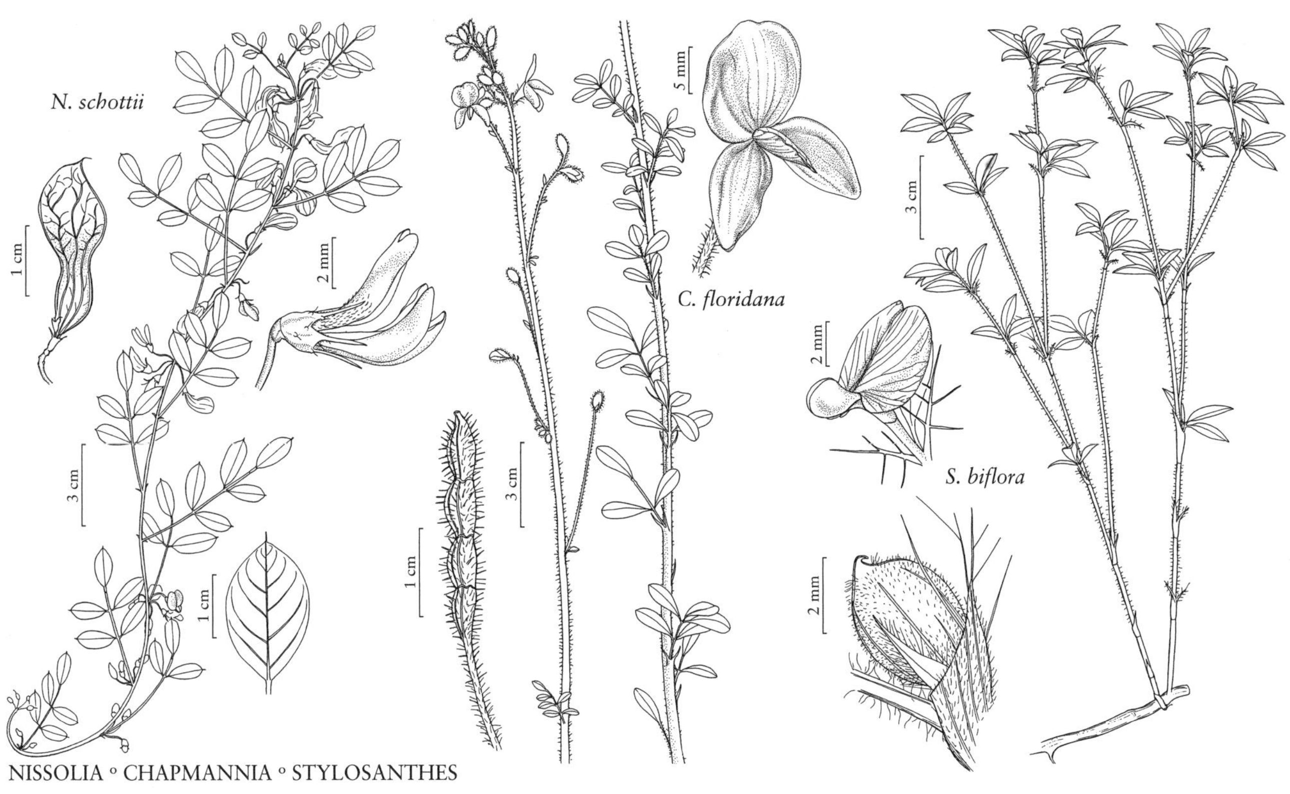

NISSOLIA ◦ CHAPMANNIA ◦ STYLOSANTHES

Flowers papilionaceous; calyx tubular, lobes 5, abaxial lobes distinct, adaxial connate nearly to apex; corolla orange-yellow; stamens 10, monadelphous; anthers sub-basifixed. **Fruits** loments, sessile, subterete, abaxial suture sinuate, adaxial suture straight, linear, dehiscent, villous. **Seeds** 1–3, ovoid, dull. $x = 11$.

Species 7 (1 in the flora): Florida, s Mexico, Central America (Guatemala), South America (Venezuela), Africa (Somalia), Indian Ocean Islands (Socotra).

Torrey and Gray, and all botanists until 1980, described *Chapmannia* as having both sterile and fertile flowers; C. R. Gunn et al. (1980) have given evidence that all flowers are fertile.

SELECTED REFERENCES Gunn, C. R., E. M. Norman, and J. S Lassetter. 1980. *Chapmannia floridana* Torrey & Gray (Fabaceae). Brittonia 32: 178–185. Thulin, M. 1999. *Chapmannia* (Leguminosae-Stylosanthinae) extended. Nordic J. Bot. 19: 597–607.

1. Chapmannia floridana Torrey & A. Gray, Fl. N. Amer. 1: 355. 1838 E F

Herbs from fleshy taproots. **Stems** to 1 m, appressed–hairy, hairs pustular-based, viscid. **Leaves:** stipules subulate, 2–4 mm; leaflets 3–9, stipels absent, blades reflexed at night, obovate to elliptic or lanceolate, 5–20 × 5–10 mm, base cuneate, apex mucronate. **Panicles** erect, lateral branches short; bracteoles 3, persistent. **Pedicels** present in terminal flower, relatively short. **Flowers:** calyx tube 2–3 mm, villous-viscid, hairs pustular-based; petals evenly graduated, banner suborbiculate, to 14 mm, wings spreading, slightly adherent to keel, obovate, with auricles, to 18 mm, keel incurved, to 12 mm, obtuse, margins slightly overlapping; filaments connate into closed tube with distinct portions alternating in length; ovary sessile, 1 mm; style filiform, to 14 mm, glabrous; stigma minute. **Loments** reddish brown, to 30 mm, with 1–4 articulations, reticulate, red-villous, hairs pustular-based. **Seeds** yellowish, 3.5 × 2.5 mm. $2n = 22$.

Flowering Apr–Oct. Open scrub, sandhills, roadsides; 0–20 m; Fla.

Chapmannia floridana is frequent in peninsular Florida (R. P. Wunderlin and B. F. Hansen 2011).

71. STYLOSANTHES Swartz, Prodr., 7, 108. 1788 • Pencil-flower [Greek *stylos*, pillar, and *anthos*, flower, alluding to long style]

Robert H. Mohlenbrock

Herbs, perennial, or subshrubs, unarmed; roots thickened. **Stems** prostrate to erect or ascending, sometimes viscid, pubescent or glabrous. **Leaves** alternate, odd-pinnate; stipules present, foliaceous, amplexicaul, adnate to petiole for most of its length; petiolate; leaflets 3, blade margins entire, surfaces glandular-punctate or epunctate, sometimes black-punctate, glabrous or pubescent. **Inflorescences** 1–15+-flowered, terminal or axillary, spikes or solitary flowers, erect, axis rudiment (aborted floral axis) sometimes present; bracts present, persistent, foliaceous; bracteoles persistent, 1 outer, 1 or 2 inner. **Flowers** papilionaceous; calyx tubular, lobes 5, unequal, adaxial 4-lobed; corolla yellow or orange-yellow, inserted near apex of calyx tube; petals evenly graduated; wings shorter and narrower than banner, not adnate to keel, clawed, auriculate; keel incurved or rostrate; stamens 10, monadelphous; anthers dimorphic, 5 versatile anthers alternating with 5 sub-basifixed; ovary subsessile; style curved, glabrous or pubescent. **Fruits** loments, sessile or stipitate, tan or brown, compressed, articulate, ovate, individual segments indehiscent, glabrous or pubescent; segments 2, breaking apart, proximal segment fertile or abortive, densely pubescent, distal segment fertile, reticulate; style persistent as a beak, beak erect, declined, or coiled. **Seeds** 1 or 2, black, compressed, ovoid, shiny. $x = 10$.

Species 37 (5 in the flora): United States, Mexico, West Indies, Central America, South America, Asia (s India, Sri Lanka), c, s Africa, Indian Ocean Islands (Madagascar), Pacific Islands (Galápagos Islands); introduced in se Asia (Malaysia), Australia.

The alternation of sub-basifixed and versatile anthers and the absence of stipels in *Stylosanthes* suggest a relationship to *Arachis*, *Chapmannia*, and *Zornia*. Molecular phylogenetic analyses support a close relationship among *Arachis*, *Chapmannia*, and *Stylosanthes* but place *Zornia* more distantly (M. Lavin et al. 2001). *Stylosanthes* resembles *Zornia* morphologically because of the large bracts subtending each flower and the often spicate inflorescences. The leaves of *Stylosanthes* are three-foliolate, the ovules are two or three, and bracteoles are present; the leaves of *Zornia* are two- or four-foliolate, the ovules are two to several, and bracteoles are absent. Species of *Stylosanthes* in sect. *Stylosanthes* have an axis rudiment (an aborted floral axis) next to the flower; species in sect. *Astyposanthes* (Herter) Mohlenbrock lack an axis rudiment.

SELECTED REFERENCE Mohlenbrock, R. H. 1957. A revision of the genus *Stylosanthes*. Ann. Missouri Bot. Gard. 44: 299–355.

1. Inflorescences: axis rudiment present; inner bracteoles 2.
   2. Loments: beak straight or slightly curved; leaflet blade surfaces glabrous (rarely with marginal cilia); teeth of distal stipules mostly longer than sheath; calyx tubes 3–4 mm .... 1. *Stylosanthes calcicola*
   2. Loments: beak hooked; leaflet blade surfaces glabrous or short-pilose; teeth of distal stipules mostly shorter than sheath; calyx tubes 4–7.5 mm .... 2. *Stylosanthes hamata*
1. Inflorescences: axis rudiment absent; inner bracteole 1.
   3. Loments: beak to 1/5 as long as distal segment .... 3. *Stylosanthes biflora*
   3. Loments: beak to 1/2 as long as or exceeding distal segment.
      4. Stems with viscid hairs; leaflet blade surfaces punctate abaxially; banners 4–7 mm; loment beak to 1/2 as long as distal segment........ 4. *Stylosanthes viscosa*
      4. Stems glabrous or short-hispid, not viscid; leaflet blade surfaces without punctations; banners 3–4 mm; loment beak equaling or surpassing distal segment........ 5. *Stylosanthes humilis*

1. Stylosanthes calcicola Small, Man. S.E. Fl., 730, 1505. 1933 • Everglades pencil-flower

Stems herbaceous, erect, branched from near base, to 5 dm, often minutely pubescent along one side, sometimes glabrous, rarely pubescent throughout. **Leaves:** stipular sheath 7-veined, glabrous or puberulent, teeth of distal stipules mostly longer than sheath; petiole 2–4 mm; leaflet blades lanceolate to ovate, 150 × 80 mm, veins 3–5 pairs, base cuneate, margins rarely ciliate, apex acute to acuminate, surfaces glabrous. **Inflorescences** 2+-flowered, narrowly oblong or ovoid, to 1.5 cm, axis rudiment present, to 5 mm; bracts 1-foliolate, averaging 4 mm wide, 5–7-veined, margins ciliate and often bristly abaxially; outer bracteole 1–3 mm, apex ciliate; inner bracteoles 2, 2–2.5 mm, apex ciliate. **Flowers:** calyx tube 3–4 mm, lobes acute; corolla yellow; banner obovate, 4.5–6 mm; wings 4–5 mm; keel 3.5–4.5 mm. **Loments** conspicuously reticulate, 1.5–2 mm wide; fertile segments (1 or)2; proximal segment 2–2.5 mm; distal segment 2.5–3 mm, usually densely white-hairy, sometimes glabrate; beak straight or slightly curved, 1.5–2.5 mm, ½ to equaling distal segment, with short, white hairs or glabrous. **Seeds** 1–2 mm. **2*n*** = 20.

Flowering year-round. Pinelands; 0–10 m; Fla.; Mexico; West Indies (Bahamas, Cuba); Central America (Guatemala).

In the flora area, *Stylosanthes calcicola* is documented from only the southernmost tips of peninsular Florida and the Florida Keys.

2. Stylosanthes hamata (Linnaeus) Taubert, Verh. Bot. Vereins Prov. Brandenburg 32: 22. 1890 • Cheesytoes

Hedysarum hamatum Linnaeus, Syst. Nat. ed. 10, 2: 1170. 1759

Stems herbaceous, ascending, spreading, prostrate, or matted, often much branched, to 10 dm, often with line of fine pubescence on one side, occasionally sericeous. **Leaves:** stipular sheath 3–11-veined, sericeous or glabrous, teeth of distal stipules mostly shorter than sheath; petiole 2–6 mm; leaflet blades lanceolate to elliptic, 150–200 × 40–60 mm, veins 3–6 pairs, base cuneate, margins entire, apex obtuse to subacute, surfaces glabrous or short-pilose abaxially. **Inflorescences** 3–15-flowered, ovoid to oblong, to 2 cm, axis rudiment present, to 7 mm; outer bracts 3-foliolate, inner bracts 1-foliolate, 5–7-veined, sheath pubescent; outer bracteole 1–5 mm, apex ciliate; inner bracteoles 2, 2–3.5 mm, apex ciliate. **Flowers:** calyx tube 4–7.5 mm, lobes ± acute; corolla yellow; banner suborbiculate, 4–5 mm; wings 3.5–4.5 mm; keel 3–4.5 mm. **Loments** reticulate, 1.8–2.2 mm wide; fertile segments (1 or)2; proximal segment (when fertile) 1.5–3.5 mm; distal segment 2–4 mm, glabrous or puberulent; beak hooked, 2–4.5 mm, equaling to surpassing distal segment, shortly pubescent or glabrous. **Seeds** 1–2 mm. **2*n*** = 20, 40.

Flowering year-round. Pinelands; 0–10 m; Fla.; Mexico; West Indies; Central America; South America (Colombia, Venezuela).

In the flora area, *Stylosanthes hamata* is documented from only southernmost peninsular Florida.

3. Stylosanthes biflora (Linnaeus) Britton, Sterns & Poggenburg, Prelim. Cat., 13. 1888 • Pencil-flower [F]

Trifolium biflorum Linnaeus, Sp. Pl. 2: 773. 1753; *Stylosanthes floridana* S. F. Blake; *S. riparia* Kearney

Stems herbaceous, erect or spreading, much branched, to 6 dm, glabrous, puberulent, or densely hispid. **Leaves:** stipular sheath 8–15-veined, glabrous or puberulent to densely hispid, teeth of distal stipules mostly shorter than sheath; petiole 1–3 mm; leaflet blades ovate to elliptic or lanceolate, 40–20 mm, veins 3–6 pairs, base cuneate, margins sometimes spinulose, apex acute to acuminate, surfaces sometimes punctate abaxially, glabrous. **Inflorescences** 1–8-flowered, ovoid, to 1 cm, axis rudiment absent; bracts usually 1-foliolate, sometimes 3-foliolate proximally, 3–6 × 2.5–5.5 mm, 5–9-veined, puberulent to densely hispid; outer bracteole 2–3 mm, apex glabrous or ciliate; inner bracteole 1, 1–2.5 mm, apex glabrous or ciliate. **Flowers:** calyx tube 2.5–5 mm, lobes ± acute; corolla yellow or orange-yellow; banner suborbiculate, 4.5–7 mm; wings 3.5–4.5 mm; keel 3–4 mm. **Loments** strongly reticulate with vertical veins, 2.5–3 mm wide; fertile segment 1; proximal segment sterile; distal segment 2.5–5 mm, puberulent; beak hooked, 0.5–1 mm, to ⅕ distal segment. **Seeds** 1–1.5 mm.

Flowering summer. Dry, open, rocky or sandy woodlands, borders, barrens, moist pine savannas, old fields, roadsides; 0–1000 m; Ala., Ariz., Ark., Del., D.C., Fla., Ga., Ill., Ind., Kans., Ky., La., Md., Miss., Mo., N.J., N.Y., N.C., Ohio, Okla., Pa., S.C., Tenn., Tex., Va., W.Va., Wis.; Mexico.

4. Stylosanthes viscosa (Linnaeus) Swartz, Prodr., 108. 1788 • Viscid pencil-flower

Hedysarum hamatum Linnaeus var. *viscosum* Linnaeus, Pl. Jamaic. Pug., 20. 1759 (as viscosa)

Stems herbaceous, ascending and spreading or prostrate and matted, much branched, to 10 dm, densely pubescent with short, viscid hairs. **Leaves:** stipular sheath 3–5-veined, teeth of distal stipules shorter than sheath; petiole 2.5–5 mm; leaflet blades elliptic to lanceolate, 25 × 5 mm, viscid, veins 2–4 pairs, base cuneate, margins entire, apex acute or obtuse, surfaces punctate abaxially, short-hairy or hispidulous. **Inflorescences** 2–5-flowered, ovoid, to 2 cm, axis rudiment absent; outer bracts 3-foliolate, inner bracts 1-foliolate, sheath 5–7-veined, hispidulous and viscid abaxially; outer bracteole 2.5–3 mm, apex ciliate; inner bracteole 1, 2.5–3 mm, apex ciliate. **Flowers:** calyx tube 3–7 mm, lobes acute; corolla yellow; banner suborbiculate, 4–7 mm; wings 4–5 mm; keel 3–4 mm. **Loments** reticulate, to 2.5 mm wide; fertile segment 1; proximal segment sterile; distal segment 2–4 mm, short-hairy; beak strongly hooked, 0.5–1.5 mm, to ½ distal segment, often curled, short-hairy. **Seeds** 1–1.5 mm. $2n$ = 20.

Flowering summer. Sandy prairies, rocky slopes; 20–2000 m; Ariz., Tex.; Mexico; West Indies; Central America; South America.

In the flora area, *Stylosanthes viscosa* is documented from Mohave County in Arizona, and Brooks, Calhoun, Denton, Kenedy, Kleberg, Neuces, and San Patricio counties in Texas.

5. Stylosanthes humilis Kunth in A. von Humboldt et al., Nov. Gen. Sp. 6(fol.): 395; 6(qto.): 506; plate 594. 1824

Stems suffruticose at base, usually ascending, sometimes prostrate, branched, to 5 dm, with short white hairs along one side of stem, glabrous or short-hispid, not viscid. **Leaves:** stipular sheath 3–7-veined, teeth of distal stipules shorter than sheath; petiole 2.5–5 mm; leaflet blades lanceolate to elliptic, 15 × 3.5 mm, veins 3–4 pairs, base cuneate, margins entire, apex acute, mucronate, surfaces bristly-ciliate or glabrous, not punctate. **Inflorescences** 3 or 4-flowered, ovoid, to 1.5 cm, axis rudiment absent; bracts 1–3-foliolate, 5–9-veined, 2.5–4.5 mm wide, bristly; outer bracteole 2.5–3.5 mm, apex ciliate; inner bracteole 1, 2–2.5 mm, apex ciliate. **Flowers:** calyx tube 4–5 mm, lobes acute; corolla yellow; banner suborbiculate, 3–4 mm; wings 3–4 mm; keel 3–3.5 mm. **Loments** reticulate, 1.5–2.5 mm wide; fertile segment 1; proximal segment sterile; distal segment 1.5–2.5(–4) mm, puberulent; beak hooked to coiled, 1.5–3.5(–5.5) mm, equaling to greatly surpassing distal segment, pubescent. **Seeds** 1–1.5 mm. $2n$ = 20.

Flowering summer. Rocky slopes, mesas; 1000–2000 m; Ariz.; Mexico; West Indies (Cuba); Central America; introduced in Asia (Malaysia), Australia.

In the flora area, *Stylosanthes humilis* is documented from Cochise and Santa Cruz counties.

72. ARACHIS Linnaeus, Sp. Pl. 2: 741. 1753; Gen. Pl. ed. 5, 329. 1754 • Peanut [Latin *arachis*, contraction of *Arachidna*; *aracus*, wild chickling, and *hudnon*, tuber, alluding to similarity between underground fruit of *arachis* and aerial fruit of *aracus*] [I]

Velva E. Rudd†

Jay A. Raveill

Herbs, annual or perennial, sometimes woody basally, unarmed. **Stems** spreading, erect, prostrate, or creeping, sometimes subterranean, glabrous or pubescent. **Leaves** alternate, usually even-pinnate; stipules present, adnate to petiole base; petiolate; leaflets usually 4, rarely 3, stipels absent, blade margins entire, surfaces glabrous or pubescent. **Inflorescences** 1–7-flowered, axillary, spikes, sometimes subpaniculate; bracts present, similar to stipules; bracteoles paired at base of elongated hypanthium. **Flowers** papilionaceous; calyx, corolla, and stamens borne at summit of an elongated, tubular hypanthium, calyx lobes 5, bilabiate, linear, 4 adaxial lobes connate to form broad lip, sometimes 2 adaxialmost lobes fused to summit and adaxial lip appearing 3-toothed; corolla yellow to orange [brick-red or white]; stamens 10, monadelphous, with 8 functional anthers and 2 sterile filaments [9 or 10 functional and 0 or 1 sterile]; anthers alternately dorsifixed, oblong, and basifixed, globose, sometimes 1 or 2 stamens reduced to sterile filaments or absent; ovary sessile at anthesis, base later greatly elongated on peg; style filiform; stigma terminal. **Fruits** geocarpic, loments, sessile, torulose, not articulate, oblong or ovoid, ± indehiscent, glabrous. **Seeds** 1–6, ovoid or oblong; hilum subapical. $x = 10$.

Species ca. 70 (2 in the flora): introduced; South America (Argentina, Brazil, Paraguay, Uruguay); introduced also in Mexico, West Indies, Central America, Asia, Africa, Australia.

Arachis is most closely related to *Chapmannia* and *Stylosanthes*, based on morphological (V. E. Rudd 1981) and molecular evidence (M. Lavin et al. 2001, 2001b). It has been divided into nine sections, with many species displaying extensive morphological variation (A. Krapovickas and W. C. Gregory 2007). Two species are cultivated in the flora area for use as food or forage. Additional species are grown in tropical climates; they may be introduced into southern Florida in the future. Some cultivated strains are difficult to identify to species and are identified only to section.

Geocarpic fruits are common to all species of *Arachis*. The flowers are chasmogamous and aerial, with a meristem at the base of the sessile ovary. After fertilization, the meristem elongates greatly to form a post-floral axis or the so-called peg that grows gravitropically until the developing fruit is below ground level (B. W. Smith 1950; A. Krapovickas and W. C. Gregory 2007).

SELECTED REFERENCES Hermann, F. J. 1954. A Synopsis of the Genus *Arachis*. Washington. [U.S.D.A., Agric. Monogr. 19.] Krapovickas, A. and W. C. Gregory. 2007. Taxonomy of the genus *Arachis* (Leguminosae). Bonplandia (Corrientes) 16(suppl.) 1–205.

1. Herbs annual; calyces 10–12 mm; corollas 10–20 mm; hypanthia elongated to (1–)2–4 cm; loments 20–60 × 10–20 mm . . . . 1. *Arachis hypogaea*
1. Herbs perennial; calyces 6–10 mm; corollas 15–24 mm; hypanthia elongated to 2.5–10 cm; loments 10 × 5–6 mm . . . . 2. *Arachis glabrata*

1. Arachis hypogaea Linnaeus, Sp. Pl. 2: 741. 1753 • Peanut, groundnut, goober, goober-pea, earthroot [F] [I]

Herbs annual. Stems spreading, erect, or prostrate, sometimes rooting at nodes, to 13 dm, glabrous or villous. **Leaves:** stipules lanceolate to subfalcate, 20–30(–50) mm; leaflet blade elliptic to ovate or obovate, 18–60 × 15–30 mm, apex often obtuse to subacute, sometimes emarginate, surfaces glabrous, or puberulent abaxially, margins villous, sometimes bristly. **Flowers:** hypanthium elongated, (1–)2–4 cm; calyx 10–12 mm, glabrous; corolla bright yellow to orange, often with reddish lines toward base of banner, 10–20 mm. **Loments** oblong, 20–60 × 10–20 mm, sometimes constricted between seeds; pericarp reticulate. **Seeds** oblong; testa reddish brown. $2n = 40$.

Flowering Jun–Sep. Waste areas, field edges; 0–800 m; introduced; Ala., Calif., Conn., Del., D.C., Fla., Ga., Ky., La., Mass., Miss., Mo., N.J., N.C., Okla., Pa., S.C., Tenn., Tex., Utah, Va., W.Va.; South America (Brazil); introduced also in Asia, Africa, Australia.

Arachis hypogaea is a major cultivated crop in tropical to warm-temperate areas worldwide (R. Prescott-Allen and C. Prescott-Allen 1990); the seeds are used most notably as food or for edible oil (J. A. Duke 1981). Archaeological evidence indicates that peanuts were in cultivation by at least 1200–1500 BCE and spread as far north as Mexico prior to European contact (R. O. Hammons 1973). Peanuts occur sporadically outside of cultivation, probably spread by birds and squirrels; they are rarely self-perpetuating. The infraspecific variation of *A. hypogaea* in its native range is extensive; it has been divided into two subspecies and six varieties (A. Krapovickas and W. C. Gregory 2007). The variation in its native range may be useful in improving the cultivated strains (J. Smartt 1990).

SELECTED REFERENCE Smith, B. W. 1950. *Arachis hypogaea*. Aerial flowers and subterranean fruit. Amer. J. Bot. 37: 802–815.

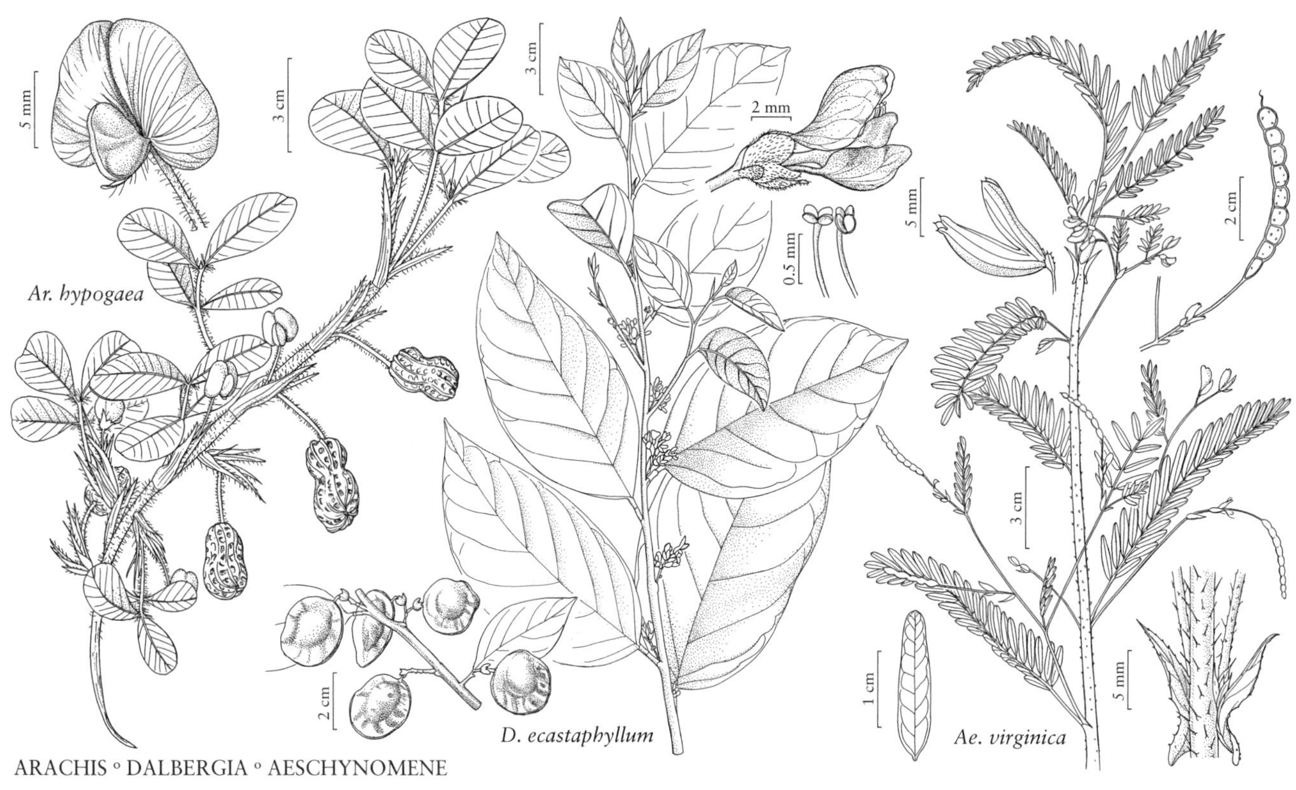

ARACHIS ∘ DALBERGIA ∘ AESCHYNOMENE

2. **Arachis glabrata** Bentham, Trans. Linn. Soc. London 18: 159. 1839 [I]

Herbs perennial. **Stems** usually prostrate and creeping, sometimes branching adventitiously, 4 dm, puberulent or glabrescent. **Leaves:** stipules linear-lanceolate, 8–27 mm; leaflet blade obovate or ovate to elliptic or oblong, 6–32 × 5–17 mm, apex obtuse to retuse or acute, surfaces often glabrescent abaxially, sometimes minutely pubescent, midrib often with persistent and longer hairs, glabrous or early glabrescent adaxially, margins glabrous, villous, or, sometimes, sparsely bristly. **Flowers:** hypanthium elongated, 2.5–10 cm; calyx 6–10 mm, villous, hairs bristly; corolla yellow or yellow-orange, 15–24 mm. **Loments** longitudinally striate, ovoid, 10 × 5–6 mm, apex acute; pericarp smooth. **Seeds** ovoid; testa pale. $2n$ = 40.

Flowering Apr–Aug. Roadsides, adjacent fields; 0–50 m; introduced; Ala., Fla., Ga.; South America (Brazil); introduced also in Mexico, West Indies, Central America, Asia, Africa.

Arachis glabrata is used as a forage crop and groundcover in Florida and, to a limited extent, other parts of southern United States (A. Flores 2008; E. C. French et al. 1994) where it has locally escaped from cultivation. The variation in *A. glabrata* is extensive; variety *hagenbeckii* (Harms ex Kuntze) F. J. Hermann is recognized by its narrower leaflets and by its unique native range. Variety *hagenbeckii* (as *A. hagenbeckii* Harms) has been reported from Georgia.

73. DALBERGIA Linnaeus f., Suppl. Pl., 52, 316. 1782, name conserved • Rosewood [For Carl Gustav Dahlberg, 1721–1781, Swedish soldier in Suriname and collector for Linnaeus, and Nils Ericsson Dahlberg, 1736–1820, Swedish royal physician]

Velva E. Rudd†

Michael A. Vincent

Amerimnon P. Browne, name rejected; *Ecastaphyllum* P. Browne, name rejected

Shrubs or trees [lianas], unarmed. **Stems** erect or scandent, young growth densely strigose or villous or glabrescent, peduncles and pedicels eglandular. **Leaves** alternate, odd-pinnate or unifoliolate; stipules present, caducous; petiolate; leaflets 1–5[+], alternate, stipels absent, blade margins entire, surfaces glabrous or pubescent. **Inflorescences** 10–50-flowered, axillary [lateral or terminal], racemes, panicles, or corymbs; bracts present; bracteoles paired proximal to calyx. **Flowers** papilionaceous; calyx campanulate, lobes 5; corolla usually white, creamy white, or yellowish, sometimes pinkish [purple], glabrous; stamens 9 or 10, monadelphous or diadelphous [triadelphous]; anthers basifixed, relatively small, dehiscing apically; style glabrous; stigma terminal, small. **Fruits** legumes, stalk present, compressed, straight, compressed, narrowly ellipsoid to oblong or subglobose to subreniform, indehiscent, often winged (samaroid), glabrous or pubescent. **Seeds** 1–4[–6], reniform; hilum lateral. $x = 10$.

Species ca. 100 (3 in the flora): Florida, Mexico, West Indies, Central America, South America, Asia, Africa; tropical to warm temperate areas.

Dalbergia includes important timber species prized for the color and grain of the wood (M. Chudnoff 1984).

1. Leaves 3–5-foliolate; leaflet blades ovate, apex abruptly acuminate or cuspidate; stamens 9; corolla creamy white to yellowish; legumes narrowly ellipsoid to oblong, stalk 5–6 mm; seeds 1 or 2(–4) . . . . 1. *Dalbergia sissoo*
1. Leaves unifoliolate; leaflet blades elliptic, ovate, or ovate-elliptic, apex usually acute, sometimes acuminate or obtuse, or abruptly narrowed to obtuse tip; stamens 10; corolla often white, sometimes pinkish; legumes ellipsoid to oblong or subglobose to subreniform, stalk 3 mm; seeds 1–4.
    2. Legumes ellipsoid to oblong, 10 mm wide; seeds 1–4; leaflet apex usually acute, sometimes acuminate or obtuse, surfaces lustrous, glabrous or lightly appressed-pubescent, hairs minute . . . . 2. *Dalbergia brownei*
    2. Legumes subglobose to subreniform, 15–20 mm wide; seed 1; leaflet apex abruptly narrowed to obtuse tip, surfaces sublustrous, subsericeous becoming moderately appressed-pubescent or glabrous . . . . 3. *Dalbergia ecastaphyllum*

1. Dalbergia sissoo Roxburgh ex de Candolle in A. P. de Candolle and A. L. P. P. de Candolle, Prodr. 2: 416. 1825 • Indian rosewood, sissoo [I]

Trees, to 25 m. **Leaves** 3 or 5-foliolate, 15 cm; stipules lanceolate, 4 × 1 mm, apex acuminate; petiole (2–)3–6 cm, usually densely pilose or villous, sometimes glabrate; rachis flexuous; petiolules 2–6 mm, usually densely pilose or villous, sometimes glabrate; leaflet blades ovate, 20–65 × 20–65 mm, base rounded, apex abruptly acuminate or cuspidate, surfaces lustrous with age, puberulent or glabrous. **Inflorescences** subcymose or paniculate, axes puberulent; bracts caducous, blade obovate, 2 × 0.5–1 mm, apex truncate or obtuse; bracteoles caducous, blade elliptic, 2 × 1 mm, apex subacute. **Pedicels** 0.2–0.7 mm. **Flowers:** calyx 3–5 mm, base rounded, puberulent, abaxial lobe usually 2 mm longer than lateral lobes, adaxial lobes rounded, connate nearly to apex; corolla creamy white to yellowish, 8–10 mm; stamens 9, monadelphous; filaments alternately long and short; pistil puberulent. **Legumes** stalk 5–6 mm; narrowly ellipsoid to oblong, 40–100 × 6–15 mm, base attenuate to cuneate, apex acute to rounded, surface sublustrous to reticulate, glabrous. **Seeds** 1 or 2(–4). **2*n*** = 20.

Flowering Mar–Jul. Thickets, pinelands; 0–50 m; introduced; Fla.; Asia; widely cultivated worldwide in tropical areas.

Dalbergia sissoo is a cultivated timber tree in India, where it is used for cabinetry, furniture, carvings, and musical instruments (M. Chudnoff 1984). In southern Florida, it is grown as an ornamental and has escaped; it is listed as a Category II invasive species by the Florida Exotic Pest Plant Council (www.fleppc.org).

2. Dalbergia brownei (Jacquin) Schinz, Bull. Herb. Boissier 6: 731. 1898 • Browne's Indian rosewood

Amerimnon brownei Jacquin, Enum. Syst. Pl., 27. 1760 (as brownii)

Shrubs or trees, to 10 m; stems often somewhat scandent. **Leaves** unifoliolate; stipules deltate-ovate, 1–2 × 1 mm, apex acute; petiole 0.5–1.5 cm, glabrous or puberulent; petiolules 2–3 mm, glabrous or pilose; leaflet blades ovate to ovate-elliptic, 40–80 × 20–40 mm, base cordate to rounded, apex usually acute, sometimes acuminate or obtuse, surfaces lustrous, glabrous or lightly appressed-pubescent, hairs minute. **Inflorescences** corymbose-paniculate, axes pilose becoming glabrate; bracts subpersistent, blade deltate, 1–2 × 1 mm, apex acute to obtuse; bracteoles caducous, blade elliptic-ovate, to 1 mm, apex acute to obtuse. **Pedicels** 1.5–2 mm. **Flowers:** calyx 4 mm, base slightly narrowed, often subsericeous, sometimes glabrate, abaxial lobe 1 mm longer than lateral lobes, adaxial lobes connate nearly to apex, longer than lateral; corolla usually white, sometimes pinkish, 8–10 mm; stamens 10, monadelphous; filaments alternately long and short; pistil glabrous. **Legumes** stalk 3 mm; ellipsoid to oblong, 15–50 × 10 mm, base cuneate to rounded, apex usually obtuse, surface lustrous, glabrous. **Seeds** 1–4.

Flowering May. Hammocks and lagoons; 0–10 m; Fla.; Mexico; West Indies; Central America; South America.

Dalbergia brownei is listed as endangered in Florida.

3. Dalbergia ecastaphyllum (Linnaeus) Taubert in H. G. A. Engler and K. Prantl, Nat. Pflanzenfam. 101–102[III,3]: 335. 1894 (as ecastophyllum) • Coinvine [F]

Hedysarum ecastaphyllum Linnaeus, Syst. Nat. ed. 10, 2: 1169. 1759; *Ecastaphyllum brownei* Persoon; *Pterocarpus ecastaphyllum* (Linnaeus) Murray

Shrubs or trees, to 4(–6) m; stems sometimes scandent. **Leaves** unifoliolate; stipules lanceolate, 10 × 2 mm, apex acuminate; petiole 0.4–0.6 cm, puberulent to sericeous; petiolules 3–5 mm, puberulent; leaflet blades elliptic to ovate, (25–)50–80 × (20–)50–80 mm, base rounded to subcordate, apex abruptly narrowed to obtuse tip, surfaces sometimes discolorous, sublustrous, subsericeous, becoming moderately appressed-pubescent or glabrous. **Inflorescences** racemose in fascicles, axes pilose; bracts caducous, blade deltate, 1 × 0.5 mm, apex acute; bracteoles subpersistent, blade deltate-ovate, 1 × 0.3–0.5 mm, apex acute. **Pedicels** 1–1.5 mm. **Flowers:** calyx 3–3.5 mm, base rounded, pilose or subsericeous, lobes subequal, barely distinct from tube, deltate; corolla usually white, sometimes pinkish, 8–9 mm; stamens 10, monadelphous or diadelphous (5 + 5); filaments nearly equal; pistil glabrous. **Legumes** stalk 3 mm; subglobose to subreniform, 20–35 × 15–20 mm, base rounded, apex rounded, surface sericeous becoming appressed-pubescent or glabrescent. **Seed** 1. **2*n*** = 20.

Flowering Apr–Aug. Hammocks, coastal thickets, wooded dunes, swamps, shores, margins of mangroves; 0–10 m; Fla.; Mexico; West Indies; Central America; South America; Africa.

74. AESCHYNOMENE Linnaeus, Sp. Pl. 2: 713. 1753; Gen. Pl. ed. 5, 319. 1754

• Sensitive joint-vetch, bastard sensitive plant [Greek *aischyno*, shame or sensitive, and *mene*, alluding to closure of leaflets when touched]

Velva E. Rudd†

Jay A. Raveill

Secula Small

Herbs, annual or perennial, or subshrubs [shrubs or trees], unarmed. **Stems** erect to decumbent or prostrate, young stems glabrous or sparsely to densely pubescent, with or without glandular hairs. **Leaves** alternate, odd- or even-pinnate; stipules present, peltate and appendiculate proximal to point of attachment or attached at base and not appendiculate; petiolate; leaflets 5–80, alternate or subopposite, blades subsessile, pulvinate, sometimes sensitive to light and touch, margins entire or ciliate-denticulate, surfaces glabrous or pubescent. **Inflorescences** 1–15-flowered, axillary [terminal], usually racemes, sometimes fascicles (in *A. villosa* var. *villosa*), rarely solitary flowers, [panicles]; bracts present, usually stipulelike, smaller; bracteoles paired at base of calyx. **Flowers** papilionaceous; calyx campanulate, lobes 5, subequal or bilabiate and abaxial lip 3-parted and adaxial lip 2-parted; corolla yellowish, sometimes with red or purplish markings, keel acute, included, bent, or curved; stamens 10, diadelphous, 5 + 5 or filaments forming sheath, splitting adaxially; anthers usually dorsifixed, sometimes basifixed; style glabrous; stigma terminal, capitate or minutely penicillate. **Fruits** loments, sessile, gynophore present, compressed, straight or curved, pubescent; segments (1 or) 2–18, each 1-seeded, joints between seeds sometimes poorly developed, proximal segment dehiscent or indehiscent, sometimes continuous with gynophore. **Seed** 1, reniform, smooth, sublustrous; hilum lateral, circular. $x = 10$.

Species ca. 150 (9 in the flora): United States, Mexico, West Indies, Central America, South America, s Asia, Africa, Pacific Islands, Australia.

SELECTED REFERENCES Rudd, V. E. 1955. The American species of *Aeschynomene*. Contr. U.S. Natl. Herb. 32: 1–172. Rudd, V. E. 1959. Supplementary studies in *Aeschynomene*. I. Series *Viscidulae*. J. Wash. Acad. Sci. 49: 45–52.

1. Stems floating; corollas 18–30 mm . . . . 9. *Aeschynomene fluitans*
1. Stems erect, decumbent, or prostrate, not floating; corollas 4–15 mm.
    2. Stipules attached at base, not peltate; calyces campanulate with 5 subequal lobes; banner pubescent abaxially; stems prostrate.
        3. Leaflets 5–9, blades obovate, 4–10(–18) × 3–7(–10) mm, margins ciliate-denticulate; loment segments 2 or 3(–5), densely white-tomentose, usually also viscid-hispid; gynophore subglabrous; stems viscid . . . . 7. *Aeschynomene viscidula*
        3. Leaflets (8–)15–30, blades oblong-elliptic, 2–5(–6) × 1–2(–5) mm, margins entire or sparsely denticulate-ciliate; loment segments 2 or 3, appressed pubescent; gynophore hispid with yellowish hairs; stems canescent . . . . 8. *Aeschynomene histrix*
    2. Stipules peltate, appendiculate; calyces bilabiate, adaxial lip 2-parted, abaxial lip 3-parted; banner usually glabrous on abaxially, sometimes ciliate; stems usually erect, sometimes decumbent (in *A. villosa*).

[4. Shifted to left margin.—Ed.]

4. Leaflet blades asymmetric, linear-oblong, apparently 2–5-veined.
   5. Loments usually glabrous or puberulent, rarely hispidulous, hairs bulbous-based, glandular; loments with conspicuous reticulate venation, especially near margins, center of each segment usually muricate or verrucose, sutures between segments prominent . . . . 1. *Aeschynomene americana*
   5. Loments villous-hispid, hairs yellow, bulbous-based, glandular; loment segments with inconspicuous venation, center of each segment rarely muricate or verrucose, sutures between segments usually distinct, sometimes absent . . . . 2. *Aeschynomene villosa*
4. Leaflet blades nearly symmetrical, 1-veined.
   6. Gynophore separating from proximal segment of loment by distinct suture; loments with both margins crenate; plants darkening on drying; calyx lips nearly entire . . . . 3. *Aeschynomene pratensis*
   6. Gynophore continuous with proximal segment of loment; loments with abaxial margin crenate or slightly crenate, adaxial margin ± straight; plants not darkening on drying; calyx lips dentate or lobed.
      7. Gynophores (10–)12–25 mm; corollas yellowish, usually with reddish markings; leaflet blades 8–20 mm . . . . 4. *Aeschynomene virginica*
      7. Gynophores 3–10 mm; corollas yellow to purplish; leaflet blades 2–15 mm.
         8. Corollas 7–10 mm, calyces 4–6 mm; loment segments rarely muricate or verrucose near center at maturity; leaflets (30–)50–70, blades 2–10 × 1–2.5 mm. . . . . 5. *Aeschynomene indica*
         8. Corollas (8–)10–15 mm, calyces 5–8 mm; loment segments usually muricate or verrucose in center at maturity; leaflets 30–40(–50), blades 6–15 × 2–3 mm . . . . 6. *Aeschynomene rudis*

1. Aeschynomene americana Linnaeus, Sp. Pl. 2: 713. 1753 [W]

Varieties 2 (1 in the flora): se United States, Mexico, West Indies, Central America, South America; introduced in Asia, Africa.

Variety *flabellata* Rudd occurs in Mexico and Central America.

1a. Aeschynomene americana Linnaeus var. **americana** [W]

Herbs, annual or perennial, not darkening on drying. **Stems** erect, to 2.5 m, ± glabrous or glandular-hirsute, hairs bulbous-based. **Leaves** 1–7 cm; stipules peltate, (5–)10–25 × 1–4 mm, apex attenuate; leaflets 20–60, blades apparently 2–4-veined, asymmetric, subfalcate, linear-oblong, 4–15 × 1–2 mm, margins ciliate-denticulate, apex acuminate, surfaces glabrous. **Inflorescences** 1–7-flowered, racemes, axis hispidulous. **Flowers:** calyx 3–6 mm, bilabiate, abaxial lip 3-parted, adaxial lip 2-parted, glabrous or hispidulous; corolla yellowish to orange or tan, usually with red or purplish lines, 5–10 mm, banner glabrous; gynophore 1–3 mm, continuous with proximal segment, glabrate. **Loments:** abaxial margin crenate, adaxial margin straight or curved, sutures between segments prominent, margins not separating from valves; segments (3–)6–8(–9), semi-globose, 2.5–5 × 3–6 mm, reticulate venation conspicuous, especially near margins, center of each usually muricate or verrucose, faces usually glabrous or puberulent, rarely hispidulous, hairs bulbous-based, glandular. **Seeds** dark brown, 2–3 × 1.5–2 mm. **2*n*** = 20.

Flowering Aug–Nov. Disturbed areas, edges of fields, wet roadsides; 0–50 m; Fla., Ga., La., Md.; Mexico; West Indies; Central America; South America; introduced in Asia, Africa.

Variety *americana* is used for forage in Florida with various grasses in permanent pastures (A. E. Kretschmer and R. C. Bullock 1980).

2. Aeschynomene villosa Poiret in J. Lamarck et al., Encycl., Suppl. 4: 76. 1816 (as Aeschinomene)

Varieties 3 (1 in the flora): Arizona, Mexico, West Indies, Central America, n South America; introduced in tropical Asia, Pacific Islands.

Variety *longifolia* (Micheli ex Donnell Smith) Rudd occurs from Mexico to northern South America, and var. *mexicana* (Hemsley & Rose) Rudd occurs in a limited area of west-central Mexico.

2a. Aeschynomene villosa Poiret var. **villosa**

Herbs, annual or perennial, not or slightly darkening on drying. **Stems** erect to decumbent, to 1 m, usually glandular-hirsute, sometimes viscid. **Leaves** 2–7 cm; stipules peltate, (5–)10–15 × 1–1.5 mm, apex attenuate; leaflets 20–50, blades apparently 2–5-veined, asymmetric, subfalcate, linear-oblong, 3–15 × 1–3 mm, margins often ciliate-denticulate, apex acute, surfaces glabrous. **Inflorescences** 5–15-flowered, racemes or fascicles, axis hispidulous. **Flowers:** calyx 2–4 mm, bilabiate, abaxial lip 3-dentate, adaxial lip 2-parted, glandular-villous; corolla usually yellowish, sometimes lilac due to reddish venation, 3–9 mm, banner glabrous; gynophore 2.5–3.5 mm, continuous with proximal segment, villous-hispid. **Loments:** abaxial margin crenate, adaxial margin straight or slightly indented, sutures between segments often distinct, sometimes absent, margins sometimes breaking away from valves; segments (2 or)3–7, semiglobose, 2–4 × 2–4 mm, reticulate venation inconspicuous, center of each rarely muricate or verrucose, faces villous-hispid, hairs yellow, bulbous-based, glandular. **Seeds** olive to black, 1.5–2.5 × 1.5–2 mm.

Flowering Sep. Wet or dry places; 1000–1500 m; Ariz.; Mexico; West Indies; Central America; n South America; introduced in tropical Asia, Pacific Islands.

3. Aeschynomene pratensis Small, Bull. New York Bot. Gard. 3: 423. 1905 [C]

Varieties 2 (1 in the flora): Florida, West Indies, Central America, South America.

Variety *caribaea* Rudd is widespread in the West Indies, Central America, and South America.

3a. Aeschynomene pratensis Small var. **pratensis** [C] [E]

Herbs, perennial, or subshrubs, darkening on drying. **Stems** ± erect, 1–3 m, glandular-hispid. **Leaves** 4–7 cm; stipules peltate, 5–15 × 1.5–2 mm, apex acuminate; leaflets 15–37, blades 1-veined, nearly symmetric, linear-oblong, 5–10 × 1.5–2.5 mm, margins entire, apex obtuse, surfaces glabrous. **Inflorescences** 1–5-flowered, racemes, axis glabrous. **Flowers:** calyx 5–6 mm, bilabiate, lips barely lobed, glabrous; corolla yellowish with purple markings, 9–12 mm, banner glabrous, sometimes margins ciliate; gynophore 10–15 mm, separating from proximal segment by distinct suture, glabrous or hirsute, hairs bulbous-based, glandular. **Loments:** both margins crenate, abaxial margin often more deeply indented, sutures between segments well developed, margins not separating from valves; segments 3–9, subelliptic, 7–8 × 5–6 mm, reticulate venation conspicuous, center of each verrucose, faces glabrous. **Seeds** dark brown, 4–5 × 3–3.5 mm.

Flowering Dec–Apr. Wet places; of conservation concern; 0–10 m; Fla.

Variety *pratensis* occurs in southern Florida.

A chromosome count of $2n = 20$ (C. A. Berger et al. 1958) was based on var. *caribaea* Rudd, which is smaller in all parts and is not known to occur in the continental United States.

4. Aeschynomene virginica (Linnaeus) Britton, Sterns & Poggenburg, Prelim. Cat., 13. 1888 [C] [E] [F]

Hedysarum virginicum Linnaeus, Sp. Pl. 2: 750. 1753; *Aeschynomene hispida* Willdenow

Herbs, annual, not darkening on drying. **Stems** erect, to 3 m, glabrous or glandular-hispid, hairs bulbous-based. **Leaves** 5–12 cm; stipules peltate, 10 × 2–3 mm, apex acute; leaflets (25–)30–55, blades 1-veined, nearly symmetric, oblong, 8–20 × 4–5 mm, margins usually entire, rarely with scattered, tuberculate hairs, apex obtuse, surfaces glabrous. **Inflorescences** 1–5-flowered, racemes, axis hispid. **Flowers:** calyx 5–8 mm, bilabiate, abaxial lip 3-dentate, adaxial lip shallowly 2-lobed, glabrous; corolla yellowish, usually with reddish markings, 10–15 mm, banner glabrous, margins sparsely ciliate; gynophore (10–)12–25 mm, continuous with proximal segment, glabrous or somewhat hispid. **Loments:** abaxial margin crenate, adaxial margin ± straight, sutures between segments well developed, margins not separating from valves; segments 3–10, subquadrate, 4.5–7 × 4.5–7 mm, reticulate venation moderately conspicuous, center of each usually verrucose, faces sparsely hispid or glabrescent, hairs eglandular, sometimes bulbous-based. **Seeds** brown, 4.5–6 × 3 mm. $2n = 40$.

Flowering Jul–Oct. Brackish tidal shores of rivers, locally in wet fields and ditches; of conservation concern; 0–50 m; Del., Md., N.J., N.C., Pa., Va.

Aeschynomene virginica has been the subject of studies of population structure (J. P. Carulli and D. E. Fairbrothers 1988), life history traits (A. B. Griffith and I. N. Forseth 2005), and seed germination and dispersal (J. M. Baskin et al. 1998, 2005; Griffith and Forseth 2002, 2003). It is in the Center for Plant Conservation's National Collection of Endangered Plants.

5. Aeschynomene indica Linnaeus, Sp. Pl. 2: 713. 1753 [W]

Herbs, annual or perennial, not darkening on drying. **Stems** erect, to 2.5 m, glabrous or moderately glandular-hispid. **Leaves** 5–10 cm; stipules peltate, 10–15 × 2–3 mm, apex acuminate; leaflets (30–)50–70, blades 1-veined, nearly symmetric, elliptic-oblong, 2–10 × 1–2.5 mm, margins entire, apex obtuse to subacute, surfaces glabrous. **Inflorescences** 1–5-flowered, racemes, axis glabrous or hispidulous. **Flowers:** calyx 4–6 mm, bilabiate, abaxial lip 3-dentate, adaxial lip 2-dentate, glabrous; corolla yellow to purplish, 7–10 mm, banner glabrous; gynophore 3–10 mm, continuous with proximal segment, glabrous. **Loments:** abaxial margin slightly crenate, adaxial margin ± straight, sutures between segments well developed, margins not separating from valves; segments 5–8(–12), subquadrate, 5–6 × 4–6 mm, reticulate venation slightly to moderately prominent in immature fruit, not visible in mature fruit, center of each rarely muricate or verrucose, faces glabrous or sparsely hispid, hairs bulbous-based, glandular. **Seeds** dark brown, 3–4 × 2–3 mm. $2n = 40$.

Flowering May–Nov. Wet areas, roadside ditches, weedy in rice fields; 0–100 m; Ala., Ark., Fla., Ga., La., Miss., Mo., N.C., Okla., S.C., Tex., Va.; West Indies (Puerto Rico); South America (s Brazil); coastal se Asia; Africa; Pacific Islands; Australia.

Some of the Texas collections have earlier been called *Aeschynomene evenia* C. Wright, a species described from Cuba that may be a variant of *A. indica*.

6. Aeschynomene rudis Bentham, Pl. Hartw., 116. 1843 [I] [W]

Herbs, annual, not darkening on drying. **Stems** erect, to 2 m, glabrous or moderately glandular-hispid. **Leaves** 4–10 cm; stipules peltate, 7–15 × 2–3 mm, apex acute; leaflets 30–40(–50), blades 1-veined, nearly symmetric, oblong to linear-oblong, 6–15 × 2–3 mm, margins usually entire, sometimes ciliate-denticulate, apex obtuse, surfaces glabrous. **Inflorescences** 1–7-flowered, racemes, axis glabrous or glandular-hispidulous. **Flowers:** calyx 5–8 mm, bilabiate, abaxial lip 3-dentate, adaxial lip shallowly 2-lobed, glabrous, margins ciliate; corolla yellow, often drying somewhat purplish, (8–)10–15 mm, banner glabrous, glandular-ciliate; gynophore 3–6(–10) mm, continuous with proximal segment, glabrate. **Loments:** abaxial margin crenate, adaxial margin ± straight, sutures between segments well developed, margins not separating from valves; segments (3–)6–12, subquadrate, 4–6 × 4–6 mm, reticulate venation inconspicuous to moderately conspicuous, center of each usually muricate or verrucose, faces subglabrous or lightly glandular-hispidulous, hairs bulbous-based. **Seeds** dark brown or black, 3–3.5 × 2–2.5 mm.

Flowering Aug–Sep. Wet areas, in standing water, rice fields; 0–100 m; introduced; Ala., Ark., Calif., Fla., Ga., La., Mo., N.C., Pa., S.C., Tex.; Mexico; West Indies (Cuba); Central America; South America.

Aeschynomene rudis was introduced into the United States in the nineteenth century and was generally overlooked (J. P. Carulli et al. 1988).

7. Aeschynomene viscidula Michaux, Fl. Bor.-Amer. 2: 74. 1803 [F]

Secula viscidula (Michaux) Small

Herbs, perennial, not darkening on drying. **Stems** prostrate, to 1 m, viscid, hairs glandular-crisp-pubescent. **Leaves** 0.5–2.5 cm; stipules attached at base, 2–4 × 1.5–2 mm, apex acute; leaflets 5–9, blades 1-veined, slightly asymmetric, obovate, 4–10(–18) × 3–7(–10) mm, margins ciliate-denticulate, apex obtuse, surfaces glabrous or subglabrous, slightly subappressed-puberulent or glabrous adaxially. **Inflorescences** 1–8-flowered, racemes, axis glandular-hispidulous. **Flowers:** calyx 2.5–3.5 mm, not bilabiate, lobes subequal, hispidulous, margins ciliate; corolla usually yellow, sometimes orangish with reddish venation, 5–7 mm, banner pubescent abaxially; gynophore 1–3(–5) mm, continuous with proximal segment, subglabrous. **Loments:** abaxial margin deeply indented, adaxial margin ± straight, sutures between segments well developed, margins not separating from valves; segments 2 or 3(–5), semiglobose, 3.5–5 × 4.5 mm, reticulate venation slightly to moderately conspicuous, sometimes obscured by pubescence, center of each not muricate or verrucose, faces densely white-tomentose, usually viscid-hispid, terminal segment rarely glabrous. **Seeds** light brown, 2–3 × 2 mm. $2n = 20$.

Flowering Apr–Aug. Wetlands; 0–50 m; Ala., Fla., Ga., Miss., Tex.; Mexico; West Indies (Cuba, Lesser Antilles); Central America (Belize, El Salvador, Guatemala, Nicaragua); South America (Brazil, Venezuela).

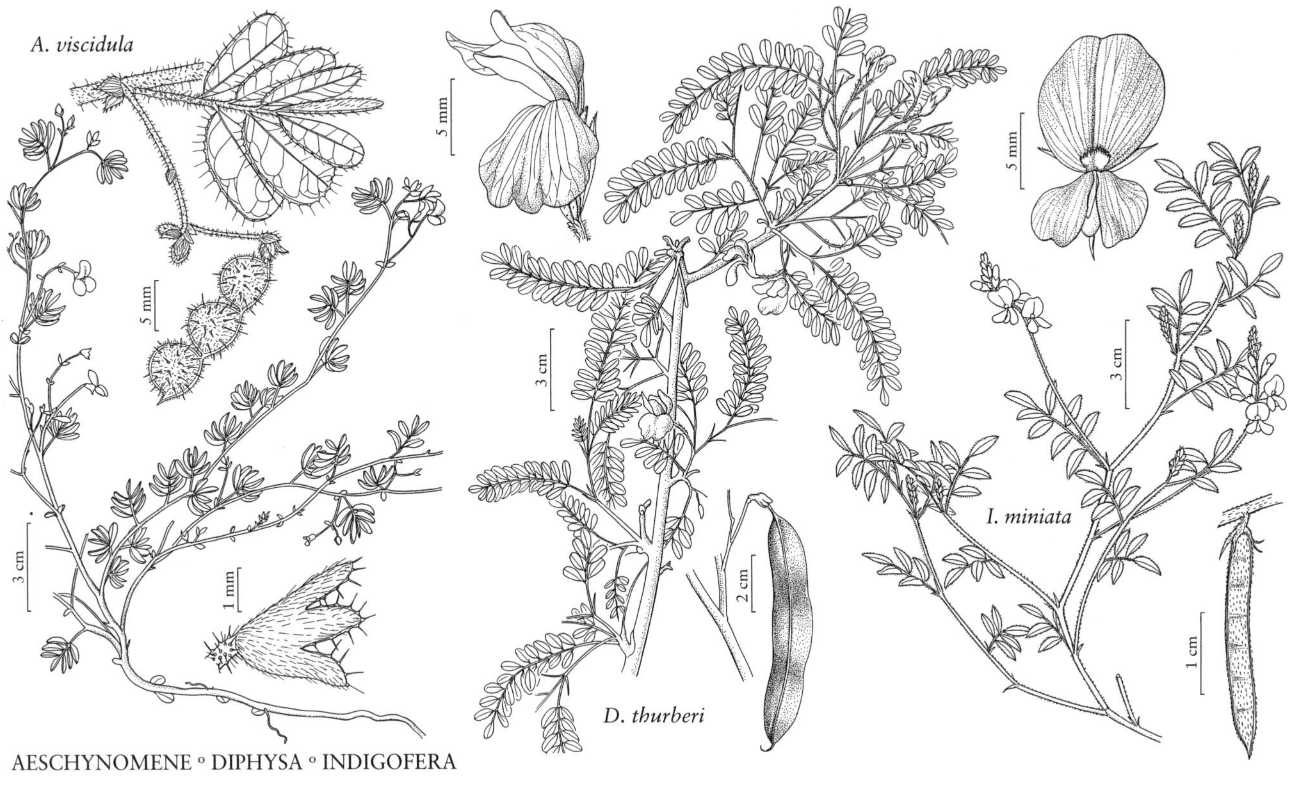

AESCHYNOMENE ◦ DIPHYSA ◦ INDIGOFERA

8. **Aeschynomene histrix** Poiret in J. Lamarck et al., Encycl., suppl. 4: 77. 1816 (as Ae schinomene) [I]

Secula histrix (Poiret) Small

Varieties 5 (1 in the flora): introduced, Florida; Mexico, Central America, South America.

8a. **Aeschynomene histrix** Poiret var. **incana** Bentham in C. F. P. von Martius et al., Fl. Bras. 15(1): 69. 1859 (as hystrix) [I]

Aeschynomene incana Vogel, Linnaea 12: 90. 1838, not (Swartz) G. Meyer 1818

Herbs, perennial, not darkening on drying. **Stems** prostrate, to 1 m, glandular-canescent. **Leaves** 1–6 cm; stipules attached at base, 4–15 × 0.2–2 mm, apex acuminate; leaflets (8–)15–30, blades 1-veined, subsymmetric, oblong-elliptic, 2–5(–6) × 1–2(–5) mm, margins entire or sparsely ciliate-denticulate, apex obtuse to subacute, surfaces canescent. **Inflorescences** 4–15-flowered, racemes, often congested, axis usually puberulent, sometimes glandular-hispidulous. **Flowers:** calyx 2–3 mm, not bilabiate, lobes subequal, glabrous or puberulent; corolla yellow, sometimes with reddish veins, (4–)5–6(–7) mm, banner puberulent abaxially; gynophore 1–2 mm, continuous with proximal segment, hispid at junction with proximal segment, hairs yellowish, 2–4 mm, otherwise glabrous. **Loments:** abaxial margin deeply constricted between seeds, adaxial margin straight, sutures between segments well developed, margins not separating from valves; segments usually 2 or 3, rarely 5, semiglobose, 2–2.5 × 2–2.5 mm, reticulate venation inconspicuous, obscured by pubescence, center of each not muricate or verrucose, faces appressed-pubescent. **Seeds** black, 1.5–2 × 1–1.5 mm.

Flowering Apr–Aug. Waste places; 0–10 m; introduced; Fla.; Central America; South America.

Aeschynomene histrix is represented in the flora area by two collections, both from Pensacola, Escambia County, in 1885 and 1976. The more recent collection was along railroad tracks in an urban area where it is unlikely to have been planted.

Demarcation between varieties in *Aeschynomene histrix* is not precise. Variety *histrix* is distinguished from var. *incana* by fruits glabrous or crisp-pubescent rather than appressed-pubescent and stems and leaflets subglabrous to moderately puberulent, as opposed to densely canescent. The 1885 collection is the only specimen of *A. histrix* observed by the authors with 5-segmented fruits. The 1976 collection has the 2-segmented loments typical of *A. histrix*.

9. Aeschynomene fluitans Peter, Abh. Königl. Ges. Wiss. Göttingen, Math.-Phys. Kl., n. s. 13: 82. 1928 • Giant water sensitive plant [I]

Herbs, perennial, aquatic, stem darkening on drying. **Stems** floating on surface, hollow, 1–4.5 m, hirsute, densely covered with adventitious roots. **Leaves** 4–8 cm; stipules peltate, appendiculate, 12–25 × 2–6.5 mm, apex attenuate; leaflets 12–24, blades 1-veined, slightly asymmetric with straight sides, narrowly oblong or oblanceolate, 11–23 × 3–6 mm, margins entire or very finely serrulate and ciliate, apex rounded and slightly mucronate, surfaces glabrous and glaucous. **Inflorescences** 1-flowered, stalk glabrous. **Flowers:** calyx 4–9 mm, bilabiate, abaxial lip 3-dentate, adaxial lip barely emarginate, glabrous; corolla yellow, 18–30 mm, banner glabrous, keel petals laciniate; gynophore 8–13 mm, jointed with proximal segment, glabrous. **Loments:** abaxial margin slightly crenate, adaxial margin ± straight, sutures between segments distinct, breaking into 1-seeded segments; segments 1–4(or 5), oblong, 9–12 × 6–9 mm, reticulate venation inconspicuous, faces glabrous. **Seeds** dark brown, 8.5 × 5 mm.

Flowering Mar–Sep. Floating in slow rivers and ponds, in floodplains, stream and pond margins; 0–10 m; introduced; Fla.; Africa.

Aeschynomene fluitans is commonly cultivated (under the names Botswana wonder, large-leaf sensitive plant, and giant water fern) as an ornamental pond or aquarium plant.

75. DIPHYSA Jacquin, Enum. Syst. Pl., 7, 28. 1760 • [Greek *dis*, double, and *physa*, bladder, alluding to legume's inflated membranous sides in *D. carthagenensis* Jacquin, the type species]

Robert H. Mohlenbrock

Shrubs [trees], unarmed [spinose]. **Stems** erect, pubescent [glabrous], hairs glandular, fine-appressed to spreading; peduncles and pedicels glandular-hirsute. **Leaves** alternate, odd-pinnate; stipules present; petiolate; leaflets [13–]19–25[–35], usually alternate, sometimes subopposite, stipels absent, blade margins entire, surfaces glabrous. **Inflorescences** 4–7-flowered, terminal and axillary, racemes; bracts present; bracteoles present. **Flowers** papilionaceous; calyx campanulate, tubular basally, lobes 5; corolla usually yellowish; stamens 10, diadelphous; anthers dorsifixed, ± uniform. **Fruits** legumes, stipitate, slightly inflated [to bladderlike], straight, oblong [lanceoloid-ellipsoid], dehiscent, pubescent. **Seeds** 4–14, oblong.

Species 19 (1 in the flora): Arizona, Mexico.

Most species in *Diphysa* have inflated, bladderlike fruit segments, reminiscent of *Sesbania*. The segments in *Diphysa thurberi*, however, are barely or not at all inflated.

1. Diphysa thurberi (A. Gray) Rydberg ex Standley, Contr. U.S. Natl. Herb. 23: 479. 1922 [F]

Daubentonia thurberi A. Gray, Pl. Nov. Thurb., 313. 1854

Shrubs to 60 cm. **Stems** branched, viscid, densely glandular-hirsute. **Leaves** to 10 cm; stipules caducous, lanceolate, to 5 mm, apex acuminate; rachis densely glandular-hirsutulous; pinna blade oval to obovate, 6–10 × 4–6 mm, base tapered or somewhat rounded, margins glandular-ciliolate, apex acute or rounded, surfaces with dark veins. **Peduncles** densely glandular-hirsute. **Inflorescences** 4–6 cm; bracts caducous, oblong, 2 mm; bracteoles caducous, 2 per flower, elliptic to obovate, 2 mm, glandular-ciliolate. **Pedicels** 7–8 mm, densely glandular-hirsute. **Flowers:** calyx usually glabrous, sometimes ciliolate, tube 5–6 mm, lobes lanceolate, 2 mm, apex acute or obtuse, glandular; corolla: banner reflexed, rounded-obovate, to 10 mm, longer than wings and keel, with 2 callosities distal to base, not clawed, apex emarginate; wings falcate, obliquely oblanceolate, shortly clawed, base auriculate, rounded, apex rounded; keel connate distal to middle, falcate, obliquely oblanceolate, shorter than wings, base auriculate, apex ± acute; ovary stipitate, densely pubescent. **Legumes** slightly inflated, barely constricted between seeds, tapering to base and apex, 60–80 × 10 mm, muricate, ± tomentose. **Seeds** usually brown or black.

Flowering year-round. Dry rocky areas; 500–1000 m; Ariz.; Mexico.

Diphysa thurberi has been documented in the United States only once, an 1882 collection from extreme southern Arizona (*J. G. Lemmon 2659*, GH). Attempts to relocate this population have been unsuccessful (F. T. Farruggia, pers. comm.).

76. INDIGOFERA Linnaeus, Sp. Pl. 2: 751. 1753; Gen. Pl. ed. 5, 333. 1754 • Indigo [Latin *indicum*, indigo, and *fero*, to bear, alluding to blue dye obtained from the plants]

Alan W. Lievens

Michael A. Vincent

Herbs, annual or perennial, subshrubs, or shrubs, unarmed. **Stems** erect, ascending, spreading, procumbent, or prostrate, usually pubescent (except glabrous in *I. decora*, *I. pilosa* pilose with biramous hairs, hairs dolabriform in part or throughout). **Leaves** alternate, odd-pinnate [unifoliolate], not glandular-punctate [or glandular-punctate]; stipules present; petiolate; leaflets (1 or)3–17(or 19)[–23], opposite or alternate, stipels absent or evanescent, blade margins entire, surfaces glabrous or pubescent. **Inflorescences** 1–60+-flowered, axillary, racemes, often appearing spicate; bracts present, caducous; bracteoles absent. **Flowers** papilionaceous; calyx campanulate, lobes 5; corolla usually pink to red, salmon to maroon, orange-mauve to orange, or greenish yellow to ochroleucous, rarely white, 2.5–12(–14) mm; petals caducous; keel shorter than wings and banner; wings auriculate; keel with a pouch or spur extending outward from lateral surface; stamens 10, diadelphous; anthers uniform, basifixed, apiculate and initially gland-tipped; ovary usually sessile. **Fruits** legumes, sessile or stipitate, terete, straight or curved, cylindric, ovoid, oblong, or ellipsoidal, 3–70 mm, ± dehiscent, usually septate, not constricted between seeds, margins smooth, often mottled inside, glabrous or pubescent. **Seeds** 1–12, ± cuboid to ellipsoidal. x = 6, 7, 8.

Species ca. 750 (14 in the flora): North America, Mexico, West Indies, Central America, South America, Asia, Africa, Pacific Islands, Australia; tropical and temperate regions.

Indigofera is easily recognized since all species have malpighian hairs that may be appressed or ascending and may have unequal branching; other types of hairs may also be present. In addition, the corollas range in color from shades of pink to red, salmon pink, orange, purplish red, or greenish yellow; petals are caducous; anthers are mucronate distally; seeds are cuboid or ellipsoid, and usually mottled. Another feature characteristic of *Indigofera* species is a floral-tripping mechanism in the flowers that results in a sudden release of pollen. If the base of the banner petal is touched, the claw splits and detaches from the calyx instantly, causing other petals to collapse and the pollen to be thrown from the anthers (F. H. G. Hildebrand 1866; G. Henslow 1867; A. W. Lievens 1992).

Indigofera includes species from which the blue dye indigo is produced. Some *Indigofera* species are grown as ornamental plants, especially woody species from southeast Asia and Australia, such as *I. australis* Willdenow, *I. decora*, *I. heterantha* Wallich ex Brandis, *I. kirilowii*, *I. pendula* Franchet, and *I. pseudotinctoria* Matsumura, some of which have escaped cultivation in the flora area.

Chromosome numbers reported in *Indigofera* are $2n$ = 8, 12, 14, 16, 32, to 48 (J. A. Frahm-Leliveld 1966; P. K. Gupta and K. Agarwal 1982; B. L. Turner 1956b).

Indigofera parviflora F. Heyne ex Wight & Arnott was collected by C. Mohr (US) as a waif on ballast spoils in Mobile, Alabama; *I. trifoliata* Linnaeus was found as a waif on chrome-ore piles in Maryland by Clyde F. Reed (MO). A specimen of *I. heterantha* Wallich ex Brandis (as *I. gerardiana* Graham ex Baker) was collected in 1979 in Los Angeles County, California.

SELECTED REFERENCE Lievens, A. W. 1992. Taxonomic Treatment of *Indigofera* L. (Fabaceae: Faboideae) in the New World. Ph.D. dissertation. Louisiana State University.

1. Flowers 12–18 mm; legumes glabrous, 25–70(–80) mm.
    2. Stems glabrous; racemes 8–15-flowered; stipules 1–2 mm; leaves 8–25 cm; leaflets 5–15[–23], 20–75(–100) mm. . . . . .13. *Indigofera decora*
    2. Stems sparsely pubescent; racemes 40–60+-flowered; stipules 4–6 mm; leaves 6–15 cm; leaflets (5 or)7–11, 15–40(–50) mm . . . . 14. *Indigofera kirilowii*
1. Flowers 2.5–12 mm; legumes pubescent, 3–35(–40) mm.
    3. Stems procumbent or prostrate; leaflets 3–11(–17), usually alternate, rarely opposite.
        4. Stems procumbent; leaflets similar in size within a leaf, blades oblanceolate, obovate, or narrowly elliptic, apex acute or truncate, surfaces glabrate to densely pubescent adaxially; peduncles 1.5–8 cm . . . . 1. *Indigofera miniata*
        4. Stems prostrate; terminal leaflet usually larger than laterals, blades obovate to broadly oblanceolate, apex rounded to truncate, surfaces glabrous adaxially; peduncles 0.5–1 cm. . . . . .2. *Indigofera spicata*
    3. Stems usually erect, ascending, spreading, prostrate, or procumbent, sometimes scrambling or sprawling; leaflets 1–19, usually opposite (at least distally).
        5. Herbs; stems erect to ascending-spreading; leaflets 1 or 3, if 3, terminal leaflet 2–3 times larger than laterals; racemes 1–3-flowered . . . . 3. *Indigofera pilosa*
        5. Herbs, subshrubs, or shrubs; stems usually erect, ascending, spreading, procumbent, or prostrate, sometimes scrambling or sprawling; leaflets 3–19, similar in size within a leaf; racemes 3–40+-flowered.
            6. Annual, biennial, or short-lived perennial herbs; stems, petioles, and legumes glandular, or brownish hirsute, or pilose, hairs long-spreading, or long-spreading intermixed with appressed.
                7. Herbs brownish hirsute or pilose, hairs long-spreading; racemes 10–20+-flowered, dense; flowers 6–7 mm . . . . .4. *Indigofera hirsuta*
                7. Herbs glandular and pubescent, hairs intermixed long-spreading and appressed; racemes 3–10-flowered, lax; flowers 2.5–3 mm . . . . 5. *Indigofera colutea*
            6. Perennial herbs, shrubs, or subshrubs; glands and brownish hairs absent, hairs appressed or ascending, or hairs crisped, curling.
                8. Perennial herbs; stems erect to procumbent; stems and petioles with crisped, curling hairs; c Texas . . . . .6. *Indigofera texana*
                8. Perennial herbs, shrubs, or subshrubs; stems usually erect or ascending (usually procumbent, sometimes scrambling in *I. oxycarpa*); stems and petioles with appressed or ascending hairs; not confined to c Texas.
                    9. Legumes ovoid, oblong, or ellipsoidal, straight, 3–9 mm; seeds 1–3.
                        10. Herbs; leaflets (7 or)9–13; flowers 6–9 mm; legumes 7–9 mm, woody; seeds 2 or 3; se United States . . . . 7. *Indigofera caroliniana*
                        10. Shrubs or subshrubs, woody; leaflets 13–19; flowers 4.5–5.2 mm; legumes 3–3.5 mm, leathery; seed 1; Arizona, California, New Mexico . . . . .8. *Indigofera sphaerocarpa*
                    9. Legumes cylindric, straight or curved, 15–40 mm; seeds 4–12.
                        11. Shrubs; stems usually procumbent, sometimes scrambling; leaflets 3–7, blade surfaces glabrate to appressed-pubescent adaxially; racemes 8–20 cm, lax, 20–40+-flowered . . . . .9. *Indigofera oxycarpa*
                        11. Herbs or subshrubs; stems erect or ascending; leaflets 7–17, blade surfaces glabrous, densely pubescent, or strigose adaxially; racemes 0.5–12 cm, lax or dense, 5–30+-flowered.

[12. Shifted to left margin.—Ed.]

12. Leaflet surfaces glabrous adaxially; legumes straight or slightly curved, or abruptly upturned distally .... 10. *Indigofera tinctoria*
12. Leaflet surfaces densely pubescent or strigose adaxially; legumes straight or slightly curved, or falcate.
    13. Legumes 18–25 mm, straight or slightly curved to falcate, cinereous-pubescent, base bulbous and reddish; racemes 5–12 cm, lax; flowers 6–8 mm .... 11. *Indigofera lindheimeriana*
    13. Legumes 15–20 mm, strongly curved, strigose to glabrate, base not bulbous or reddish; racemes 3.5–5.5 cm, dense; flowers 5–6 mm .... 12. *Indigofera suffruticosa*

1. Indigofera miniata Ortega, Nov. Pl. Descr. Dec. 8: 98. 1798 • Coastal indigo, scarlet pea [F]

Anila leptosepala (Nuttall) Kuntze; *Astragalus pasqualensis* M. E. Jones; *A. recticarpus* Alph. Wood; *Indigofera argentata* Rydberg; *I. cinerea* Willdenow; *I. hartwegii* Rydberg; *I. leptosepala* Nuttall; *I. miniata* var. *floridana* Isely; *I. miniata* var. *leptosepala* (Nuttall) B. L. Turner; *I. sphenoides* Rydberg; *Orobus coccineus* Miller

Herbs, perennial, strigose, hairs appressed, silvery. **Stems** procumbent, diffusely branched, 1–5 dm. **Leaves** 1–3.5 cm; stipules subulate, 1–7 mm; petiole 0.5–8 cm; stipels absent or of reddish hairs; petiolules 1 mm; leaflets (3 or)5–11(–17), usually alternate, rarely opposite, blades oblanceolate, obovate, or narrowly elliptic, 5–25 × 5 mm, similar in size within a leaf, base cuneate, apex acute or truncate, ± mucronate, surfaces glabrous or adaxially glabrate to densely pubescent. **Peduncles** 1.5–8 cm. **Racemes** 2–20-flowered, dense or lax, 1.5–9 cm. **Pedicels** 1 mm. **Flowers** 7–12 mm; calyx 4–6 mm, lobes usually long-subulate, sometimes triangular; corolla brick red, salmon pinkish, or salmon orange. **Legumes** brown, irregularly spreading or deflexed, cylindric, straight, 10–40 mm, leathery, densely sericeous. **Seeds** 2–8, usually brown, sometimes lighter and brown-speckled, cuboid. **2*n*** = 32.

Flowering Jan–Oct. Open woods, creek bottoms, ruderal areas, pinelands, hammocks, urban waste areas; 0–1200 m; Ala., Ark., Fla., Ga., Kans., La., Okla., Tex.; Mexico (Aguascalientes, Chiapas, Coahuila, Durango, Guanajuato, Guerrero, Jalisco, México, Morelos, Nayarit, Nuevo León, Oaxaca, San Luis Potosí, Tabasco, Tamaulipas, Veracruz); West Indies (Cuba); Central America.

Indigofera miniata is sometimes subdivided into vars. *floridana*, *leptosepala*, and *miniata*. They intergrade and are not clearly differentiated.

Indigofera mexicana Bentham, *I. nana* Rydberg, and *I. ornithopodioides* Chamisso & Schlechtendal are illegitimate names that pertain here.

2. Indigofera spicata Forsskål, Fl. Aegypt.-Arab., 138. 1775 • Creeping indigo [I] [W]

Herbs, perennial, densely strigulose to glabrate, hairs appressed. **Stems** prostrate, often mat-forming, branching freely, 1–3 dm. **Leaves** 1–7.5 cm; stipules deltate to lanceolate, 5–7(–9) mm; petiole 0.1–0.2 cm; stipels absent or of a few hairs; petiolules 1 mm; leaflets 3–9, alternate, blades obovate to broadly oblanceolate, 5–30 × 2–18 mm, terminal leaflet usually larger than laterals, base cuneate, apex rounded to truncate, surfaces strigulose abaxially, glabrous adaxially. **Peduncles** 0.5–1 cm. **Racemes** 20–40+-flowered, dense, 4–9 cm. **Pedicels** 0.5–1 mm. **Flowers** 6–8 mm; calyx 2.5–4 mm, lobes subulate; corolla pinkish salmon to pale carmine. **Legumes** brown, deflexed, cylindric, straight, 10–20 mm, leathery, strigulose. **Seeds** 4–9, greenish, cuboid. **2*n*** = 16.

Flowering year-round. Disturbed, ruderal areas, roadsides, lawns, hammocks, beaches; 0–10 m; introduced; Ala., Fla., Ga., S.C.; Africa; introduced also in Mexico, West Indies (Bahamas, Jamaica, Lesser Antilles, Puerto Rico, Virgin Islands), Central America, South America (Bolivia, Brazil, Colombia, French Guiana), Pacific Islands (Hawaii), Australia.

Indigofera spicata has been confused with *I. hendecaphylla* Jacquin (sometimes spelled incorrectly as *endecaphylla*); distinctions between them were clarified by D. J. Du Puy et al. (1993) and A. S. Weakley et al (2018). The former is toxic to some grazing animals and has been linked to a fatal central nervous system syndrome in horses (J. F. Morton 1989).

3. Indigofera pilosa Poiret in J. Lamarck et al., Encycl., suppl. 3: 151. 1813 • Softhairy indigo [I] [W]

Herbs, annual, pilose, hairs appressed or spreading. **Stems** erect to spreading or ascending-spreading, branched, wiry, 3–7 dm. **Leaves** 1.5–3.5 cm; stipules subulate, 3–5 mm; petiole 0.5–1 cm; stipels absent; petiolules 1 mm; leaflets 1 (proximal leaves) or 3 (distal leaves), opposite, blades broadly to narrowly elliptic, 5–45 × 3–15 mm, terminal leaflet 2–3 times larger than laterals, base cuneate, apex acute, short-mucronate, surfaces sericeous, hairs spreading, one arm much longer than other. **Peduncles** filiform, 0.5–1.5 cm. **Racemes** 1–3-flowered, lax, 1–2 cm. **Pedicels** 1.5 mm. **Flowers** 5 mm; calyx 2–3 mm, lobes linear-subulate; corolla salmon reddish. **Legumes** brown, spreading to strongly ascending, cylindric, straight, 15–22 mm, leathery, hirsute, glandular. **Seeds** 3–6, yellowish brown, cuboid. $2n = 32$.

Flowering Aug–Oct. Disturbed, ruderal areas; 0–10 m; introduced; Fla.; Africa.

In the flora area, *Indigofera pilosa* is found only in central peninsular Florida.

4. Indigofera hirsuta Linnaeus, Sp. Pl. 2: 751. 1753 • Hairy indigo [I] [W]

Anila hirsuta (Linnaeus) Kuntze

Herbs, annual or biennial, brownish hirsute or pilose, hairs long-spreading. **Stems** erect or sprawling, unbranched or branched, 3–10 dm. **Leaves** 4–12.5 cm; stipules narrowly subulate, 10–13 mm; petiole 0.8–1.2 cm; stipels 1–3 mm; petiolules 1.5–2 mm; leaflets 3–7(or 9), opposite, blades elliptic to obovate, 15–60 × 7–25 mm, base cuneate, apex rounded, short-mucronate, surfaces pubescent. **Peduncles** 4–9 cm. **Racemes** 10–20+-flowered, dense, 6–20 cm. **Pedicels** 1–2 mm. **Flowers** 6–7 mm; calyx 3.5–5 mm, lobes setaceous, bristly-plumose; corolla salmon red to maroon. **Legumes** dark brown, deflexed, cylindric, straight, 15–22 mm, leathery, hispid. **Seeds** 6–8, greenish, cuboid. $2n = 16$.

Flowering year-round. Roadsides, old fields, disturbed woodlands, urban waste areas; 0–50 m; introduced; Ala., Fla., Ga., Miss., S.C.; se Asia; Africa; introduced also in Mexico (Guerrero, Oaxaca, Tabasco), West Indies (Lesser Antilles, Puerto Rico), South America (Brazil, Ecuador, Guyana, Paraguay, Peru, Venezuela), Pacific Islands, Australia.

5. Indigofera colutea (Burman f.) Merrill, Philipp. J. Sci. 19: 355. 1921 • Rusty indigo [I]

Galega colutea Burman f., Fl. Indica, 172. 1768; *Indigofera viscosa* Lamarck

Herbs, annual or short-lived perennial, pubescent, hairs long, simple, erect, spreading, glandular, intermixed with appressed hairs. **Stems** ascending and spreading or prostrate, branched, 3–30 dm. **Leaves** 1.5–4.5 cm; stipules narrowly linear, 2.5–3.5 mm; petiole 1–1.5 cm; stipels of brown hairs; petiolules 0.5 mm; leaflets 5–11, sometimes subopposite or alternate proximally, opposite distally, blades elliptic or obovate, 7–14 × 3–4 mm, base cuneate to broadly cuneate, apex broadly acute or obtuse, apiculate, surfaces pubescent, hairs erect, spreading, and appressed. **Peduncles** 0.7–1.2 cm. **Racemes** 3–10-flowered, lax, 2.5–3.5 cm. **Pedicels** 0.5–1 mm. **Flowers** 2.5–3 mm; calyx 1.5–1.9 mm, lobes subulate; corolla reddish or salmon pink. **Legumes** brown, spreading, slightly deflexed, or slightly ascending, cylindric, straight, 18–26 mm, papery, pubescent. **Seeds** 8–12, amber-brown, cuboid. $2n = 16$.

Flowering year-round. Disturbed areas, roadsides, rocky areas, coastal sand; 0–50 m; introduced; Fla.; Asia; Africa; introduced also in West Indies (Hispaniola, Jamaica), Pacific Islands, Australia.

In the flora area, *Indigofera colutea* is known only from Hillsborough, Manatee, and Polk counties.

6. Indigofera texana Buckley, Proc. Acad. Nat. Sci. Philadelphia 13: 451. 1862 • Texas indigo [E]

Indigofera miniata Ortega var. *texana* (Buckley) B. L. Turner

Herbs, perennial, pubescent, glabrate, hairs crisped, curling. **Stems** erect to procumbent, branched, 3–5 dm; from stout rootstock. **Leaves** 2.5–4.5 cm; stipules subulate, 5–8 mm; petiole 0.4–0.6 cm; stipels absent; petiolules 0.5–1 mm; leaflets (3 or)5–9, usually opposite, rarely subopposite, blades obovate, 18–25 × 5–7 mm, terminal leaflet equal to or slightly larger than laterals, primarily wider distally, base cuneate, apex acute, mucronate, surfaces strigose abaxially, glabrous or glabrate adaxially. **Peduncles** 2–5 cm. **Racemes** 20–30+-flowered, lax, 3–10 cm. **Pedicels** 1–1.5 mm. **Flowers** 8–10 mm; calyx 3–4 mm, lobes narrowly long-triangular; corolla reddish. **Legumes** gray-brown, deflexed, cylindric, straight, 18–27 mm, leathery, glabrate. **Seeds** 7 or 8, yellowish green becoming brown in age, often with brown mottling, cuboid. $2n = 32$.

Flowering Apr–Jun. Granite-based soils; 200–700 m; Tex.

Indigofera texana is known only from central Texas, in Blanco, Burnet, Gillespie, Kerr, Llano, Mason, and Menard counties.

7. **Indigofera caroliniana** Miller, Gard. Dict. ed. 8, Indigofera no. 3. 1768 • Carolina indigo [E]

Anila caroliniana Kuntze; *Indigofera disperma* Linnaeus

Herbs, perennial, herbaceous or suffrutescent, sparsely strigose, hairs appressed. **Stems** erect or ascending, often bushy, branched, 7–15 dm. **Leaves** 2–8.5 cm; stipules narrowly triangular, 0.5–1 mm; petiole 0.5–1.3 cm; stipels 0.5–1 mm; petiolules 1–1.3 mm; leaflets (7 or)9–13, ± opposite, blades obovate to oblanceolate, 8–20(–25) × 2–12 mm, base cuneate, apex broadly acute or obtuse, mucronate, surfaces strigulose, pale abaxially. **Peduncles** 1–2 cm. **Racemes** 15–40-flowered, lax, 4–12 cm. **Pedicels** 1–2(–3) mm. **Flowers** 6–9 mm; calyx 1.5–2 mm, lobes deltate; corolla dark pinkish buff to ochroleucous. **Legumes** dark brown, deflexed, ovoid or oblong, straight, 7–9 mm, woody, glabrate or sparsely strigulose. **Seeds** 2 or 3, yellowish tan, bluntly ellipsoidal.

Flowering Jun–Jul. Pinelands, pine-palmetto, scrub oak communities, sandhills, hammocks, roadsides; 0–200 m; Ala., Fla., Ga., La., N.C., S.C.

Indigofera caroliniana Walter is an illegitimate later homonym that pertains here; the name by Walter is also the basis of *Anila caroliniana*.

8. **Indigofera sphaerocarpa** A. Gray, Smithsonian Contr. Knowl. 5(6): 37. 1853 • Sonoran indigo

Amorpha ovalis M. E. Jones; *Anila sphaerocarpa* (A. Gray) Kuntze

Shrubs or subshrubs (woody), strigose, hairs appressed. **Stems** erect, diffusely branched, 3–15 dm. **Leaves** 2.5–9 cm; stipules linear-triangular, 1–2 mm; petiole 0.3–1.5 cm; stipels 0.5 mm; petiolules 1.3 mm; leaflets 13–19, opposite, blades elliptic to obovate-oblong, sometimes folded, 20–30 × 2–5 mm, base cuneate, apex broadly rounded or truncate, mucronate, surfaces strigose and pale abaxially, glabrate adaxially. **Peduncles** 0.8–1.2 cm. **Racemes** 20–35+-flowered, lax, 2.5–11 cm. **Pedicels** 1–2 mm. **Flowers** 4.5–5.2 mm; calyx 1.5–2 mm, lobes broadly triangular; corolla orange-mauve or pinkish. **Legumes** brown, divergent or deflexed, ellipsoidal, straight, 3–3.5 mm, leathery, glabrate. **Seed** 1, brown, bluntly ellipsoidal.

Flowering Jul–Oct. Dry, rocky slopes, with grasses, oaks; 1000–1800 m; Ariz., Calif., N.Mex.; Mexico (Chihuahua, Jalisco, Sonora).

Indigofera sphaerocarpa is known in the flora area from Cochise, Graham, Pima, and Santa Cruz counties, Arizona, and Hidalgo County, New Mexico. A single specimen from the Joshua Tree National Monument, Riverside County, California, was collected in 1973 (*Smith & Sawyer 6890*, HSC).

9. **Indigofera oxycarpa** Desvaux, J. Bot. Agric. 3: 79. 1814 • Florida Keys indigo [E]

Galega frutescens Miller; *Indigofera jamaicensis* Sprengel; *I. keyensis* Small; *I. laevis* Rydberg; *I. macilenta* Standley; *I. mucronata* Sprengel ex de Candolle var. *keyensis* (Small) Isely; *I. rosei* Rydberg; *I. trita* Linnaeus f. var. *keyensis* (Small) Kartesz & Gandhi; *Tephrosia frutescens* (Miller) de Candolle

Shrubs, pubescent, hairs appressed, silvery gray. **Stems** usually procumbent, sometimes scrambling, branched, younger ones with faint zigzag pattern, from main stem at angle (30–90°), those arising from main axis usually short and stubby, 3–20 dm. **Leaves** 2–10 cm; stipules narrowly long-triangular, attenuate, 1–1.3 mm; petiole 1–2 cm; stipels absent; petiolules 0.5 mm; leaflets 3–7, opposite, blades ovate or elliptic, 4.5–19 × 2.5–16 mm, base cuneate, apex acute or broadly rounded, sometimes emarginate, mucronate, surfaces glabrate to appressed-pubescent adaxially, less so abaxially. **Peduncles** 2–6 cm. **Racemes** 20–40+-flowered, lax, 8–20 cm. **Pedicels** 1–2 mm. **Flowers** 5–6 mm; calyx 1.5–3.1 mm, lobes narrowly triangular; corolla pink. **Legumes** brown, strongly reflexed or spreading, cylindric, straight to slightly curved, 24–40 mm, papery, sparsely strigose. **Seeds** 9 or 10, yellowish brown, cuboid. $2n = 16$.

Flowering Oct–Mar. Rocky coasts; 0–10 m; of conservation concern; Fla.; West Indies (Cuba, Jamaica); Central America; South America (Brazil).

Indigofera oxycarpa is endangered in Florida, known only from Collier, Miami-Dade, and Monroe counties.

The nomenclature of *Indigofera oxycarpa* has a confusing history (A. W. Lievens 1992). The earliest name for the species, as treated here, is *Galega frutescens* Miller [*Tephrosia frutescens* (Miller) de Candolle]. Since the name *I. frutescens* is preoccupied, the name *I. oxycarpa* is the oldest available name for the species, if it is recognized as separate from Old World taxa. *Indigofera mucronata* Sprengel ex de Candolle is an illegitimate name sometimes used for this taxon. Sprengel published *I. jamaicensis* in 1826; P. S. White (1980) adopted this name in his treatment of the genus for the *Flora of Panama*. Lievens provided a complete synonymy.

R. D. Meikle (1950) discussed the similarities of these New World plants with *Indigofera subulata* Vahl ex Poiret, an African species, and *I. scabra* Roth, an Indian species, creating *I. subulata* var. *scabra* (Roth) Meikle, and placing the New World names *I. mucronata* and *I. jamaicensis* under it as synonyms. Subsequently, S. I. Ali (1958) placed *I. subulata* and all its varieties in synonymy under *I. trita* Linnaeus f., creating a new combination, *I. trita* var. *scabra* (Roth) Ali for the New World taxon, later placed as *I. trita* subsp. *scabra* (Roth) de Kort & G. Thijsse.

10. Indigofera tinctoria Linnaeus, Sp. Pl. 2: 751. 1753 • Mu lan [I]

Anila tinctoria (Linnaeus) Kuntze

Herbs or subshrubs, perennial, pubescent, hairs appressed, silvery, young growth and flowering parts covered with brownish hairs, becoming glabrate. **Stems** erect or ascending, much branched, 5–20 dm. **Leaves** 3–10 cm; stipules caducous, subulate, 1–2 mm; petiole 0.4–1.2 cm; stipels 1–1.5 mm; petiolules 1–1.5 mm; leaflets 7–15, opposite, blades broadly oblanceolate to obovate or elliptic, 10–25 × 3–10 mm, base cuneate, apex broadly rounded or truncate, slightly apiculate, surfaces pubescent abaxially, glabrous adaxially. **Peduncles** 0.1–0.5 cm. **Racemes** 5–25-flowered, dense, 0.5–4.5 cm. **Pedicels** 1–2 mm. **Flowers** 5–6 mm; calyx 1.5 mm, lobes triangular; corolla pink or salmon pink. **Legumes** red-brown or dark brown, spreading or reflexed, cylindric, straight or slightly curved or abruptly upturned distally, 20–35 mm, thinly leathery, strigose. **Seeds** 6–12, greenish to dark brown, cuboid-ellipsoidal. **2*n*** = 16.

Flowering year-round. Ruderal areas, disturbed pinelands, hammocks; 0–200 m; introduced; Ala., Fla., N.C., S.C., Tenn.; s Asia (India); introduced also in Mexico (Tabasco), West Indies (Bahamas, Cayman Islands, Cuba, Hispaniola, Jamaica, Lesser Antilles, Puerto Rico, Virgin Islands), Central America, South America (Argentina, Venezuela), elsewhere in Asia, Africa, Australia.

Indigofera tinctoria was an early source of a blue fabric dye (J. A. Duke 1981). It was widely cultivated in tropical areas around the world, and it has naturalized in many regions. Use of the plant as a dye source waned after introduction of a synthetic dye.

11. Indigofera lindheimeriana Scheele, Linnaea 21: 464. 1848 • Lindheimer's indigo

Anila lindheimeriana (Scheele) Kuntze

Herbs, perennial, suffrutescent, cinereous-pubescent, hairs silvery greenish, appressed or ascending. **Stems** erect, several from rootstock, sparsely branched distally, 5–15 dm. **Leaves** 8.5–10.5 cm; stipules sometimes clusters of hairs, 0.5–2 mm; petiole 1–1.5 cm; stipels 0.5–1 mm; petiolules 0.5–1 mm; leaflets 7–15, opposite, blades obovate, narrowly or broadly oblanceolate, or elliptic, 8–16 × 4–8 mm, base cuneate, apex acute to obtuse, apiculate, surfaces densely pubescent. **Peduncles** 0.8–1.2 cm. **Racemes** 8–30+-flowered, lax, 5–12 cm. **Pedicels** 1 mm. **Flowers** 6–8 mm; calyx 1.5–2 mm, lobes narrowly triangular; corolla reddish. **Legumes** brown, divergent or reflexed, cylindric, straight or slightly curved to falcate, 18–25 mm, leathery, base bulbous and reddish, cinereous-pubescent. **Seeds** 4–6, brown, cuboid. **2*n*** = 16.

Flowering May–Sep. River and creek bottoms or banks, dry beds, limestone, roadsides; 200–1300 m; Tex.; Mexico (Coahuila, Nuevo León).

Indigofera lindheimeriana is found in the flora area in southwest Texas, from its eastern extent in Comal and Llano counties west to Brewster and Terrell counties.

12. Indigofera suffruticosa Miller, Gard. Dict. ed. 8, Indigofera no. 2. 1768 • Anil de pasto [F] [I]

Indigofera anil Linnaeus

Herbs, perennial, strigose, hairs appressed, grayish silvery. **Stems** erect or ascending, many stems from ground, much-branched distally, stems angled, 5–20 dm. **Leaves** 6–11 cm; stipules narrowly triangular, attenuate, 5–6 mm; petiole 10–20 mm; stipels 0.5–1.5 mm; petiolules 0.5–1.5 mm; leaflets 9–17, opposite, blades elliptic or oblanceolate, 15–20(–40) × 5–10(–15) mm, base cuneate, apex acute, mucronate, surfaces strigose, abaxially sometimes glabrate. **Peduncles** 0.5 cm. **Racemes** 20–30+-flowered, dense, 3.5–5.5 cm. **Pedicels** 1 mm. **Flowers** 5–6 mm; calyx 1.5–2 mm, lobes deltate to lanceolate; corolla greenish yellow, orange, or purple-pink. **Legumes** dark brown, reflexed, cylindric, strongly curved, 15–20 mm, leathery, base not bulbous or reddish, strigose to glabrate. **Seeds** 4–6, reddish brown, cuboid. **2*n*** = 16, 32.

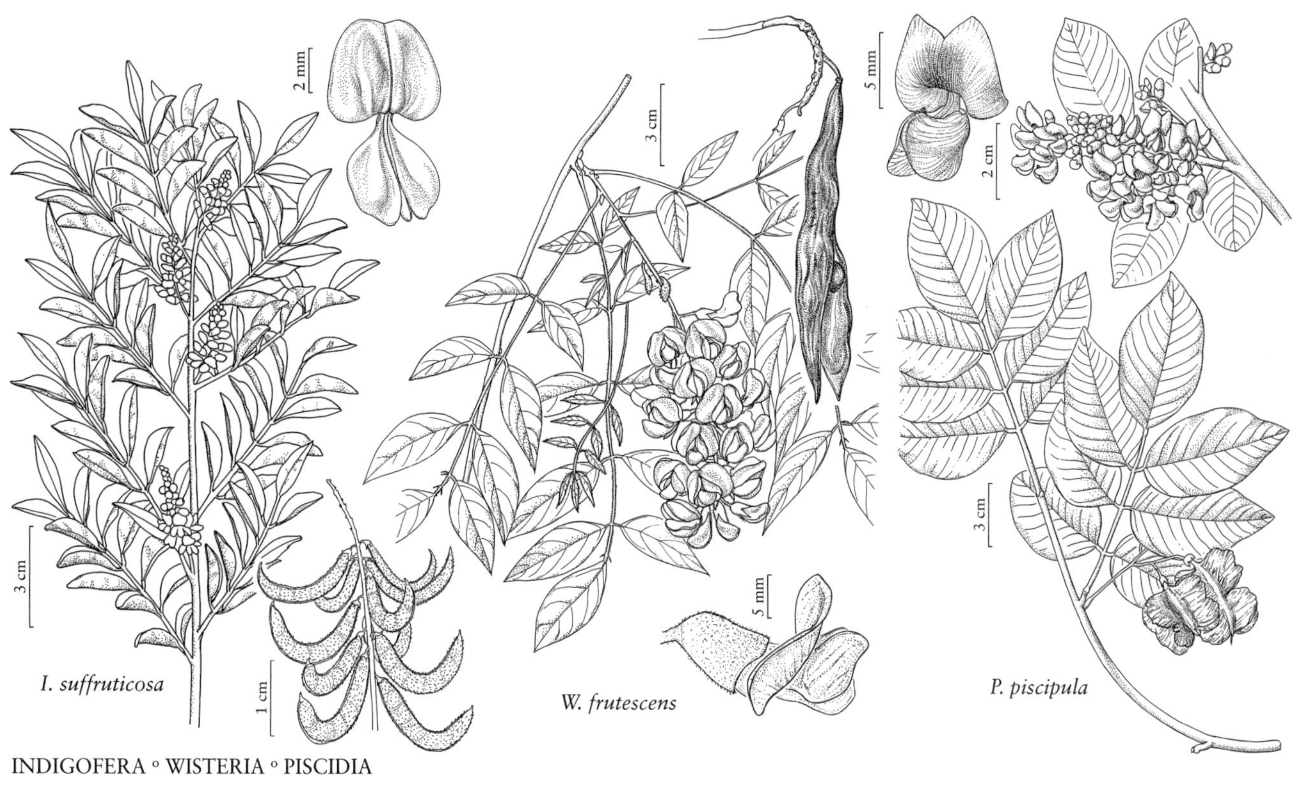

INDIGOFERA ◦ WISTERIA ◦ PISCIDIA

Flowering year-round. Dry, sandy, open woodlands, along streams, abandoned fields, ruderal or agricultural areas; 0–300 m; introduced; Fla., Ga., La., Miss., N.C., S.C., Tex.; Central America; South America (Argentina, Brazil, Paraguay, Uruguay); introduced also in Asia, Africa, Pacific Islands, Australia.

Indigofera suffruticosa is probably native to the New World tropics and subtropics. In the New World, it became a major source of blue dye. It was spread through cultivation to other regions of the world (P. C. Standley and J. A. Steyermark 1946).

13. Indigofera decora Lindley, J. Hort. Soc. London 1: 68. 1846 • Chinese indigo [I]

Shrubs, glabrous. **Stems** erect, arching, branched, 4–20 dm; rhizomatous. **Leaves** 8–25 cm; stipules early-deciduous, linear, 1–2 mm; petiole 1–2.5 cm; stipels 1.5 mm; petiolules 1.5 mm; leaflets 5–15[–23], usually opposite, rarely alternate or alternate proximally and opposite distally, blades ovate-lanceolate, ovate-oblong, or lanceolate, 20–75(–100) × 10–35 mm, base cuneate to broadly cuneate, apex usually acuminate, acute, rarely obtuse and mucronate, surfaces glabrous or pubescent. **Peduncles** 2–4 cm. **Racemes** 8–15-flowered, lax, 7–8.5 cm. **Pedicels** 3 mm. **Flowers** 12–18 mm; calyx 2.5–3.5 mm, lobes triangular; corolla usually light purple or pink, rarely white. **Legumes** brown, pendulous, cylindric, straight, 25–65(–80) mm, leathery, glabrous. **Seeds** 7 or 8, brown, ellipsoidal. $2n = 48$.

Flowering Apr–Nov. Sunny margins of pine-mixed hardwood forests; 150–200 m; introduced; Ga.; Asia (China, Japan); introduced also in Pacific Islands (New Zealand).

Indigofera decora is cultivated as an ornamental shrub in the United States and elsewhere (M. A. Dirr 2011). It is known in the flora area only from populations in Greene County.

14. Indigofera kirilowii Maximowicz ex Palibin, Trudy Glavn. Bot. Sada 17: 62, plate 4. 1898 • Kirilow's indigo [I]

Shrubs, pubescent, hairs sparse, appressed. **Stems** erect, arching, branched, 3–10 dm. **Leaves** 6–15 cm; stipules narrowly long-triangular, attenuate, 4–6 mm; petiole 0.1–2.5(–3) cm; stipels 2–3 mm; petiolules 2–2.5 mm; leaflets (5 or)7–11, opposite, blades broadly ovate, ovate-rhombic, or elliptic, 15–40(–50) × 10–23(–30) mm, base cuneate to broadly cuneate, apex rounded to acute, surfaces appressed-pubescent, pale abaxially. **Peduncles** 2–3 cm. **Racemes** 40–60+-flowered, dense, 7–8.5 cm. **Pedicels** 3–5 mm, glabrous. **Flowers** 12–14(–18) mm; calyx 2.5–4 mm, lobes triangular; corolla usually pink, rarely white. **Legumes** brown, deflexed, cylindric, straight, 35–70 mm, leathery, glabrous. **Seeds** 8–12, reddish brown, ellipsoidal. **2*n*** = 16.

Flowering May–Oct. Ruderal areas, edges of woods; 100–150 m; introduced; Tenn.; Asia (China, Japan, Korea).

Indigofera kirilowii has been in cultivation in the United States since about 1899 (A. J. Rehder 1940). It is known in the flora area only from Madison County.

77. WISTERIA Nuttall, Gen. N. Amer. Pl. 2: 115. 1818, name conserved • [For Caspar Wistar, 1761–1818, American physician and human anatomist]

Lawrence R. Stritch

Rehsonia Stritch

Vines, perennial, woody, unarmed; with long-creeping rhizomes. **Stems** twining counterclockwise or clockwise, high-climbing or scandent, pubescent or glabrescent; peduncles and pedicels usually eglandular, pedicels sometimes with clavate glands. **Leaves** alternate, odd-pinnate; stipules present, linear-lanceolate; petiolate; leaflets (7 or)9–17(or 19), stipels linear-lanceolate, blade margins entire, surfaces glabrous or villous. **Inflorescences** 30–100-flowered, terminal, pendent racemes; bracts present, caducous, lanceolate, pubescent, sometimes with clavate glands. **Pedicels** ebracteolate, sometimes with clavate glands, pubescent. **Flowers** papilionaceous; calyx campanulate, bilabiate, pubescent, lobes 5, abaxial lip 3-lobed, middle lobe long-acuminate, adaxial lip 2-lobed; corolla azure, purple, rose, or white, petals subequal, banner reflexed at a 2-auricled callosity near middle or base, wings oblong-falcate, 1-clawed with auricle at one or both sides of base, keel incurved, petals connate at apices; stamens 10, diadelphous; anthers basifixed; ovary stipitate, with disc surrounding stipe. **Fruits** legumes, stipitate, erect, flattened bilaterally or cylindric, torulose, oblong-elliptic, oblanceolate, or linear-oblong, 2-valved, explosively or tardily dehiscent, constricted between seeds, glabrous or pubescent. **Seeds** 1–5 (rarely more in *W. frutescens*), black, sometimes mottled brown, reniform or lenticular. $x = 8$.

Species 8 (4, including 1 hybrid, in the flora): c, s, e United States, e Asia; introduced in South America, Europe, Africa, Australia.

Wisteria japonica, *W. sinensis*, and *W.* ×*formosa* are commonly cultivated and have become naturalized in the flora area. Native *W. frutescens* is becoming more popular in cultivation as the invasive nature of the Asian taxa is better understood by consumers. All parts of *Wisteria* plants contain toxins that can cause severe nausea, vomiting, and abdominal cramping (L. S. Nelson et al. 2007).

Four additional generic names pertain here: *Diplonyx* Rafinesque and *Phaseoloides* Duhamel are both rejected names against which *Wisteria* is conserved; *Kraunhia* Rafinesque is an invalid name; and *Thyrsanthus* Elliott, not Schrank 1814, is illegitimate.

Recognition of *Rehsonia* as separate from *Wisteria* (L. R. Stritch 1984) was based on differences in position of the banner petal callosity and the place of reflexing of the banner petal, legume characters, and seed traits. In *Rehsonia*, the banner is reflexed at the base at the auricled callosity, the ovary is pubescent, the legume is thick and coriaceous, tardily dehiscent, flattened, and pubescent, with valves that split easily into an endocarp and exocarp, and the seeds are flat and lenticular. In *Wisteria* in the narrow sense, the banner is reflexed at the middle of its length at the auricled callosity, the ovary is glabrous, the legume is thin, explosively dehiscent, cylindric, and glabrous, with valves that do not split into an endocarp and exocarp, and the seeds are plump and reniform. Recognition of these as separate genera has not been borne out in subsequent molecular studies (Hu J. M. et al. 2000; Li J. H. et al. 2014), and *Wisteria* is consequently being recognized here in the broader, traditional sense.

Anthesis within a raceme may be gradual, with anthers of flowers at the inflorescence base abscising while those at the apex are still in bud, or more or less simultaneous, with the anthers abscising at about the same time.

SELECTED REFERENCE Wyman, D. 1949. The wisterias. Arnoldia (Jamaica Plain) 9: 17–28.

1. Banners reflexed at middle; ovaries glabrous; legumes plump, glabrous, explosively dehiscent; seeds plump, reniform . . . . 1. *Wisteria frutescens*
1. Banners reflexed at base; ovaries pubescent; legumes flattened, pubescent, tardily dehiscent; seeds flat, lenticular.
   2. Flowers unscented, appearing before leaves, anthesis within a raceme nearly simultaneous; banners 2.1–2.4 × 2.1–2.3 cm; stems twining counterclockwise . . . . 2. *Wisteria sinensis*
   2. Flowers scented, appearing with or after leaves, anthesis within a raceme gradual, those at base abscising while those at apex still in bud; banners 1.6–1.8 × 1.6–1.8 cm; stems usually twining clockwise, rarely counterclockwise.
      3. Banners: auricles of callosity 1.1–1.2 mm, apex acuminate; stems twining clockwise . . . . 3. *Wisteria floribunda*
      3. Banners: auricles of callosity 0.7–0.8 mm, apex rounded; stems usually twining counterclockwise, rarely clockwise . . . . 4. *Wisteria* ×*formosa*

1. Wisteria frutescens (Linnaeus) Poiret in J. Lamarck and J. Poiret, Tabl. Encyl. 3: 674. 1823 • American wisteria [E] [F]

Glycine frutescens Linnaeus, Sp. Pl. 2: 753. 1753; *Kraunhia macrostachys* (Torrey & A. Gray) Small; *Wisteria frutescens* var. *macrostachya* Torrey & A. Gray; *W. macrostachya* (Torrey & A. Gray) Nuttall ex B. L. Robinson & Fernald

Stems twining counterclockwise. **Leaves:** leaflets 9–15, blades elliptic to lanceolate, 6 × 3 cm. **Racemes** 5–15(–22) cm; anthesis gradual. **Pedicels** 0.5–0.8 cm. **Flowers** appearing after leaves, unscented; calyx middle lobe of abaxial lip to 3 mm; corolla usually azure or purple, rarely white, 1.5–2 cm; banner 1.7–1.8 × 1.4–1.5 cm, reflexed at middle, apex rounded, auricles of median callosity 0.7–0.8 mm; wings 1.7–1.8 × 0.6 cm; keel 1.2–1.3 × 0.6–0.7 cm; ovary glabrous. **Legumes** plump, linear-oblong, 5–12 (–15) cm, explosively dehiscent, glabrous, endocarp not readily separable from exocarp. **Seeds** plump, reniform. 2*n* = 16.

Flowering Apr–Jun. Bottomland forests, riverbanks, stream banks, bayheads; 0–300 m; Ala., Ark., Conn., Fla., Ga., Ill., Ind., Kans., Ky., La., Mass., Mich., Miss., Mo., N.J., N.Y., N.C., Ohio, Pa., S.C., Tenn., Tex., Va., W.Va.

2. Wisteria sinensis (Sims) de Candolle in A. P. de Candolle and A. L. P. P. de Candolle, Prodr. 2: 390. 1825 (as chinensis) • Chinese wisteria [I]

Glycine sinensis Sims, Bot. Mag. 46: plate 2083. 1819; *Rehsonia sinensis* (Sims) Stritch

Stems twining counterclockwise. **Leaves:** leaflets (7 or) 9 or 11(or 13), blades ovate-elliptic to obovate, 9 × 3.5 cm. **Racemes** to 33 cm; anthesis ± simultaneous. **Pedicels** to 3 cm. **Flowers** appearing before leaves, unscented; calyx middle lobe of abaxial lip to 6 mm; corolla azure, purple, rose, or white, 2–2.5 cm; banner 2.1–2.4 × 2.1–2.3 cm, reflexed at base, apex rounded, auricles of basal callosity 0.7–0.8 mm; wings 1.7–1.8 × 0.7 cm; keel 1.7–1.8 × 0.7–0.8 cm; ovary pubescent. **Legumes** flattened, oblong-elliptic or oblanceolate, 8–21 cm, tardily dehiscent, pubescent, endocarp readily separable from exocarp. **Seeds** flat, lenticular. 2*n* = 32.

Flowering May–Jun. Abandoned home sites, wooded edges of low fields, disturbed bottomland hardwood forests, wet ground; 0–500 m; introduced; Ala., Ariz., Ark., Conn., Fla., Ga., Ill., Ind., Ky., La., Maine, Mass., Mich., Miss., Mo., N.Y., N.C., Pa., S.C., Tenn., Tex., Va.; Asia (c, e China); introduced also in South America (Argentina), Australia.

Wisteria sinensis is native to China, where it is common in moist, deciduous forests and riparian habitats from near sea level to 1000 m. Extensively cultivated as an ornamental in China, it is also a popular introduction in the eastern United States. In the flora area, it has become invasive, naturalizing readily in habitats similar to its native environs.

Petals of *Wisteria sinensis* are a delicacy in China, where they are eaten steamed or fried (D. Wyman 1949).

Wisteria sinensis differs from *W. floribunda* in having fewer leaflets per leaf (typically 9–11 versus 13–17 in *W. floribunda*) and in the counterclockwise (versus clockwise) twining of the stem.

3. **Wisteria floribunda** (Willdenow) de Candolle in A. P. de Candolle and A. L. P. P. de Candolle, Prodr. 2: 390. 1825, name conserved • Japanese wisteria [I]

Glycine floribunda Willdenow, Sp. Pl. 3: 1066. 1802, name conserved; *Kraunhia floribunda* (Willdenow) Taubert; *Rehsonia floribunda* (Willdenow) Stritch

Stems twining clockwise. **Leaves:** leaflets (11 or)13–17(or 19), blades elliptic to lanceolate, to 11.2 × 2.6 cm. **Racemes** to 132 cm; anthesis gradually acropetal. **Pedicels** to 2.8 cm. **Flowers** appearing with or after leaves, pleasantly scented; calyx middle lobe of abaxial lip to 4 mm; corolla azure, purple, rose, or white; banner 1.6–1.8 × 1.6–1.7 cm, reflexed at base, apex acuminate, auricles of basal callosity 1.1–1.2 mm; wings 1.4–1.5 × 0.7–0.8 cm; keel 1.4–1.5 × 0.7–0.8 cm; ovary pubescent. **Legumes** flattened, oblong-elliptic or oblanceolate, 12–22(–30) cm, tardily dehiscent, pubescent, endocarp readily separable from exocarp. **Seeds** flat, lenticular. **2*n*** = 16.

Flowering May–Jun. Abandoned home sites, wooded edges of low fields, disturbed bottomland hardwood forests, wet ground; 0–500 m; introduced; Ala., Ark., Fla., Ga., Ill., Ind., Ky., La., Maine, Miss., N.H., N.C., Ohio, Pa., S.C., Tenn., Va.; e Asia (Japan); introduced also in South America (Argentina), Europe, Africa (South Africa).

Wisteria floribunda is native to Japan, ranging from northern Hondo southward. It is common in moist, deciduous forests and riparian habitats, from near sea level to 1200 m. Extensively cultivated in Japan, *W. floribunda* is also popular in the eastern United States, where it has become invasive and naturalized in habitats similar to those in its native Japan.

4. **Wisteria ×formosa** Rehder, J. Arnold Arbor. 3: 36. 1922 (as Wistaria) • Formosa wisteria

Rehsonia ×formosa (Rehder) Stritch

Stems usually twining counterclockwise, rarely clockwise. **Leaves:** leaflets (7 or)9–13 (or 15), blades oblong-elliptic, 8.2 × 3.3 cm. **Racemes** to 36 cm; anthesis gradually acropetal. **Pedicels** to 2.8 cm. **Flowers** appearing with or after leaves, pleasantly scented; calyx middle lobe of abaxial lip to 5 mm; corolla azure, purple, or white, 1.5– 2 cm; banner 1.6–1.8 × 1.6–1.8 cm, reflexed at base, apex rounded, auricles of basal callosity 0.7–0.8 mm; wings 1.7–1.8 × 0.8–0.9 cm; keel 1.5–1.6 × 0.7–0.8 cm; ovary pubescent. **Legumes** flattened, oblong-elliptic or oblanceolate, 6–9.5 cm, tardily dehiscent, pubescent, endocarp readily separable from exocarp. **Seeds** flat, lenticular.

Flowering May–Jun. Abandoned home sites, wooded edges of low fields, disturbed bottomland hardwood forests, wet ground; 0–500 m; Ala., Ark., Fla., Ga., Ky., La., Mich., N.C., S.C., Tex., Va.

Wisteria ×formosa originated spontaneously about 1905 at Holm Lea, the 150-acre estate owned by botanist Charles Sprague Sargent in Brookline, Massachusetts. The hybrid grew from seed borne by a white-petaled plant of *W. floribunda*; the pollen parent was assumed to have been *W. sinensis*, which was also cultivated on the estate. As an ornamental, it is regarded as superior to both parents, with large, fragrant flowers, and sequential anthesis combined with precocious blooming of *W. sinensis* (A. J. Rehder 1922).

Wisteria ×formosa has been a source of confusion for botanists. Although D. Wyman (1949, 1969, 1977) indicated that it is more common in American horticulture than either parent, no major North American flora has included it in its keys and descriptions. As a result, its existence in the spontaneous flora of the continent has gone unrecognized. For example, D. Isely (1990) experienced difficulty in attempting to discriminate *W. floribunda* from *W. sinensis* in the southeastern United States. The lack of consistent character-state correlations he noted is exactly what would be seen if much of the studied material was actually *W. ×formosa*, as was borne out by molecular studies of weedy *Wisteria* in the southeastern United States (J. L. Trusty et al. 2007).

78. PISCIDIA Linnaeus, Syst. Nat. ed. 10, 2: 1151, 1155, 1376. 1759, name conserved [Latin *piscis*, fish, and *caedo*, kill, alluding to use of plant extract for stupefying process]

Velva E. Rudd†

Michael A. Vincent

Ichthyomethia P. Browne, name rejected

Shrubs or trees, unarmed. **Stems** ascending, sericeous to strigulose or glabrescent. **Leaves** alternate, odd-pinnate; stipules present; petiolate; leaflets [5 or]7–11[–27], stipels absent, blade margins entire, surfaces pubescent. **Inflorescences** 30–100+-flowered, axillary or pseudoterminal, usually racemes, sometimes panicles [spikes]; bracts and bracteoles present. **Flowers** papilionaceous; calyx campanulate, lobes 5, short; corolla white with pink or reddish markings [pinkish or with purplish markings]; stamens 10, monadelphous, adaxial filament distinct nearly to base; anthers dorsifixed. **Fruits** loments, stipitate, compressed, straight, oblong, not beaked, leathery, with 4 papery wings (10–20 mm wide), indehiscent, pubescent. **Seeds** [1–]3–8[–10], reddish brown to dark brown, reniform. x = 11.

Species 7 (1 in the flora): Florida, Mexico, West Indies, Central America, n, nw South America.

SELECTED REFERENCE Rudd, V. E. 1969. A synopsis of the genus *Piscidia* (Leguminosae). Phytologia 18: 473–499.

1. Piscidia piscipula (Linnaeus) Sargent, Gard. & Forest 4: 436. 1891 • Dogwood, fishfuddle tree, fish poison, Jamaican dogwood [F]

Erythrina piscipula Linnaeus, Sp. Pl. 2: 707. 1753; *Ichthyomethia communis* S. F. Blake; *I. piscipula* (Linnaeus) Hitchcock; *Piscidia communis* (S. F. Blake) Harms

Shrubs or trees to 20 m. **Leaves:** stipules obliquely reniform, 3–5 × 3–6 mm; pinna blade ovate to elliptic, 40–170 × 20–110 mm, base rounded to cuneate, apex obtuse to acute or acuminate, surfaces micro-alveolate or sericeous, or hairs slightly crispate abaxially, sometimes glabrescent, veinlets usually more densely pubescent, sericeous or minutely pilose to glabrescent adaxially. **Inflorescences** with densely gray-puberulent axis; bracts at base of pedicel, ovate to elliptic, 1–1.5 × 1 mm, apex obtuse; bracteoles caducous, paired at base of calyx, ovate to elliptic, 2–3 × 1 mm, apex acute. **Pedicels** 4 mm. **Flowers:** calyx subactinomorphic, 4–6 mm, silvery-sericeous or subsericeous; lobes relatively short, subequal, adaxial lobes often connate; corolla 12–15 mm; banner pubescent abaxially; anthers oblong; ovary sessile to shortly stipitate; style filiform, glabrous distally; stigma terminal, minutely penicillate. **Loments:** stipe 1–3 mm; 40–100 × 30–45 mm. **Seeds** laterally compressed, 4.5–6 × 2.5–3 mm, lustrous; hilum lateral, orbiculate, to 1 mm diam. $2n$ = 22.

Flowering Apr–Jun, fruiting Jul–Sep. Hammocks, shell middens, pine rocklands; 0–30 m; Fla.; Mexico; West Indies; Central America.

In the flora area, *Piscidia piscipula* is known in peninsular Florida, from Miami-Dade and Monroe counties, including the Florida Keys, northward through the western coastal counties to Hillsborough and Pinellas counties.

Piscidia erythrina Linnaeus, *P. inebrians* Medikus, *P. toxicaria* Salisbury, and *Robinia alata* Miller are superfluous, illegitimate names that pertain here.

79. MILLETTIA Wight & Arnott, Prodr. Fl. Ind. Orient. 1: 263. 1834, name conserved • Pongam, Indian beech [For Charles Millett, fl. 1825–1834, of Canton, China, in service of British East India Company, collector of Chinese plants] [I]

Velva Rudd†

Neil A. Harriman†

Pongamia Adanson

Trees [shrubs, vines], unarmed. **Stems** spreading, glabrous. **Leaves** alternate, odd-pinnate; stipules present, caducous; petiolate; leaflets 5–9[–35], stipels absent [present], blade margins entire, surfaces glabrous or glabrate. **Inflorescences** 25–40-flowered, axillary [terminal], pseudoracemes [racemes or panicles], flowers mostly paired, rarely fasciculate, at nodes; bracts present, caducous; bracteoles 2, at pedicel apex. **Flowers** papilionaceous; calyx broadly campanulate, truncate, lobes obsolete [short]; corolla white to pink or lavender; stamens 10, submonadelphous, vexillary stamen distinct at base; anthers dorsifixed. **Fruits** legumes, within persistent calyx, sessile, compressed, straight, narrowly ovoid, not beaked, woody or rigidly leathery, tardily dehiscent or 2-valved, glabrous. **Seed** 1 [several], brown, reniform. x = 11.

Species ca. 150 (1 in the flora): introduced, Florida; Asia, Africa, Pacific Islands, n Australia; introduced also in tropical areas worldwide.

S. T. Dunn (1912) recognized 134 species in *Millettia*. R. Geesink (1984) claimed that *Millettia* encompasses about 90 species distributed from Africa to Malesia, with one species from India to northern Australia and the western Pacific; he also included the genus *Hesperothamnus* Brandegee, with about five species in Mexico, in his concept of *Millettia*. G. P. Lewis et al. (2005) maintained *Hesperothamnus* as separate from *Millettia*, stating that the latter contains 150 species.

Millettia is conserved against *Pongamia* Adanson (1763), which is itself conserved, making *Pongamia* Ventenat (1803), an unnecessary renaming of the genus; the Ventenat name appears in some regional treatments of legumes.

SELECTED REFERENCES Dunn, S. T. 1912. A revision of the genus *Millettia* Wight et Arn. J. Linn. Soc., Bot. 41: 123–243. Geesink, R. 1984. Scala *Millettiearum*. Leiden Bot. Ser. 8: 1–131.

1. **Millettia pinnata** (Linnaeus) Panigrahi in G. Panigrahi and S. K. Murti, Fl. Bilaspur Distr. 1: 210. 1989 • Pongame oiltree [F] [I]

Cytisus pinnatus Linnaeus, Sp. Pl. 2: 741. 1753; *Derris indica* (Lamarck) Bennet; *Pongamia pinnata* (Linnaeus) Pierre

Trees to 30 m. **Leaves** 6–17 cm; petiole 2.5–5 cm; petiolules 0.5–1 cm, leaflet blades ovate to elliptic-oblong, 3–10 × 2–5 cm, base rounded, apex acuminate. **Inflorescences:** axis and pedicels glabrous or sparsely hairy. **Flowers** 12–14 mm; calyx 3–4 mm, sericeous; banner sericeous outside; style glabrous. **Legumes** 5–8 × 2.5–3 cm. **Seeds** compressed, 2 × 1 cm, lustrous; hilum lateral, elliptic, 1 mm. 2n = 22.

Flowering year-round. Waste places, thickets; 0–50 m; introduced; Fla.; s Asia (India); Australia; introduced also throughout tropics.

Millettia pinnata has escaped from cultivation in Broward, Lee, Palm Beach, and Sarasota counties. Its seeds contain oil that may be used as a substitute for diesel fuel.

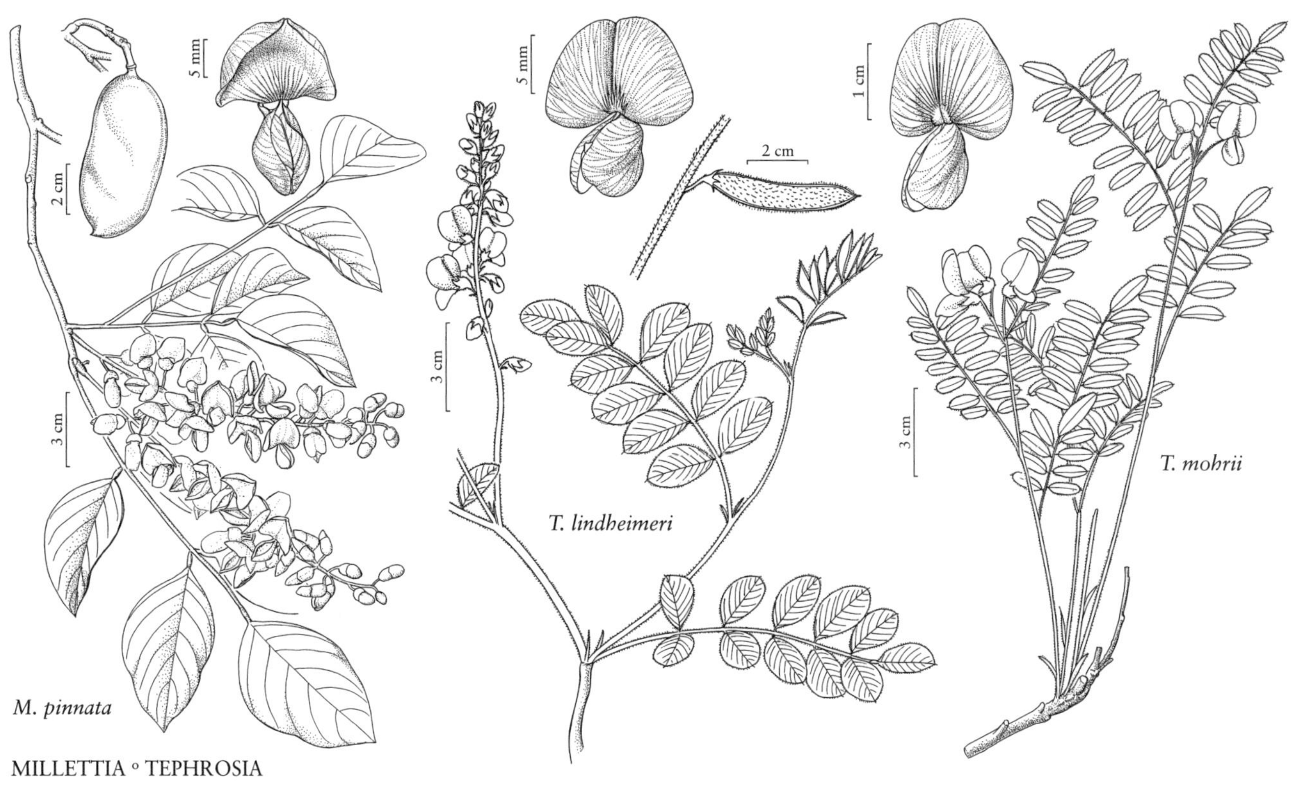

MILLETTIA ◦ TEPHROSIA

80. TEPHROSIA Persoon, Syn. Pl. 2: 328. 1807, name conserved • Hoary-pea [Greek *tephros*, ash-colored, probably alluding to foliage appearance in some species]

Guy L. Nesom

Cracca Linnaeus, name rejected

Herbs, usually perennial, rarely annual, or subshrubs [**shrubs**], unarmed. **Stems** erect, procumbent, ascending, reclining, prostrate, decumbent, or sprawling, pubescent or glabrous. **Leaves** alternate, odd-pinnate; stipules present; petiolate; leaflets (3 or)5–27(–35), often opposite, sometimes subopposite, stipels absent, blade margins entire, with 8–25 parallel, straight, lateral veins extending to margins, surfaces glabrous or pubescent. **Inflorescences** (1 or)2–45-flowered, terminal (bracteal leaves reduced) distal to level of leaves, or axillary, pseudoracemes (opposite unreduced leaves) in distal portions of leafy stems; bracts present, persistent or caducous. **Flowers** papilionaceous; calyx campanulate, lobes 5, 2 lobes superior, ± connate, shorter; corolla reddish to purple, pink, pink-purple, violet-red, yellow, cream, or white, 6–20 mm; stamens 10, monadelphous or diadelphous, vexillary stamen free or apically adnate to staminal tube and basally distinct; anthers dorsifixed; style bearded or glabrous, stigma glabrous or penicillate. **Fruits** legumes, sessile or subsessile, flat, laterally compressed, straight or slightly curved or apically incurved, oblong, dehiscent by 2 sutures, pubescent. **Seeds** 6–12, terete to suborbicular or reniform. $x = 11$.

Species ca. 400 (17 in the flora): North America, Mexico, West Indies, Central America, South America, Asia, Africa, Pacific Islands; tropical and subtropical regions.

Some species of *Tephrosia* produce rotenone, which is widely used as an insect and fish poison. The name barbasco is used for some of the fish-poison species in Mexico and Central America. *Tephrosia purpurea* (Linnaeus) Persoon was collected by C. F. Reed from chrome ore piles (originating from Rhodesia) in Baltimore, Maryland, [1958, 1959, 1969 (MO)] and in Newport News, Virginia [1959 (MO)]. *Tephrosia purpurea* and *T. tenella* are closely similar. *Tephrosia cinerea* (Linnaeus) Persoon was collected in Florida in 1842–1849 [*Rugel 748* (MO)] and was reported in Mobile, Alabama, as a ballast waif as early as 1886, later becoming established (C. T. Mohr 1901). Neither *T. cinerea* nor *T. purpurea* has been reported as naturalized in the flora area.

SELECTED REFERENCES Raina, S. N., P. K. Srivastav, and S. Rama Rao. 1986. Nuclear DNA variation in *Tephrosia*. Genetica 69: 27–33. Wood, C. E. Jr. 1949. The American barbistyled species of *Tephrosia* (Leguminosae). Rhodora 51: 193–231, 233–302, 305–364, 369–384.

1. Leaflet blades obovate to obtriangular or suborbiculate; stamens monadelphous; Texas.
    2. Leaflets (5–)9–13(–17); flowers separate in racemes, 1 per node . . . . 1. *Tephrosia lindheimeri*
    2. Leaflets (3 or)5 or 7(or 9); flowers clustered in racemes, 2–4 per node . . . . 2. *Tephrosia potosina*
1. Leaflet blades usually oblong to elliptic, lanceolate, or oblanceolate, often more elongate, rarely obovate; stamens monadelphous or diadelphous; widespread, including Texas.
    3. Corollas 6–11 mm; styles glabrous; leaflet blade length 3–9 or 12–30 times width.
        4. Leaflets (3 or)5–9(or 11), apices acute to obtuse or rounded; Arizona, New Mexico, Texas . . . . 14. *Tephrosia tenella*
        4. Leaflets (9 or)11–15(–19), apices acute or rounded to truncate or retuse; Florida.
            5. Stems hirsute; leaflet surfaces villous-hirsute, apices rounded to truncate . . . . 17. *Tephrosia corallicola*
            5. Stems glabrous; leaflet surfaces glabrate or strigulose, apices acute, rounded to truncate, or retuse.
                6. Leaflet blades linear to linear-lanceolate, 20–50 × 0.5–1.5 mm, length 12–30 times width, apices acute. . . . . 15. *Tephrosia angustissima*
                6. Leaflet blades oblong-elliptic to oblanceolate-oblong, (9–)12–25(–30) × 3–6 mm, length 3–6 times width, apices rounded to truncate or retuse . . . . 16. *Tephrosia curtissii*
    3. Corollas (8–)10–20 mm; styles bearded; leaflet blade length 1.3–6(–6.5) times width.
        7. Leaflets (9 or)11–27(–35).
            8. Stamens weakly diadelphous; Arizona.
                9. Legumes glabrous; inflorescences loose racemes, 4–8(–10)-flowered, 5–8 (–15) cm; corollas white, darkening reddish; leaflet blades 5–7(–9) mm wide. . . . . 4. *Tephrosia leiocarpa*
                9. Legumes villosulous; inflorescences congested racemes, 8–14-flowered, 2–4 cm; corollas pink and pink-purple or yellowish aging pink-purple; leaflet blades (5–)7–13 mm wide . . . . 5. *Tephrosia thurberi*
            8. Stamens monadelphous; United States from Texas to Minnesota and eastward, Ontario.
                10. Racemes (10–)20–40 cm, (12–)20–45-flowered . . . . 3. *Tephrosia onobrychoides*
                10. Racemes 2–8 cm, 10–40-flowered, or flowers axillary, 4–12.
                    11. Racemes 2–8 cm, 10–40-flowered . . . . 6. *Tephrosia virginiana*
                    11. Racemes: flowers mostly axillary, 4–12. . . . . 7. *Tephrosia mohrii*
        7. Leaflets (3 or)5–17(or 19).
            12. Racemes not evident (flowers axillary in distal portions of leafy stems, nodes initially congested but elongating); floral bracts foliaceous, enlarging with floral and fruit development. . . . . 8. *Tephrosia rugelii*
            12. Racemes evident (flowers well above level of leaves) floral bracts lanceolate to linear-lanceolate or linear-subulate, not foliaceous.

[13. Shifted to left margin.—Ed.]

13. Leaflet blades bicolored (darker abaxially), surfaces usually finely and evenly sparsely strigulose abaxially, hairs relatively short, not overlapping, abaxial venation distinctly reddish.
    14. Leaflet blades 17–35 × (1.5–)3–9(–11) mm, narrowly oblanceolate to oblong-oblanceolate or obovate-elliptic, length (2.5–)3–6 times width, apices obtuse to rounded or truncate and slightly retuse; petioles (10–)20–40 mm; legumes sparsely strigulose .... 12. *Tephrosia florida*
    14. Leaflet blades 9–20(–25) × 2–6 mm, narrowly elliptic to oblong-elliptic or elliptic-lanceolate, length 2.5–5 times width, apices acute; petioles 2–8(–15) mm; legumes hirsute-villous .... 13. *Tephrosia hispidula*
13. Leaflet blades concolorous, surfaces moderately to densely strigose to strigose-sericeous or -hirsute abaxially, hairs relatively long and overlapping, abaxial venation greenish.
    15. Stems erect to ascending or decumbent-ascending; leaflets (7 or)9–13(–17), blade length 1.5–3.5(–5) times width; petioles (2–)5–15 mm; inflorescences (3–)5–15 (–20)-flowered........ 9. *Tephrosia spicata*
    15. Stems prostrate; leaflets (3 or)5 or 7, or (5 or)7–11(or 13), blade length 1.3–2.2 times width; petioles 0 or 1–5 mm; inflorescences 2–6-flowered.
        16. Leaflets (3 or)5 or 7(or 9), surfaces glabrous adaxially, shiny, bright green .... 10. *Tephrosia chrysophylla*
        16. Leaflets (5 or)7–11(or 13), surfaces usually minutely hirtellous or glabrate adaxially, dull, light olive green to brownish........ 11. *Tephrosia mysteriosa*

1. **Tephrosia lindheimeri** A. Gray, Boston J. Nat. Hist. 6: 172. 1850 • Lindheimer's hoary-pea [E] [F]

Cracca lindheimeri (A. Gray) Kuntze

Herbs. Stems prostrate to procumbent or decumbent, 40–100 cm, densely hirsute-pilose, hairs deflexed to spreading, to hirsute or strigose. **Leaves:** petiole 15–35 mm; leaflets (5–)9–13(–17), blades obovate to obtriangular or suborbiculate, 12–30(–35) × 12–23 mm, length 1–2 times width, apex obtuse to retuse, surfaces finely and loosely strigose, adaxial sometimes glabrescent. **Racemes** 8–25-flowered, flowers 1 per node, 6–15 cm; floral bracts caducous, linear-subulate. **Flowers:** corolla pink to pink-purple or violet-red, 12–15 mm; stamens monadelphous; style bearded. **Legumes** 40–50 × 6–8 mm, hirsute. $2n = 22$.

Flowering Apr–Jun(–Jul). Deep sand, sandy loam, limestone ridges, roadsides, fields, pastures, open oak-hickory and oak woodlands, brushy prairies, live-oak savannas, mesquite uplands; 0–600 m; Tex.

Tephrosia lindheimeri is relatively widespread in south-central Texas.

2. **Tephrosia potosina** Brandegee, Univ. Calif. Publ. Bot. 4: 272. 1912 • Edwards Plateau hoary-pea

Cracca potosina (Brandegee) Standley

Herbs. Stems decumbent, 25–50 cm, hirsute to hirsute-pilose, hairs spreading to deflexed. **Leaves:** petiole 2.5–6 mm; leaflets (3 or)5 or 7(or 9), blades obovate to suborbiculate, 12–30(–38) × 12–25(–32) mm, length 1.1–1.7 times width, apex obtuse to retuse, abaxial surface loosely strigose-villous, adaxial glabrous. **Racemes** 8–20-flowered, flowers clustered, 2–4 per node, 6–10 cm; floral bracts persistent, linear-lanceolate. **Flowers:** corolla reddish purple, 12–15(–18) mm; stamens monadelphous; style bearded. **Legumes** 32–50 × 6–8 mm, hirsute to hirsute-pilose.

Flowering Apr–Aug. Rocky hillsides, roadsides; 200–400 m; Tex.; Mexico (Coahuila, Nuevo León, San Luis Potosí, Tamaulipas, Zacatecas).

Tephrosia potosina is rare in the flora area, known only from Comal, Hays, and Uvalde counties in south-central Texas.

3. Tephrosia onobrychoides Nuttall, J. Acad. Nat. Sci. Philadelphia 7: 104. 1834 • Multi-bloom hoary-pea [E]

Cracca angustifolia (Featherman) Pennell; *C. onobrychoides* (Nuttall) Kuntze; *C. texana* Rydberg; *Tephrosia angustifolia* Featherman; *T. multiflora* Featherman; *T. onobrychoides* var. *texana* (Rydberg) J. F. Macbride; *T. texana* (Rydberg) Cory

Herbs. Stems usually ascending to decumbent or reclining, rarely erect, 2–6(–10) cm, strigose to hirsute. **Leaves:** petiole 20–60 mm; leaflets (9–)13–25(–29), blades obovate, elliptic to oblong-oblanceolate, or linear-oblanceolate, (15–)20–50 × 4–16(–20) mm, length 2.5–5 times width, apex obtuse to rounded or truncate, abaxial surface strigose, adaxial glabrous. **Racemes** (12–)20–45-flowered, (10–)20–40 cm; floral bracts persistent, linear-subulate. **Flowers:** corolla white or pink and white, becoming red to purple, 15–18 mm; stamens monadelphous; style bearded. **Legumes** 40–80 × 4–5 mm, evenly hirsute to hirsutulous or short-strigose.

Flowering May–Sep. Fencerows, roadsides, fields, wet ditches, prairie strips along railroads, prairies, pine and pine-oak woods, longleaf pine woodlands, pineland bogs, sand, sandy clay, gravelly clay; 10–200 m; Ala., Ark., La., Miss., Okla., Tex.

In Texas, *Tephrosia onobrychoides* is known from numerous counties in the eastern half of the state.

4. Tephrosia leiocarpa A. Gray, Smithsonian Contr. Knowl. 5(6): 36. 1853 • Smooth-pod hoary-pea

Cracca leiocarpa (A. Gray) Kuntze

Varieties 2 (1 in the flora): Arizona, n Mexico.

Variety *costenya* McVaugh occurs in Mexico. F. Shreve and I. L. Wiggins (1964) described the corollas as pink to deep red or purplish.

4a. Tephrosia leiocarpa A. Gray var. **leiocarpa**

Tephrosia affinis S. Watson; *T. viridis* M. E. Jones

Herbs or subshrubs. Stems erect, 30–100 cm, strigose. **Leaves:** petiole 7–20 mm; leaflets 11–23, blades oblong to elliptic-oblanceolate, (15–)20–40 × 5–7(–9) mm, length 3–6.5 times width, apex obtuse, rounded to truncate, or retuse, abaxial surface strigulose, adaxial glabrate. **Racemes** loose, 4–8(–10)-flowered, 5–8 (–15) cm; floral bracts caducous, setaceous. **Flowers:** corolla white, darkening reddish, 13–16 mm; stamens weakly diadelphous; style bearded. **Legumes** 40–65 × 5–6 mm, glabrous.

Flowering Jun–Aug(–Sep). Pine, pine-oak, oak, oak-*Agave-Dasylirion* communities, open slopes, canyons; 1300–1600 m; Ariz.; Mexico (Chihuahua, Durango, Sonora).

Variety *leiocarpa* is restricted to Pima and Santa Cruz counties in southeastern Arizona.

5. Tephrosia thurberi (Rydberg) C. E. Wood, Rhodora 51: 265. 1949 • Thurber's hoary-pea

Cracca thurberi Rydberg in N. L. Britton et al., N. Amer. Fl. 24: 165. 1923

Herbs. Stems erect, 30–60 cm, hirsute to hirsute-villous. **Leaves:** petiole 10–30(–40) mm; leaflets (9–)11–27, blades elliptic to narrowly oblong, 15–30 × (5–)7–13 mm, length 2.5–3.5 (–4) times width, apex obtuse to rounded, surfaces loosely strigose to sericeous. **Racemes** congested, 8–14-flowered, 2–4 cm; floral bracts setaceous, caducous. **Flowers:** corolla pink and pink-purple or yellowish, aging pink-purple, 15–18 mm; stamens weakly diadelphous; style bearded. **Legumes** 30–60 × 4 mm, villosulous.

Flowering Jun–Sep. Oak or pine woodlands, roadsides; 1600–2000 m; Ariz.; Mexico (Chihuahua, Sonora).

Tephrosia thurberi is similar to *T. virginiana* but far disjunct and in a different biome. In the flora area, it is restricted to Cochise and Santa Cruz counties in southeastern Arizona.

6. Tephrosia virginiana (Linnaeus) Persoon, Syn. Pl. 2: 329. 1807 • Goat's-rue, Virginia goat's-rue [E]

Cracca virginiana Linnaeus, Sp. Pl. 2: 752. 1753; *Tephrosia latidens* (Small) Standley; *T. virginiana* var. *glabra* Nuttall; *T. virginiana* var. *holosericea* (Nuttall) Torrey & A. Gray; *T. virginica* Bigelow

Herbs. Stems erect, 30–70 cm, densely villous or sericeous to sparsely strigulose or glabrate. **Leaves:** petiole 1–5(–10) mm; leaflets (9–)13–23(–35), blades elliptic to oblong, 10–25(–30) × (3–)4–7 mm, length 2–5(–6) times width, apex obtuse or rounded to truncate, surfaces strigose to sericeous. **Racemes** 10–40-flowered, 2–8 cm, mostly above level of leaves; floral bracts caducous, setaceous. **Flowers:** corolla yellow and pink (banner yellow, wings pink, keel yellow-pink striped), 15–20 mm; stamens monadelphous; style bearded. **Legumes** 30–55 × 4–5 mm, strigose to villous. $2n = 22$.

Flowering May–Jun(–Aug). Sandhills, pinelands, dry, sandy oak-pine savannas, xeric and/or rocky woodlands and forests, outcrops, barrens, dry roadbanks; 50–700 m; Ont.; Ala., Ark., Conn., Del., D.C., Fla., Ga., Ill., Ind., Iowa, Kans., Ky., La., Maine, Minn., Miss., Mo., Nebr., N.H., N.J., N.Y., N.C., Ohio, Okla., Pa., R.I., S.C., Tenn., Tex., Va., W.Va., Wis.

Tephrosia virginiana is the only member of the genus that occurs in Canada, where it is known only from the vicinity of Turkey Point in southern Ontario.

7. **Tephrosia mohrii** (Rydberg) R. K. Godfrey, Brittonia 10: 169. 1958 • Dwarf goat's-rue [E] [F]

Cracca mohrii Rydberg in N. L. Britton et al., N. Amer. Fl. 24: 163. 1923; *Tephrosia virginiana* (Linnaeus) Persoon var. *mohrii* (Rydberg) D. B. Ward

Herbs. Stems erect, 10–15(–20) cm, strigulose. **Leaves:** petiole 3–10 mm; leaflets (9–)13–27, blades elliptic to oblong or obovate-oblong, 6–12 × 4–5.5 mm, length 1.8–2.8 times width, apex obtuse or rounded to truncate, surfaces strigose, adaxial sparsely so. **Racemes** 4–12-flowered, flowers mostly axillary in distal portion of leafy stems; floral bracts caducous, setaceous. **Flowers:** corolla cream, pink, and white (banner cream, wings and keel dark pink to white), 13–17 mm; stamens monadelphous; style bearded. **Legumes** 36–58 × 4–5.5 mm, strigose.

Flowering (Mar–)Apr–May(–Jul). Sandhills and sand ridges with turkey oak or longleaf pine, mixed with yaupon, turkey oak, sand live-oak, and laurel oak, sandy roadsides; 10–100 m; Ala., Fla., Ga.

Tephrosia mohrii is known from Covington and Houston counties in Alabama; Okaloosa, Santa Rosa, and Walton counties in Florida; and Ben Hill and Grady counties in Georgia. The species appears to intergrade with *T. virginiana*.

8. **Tephrosia rugelii** Shuttleworth ex B. L. Robinson, Bot. Gaz. 28: 197. 1899 • Rugel's hoary-pea [E]

Cracca rugelii (Shuttleworth ex B. L. Robinson) A. Heller

Herbs. Stems ascending to decumbent, 10–50 cm, closely strigose. **Leaves:** petiole 3–10(–20) mm; leaflets (5–)9–15, blades elliptic to obovate-cuneate, 10–16(–22) × 4–10 mm, length 1.5–2.5 times width, apex rounded to retuse, surfaces strigose-sericeous. **Racemes** 2–6-flowered, not evident, flowers axillary, 1 or 2 per node, in distal portions of leafy stems, nodes initially congested but elongating; foliaceous bracts enlarging with floral and fruit development. **Flowers:** corolla yellow-white with red veins, aging purplish, 14–18 mm; stamens diadelphous; style bearded. **Legumes** 25–40 × 4–5 mm, loosely strigose-villous to strigose-hirsute.

Flowering Mar–May(–Sep). Sandhills, pine savannas, pine flatwoods, oak barrens, roadsides, sandy soils; 0–20 m; Fla.

Tephrosia rugelii is widespread in peninsular Florida.

9. **Tephrosia spicata** (Walter) Torrey & A. Gray, Fl. N. Amer. 1: 296. 1838 • Spiked hoary-pea [E]

Galega spicata Walter, Fl. Carol., 188. 1788; *Cracca spicata* (Walter) Kuntze; *Tephrosia spicata* var. *semitonsa* Fernald

Herbs. Stems erect to ascending or decumbent-ascending, 30–60 cm, strigose to hirsute or glabrate. **Leaves:** petiole (2–)5–15 mm; leaflets (7 or)9–13(–17), blades concolorous, oblanceolate to obovate, elliptic-obovate, or oblong-obovate, 8–28(–40) × 6–16 mm, length 1.5–3.5(–5) times width, apex rounded to truncate, abaxial surface moderately to densely strigose to strigose-hirsute, hairs relatively long and overlapping, venation greenish, adaxial glabrous or strigose-hirsute, venation raised. **Racemes** (3–)5–15(–20)-flowered, evident (flowers well above level of leaves), 10–20(–40) cm; floral bracts persistent, lanceolate. **Flowers:** corolla yellowish white, becoming pink to red, drying purple, 13–18 mm; stamens diadelphous; style bearded. **Legumes** 20–40 × 3.5–4.5 mm, hirsute-villous, glabrescent. $2n = 22$.

Flowering Jun–Aug. Dry or wet, open pine or mixed woods, pine-palmetto scrub, pineland bogs, pine savannas, clearings, field margins, roadsides; 10–200 m; Ala., Del., Fla., Ga., Ky., La., Md., Miss., N.C., S.C., Tenn., Va.

Tephrosia spicata is recognized by its numerous leaflets with raised adaxial venation and long, ebracteate peduncles with long racemes.

Cracca flexuosa (Vail) A. Heller is a later homonym that pertains here.

10. Tephrosia chrysophylla Pursh, Fl. Amer. Sept. 2: 489. 1813 • Scurf hoary-pea, sprawling goat's-rue [E]

Cracca carpenteri Rydberg; *C. chapmanii* (Vail) Small; *C. chrysophylla* (Pursh) Kuntze; *Tephrosia carpenteri* (Rydberg) Killip

Herbs. Stems prostrate, 20–50 cm, densely strigose to hirsutulous or hispid-hirsute, hairs spreading to deflexed. **Leaves:** petiole (0 or) 1–5 mm, leaflets (3 or)5 or 7, blades concolorous, obovate-obtriangular to oblong-obovate, elliptic, or obovate, 12–35 × 7–20 mm, length 1.3–2 times width, apex truncate to retuse, abaxial surface densely strigose, hairs relatively long and overlapping, venation greenish, adaxial bright green, glabrous or sparsely strigose, venation raised. **Racemes** axillary, 2–6-flowered, evident (flowers well above level of leaves), 2–10(–15) cm; floral bracts persistent, linear-lanceolate. **Flowers:** corolla white to pale pink, aging pink to reddish, (8–)10–14 mm; stamens diadelphous; style bearded. **Legumes** 30–40(–50) × 4–5 mm, sparsely strigulose to strigose-hirsute.

Flowering May–Jul. Sandhills, ridges, flats, pine flatwoods, slash pine-wiregrass, longleaf pine forests, turkey oak woodlands, roadsides; 10–50 m; Ala., Fla., Ga., Miss.

Tephrosia chrysophylla is recognized by its prostrate habit and sessile or subsessile leaves with relatively few, broad and short leaflets with raised adaxial venation.

A "Panhandle Entity" of *Tephrosia chrysophylla* was recognized by K. R. DeLaney (2010b) as a likely distinct species, possibly correctly identified as *T. carpenteri* or *T. chapmanii.* It is said to replace typical *T. chrysophylla* west of the Ochlockonee River in Florida, southwestern Georgia, southern Alabama, and southeastern Mississippi. In this view, the only localities of typical *T. chrysophylla* outside of Florida are in coastal or near-coastal southeastern Georgia.

11. Tephrosia mysteriosa DeLaney, Bot. Explor. 4: 101, figs. 1, 2A, 3, 6. 2010 • Lake Wales hoary-pea, sandhill tippitoes [E]

Herbs. Stems prostrate, 20–60 cm, densely hirsute, hairs tawny. **Leaves:** petiole 1–2(–3) mm; leaflets (5 or)7–11(or 13), blades concolorous, elliptic to oblong- or obovate-elliptic, (8–)14–18(–25) × (6–)8–12(–16) mm, length 1.6–2.2 times width, apex truncate to slightly retuse, abaxial surface moderately to densely strigose-sericeous, hairs relatively long and overlapping, venation greenish, adaxial dull, light olive green to brownish, usually hirtellous, becoming glabrate or glabrescent. **Racemes** axillary, 2–6-flowered, evident (flowers well above level of leaves), (5–)10–16(–20) cm; floral bracts persistent, linear-lanceolate. **Flowers:** corolla white to pinkish, aging red to deep maroon, 8–12 mm; stamens diadelphous; style bearded. **Legumes** 40–55 × 4–5 mm, minutely and closely strigulose.

Flowering Mar–Oct(–Nov). Sandhills, sand ridges, within and along edges of turkey oak and hickory scrub woodlands, less commonly in high pineland and pine flatwoods; 50–100 m; Fla.

Tephrosia mysteriosa is known from two major ridge systems, the Lake Wales Ridge and the Mount Dora Ridge, in the northern half of peninsular Florida. The species had previously been identified as *T. chrysophylla*; variant populations of *T. mysteriosa* found in disturbed sites on the periphery of its range probably reflect hybridization with *T. chrysophylla. Tephrosia* ×*varioforma* DeLaney is a hybrid of *T. florida* and *T. mysteriosa* and is apparently formed sporadically.

12. Tephrosia florida (F. Dietrich) C. E. Wood, Rhodora 51: 305. 1949 • Florida hoary-pea or goat's-rue [E]

Galega florida F. Dietrich, Nachtr. Vollst. Lex. Gärtn. 3: 422. 1817; *Cracca ambigua* (M. A. Curtis) Kuntze; *C. gracillima* (B. L. Robinson) A. Heller; *Tephrosia ambigua* (M. A. Curtis) Chapman; *T. ambigua* var. *gracillima* B. L. Robinson; *T. florida* var. *gracillima* (B. L. Robinson) Shinners

Herbs. Stems prostrate to procumbent, 10–80 cm, glabrous or strigulose. **Leaves:** petiole usually (10–)20–40 mm; leaflets (5 or)7–13(or 15), blades bicolored (darker abaxially), narrowly oblanceolate to oblong-oblanceolate or obovate-elliptic, 17–35 × (1.5–)3–9(–11) mm, length (2.5–)3–6 times width, apex obtuse to rounded or truncate and slightly retuse, abaxial surface usually finely and evenly sparsely strigose, rarely hirsute to hirsute-strigose, hairs relatively short, not overlapping, venation distinctly reddish, adaxial glabrate. **Racemes** axillary and terminal, 2–6-flowered, evident (flowers well above level of leaves), 5–15(–25) cm; floral bracts persistent, linear-subulate. **Flowers:** corolla yellowish white to white, aging dark purple, 10–14 mm; stamens diadelphous; style bearded. **Legumes** 25–40 × 4–5 mm, sparsely strigulose.

Flowering May–Jul. Fields, dunes, turkey oak scrub, longleaf pine savannas, pine barrens, pine-palmetto, pine-oak, pine-hardwood uplands; 10–50 m; Ala., Fla., Ga., La., Miss., N.C., S.C.

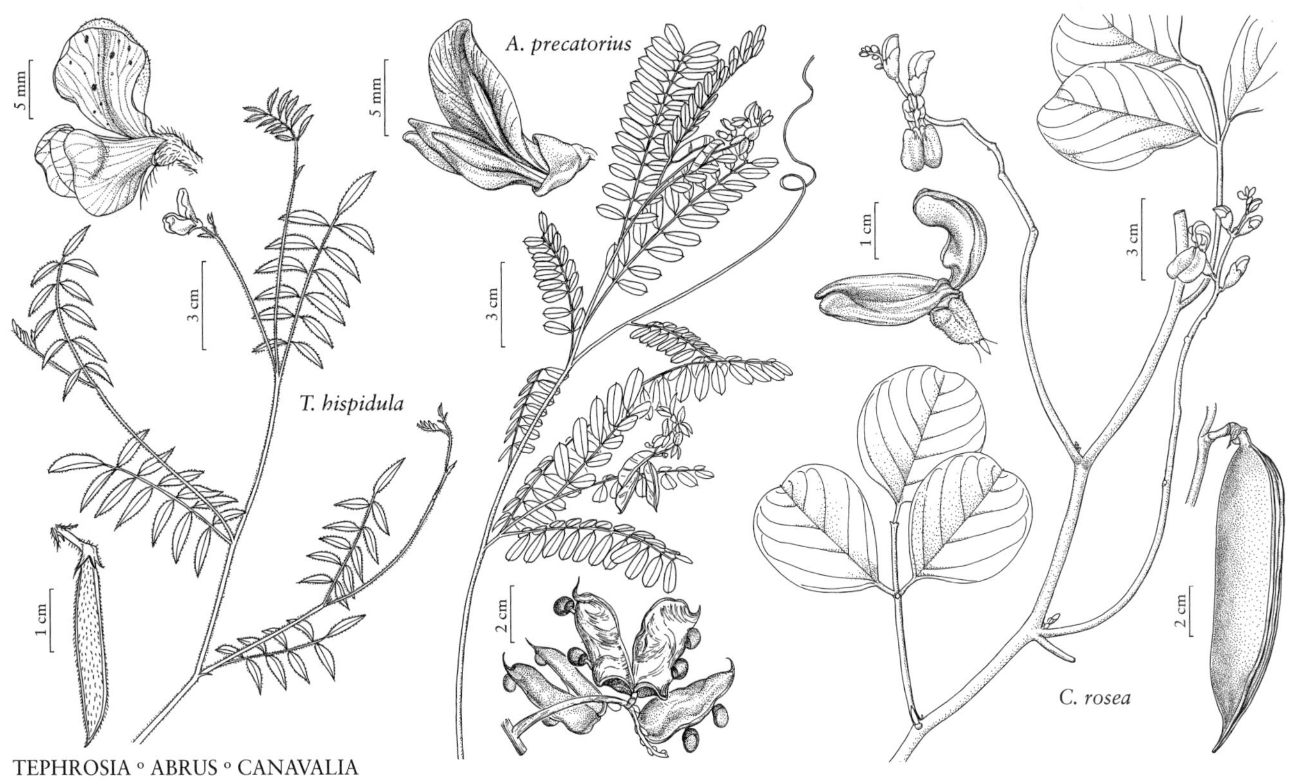

TEPHROSIA ∘ ABRUS ∘ CANAVALIA

Tephrosia florida is recognized by its relatively small, elongate, bicolored leaves with abaxial surfaces strigulose and with reddish venation (including secondary and tertiary veins).

Tephrosia ×*intermedia* (Small) G. L. Nesom & Zarucchi is a putative hybrid between *T. chrysophylla* and *T. florida* (C. E. Wood Jr. 1949; D. Isely 1998; G. L. Nesom and J. L. Zarucchi 2009). Synonyms are *Cracca intermedia* Small, *C. floridana* Vail, *C. smallii* Vail, and *T.* ×*floridana* (Vail) Isely. The hybrid is said to occur in association with the two putative parents, sporadically from Alabama, Florida, Georgia, and Mississippi, and its origin as a recurrent hybrid seems a reasonable hypothesis. According to Isely, it most closely resembles *T. florida*, differing in its shorter petioles and broader, fewer leaflets; both parents are variable in these features, and it is difficult to confirm that the putative hybrids are consistently intermediate in morphology. Perhaps the only sure way to identify the hybrid is to see it in the field, in company with the parents and in contrast to them.

13. Tephrosia hispidula (Michaux) Persoon, Syn. Pl. 2: 329. 1807 • Sprawling hoary-pea [E] [F]

Galega hispidula Michaux, Fl. Bor.-Amer. 2: 68. 1803; *Cracca hispidula* (Michaux) Kuntze

Herbs. Stems decumbent to erect, 10–50 cm, loosely strigose to villous. **Leaves:** petiole 2–8(–15) mm; leaflets (9 or)11–17(or 19), blades bicolored (darker abaxially), narrowly elliptic to oblong-elliptic or elliptic-lanceolate, 9–20(–25) × 2–6 mm, length 2.5–5 times width, apex acute, abaxial surface finely and evenly sparsely strigose, hairs relatively short, not overlapping, venation distinctly reddish, adaxial glabrate. **Racemes** axillary and terminal, (1–)3–8-flowered, evident (flowers well above level of leaves), 1.5–15 cm; floral bracts persistent, linear-lanceolate. **Flowers:** corolla yellowish white, aging reddish to purple, 10–15 mm; stamens diadelphous; style bearded. **Legumes** 30–50 × 5–6 mm, hirsute-villous.

Flowering May–Aug. Riverbanks, sedge bogs, meadows, pine flatwoods, roadsides, ditches, wet habitats, pine savannas, dry woodlands; 10–50 m; Ala., Fla., Ga., La., Miss., N.C., S.C., Va.

Tephrosia hispidula is recognized by its relatively small leaflets with sharply acute apices and strigulose abaxial surfaces with reddish venation.

14. Tephrosia tenella A. Gray, Smithsonian Contr. Knowl. 5(6): 36. 1853 • Slender hoary-pea

Cracca tenella (A. Gray) Rose

Herbs. Stems erect to decumbent or ascending, (8–)10–50(–100) cm, sparsely strigulose to glabrescent. **Leaves:** petiole 10–30 mm; leaflets (3 or)5–9(or 11), blades linear to linear-oblong, narrowly oblong, or oblong-elliptic, 15–40 × 2–6 mm, length 5–9 times width, apex acute to obtuse or rounded, abaxial surface sparsely strigulose, adaxial glabrous. **Racemes** terminal and axillary, (1–)8–17-flowered, 10–30 cm; floral bracts subpersistent, setaceous-subulate. **Flowers:** corolla pink to rose-pink or rose-purple, aging darker reddish to purple, 6–9 mm; stamens diadelphous; style glabrous. **Legumes** 30–50 × 3–4 mm, sparsely strigulose.

Flowering Apr–Oct(–Nov). Open slopes and flats, canyon slopes and bottoms, ledges, crevices, among boulders, washes, gravelly alluvium, desert scrub, desert grasslands, mesquite-acacia grasslands, oak savannas, oak-juniper woodlands, pine-oak woodlands, roadsides; (700–)800–1900(–2000) m; Ariz., N.Mex., Tex.; Mexico; Central America.

D. Isely (1998) noted that *Tephrosia tenella* seems a peripheral manifestation of the widespread *T. purpurea* complex. F. Shreve and I. L. Wiggins (1964) identified the species in the Sonoran Desert as *T. purpurea* (the type of which is from Africa) and observed that plants in the northern part of its range (called *T. tenella*) seem to have narrower, more acute leaflets but intergrade completely with ones at more southern localities.

Tephrosia vicioides Schlechtendal has been suggested to be the correct name for these plants (R. McVaugh 1987).

In *Tephrosia tenella* as identified here, most commonly the taproot becomes thick and distinctly perennial, and the plants often develop a woody, caudex-like region as well. Some plants arise from a slender taproot, with stems 8–30 cm and (1 or)2–5 flowers per raceme. Glabrous-styled taxa were not included in the study of *Tephrosia* by C. E. Wood Jr. (1949).

15. Tephrosia angustissima Shuttleworth ex Chapman, Fl. South. U.S., 96. 1860 • Narrowleaf hoary-pea [C] [E]

Cracca angustissima (Shuttleworth ex Chapman) Kuntze

Subshrubs. Stems ascending-erect to sprawling, 10–45 cm, glabrous. **Leaves:** petiole 10–20 mm; leaflets 11 or 13, blades linear to linear-lanceolate, 20–50 × 0.5–1.5 mm, length 12–30 times width, apex acute, surfaces minutely strigulose to glabrate. **Racemes** 5–11-flowered, 4–8 cm; floral bracts persistent, linear. **Flowers:** corolla white to pink, darkening to red, 7–10 mm; stamens monadelphous; style glabrous. **Legumes** 38–50 × 3–4 mm, sparsely hirsutulous.

Flowering May–Dec. Roadsides, coastal scrub; of conservation concern; 0–10 m; Fla.

Tephrosia angustissima is known from Brevard and Miami-Dade counties.

Tephrosia angustissima, *T. corallicola*, and *T. curtissii* have been regarded as distinct species (L. H. Shinners 1962e; R. W. Long and O. Lakela 1967); D. Isely (1982, 1998) considered them a single species. These three taxa are sympatric with apparently few, if any, morphological intermediates. They are part of the *T. purpurea* complex (see discussion under 14. *T. tenella*).

16. Tephrosia curtissii (Small ex Rydberg) Shinners, Sida 1: 60. 1962 • Curtiss's hoary-pea [C] [E]

Cracca curtissii Small ex Rydberg in N. L. Britton et al., N. Amer. Fl. 24: 179. 1923; *Tephrosia angustissima* Shuttleworth ex Chapman var. *curtissii* (Small ex Rydberg) Isely; *T. seminole* Shinners

Subshrubs. Stems ascending-erect to sprawling, becoming prostrate, 10–45 cm, glabrous. **Leaves:** petiole 6–16 mm; leaflets (9 or)11–15(–19), blades oblong-elliptic to oblanceolate-oblong, (9–)12–25(–30) × 3–6 mm, length 3–6 times width, apex rounded to truncate or retuse, surfaces minutely strigulose, abaxial veins greenish to reddish. **Racemes** 5–11-flowered, 4–10 cm; floral bracts persistent, linear. **Flowers:** corolla pale pink to purple, 7–10 mm; stamens monadelphous; style glabrous. **Legumes** 35–47 × 3–4 mm, sparsely hirsutulous.

Flowering May–Sep. Coastal dunes, beach ridges, coastal scrub, live-oak woods, roadsides; of conservation concern; 0–10 m; Fla.

Tephrosia curtissii is known from Brevard, Broward, Hendry, Hillsborough, Miami-Dade, Palm Beach, and Volusia counties.

17. Tephrosia corallicola (Small) León, Contr. Ocas. Mus. Hist. Nat. Colegio "De La Salle" 10: 304. 1951 • Coral hoary-pea 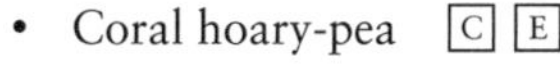

Cracca corallicola Small, Bull. Torrey Bot. Club 36: 160. 1909; *Tephrosia angustissima* Shuttleworth ex Chapman var. *corallicola* (Small) Isely

Subshrubs. Stems erect to ascending-sprawling, 5–70 cm, densely fine-hirsute to hirsute. **Leaves:** petiole 6–15 mm; leaflets 11–15, blades linear to oblong-elliptic or oblong-oblanceolate, (9–)12–30 × 3–6 mm, length 3–5 times width, apex rounded to truncate, surfaces villous-hirsute, abaxial veins reddish. **Racemes** 5–11-flowered, 4–8 cm; floral bracts persistent, linear. **Flowers:** corolla pale pink to purple, 7–11 mm; stamens monadelphous; style glabrous. **Legumes** 35–45 × 3–4 mm, sparsely hirsutulous.

Flowering May–Dec. Slash pine-saw palmetto communities; of conservation concern; 0–10 m; Fla.

Tephrosia corallicola is known from Collier and Miami-Dade counties; it has been established by cuttings from a Miami-Dade locality in a nearby, similar habitat (K. Wendelberger, http://www.virtualherbarium.org/GardenViews/TephrosiaAngustissima.html).

81. ABRUS Adanson, Fam. Pl. 2: 327, 511. 1763 • [Derivation uncertain; probably Greek *habros* or Arabic *abruz*, elegant, alluding to appearance of leaves and/or seeds] I

Velva E. Rudd†

Michael A. Vincent

Vines, perennial, woody or suffrutescent, unarmed. **Stems** twining, pubescent becoming glabrescent. **Leaves** alternate, even-pinnate; stipules present; petiolate; leaflets 16–40, opposite, stipels absent or minute, blade margins entire, surfaces glabrous or pubescent. **Inflorescences** 10–30-flowered, axillary or terminal, racemes [pseudoracemes or fascicles]; bracts and bracteoles present. **Flowers** papilionaceous; calyx campanulate, lobes 5; corolla pink or lavender to white, [yellowish, blue, or purplish]; stamens 9, vexillary stamen absent, connate ½ length; anthers dorsifixed, uniform or 4 smaller; ovary densely strigose; style slightly curved, relatively short, glabrous; stigma terminal, capitate, penicillate. **Fruits** legumes, subsessile, slightly inflated [compressed], curved, oblong [linear], beaked, elastically dehiscent, puberulent. **Seeds** (1–)3–7, subglobose [ellipsoid and compressed].

Species ca. 17 (1 in the flora): introduced, Florida; Asia, Africa; introduced also in Mexico, West Indies, Central America, South America, Indian Ocean Islands, Pacific Islands, Australia; pantropical, tropical, and subtropical regions.

SELECTED REFERENCE Breteler, F. J. 1960. Revision of *Abrus* Adanson (Papilionoideae) with special reference to Africa. Blumea 10: 607–624.

1. Abrus precatorius Linnaeus, Syst. Nat. ed. 12, 2: 472. 1767 • Crab's eye, Indian licorice, rosary pea [F] [I] [W]

Glycine abrus Linnaeus, Sp. Pl. 2: 753. 1753

Stems to 50 cm. **Leaves** 4–10 cm; stipules caducous, linear, 5 × 1 mm; pinna blade oblong to elliptic, 5–30 × 3–10 mm, base obtuse, apex obtuse, usually terminated by bristle, surfaces sparsely pubescent abaxially, hairs appressed, minute, glabrous adaxially. **Racemes** shorter than leaves. **Flowers:** calyx subactinomorphic, 2–4 mm, sparsely pubescent; corolla 9–12 mm, glabrous. **Legumes** (2–)3–4(–5) × 1–1.5 cm, smooth or muriculate; 2-valved, lightly septate. **Seeds** usually red with black spot surrounding hilum, sometimes black throughout, black and white, or whitish, 5–7 × 4–5 mm, lustrous; hilum eccentric, elliptic, to 1 mm diam. **2*n*** = 22.

Flowering Jun–Nov. Borders of woods, hedges, fields, waste places; 0–10 m; introduced; Fla.; s, se Asia; Africa; introduced also in Mexico, West Indies, Central America, South America, elsewhere in Asia, Indian Ocean Islands, Pacific Islands, Australia.

B. Verdcourt (1970) pointed out that there are two entities, or subspecies, of *Abrus precatorius*: the typical subspecies, with smooth fruit surfaces, from Sri Lanka, India, and southeast Asia; and subsp. *africanus* Verdcourt from Africa, with muriculate fruit surfaces covered with low tubercles. There appear to be separate introductions to Florida, perhaps by way of the West Indies, as both subspecies and intermediates are to be found. Distinction of the two subspecies in the flora area is problematic.

The seeds are poisonous and importation of the species is prohibited in Canada (Canadian Food Inspection Agency, http://www.inspection.gc.ca/english/plaveg/oper/prohibintere.shtml). They have been used historically as standard weights in East Asia and are commonly used for rosaries and novelty jewelry (O. N. Allen and E. K. Allen 1981); this use is now prohibited in the United States (R. C. Dart 2004).

82. CANAVALIA Adanson, Fam. Pl. 2: 325, 531. 1763 (as Canavali), name and orthography conserved • [Konkani (southwest India) *cana*, corruption of *rana*, wild, forest, and *val*, bean, or *vaal*, sword, probably alluding to form and/or taste of pods]

Alexander Krings

Wenderothia Schlechtendal

Herbs or vines, annual or perennial, woody or herbaceous, unarmed. **Stems** twining, trailing, prostrate, or erect, glabrous, glabrate, strigulose, or glabrescent. **Leaves** alternate, odd-pinnate; stipules present, caducous, deltate and small or obsolete; petiolate; stipels deciduous; leaflets 3, blade margins entire, surfaces strigose, glabrate, or glabrous. **Inflorescences** 8–50-flowered, axillary, panicles; bracts present, caducous; axis retrorsely pubescent basally, antrorsely pubescent apically; bracteoles present, calycine. **Flowers** papilionaceous; calyx campanulate, 2-lipped, lobes 5, abaxial lip with 3 short lobes, adaxial lip with 2 massive connate lobes; corolla lavender, pink-purple, purple and white (bicolored), white, blue-violet, or reddish purple [pink-white], 20–35 mm, glabrous; stamens 10, monadelphous; anthers basifixed, dehiscing apically, relatively small. **Fruits** legumes, stipitate, straight or ± falcate, ± compressed, sometimes turgid, oblong or narrowly oblong [linear], 6–40 cm, well exceeding calyx, ventral margin 3–5-ribbed, adaxial (upper) margins 3-costate, dehiscent, strigose to glabrate. **Seeds** (1–)4–15, oblong to elliptic in silhouette; hilum lateral. x = 11.

Species ca. 60 (4 in the flora): s, c United States, Mexico, West Indies, Central America, South America, Asia, Africa, Atlantic Islands, Pacific Islands, Australia.

Some *Canavalia* species are grown for cover crops, green manures, forage, and human consumption (G. P. Lewis et al. 2005). Coastal species produce drift-seeds.

SELECTED REFERENCE Sauer, J. D. 1964. Revision of *Canavalia*. Brittonia 16: 106–181.

1. Leaflet blades suborbiculate, elliptic, or oblong, apices emarginate or obtuse; legumes turgid to moderately compressed; seeds marbled, red to brown; hilum to ½ length of seed; coastal habitats . . . . 4. *Canavalia rosea*
1. Leaflet blades ovate to ovate-elliptic, apices obtuse, acute, subacute, subacuminate, or acuminate; legumes slightly compressed; seeds usually not marbled (sometimes darkly so in *C. brasiliensis*), olive, brown, red, red-brown, white, or off-white; hilum shorter to longer than ½ length of seed; disturbed areas.
    2. Leaflet apices acuminate; calyces with central lobe of abaxial lip equaling obtuse lateral lobes; seeds usually red to red-brown, rarely white . . . . 3. *Canavalia gladiata*
    2. Leaflet apices obtuse, subacute, or emarginate; calyces with central lobe of abaxial lip exceeding ± acute lateral lobes; seeds white, off-white, olive, brown, or red.
        3. Stems twining or prostrate; petiolule hairs 0.5–0.9 mm; legumes 6–20 × 2–3 cm; seeds olive, brown, or red . . . . 1. *Canavalia brasiliensis*
        3. Stems twining or erect; petiolule hairs 0.3 mm; legumes 15–35 × 3–3.5 cm; seeds white or off-white . . . . 2. *Canavalia ensiformis*

1. Canavalia brasiliensis Martius ex Bentham, Comm Legum. Gen., 71. 1837 [I]

Vines, perennial, herbaceous or woody, to 3 m. **Stems** twining or prostrate, sparsely pubescent to glabrate. **Leaves:** petiole 3.9–11.6 cm; petiolules 7–8.7 mm, moderately to densely pubescent, hairs 0.5–0.9 mm; leaflet blades ovate, 30–142 × 28–97 mm, base cuneate, apex obtuse, acute, or subacuminate, surfaces strigose to glabrate. **Panicles** to 25 cm; bracteoles 1.3–1.5 × 1.2–1.3 mm, apex obtuse. **Pedicels** 0.3–2 mm, glabrous or strigillose. **Flowers:** calyx 6.3–12 mm; central lobe of abaxial lip exceeding ± acute lateral lobes; corolla lavender to blue-violet, 20–24 mm. **Legumes** slightly compressed, oblong, 6–20 × 2–3 cm. **Seeds** 4–12, olive, brown, or red, sometimes darkly marbled, moderately compressed, oblong, 1.4–1.9 × 1–1.2 cm; hilum ½+ length of seed. $2n = 22$.

Flowering Feb–Apr, Nov–Dec. Sandy soils of pineland margins, disturbed woodlands, waste areas; 0–20 m; introduced; Fla.; Mexico; West Indies; Central America; South America.

Canavalia brasiliensis was cultivated historically also in Mississippi; no recent records of escaped or persisting populations exist. It is known from Miami-Dade County.

2. Canavalia ensiformis (Linnaeus) de Candolle in A. P. de Candolle and A. L. P. P. de Candolle, Prodr. 2: 404. 1825 • Jack bean [I]

Dolichos ensiformis Linnaeus, Sp. Pl. 2: 725. 1753

Herbs or vines, annual or perennial, herbaceous, 1–2(–10) m. **Stems** twining or erect, glabrous or glabrate. **Leaves:** stipules 0.6–1.3 × 0.4–1 mm; petiole 5–12 cm; petiolules 3.6–7.8 mm, moderately to densely pubescent, hairs 0.3 mm; leaflet blades ovate-elliptic, 60–150(–200) × 26–82 mm, base cuneate, apex obtuse or subacute, surfaces glabrate. **Panicles** to 15 cm; bracteoles 2 × 1 mm, apex obtuse. **Pedicels** 2–2.3 mm, strigillose. **Flowers:** calyx 9.7–14 mm; central lobe of abaxial lip exceeding ± acute lateral lobes; corolla lavender to pink-purple, 20–28 mm. **Legumes** slightly compressed, narrowly oblong, 15–35 × 3–3.5 cm. **Seeds** 9–15, white or off-white, moderately compressed, oblong, 2 × 1.5 cm; hilum shorter to longer than ½ length of seed. $2n = 22$.

Flowering Jul–Sep. Waste places; 0–200 m; introduced; Ala., Ark., Fla., Ga., Kans., La., Miss., Mo., N.C., Okla., Tex.; West Indies; Central America; introduced also in Mexico, South America, Asia, Africa, Pacific Islands.

J. D. Sauer (1964) cited a Palmer collection (GH) of *Canavalia ensiformis* from plants grown at Harvard from seed, from either Arizona or Sonora; this specimen was not seen. *Canavalia ensiformis* is reported adventive in White County, Illinois (R. H. Mohlenbrock 1986); corresponding specimens have not been seen. It is cultivated for forage, erosion control, and as a green manure (D. Isely 1990).

3. Canavalia gladiata (Jacquin) de Candolle in A. P. de Candolle and A. L. P. P. de Candolle, Prodr. 2: 404. 1825 • Sword bean [I]

Dolichos gladiatus Jacquin, Icon. Pl. Rar. 3: plate 560. 1788

Herbs or vines, annual or perennial, herbaceous, 1–2(–9) m. **Stems** erect or twining, sparsely pubescent to glabrate. **Leaves:** petiole 5.8–8 cm; petiolules 5–7.5 mm, sparsely pubescent, hairs 0.3–0.6 mm; leaflet blades ovate-elliptic or ovate, 70–200 × 50–90 mm, base cuneate, apex acuminate, surfaces glabrate. **Panicles** to 45 cm; bracteoles 0.5–1 × 0.7–1.4 mm, apex obtuse. **Pedicels** 2–2.2 mm, glabrous or strigillose. **Flowers:** calyx 11–16 mm; central lobe of abaxial lip equaling obtuse lateral lobes; corolla bicolored (purple and white) or white, 25–35 mm. **Legumes** slightly compressed, narrowly oblong, 20–40 × 2.5–5 cm. **Seeds** 6–9, usually red to red-brown, rarely white, moderately compressed, oblong, to 2–3.5 × 1.5–2 cm; hilum ½+ length of seed. **2*n*** = 22.

Flowering Aug–Sep. Waste places; 0–100 m; introduced; La., Miss., Mo., S.C., Tex.; se Asia; introduced also in Mexico, West Indies, Central America, South America, Africa, Pacific Islands, Australia.

4. Canavalia rosea (Swartz) de Candolle in A. P. de Candolle and A. L. P. P. de Candolle, Prodr. 2: 404. 1825 • Baybean [F]

Dolichos roseus Swartz, Prodr., 105. 1788; *Canavalia maritima* Thouars; *D. maritimus* Aublet

Vines, perennial, herbaceous or woody, to 10 m. **Stems** twining or prostrate-trailing, pubescent to glabrate. **Leaves:** petiole 2–5.8 cm; petiolules 3–8.5 mm, moderately densely pubescent, hairs 0.2–0.4 mm; leaflet blades suborbiculate, elliptic, or oblong, 40–120 × 23–62 mm, base cuneate to rounded, apex emarginate or obtuse, surfaces moderately or densely pubescent or glabrous abaxially, sparsely pubescent adaxially. **Panicles** 9–21 cm; bracteoles 1.2–1.5 × 0.8–1.6 mm, apex obtuse. **Pedicels** 1.5–3 mm, strigillose. **Flowers:** calyx 10–12 mm; central lobe of abaxial lip slightly exceeding acute lateral lobes; corolla lavender to reddish purple, 25–30 mm. **Legumes** turgid to moderately compressed, oblong, 10–15 × 2–3.5 cm. **Seeds** (1–)4–8, red to brown, darkly marbled, slightly compressed, elliptic, 1.5–1.8 × 1.3–2 cm; hilum to ½ length of seed. **2*n*** = 22.

Flowering year-round. Dunes, beaches, scrub hammocks, palm groves, salt marsh edges; 0–100 m; Fla., La., Tex.; Mexico; West Indies; Central America; South America; Asia; Africa; Atlantic Islands; Pacific Islands; Australia.

Canavalia rosea is frequent in Dixie County and central and southern peninsular Florida (R. P. Wunderlin and B. F. Hansen 2011), as well as being found in south coastal Texas in Cameron and Kenedy counties. D. Isely (1990) reported *Canavalia rosea* also from Alabama and Mississippi; corresponding specimens from those localities were not seen.

83. GALACTIA P. Browne, Civ. Nat. Hist. Jamaica, 298, plate 32, fig. 2. 1756 • Milkpea [Greek *galaktos*, milk, alluding to milky sap in *Galactia pendula*, the type species]

Guy L. Nesom

Heterocarpaea Scheele; *Odonia* Bertoloni

Herbs, perennial, [subshrubs, rarely shrubs], unarmed; with rhizomes, from woody taproot elongate or fusiform. **Stems** procumbent or twining and climbing, glabrous or with spreading or appressed hairs. **Leaves** alternate, unifoliolate or odd-pinnate; stipules present, deciduous or persistent; petiolate; leaflets 1 or 3(–9), stipels persistent, blades 6–85 mm, margins entire, surfaces pubescent or glabrous. **Inflorescences** 1–25(–38)-flowered, axillary [terminal], usually pseudoracemes, pedunculate or without axis and flowers in axillary fascicles, sometimes flowers solitary; rachis with slightly swollen nodes; bracts present, setaceous; bracteoles minute, caducous, rarely tardily so. **Flowers** papilionaceous, solitary, paired, or fascicles of 2 or 3 at nodes; calyx campanulate, lobes 5 appearing as 4, adaxial 2 completely connate; corolla usually purplish to bluish, pink, rose, violet, or lavender, rarely white [red], 6–15(–17) mm; petals subequal, banner orbiculate to ovate or obovate-orbiculate, margins slightly inflexed or appendaged, apex rounded, wings narrow or obovate, adherent to keel, keel obtuse and almost straight, subequal to or longer than wings, carinate or moderately incurved; stamens 10, diadelphous [pseudomonadelphous], vexillary stamen free or proximally connate from middle; anthers dorsifixed; ovary subsessile; style filiform, glabrous; stigma terminal, capitate; nectary at ovary base. **Fruits** legumes, sessile, brown, laterally compressed, straight or weakly to strongly falcate, linear, with false septae between seeds, elastically dehiscent, pubescent. **Seeds** 1–12, brown or brownish orange, flattened, oblong, 3–7 mm, estrophiolate. $x = 10$.

Species ca. 110 (21 in the flora): United States, Mexico, West Indies, Central America, South America, Asia, Africa, Australia.

Most *Galactia* species are native to the Americas, distributed fairly evenly across the southeastern and south-central United States, Mexico, West Indies, Central America, and South America. Diversity in the flora area is concentrated in Florida and Texas, with relatively fewer species in Mexico and Central America. Three species of *Galactia* are native to Asia, Africa, and Australia. An overview of the genus in the flora area and a summary of previous studies worldwide were provided in G. L. Nesom (2015). The Texas species *G. watsoniana* W. C. Holmes & Singhurst is a synonym of *Cologania pallida* Rose (Nesom).

Three sections have been recognized within *Galactia* (A. Burkart 1971), emphasizing the South American species. Most species of *Galactia*, including all of those in the flora area, are placed in sect. *Odonia* (Bertoloni) Burkart in the sense of Burkart.

Galactia forms a group in the Diocleinae Bentham together with three or four other genera: *Camptosema* Hooker & Arnott, *Collaea* de Candolle, and *Lackeya*. R. H. Maxwell and D. W. Taylor (2003) included the Caribbean *Rhodopis* Urban in their *Galactia* clade. Phylogenetic studies indicate that *Galactia* is not monophyletic (L. P. de Queiroz et al. 2003; S. M. Sede et al. 2008, 2009; G. B. Ceolin 2011), but relatively few species have been included in analyses. *Galactia* appears to be paraphyletic without the inclusion of some species of *Camptosema* and perhaps the entire genus *Collaea*. In addition, the sections as circumscribed by Burkart do not appear to be monophyletic.

R. H. Maxwell (1979) placed the eastern North American *Dioclea multiflora* in *Galactia* as *G. mohlenbrockii* R. H. Maxwell; R. H. Fortunato et al. (1996) segregated *D. multiflora* as the monospecific *Lackeya*. This placement is supported by molecular analyses (L. P. de Queiroz et al. 2015).

SELECTED REFERENCES Duncan, W. H. 1979b. Changes in *Galactia* (Fabaceae) of the southeastern United States. Sida 8: 170–180. Franck, A. R. 2017. Notes on trifoliolate species of *Galactia* (Fabaceae) in Florida. Phytologia 99: 139–185. Nesom, G. L. 2015. Taxonomy of *Galactia* (Fabaceae) in the USA. Phytoneuron 2015-42: 1–53. Nesom, G. L. 2017b. *Galactia* (Fabaceae) in Florida: Comments on Franck's recent study. Phytoneuron 2017-39: 1–7. Rogers, H. J. 1949. The Genus *Galactia* in the United States. Ph.D. dissertation. Duke University. Vail, A. M. 1895. A study of the genus *Galactia* in North America. Bull. Torrey Bot. Club 22: 374–378. Ward, D. B. and D. W. Hall. 2004. Keys to the flora of Florida—10. *Galactia* (Leguminosae). Phytologia 86: 65–74.

1. Leaflets 1 . . . . 21. *Galactia marginalis*
1. Leaflets 3 or 5–9.
   2. Leaflets 5–9.
      3. Leaflets (5 or)7(or 9); corollas white; flowers 3–11, distal on axis; Florida, Georgia, South Carolina . . . . 19. *Galactia elliottii*
      3. Leaflets 5; corollas pink to purple, purple-red, violet-red, or lavender; flowers axillary, solitary or 2–5 in pseudoracemes; Texas . . . . 20. *Galactia heterophylla*
   2. Leaflets usually 3, rarely 5.
      4. Stems mostly erect, not twining, usually alternately bent at nodes; inflorescences subsessile, flowers 1–6 . . . . 16. *Galactia erecta*
      4. Stems procumbent or climbing-twining, not bent at nodes; inflorescences pedunculate, flowers 2–25(–38), or sessile or subsessile and 1-flowered.
         5. Stems climbing-twining.
            6. Corollas 11–14(–15) mm; stems loosely strigose with short, loosely appressed, retrorse hairs, strongly lignescent . . . . 5. *Galactia fasciculata*
            6. Corollas 7–11(–14) mm; stems strigose to hirsute or hirsute-pilose, herbaceous to ± lignescent (*G. striata*).
               7. Banners striped with white lines; localities coastal and near-coast . . . . . 4. *Galactia striata*
               7. Banners not striped; localities inland to coastal.
                  8. Legumes falcate; flowers 1–5, solitary and subsessile or 2–5 on inflorescence axis 1–4(–40) mm . . . . 12. *Galactia texana*
                  8. Legumes straight; flowers 1–8(–16), solitary and pedicellate or 2–8(–16) on inflorescence axis 10–150(–280) mm.
                     9. Stems strigose with antrorse hairs; leaflet blades linear-oblong to narrowly oblong or narrowly elliptic, 2–4(–6) mm wide; Florida . . . . 18. *Galactia grisebachii*
                     9. Stems strigose or hirsute to hirsute-villous with spreading-deflexed or retrorse hairs; leaflet blades oblong to elliptic, elliptic-lanceolate, or oblong-lanceolate, 5–21(–25) mm wide; Texas, or broadly distributed in c, e United States.
                        10. Leaflet blades narrowly oblong to oblong-lanceolate, 6–14 mm wide; legumes 35–65 mm; seeds 12–15; Florida, Texas . . . . 3. *Galactia longifolia*
                        10. Leaflet blades elliptic to broadly elliptic or oblong to lanceolate-elliptic, 5–21(–25) mm wide; legumes 20–50 (–52) mm; seeds 5–11; c, e United States including Texas.
                            11. Leaflet blades mostly elliptic to broadly elliptic, (5–) 10–21(–25) mm wide; stems moderately to densely hirsute to hirsute-villous with spreading-deflexed hairs; corollas 7–10 mm . . . . 1. *Galactia regularis*
                            11. Leaflet blades oblong to lanceolate-elliptic, 5–15 (–17) mm wide; stems sparsely to moderately strigose with tightly to loosely appressed, retrorse hairs, sometime glabrate; corollas 9–14 mm . . . . 2. *Galactia volubilis*
         5. Stems procumbent at least proximally, not distinctly climbing-twining, sometimes weakly twining distally.
            12. Herbs usually producing filiform rhizomes at nodes, these producing subterranean flowers and 1-seeded fruits . . . . 15. *Galactia canescens*
            12. Herbs without rhizomes at nodes, without subterranean flowers and fruits.
                13. Calyx lobes brown to reddish brown on inner surface when dry; corollas distinctly dark reddish when dry, persisting after anthesis, sometimes still present in mature fruit . . . . 6. *Galactia mollis*
                13. Calyx lobes greenish yellow to tan on inner surface when dry; corollas light whitish to blue, pinkish, or purplish when dry, not persisting after anthesis.

[14. Shifted to left margin.—Ed.]

14. Leaflets ± leathery to leathery, veins raised on both surfaces.
    15. Leaflet blades mostly linear-oblong or narrowly oblong, 2–8(–11) mm wide; Florida . . . . 17. *Galactia pinetorum*
    15. Leaflet blades elliptic, oblanceolate-elliptic, oblong-elliptic, elliptic-lanceolate, or broadly lanceolate, (4–)7–25(–32) mm wide; Florida and Alabama north to New Jersey.
        16. Stems: several to most internodes (especially those toward base) longer than largest leaflet of adjacent nodes, hairs on stem 0.1–0.8 mm; leaflet blades (4–)10–25 (–32) mm wide; flowers usually (3–)5–15(–25), rarely 1 or 2 . . . . 10. *Galactia brachypoda*
        16. Stems: internodes usually shorter, sometimes longer, than largest leaflet of adjacent nodes, hairs on stems 0.1–0.3 mm; leaflet blades (4–)7–10(–18) mm wide; flowers solitary or 2–4 . . . . 11. *Galactia minor*
14. Leaflets herbaceous, veins not raised (except strong raised abaxially in *G. joselyniae*).
    17. Stems strigose; Arizona, New Mexico, Texas.
        18. Leaflet blades oblong-elliptic to elliptic-ovate; flowers (2–)5–18(–30), corollas 11–12 mm . . . . 13. *Galactia wrightii*
        18. Leaflet blades mostly broadly oblong-elliptic to suborbiculate; flowers solitary or 2–8, corollas 6–8 mm . . . . 14. *Galactia joselyniae*
    17. Stems tomentose to hirsute-villous or hirsute; se United States.
        19. Leaflet blades (14–)20–55 × (10–)15–35 mm; flowers 5–12(–25) . . . . 7. *Galactia floridana*
        19. Leaflet blades 8–30 × 5–20 mm; flowers solitary and axillary or 2–6.
            20. Inflorescence axis 10–20 mm; calyces 3–4 mm; corollas 6–7 mm; Florida panhandle, s Alabama . . . . 8. *Galactia microphylla*
            20. Inflorescence axis (5–)20–60(–90) mm; calyces 6–7 mm; corollas 10–15 mm; s Florida . . . . 9. *Galactia smallii*

1. Galactia regularis (Linnaeus) Britton, Sterns & Poggenburg, Prelim. Cat., 14. 1888 • Eastern or downy milkpea [E] [F]

Dolichos regularis Linnaeus, Sp. Pl. 2: 726. 1753; *Galactia volubilis* (Linnaeus) Britton var. *mississippiensis* Vail

Herbs from an elongate woody taproot. **Stems** climbing-twining, herbaceous, moderately to densely hirsute to hirsute-villous with spreading-deflexed hairs. **Leaflets** 3, blades elliptic to broadly elliptic, oblong-elliptic, or lanceolate-elliptic, (10–)14–40(–50) × (5–)10–21(–25) mm, herbaceous, veins not raised, apex obtuse to rounded, surfaces sparsely strigose abaxially (often glaucous), minutely and sparsely short-strigose adaxially. **Inflorescences:** flowers solitary and axillary or 2–7(–9) in reduced pseudoracemes on distal ½–¾ of axis; axis 10–70(–150) mm. **Flowers:** calyx 4–6 mm, hirsute-villous; corolla pink to rose, light violet, pink-purple, or rose-purple, 7–10 mm. **Legumes** straight, 20–50 × 3–5 mm, loosely strigose. **Seeds** 5–9.

Flowering (Jun–)Jul–Aug. Oak, pine-oak woods, woodland borders, fence rows, low fields, pond and stream margins, ditches, roadbanks, open disturbed sites; 20–500(–900) m; Ala., Ark., Del., Fla., Ga., Ill., Ind., Kans., Ky., La., Md., Miss., Mo., N.J., N.Y., N.C., Ohio, Okla., Pa., S.C., Tenn., Tex., Va., W.Va.

Galactia regularis is the most widespread species of the genus in the eastern United States and is characterized by its relatively small flowers, elliptic leaflets, and twining, deflexed-hirsute-villous stems.

2. Galactia volubilis (Linnaeus) Britton, Mem. Torrey Bot. Club 5: 208. 1894 • McRee's milkpea [E] [F]

Hedysarum volubile Linnaeus, Sp. Pl. 2: 750. 1753; *Galactia macreei* M. A. Curtis

Herbs from a woody taproot. **Stems** climbing-twining, herbaceous, usually sparsely to moderately strigose with tightly to loosely appressed, retrorse hairs, sometimes glabrate. **Leaflets** 3, blades oblong to narrowly elliptic or narrowly lanceolate-elliptic, (10–)12–40(–45) × 5–15(–17) mm, herbaceous, veins not raised, apex rounded to truncate or shallowly retuse, surfaces short-strigose abaxially, glabrous or sparsely strigose adaxially. **Inflorescences:** flowers solitary and axillary or 2–6(–10) in reduced pseudoracemes on distal ⅓–¾ of axis, sometimes in fascicles; axis (10–)20–90(–240) mm. **Flowers:** calyx 6–8 mm, sparsely strigose to glabrate; corolla pink to pink and purple, 9–14 mm. **Legumes** straight, (20–)25–52 × 3–4 mm, short-strigose. **Seeds** (5–)7–11.

Flowering (Apr–)May–Aug(–Sep). Swamp forests and borders, brackish marshes, ditches, shell mounds, hammock edges, live oak woods, pine and oak-pine woods, roadsides, cutover woods, disturbed sites; 20–600 m; Ala., Fla., Ga., La., Miss., N.C., S.C., Tex.

Galactia volubilis is characterized by its slightly larger flowers, characteristically narrow oblong leaflets, and twining, thin, sparsely, antrorsely strigose to glabrate stems; it is distributed mostly on the coastal plain from North Carolina to Alabama; scattered localities are known westward to Texas.

Galactia volubilis and *G. regularis* appear to be mostly distinct in their area of sympatry (*G. regularis* has a wider geographic range); apparent intermediates are encountered. Flowering times coincide and there is at least some overlap in habitat, allowing opportunities for hybridization, but the relative stability of the two forms even where sympatric suggests that some kind of reproductive isolation is in effect, perhaps post-zygotic. The most prominent distinction between the two species is in leaf shape; leaves of *G. volubilis* also tend to be thinner and glaucous on the abaxial surface. Vestiture of *G. volubilis* is relatively sparse or surfaces may be glabrous or nearly so.

Galactia glabella Michaux is a superfluous and illegitimate name that pertains here.

3. **Galactia longifolia** (Jacquin) Bentham, Comm. Legum. Gen., 63. 1837 • Longleaf milkpea

Galega longifolia Jacquin, Collectanea 2: 349. 1789

Herbs: basal parts not seen. **Stems** climbing-twining, moderately strigose, hairs loosely appressed, retrorse. **Leaflets** 3, blades narrowly oblong to oblong-lanceolate, 25–75 × 6–14 mm, herbaceous, veins not raised, apex rounded to obtuse, surfaces moderately to densely minutely strigulose, with closely appressed hairs. **Inflorescences:** flowers solitary and axillary or 2–8(–16) in pseudoracemes on distal 1/4 of axis, sometimes in fascicles; axis 30–120(–280) mm. **Flowers:** calyx 5–6 mm, strigulose; corolla lavender, 10–11 mm. **Legumes** straight, 35–65 × 4–6 mm, sparsely minutely strigulose, hairs closely appressed. **Seeds** 12–15.

Flowering Apr–Aug(–Sep). Coastal prairies, clay, poorly drained sandy loam; 10–30 m; Fla., Tex.; West Indies (Hispaniola, Lesser Antilles, Puerto Rico); South America (Argentina, French Guiana, Paraguay).

In Texas, *Galactia longifolia* is known from a cluster of five coastal counties in the south: Aransas, Brazoria, Calhoun, Jackson, and Victoria. The irregularly scattered distribution of this species (Florida, Texas, Caribbean, French Guiana, and southern South America) suggests that it may not be monophyletic.

4. **Galactia striata** (Jacquin) Urban, Symb. Antill. 2: 320. 1900 • Florida hammock milkpea

Glycine striata Jacquin, Hort. Bot. Vindob. 1: 32, plate 76. 1771; *Galactia berteroana* de Candolle; *G. cubensis* Kunth; *G. spiciformis* Torrey & A. Gray

Herbs from an elongate woody taproot. **Stems** climbing-twining, often high-climbing, strongly lignescent, densely hirsute-pilose. **Leaflets** 3, blades elliptic to lanceolate-elliptic, ovate-elliptic, or broadly elliptic, (20–)32–70 × 9–40(–50) mm, herbaceous, veins not raised, apex rounded to obtuse or subacute, surfaces hirsute, hairs erect to ascending. **Inflorescences:** flowers 10–20(–38) in pseudoracemes on distal 2/3–4/5 of axis, often fasciculate; axis (70–)100–280 mm. **Flowers:** calyx 5–7 mm, strigose; corolla lavender, bluish, pink-purple, purple, pink, banner striped with white lines, 8–11 mm. **Legumes** straight, 30–60 × 6–8 mm, loosely strigose. **Seeds** 5–12.

Flowering year-round. Hammocks, mangroves, thickets, scrubland, beaches, roadsides; 0–20 m; Fla.; Mexico; West Indies; Central America; South America.

Galactia striata is known from the southern half of Florida.

A. Burkart (1971) recognized three varieties within *Galactia striata*: var. *striata* and var. *tenuiflora* (Klein ex Willdenow) Burkart, both widespread and widely sympatric, and var. *crassirachis* Burkart, endemic to Argentina. At least seven other varieties have been recognized, as well as various synonyms at specific rank, and this variable complex needs study before evolutionary morpho-geographic patterns are clearly evident. *Galactia tenuiflora* Klein ex Willdenow is treated as a distinct species in many accounts and is widely distributed.

Galactia striata and *G. spiciformis* sometimes have both been recognized in Florida and in the West Indies; distinctions observed between them have varied. Most Florida botanists (as well as D. Isely 1998) have treated *G. striata* more broadly, treating *G. spiciformis* as a synonym.

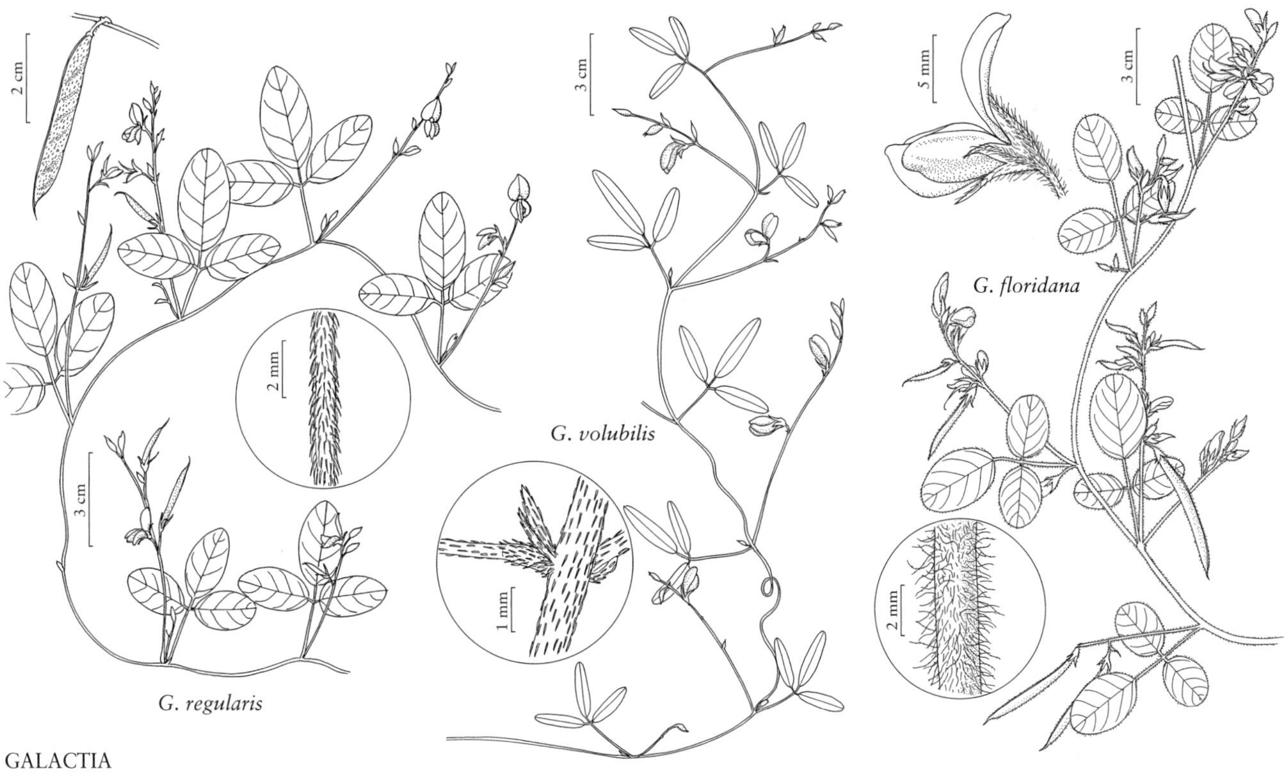

GALACTIA

5. Galactia fasciculata Vail, Bull. Torrey Bot. Club 22: 505. 1895 • Large trailing milkpea [E]

Galactia floridana Torrey & A. Gray var. *longeracemosa* Vail; *G. volubilis* (Linnaeus) Britton var. *baltzelliana* D. B. Ward & D. W. Hall; *G. volubilis* var. *fasciculata* (Vail) D. B. Ward & D. W. Hall

Herbs from a woody taproot. **Stems** climbing-twining, strongly lignescent, loosely strigose, hairs loosely appressed, retrorse. **Leaflets** 3, blades elliptic, broadly elliptic, or suborbiculate, (12–)25–45 (–64) × 10–30(–39) mm, leathery, veins not raised, apex rounded to obtuse, sometimes retuse, surfaces short-strigulose and lighter abaxially, glabrous and darker adaxially. **Inflorescences:** flowers (3–)6–25, fasciculate in pseudoracemes along distal ½–¾ of rachis; axis (10–)30–160 mm. **Flowers:** calyx 6–7 mm, sparsely minutely strigose to glabrate; corolla lavender or purplish to pinkish, 11–14(–15) mm. **Legumes** straight, 30–60 × 4–6 mm, densely short-strigose to strigose-sericeous, hairs loosely appressed. **Seeds** 5–9.

Flowering (Jun–)Jul–Sep. Sand pine scrub, dunes and hills with sand pine-oak, oak-hickory, scrubby flatwoods, river banks with live oak, longleaf pine, and saw palmetto, disturbed areas; 10–30 m; Fla.

Galactia fasciculata, which is widespread in central peninsular Florida, is distinguished by lignescent, twining and high-climbing stems with densely and loosely retrorse-strigose vestiture, coriaceous leaves dark and glossy adaxially, and short inflorescences with relatively large, densely clustered flowers. It has sometimes been identified as *G. floridana*; the latter is distinct from *G. fasciculata* in its prostrate habit, persistently hairy adaxial leaf surfaces, elongate inflorescences with distally positioned flowers, and villous calyces.

6. Galactia mollis Michaux, Fl. Bor.-Amer. 2: 61. 1803 • Soft milkpea [E]

Galactia pilosa Nuttall

Herbs from an elongate taproot. **Stems** procumbent and trailing at least proximally, often weakly climbing-twining distally, hirsute to villous-hirsute, hairs spreading to slightly upcurved or slightly to strongly deflexed. **Leaflets** 3, blades narrowly to broadly oblong to elliptic-oblong, elliptic, or ovate, (20–)25–50 × 10–30 mm, herbaceous, veins not raised, apex rounded to obtuse, surfaces loosely strigose to pilose or villous. **Inflorescences:** flowers 6–10, usually on distal ¼–½ of axis, often in fascicles; axis (3–)5–15 (–20) mm. **Flowers:** calyx 5–8 mm, densely villous, lobes brown to reddish brown on inner surface when dry; corolla persisting after anthesis, sometimes still present in mature fruit, purplish pink to red or rose-purple, distinctly dark reddish when dry, 7–10 mm. **Legumes** straight, 25–35 × 4–5 mm, loosely densely strigose-sericeous to villous-sericeous. **Seeds** 7–12.

Flowering May–Jul. Longleaf pine savannas, turkey oak, pine barrens, sandhills, sandy roadsides; 20–100 m; Ala., Fla., Ga., N.C., S.C.

Galactia mollis is known from northern peninsular Florida and from scattered counties in the other adjacent states in the flora area.

Galactia mollis is distinctive and rarely misidentified; it is characterized especially by its procumbent habit, hirsute stems, and red, relatively small corollas.

7. Galactia floridana Torrey & A. Gray, Fl. N. Amer. 1: 288. 1838 • Florida milkpea [E] [F]

Galactia brevipes Small

Herbs from an elongate, narrowly fusiform, woody taproot. **Stems** procumbent or creeping, rooting at nodes, sometimes climbing-sprawling but not twining, densely short-tomentose to hirsute-villous, hairs spreading to erect, irregularly oriented. **Leaflets** 3, blades elliptic to broadly elliptic, (14–)20–55 × (10–)15–35 mm, herbaceous, thickened-leathery, veins not raised, apex rounded to truncate, commonly shallowly retuse, surfaces much darker adaxially, sparsely, persistently strigose-sericeous adaxially with loosely appressed hairs. **Inflorescences:** flowers 5–12(–25) in pseudoracemes on distal ¼–½ of axis, in fascicles; axis 20–100(–130) mm. **Flowers:** calyx 7–8 mm, villous, lobes greenish yellow to tan on inner surface when dry; corolla not persisting after anthesis, pink to purple or rose-purple, lighter when dry, 12–15 mm. **Legumes** straight, 30–45 × 3–4(–5) mm, densely villous-hirsute. **Seeds** 7–11.

Flowering Mar–Aug(–Sep). Open pine woods, pine barrens, longleaf pine-turkey oak-blue oak woods, sandhill scrub, sandhills, roadsides; 10–30 m; Ala., Fla., Ga., La., Miss.

J. K. Small (1903, 1913, 1933) distinguished *Galactia brevipes* from *G. floridana* by its panicles longer than leaves and its separated flower clusters (versus panicles shorter or slightly longer than leaves and flower clusters approximate). Intermediate forms are common. Isolated localities in Alabama and Louisiana are disjunct from the main range.

8. Galactia microphylla (Chapman) H. J. Rogers ex D. W. Hall & D. B. Ward, Brittonia 38: 54. 1986 • Littleleaf milkpea [E]

Galactia floridana Torrey & A. Gray var. *microphylla* Chapman, Fl. South. U.S., 108. 1860

Herbs from an elongate, often napiform taproot. **Stems** procumbent, not twining, herbaceous to lignescent, hirsute-villous, hairs irregularly to strongly deflexed, rarely nearly appressed-retrorse. **Leaflets** 3, blades elliptic, 10–30 × 5–16 mm, herbaceous, veins not raised, apex rounded to obtuse, surfaces glossy, glaucous, and sparsely short-strigose abaxially with appressed to ascending hairs, strigose to glabrescent or glabrate adaxially. **Inflorescences:** flowers solitary and axillary or 2–6 in reduced pseudoracemes; axis 10–20 mm. **Flowers:** calyx 3–4 mm, closely strigulose, lobes greenish yellow to tan on inner surface when dry; corolla not persisting after anthesis, light purple, lighter when dry, 6–7 mm. **Legumes** straight, 25–45 × 4–5 mm, short-hirsute, hairs spreading. **Seeds** 3–8.

Flowering Apr–Sep(–Oct). Longleaf pine woodlands, scrub, dunes, sandy hills and slopes; 0–10 m; Ala., Fla.

Galactia microphylla is characterized by its prostrate habit, hirsute-villous stems, and relatively small leaves; it is known from the western Florida panhandle and adjacent Alabama. Compared to *G. floridana*, *G. microphylla* has shorter internodes, smaller and thinner leaves light green on both surfaces and glaucous beneath, shorter inflorescences with fewer flowers, and minutely and closely strigillose calyces.

9. Galactia smallii H. J. Rogers ex A. Herndon, Rhodora 83: 471. 1981 • Small's milkpea [C] [E]

Galactia prostrata Small, Man. S.E. Fl., 719, 1505. 1933, not Bentham 1837

Herbs from a thick-fusiform, woody taproot. **Stems** procumbent, distally twining, densely to sparsely hirsute-villous to hirsute, hairs loosely retrorsely spreading or antrorsely spreading-ascending. **Leaflets** 3, blades broadly elliptic to broadly elliptic-oblong or suborbiculate, 8–25 × 6–20 mm, herbaceous, veins not raised, apex rounded or usually shallowly retuse, surfaces villous-hirsute, with ascending hairs or adaxially minutely hirsute. **Inflorescences:** flowers solitary and axillary or 2–6 in reduced pseudoracemes on distal ⅛–¼ of axis; axis (5–)20–60(–90) mm. **Flowers:** calyx 6–7 mm, strigose to

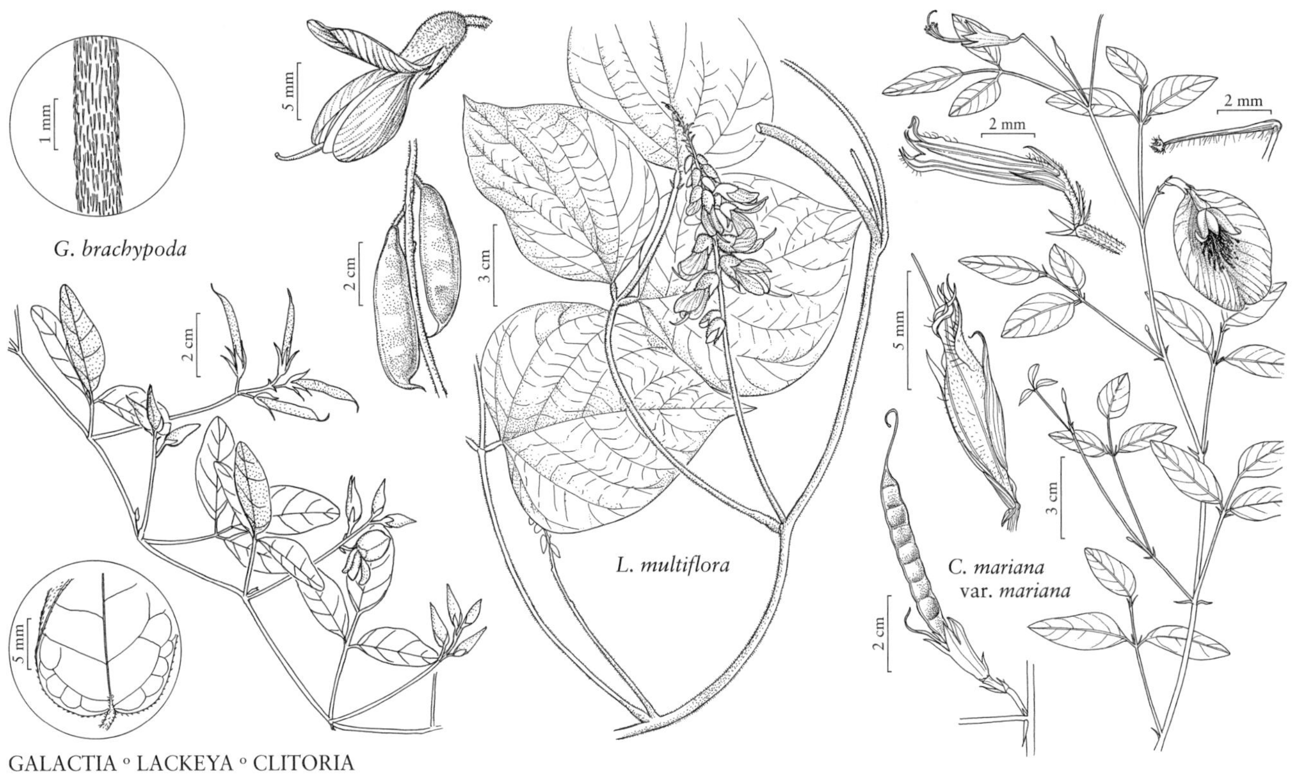

GALACTIA ◦ LACKEYA ◦ CLITORIA

hirsute, lobes greenish yellow to tan on inner surface when dry; corolla not persisting after anthesis, lavender-pink to purple, lighter when dry, 10–15 mm. **Legumes** straight, 25–50 × 5 mm, densely strigose, sometimes white-glaucous. **Seeds** 7–11.

Flowering Mar–Oct (or year-round). Pine rockland-slash pine with a shrub canopy of saw palmetto (*Serenoa repens*), wax myrtle (*Myrica cerifera*), poisonwood (*Metopium toxiferum*), and willow Bustic (*Sideroxylon salicifolium*) over outcropping oolitic limestone; of conservation concern; 0–10 m; Fla.

Galactia smallii is endemic to rocky habitats in Miami-Dade County and is recognized by its prostrate habit with stems distally twining, stems and leaves variably spreading-hairy to strigose (antrorse or retrorse), and relatively large flowers, which often appear abundantly after fires. The lectotype (*Small 8633*, NY) has spreading cauline vestiture (though strongly glabrescent and not evident on portions of the stems). Other collections from the Miami-Dade County rocklands essentially identical otherwise in morphology have either spreading hairs or retrorse or antrorse hairs, and it appears that all of these plants should be considered as a single population system with variable vestiture. Other species apparently with variable orientation of vestiture are *G. brachypoda*, *G. joselyniae*, *G. microphylla*, and *G. pinetorum*.

Galactia smallii is in the Center for Plant Conservation's National Collection of Endangered Plants.

10. Galactia brachypoda Torrey & A. Gray, Fl. N. Amer. 1: 288. 1838 • Smooth creeping milkpea [E] [F]

Galactia michauxii A. R. Franck; *G. mollis* Michaux unranked *nashii* Vail ex Small

Herbs from elongate, narrowly fusiform to cylindric, woody taproot. **Stems** procumbent, creeping, not rooting at nodes, sometimes weakly twining distally, minutely strigose, hairs retrorsely or antrorsely appressed; some or most internodes, especially proximally, longer than largest leaflet of adjacent node. **Leaflets** 3, blades elliptic to elliptic-lanceolate or broadly lanceolate to oblong-elliptic, sometimes linear-elliptic, (8–)15–45(–60) × (4–)10–25 (–32) mm, ± leathery, veins slightly but distinctly raised on adaxial or both surfaces, apex obtuse to rounded or shallowly retuse, surfaces moderately to densely short-strigose with closely appressed hairs and lighter green but not glaucous abaxially, glabrous or sparsely short-strigose or minutely hirtellous and darker, slightly glossy or not adaxially. **Inflorescences:** flowers usually (3–)5–15(–25), rarely 1 or 2, in pseudoracemes on distal $^{3}/_{4}$ of shorter axes or usually on distal $^{1}/_{5}$–$^{1}/_{4}$ of longer axes, often fasciculate distally; axis (5–)20–80 (–150) mm. **Flowers:** calyx 5–7 mm, sparsely strigose to glabrate, lobes greenish yellow to tan on inner surface when dry; corolla not persisting after anthesis, lavender or violet to purplish, bright pink, or pinkish, lighter when dry, 11–15 mm. **Legumes** straight, (25–)30–60 × 4–5(–6) mm, densely strigose to strigose-sericeous, glabrescent. **Seeds** (3–)5–8(–12).

Flowering (Mar–)Apr–Sep. Sand pine-slash pine, white sand scrub, oak and pine-oak scrub, turkey oak woodlands, longleaf pine savannas, pine flatwoods, oak-hickory woods, pine-oak margins, xeric hammocks, low dunes, sandhills and ridges, sandy fields, roadsides, swamp margins, ditches, canal and river banks, river terraces, vacant lots, disturbed sites; 0–100 m; Ala., D.C., Fla., Ga., Md., N.J., N.C., S.C., Va.

Galactia brachypoda is a coastal plain species that ranges from Maryland and Virginia to Alabama. The species is characterized by its essentially prostrate habit, mostly non-twining, short-strigose (antrorse or retrorse) stems (sometimes weakly twining distally), subcoriaceous leaflets with raised venation, and relatively large corollas. Plants of *G. brachypoda* with distally twining stems and relatively small leaves might be mistaken for *G. regularis*; the latter has climbing and consistently twining stems with looser and non-appressed vestiture, thinner leaves, and longer inflorescences with curved axes and smaller, less congested flowers.

W. H. Duncan (1979b) mapped three morphogeographic entities of *Galactia brachypoda*, emphasizing stem vestiture; the widespread entity has appressed-retrorse hairs, while the other two have appressed-antrorse hairs. There appears to be no other difference that would consistently distinguish among these population systems and thus all are identified here as *G. brachypoda*. Analogous, alternate orientation of cauline vestiture occurs in *G. joselyniae*, *G. microphylla*, *G. pinetorum*, and *G. smallii* (G. L. Nesom 2015).

Many plants having antrorse hairs are encountered in Georgia, South Carolina, and southeastern North Carolina; these have narrower leaflets than elsewhere in the range.

11. Galactia minor W. H. Duncan, Phytologia 37: 59. 1977 • Duncan's milkpea [E]

Herbs from elongate, cylindric, woody taproot. **Stems** procumbent or trailing, not twining, densely short-strigose, hairs closely antrorse-appressed, hairs 0.1–0.3 mm; internodes usually shorter, sometimes longer, than largest leaflet of adjacent node. **Leaflets** 3, blades elliptic, oblanceolate-elliptic, or oblong-elliptic, (7–)9–25(–30) × (4–)7–10(–18) mm, ± leathery, veins raised on both surfaces, apex rounded to slightly retuse, rarely acute, surfaces sparsely strigose abaxially and lighter colored but not glaucous, glabrous adaxially. **Inflorescences:** flowers solitary and axillary or 2–4 in reduced pseudoracemes; axis (5–)10–20(–35) mm. **Flowers:** calyx 7–10 mm, strigose, lobes greenish yellow to tan on inner surface when dry; corolla not persisting after anthesis, pink, lighter when dry, 11–17 mm. **Legumes** straight, 25–45 × 4–5 mm, strigose. **Seeds** 3–8.

Flowering Jun–Aug(–Oct). Sandhills, sandy ridges, roadsides, pine flats, pine-scrub oak, turkey oak, longleaf pine woodlands; 0–100 m; Ala., Fla., Ga., Miss., N.C., S.C.

Galactia minor is known from the Florida panhandle and southern Mississippi and from scattered counties in the other named states.

Galactia minor is distinguished by procumbent, antrorsely strigulose stems, relatively small, congested leaves with glabrous adaxial surfaces and raised venation, few flowers on a short inflorescence axis, and relatively large corollas.

12. Galactia texana (Scheele) A. Gray, Boston J. Nat. Hist. 6: 170. 1850 • Texas milkpea

Lablab texanus Scheele, Linnaea 21: 467. 1848

Herbs from a slender, elongate, woody taproot. **Stems** climbing-twining, proximally lignescent, hirsute-strigose to strigose, hairs loosely appressed, retrorse. **Leaflets** 3, blades elliptic to broadly elliptic or oblong-elliptic, (15–)20–42 × 10–25(–32) mm, herbaceous, veins raised or not on both surfaces, apex obtuse to rounded or shallowly retuse, surfaces not glaucous, sparsely strigose with closely appressed hairs to softly hirsute with ascending hairs abaxially, glabrous to sparsely strigose adaxially. **Inflorescences:** flowers solitary and axillary or 2–5 in reduced pseudoracemes; axis 1–4(–40) mm. **Flowers:** calyx 6 mm, loosely strigose to hirsute-strigose or hirsute; corolla pink, rose, reddish, or purple-cream, 8–11 mm. **Legumes** falcate, 30–60 × 4–6 mm, sparsely minutely strigulose, hairs closely appressed. **Seeds** (3–)6–10.

Flowering Jun–Jul(–Aug). Oak-juniper, ash-juniper, and oak woodlands, valley and canyon bottoms, roadbanks, gravelly limestone outcrops and slopes, streamsides, terraces, limestone alluvium, rocky clay; 300–1500 m; Tex.; Mexico (Coahuila, Nuevo Léon, Tamaulipas); South America (Argentina).

In Texas, *Galactia texana* is known from east-central counties southwestward to the Big Bend region.

Galactia texana is characterized by its twining stems, relatively short, few-flowered inflorescences, and falcate fruits.

13. Galactia wrightii A. Gray, Smithsonian Contr. Knowl. 3(5): 44. 1852 • Wright's milkpea

Galactia tephrodes A. Gray; *G. wrightii* var. *mollissima* Kearney & Peebles

Herbs from woody taproot. **Stems** procumbent proximally, weakly twining distally, strongly lignescent, densely to sparsely strigose, hairs retrorsely appressed to slightly spreading. **Leaflets** 3, blades oblong-elliptic to elliptic-ovate, 15–48 × 5–18 mm, herbaceous, veins not raised, apex rounded to obtuse or shallowly retuse, surfaces moderately to densely strigose-sericeous and glaucous abaxially, sparsely to densely short-strigose-sericeous with closely appressed hairs to pubescent with soft, spreading-erect hairs, sometimes strigose to glabrous, adaxially. **Inflorescences:** flowers (2–)5–18(–30) in pseudoracemes, usually in fascicles, axis rarely 10 mm and 2- or 3-flowered; axis (10–)35–200(–250) mm. **Flowers:** calyx 5–7 mm, loosely short-strigose to hirsute-pubescent, lobes greenish yellow to tan on inner surface when dry; corolla not persisting after anthesis, pink to purple-rose to lavender, lighter when dry, 11–12 mm. **Legumes** straight, 25–50 × 4–5 mm, moderately to densely strigose to strigose-sericeous. **Seeds** (3–)5–9.

Flowering May–Aug. Grasslands, desert scrub, oak-juniper and oak woodlands, granite crevices, igneous talus, among boulders, gravelly alluvium; 700–1900 m; Ariz., N.Mex., Tex.; Mexico (Chihuahua, Sonora).

Galactia wrightii is characterized by twining stems, mostly oblong-elliptic leaflets with glaucous abaxial surfaces, relatively long inflorescences with numerous flowers and relatively large corollas, and strigose-sericeous fruits. The type of var. *mollissima* is a plant with vestiture more spreading than normal; such variants are scattered through the range in Arizona, as cited by Kearney and Peebles, as well as in Texas.

Plants in southwestern New Mexico and southeastern Arizona (especially the Huachuca Mountains but not the Chiricahua Mountains) tend to have reduced vestiture; the leaves are sometimes completely glabrous. Such plants extend southward in Mexico along the Chihuahua-Sonora border region. Intermediates are numerous, especially in Arizona, and no distinct boundary seems evident. In Texas, *G. wrightii* is known from four counties of the trans-Pecos and Big Bend regions.

14. Galactia joselyniae G. L. Nesom, Phytoneuron 2015-42: 29, figs. 8–12. 2015 • Joselyn's milkpea

Herbs from woody taproot. **Stems** procumbent, sometimes weakly twining distally, herbaceous or proximally lignescent, loosely strigose, hairs antrorse or retrorse. **Leaflets** 3(rarely 5), blades usually broadly oblong-elliptic to suborbiculate, sometimes broadly oblong to broadly oblong-oblanceolate, (9–)11–29(–37) × 6–24(–34) mm, herbaceous, veins strongly raised on abaxial surface but not adaxially, apex rounded to truncate or retuse, surfaces light green to glaucous (beneath vestiture), densely hirsute-strigose to loosely strigose-sericeous, sometimes more densely so along abaxial veins. **Inflorescences:** flowers solitary and axillary or 2–8 in pseudoracemes, not fasciculate; axis (10–)40–130(–150) mm. **Flowers:** calyx 4–5 mm, loosely strigose, lobes greenish yellow to tan on inner surface when dry; corolla not persisting after anthesis, pink to rose-pink, dull blue-purple when dry, 6–8 mm. **Legumes** straight, 25–40 × 4–6 mm, sparsely strigose, hairs filiform. **Seeds** (4 or)5 or 6.

Flowering Jun(–Aug). Gravelly canyon washes, rock cracks, under shrubs (such as *Agave*, *Diospyros*, *Fallugia*, *Porophyllum*, *Viguiera*, *Yucca*); 600–1500 m; Tex.; Mexico (Coahuila).

Galactia joselyniae is similar to *G. wrightii* in its mostly trailing stems and densely hairy leaves but different in its cauline vestiture with hairs either antrorse or retrorse, smaller, broadly oblong to suborbiculate leaves, and smaller and fewer flowers. It is known from Texas populations in Brewster County (Dead Horse Mountains, near the Rio Grande within side drainages of Boquillas Canyon) and Jeff Davis County (Wild Rose Pass) and from one collection in central Coahuila about 300 km south of the Brewster County sites. Plants in Brewster County have loosely strigose stems with antrorse hairs; those in Jeff Davis County and in Coahuila have strigose stems with retrorse hairs.

15. Galactia canescens Bentham, Comm. Legum. Gen., 62. 1837 • Hoary milkpea

Heterocarpaea texana Scheele

Herbs from slender, elongate woody taproot, usually producing filiform rhizomes at nodes, these producing subterranean flowers and 1-seeded fruits. **Stems** procumbent, not twining, proximally lignescent, moderately strigose, hairs loosely appressed, retrorse. **Leaflets** 3, blades broadly oblong to oblong-obovate, oblong-elliptic, or suborbiculate,

11–35(–42) × 8–30(–35) mm, herbaceous, veins not raised, apex rounded to flat or shallowly retuse, surfaces blue-green glaucous and densely strigose abaxially, sparsely strigose adaxially with closely appressed hairs. **Inflorescences:** flowers 5–8 in pseudoracemes; axis 60–120 mm. **Flowers:** calyx 5–8 mm, hirsute to strigose-hirsute; corolla pink to pink-red or light purple, 9–11 mm. **Legumes** straight or slightly curved, 30–50 × 6–9 mm, densely strigose-sericeous. **Seeds** 1–5.

Flowering Apr–Oct. Sandy prairies, dunes, sand mounds, sandy roadsides, disturbed sites, sandy loam, alluvial sands; 0–200 m; Tex.; Mexico (Tamaulipas).

Galactia canescens is characterized by its prostrate, strigose stems rooting at the nodes, slender rhizomes often bearing subterranean flowers and fruits, and broadly oblong to suborbiculate leaflets with glaucous and densely strigose abaxial surfaces. It is found in more than 20 counties in Texas.

16. Galactia erecta (Walter) Vail, Bull. Torrey Bot. Club 22: 502. 1895 • Erect milkpea [E]

Ervum erectum Walter, Fl. Carol., 187. 1788; *Galactia sessiliflora* Torrey & A. Gray

Herbs from a slender, irregularly thickened to nearly moniliform taproot, also commonly producing very slender rhizomes. **Stems** mostly erect, not twining, usually alternately bent at nodes, (10–)20–30(–40) cm, herbaceous, glabrous or glabrate to sparsely strigose, hairs closely appressed, retrorse. **Leaflets** 3, blades oblong or narrowly oblong to narrowly elliptic or oblong-lanceolate, (15–)25–40(–50) × 7–18 mm, leathery, veins closely reticulate (areoles isodiametric) and raised on both surfaces, with a thickened, continuous, marginal vein, apex rounded to obtuse, sometimes retuse, surfaces glabrous. **Inflorescences:** axillary, subsessile fascicles, flowers solitary and axillary or 2–6 in reduced pseudoracemes. **Flowers:** calyx 5–6 mm, short-strigose; corolla pale purple to white, 7–8 mm. **Legumes** straight or falcate, 20–40 × 5–8 mm, densely hirsute. **Seeds** 6–10.

Flowering Apr–Jul. Longleaf pine, longleaf pine-oak scrub, oak scrub, wiregrass-slash pine woodlands, pine flatwoods; 10–150 m; Ala., Fla., Ga., La., Miss., N.C., S.C., Tex.

Galactia erecta is distinct in its erect habit, slender rhizomes, subsessile leaflets, and flowers in axillary-sessile clusters. In Florida, *G. erecta* is restricted to the northern counties, and in Texas it is found only in six eastern counties.

17. Galactia pinetorum Small, Fl. Miami, 93, 200. 1913 • Pineland milkpea [C] [E]

Herbs from a woody, elongate, cylindric to fusiform or obfusiform taproot. **Stems** procumbent, not twining, herbaceous, minutely and sparsely strigulose, hairs usually retrorse, rarely antrorse. **Leaflets** 3, blades linear-oblong or narrowly oblong to narrowly lanceolate, narrowly elliptic-lanceolate, or linear-elliptic, 20–55 × 2–8(–11) mm, leathery, veins prominently raised on both surfaces, apex rounded to obtuse, surfaces glabrate to sparsely strigulose abaxially, sometimes glaucous, glabrous adaxially. **Inflorescences:** flowers solitary and axillary or 2–8(–10) in reduced pseudoracemes, usually on distal ¼–½ of axis; axis 30–150 mm. **Flowers:** calyx 5–9 mm, strigulose, lobes greenish yellow to tan on inner surface when dry; corolla not persisting after anthesis, blue to purple or purplish or pink-purple, lighter when dry, 11–15 mm. **Legumes** straight, 25–50 × 4 mm, densely strigose to strigulose, hairs minute. **Seeds** 5–7.

Flowering year-round. Disturbed sites, among palmettos, dry sands; of conservation concern; 0–30 m; Fla.

Galactia pinetorum is distinctive in its prostrate (non-twining) stems usually with retrorse hairs, very narrow leaflets with raised venation, and relatively large flowers. Stems of Moldenke collections have antrorsely oriented hairs; this variation is analogous to that seen also in *G. brachypoda*, *G. joselyniae*, *G. microphylla*, and *G. smallii*. *Galactia pinetorum* is known only from Brevard, Miami-Dade, and Monroe counties. The other linear-leaflet species of southern Florida, *G. grisebachii*, has twining stems with consistently antrorse hairs, leaflets without prominently raised venation, and smaller flowers.

18. Galactia grisebachii Urban, Symb. Antill. 5: 372. 1908 • Grisebach's milkpea

Galactia stenophylla Urban, Symb. Antill. 2: 313. 1900, not Hooker & Arnott 1833; *Dolichos filiformis* Linnaeus 1759, not *G. filiformis* (Jacquin) Bentham 1837; *G. angustifolia* Kunth var. *retusa* C. Wright ex Grisebach

Herbs from elongate taproot. **Stems** climbing-twining, filiform, herbaceous, sparsely and minutely strigose, hairs antrorse. **Leaflets** 3, blades linear-oblong to narrowly oblong or narrowly elliptic, (10–)15–40 × 2–4(–6) mm, herbaceous, veins not raised, apex rounded to obtuse, surfaces weakly glaucous and sparsely minutely strigose abaxially, sparsely strigose or glabrous adaxially. **Inflorescences:** flowers solitary and axillary or 2–5(–10) in reduced pseudoracemes; axis 10–40(–130) mm. **Flowers:** calyx 5–6 mm, strigose; corolla pink to blue, purple, or lavender, 7–9 mm. **Legumes** straight, (20–)25–45 × 3–5 mm, sparsely strigose. **Seeds** (3–)8–10.

Flowering year-round. Pinelands, pine-palmetto scrublands, hammocks, weedy grasslands, sandy fields, beaches; 0–20 m; Fla.; West Indies.

Galactia grisebachii is characterized by its twining habit, uniformly linear to linear-oblong leaflets sparsely strigose or glabrous adaxially, weakly glaucous and sparsely minutely strigose abaxially, and flowers solitary and axillary or 2–5(–10) in reduced pseudoracemes. In the flora area, this species is known only from Lee, Miami-Dade, and Monroe counties. These plants have previously been identified by the misapplied name *G. parvifolia* A. Richard, a different species (G. L. Nesom 2015).

A. R. Franck (2017) observed that plants matching the lectotype of *Galactia grisebachii* (from Cuba) are restricted to the West Indies and regarded the Florida plants as *G. austrofloridensis* A. R. Franck, distinguishing them by: long inflorescences often exserted beyond the leaves, 1–9 flowers (versus short inflorescences of *G. grisebachii* rarely exserted beyond the leaves, with 1–5 flowers); and conspicuously raised-reticulate venation adaxially (versus leaflets without raised-reticulate venation in *G. grisebachii*). The hypothesis by Franck may prove to be correct, but inflorescence axis length and number of flowers in the Florida plants are variable and overlap with the West Indian plants, and the putative distinction in venation remains to be clearly documented and affirmed.

19. Galactia elliottii Nuttall, Gen. N. Amer. Pl. 2: 117. 1818 • Elliott's milkpea [E]

Galactia elliotii var. *leavenworthii* Torrey & A. Gray

Herbs: taproot slender and fusiform, producing long, white rhizomes that at intervals produce shoots as well as slender, adventitious, fusiform roots. **Stems** procumbent and trailing at least proximally, often climbing-twining distally, strigose, hairs loosely appressed. **Leaflets** (5 or)7(or 9), blades elliptic to oblong-elliptic, oblong-lanceolate, or elliptic-oblanceolate, 17–39 × 6–21 mm, herbaceous, veins not raised, apex obtuse to rounded or shallowly retuse, surfaces lighter abaxially but not glaucous, dark adaxially, sparsely strigose abaxially, sparsely strigose to scabrous adaxially. **Inflorescences:** flowers 3–11, on distal 1/5–1/2 of axis, sometimes in fascicles; axis 50–150 mm. **Flowers:** calyx 7–9 mm, loosely strigose; corolla white, 11–14 mm. **Legumes** straight, 30–45 × 10–14 mm, loosely strigose to strigose-hirsute. **Seeds** 3–7.

Flowering May–Aug. Pine-live oak flats, slash pine and sand pine flats, marshes, marsh edges, peat bogs, ditches, roadsides, spoil areas, marl, sandy peat, white sands; 0–50 m; Fla., Ga., S.C.

Galactia elliottii is distinct in its pinnate leaves (leaflets 5–9) with coriaceous, dark-drying leaflets, broad fruits, and relatively large white flowers clustered distally on the inflorescence axis.

Galactia elliottii is known from scattered areas of Florida plus coastal areas of Georgia and South Carolina.

20. Galactia heterophylla A. Gray, Boston J. Nat. Hist. 6: 171. 1850 • Gray's milkpea

Herbs from a very slender, elongate, woody taproot, also sometimes with rhizomes or rhizome-like caudex branches from root apex. **Stems** procumbent, not twining, densely strigose, hairs closely appressed, retrorse. **Leaflets** 5, blades elliptic or broadly elliptic to elliptic-obovate or oblong-elliptic, 6–24 × 2–12 mm, herbaceous, veins not raised, margins strigose, apex obtuse to rounded or shallowly retuse, surfaces smooth-glaucous abaxially and moderately strigose, hairs closely appressed, usually glabrous adaxially, rarely sparsely strigose. **Inflorescences:** flowers solitary and axillary or 2–5 in reduced pseudoracemes; axis 1–10 mm. **Flowers:** calyx 7–9 mm, short-strigose with closely appressed hairs; corolla pink, deep pink, cerise, rose-purple, lavender, purple, violet-red, 11–15 mm. **Legumes** straight, (20–)30–45 × 5–7 mm, moderately strigose, hairs closely appressed. **Seeds** 3–5.

Flowering (Mar–)Apr–Sep. Blackbrush-cenizo brush, mesquite brush, openings in live oak-thorn scrub, granite slopes, limestone ridges, roadsides, caliche outcrops, sandy prairies, hard-packed sands, sandy silt, sandy clay, gravelly sandy loam; 10–150(–400) m; Tex.; Mexico (Coahuila, Nuevo León, Tamaulipas).

Galactia heterophylla is characterized by its prostrate, non-twining stems and particularly by its five leaflets with glabrous adaxial surfaces. It occurs in about 15 counties in central and south-central Texas.

Galactia grayi Vail is an illegitimate, superfluous name that pertains here.

21. Galactia marginalis Bentham, Comm. Legum. Gen., 62. 1837 • Edible milkpea

Cologania heterophylla Gillies ex Hooker 1833, not *Galactia heterophylla* A. Gray 1850

Herbs from a short, ovoid-fusiform tuber sometimes producing slender rhizomes or rhizomelike caudex branches from apex. **Stems** procumbent, not twining, lignescent, sparsely to moderately short-strigose, hairs retrorse. **Leaflets** 1, blade narrowly elliptic to narrowly lanceolate, 25–85 × 4–10(–16) mm, leathery, veins closely reticulate and strongly raised, thickened marginal vein completely encircling entire margin, apex rounded to obtuse, surfaces not glaucous abaxially, glabrous throughout. **Inflorescences:** flowers solitary, axillary; axis 3–8 mm. **Flowers:** calyx 5–6 mm, short-strigose; corolla pink to purple, purple-red, or deep lavender, 13–15 mm. **Legumes** straight, 25–35 × 5–7 mm, short-strigose, hairs closely appressed. **Seeds** (5–)7–9.

Flowering (Feb–)Apr–Oct. Oak-juniper woodlands, blackjack-post oak woods, coastal prairies, sands, sandy loam, gravelly hillsides, ditch banks; 0–200 m; Tex.; Mexico (Coahuila, Tamaulipas); South America (Argentina, Brazil, Paraguay, Uruguay).

Galactia marginalis is characterized by prostrate stems, glabrous, 1-foliolate leaves with closely reticulate, raised venation and a completely encircling marginal vein, and relatively large, solitary, axillary flowers. The species is known from at least 14 counties, mostly on the Coastal Plain of southeastern Texas.

A. Burkart (1971) described *Galactia marginalis* var. *columbiana* Burkart based on a specimen from Cundinamarca, Colombia, that was thought to represent an intermediary between the population of *G. marginalis* in southeastern Texas and in southern South America. The Colombia collection has subsequently been identified as *G. glaucescens* Kunth.

84. LACKEYA Fortunato, L. P. Queiroz & G. P. Lewis, Kew Bull. 51: 365, fig. 1. 1996 • Drift seeds, clusterpeas [For James Andrew Lackey, b. 1948, American botanist and researcher of Fabaceae] E

Brian R. Keener

Lianas, to 5 m, woody, unarmed. **Stems** twining or clambering, pubescent. **Leaves** alternate, odd-pinnate; stipules present, caducous, 2.5–3 mm; petiolate; leaflets 3, stipels present, caducous, blades 50–130 mm, margins entire, apex obtuse or abruptly acuminate to mucronate, surfaces pubescent. **Inflorescences** 3–60-flowered, axillary, pseudoracemes, flowers fasciculate on tubercles of rachis; bracts present, caducous; bracteoles caducous, paired proximal to calyx. **Flowers** papilionaceous; calyx campanulate, 5.5–7.5 mm, lobes 4; corolla pink, magenta, and white, 11–14 mm, striate, glabrous; stamens 10, pseudomonadelphous; anthers basifixed, dehiscing longitudinally; ovary pubescent; style glabrous; stigma terminal. **Fruits** legumes, sessile, brown, compressed, narrowly elliptic to oblong, flanged or narrowly winged on ventral suture, indehiscent, sparsely pubescent. **Seeds** 2–5, reddish brown, globose, 4–9 mm; hilum lateral, oblong. $x = 11$.

Species 1: sc, se United States.

Lackeya is closely allied with *Dioclea* Kunth and *Galactia* and has been treated historically by different authors as part of one or the other (C. T. Mohr 1901; R. H. Maxwell 1979). The woody stem habit and caducous stipules of *Lackeya* can be used to distinguish it from climbing members of *Galactia*, which have herbaceous stems and persistent stipules. Within *Dioclea*, species of sect. *Macrocarpon* Amshoff are more closely aligned morphologically with *Lackeya*. These species of *Dioclea* have larger, strongly compressed fruits with a woody pericarp, which differ from the smaller, less compressed fruit with a herbaceous pericarp found in *Lackeya*. *Dioclea* is more tropically distributed; its range does not overlap with that of *Lackeya* (R. H. Fortunato et al. 1996).

1. Lackeya multiflora (Torrey & A. Gray) Fortunato, L. P. Queiroz & G. P. Lewis, Kew Bull. 51: 366. 1996 • Boykin's clusterpea E F

Dolichos multiflorus Torrey & A. Gray, Fl. N. Amer. 1: 281. 1838; *Dioclea multiflora* (Torrey & A. Gray) C. Mohr; *Galactia mohlenbrockii* R. H. Maxwell

Lianas to 5 m, herbage pubescent. **Stems** sulcate to striate, hairs appressed. **Leaves:** stipules lanceolate, 2.5–3 × 0.7–1 mm, apex acute; petiole 3–15 cm; rachis 1.5–4.5 cm; stipels awl-shaped, 1.5–2 × 0.2–0.3 mm; petiolules 2–7 mm, densely pubescent; leaflet blades ovate to ovate-orbiculate, 50–130 × 40–120 mm, membranous, base truncate, rounded, or cuneate, surfaces sparsely pubescent abaxially, pubescent adaxially, with denser pubescence along veins. **Peduncles** 3.5–15 cm, pubescent. **Inflorescences:** bracts lanceolate, 1.8–2 × 0.5–1 mm, apex acute; bracteoles ovate, 0.8–1 × 0.5 mm, apex acute. **Pedicels** 1–2 mm, densely pubescent. **Flowers:** calyx puberulent, tube 3–3.5 mm, abaxial lobe 3–3.5 × 1.3–1.5 mm, acuminate, lateral lobes deltate, 2–2.5 × 1.8–2.1 mm, adaxial lobe 2.8–3.2 × 2.9–3.3 mm, obtuse, apiculate, or 2-fid; corolla banner magenta with lighter striations, wings pink, keel whitish. **Legumes** 3–7 × 1–1.8 cm, base acuminate to acute, apex beaked, bent abaxially, acuminate. **Seeds:** hilum 2.5–3 mm.

Flowering late spring–summer. Woods along rivers and creeks, alluvial soils; 20–500 m; Ala., Ark., Ga., Ky., La., Miss., S.C., Tenn., Tex.

No correctly identified Florida specimens of *Lackeya multiflora* were located. The name *Dioclea boykinii* A. Gray ex S. Watson, which pertains here, is superfluous and illegitimate.

85. CLITORIA Linnaeus, Sp. Pl. 2: 753. 1753; Gen. Pl. ed. 5, 334. 1754 • Butterfly-pea, pigeon-wing [Greek *kleitoris*, female genitalia, alluding to fancied resemblance of closed flowers]

Paul R. Fantz

Martiusia Schultes

Subshrubs [lianas, trees], unarmed; rhizomes (xylopodia) woody, subterranean, erect or horizontal, with slender, distal portion tapering deeply underground. **Stems** erect or distally lax and twining or trailing [scandent], uncinate-pubescent. **Leaves** alternate, odd-pinnate; stipules present, persistent, striate; petiolate; leaflets 3–7, stipels striate, blade margins entire, surfaces glabrous or pubescent. **Inflorescences** 1 or 2(–4)-flowered, axillary, pseudoracemes, erect to lax, flowers chasmogamous, sometimes also cleistogamous; bracts present, persistent; bracteoles persistent or tardily deciduous, appressed to calyx, rarely enlarged and obscuring calyx. **Pedicels** paired, borne laterally at apex, spirally twisted to invert flowers. **Flowers** usually papilionaceous, actinomorphic in *C. ternatea* var. *pleniflora*; chasmogamous flowers resupinate, rarely all petals subequal, bannerlike, 35–60 mm; cleistogamous flowers apetalous, banner rarely hidden within calyx, reduced, inconspicuous except in fruit; calyx persistent, funnelform, lobes 5, adaxial 2 subconnate, 4 wider, often shorter than abaxial lobe, shorter than tube; corolla lilac, blue, purplish, or blue-violaceous, sometimes with white to yellow medial strip [white with purplish venation on banner]; banner conduplicate, short-clawed, spurless, obovate-orbiculate, 40–60 mm, much larger than other petals, arising from lower side of resupinate flower, emarginate; wings slightly adherent to keel, long-clawed, falcate-oblong or spatulate, shorter than banner and extending beyond keel, base without auricles; keel incurved, long-clawed; stamens 10, diadelphous, usually distinct apically, rarely ± distinct and some in bundles; anthers dorsifixed; ovary stipitate; style elongated, flattened, base persistent as beak in fruit, apex dilated and geniculate distally, bearded lengthwise. **Fruits** legumes, stipitate to subsessile, straight to subfalcate, convex and depressed between seeds or flat, linear, 6–11 mm wide, dehiscent by valves breaking from replum, spirally twisting to expel seeds, leathery, margins thickened, apex beaked, uncinate-pubescent. **Seeds** 1–10[–12], cuboidal, globose, or subreniform [reniform]. x = 8, (12).

Species ca. 60 (3 in the flora): United States, Mexico, West Indies, Central America, South America, Asia, Africa, Pacific Islands, Australia.

Species of *Clitoria* are usually associated with sandy soils. Fruits and seeds are variable; floral traits are consistent.

Clitoria is divided into three subgenera and eight sections; the introduced species in the flora area belongs to subg. *Clitoria*, and the two native species belong to subg. *Neurocarpum* (Desvaux) Baker sect. *Mexicana* Fantz.

Cleistogamy has been reported for species of *Clitoria* only recently. Cleistogamous flowers are inconspicuous. In the flora area, chasmogamous flowers occur predominately from May to mid July (to September); cleistogamous flowers occur from mid July onward. Both flower forms occur on the same plant. Inflorescences with both chasmogamous and cleistogamous flowers are rare.

Clitoria and *Centrosema* have resupinate, papilionaceous flowers. Historically, the similarity in appearance has resulted in frequent misidentifications. Both genera have microuncinate or uncinate hairs (viewed at 20–30×) on their vegetative and reproductive structures. Suffrutescent members have aerial stems arising seasonally from a subterranean woody rhizome (xylopodium) that is seldom collected. The proximal portion of the xylopodium is thickened and scarred with nodes of prior aerial stems. Extending from this is an elongated, narrow, distal portion that extends laterally away from the aerial plant, which extends deeper into the ground, and breaks easily as one attempts to collect it. *Centrosema* is distinguished by campanulate calyces, U-curved styles, corollas V-shaped basally, wings subequal to keels, and fruits flat, each with a raised costa near each margin.

Some species of *Clitoria* are tropical agronomic crops and medicinal plants and are useful for pesticidal properties, fish poisons, and natural dyes. Some species are valued as cultivated ornamentals, including the three species treated here plus *C. biflora* Dalzell, *C. brachystegia* Bentham, *C. fairchildiana* R. A. Howard, *C. heterophylla* Lamarck, and *C. laurifolia* Poiret (P. R. Fantz 1991).

Nauchea Descourtilz, *Ternatea* Miller, and *Vexillaria* Eaton are illegitimate names that pertain here.

SELECTED REFERENCES Fantz, P. R. 1991. Ethnobotany of *Clitoria* (Leguminosae). Econ. Bot. 45: 511–520. Fantz, P. R. 1993. Revision of cultivated *Centrosema* and *Clitoria* in the United States. HortScience 28: 674–676.

1. Leaflets 5 or 7; petioles 1–4 cm; rachis 2–7 cm; legumes subsessile, flat, yellowish green to green becoming light brownish to tan; seeds not viscid; bracteoles broadly ovate to suborbiculate; cleistogamous flowers absent . . . . . 3. *Clitoria ternatea*
1. Leaflets 3; petioles 1.5–10 cm; rachis 0.7–2(–2.5) cm; legumes stipitate, convex, brown; seeds viscid; bracteoles (of chasmogamous flowers) linear-lanceolate or lanceolate to lanceolate-ovate; cleistogamous flowers present.
    2. Calyx tubes 7–10 mm, purplish tinged near base; leaflet blades linear, linear-lanceolate to oblong-lanceolate or, sometimes, proximal ones narrowly elliptic, 5–15 mm wide, primary lateral veins 6–8 pairs; stipules 2–4 mm; stipels 1–3 mm; legume stipes 15–21 mm; cleistogamous flowers: bracteoles 2(–3) mm, calyx tube 3–4 mm, legume stipe 9–14 mm; s Florida . . . . . 1. *Clitoria fragrans*
    2. Calyx tubes 10–14 mm, greenish; leaflet blades ovate, oblong-ovate, elliptic-oblong, lanceolate, lanceolate-ovate, oblong, or elliptic, 10–40(–65) mm wide, primary lateral veins 7–12 pairs; stipules 4–8 mm; stipels 3–8 mm; legume stipes 12–17 mm; cleistogamous flowers: bracteoles 3–5 mm, calyx tube 4–5 mm, legume stipe 5–10 mm; e, se United States to e Texas, se Arizona. . . . . . 2. *Clitoria mariana*

1. Clitoria fragrans Small, Torreya 26: 57. 1926 [C] [E]

Martiusia fragrans (Small) Small

Xylopodium: proximal portion horizontal, cylindric, 5–15 × 0.4–1 cm, ligneous; distal portion 2+ m × 2–5 mm, bearing rootlets. **Stems** 1–4 from crown, erect, purplish, 15–50 cm; internodes nearly straight proximally, weak to moderately zigzag distally; branches few, mostly basal; branchlets glaucous. **Leaves:** stipules ovate to lanceolate-ovate, 2–4 × 1–2 mm, apex acute; petiole purplish, wiry, angular, ± canaliculate adaxially, 1.5–3(–3.5) cm, glaucescent; stipels linear to subulate, 1–3 mm; petiolules 2 mm; rachis 0.7–1.5 cm; leaflets 3, blades linear, linear-lanceolate to oblong-lanceolate, or (proximal) narrowly elliptic, 20–45 × 5–15 mm, thickly membranous to ± leathery, base rounded, primary lateral veins 6–8 pairs, apex obtuse to retuse and mucronate, surfaces glaucous, glabrous abaxially, pubescent adaxially. **Peduncles** 0.5–4 cm (chasmogamous flowers) or 0.4–0.8 cm (cleistogamous flowers). **Inflorescences** 1 or 2(–4)-flowered, to 4 cm, flowers cleistogamous and/or chasmogamous; bracts linear-lanceolate, 2–5 × 1 mm. **Pedicels** 2–7 mm; bracteoles of chasmogamous flowers linear-lanceolate, (3–)4–5 × 1 mm, cleistogamous flowers 2(–3) mm, apex acute, uncinate-pubescent. **Chasmogamous flowers:** calyx tube purplish tinged near base, 7–10 × 2–3 mm at base becoming 5–6 mm wide; lobes ovate, 5–6 × 2–2.5 mm (at base, abaxial lobe 6–8 mm), apex gradually narrowed to short-acuminate; corolla lilac; banner 35–45 mm, claw 4–5 mm; wing blades 21–24 × 4–6 mm, claw 13–15 mm; keel 8–11 × 3–5 mm, claw 14–17 mm; staminal tube 17–22 mm; filaments distinct, 1–3 mm; anthers lanceolate, 1.2–1.5 mm; ovary 6–7 mm, densely uncinate-pubescent; style 13–17 mm. **Cleistogamous flowers:** calyx tube 3–4 × 1 mm at base becoming 1.5(–2) mm wide; lobes 1.5–3 mm; staminal tube 0.1 mm; ovary 4 mm; style 5–6 mm, bent backwards and in contact with anthers. **Legumes** brown, convex, conspicuously depressed between seeds, 30–55 × 6–8 mm; stipe 15–21 mm (9–14 mm in cleistogamous). **Seeds** 2–5(–8), reddish brown, cuboidal, 4 × 4–5 mm, viscid. $2n = 16$.

Flowering and fruiting (chasmogamous) May–Jun; (cleistogamous) May–Sep. Scrub and secondary regrowth, sandy soils with humus layer, open areas in bare, sandy soils; of conservation concern; 0–30 m; Fla.

Clitoria fragrans is known from central Florida, primarily in Highlands and Polk counties. Plants are found infrequently in bare sand in open, sunny areas, commonly bearing cleistogamous flowers. Denser populations occur in scrub and secondary regrowth on sandy soils with a humus layer. Native habitats for this species are being destroyed.

Individual plants of *Clitoria fragrans* are more robust in partial shade, and chasmogamous flowers are more frequent. The erect, aerial stems usually die back each year. The flowers are faintly fragrant, not pungently sweet as the name implies.

2. Clitoria mariana Linnaeus, Sp. Pl. 2: 753. 1753 [F]

Martiusia mariana (Linnaeus) Small

Xylopodium: proximal portion horizontal, cylindric, 4–15 × 3–12 cm; distal portion 1+ m × 1.5–6 mm. **Stems** 1–4 from crown, trailing, to 150 cm, or erect to lax, apex sometimes twining, to 60 cm; internodes ± straight to weakly flexuous; branches few, primarily basal. **Leaves:** stipules lanceolate to lanceolate-ovate, 4–8 × 2–5 mm, apex acute; petiole subterete, often weakly to strongly canaliculate adaxially, 2–10 cm; stipels linear to subulate, 3–8 mm; petiolules 2–4 mm; rachis 1–2(–2.5) cm; leaflets 3, blades ovate, oblong-ovate, elliptic-oblong, lanceolate, lanceolate-ovate, oblong, or elliptic, 20–90(–115) × 10–40(–65) mm, thick membranous to thick papery, base broadly cuneate to subcordate, primary lateral veins 7–12 pairs, apex usually acute to obtuse, rarely short-acuminate or mucronate, surfaces glaucescent, glabrate or sparsely pubescent abaxially on major veins or moderately to densely piloso-sericeous, glabrate or uncinate-pubescent adaxially. **Peduncles** 1–4.5 cm (chasmogamous flowers) or 0.5–3 cm (cleistogamous flowers). **Inflorescences** 2(–4)-flowered, 1–5 cm, flowers cleistogamous and/or chasmogamous; bracts lanceolate, 3–4 × 1 mm. **Pedicels** 3–7 mm; bracteoles of chasmogamous flowers lanceolate to lanceolate-ovate, 4–9 × 2–3 mm, cleistogamous flowers 3–5 mm, apex acute, uncinate-pubescent. **Chasmogamous flowers:** calyx tube greenish, 10–14 × 3–5 mm at base becoming 5–8 mm wide; lobes ovate, 5–9 × 2.5–3.5 mm (at base, abaxial lobe 7–9 mm), apex short-acuminate; corolla blue to pale purplish; banner 40–60 mm, claw 5–8 mm; wing blades 21–24 × 5–10 mm, claw 7–12 mm; keel 8–13 × 3–5 mm, claw 14–21 mm; staminal tube 21–30 mm; filaments distinct, 2–4 mm; anthers lanceolate, 1–2 mm; ovary 7–9 mm, densely uncinate-pubescent; style 16–20 mm. **Cleistogamous flowers:** calyx tube 4–5 × 1–2 mm becoming 2 mm wide; lobes 2–3 mm; staminal tube 0.1 mm; ovary 5–6 mm; style 4–6 mm, bent backwards and in contact with anthers. **Legumes** brown, convex, 25–55(–70) × 6–9 mm; stipe 12–17 mm (5–10 mm in cleistogamous). **Seeds** 1–10, black, cuboidal to globular, 3–5 × 4–6 mm, viscid.

Varieties 3 (2 in the flora): se United States, n Mexico, Asia.

Variety *orientalis* Fantz occurs in China, eastern India, Myanmar (Burma), and Thailand. It is characterized as a vine with inflorescences bearing two to six slightly smaller flowers than those in the flora area and without cleistogamous flowers.

Clitoria mariana is cultivated for its showy chasmogamous flowers. Plants in the wild grow as isolated individuals or in clusters.

Historically, *Clitoria mariana* has been misidentified as *Centrosema virginianum*, which is distinguished as a vine with a campanulate calyx bearing lobes that are narrow and longer than the tube, bracteoles that nearly hide the calyx, a spurred banner, wings subequal in length to the keel, and flat fruits with two marginal veins.

1. Leaflet blades sparsely pubescent or glabrate abaxially, hairs scattered or confined to major veins; calyces glabrate, macrotrichomes sparse, scattered . . . . 2a. *Clitoria mariana* var. *mariana*
1. Leaflet blades moderately to densely pilose-sericeous abaxially, hairs suberect to erect, not widely scattered or confined to veins; calyces uncinate-pubescent or glabrate, macrotrichomes moderately dense to scattered . . . . 2b. *Clitoria mariana* var. *pubescentia*

2a. Clitoria mariana Linnaeus var. **mariana** [F]

Leaflet blades: abaxial surface sparsely pubescent or glabrate, macrotrichomes inconspicuous (0.3–1 mm), scattered and confined to major veins, adaxial surface glabrate, trichomes scattered, inconspicuous, microuncinate, macrotrichomes absent. **Calyces** glabrate, macrotrichomes sparse, scattered. **2*n*** = 16.

Flowering (chasmogamous) May–Jul(–Sep), (cleistogamous) mid Jul–Nov; fruiting (chasmogamous) (May–)Jun–Nov, (cleistogamous) mid Jul–Nov. Dry sandy soils, gravelly or rocky soils, open areas of pine, pine-oak, oak-hickory associations, bluff outcrops; 0–1900 m; Ala., Ariz., Ark., Del., D.C., Fla., Ga., Ill., Ind., Kans., Ky., La., Md., Miss., Mo., N.J., N.Y., N.C., Ohio, Okla., Pa., S.C., Tenn., Tex., Va., W.Va.; Mexico (Nuevo León).

Reports of var. *mariana* from Iowa, Minnesota, Nebraska, and Wisconsin are based on misidentifications.

2b. Clitoria mariana Linnaeus var. **pubescentia** Fantz, Sida 16: 727. 1995 [E]

Leaflet blades: abaxial surface moderately to densely piloso-sericeous, macrotrichomes conspicuous, not widely scattered or confined to veins, adaxial surface glabrate, trichomes inconspicuous, microuncinate, whitish macrotrichomes, trichomes scattered, falcate to subappressed, 0.3–1 mm. **Calyces** uncinate-pubescent or glabrate, macrotrichomes moderately dense to scattered. **2*n*** = 16.

Flowering (chasmogamous) May–Jul(–Sep), (cleistogamous) mid Jul–Nov; fruiting (chasmogamous) (May–)Jun–Nov, (cleistogamous) mid Jul–Nov. Dry, sandy soils in open areas of pine, pine-oak, oak-hickory associations; 0–100 m; Fla.

Variety *pubescentia* is known from central and southern Florida. The variety is commonly found south of an imaginary line drawn across north-central Florida (Cedar Key to Ponte Verda Beach).

3. Clitoria ternatea Linnaeus, Sp. Pl. 2: 753. 1753
• Blue pea, conchitas, zapatico de la reina [I]

Xylopodium: proximal portion erect, cylindric, 6–15 × 0.9–1.5 cm; distal portion 0.3+ m × 3–6 mm. **Stems** 1–6 from crown, trailing and intertwining to form tangled mats or climbing, terete, weakly striate, 500 cm; internodes ± straight to weakly flexuous, distal internodes nodding; branches mostly proximal, sometimes distal. **Leaves:** stipules linear, 4–10 × 0.5–1 mm, apex acuminate; petiole subangular, canaliculate adaxially, 1–4 cm; stipels linear, 1–3 mm; petiolules 1–3 mm; rachis canaliculate adaxially, 2–7 cm; leaflets 5 or 7, blades polymorphic, ovate, elliptic, obovate- or ovate-elliptic, or oblong, 10–50(–70) × (4–)10–30 mm, membranous, base cuneate to rounded, primary lateral veins 5 or 6 pairs, apex acute to obtuse or retuse, surfaces glabrate. **Peduncles** 0.3–1.5 cm. **Inflorescences** 1(or 2)-flowered, 0.5–1 cm, flowers chasmogamous; bracts ovate to lanceolate, 2–4(–5) × 1 mm. **Pedicels** 3–6 mm; bracteoles deciduous by fructification, broadly ovate to suborbiculate, conspicuous, shorter than calyx tube or subequaling and obscuring calyx, (4–)6–11(–15) × (4–)6–11(–15) mm, apex acute to rounded, apiculate, glabrous. **Papilionaceous flowers:** calyx tube greenish, 8–14 × 3–4 mm near base becoming 6–9(–11) mm wide, shrinking slightly in fruit; lobes oblong, 7–12 × 3 mm, apex acute; corolla pale blue to azure or blue-violaceous with white to yellow medial strip, or white with greenish white medial strip; banner 40–55 mm, claw 2–4 mm; wing blades 17–28 × 7–13 mm, claw 7–11 mm; keel 7–10 × 4–6 mm, claw 14–18 mm; staminal tube 16–20 mm; filaments distinct, 3–4 mm; anthers lanceolate, 1–1.5 mm; ovary 6–9 mm, densely white-strigose; style 14–17 mm, geniculate 5–8 mm from distal end. **Actinomorphic flowers** ("double"): calyx similar to papilionaceous flowers; corolla azure to dark blue, petals bannerlike; stamens usually diadelphous or distinct, sometimes with fused bundles of 2–5; ovary 6–9 mm, densely white-strigose; style 14–17 mm. **Legumes** yellowish green to green becoming light brownish to tan, flat, (50–)70–110 × 8–11 mm; stipe 1–2 mm, enclosed within calyx with base of valves. **Seeds** 7–10, brown becoming black, subreniform, compressed, 4–5 × 5–6 mm, not viscid.

Varieties 3 (2 in the flora): introduced; Africa; introduced also in West Indies, Central America, South America, Asia, Pacific Islands, Australia.

Variety *angustifolia* Hochstetter ex Baker f. is distinguished by having white petals and narrow leaflet blades; it is native to eastern Africa from Mozambique northward.

Clitoria ternatea is anthropogenic; it is cultivated and naturalized pantropically. The species is used medicinally for treating human ailments, as a dye, in treatment of scorpion stings and venomous snakebites, as a forage crop, and as an ornamental vine. It is cultivated in the United States outdoors as an annual or under glass as a perennial. This species is a profuse bloomer and seed producer, blooming year-round in tropical areas.

1. Flowers papilionaceous, with 1 bannerlike petal; stamens diadelphous . . . . 3a. *Clitoria ternatea* var. *ternatea*
1. Flowers actinomorphic, with 5 bannerlike petals; stamens distinct or connate in bundles of 2–5 . . . . 3b. *Clitoria ternatea* var. *pleniflora*

3a. Clitoria ternatea Linnaeus var. **ternatea** [I]

Flowers papilionaceous; calyx tube 6–9 mm wide at throat; bannerlike petals 1; stamens diadelphous, adaxial stamen connate basally, distinct most of its length. **2*n*** = 16.

Flowering Mar–Nov (year-round). Sandy soils; 0–200 m; introduced; Fla., Tex.; Africa; introduced also in Central America.

A population of var. *ternatea* is naturalized in the Florida Keys. Plants in supposedly wild populations in eastern Texas probably do not survive the winter. Reports of var. *ternatea* from California and Georgia are likely based on misidentifications. A form with white petals is common in Africa and introduced elsewhere.

3b. Clitoria ternatea Linnaeus var. **pleniflora** Fantz, Moscosoa 6: 164. 1990 [I]

Flowers actinomorphic; calyx tube 6–11 mm wide at throat, sometimes splitting longitudinally; bannerlike petals 5; stamens usually distinct, sometimes connate in bundles of 2–5. **2*n*** = 16.

Flowering May–Nov (year-round). Sandy soils; 0–50 m; introduced; Fla.; Africa; introduced also in West Indies, South America, Asia (India), Pacific Islands (Fiji, Java, Philippines).

Variety *pleniflora* is probably of garden origin; it is currently naturalized pantropically. Botanists not familiar with this variety often file vouchers in herbaria as unidentified caesalpinoid legumes or as unidentified taxa of Convolvulaceae. The variety is prized as an ornamental, blue-flowering vine. A form with white petals has been vouchered from Cuba and Thailand. Some early collections of var. *pleniflora* (*Anonymous* [undated], S; *Anonymous* in 1812, W) may possibly be from outside of cultivation; more recent specimens are more likely from cultivation.

86. CENTROSEMA (de Candolle) Bentham, Comm. Legum. Gen., 53. 1837, name conserved • Butterfly-pea, spurred butterfly-pea [Greek *kentron*, point, and *sema*, sign, alluding to spur of banner]

Paul R. Fantz

Clitoria Linnaeus sect. *Centrosema* de Candolle in A. P. de Candolle and A. L. P. P. de Candolle, Prodr. 2: 234. 1825; *Bradburya* Rafinesque, name rejected

Herbs, perennial, suffrutescent, [shrubs, lianas], unarmed; rhizomes (xylopodia) horizontal, lignose. **Stems** trailing to scandent and twining, wiry, pubescent, hairs microuncinate. **Leaves** alternate, odd-pinnate; stipules present, persistent, striate; petiolate; leaflets 3, blade margins entire, surfaces glabrate abaxially, uncinulate-hairy adaxially. **Inflorescences** 1 or 2(–4)-flowered, axillary, pseudoracemes; bracts present, persistent; bracteoles deciduous in fruit, appressed to calyx, often obscuring calyx tube and distal and lateral lobes. **Pedicels** paired, borne laterally at peduncle apex, spirally twisted to invert flowers. **Flowers** papilionaceous, resupinate, showy; calyx campanulate, lobes 5, equal to or longer than tube, 2 abaxial lobes connate, adaxial lobe conspicuous, often extending between bracteoles; corolla lavender, pinkish lavender, bluish violet, or purple, 20–35(–40) mm, banner conduplicate, spurred or gibbous, distal to claw, obovate-orbiculate, emarginate, with medial white stripe on adaxial surface; wings slightly adherent to keel, falcate-obovate, with auricles distal to claw, subequal to keel; keel incurved, adaxial margin broadly U-shaped; stamens 10, diadelphous, distinct apically; anthers dorsifixed or basifixed, uniform; style strongly incurved, broadly U-shaped, flattened, base persistent as beak in fruit, ± dilated apically, barbellate near apex. **Fruits** legumes, sessile, green, straight, compressed, flat with raised rib near margin, linear, 3–6 mm wide, dehiscent by valves breaking from replum and spirally twisting to expel seeds, glabrate. **Seeds** 8–18, reniform, smooth. $x = 10$.

Species ca. 35 (2 in the flora): c, e, s United States, Mexico, West Indies, Central America, South America; introduced in paleotropics.

Centrosema is a woody genus of shrubs, lianas, and suffrutescent herbs with scandent aerial stems. It has become an important agronomic crop in the past several decades, with germplasm being spread throughout the paleotropics. *Centrosema molle* Martius ex Bentham (reported as *C. pubescens* Bentham), *C. plumieri* (Turpin ex Persoon) Bentham, and *C. sagittatum* (Humboldt & Bonpland ex Willdenow) Brandegee are reported in references and on the internet as native to Florida. All vouchers are from cultivated specimens; those taxa are excluded here. A specimen of *C. sagittatum* collected by Erdman West (FLAS, 61296, "Alachua Co. seeds collected winter 1949–1950, collected in hammock near Newman's Lake on Oct 1950") has been cited as documentation for being native in Florida; the plant was introduced from Mexico and grown in a cultivated legume plot.

Centrosema and *Clitoria* are unique legumes with relatively large, resupinate flowers. Both genera have microuncinate hairs (viewed at 20–30×) on their vegetative and reproductive structures. Both have aerial stems arising seasonally from a subterranean xylopodium that often is not collected. The proximal portion of the xylopodium is thickened, lignose, and scarred with bases of prior aerial stems. Extending from this is an elongated, narrow, distal portion that extends laterally away from the aerial plant and deeper into the ground, easily breaking apart as one attempts to collect it, leaving much in the ground. Historically, the similar appearances of *Centrosema* and *Clitoria* have resulted in misidentifications. *Clitoria* is distinguished easily by the funnelform calyx, geniculate styles, U-shaped corollas, wings extending beyond the keel, and, in the flora area, turgid fruits that are depressed between the seeds, or flat and ecostate.

SELECTED REFERENCES Fantz, P. R. 1993. Revision of cultivated *Centrosema* and *Clitoria* in the United States. HortScience 28: 674–676. Fantz, P. R. 2002. Distribution of *Centrosema* (Leguminosae: Phaseoleae: Clitoriinae) for the Flora of North America Project. Vulpia 1: 41–81. Schultz-Kraft, R. and R. J. Clements. 1990. *Centrosema*: Biology, Agronomy, and Utilization. Cali.

1. Calyx lobes unequal; inflorescence bracteoles 8–10 mm; stipules and stipels 1–2 mm; pedicels 10–14 mm in fruit; legumes 5–6 mm wide . . . . 1. *Centrosema arenicola*
1. Calyx lobes subequal; inflorescence bracteoles 6–8 mm; stipules and stipels 3–5 mm; pedicels 7–11 mm in fruit; legumes 3–5 mm wide . . . . 2. *Centrosema virginianum*

1. Centrosema arenicola (Small) F. J. Hermann, J. Wash. Acad. Sci. 38: 237. 1948 • Pineland butterfly-pea [C] [E]

Bradburya arenicola Small, Fl. S.E. U.S., 651, 1332. 1903; *B. floridana* Britton; *Centrosema floridanum* (Britton) Lakela

Rhizomes 4–6 cm × 5–10 mm proximally, to 20+ cm × 1–2 mm distally. **Stems** 1–4, 2–3 m × 1–2 mm. **Leaves:** stipules deltate, 1 mm; petiole angular, sulcate adaxially, 1–4 cm; stipels persistent, striate, linear to subulate, 1–2 mm; petiolules 1.5–2 mm; rachis 0.5–1.5 cm; leaflet blades elliptic or elliptic-lanceolate to lanceolate, 15–55 × 8–25 mm, leathery, base rotund to truncate, primary lateral veins 5–7 pairs, apex broadly acute. **Inflorescences** 1 per node, 3–8 cm; bracts striate, concave around pedicel, elliptic-ovate, 4–6 mm; bracteoles striate, lanceolate-ovate, 8–10 × 4–5 mm, adaxial surface with uncinulate hairs; rachis flexuous, 1–1.5 cm, strigose. **Pedicels** 5–8 mm, 10–14 mm in fruit, thinly pilose. **Flowers:** calyx tube 3–4 × 5–7 mm, lobes unequal, abaxial and lateral ones 4–6 mm, adaxial one 8–11 mm, hairs uncinulate; corolla lavender to pinkish lavender; banner 20–30 mm, claw 5–6 mm, spur 2 mm; wings 20–24 × 4 mm, claw 5–6 mm; keel 20–25 × 10–11 mm, claw 4–5 mm; staminal tube 32–34 mm; apical distinct filaments 3–4 mm; ovary 16–19 mm; style 17–20 mm, apex dilated 2 × 1 mm, barbate. **Legumes:** dehiscence causing valve to twist 2–3 turns, (70–)90–125 × 5–6 mm; beak 8–12 mm. **Seeds** 8–12, brownish black, 3–4 × 4–5 × 1 mm.

Flowering and fruiting Jun–Sep. Sandy soils in open areas, roadsides, railroads, scrub, open pinewoods, margins of oak-sabal palmetto woods; of conservation concern; 0–20 m; Fla.

Centrosema arenicola is known from central Florida.

2. Centrosema virginianum (Linnaeus) Bentham, Comm. Legum. Gen., 56. 1837 [F]

Clitoria virginiana Linnaeus, Sp. Pl. 2: 753. 1753; *Bradburya virginiana* (Linnaeus) Kuntze; *Centrosema virginianum* var. *angustifolium* (de Candolle) Grisebach; *C. virginianum* var. *ellipticum* (de Candolle) Fernald

Rhizomes 4–8 cm × 5–11 mm proximally, to 30+ cm × 1–2 mm distally. **Stems** 1–5, to 1–3 m × 1–2 mm. **Leaves:** stipules ovate-deltate, 3–5 mm; petioles angular, canaliculate adaxially, 1–5 cm; stipels persistent, striate, linear, 3–5 mm; petiolules 2 mm; rachis 0.5–1.5 cm; leaflet blades ovate to elliptic, ovate to lanceolate, or oblong to linear, (12–)20–65(–100) × 8–45 mm, thinly leathery, base rotund, primary lateral veins of 6–8 pairs, to 15 pairs in linear leaflets, veins with uncinulate hairs, apex broadly acute. **Inflorescences** 1(or 2) per node, 1–3 cm; bracts striate, concave around pedicel, oval-ovate, 4–6 mm; bracteoles striate, lanceolate-ovate, 6–8 × 3–5 mm, surfaces with uncinulate hairs; rachis subflexuous, 1–2(–3) cm, strigose. **Pedicels** 5–8 mm, 7–11 mm in fruit, thinly pilose. **Flowers:** calyx tube 3–4 × 4–6 mm, lobes subequal, abaxial ones 4–7 mm, lateral ones 5–8 mm, adaxial ones 6–10 mm, hairs uncinulate; corolla lavender to bluish violet or purple; banner 25–35(–40) mm, claw 2–4 mm, spur 1–2 mm; wings 14–19 × 5–9 mm, claw 5–7 mm; keel 16–20 × 7–10 mm, claw 3–5 mm; staminal tube 19–25 mm; apical distinct filaments 1–3 mm; ovary 12–15 mm; style 20–27 mm, apex dilated 9–12 × 1 mm. **Legumes:** dehiscence causing valve to twist (1–)3–5 turns, (60–)80–110 × 3–5 mm; beak 9–17 mm. **Seeds** 14–18, dark brown, 3–4 × 4–6 × 1 mm. $2n$ = 14, 18, 22.

Flowering and fruiting Jun–early Oct. Sandy soils in pine-oak woodlands, oak-hickory woodlands, shale bluffs, roadsides, railroads, grasslands, old fields, sand dunes, alluvial woods, swamps, pocosins, marshes, bogs, river banks; 0–600 m; Ala., Ark., Del., Fla., Ga., Ky., La., Md., Miss., Mo., N.J., N.C., Okla., Pa., S.C., Tenn., Tex., Va.; Mexico; West Indies; Central America; South America; introduced in Asia.

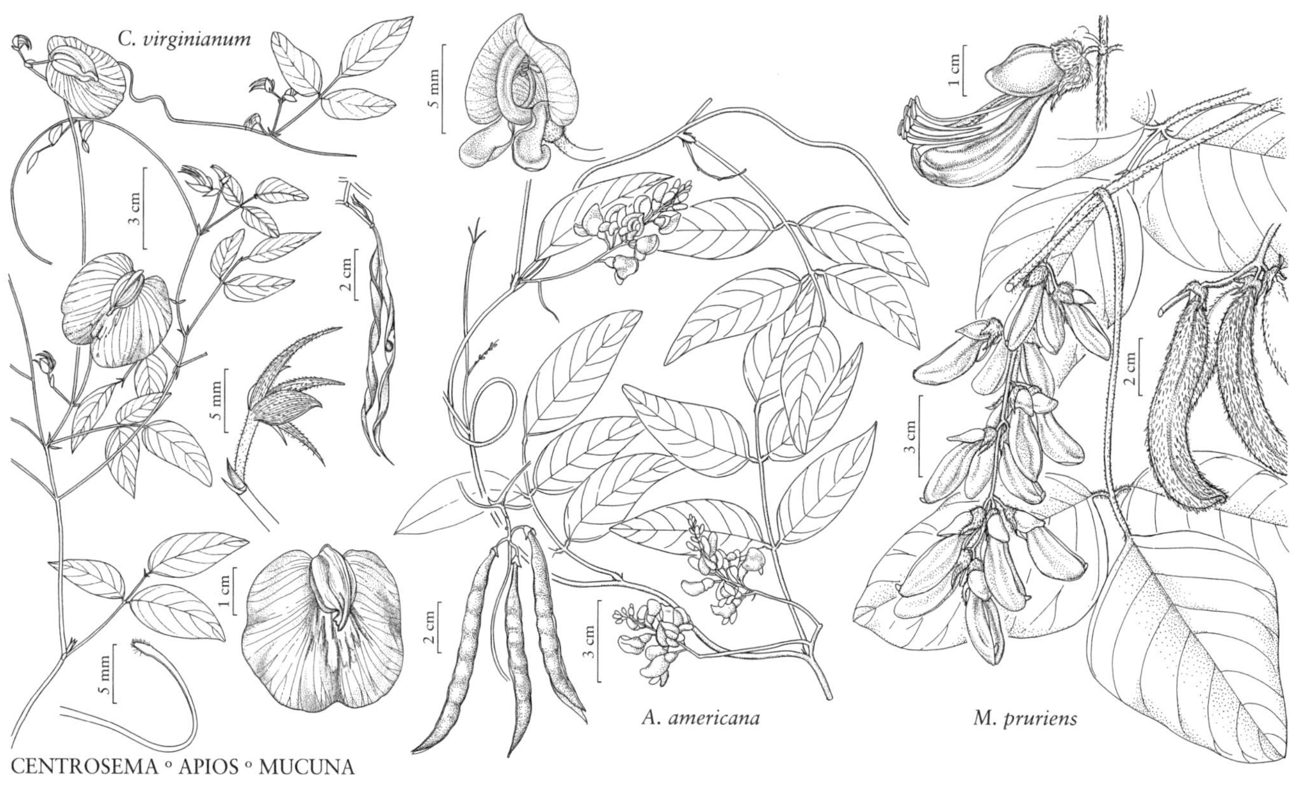

CENTROSEMA ◦ APIOS ◦ MUCUNA

Historically, *Centrosema virginianum* has been misidentified as *Clitoria mariana* by collectors in the United States. The latter species is distinguished easily by the non-scandent, erect stems, funnelform calyces with lobes broader and shorter than tubes, spurless banners, wings longer than keel petals, presence of cleistogamy, and turgid, ecostate fruits depressed slightly between the seeds.

Two varieties of *Centrosema virginianum* have been described based upon leaflet width. Specimens with narrow, linear leaves (var. *angustifolium*) found in the southern coastal areas appear distinct from those found inland with broader and shorter leaves (var. *ellipticum*, var. *virginianum*). Examined specimens exhibit a gradation in leaflet width and length, from multiple collections within a population, to variation within one plant, bearing shorter and broader leaves at proximal nodes and narrower and longer leaves at distal nodes. Varieties are not recognized here.

87. APIOS Fabricius, Enum., 176. 1759, name conserved • Groundnut [Greek name for pear, alluding to shape of root tubers]

Michael Woods

Vines, perennial, unarmed, latex present, white; rhizomatous, tuber single or several (moniliform) [absent]. **Stems** usually herbaceous, sometimes woody at base, twining or clambering, slightly striate [smooth], glabrous or pubescent. **Leaves** alternate, odd-pinnate; stipules present, 2, persistent or deciduous, linear-triangular, glabrous or sericeous; petiolate, petiole striate or smooth; rachis striate or smooth; leaflets (3 or)5 or 7(or 9), stipels deciduous or persistent, 2 proximal to terminal leaflet, 1 proximal to lateral leaflets, margins entire, petiolules reduced to pulvinus, blade abaxially pale green, adaxially darker, 47–100 mm, margins entire, glabrous or ciliate, veins anastomosing before margins, surfaces glabrous or pubescent. **Inflorescences**

40–70-flowered, axillary, pseudoracemes, nodose, or flowers paired apically in leaf axils, simple or branched; bracts present, 2, caducous, margins entire, ciliate, surfaces glabrous or pubescent; bracteoles 2, caducous. **Flowers** papilionaceous; calyx hemispheric or campanulate, bilobed, lobes 4; corolla maroon and white, or pale green and rose-purple [yellow-green], 10.5–26 mm; banner apex fused into stylobos; keel incurved, narrowly elliptic, connate distally, sometimes slit distally after pollination, narrowly linear to oblong; stamens 10, diadelphous; anthers basifixed; pistil stipitate, disc surrounding and free from stipe; style spirally coiled; stigma capitate. **Fruits** legumes, stipitate, cylindric, linear-oblong, apex short-aristate or acuminate, dehiscent, glabrous or pubescent; endocarp silvery or white [off-white]. **Seeds** 6–12, elliptic or oblong [circular-oblate], glabrous. x = 11.

Species 5 (2 in the flora): North America, Asia.

The term stylobos refers to an involute apical appendage of the banner that holds the keel in place until tripped by a visiting pollinator (J. A. E. Seabrook 1973).

SELECTED REFERENCE Woods, M. 2005. A revision of the North American species of *Apios* (Fabaceae). Castanea 70: 85–100.

1. Banners oblate, 10.5–12.5 mm, stylobos 1.5–2 mm; styles glabrous; legumes 6–10(–12) cm; seeds 5–6 mm; corollas deep to pale maroon and white; tubers 4–12, 2–10 cm diam. . . . . . 1. *Apios americana*
1. Banners broadly elliptic, 23–26 mm, stylobos 5.8–7.8 mm; styles bearded; legumes 12–15(–18) cm; seeds 7.2–11 mm; corollas pale green and rose-purple; tuber 1, 15–20 cm diam. . . . . 2. *Apios priceana*

1. Apios americana Medikus, Vorles. Churpfälz. Phys.-Öcon. Ges. 2: 355. 1787 [E] [F]

Glycine apios Linnaeus, Sp. Pl. 2: 753. 1753; *Apios americana* var. *turrigera* Fernald

Vines twining or clambering; tubers 4–12, oblong, oval, or globose, 2–10 cm diam., fleshy. **Stems** green to brownish green or brown, glabrous or tomentose. **Leaves** 10–22 cm; rachis terete, 10–32 mm between lateral and terminal leaflets, 16–37 mm between lateral leaflets, glabrous or velutinous; stipules 4–6.5 × 0.3–0.6 mm; petiole 20–58 mm, glabrous or velutinous; pulvinus 4.5–7 mm, glabrous or velutinous; stipels linear-triangular, 0.5–1 × 0.1–0.3 mm, hairs scattered or sericeous; petiolule (1.5–)2.8–4 mm, slightly hairy to velutinous; leaflet blades ovate to ovate-lanceolate, 47–70(–90) × 21–42 mm (blades of ramal branches 30–45 × 12–20 mm), base rounded (often asymmetrical), apex acuminate to acute, apiculate, surfaces glabrate to tomentose abaxially, usually denser on major veins, glabrous or puberulous adaxially, usually denser on major veins. **Inflorescences** 40–60-flowered, 3–14 cm; bracts usually deciduous, rarely persistent, 2–2.8 mm; bracteoles 2–3 × 0.3–0.5 mm. **Pedicels** 2–3 mm, glabrous or velutinous. **Flowers** in clusters of 2 or 3 on inflated tubercles; calyx green, red and green, or pink-red, hemispheric to campanulate, 2.8–3.4 mm, glabrous or puberulous, abaxial lobe lanceolate to narrowly triangular, 1.3–1.8 × 0.4–0.6 mm, lateral lobes triangular to shallowly so, 0.2–0.4 × 0.7–0.9 mm, adaxial lobe almost obsolete or broadly rounded with acute, triangular apex, 0.2–0.3 × 0.1–0.2 mm; corolla deep to pale maroon and white; banner oblate, 10.5–12.5 × 14–16 mm, stylobos 1.5–2 mm; wings obovate, falcate, 9.5–10.5 × 4.3–4.8 mm; keel strongly incurved, slit apically after pollination, 12–14 × 2–4 mm; stamens 15.5–17 mm, filaments connate most of their length; pistil disk 0.9–1.2 mm; ovary 5.5–7 × 0.4–0.6 mm, glabrous or slightly hairy along sutures; style 6–7.5 mm, glabrous; ovules 6–11. **Legumes** olive green to tannish brown, 6–10(–12) × 0.6–0.7 cm, base acute, apex aristate to acuminate; endocarp white. **Seeds** 6–11, olive green becoming brown to reddish brown when dry, ellipsoid to broadly oblong, 5–6 × 3.5–4.5 mm, not glaucous; hilum 0.8–2 × 0.3–0.4 mm. $2n$ = 22.

Flowering summer–fall. Wet soils, along streams and lakes; 0–1600 m; N.B., N.S., Ont., Que.; Ala., Ark., Colo., Conn., Del., D.C., Fla., Ga., Ill., Ind., Iowa, Kans., Ky., La., Maine, Md., Mass., Mich., Minn., Miss., Mo., Nebr., N.H., N.J., N.Y., N.C., Ohio, Okla., Pa., R.I., S.C., S.Dak., Tenn., Tex., Vt., Va., W.Va., Wis.

Six infraspecific taxa of *Apios americana* have been described. The highly variable characters of *A. americana* are so overlapping that no definite lines of demarcation can adequately separate the infraspecific taxa (M. Woods 2005).

Species of *Megachile* (leaf-cutter bees) are the only visitors reported to trip the flowers of *Apios americana* in the northern half of its range and are the only likely pollinators there. *Megachile* species are the only insects observed tripping the flowers in the southern part of its range; two additional types of bees, honeybees (Apidae) and members of the Halictidae, are frequent visitors there but have not been observed tripping the flowers (A. Bruneau and G. J. Anderson 1988, 1994).

Diploid and triploid populations of *Apios americana* are almost entirely restricted to different sections of the overall geographical range. Triploid individuals are primarily located in the section of eastern North American that was covered by ice during the Wisconsinan glaciation (areas north of central Ohio, southern Indiana, central Iowa, Pennsylvania, and central Wisconsin). Diploid individuals also occur in the Wisconsinan glaciation area but are more abundant outside of the area in the southern part of the range. Triploidy is considered to have evolved at least four times. Clones east of the Appalachian Mountains have light-colored petals and little stem indument; the western clones have dark-colored petals and heavy stem indument (S. Joly and A. Bruneau 2004).

Apios tuberosa Moench (1794) is an illegitimate, superfluous name that pertains here.

2. Apios priceana B. L. Robinson, Bot. Gaz. 25: 451, fig. s.n. [p. 451]. 1898 • Price's groundnut or potato-bean [C] [E]

Glycine priceana (B. L. Robinson) Britton

Vines twining; tuber 1, oblate-spheroidal, 15–20 cm diam. **Stems** terete, brownish green, glabrous or reflexed-pubescent. **Leaves** 18–27 cm; rachis 30–37 mm between lateral and terminal leaflets, 34–52 mm between lateral leaflets, glabrous or slightly hairy; stipules 7–8.6 × 0.5–0.7 mm; petiole 70–7 mm, glabrous or slightly hairy; pulvinus 3–4 mm, glabrous or hairs scattered; stipels narrowly triangular, 0.3–0.4 × 0.1–0.2 mm, sericeous; petiolule 3.5–4 mm, slightly hairy to tomentose; leaflet blades ovate to ovate-lanceolate, 50–100 × 5–60 mm, base obtuse or rounded, apex caudate, apiculate, surfaces glabrous or strigose, mostly along major veins. **Inflorescences** 55–70-flowered, 12–16 cm; bracts early deciduous, 2.5–3.25 mm; bracteoles 5–6.5 × 1–1.8 mm. **Pedicels** 4–5 mm, glabrous or sparsely pubescent. **Flowers** in clusters of 2 or 3 on small tubercles; calyx green, hemispheric, 4.8–5.3 mm, glabrous or sericeous, abaxial lobe lanceolate-acuminate, 3–4 × 1.9–2.1 mm, lateral lobes shallowly triangular, 0.9–1.1 × 2–2.3 mm, adaxial lobe almost obsolete, shallowly triangular, 0.8–1 × 1.9–2.3 mm; corolla pale green and rose-purple; banner broadly elliptic, 23–26 × 15–20 mm, stylobos 5.8–7.8 mm; wings narrowly elliptic, falcate, 19–21 × 2.3–2.8 mm (to 4.5–5 mm wide at apex); keel incurved, 18–19 × 8–9 mm, triangular pouch present at middle; stamens 20–24 mm, filaments connate most of their length; pistil disk 0.8–1 mm; ovary 13–15 × 0.9–1.1 mm, glabrous or slightly hairy, mostly along sutures; style 8–11 mm, bearded with simple hairs; ovules 8–12. **Legumes** brownish red (with tan lines when dry), 12–15(–18) × 0.6–1 cm, base attenuate, apex acuminate; endocarp silvery white. **Seeds** 8–12, olive green becoming brown when dry, ellipsoid to oblong, 7.2–11 × 4.5–5.5 mm, glaucous; hilum 3.3–4 × 1.4–1.6 mm. **2*n*** = 22.

Flowering summer. Rocky, open woods, forest borders, mixed oak woods, limestone, drainage areas; of conservation concern; 60–200 m; Ala., Ky., Miss., Tenn.

Apios priceana is designated as threatened throughout its range. The species is apparently extirpated from Illinois (M. Woods 2005).

Apios priceana is in the Center for Plant Conservation's National Collection of Endangered Plants.

88. MUCUNA Adanson, Fam. Pl. 2: 325, 579 [as Mukuna]. 1763, name and orthography conserved • Sea bean [Brazilian mucuna-guaca, name for *M. urens* (Linnaeus) Medikus]

Rachel K. Clark

Alexander Krings

Stizolobium P. Browne, name rejected

Vines, annual or perennial, herbaceous or woody, unarmed. **Stems** trailing or climbing, pubescent. **Leaves** alternate, odd-pinnate; stipules present, lanceolate; petiolate; leaflets 3, stipels present, blade margins entire, surfaces pubescent. **Inflorescences** 10–40-flowered, axillary, racemes or umbelliform, pendent; bracts present, caducous. **Flowers** papilionaceous; calyx 2-lipped, lobes 5, pubescent; corolla white, yellow, or purple, 30–65 mm; stamens 10, diadelphous; anthers dorsifixed; ovary pubescent. **Fruits** legumes, pendent, pedicellate, brown, oblong, compressed between seeds, dehiscent, pubescent, often with stinging hairs, ridges longitudinal or transverse. **Seeds** 1–6, black to brown or white, 1–2 cm diam., spherical to oblong, smooth; hilum lateral. $x = 11$.

Species ca. 100 (2 in the flora): se United States, Mexico, West Indies, Central America, South America, Asia, Africa, Pacific Islands (Hawaii), Australia.

Pending resolution of generic relationships, we follow G. P. Lewis et al. (2005) in treating *Mucuna* in a broad sense to encompass *Stizolobium*. The status of putative cultigens, such as *M. aterrima* (Piper & Tracy) Holland and *M. deeringiana* (treated here as a synonym of *M. pruriens*), needs further study. Phylogenetic studies are also needed to resolve issues in species circumscription and the proper application of names, particularly for extralimital taxa.

In addition to the taxa treated below, some species of *Mucuna* collected from tropical Asia were grown experimentally at the United States Department of Agriculture Experiment Station in Biloxi, Mississippi. These include *M. aterrima* (= *M. pruriens* according to R. A. Howard 1974–1989, vol. 4), *Stizolobium cinereum* Piper & Tracy (no name yet available in *Mucuna*), *M. hassjoo* (Piper & Tracy) Mansfeld (= *M. pruriens* var. *utilis* according to V. A. Funk et al. 2007), *M. lyonii* Merrill, *M. nivea* (Roxburgh) de Candolle ex Wight & Arnott, *M. pachylobia* Rock, *M. stans* Welwitsch ex Baker, and *M. velutina* Hasskarl. There is no evidence that these taxa have escaped.

1. Legumes 5–9 cm, transverse ridges absent; hilum to 1/4 circumference of seeds, elevated; inflorescences racemes; terminal leaflet blades rhombic-ovate . . . . 1. *Mucuna pruriens*
1. Legumes 9–12(–16) cm, transverse ridges conspicuous; hilum nearly circling seeds, not elevated; inflorescences umbelliform; terminal leaflet blades ovate. 2. *Mucuna sloanei*

1. Mucuna pruriens (Linnaeus) de Candolle in A. P. de Candolle and A. L. P. P. de Candolle, Prodr. 2: 405. 1825 • Cow itch, velvet bean, cowhage [F] [I]

Dolichos pruriens Linnaeus, Herb. Amb., 23. 1754; *Mucuna deeringiana* (Bort) Merrill; *M. pruriens* var. *utilis* (Wallich ex Wight) Baker ex Burck; *M. utilis* Wallich ex Wight; *Stizolobium deeringianum* Bort

Vines annual. Stems climbing or trailing. **Leaves:** stipules 3–5 mm; petiole (3–)6–20 cm, pubescent; terminal leaflet blade rhombic-ovate, (5–)9–22 cm, base rounded, lateral blade base oblique, apex acuminate to cuspidate, surfaces strigose abaxially, sparsely pubescent adaxially. **Inflorescences** racemes. **Pedicels** 0.5–1.1 cm, pubescent. **Flowers:** calyx 12–15 mm, abaxial lip 3-lobed, adaxial lip broad, acuminate; corolla white to dark purple, 30–40 mm. **Legumes** 5–9 × 0.7–1.7 cm, velutinous, irritating hairs present or absent, longitudinal ridges obscure to prominent, transverse ridges absent. **Seeds** (1–)3–6, black-brown to white with dark mottling, spherical to oblong; hilum cream or black, to 1/4 circumference of seed, elevated. $2n = 22$.

Flowering summer–fall. Pastures, waste areas, old fields, pinelands; 0–100 m; introduced; Ala., Fla., N.C., S.C.; Asia; introduced also in Mexico, West Indies, Central America, South America, Africa, Australia.

Mucuna pruriens is introduced and widely cultivated in tropical areas; it is used for many herbal remedies worldwide and extracts from the seeds are sold as dietary supplements. The seeds contain L-DOPA, a precursor to the neurotransmitter dopamine. The species is being investigated as an alternative treatment for Parkinson's Disease (M. Daniels 2006).

In addition to its medicinal properties, *Mucuna pruriens* is used in agriculture as a cover crop and as forage for domesticated animals (E. C. Rich and A. A. Teixeira 2005).

The hairs covering the seed pods can be very irritating and have been used in so-called itching powder (W. Shelly and R. P. Arthur 1955).

2. Mucuna sloanei Fawcett & Rendle, J. Bot. 55: 36. 1917 • Horse-eye bean

Vines perennial. Stems climbing. **Leaves:** stipules 1–3 mm; petiole 2.9–11.1 cm, pubescent; terminal leaflet blade ovate, 7–15 cm, base rounded, lateral blade base oblique, apex acuminate, surfaces silver-gray, strigose abaxially, pubescent adaxially. **Inflorescences** umbelliform. **Pedicels** 0.5–1.5 cm, pubescent. **Flowers:** calyx 15–20 mm, abaxial lip 3-lobed, adaxial lip broad, rounded; corolla yellow, 45–65 mm. **Legumes** 9–12

(–16) × 4–6 cm, setose, irritating hairs present, transverse ridges conspicuous. **Seeds** 1–3, brown to black, spherical, 2–3 cm; hilum black, nearly encircling seed, not elevated. $2n$ = 22.

Flowering year-round. Hammocks, beaches; 0–20 m; Fla.; Mexico; West Indies; Central America; South America; Africa; Pacific Islands (Hawaii).

In the flora area, *Mucuna sloanei* is known from Broward and Miami-Dade counties.

The seeds of *Mucuna sloanei* can be found in decorative jewelry, and, in Nigeria, a black dye is extracted from the plant and used to dye fabric and leather (P. C. M. Jansen 2005). *Mucuna sloanei* is used as a cover crop in tropical areas to supply nitrogen to soil and for weed suppression (I. I. Ibeawuchi 2007). G. O. Obochi et al. (2007) noted that the high protein content of the seed led to use as food and soup thickener in tropical Africa. The mitogenic properties of the seeds are being investigated for their potential in the treatment and diagnosis of human diseases affecting white blood cell production (Obochi et al.).

89. RHYNCHOSIA Loureiro, Fl. Cochinch. 2: 425 [as Phynchosia], 460. 1790, name conserved • Snoutbean [Greek *rhynchos*, beak or snout, alluding to keel shape in *Rhynchosia volubilis*, the type species]

Michael Woods

Leucopterum Small

Herbs, perennial, subshrubs, or vines, unarmed; from woody taproots. **Stems** prostrate, procumbent, twining, ascending, or erect, pubescent or glabrous. **Leaves** alternate, unifoliolate or trifoliolate; stipules present, striate; petiolate; stipels deciduous; leaflets 1 or 3, 0.5–2.5 mm, blade margins entire, surfaces gland-dotted abaxially, sometimes also adaxially, pubescent or glabrous. **Inflorescences** 1–3-flowered, usually axillary, rarely terminal, usually racemes; bracts present, striate. **Flowers** papilionaceous; calyx campanulate with relatively long lobes, or tubulous-campanulate with relatively short lobes, lobes 5; corolla yellow, yellow-orange, or green-yellow, often with purple or brown tinge or streaks, (4–)6–12(–14) mm; stamens 10, diadelphous; anthers dorsifixed. **Fruits** legumes, sessile or subsessile, usually compressed, ovoid to ellipsoid, falcate, or acinaciform, beaked, dehiscent, gland-dotted, pubescent or glabrous. **Seeds** 1 or 2, subglobose, ovoid to ellipsoid, or reniform. x = 11.

Species ca. 200 (14 in the flora): United States, Mexico, West Indies, Bermuda, Central America, South America, Asia (Japan, South Korea); warm temperate and tropical areas.

SELECTED REFERENCE Grear, J. W. 1978. A revision of the New World species of *Rhynchosia* (Leguminosae-Faboideae). Mem. New York Bot. Gard. 31(1): 1–168.

1. Leaves usually unifoliolate, distalmost rarely trifoliolate.
    2. Calyces 14–16 mm; wings oblong, 9–11 mm; stamens 9–10 mm; leaflet surfaces tomentose-woolly abaxially. . . . . 1. *Rhynchosia michauxii*
    2. Calyces 7–13 mm; wings narrowly oblong, 6.5–7.7 mm; stamens 6–8.5 mm; leaflet surfaces hirtellous or villosulous abaxially.
        3. Stems usually ascending or erect, rarely twining; calyces densely hirtellous and gland-dotted; banners 6.5–7 mm; keel petals 6.7–7 × 2–2.5 mm; stamens 6–7 mm . . . . 2. *Rhynchosia reniformis*
        3. Stems procumbent, trailing, or twining; calyces villosulous; banners 8.5–10 mm; keel petals 8–9 × 3–3.5 mm; stamens 7.5–8.5 mm . . . . 3. *Rhynchosia americana*

1. Leaves usually trifoliolate, proximalmost sometimes unifoliolate.
    4. Calyces: lateral lobes 3+ times tubes.
        5. Inflorescences longer than leaves; leaflet surfaces villous abaxially; seeds brown-gray or mottled . . . . 11. *Rhynchosia latifolia*
        5. Inflorescences shorter than leaves; leaflet surfaces puberulent, villosulous, hirtellous, strigulose, or strigose abaxially; seeds brown, black, or mottled.
            6. Stems ascending or erect; calyces: adaxial lobes 2–2.5 mm. . . . . 12. *Rhynchosia tomentosa*
            6. Stems usually prostrate or twining, rarely climbing or erect; calyces: adaxial lobes 3–5 mm.
                7. Petioles strigulose; stems prostrate, rarely climbing . . . . 13. *Rhynchosia cinerea*
                7. Petioles hirsute; stems prostrate or twining . . . . 14. *Rhynchosia difformis*
    4. Calyces: lateral lobes to 2.5 times tubes.
        8. Stem hairs yellowish; Santa Cruz County, Arizona . . . . 4. *Rhynchosia edulis*
        8. Stem hairs silvery or grayish; Alabama, Arizona, Arkansas, Florida, Louisiana, Mississippi, Missouri, New Mexico, Texas.
            9. Stamens 3.5–7 mm.
                10. Legumes falcate to oblong-ovoid; seeds ovoid-reniform; wings puberulent apically . . . . 5. *Rhynchosia minima*
                10. Legumes oblong or acinaciform; seeds reniform or subglobose; wings glabrous.
                    11. Leaflets ± leathery, blades lanceolate-ovate, margins revolute; flowers solitary, 1(2 or 3)-clustered; inflorescences shorter than leaves . . . . 6. *Rhynchosia texana*
                    11. Leaflets membranous, blades ovate, margins flat; flowers in solitary racemes; inflorescences longer than leaves . . . . 7. *Rhynchosia swartzii*
            9. Stamens 8–12 mm.
                12. Calyces: lateral lobes 2–3 mm; wings puberulent apically, 6–7 mm; seeds red and black, 5–8 mm . . . . 8. *Rhynchosia precatoria*
                12. Calyces: lateral lobes 4–5 mm; wings glabrous, 8–10 mm; seeds brown, black, or mottled, 2–4 mm.
                    13. Banners glabrous, keel petals 4–5 mm wide; seeds subglobose; hilum ovate; calyces hirtellous; leaflet surfaces gland-dotted and puberulent abaxially, strigose adaxially, blade bases cuneate . . . . 9. *Rhynchosia cytisoides*
                    13. Banners puberulent (and gland-dotted), keel petals 2–2.5 mm wide; seeds ovoid-ellipsoid; hilum linear; calyces tomentose, viscid; leaflet surfaces grayish tomentulose, blades bases obtuse . . . . 10. *Rhynchosia parvifolia*

1. Rhynchosia michauxii Vail, Bull. Torrey Bot. Club 22: 458. 1895 • Michaux's snoutbean [E]

Dolicholus michauxii (Vail) Vail

Vines, herbaceous. **Stems** prostrate (twining distally), hirtellous, hairs grayish. **Leaves** usually unifoliolate, distalmost rarely trifoliolate; stipules persistent, ovate-lanceolate, 3–5 × 1.5–2 mm, apex acuminate; petiole 20–40 mm, densely hirsute; leaflet blades reniform or orbiculate, 20–50 × 20–70 mm, leathery, gland-dotted, base truncate or subcordate, apex obtuse, obscurely mucronulate, surfaces reticulate and tomentose-woolly abaxially, rugose and finely strigose adaxially. **Inflorescences** in clusters on peduncles, shorter than leaves, 2–6 cm. **Pedicels** 3–8 mm. **Flowers:** calyx 14–16 mm, hirsute, tube 2 mm, lobes lanceolate or elliptic, laterals 12–14 mm, adaxials 5 mm; corolla yellow-orange; banner obovate, 10–12 × 5–6 mm, emarginate, puberulent, with a pair of internal callosities; wings oblong, 9–11 × 2–2.5 mm, glabrous; keel 9–10 × 2–2.5 mm, glabrous; stamens 9–10 mm. **Legumes** ovoid-oblong, compressed, 10–18 × 5–9 mm, gland-dotted, tomentose. **Seeds** brown, black, or mottled, subglobose, compressed, 3.5–4 × 3.5–4 mm.

Flowering year-round. Sandy soils in pine and oak woodlands, fields, disturbed areas; 0–20 m; Fla., N.C.

In North Carolina, *Rhynchosia michauxii* is found only in Brunswick County.

2. Rhynchosia reniformis de Candolle in A. P. de Candolle and A. L. P. P. de Candolle, Prodr. 2: 384. 1825 • Dollarleaf [E] [F]

Arcyphyllum simplicifolium (Walter) Elliott; *Dolicholus intermedius* (Torrey & A. Gray) Vail; *D. simplicifolius* (Walter) Vail; *Glycine simplicifolia* (Walter) Elliott; *G. tomentosa* Linnaeus var. *monophylla* Michaux; *Psoralea alnifolia* Bertoloni; *P. alopecurina* Bertoloni; *Rhynchosia simplicifolia* de Candolle var. *intermedia* (Torrey & A. Gray) F. J. Hermann; *R. tomentosa* (Linnaeus) Hooker & Arnott var. *intermedia* Torrey & A. Gray; *R. tomentosa* var. *monophylla* (Michaux) Torrey & A. Gray; *Trifolium simplicifolium* Walter 1788, not *R. simplicifolia* de Candolle 1825

Vines, herbaceous. **Stems** usually ascending or erect, rarely twining, glabrous or sparsely to densely hirtellous, hairs grayish. **Leaves** usually unifoliolate, distalmost rarely trifoliolate; stipules persistent, lanceolate to ovate-lanceolate, 4–15 × 1–4.5 mm, apex acute to acuminate; petiole 15–45 mm, hirtellous; leaflet blades suborbiculate to reniform or ovate to oblong, 20–50 × 25–70 mm, leathery, gland-dotted, base truncate, broadly rounded to cuneate, or subcordate, apex obtuse, broadly rounded, emarginate to mucronate, surfaces reticulate and hirtellous abaxially, rugose and strigulose, glabrescent adaxially. **Inflorescences** crowded in densely packed heads, flowers numerous, shorter than leaves, 1–3.5 cm. **Pedicels** 1–3 mm. **Flowers:** calyx 7–10 mm, densely hirtellous, gland-dotted, tube 1.5–2 mm, lobes linear-lanceolate, laterals 7–8 mm, adaxials 2 mm; corolla yellow; banner elliptic-ovate, 6.5–7 × 6–6.5 mm, emarginate, glabrous; wings narrowly oblong, 6.5–7 × 1.5–2.5 mm, glabrous; keel 6.7–7 × 2–2.5 mm, glabrous; stamens 6–7 mm. **Legumes** oblong-ellipsoid, compressed, 13–18 × 5–7 mm, gland-dotted, hirtellous. **Seeds** brown, black, or mottled, subglobose, compressed, 3 × 3 mm.

Flowering spring–summer. Dry woodlands, sandhills, savannas, prairie openings, fields, roadsides; 20–300 m; Ala., Fla., Ga., La., Miss., N.C., S.C., Tenn., Tex.

In Texas, *Rhynchosia reniformis* is known from relatively few counties in the easternmost part of the state.

Glycine monophylla (Michaux) Nuttall, *G. reniformis* Pursh, *Rhynchosia intermedia* (Torrey & A. Gray) Small, and *R. simplicifolia* (Walter) Alph. Wood are illegitimate names that pertain here.

3. Rhynchosia americana (Miller) Metz, Catholic Univ. Amer., Biol. Ser. 16: 126. 1934 • American snoutbean

Lathyrus americanus Miller, Gard. Dict. ed. 8, Lathyrus no. 19. 1768 (as americana); *Glycine menispermoides* (de Candolle) Sprengel; *Phaseolus menispermoideus* (de Candolle) Eaton & Wright; *Rhynchosia menispermoidea* de Candolle

Vines, herbaceous. **Stems** procumbent, trailing, or twining, villous or villosulous, hairs silvery, spreading. **Leaves** usually unifoliolate, distalmost rarely trifoliolate; stipules persistent, ovate-lanceolate, 2–5 × 1–2.5 mm, apex acuminate; petiole 10–45 mm, villosulous; leaflet blades suborbiculate to reniform, 15–40 × 20–55 mm, leathery, gland-dotted, base cordate, apex broadly rounded, surfaces villosulous abaxially, rugose and finely strigose adaxially. **Inflorescences** racemes, shorter than leaves, 1.5–5 cm. **Pedicels** 2–5 mm. **Flowers:** calyx 7–13 mm, villosulous, tube 1.5–2 mm, lobes lanceolate, laterals 6–10 mm, adaxials 2–4 mm; corolla yellow, often tinged brown; banner obovate, 8.5–10 × 6.5–7.5 mm, emarginate, puberulous; wings narrowly oblong, 6.5–7.7 × 2–2.5 mm, glabrous; keel 8–9 × 3–3.5 mm, glabrous; stamens 7.5–8.5 mm. **Legumes** oblong-ovoid, compressed, 10–15 × 5–8 mm, villosulous. **Seeds** brown, black, or mottled, subglobose, compressed, 3–4 × 3–3.5 mm. $2n = 22$.

Flowering spring–summer. Sandy soils, prairies, fields, oak woodlands, roadsides, sand dunes; 0–300 m; Tex.; Mexico (Chiapas, Durango, San Luis Potosí, Sinaloa, Tamaulipas, Veracruz).

In Texas, *Rhynchosia americana* occurs in coastal and southern counties.

4. Rhynchosia edulis Grisebach, Abh. Königl. Ges. Wiss. Göttingen 19: 123. 1874 • Chihuahuan snoutbean

Dolicholus apoloensis Rusby; *D. ixodes* Standley; *Eriosema edule* (Grisebach) Burkhart; *E. nigropunctatum* Brandegee; *E. volubile* Micheli; *Rhynchosia apoloensis* (Rusby) J. F. Macbride; *R. ixodes* (Standley) Standley; *R. melanosticta* Grisebach; *R. nigropunctata* S. Watson; *R. pinetorum* Standley; *R. rariflora* Standley; *R. rupicola* Brandegee

Herbs. Stems erect, suberect, decumbent, procumbent, or twining, viscid, hirsute, hairs yellowish. **Leaves** trifoliolate; stipules persistent, linear to narrowly lanceolate, 3–9 × 0.5–1.5 mm, apex acute to acuminate, surfaces hirsute; petiole 15–55 mm, hirsute; leaflet blades lanceolate to obovate-oblong or ovate-deltate, 15–70 × 10–60 mm, membranous or leathery, gland-dotted, often viscid, base obtuse to rounded or truncate, margins ciliate, slightly revolute, apex acute to acuminate, surfaces strongly reticulate and sparsely to densely hirsute abaxially, strigulose to strigose adaxially. **Inflorescences** racemes, equal to or longer than leaves, 2.5–20 cm. **Pedicels** 1–3 mm. **Flowers:** calyx 4–7 mm, hirsute, tube 1.5–2 mm, lobes lanceolate, laterals 2–2.5 mm, lengths to 2.5 times tube, adaxials 1.5–3 mm; corolla yellow, striped reddish brown or purple; banner widely ovate to obovate, 7–10 × 4–5 mm, slightly apiculate, hirtellous and gland-dotted; wings narrowly oblong, 6.5–9 × 1.5–2 mm, gland-dotted, puberulent apically; keel 6.5–9 × 2–3 mm, glabrous; stamens 6–9 mm. **Legumes** oblong-ovoid, compressed, 16–26 × 6–8 mm, often viscid, long-hirsute to puberulent, hairs intermixed, glabrescent. **Seeds** greenish brown or mottled, widely ovoid to subglobose, compressed, 4–5 × 3–4 mm.

Flowering spring–summer. Sandy or clay soils of woodland, thickets, ravines, pastures, stream banks, roadsides; 800–1500 m; Ariz.; Mexico (Chiapas, Durango, Guerrero, Jalisco, Michoacán, Nayarit, San Luis Potosí, Sonora, Veracruz); Central America; South America.

In Arizona, *Rhynchosia edulis* is found only in Santa Cruz County.

Dolicholus melanostictus (Grisebach) Kuntze is an illegitimate name that pertains here.

5. **Rhynchosia minima** (Linnaeus) de Candolle in A. P. de Candolle and A. L. P. P. de Candolle, Prod. 2: 385. 1825 • Least snoutbean

Dolichos minimus Linnaeus, Sp. Pl. 2: 726. 1753; *Dolicholus minimus* (Linnaeus) Medikus; *Glycine lamarckii* Kunth; *G. reflexa* Baldwyn ex Nuttall; *Phaseolus caribaeus* Eaton & Wright; *Rhynchosia aureoguttata* Andersson; *R. exigua* Andersson; *R. mexicana* Hooker & Arnott; *R. minima* var. *diminifolia* Walraven; *R. minima* var. *lutea* Eggers; *R. minima* var. *pauciflora* Kuntze; *R. punctata* de Candolle

Herbs or subshrubs. Stems usually prostrate or twining, rarely ascending, rarely viscid, glabrous, puberulent, or villosulous, hairs silvery or grayish, spreading or reflexed. **Leaves** trifoliolate; stipules persistent, linear to lanceolate, 1–6 × 1–2 mm, apex acuminate, surfaces puberulent to villosulous; petiole 4–100 mm, glabrous, tomentulose, or villosulous; leaflet blades rhombic-orbiculate, rhombic, subrhombic, or ovate, 30–90 × 5–70 mm, membranous or nearly leathery, gland-dotted, base obtuse to rounded, cuneate, or truncate, apex acuminate to obtuse, surfaces glabrous, puberulent, or sparsely to densely villosulous abaxially, glabrous or finely strigose, villosulous, or puberulent adaxially. **Inflorescences** racemes, longer than leaves, 2–20 cm. **Pedicels** 1–5 mm. **Flowers:** calyx 3–6 mm, puberulent or villosulous, tube 1.5–2 mm, lobes lanceolate, laterals 1.5–4 mm, lengths to 2.5 times tube, adaxials 0.5–1 mm; corolla yellow, veined purple or brown; banner orbiculate-ovate, 4–6 × 3–5 mm, emarginate, puberulent, gland-dotted; wings narrowly oblong, 4.5–5 × 1–2 mm, narrowly gland-dotted, puberulent apically; keel 5–6 × 2–3 mm, glabrous; stamens 5–7 mm. **Legumes** falcate to oblong-ovoid, compressed, 9–20 × 3–5 mm, glabrous, puberulent, or villosulous. **Seeds** grayish, brown, black, or mottled, ovoid-reniform, plump, 3–4 × 2–3 mm. $2n = 22$.

Flowering spring–summer. Disturbed areas, forests, edges, prairies, sand dunes; 0–100 m; Ala., Ark., Fla., La., Miss., Mo., Tex.; West Indies; Bermuda; Central America; South America.

Rhynchosia minima was recently collected in Alabama after an absence of over 100 years (A. R. Diamond 2015).

Glycine littoralis Vahl ex de Candolle is an illegitimate name that pertains here.

6. **Rhynchosia texana** Torrey & A. Gray, Fl. N. Amer. 1: 687. 1840 • Texas snoutbean

Rhynchosia senna Gillies ex Hooker var. *angustifolia* (A. Gray) Grear; *R. senna* var. *cordobensis* (Grisebach) Burkart; *R. senna* var. *texana* (Torrey & A. Gray) M. C. Johnston; *R. texana* var. *angustifolia* A. Gray; *R. texana* var. *microphylla* Hassler

Herbs. Stems usually prostrate or twining, rarely subascending, puberulent to strigulose or villosulous, hairs silvery. **Leaves** trifoliolate; stipules persistent, linear or linear-lanceolate, 1.5–3 × 0.5 mm, acute to acuminate; petiole 5–35 mm, puberulous, strigulose, or villosulous; leaflet blades lanceolate-ovate, 5–45 × 20–25 mm, leathery, gland-dotted, base obtuse or subcordate, margins revolute, apex acute or obtuse, surfaces puberulent, strigulose, or villosulous. **Inflorescences** 1(2 or 3) simple flowers per axil, shorter than leaves, 0.6–1.5 cm. **Pedicels** 1–6 mm. **Flowers:** calyx 3–5 mm, villous or villosulous, tube 1.5–2.5 mm, lobes subulate, laterals 1–3.5 mm, lengths to 2.5 times tube, adaxials 0.5–2 mm; corolla yellow, veined brown; banner widely ovate, 5–7 × 3.5–5 mm, apex emarginate, puberulent; wings oblong to ovate, 5–6 × 1–2 mm, glabrous; keel 5–6.5 × 2–2.5 mm, glabrous; stamens

4–6 mm. **Legumes** oblong, compressed, 15–25 × 4–6 mm, puberulent-hirtellous, hairs intermixed. **Seeds** brown, black or mottled, subglobose, compressed, 3–4 × 3–4 mm. 2*n* = 22.

Flowering spring–summer. Dry limestone, sandy or igneous soils, grasslands, canyons, mountain slopes, roadsides, forest clearings; 40–2700 m; Ariz., N.Mex., Tex.; Mexico (Chiapas, Chihuahua, Coahuila, Durango, Nuevo León, Puebla, San Luis Potosí, Sonora, Tamaulipas, Veracruz); South America.

Rhynchosia angustifolia Engelmann ex A. Gray is an illegitimate name that pertains here. *Dolicholus texensis* Vail and its var. *angustifolius* (A. Gray) Vail are illegitimate and superfluous names that also pertain here.

7. **Rhynchosia swartzii** (Vail) Urban, Repert. Spec. Nov. Regni Veg. 15: 320. 1918 • Swartz's snoutbean

Dolicholus swartzii Vail, Bull. Torrey Bot. Club 26: 108. 1899; *Rhynchosia gundlachii* Urban

Herbs or subshrubs. Stems trailing or twining, gland-dotted, soft-hirsute, hairs silvery. **Leaves** trifoliolate; stipules persistent, narrowly lanceolate to lanceolate, 3–4 × 0.5–1.5 mm, acuminate, surfaces hirtellous; petiole 10–60 mm, hirsute; leaflet blades ovate, 20–60 × 15–45 mm, membranous, gland-dotted abaxially, base obtuse, rounded, or truncate, apex acute or long-acuminate, surfaces hirsute abaxially, glabrous or hirsute adaxially. **Inflorescences** racemes, longer than leaves, 1–6 cm. **Pedicels** filiform, 2–4 mm, viscid. **Flowers:** calyx 3.5–5 mm, hirsute-viscid, tube 2.5–5 mm, lobes broadly lanceolate, laterals 1.5–2 mm, lengths to 2.5 times tube, adaxials 0.5–1 mm; corolla yellow; banner obovate, 5–8 × 3–4.5 mm, marginate, puberulent, gland-dotted; wings oblong, 4–5 × 1–1.5 mm, glabrous; keel 4.5–5 × 2-2.5 mm, glabrous; stamens 3.5–5 mm. **Legumes** brown, acinaciform, compressed, 25–40 × 5–9 mm, tapered toward base, densely puberulent, hairs long, scattered. **Seeds** brown to red, reniform, barely compressed, 4–6 × 3–3.5 mm.

Flowering spring. Sandy soils, hammocks, thickets, open woods, pastures, roadsides; 0–10 m; Fla.; s Mexico; West Indies (Bahamas, Greater Antilles).

In the flora area, *Rhynchosia swartzii* is found in Miami-Dade and Monroe counties.

8. **Rhynchosia precatoria** de Candolle in A. P. de Candolle and A. L. P. P. de Candolle, Prodr. 2: 385. 1825 • Praying snoutbean [C]

Dolicholus vailiae Rose; *Indigofera volubilis* J. C. Wendland 1798, not *Rhynchosia volubilis* Loureiro 1790; *R. bicolor* Micheli

Subshrubs. Stems sprawling or twining, gland-dotted, rarely viscid, villous or villosulous, hairs silvery or grayish and silvery intermixed. **Leaves** trifoliolate; stipules early deciduous, ovate or lanceolate, 4–6 × 1.5–2 mm, apex acute or acuminate, surfaces villosulous; petiole 1–7 mm, rarely viscid, villous or villosulous; leaflet blades obovate to ovate-lanceolate or ovate-rhombic to rhombic, 20–130 × 15–100 mm, leathery, gland-dotted, base rounded to obtuse or cuneate, apex acute to acuminate, surfaces villous or villosulous abaxially, villous or villosulous adaxially, rarely glabrescent. **Inflorescences** racemes, longer than leaves, 5–30 cm. **Pedicels** 1–2 mm. **Flowers:** calyx 4–5 mm, villosulous, often viscid, tube 2–2.5 mm, lobes lanceolate, laterals 2–3 mm, lengths to 2.5 times tube, adaxials 1–1.5 mm; corolla green-yellow, streaked purple or brown; banner orbiculate, 8–9 × 6–7 mm, emarginate, villosulous, gland-dotted; wings oblong, 6–7 × 2–2.5 mm, often gland-dotted, puberulent apically; keel 6–8 × 3–3.5 mm, puberulent apically; stamens 8–9 mm. **Legumes** brown or greenish, widely ovoid-oblong, subinflated, constricted, 20–30 × 7–12 mm, gland-dotted, rarely viscid, densely villosulous to puberulent. **Seeds** red and black, subglobose to ovoid, plump, 5–8 × 4–6 mm.

Flowering spring–summer. Sandy soils or limestone, open areas, thickets, forests; of conservation concern; (0–20) or 600–1200 m; Ariz., Fla.; Mexico (Baja California Sur, Chiapas, Chihuahua, Colima, Guerrero, Jalisco, México, Michoacán, Nayarit, Oaxaca, San Luis Potosí, Sonora, Veracruz); Central America; South America.

Rhynchosia precatoria is native in Santa Cruz County, Arizona; it is considered introduced in Florida, where it is found in Miami-Dade County.

Glycine precatoria Humboldt & Bonpland ex Willdenow is a superfluous and illegitimate name that pertains here.

9. Rhynchosia cytisoides (Bertoloni) Wilbur, Rhodora 64: 60. 1962 • Royal snoutbean [E]

Lespedeza cytisoides Bertoloni, Mem. Reale Accad. Sci. Ist. Bologna 2: 278, plate 16. 1851; *Pitcheria galactoides* Nuttall; *Rhynchosia pitcheria* Burkart

Herbs or subshrubs. Stems erect and wiry, villosulous to puberulent, hairs silvery. **Leaves** trifoliolate; stipules persistent, linear, 1 × 0.5 mm, apex acuminate; petiole 1–3 mm, puberulent; leaflet blades elliptic, 5–20 × 4–10 mm, leathery, gland-dotted abaxially, base cuneate, margins revolute, apex acute to obtuse, frequently apiculate, surfaces puberulent abaxially, finely strigose adaxially. **Inflorescences** 1(2 or 3) simple flowers per axil, longer than leaves, 0.7–1.5 cm. **Pedicels** 3–5 mm. **Flowers:** calyx 5–8 mm, hirtellous, tube 1.5–3 mm, lobes lanceolate, laterals 4.5–5 mm, lengths to 2.5 times tube, adaxials 1–1.5 mm; corolla yellow, veined purple; banner obovate to orbiculate, 8–10 × 7–10 mm, emarginate, glabrous; wings narrowly oblong, 8.5–10 × 2–2.5 mm, glabrous; keel 9–10 × 4–5 mm, glabrous; stamens 10–12 mm. **Legumes** oblong or oblong-lanceoloid, compressed, 10–20 × 5–9 mm, puberulent. **Seeds** brown, black, or mottled, subglobose, compressed, 2–3 × 2–3 mm; hilum ovate, 0.5–1 mm.

Flowering spring–summer. Sandy soils of pinehills, fields, oak woodlands, roadsides, sand dunes; 0–50 m; Ala., Fla., Miss.

Rhynchosia galactoides (Nuttall) Endlicher ex Walpers is an illegitimate name that pertains here.

10. Rhynchosia parvifolia de Candolle in A. P. de Candolle and A. L. P. P. de Candolle, Prodr. 2: 385. 1825 • Small-leaf snoutbean

Dolicholus parvifolius (de Candolle) Vail; *Leucopterum parvifolium* (de Candolle) Small

Herbs. Stems prostrate or twining, tomentulose, hairs silvery or grayish. **Leaves** trifoliolate; stipules persistent, subulate, 1–2 × 0.5–1 mm, apex acute to acuminate, surfaces tomentulose; petiole 4–30 mm, tomentulose; leaflet blades obovate or elliptic-lanceolate, 10–45 × 5–20 mm, leathery, gland-dotted, base obtuse, apex usually rounded or obtuse, rarely acuminate, surfaces strongly reticulate and densely grayish tomentulose abaxially, densely grayish tomentulose adaxially. **Inflorescences** racemes, shorter than or equal to leaves, 2–6 cm. **Pedicels** 2–4 mm, viscid. **Flowers:** calyx 5–7 mm, tomentose, viscid, tube 2–2.5 mm, lobes lanceolate, laterals 4–5 mm, lengths to 2.5 times tube, adaxials 2.5–5 mm; corolla pale yellow; banner suborbiculate, 8–10 × 6–7 mm, emarginate, puberulent, gland-dotted; wings oblong, 8–9 × 2.5–3 mm, glabrous; keel 8–9.5 × 2–2.5 mm, glabrous; stamens 8–10 mm. **Legumes** ellipsoid, compressed, 15–17 × 4–6 mm, yellow-hirsute and puberulent, hairs intermixed. **Seeds** brown, black, or mottled, ovoid-ellipsoid, compressed, 2.5–4 × 2.5–3 mm; hilum linear, 1–1.5 mm.

Flowering spring–summer. Sandy pinelands and grasslands, limestone, trails, roads, beaches; 0–10 m; Fla.; West Indies (Greater Antilles).

In the flora area, *Rhynchosia parvifolia* is found in Miami-Dade and Monroe counties.

11. Rhynchosia latifolia Nuttall ex Torrey & A. Gray, Fl. N. Amer. 1: 285. 1838 • Prairie snoutbean [E]

Dolicholus torreyi (Vail) Vail; *Rhynchosia torreyi* Vail

Herbs. Stems usually trailing or twining, rarely suberect, hirsute, hairs tawny. **Leaves** usually trifoliolate, proximalmost sometimes unifoliolate; stipules deciduous, subulate-lanceolate, 2.5–7.5 × 2–2.5 mm, apex acuminate; petiole 20–60 mm, hirsute; leaflet blades oval to ovate-rhombic or orbiculate, 30–80 × 10–60 mm, leathery, gland-dotted abaxially, base obtuse or subcordate, apex obtuse, acute, or abruptly acuminate, often mucronate, surfaces villous abaxially, strigose adaxially. **Inflorescences** racemes, longer than leaves, 5–20 cm. **Pedicels** 1–3 mm. **Flowers:** calyx 8–15 mm, hirsute, tube 2–3 mm, lobes lanceolate, laterals 7–10 mm, lengths 3+ times tube, adaxials 4 mm; corolla yellow; banner obovate, 9.5–14 × 6–7 mm, emarginate, hirtellous, gland-dotted; wings oblong, 8.5–13 × 2–2.5 mm, glabrous; keel 8.5–13 × 3–4 mm, glabrous; stamens 8–12 mm. **Legumes** ovoid-oblong, compressed, 15–20 × 7–9 mm, villous and puberulent, hairs intermixed. **Seeds** brown-gray or mottled, subglobose, compressed, 3–4 × 3–4 mm. $2n = 22$.

Flowering spring–summer. Sandy soils, pine and oak woodlands, sandy prairies, limestone glades, along streams, thickets; 0–400 m; Ark., La., Miss., Mo., Okla., Tex.

Dolicholus latifolius (Nuttall ex Torrey & A. Gray) Vail and *Phaseolus latifolius* (Nuttall ex Torrey & A. Gray) Eaton & Wright are illegitimate names that pertain here.

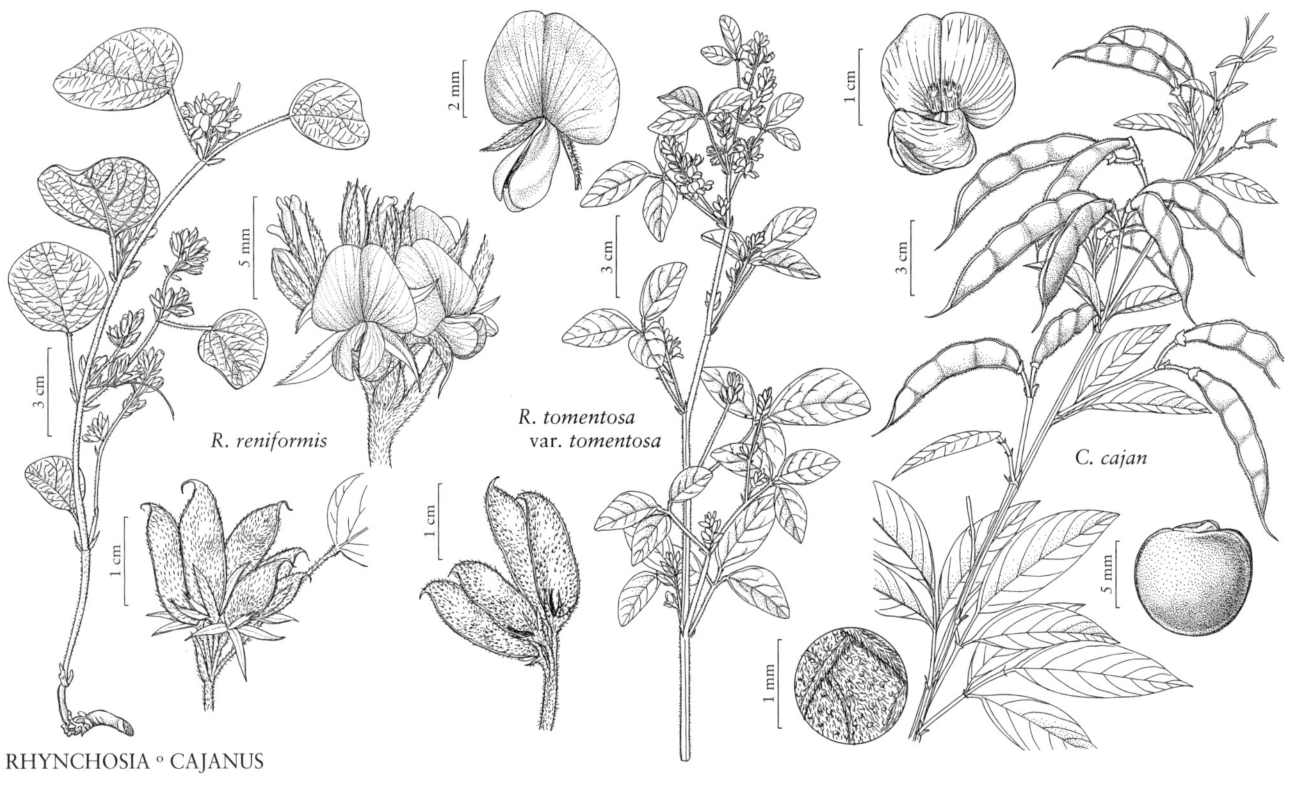

RHYNCHOSIA ◦ CAJANUS

12. Rhynchosia tomentosa (Linnaeus) Hooker & Arnott, Compan. Bot. Mag. 1: 23. 1835 • Twining snoutbean [E] [F]

Glycine tomentosa Linnaeus, Sp. Pl. 2: 754. 1753

Herbs or subshrubs. Stems ascending or erect, tomentulose to hirtellous, hairs silvery to tawny. **Leaves** usually trifoliolate, proximalmost sometimes unifoliolate; stipules caducous or persistent, lanceolate to linear-lanceolate, 3–12 × 1.5–3.5 mm, apex acuminate; petiole 5–35 mm, densely canescent-tomentose abaxially, villous adaxially; leaflet blades oblong or ovate to rhombic-ovate, elliptic, or obovate, 20–50(–60) × 10–40(–50) mm, leathery, gland-dotted, base obtuse, subcordate, or broadly cuneate, apex acute, obtuse, or rounded, minutely apiculate, surfaces puberulent, strigulose, or villosulous. **Inflorescences** racemes, shorter than leaves, axillary ones 1.5–4(–5) cm, terminal ones 6.5–23 cm. **Pedicels** 1–3 mm. **Flowers:** calyx 6–9 mm, hirtellous, tube 1.5–2.5 mm, lobes narrowly lanceolate to linear-subulate, laterals 4.5–7.5 mm, lengths 3+ times tube, adaxials 2–2.5 mm; corolla yellow or bright yellow; banner orbiculate, 6–9 × 5–7 mm, emarginate, glabrous; wings oblong, 6–8 × 1.5–2.5 mm, glabrous; keel 5–7.5 × 2–2.5 mm, glabrous; stamens 5.5–7.5 mm. **Legumes** ovoid-oblong, compressed, 15–20 × 5–7 mm, hirtellous and puberulent, hairs intermixed. **Seeds** brown, black, or mottled, subglobose, compressed, 3–4 × 3–4 mm. **2*n*** = 22.

Varieties 2 (2 in the flora): s, e United States.

1. Stipules persistent; inflorescences axillary . . . . .12a. *Rhynchosia tomentosa* var. *tomentosa*
1. Stipules caducous; inflorescences mostly terminal . . . . 12b. *Rhynchosia tomentosa* var. *mollissima*

12a. Rhynchosia tomentosa (Linnaeus) Hooker & Arnott var. **tomentosa** [E] [F]

Arcyphyllum erectum (Walter) Elliott; *Dolicholus drummondii* Vail; *D. erectus* (Walter) Vail; *Glycine caroliniana* Sprengel; *G. tomentosa* Linnaeus var. *erecta* (Walter) Michaux; *Rhynchosia drummondii* (Vail) K. Schumann; *R. erecta* (Walter) de Candolle; *Trifolium erectum* Walter

Stipules persistent. **Inflorescences** axillary.

Flowering spring–summer. Sandy soils, dry woods, clearings, roadsides, waste places; 0–900 m; Ala., Del., D.C., Fla., Ga., Ky., Md., Miss., N.C., Tenn., Tex., Va.

Glycine erecta (Walter) Nuttall is an illegitimate name that pertains here.

12b. Rhynchosia tomentosa (Linnaeus) Hooker & Arnott var. **mollissima** (Elliott) Torrey & A. Gray, Fl. N. Amer. 1: 285. 1838 [E]

Glycine mollissima Elliott, Sketch Bot. S. Carolina 2: 235. 1823; *Dolicholus mollissimus* (Elliott) Vail

Stipules caducous. **Inflorescences** mostly terminal.

Flowering spring–summer. Sandy soils, dry pine barrens, roadsides, fields; 0–100 m; Fla., Ga., S.C.

Variety *mollissima* is found in the northern half of the Florida peninsula, east Georgia, and a single collection from Beaufort County, South Carolina.

Rhynchosia mollissima (Eliott) Shuttleworth ex S. Watson is an illegitimate name that pertains here.

13. Rhynchosia cinerea Nash, Bull. Torrey Bot. Club 22: 149. 1895 • Brown-hair snoutbean [E]

Dolicholus cinereus (Nash) Vail

Herbs. Stems usually prostrate, rarely climbing, strigose or villosulous, hairs cinereous, appressed or slightly spreading. **Leaves** usually trifoliolate, proximalmost sometimes unifoliolate; stipules persistent, lanceolate-ovate, 2–5 × 1–2 mm, apex acuminate; petiole strigulose; leaflet blades oval to orbiculate-ovate, obovate, or rhombic, 15–35 × 6–50 mm, leathery, gland-dotted, base obtuse or subcordate, apex obtuse or acute, surfaces hirtellous abaxially, rugose and finely strigose adaxially. **Inflorescences** 1(2 or 3) simple flowers per axil, shorter than leaves, 1–3 cm. **Pedicels** 1–4 mm. **Flowers:** calyx 10–12 mm, hirtellous, tube 2 mm, lobes lanceolate, laterals 9–10 mm, lengths 3+ times tube, adaxials 3–3.5 mm; corolla light yellow; banner obovate, 8–11 × 6–8 mm, emarginate, puberulent; wings oblong, 8.5–13 × 2.5–3 mm, glabrous; keel 8–9.5 × 3–4 mm, glabrous; stamens 8–10 mm. **Legumes** ovoid-oblong, compressed, 13–17 × 6–8 mm, puberulent. **Seeds** brown, black, or mottled, subglobose, compressed, 2.5–4 × 2–4 mm.

Flowering spring–summer. Sandy soils, pine forests, coastal dunes, waste places, disturbed areas; 0–100 m; Fla.

Rhynchosia cinerea is known from peninsular Florida.

14. Rhynchosia difformis (Elliott) de Candolle in A. P. de Candolle and A. L. P. P. de Candolle, Prodr. 2: 384. 1825 • Double-form snoutbean [E]

Arcyphyllum difforme Elliott, J. Acad. Nat. Sci. Philadelphia 1: 372. 1818, based on *Glycine tomentosa* Linnaeus var. *volubilis* Michaux, Fl. Bor.-Amer. 2: 63. 1803; *Dolicholus tomentosus* (Linnaeus) Vail var. *undulatus* Vail; *Rhynchosia lewtonii* (Vail) K. Schumann; *R. tomentosa* (Linnaeus) Hooker & Arnott var. *volubilis* (Michaux) Torrey & A. Gray

Herbs. Stems usually prostrate or twining, rarely erect, strigose or hirsute, hairs tawny or silvery. **Leaves** usually trifoliolate, proximalmost sometimes unifoliolate; stipules persistent, ovate or ovate-lanceolate, 3–10 × 1.5–3 mm, apex acute or long-acuminate; petiole 10–65 mm, hirsute; leaflet blades ovate to ovate-rhombic and orbiculate, or obovate to obovate-elliptic and elliptic, 20–60 × 10–70 mm, leathery, gland-dotted, base obtuse to rounded or subcordate, apex usually acute, obtuse, or rounded, rarely retuse, surfaces hirtellous or strigulose to loosely strigose abaxially, glabrous or strigose adaxially. **Inflorescences** racemes, shorter than leaves, 1–4 cm. **Pedicels** 2–5 mm. **Flowers:** calyx 9–12 mm, hirsute or hirtellous, tube 1–2 mm, lobes widely lanceolate or ovate-lanceolate, laterals 6–10 mm, adaxials 3–5 mm; corolla deep yellow or orange-yellow; banner broadly-obovate, 8–10.5 × 5–6 mm, emarginate, glabrous or puberulent, with a pair of internal callosities; wings oblong, 7–8 × 2–3 mm, glabrous; keel 7–8 × 2–3 mm, glabrous; stamens 7–9 mm. **Legumes** ovoid-oblong, compressed, 14–20 × 6–9 mm, gland-dotted, puberulent and hirsute, hairs intermixed. **Seeds** brown, black, or mottled, subglobose, compressed, 3–4 × 3–4 mm. 2*n* = 22.

Flowering spring–summer. Sandy soils, pinelands, fallow fields, clearings; 0–200 m; Ala., Ga., La., Miss., Mo., N.C., S.C., Tenn., Tex., Va.

Rhynchosia difformis is common in the coastal plain but rare in the mountains of eastern Tennessee in Cocke County.

90. CAJANUS Adanson, Fam. Pl. 2: 326 (as Cajan), 529 (as Kajan). 1763, name and orthography conserved • [Malay *catjang* (*kacang*) or Tamil *kecca-kai* (*karamini*), name for pods in general] I

L. J. G. van der Maesen

Atylosia Wight & Arnott; *Cantharospermum* Wight & Arnott; *Endomallus* Gagnepain

Shrubs [herbs, vines], short-lived, unarmed. **Stems** spreading to erect, pubescent. **Leaves** alternate, odd-pinnate [palmate]; stipules present; petiolate; leaflets 3, stipels present [absent], setiform, blade margins entire, with vesicular glands (gland-dotted) abaxially, surfaces pubescent or glabrous abaxially, pubescent adaxially. **Inflorescences** 1–10(–30)-flowered, axillary [terminal], racemes; bracts present, caducous. **Flowers** papilionaceous; calyx campanulate, lobes 5, unequal, ± connate distally; corolla yellow, orange, red, or purplish, to 30 mm; stamens 10, diadelphous; anthers dorsifixed. **Fruits** legumes, pedicellate, green to purplish, sometimes variegated, flattened, with transverse lines, oblong [linear-oblong], dehiscent, depressed between seeds, septate, glandular-punctate, densely pubescent. **Seeds** [1 or]2–9[or 10], white to cream and brown, purplish, or nearly black, sometimes mottled, globose to ellipsoid-reniform [subglobose]. $x = 11$.

Species 34 (1 in the flora): introduced, Florida; Asia, Africa, Australia; introduced also in Mexico, West Indies (Antilles, Bahamas), Central America, South America, Australia.

Cajanus is the type genus of subtribe Cajaninae in tribe Phaseoleae, all species of which possess glandular dots.

SELECTED REFERENCES van der Maesen, L. J. G. 1986. *Cajanus* DC. and *Atylosia* W. & A. (Leguminosae). Wageningen Agric. Univ. Pap. 85(4): 1–225. van der Maesen, L. J. G. 1990. Origin, history and taxonomy of pigeonpea. In: Y. L. Nene et al., eds. 1990. The Pigeonpea. Wallingford and Patancheru. Pp. 15–46.

1. Cajanus cajan (Linnaeus) Huth, Helios 11: 133. 1893 (as Cajan cajan) • Pigeonpea F I

Cytisus cajan Linnaeus, Sp. Pl. 2: 739. 1753

Shrubs 0.5–4 m. **Leaves:** stipules triangular-lanceolate, 2–6 mm; petiole 1–8 cm; stipels 1–4 mm, leaflet blade elliptic, ovate, or lanceolate, 40–140 × 14–45 mm, discolorous, medium green abaxially, grayish green to almost silvery adaxially, soft-leathery, base cuneate, apex acute to acuminate. **Peduncles** 1–8 cm. **Inflorescences** 4–6 cm; bracts scalelike, 1–4 mm. **Pedicels** 7–15 mm. **Flowers:** calyx pubescent, tube 3–6 mm, lobes lanceolate, 3–7 mm; corolla banner sometimes red or orange abaxially, veins prominent; stamens 15–18 mm; anthers with distinct part upturned; ovary ovoid, 5–8 mm, pubescent; style 10–12 mm, glabrous; stigma relatively small. **Legumes** straight to falcate, 20–80(–130) × 4–10(–17) mm, hairs simple and bulbous-based. **Seeds** 4–9 × 3–8 mm, shiny, smooth; hilum with vestigial strophiole/rim aril, visible in developing seed, mostly disappearing at maturity. $2n = 22, 44, 66$.

Flowering late summer–mid winter. Fields, waste places; 0–50 m; introduced; Fla.; Africa; introduced also in Mexico, West Indies (Antilles, Bahamas), Central America, South America, Asia, Australia.

Cajanus cajan is widely cultivated as a rainy-season crop in semiarid and semihumid tropical areas of the world. The species is cultivated in the United States in Florida, Hawaii, and Puerto Rico; it sometimes escapes but is not invasive. Pigeonpea is the sixth most important pulse crop in the world, and was introduced into the Americas from India via Africa (Angola and Congo), in post-Columbian times prior to, or with, the slave trade. In Central America, the large-seeded vegetable pigeonpea cultivars usually are canned fresh and are used in Latin-American cuisine; the dry pulse makes good stews and Indian dishes. The world's largest producer is India, where decorticated pigeonpea is prepared mainly as the protein-rich side dish "dhal" and savory snacks.

The English vernacular name pigeonpea was first used by L. Plukenet (1691–1705) pertaining to the Lesser Antilles (Barbados); it is sometimes written in two words (pigeon pea). Other names include Angola pea, Congo bean, gandul, gungo pea, or red gram.

91. ERYTHRINA Linnaeus, Sp. Pl. 2: 706. 1753; Gen. Pl. ed. 5, 316. 1754 • Coral tree [Greek *erythros*, red, alluding to bright red or red-orange corollas]

Guy L. Nesom

Micropteryx Walpers

Trees, shrubs, or herbs, perennial, armed, with recurved prickles. **Stems** erect or sprawling, glabrous. **Leaves** alternate, odd-pinnate; stipules present, persistent or caducous, narrowly oblong to lanceolate, triangular, or foliaceous; petiolate; leaflets 3, stipels present [absent], caducous [persistent], swollen, glandlike, 1 mm, blade margins entire, surfaces glabrous; prickles sometimes on petioles, petiolules, and laminar veins. **Inflorescences** 20–80[–100]-flowered, terminal or axillary, pyramidal columnar pseudoracemes, flowers often in whorls; bracts and bracteoles absent or small and caducous. **Flowers** papilionaceous; calyx zygomorphic, broadly campanulate, with reduced lobes or spathiform-tubular and 2-lipped, lobes 0(or 5); corolla red [red-orange], petals with connate proximal margins, glabrous, banner much longer than wings and keel, not reflexed, pseudotubular and enclosing wings, keel, and stamens; stamens 10, diadelphous, vexillary stamen distinct, others connate into a sheath along ⅔–⅘ their length, exserted, shorter than banner, [monadelphous, or mostly distinct]; anthers dorsifixed, uniform, dehiscing longitudinally; style glabrous; stigma terminal, relatively small, usually 2-lobed. **Fruits** legumes, stipitate, terete to laterally compressed, narrowly oblong-cylindric, dehiscent, regularly or irregularly constricted between seeds, leathery to woody, glabrous. **Seeds** (1–)3–10, slightly compressed, red to orange-red or orange, sometimes with black markings, oblong to oblong-elliptic or oblong-reniform in outline; hilum narrowly elliptic, without aril. $x = 21$.

Species ca. 120 (2 in the flora): s United States, Mexico, West Indies, Central America, South America, Asia, Africa, Indian Ocean Islands (Madagascar), Australia.

Seeds of most *Erythrina* species are highly toxic, but *E. edulis* Triana ex M. Micheli has long been cultivated as a food source in the tropical highlands of South America. The seeds must be boiled or fried; they contain amino acids and provide a base for tortillas, desserts, pies, soups, and food for infants (F. R. Ruskin 1989).

Red is the characteristic flower color in the genus, but white-flowered individuals and orange-flowered species occur, and orange, yellow, salmon, green, and white variants are found within natural populations of *Erythrina sandwicensis* O. Degener, the only member of the genus endemic to the Hawaiian Islands.

Shrubby and arboreal species of *Erythrina* are planted as ornamentals in the flora area for their brilliant red to scarlet petals. The native South American *Erythrina crista-galli* Linnaeus is widely planted as a street or garden tree in California and in towns along the Gulf Coast; plants underlying a view of it as naturalized are either persisting from cultivation or better regarded as waifs (G. L. Nesom 2015b).

Erythrina caffra Thunberg, the African coral tree, may be naturalized in California, as documented by records in the Consortium of California Herbaria database from Orange and San Diego counties. It was included in the San Diego County flora by J. P. Rebman and M. G. Simpson (2014). It is a tree to 12 m (rarely to 21 m) with orange-scarlet corollas in which the banner curves upward, exposing the other corolla parts and the stamens.

SELECTED REFERENCES Krukoff, B. A. and R. C. Barneby. 1973. Notes on species of *Erythrina*. VII. Phytologia 27: 108–114. Krukoff, B. A. and R. C. Barneby. 1974. Conspectus of species of the genus *Erythrina*. Lloydia 37: 332–459. Nesom, G. L. 2015b. Key to native and cultivated species of *Erythrina* (Fabaceae) in the USA and comments on naturalization of *E. crista-galli*. Phytoneuron 2015-29: 1–8. Nesom, G. L. 2016. *Erythrina herbacea* (Fabaceae) and two close relatives from Mexico. Phytoneuron 2016-40: 1–13.

1. Leaflet blades ovate-acuminate to hastate-ovate, subtrilobed; herbs or shrubs; s, se United States . . . . 1. *Erythrina herbacea*
1. Leaflet blades broadly ovate to depressed ovate, unlobed; shrubs or small trees; Arizona, New Mexico . . . . 2. *Erythrina flabelliformis*

1. Erythrina herbacea Linnaeus, Sp. Pl. 2: 706. 1753 • Red cardinal, eastern coral or Cherokee bean [F]

Erythrina arborea (Chapman) Small; *E. herbacea* var. *arborea* Chapman

Herbs or shrubs, 1–2.5(–5) m; main branches erect or sprawling, new shoots erect or arching, glabrous or minutely puberulent and glabrescent. **Leaflets** thin-herbaceous, blades ovate-acuminate to hastate-ovate, subtrilobed, terminal blade (2–)3–8(–13) × 2–11 cm, base truncate to broadly cuneate. **Inflorescences** of herbaceous forms appearing before or with leafy stems, flowers and leaves usually on separate stems, 20–60(–75)-flowered. **Flowers:** calyx tube short-cylindric to obconic, 5–8 mm, apex truncate and unlobed; corolla banner elliptic-oblong, 3–5 cm, folded and pseudotubular, wings and keel short, slightly protruding from calyx. **Legumes** 6–15(–21) cm. **Seeds** (1–)3–6, red to orange-red or orange.

Flowering Apr–Jun. Thickets, turkey oak woodlands, longleaf pine savannas, scrub live oak, post oak-hickory-pine, mixed oak-pine, mixed hardwoods, pine-sweetgum-palmetto woodlands, coastal dunes, hammocks, sandy or sandy clay soils; 0–100 m; Ala., Ark., Fla., Ga., La., Miss., N.C., Okla., S.C., Tex.; Mexico (Tamaulipas).

Over most of the range of *Erythrina herbacea*, the plants are herbaceous perennials with flowers and leaves on separate stems (flowers borne on leafless stems) arising separately from the underground root. In many counties of Florida, as well as Gulf states from Georgia to Texas, flowers and leaves are often borne on the same stem; the flowers usually in a dense to loose raceme and usually distal to the leaves, sometimes axillary. Some of these plants are herbaceous. In southernmost Florida, the stems are usually distinctly woody and perennial with deciduous leaves. J. K. Small (1933) distinguished *E. arborea* on this basis, noting also that the banner was slightly shorter in *E. arborea* (35–40 versus 45–50 mm in *E. herbacea*); these forms are conspecific.

A single white-petaled plant in a population of red-petaled ones from Pinellas County, Florida, has been described (*Erythrina herbacea* forma *albiflora* Moffler & Crewz).

Plants of Mexico previously treated as the strictly Mexican *Erythrina herbacea* subsp. *nigrorosea* Krukoff & Barneby have been treated as *E. nigrorosea* (Krukoff & Barneby) G. L. Nesom (G. L. Nesom 2016). They differ from *E. herbacea* in their pink corollas and black calyces and consistently shrubby habit; *E. nigrorosea* may be more closely related to the Mexican-Central American *E. goldmanii* Standley and *E. standleyana* Krukoff. *Erythrina herbacea* and *E. nigrorosea* are sympatric in southern Tamaulipas, Mexico.

2. Erythrina flabelliformis Kearney, Trans. New York Acad. Sci. 14: 32. 1894 • Coral or western coral bean

Shrubs or small trees, 0.6–2 [–6] m; branches erect, glabrous. **Leaflets** thin-herbaceous, blades broadly ovate to depressed ovate, unlobed, terminal blade (3–)5–7.5 × (3–)4–11 cm, base truncate to slightly obtuse. **Inflorescences** appearing before or with developing leaves, flowers and leaves on same stem, 25–80-flowered. **Flowers:** calyx tube short-obconic, 6–8 mm, apex truncate and unlobed; corolla banner elliptic-oblong, 4–7 cm, folded and pseudotubular, wings and keel reduced, not protruding from calyx. **Legumes** 12–25 (–35) cm. **Seeds** 5–10, red to orange-red or orange with black marking.

Flowering Apr–Jul. Grasslands, mesquite-grasslands, mesquite-*Opuntia*-*Agave* communities, oak-grasslands, chaparral, oak-beargrass-yucca, oak-juniper woodlands, riparian areas, hackberry communities, hills, flats, rocky slopes; 1000–1800 m; Ariz., N.Mex.; Mexico (Aguascalientes, Baja California, Chihuahua, Durango, Jalisco, Michoacán, Sinaloa, Sonora, Zacatecas).

In the flora area, *Erythrina flabelliformis* is found mostly in mountains of south-central and southeastern Arizona and southwestern and southern New Mexico.

92. COLOGANIA Kunth, Mimoses, 205, plates 57, 58. 1824 [For the Cologan family, patrons of arts, science, and navigation in Tenerife, Canary Islands]

Gabriel Flores-Franco

Alfonso Delgado-Salinas

Herbs or vines, perennial, unarmed. **Stems** usually twining or prostrate, rarely erect, densely strigose or hirsute, glabrescent; arising from subterranean, lignescent to woody taproots. **Leaves** alternate, odd-pinnate; stipules present, persistent, striate; petiolate; leaflets (1–)3(or 5), stipels persistent or caducous, sometimes absent, blade margins entire, often revolute, apex mucronate, surfaces usually pubescent, sometimes glabrous adaxially. **Inflorescences** 1–6-flowered, axillary, racemes, fasciculate (usually with both chasmogamous and cleistogamous flowers), or with solitary flowers; bracts present, subtending peduncles and pedicels, persistent, usually relatively small; bracteoles persistent, paired or alternate proximal to calyx. **Flowers** papilionaceous; calyx tubular [cylindric], lobes 5, sometimes adaxial pair fused, adaxial gibbous at base; corolla purple, purple-pink, purplish blue, blue, pink, magenta, red-purple, violet, lilac, or lavender, glabrous; banner base auriculate, short-clawed; wings longer than keel, long-clawed, auriculate, distally spreading; keel slightly incurved, long-clawed; stamens 10, diadelphous; anthers sub-basifixed, dehiscing laterally, pollen tricolporate; ovary usually stipitate, pubescent, nectary disc at base; style filiform, ± incurved, glabrous, stigma terminal with a crown of short cilia. **Fruits** legumes, sessile or stipitate, compressed or slightly turgid, linear to falcate or strongly curved, dehiscent, cleistogamous fruits smaller, pubescent. **Seeds** 2–10(or 11), compressed, usually oblong, orbicular, or subquadrate, rarely rhombic or elliptic; testa smooth, hilum lateral, ovate, rim-aril and epihilum conspicuous. $x = 11$.

Species ca. 15 (3 in the flora): sc, sw United States, Mexico, Central America, South America (n Argentina, Bolivia, Colombia, Ecuador, Peru, Venezuela).

Cologania is found mostly in montane temperate areas, with Mexico as its center of diversity (G. Flores-Franco 2013).

Species of *Cologania* can be distinguished by the combination of the following features: woody taproots; commonly trifoliolate leaves; inflorescences with few papilionaceous flowers that have either tubular calyces and brightly colored petals in anthesis (chasmogamous) or funnelform calyces that do not fully open (cleistogamous). The cleistogamous flowers may be found with chasmogamous ones or in short, separate inflorescences that are often smaller and have fewer flower parts, such as the androecium reduced to one or two stamens, and the style shorter and reflexed towards the stamens. Two distinctive fruits are set (amphicarpy); the cleistogamous fruits are shorter and often broader with fewer seeds (2–6). Its polyploid nature, proposed interspecies hybridization, and species leaf polymorphism have made the taxonomy of this genus unstable (O. S. Fearing 1959; R. McVaugh 1987; B. L. Turner 1992).

Plants of *Cologania pulchella* Kunth, classified under *C. broussonetii* (Balbis) de Candolle by O. S. Fearing (1959) and B. L. Turner (1992), have been reported to occur within the flora area; however, according to recent studies, *C. pulchella* is known only from northern Mexico to Panama (G. Flores-Franco 2013).

SELECTED REFERENCES Fearing, O. S. 1959. A Cytotaxonomic Study of the Genus *Cologania* and its Relationship to *Amphicarpaea* (Leguminosae-Papilionoideae). Ph.D. dissertation. University of Texas. Flores-Franco, G. 2013. Análisis Taxonómico del Género *Cologania* (Leguminosae). M.Ci.(Biol.) tesis. Universidad Nacional Autónoma de México. Turner, B. L. 1992. Taxonomic overview of the genus *Cologania* (Fabaceae, Phaseoleae). Phytologia 73: 281–301.

1. Herbs prostrate; petioles 0.2–0.5 cm; leaflet blades nearly as long as wide, obovate or obovate-elliptic to orbiculate, apex obtuse; stipels usually caducous; inflorescences pedunculate . . . . 3. *Cologania obovata*
1. Herbs usually twining, sometimes erect, rarely prostrate; petioles 0.8–8 cm, leaflet blades mostly 2–10 times as long as wide, usually linear-oblong, oblong-elliptic, elliptic, lanceolate, ovate, ovate-oblong, or ovate-elliptic, rarely orbiculate, obovate, oblong, or oblong-obovate, apex usually acute to obtuse, rarely acuminate; stipels not caducous; inflorescences sessile or pedunculate.
   2. Leaflets 3(or 5), green, blades usually linear-oblong, oblong, oblong-elliptic, lanceolate, ovate, elliptic, or ovate-oblong, rarely orbiculate or obovate, apex usually acute or obtuse, rarely acuminate; calyx green to purple; legumes of chasmogamous flowers 5 × 0.4 cm, linear to slightly falcate, sessile, valves densely appressed pilose or hirsute . . . . 1. *Cologania angustifolia*
   2. Leaflets 3, pallid green, blades usually elliptic, oblong-elliptic, ovate, or ovate-elliptic, rarely oblong or oblong-obovate, apex usually acute or obtuse, rarely acuminate; calyx pallid green, not purple; legumes of chasmogamous flowers 4.6–6.8 × 0.3–0.4 cm, slightly to strongly curved, stipe 1.6–3.2 mm, valves usually strigose, rarely pilose-hirsute . . . . 2. *Cologania pallida*

1. Cologania angustifolia Kunth, Mimoses, 209, plate 58. 1824 • Longleaf cologania [F]

Amphicarpaea angustifolia (Kunth) Taubert; *Cologania confusa* Rose; *C. intermedia* Kunth; *C. longifolia* A. Gray; *C. longifolia* var. *stricta* M. E. Jones; *C. martia* S. Watson; *Galactia radicata* de Candolle; *Martia mexicana* Zuccarini; *Neurocarpum mexicanum* (Zuccarini) Steudel

Herbs or vines twining, erect, or prostrate, to 1 m. **Stems** canaliculate-striate, strigose, pilose, or hirsute to glabrescent, hairs mostly white, rarely yellow. **Leaves:** stipules striate, oblong-ovate, oblong, linear-oblong, linear-lanceolate, lanceolate, or triangular, 1.1–6.7 × (0.2–)0.3–2.8 mm, hirsutulous, pilose, strigose, or glabrate; petiole striate, canaliculate, 1–8 cm, hirsute or strigose to glabrescent; rachis canaliculate, corrugate, 7–17 mm, hirsute or strigose; stipels not caducous, linear, 0.3–0.5 mm, strigose, glabrescent, or glabrous; leaflets 3(or 5), green, blades usually linear-oblong, oblong, oblong-elliptic, lanceolate, ovate, elliptic, or ovate-oblong, rarely orbiculate or obovate, 0.4–17 × 0.1–1.6 cm, base cuneate, obtuse, rounded, or attenuate, sometimes subcordate, apex usually acute or obtuse, rarely acuminate, venation conspicuous abaxially, conspicuous or slightly conspicuous adaxially, surfaces abaxially slightly to densely strigose, glabrescent, adaxially strigose. **Peduncles** 0.5–4.8(–18) mm, strigose, pilose, hirsutulous, pilosulous, or strigulose; bracts striate, lanceolate, linear-lanceolate, linear-oblong, or oblong, 2–7.8 × 0.4–1.3 mm, strigose or densely hirsute, glabrescent. **Inflorescences** with 1–3(or 4) chasmogamous flowers, usually together with 1 or 2 cleistogamous flowers, 1.8–4.9 cm. **Pedicels** 2–22 mm, densely to slightly strigose or pilose; bracts striate, linear, 1.3–4.5 mm, strigose, strigulose, hirsute, or glabrescent; bracteoles linear, (0.7–)1.2–3.3(–4.6) mm, strigose, strigulose, hirsutulous, or glabrescent. **Flowers:** calyx green to purple, 7.5–16 × 2.1–5.9 mm, strigose, hirsute, pilose, or glabrescent, lobes triangular, strigose, (1.6–)2.2–4.5(–5.2) × 1.1–2.3(–3.1) mm, adaxial lobe deltate, 2.5–4.8 × 2–3.6 mm, rarely divided; corolla usually purple, pink-purple, pink, or bluish, rarely magenta; banner obovate, 17–33 × 7.6–19 mm, claw slightly lobulate, apex obcordate, rarely emarginate; wings obovate-oblong or obovate, 14–30 × 2.5–7 mm, claw 6.8–13 mm; keel oblong or obovate, 11–18 × 2.1–3.4 mm, claw 6.8–12 mm; staminal tube 10.5–18.5 × 1.6–3.5 mm, free filaments 0.5–2.6 mm, vexillary filament 9.5–17 mm; anthers elliptic, oblong, or oblong-elliptic, 0.4–0.7 × 0.2–0.4(–0.5) mm; ovary linear-oblong, (8–)11–19 × 0.4–0.8 mm, sericeous to densely strigose; style 1.5–3.8 mm; stigma 0.2–0.3 mm diam. **Legumes** (chasmogamous) linear to slightly falcate, 5 × 0.4 cm, valves densely appressed-pilose or hirsute; stipe 0 mm. **Seeds** (chasmogamous) 10, brown, oblong or subquadrangular, 5 mm. **Legumes** (cleistogamous) straight to slightly or strongly curved, (1.4–)1.8–4.6 × 0.2–0.4 cm, valves densely strigose or pilose; stipe (0–) 0.8–1 mm. **Seeds** (cleistogamous) (2–)4–10, brown, with darker patterns, oblong, orbicular, or subquadrate, 2–4.8 mm. 2*n* = 44.

Flowering Mar–Oct. Open or shady understory of pine or pine-oak, juniper-pine or mixed forests of pine, Douglas-fir, and oak, grasslands, canyon slopes, streamsides, roadsides, rocky soils from limestone or igneous rock; 800–2800 m; Ariz., N.Mex., Tex.; Mexico.

Cologania angustifolia is characterized by its high variability, not only in leaflets and fruit morphology,

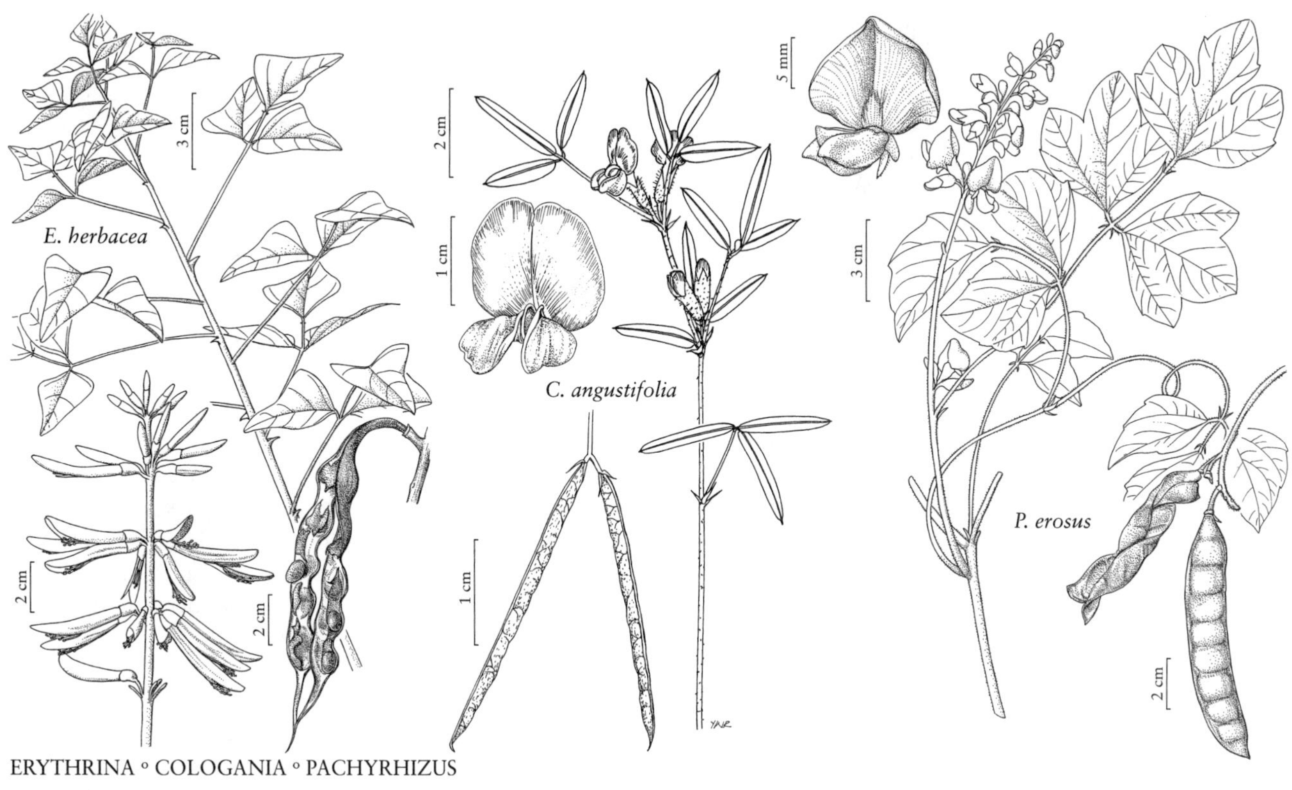

ERYTHRINA ∘ COLOGANIA ∘ PACHYRHIZUS

but also in its habit. Several of the different morphs displayed throughout its distribution have received species names. Hybridization with other species has also been proposed (O. S. Fearing 1959; B. L. Turner 1992).

Cologania angustifolia is widespread in Mexico.

2. **Cologania pallida** Rose, Contr. U.S. Natl. Herb. 8: 38. 1903 • Pale cologania

Galactia watsoniana W. C. Holmes & Singhurst

Herbs or vines twining, 0.2–0.5 m. **Stems** canaliculate, corrugate, hirsute to strigose, basal more hairy. **Leaves:** stipules striate, lanceolate, oblong, or linear-lanceolate, 1.7–6 × (0.3–)0.8–1.8(–3) mm, strigose, glabrescent; petiole canaliculate, corrugate, 0.8–6.5 cm, strigose to slightly strigose; rachis sulcate, corrugate, (5–)10–20 mm, strigose; stipels not caducous, linear, 0.8–2.5 mm, glabrescent; leaflets 3, pallid green, blades usually elliptic, oblong-elliptic, ovate, or ovate-elliptic, rarely oblong or oblong-obovate, 0.6–5.8 × (0.2–)0.3–3.2 cm (lateral leaflets conspicuously shorter than terminal), base usually obtuse, cuneate, or rounded, rarely subcordate, apex usually acute or obtuse, rarely acuminate, venation conspicuous to prominent abaxially, slightly conspicuous adaxially, surfaces usually strigose, sometimes, glabrous adaxially. **Peduncles** 0 mm; bracts linear-lanceolate or lanceolate, 3.3–5.1 × 0.3–0.8 mm, strigose to glabrescent. **Inflorescences** with 1 or 2 chasmogamous flowers, sometimes mixed with 1 or 2 cleistogamous flowers, 2–3.8 cm. **Pedicels** flexible, 4–18 mm, strigulose or pilosulous; bracts linear, 1.5–2.2 mm, strigose; bracteoles linear, 1 mm, strigulose. **Flowers:** calyx pallid green, not purple, 8.5–13 × 2.8–4.1 mm, usually hirsute, strigulose, or strigose, rarely hirsutulous, lobes 1.5–3.4(–5) × 1–2.2 mm, adaxial lobe deltate, 2.1–3 × 2.1–3.7 mm, not divided; corolla purple or purplish blue; banner obovate, (16–)21–24.5 × 7.4–14 mm, apex obcordate; wings obovate-oblong, 12–21.5 × 2.6–4.8(–5) mm, claw 7–10 mm; keel obovate, 9–15.5 × 2–3.6 mm, claw 7–10 mm; staminal tube 14–15.5 × 1.6–2.9 mm, free filaments (0.5–)0.8–2.8 mm, vexillary filament 9–13.5 mm; anthers elliptic-oblong, 0.3–0.6 × 0.2–0.4 mm; ovary linear-oblong, 11.5–14.5 × 0.5–0.6 mm, sericeous; style 2.2–2.8 mm; stigma 0.1–0.3 mm diam. **Legumes** (chasmogamous) slightly to strongly curved, 4.6–6.8 × 0.3–0.4 cm, valves usually strigose, rarely pilose-hirsute; stipe 1.6–3.2 mm, glabrous. **Seeds** (chasmogamous) 5–11, brown, oblong, 3.3–3.5 mm. **Legumes** (cleistogamous) strongly curved, 1.9–5.2 × 0.3–0.4 cm, valves usually strigose (hairs white), rarely glabrescent; stipe 0.5 mm. **Seeds** (cleistogamous) 2–6, mature seeds not seen. $2n = 44$.

Flowering May–Sep. Open pine, juniper-pine or pine-oak forests, grasslands, rocky limestone or igneous soils; 1300–2500 m; Ariz., N.Mex., Tex.; Mexico (Chihuahua, Coahuila, Sonora).

Cologania pallida is still poorly known and is distinguished by its fascicles of one or two chasmogamous flowers rarely mixed with one or two cleistogamous, and by its pallid green leaves, with usually elliptic to ovate-elliptic, strigose or glabrous leaflets. The legumes are often strongly curved.

Cologania pallida is uncommon in Arizona. Extant populations are known only from the Huachuca Mountains in southern Cochise County, though it is also known historically from the White Mountains in Apache County.

3. **Cologania obovata** Schlechtendal, Linnaea 12: 287. 1838 • Lemmon's cologania

Cologania houghii Rose; *C. humifusa* Hemsley; *C. lemmonii* A. Gray; *C. pringlei* S. Watson

Herbs or vines prostrate, 0.2–0.5 m. **Stems** canaliculate, densely hirsute. **Leaves:** stipules striate, oblong to broadly oblong or lanceolate, 1.8–6.5(–7) × 0.4–3.2(–5.8) mm, slightly pubescent; petiole canaliculate, 0.2–0.5 cm, hirsutulous, hairs sometimes retrorse; rachis canaliculate, (0.7–)1–5.1 mm, hirsute; stipels usually caducous, rarely present, acicular, 0.8–1.2 mm, densely pubescent; leaflets 3 (sometimes basal leaves with 1–3), green, blades obovate or obovate-elliptic to orbiculate, (0.8–)1–5.4 × (0.6–)1–3.6 cm, base cuneate to obtuse, apex obtuse, venation conspicuous abaxially, slightly conspicuous adaxially, surfaces pubescent to densely pubescent. **Peduncles** sulcate, (0.3–)2–35 mm, pubescent to slightly pubescent; bracts striate, usually oblong, linear-oblong, ovate, or obovate-oblong, rarely lanceolate, 1.8–6.2 × 0.5–3.3 mm, apex acute or obtuse, densely pubescent, glabrescent. **Inflorescences** with 1 or 2(–4) flowers, 2.1–10 cm. **Pedicels** 0.5–6 (–17) mm, densely to slightly pubescent, hairs sometimes retrorse; bracts linear, linear-lanceolate, lanceolate, or linear-oblong, 1.2–5 mm, slightly pubescent; bracteoles linear to lanceolate, 1.2–7.2 mm, slightly pubescent. **Flowers:** calyx green to purple, (10–)13–19 × 3–6 mm, pubescent, lobes 2.4–7.5 × 1.7–3.6(–5) mm, adaxial lobe deltate, 2.3–9.5 × 1.5–2.8(–5.2) mm, entire; corolla purple, blue, magenta, red-purple, violet, lilac, or lavender; banner broadly obovate to obovate or orbiculate, 22–35 × 11–29 mm, apex rounded or obcordate, rarely emarginate; wings slightly obovate to oblong, 22–28.5 × 3–10.5 mm, claw 11–15 mm; keel obovate-oblong, 15–20 × 3.2–4.5 mm, claw 9.5–15 mm; staminal tube 12–19.5 mm, free filaments 1–2.7 mm, vexillary stamen 9.5–13 mm; anthers oblong-elliptic, (0.4–)0.5–0.9 × 0.2–0.7 mm; ovary linear-oblong, 15–19.5 × 0.7–0.8 mm, densely pubescent; style 1.9–3.5 mm; stigma 0.2–0.4 mm diam. **Legumes** (chasmogamous) slightly curved, 3–4.4 × 0.4–0.5 cm, valves densely pubescent. **Seeds** (chasmogamous) 7–10, light to dark brown, with darker patterns, usually orbicular, rarely oblong, rhombic, or elliptic, 2.1–2.8 mm. **Legumes** (cleistogamous) straight, (1.5–)2–3.8 × 0.4–0.5 cm, valves densely pubescent; stipe 1.5 mm. **Seeds** (cleistogamous) (1 or)2–8(–11), brown, with darker patterns, usually orbicular, rhombic, or elliptic, rarely oblong, 1.8–3.3 mm. 2*n* = 44.

Flowering Jan–Sep. Open pine, pine-oak or mixed forests, grasslands, slopes or roadsides, on rocky, sandy or clayish soils from limestone or igneous rock; 1100–2800 m; Ariz., Nev.; Mexico (Aguascalientes, Chihuahua, Coahuila, Durango, Hidalgo, México, Michoacán, Nayarit, Oaxaca, Puebla, Querétaro, San Luis Potosí, Sinaloa, Sonora, Tlaxcala, Zacatecas).

Cologania obovata is known only from Cochise, Pima, and Santa Cruz counties in Arizona, and in Meadow Valley Wash in southern Nevada. It is characterized by its prostrate habit, almost sessile leaves on short petioles, and by having legumes either short and wide, or long and wide. Also, the leaves in some plants were found to vary at the base from one to three leaflets, these almost sessile. Due to this variability O. S. Fearing (1959) and B. L. Turner (1992) proposed that this species possibly hybridized with *C. angustifolia*.

93. PACHYRHIZUS Richard ex de Candolle in A. P. de Candolle and A. L. P. P. de Candolle, Prodr. 2: 402. 1825, name conserved • Yam bean [Greek *pachys*, thick, and *rhiza*, root, alluding to edible tuberous roots] [I]

Guy L. Nesom

Vines, perennial, herbaceous, 2–5(–10) m, unarmed; roots tuberous. **Stems** trailing or climbing to semi-erect, strigose to hirsute or villous [hirsutulous], hairs spreading to deflexed. **Leaves** alternate, odd-pinnate; stipules present, caducous, linear-lanceolate, 5–11 mm; petiolate;

leaflets 3, alternate, stipels caducous, blade margins entire, toothed, or lobed, surfaces strigose or glabrous. **Inflorescences** 4–11-flowered, axillary or terminal, pseudoracemes, fasciculate, nodose; bracts and bracteoles present, caducous, setaceous. **Flowers** papilionaceous; calyx tubular, 8–12 mm, lobes 5; corolla white, pink, or purplish; stamens 10, diadelphous; anthers basifixed, relatively small, dehiscing apically; style glabrous; stigma relatively small, terminal. **Fruits** legumes, pedicellate, sides straight, strongly compressed, oblong, dehiscent, constricted between seeds, septate, pubescent or glabrescent. **Seeds** 4–10, somewhat flattened, 4-angled with rounded corners or suborbicular [reniform]; hilum lateral. $x = 11$.

Species 5 (1 in the flora): introduced, Florida; Mexico, West Indies, Central America, South America; introduced also widely in tropical and subtropical areas.

Three species of *Pachyrhizus* are widely cultivated for their edible tuberous roots: *P. ahipa* (Weddell) Parodi (known only in cultivation), *P. erosus*, and *P. tuberosus* (Lamarck) Sprengel. Two species occur only in the wild: *P. ferrugineus* (Piper) M. Sørensen and *P. panamensis* R. T. Clausen.

SELECTED REFERENCE Sørensen, M. 1988. A taxonomic revision of the genus *Pachyrhizus* (Fabaceae-Phaseoleae). Nordic J. Bot. 8: 167–192.

1. Pachyrhizus erosus (Linnaeus) Urban, Symb. Antill. 4: 311. 1905 (as Pachyrrhizus) • Mexican turnip, jicama [F] [I]

Dolichos erosus Linnaeus, Sp. Pl. 2: 726. 1753; *Cacara erosa* (Linnaeus) Kuntze; *Pachyrhizus erosus* var. *palmatilobus* (de Candolle) R. T. Clausen; *P. strigosus* R. T. Clausen

Vines 2–5(–10) m; roots white to brownish, usually round and beet-shaped with distinct taproot, sometimes elongated, to 2–2.5 m. **Leaves:** leaflet blades ovate to rhombic or ovate-reniform, sometimes broadly palmately 3- or 5-lobed, terminal blade often 5–8(–18) × 6–13(–20) cm, lateral blades smaller, margins entire or coarsely sinuate-dentate on distal ½. **Inflorescences** erect to spreading, 10–45(–70) cm. **Pedicels** 1–5 mm. **Flowers:** calyx 8–12 mm; corolla 14–22 mm, banner blue-violet to red-purple, white, or bicolored, suborbiculate. **Legumes** pale brown to olive green, 6–15 × 1–1.8 cm, strigose to glabrate. **Seeds** 5–10 mm, olive green to brown or reddish brown. $2n = 20, 22$.

Flowering Sep–Dec. Pine-palmetto savannas, rocky pinelands, woodlots, disturbed sites; 0–10 m; introduced; Fla.; Mexico; West Indies; Central America; South America; introduced also widely in tropical and subtropical areas.

In the flora area, *Pachyrhizus erosus* is known from Brevard and Miami-Dade counties.

In Mexico, Central America, southeast Asia, and China, *Pachyrhizus erosus* is a major food plant and source of starch, popular in salads, fresh fruit mixes, fruit bars, soups, and cooked dishes. Its sweet flavor comes from an oligosaccharide. In contrast to the roots, the stems and leaves are toxic, and the seeds contain rotenone, which is used as an insect and fish poison.

Morphological variation among apparent native races and cultivars is greatest in the Mexican states of Chiapas, Oaxaca, Tabasco, and Veracruz, and in Guatemala.

94. PUERARIA de Candolle, Ann. Sci. Nat. (Paris) 4: 97. 1825 • Kudzu [For Marc Nicolas Puerari, 1766–1845, Swiss naturalist and professor in Copenhagen] [I]

L. J. G. van der Maesen

Vines, perennial [**shrubs**], robust, woody or coarsely herbaceous, to 30 m, unarmed; roots often tuberous. **Stems** climbing and creeping, glabrous or densely pubescent. **Leaves** alternate, odd-pinnate; stipules present, persistent, peltate, 8–16(–25) mm; petiolate; leaflets 3, stipels present, blades 8–20(–26) cm, margins lobed or entire, surfaces pubescent. **Inflorescences** 15–40-flowered, axillary or terminal, pseudoracemes, unbranched or paniculate; bracts present, caducous, ovate to lanceolate; bracteoles 2. **Flowers** papilionaceous, (2 or)3[4–10] per node; calyx campanulate, (6–)10–18 mm, lobes 5, adaxial ones ± connate, pubescent; corolla purplish, blue, or white, 10–25 mm, veins evident; stamens 10, monadelphous, vexillary stamen becoming distinct as ovary expands, distinct part upturned; anthers dorsifixed, on alternating long and short filaments; ovary elongate, pubescent. **Fruits** legumes, sessile, flattened, cylindrical [flattened-oblong], well exceeding calyx, dehiscent, with or without transverse lines between seeds, septate, pubescent. **Seeds** [2–](5–)10–15[–20], flattened-ovoid [oblong or barrel-shaped]. x = 11.

Species 19 (1 in the flora): introduced; Asia (China, India, Indochina, Japan, Malesia), Pacific Islands; introduced also in Mexico, s Europe, Pacific Islands, Australia.

Pueraria montana (kudzu) and *P. phaseoloides* (Roxburgh) Bentham have been widely spread by human activity from Asia to other continents. The latter species is now treated as *Neustanthus phaseoloides* (Roxburgh) Bentham.

SELECTED REFERENCES Egan, A. N. and Pan B. 2015. Resolution of polyphyly in *Pueraria* (Leguminosae: Papilionoideae): The creation of two new genera, *Haymondia* and *Toxicopueraria*, the resurrection of *Neustanthus*, and a new combination in *Teyleria*. Phytotaxa: 218: 201–226. Egan, A. N, M. Vatanparast, and W. Cagle. 2016. Parsing polyphyletic *Pueraria*: Delimiting distinct lineages through phylogeny. Molec. Phylog. Evol. 104: 44–59. van der Maesen, L. J. G. 1985. Revision of the genus *Pueraria* de Candolle, with some notes on *Teyleria* Backer. Wageningen Agric. Univ. Pap. 85(1). van der Maesen, L. J. G. 1994. *Pueraria*, the kudzu and its relatives. An update of the taxonomy. In: M. Sørensen, ed. 1994. Proceedings of the First International Symposium on Tuberous Legumes, Guadeloupe, F.W.I., 21–24 April 1992. Copenhagen. Pp. 55–86.

1. **Pueraria montana** (Loureiro) Merrill, Trans. Amer. Philos. Soc., n. s. 24(2): 210. 1935 [F] [I] [W]

Dolichos montanus Loureiro, Fl. Cochinch. 2: 440. 1790; *Pueraria lobata* (Willdenow) Ohwi var. *montana* (Loureiro) Maesen

Varieties 3 (1 in the flora): introduced; Asia; introduced also widely elsewhere.

1a. **Pueraria montana** (Loureiro) Merrill var. **lobata** (Willdenow) Maesen & S. M. Almeida ex Sanjappa & Predeep in M. Sanjappa, Legumes India, 288. 1992 • Mason-Dixon vine, Japanese arrowroot [F] [I] [W]

Dolichos lobatus Willdenow, Sp. Pl. 3: 1047. 1802; *Pueraria lobata* (Willdenow) Ohwi

Vines to 30 m, producing new growth after winter, perennial from tuber; tuber to 18–45 cm diam. **Stems** relatively strong, 0.6–2.5(–10) cm diam. **Leaves:** stipule margins entire or 2-fid, or fringed proximal to point of insertion; petiole 8–13 cm; rachis 2.5–7 cm; leaflets: stipels lanceolate, 5–18 × 0.5–1.5 mm, margins ciliate, blades light to grayish green abaxially, green adaxially, ovate to orbiculate, 8–20(–26) × 5–19(–22) cm, ± leathery, base cuneate, margins usually 3-lobed, apex acute to acuminate, surfaces appressed-pubescent. **Inflorescences** unbranched or with 1 lateral, 10–25(–35) cm; bracts 4–10 × 0.5–1(–2) mm; bracteoles 2–4 × 1–2 mm. **Pedicels** 7–15 mm. **Flowers** fragrant; calyx gray to golden brown, tube 3–5 mm, lobes 3–13 mm, unequal (proximal ones longer), broad-acute to acuminate; corolla ± with green or yellow spot, 10–25 × 9–16 mm, banner veined; stamens 9–22 mm; ovary 8–15 mm; style 5–8 mm, glabrous; stigma globular, often penicillate. **Legumes** straight or falcate, 4–13 × 0.6–1.3 cm, hairs golden brown, dense, somewhat bulbous-based. **Seeds** reddish brown with black mottling, purplish, or almost black, sometimes variegated, 4–5 × 2.5–4 mm, minutely pitted; hilum relatively small; strophiole elliptic, 1 mm. $2n$ = 22.

Flowering summer. Fields, waste places, forest edges; 0–900 m; introduced; Ont.; Ala., Ark., Conn., Del., D.C., Fla., Ga., Ill., Ind., Kans., Ky., La., Maine, Md., Mass., Mich., Miss., Mo., Nebr., N.J., N.Y., N.C., Ohio, Okla., Oreg., Pa., S.C., Tenn., Tex., Va., Wash., W.Va.; e Asia; introduced also in Mexico, s Europe (Italy), Pacific Islands, Australia.

Variety *lobata* (kudzu) is cultivated as a specialty flour crop in Japan, as a tuber crop in New Guinea, and as a cover crop in humid (sub)tropical and warm-temperate areas of the world, mainly in Asia. Kudzu was introduced into the United States from Japan in 1876 at the Philadelphia Centennial Exposition (M. A. Stewart 1997). Useful for erosion control and fodder, kudzu has become invasive in the southern United States. It is no longer recommended as a cover crop or ornamental and is banned from trade and planting in some states as a noxious weed. In China, kudzu is used medicinally, as a diaphoretic and febrifuge, and for the treatment of alcoholism, diarrhea, and dysentery (L. J. G. van der Maesen 2002).

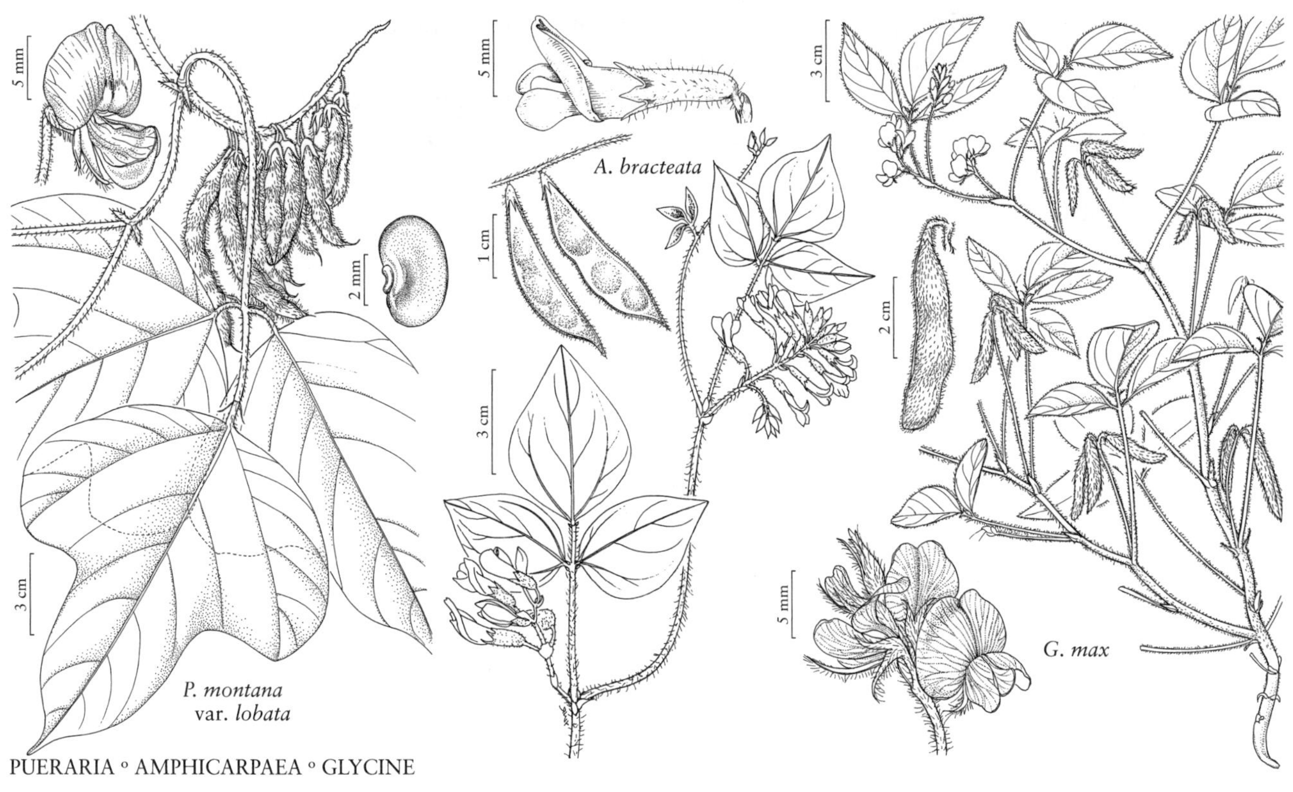

PUERARIA ◦ AMPHICARPAEA ◦ GLYCINE

95. AMPHICARPAEA Elliott ex Nuttall, Gen. N. Amer. Pl. 2: 113. 1818 (as Amphicarpa), name and orthography conserved • Hog peanut [Greek *amphi*, on both sides, and *karpos*, fruit, alluding to plants bearing aerial and subterranean fruits]

Alfonso Delgado-Salinas

Matthew A. Parker

Falcata J. F. Gmelin, name rejected; *Lobomon* Rafinesque; *Xypherus* Rafinesque

Vines, annual, unarmed, 2–3 m. **Stems** prostrate to climbing, base sometimes corky, strigose or hirtellous, hairs retrorse. **Leaves** alternate, odd-pinnate; stipules present, persistent, partly connate, membranous to firm, ca. 10-veined; petiolate, petiole longer than rachis, both canaliculate; leaflets 3, stipels present, persistent, blades 3–10.5 cm, margins entire, surfaces darker adaxially, strigillose. **Inflorescences** 6–24-flowered, axillary, racemes, with chasmogamous or cleistogamous flowers, or on short shoots or fertile brachyblasts, with distal stipular sheath, [1–]6–12 non-swollen floral nodes, each floral node 1 or 2-flowered; bracts present, persistent, firm, veined, pubescent; secondary bracts or bracts at base of pedicels, mostly caducous, subulate, glabrous; bracteoles obsolescent or absent. **Pedicels** different lengths, accrescent at fruit, with minute, retrorse hairs. **Flowers** papilionaceous, chasmogamous or cleistogamous; chasmogamous: calyx campanulate to tubular, 5–8 mm, basally gibbous, lobes 4, by connation of upper lobes, lobes subequal; corolla white to pale lavender or violet to purple, 15 mm, petals subequal, banner larger, bent slightly backwards in anthesis, not or slightly auriculate, margins revolute at anthesis, wings with ovate lamina and long-clawed, keel slightly smaller than other petals, slightly incurved and distally connate, long-clawed, articulate at base of lamina with wings; stamens 10, diadelphous; anthers sub-basifixed, relatively small; ovary subsessile, with nectarial strap at base; style glabrous, sometimes with hairs at base, slightly incurved; stigma terminal, relatively small, with a ring of papillae or cilia; cleistogamous: aerial or subterranean, on shorter and reduced flowering axes, much reduced in size and flower parts, stamens 2 or 3. **Fruits** legumes, stipitate, dimorphic, calyx persistent; aerial legumes (from chasmogamous and cleistogamous flowers) compressed, oblong to slightly falcate, elastically dehiscent, valves thin, reticulate-veined; subterranean orbicular to ellipsoidal, indehiscent, valves adjoining seed, papery, strigose or glabrous. **Seeds** 1–4[or 5], those from aerial fruits compressed, oblong, surface smooth; hilum lateral and centric, with 2-lipped rim aril, cartilaginous, 2 flaps or tongues on each lip, lens discernible dark colored, epihilum present; subterranean subglobose, fleshy, 3–4 times larger than aerial seeds. $x = 10, 11$.

Species ca. 3 (1 in the flora): North America, n Mexico, e Asia; tropical montane to temperate areas.

Amphicarpaea has a close morphological resemblance with *Cologania* due to the tubular calyx and elongated chasmogamous flowers. Both genera are vines with aerial cleistogamous flowers (where there is partial suppression of petals and stamens) and an incurvature of the style towards the anthers, securing obligate self-pollination (Zhang Y. et al. 2006). In contrast, molecular evidence indicate that *Amphicarpaea* is sister to *Glycine* and *Teramnus* P. Browne (J. K. Lee and T. Hymowitz 2001).

Prior to 1995, *Amphicarpaea* in eastern and central North America was generally considered to consist of only a single species, although many authors recognized two infraspecific taxa (H. A. Gleason and A. Cronquist 1963; B. L. Turner and O. S. Fearing 1964). *Amphicarpaea bracteata* has been the subject of more thorough investigations by M. A. Parker (1995, 1996) and H. S. Callahan (1997). Parker (1996) proposed the existence of three taxa within North American *Amphicarpaea*: var. *bracteata*, var. *comosa*, and a third unnamed variety. However, recent population genetic studies have shown that these three taxa co-occur in woodlands or forest edges with high self-pollination rates but without clear-cut phenotypic differences to separate them (R. Y. Kartzinel et al. 2016). Therefore, it is best to treat them as one species until a better systematic solution is achieved.

Amphicarpaea beans (mostly the subterranean seeds) have been food for different North American and Mexican ethnic groups and wild animals (F. Basurto-Peña et al. 1999). Also, foliage and roots have been used as a medicine (D. E. Moerman 1986). However, seed extracts of *A. edgeworthii* Bentham, occurring and eaten in Japan, could lead to atherosclerosis (Yang L. et al. 2015).

SELECTED REFERENCES Callahan, H. S. 1997. Infraspecific differentiation in the *Amphicarpaea bracteata* (Fabaceae) species complex: Varieties and ecotypes. Rhodora 99: 64–82. Kartzinel, R. Y. et al. 2016. Divergence and isolation of cryptic sympatric taxa within the annual legume *Amphicarpaea bracteata*. Ecol. & Evol. 6: 3367–3379. Ohashi, H. and K. Ohashi. 2016. A taxonomic revision of *Amphicarpaea* (Leguminosae), including a pollen morphological comparison with *Shuteria*. J. Jap. Bot. 91(suppl.): 231–249. Parker, M. A. 1996. Cryptic species within *Amphicarpaea bracteata* (Leguminosae): Evidence from isozymes, morphology, and pathogen specifity. Canad. J. Bot. 74: 1640–1650. Turner B. L. and O. S. Fearing. 1964. A taxonomic study of the genus *Amphicarpaea* (Leguminosae). SouthW. Naturalist 9: 207–218.

1. Amphicarpaea bracteata (Linnaeus) Fernald, Rhodora 35: 276. 1933 (as Amphicarpa) [F]

Glycine bracteata Linnaeus, Sp. Pl. 2: 754. 1753; *Amphicarpaea bracteata* var. *comosa* (Linnaeus) Fernald; *A. bracteata* var. *pitcheri* (Torrey & A. Gray) Fassett; *A. chamaecaulis* B. Boivin & Raymond; *A. ciliata* Rafinesque; *A. monoica* Nuttall; *A. monoica* var. *comosa* (Linnaeus) Eaton; *A. pitcheri* Torrey & A. Gray; *Falcata bracteata* (Linnaeus) Farwell; *F. comosa* (Linnaeus) Kuntze; *F. pitcheri* (Torrey & A. Gray) Kuntze; *G. comosa* Linnaeus; *Phaseolus pitcheri* (Torrey & A. Gray) Eaton & Wright

Stems slender, filiform, mainly with whitish or pale hairs. **Leaves:** stipules lanceolate or ovate-lanceolate, 3.5–8.5 × 1–3 mm, in younger stems basally connate, sparsely strigillose; petiole 2.5–9.5(–17) cm, covered with retrorse hairs; rachis 1–1.5(–3.5) cm, covered with antrorse hairs; stipels narrowly triangular, relatively small; lateral leaflet blades asymmetrically ovate to broadly ovate, smaller than terminal; terminal blade broadly ovate to rhomboid-ovate, 3–10.5 × 1.6–8 cm, base rounded, apex acute, rarely with mucro. **Peduncles** 2–6 cm, 6–12 floral nodes; bracts firm, widely ovate to truncate at apex, flabellate or bilobed, 2–5 × 1–3.5 mm, often silky-canescent. **Flowers:** chasmogamous with pedicels 2–5 mm; calyx 5–8 × 3 mm, cleistogamous 3 × 1 mm, lobes triangular to lanceolate, 1–2 mm; corolla becoming darker in age; banner obovate to suborbiculate, 13–15 × 4–5 mm; wings oblong, with claws 7 mm, auriculate above claws; keel similar to wings; ovary pubescent. **Legumes:** those of chasmogamous and cleistogamous aerial flowers oblong to slightly falcate, narrow at base and apex, 3–3.7 × 0.7 cm; valves strigose or glabrous, sutures with mostly ascending hairs or often at base with retrorse hairs. **Seeds:** 2 or 3(or 4) in chasmogamous and cleistogamous aerial fruits, dark red-brown, 3.5–4 × 3 mm; hilum reniform to broadly ovate, 1.5 mm; subterranean 1–1.5 cm diam. $2n = 22$.

Flowering Aug–Oct. Rich, moist woodlands, edges of woods, along railroad tracks, sandy-loam roadsides, sand dunes; 100–600 m; Man., N.B., Nfld. and Labr., N.S., Ont., P.E.I., Que., Sask.; Ala., Ark., Conn., Del., D.C., Fla., Ga., Ill., Ind., Iowa, Kans., Ky., La., Maine, Md., Mass., Minn., Miss., Mo., Mont., Nebr., N.H., N.J., N.Y., N.C., N.Dak., Ohio, Okla., Pa., R.I., S.C., S.Dak., Tenn., Tex., Vt., Va., W.Va., Wis.; Mexico (Nuevo León, Puebla).

Several local or regional floras have treated *Amphicarpaea bracteata* as comprising two varieties, var. *bracteata* and var. *comosa*. The latter is characterized by having stout stems, often densely covered with brownish hirsute-villous hairs, calyx 1 cm, corolla mostly purple, ca. 15 mm, keel petal blades equaling claws, aerial legumes with strigose valves, pubescence of the adaxial (placentar) suture with ascending (antrorse) hairs, and the abaxial suture with retrorse hairs proximally.

96. GLYCINE Willdenow, Sp. Pl. 3: 854, 1053. 1802, name conserved • Soybean [Greek *glykys*, sweet, alluding to medicinal use of leaves and roots of some species] [I]

Gordon C. Tucker

Robert J. Alier

Herbs, annual [perennial], unarmed. **Stems** erect [climbing], pilose-pubescent. **Leaves** alternate, odd-pinnate; stipules present, persistent, linear-lanceolate; petiolate; leaflets 3, stipels present, lateral leaflets sessile or short-petiolulate, terminal petiolulate, blade margins entire, surfaces pubescent. **Inflorescences** 5–8-flowered, axillary, racemes [paniculate or flowers fascicled, solitary, or paired]; bracts present. **Flowers** papilionaceous; calyx campanulate, lobes 5; corolla violet, pink, or white, 4.5–7(–10) mm; stamens 10, diadelphous, vexillary stamen auriculate basally, sometimes becoming distinct in age; anthers basifixed, uniform; ovary ± sessile; style glabrous; stigma terminal, capitate. **Fruits** legumes, stipitate, straight or falcate, linear or oblong, laterally dehiscent, ± constricted between seeds, pubescent. **Seeds** 2–4(or 5), ovoid; hilum lateral; aril scalelike. $x = 20$.

Species 9 (1 in the flora): introduced; e Asia, Africa, Pacific Islands, Australia; introduced nearly worldwide.

SELECTED REFERENCE Hermann, F. J. 1962. A Revision of the Genus *Glycine* and Its Immediate Allies. Washington. [U.S.D.A. Techn. Bull. 1268.

1. Glycine max (Linnaeus) Merrill, Interpr. Herb. Amboin., 274. 1917 F I W

Phaseolus max Linnaeus, Sp. Pl. 2: 725. 1753; *Dolichos soja* Linnaeus; *Glycine hispida* (Moench) Maximowicz; *Soja hispida* Moench

Herbs 0.2–1 m. **Stems** ± ribbed, hairs reddish brown. **Leaves:** petiole (2–)8–15(–24) cm; rachis 5–30 mm, sparsely hairy; stipels linear-lanceolate; leaflet blades ovate-elliptic to orbiculate, 3–10(–15) × 2.5–8 cm, base broadly rounded, apex obtuse to subacute. **Racemes:** bracteoles lanceolate, 2–3 mm, hairy. **Pedicels** 2–4 mm. **Flowers:** calyx 4–7 mm; stamens 2.5 mm; anthers broadly ellipsoid, 0.3 mm. **Legumes** 2.5–8.5 cm × 8–15 mm, often tardily dehiscent. **Seeds** light to dark brown, sometimes mottled, 6–11 mm. $2n$ = 40.

Flowering summer–early fall. Disturbed areas, roadsides, railroad ballast, drainage ditches; 0–300 m; introduced; Ont., Que.; Ala., Ark., Del., Ga., Ill., Ind., Iowa, Ky., La., Md., Mass., Mich., Minn., Miss., Mo., Nebr., N.J., N.Y., N.C., Ohio, Pa., S.C., Tenn., Vt., Va., W.Va., Wis.; Asia (China); introduced also in South America, s Europe, elsewhere in Asia, Africa, Australia.

Glycine max is cultivated for the extraction of oil, for the edible seeds, and for animal fodder; it is estimated that it provides about one-third of all protein used by humans. It is not known as a wild plant in its native China, and is believed to have originated as a selection from *G. soja* Siebold & Zuccarini. The latter is a twining herb with seeds 2.5–4 mm. *Glycine max* probably is not truly naturalized in Canada and some of the states listed for the flora area.

97. DIPOGON Liebmann, Ann. Sci. Nat., Bot., sér. 4, 2: 374. 1854/1855; Index Seminum (Copenhagen) 1854: 27. 1855 • [Greek *di-*, two, and *pogon*, beard, alluding to two lines of hairs on style] I

Alfonso Delgado-Salinas

Verdcourtia R. Wilczek

Vines, perennial, unarmed, base woody. **Stems** twining, climbing, young growth densely strigose or villous, hairs not uncinate, glabrescent. **Leaves** alternate, odd-pinnate; stipules present, persistent, sessile, not produced below point of insertion; petiolate; leaflets 3, stipels present, blade margins entire, surfaces pubescent. **Inflorescences** 5–10[–30]-flowered, axillary, pseudoracemes, with non-swollen floral nodes, 2 flowers per node; bracts and bracteoles present, persistent, lanceolate. **Pedicels** longer than calyx tube. **Flowers** papilionaceous; calyx campanulate, lobes 5; corolla rose-purple or pink, 10–15 mm, glabrous, banner with 1 prominent appendage at base; stamens 10, diadelphous; anthers basifixed, dehiscing laterally, pollen tricolporate; ovary with nectary disc at base, linear; style with 2 lines of hairs; stigma terminal, fringed with hairs. **Fruits** legumes, sessile or subsessile, brown, compressed, straight or falcate, oblong, 3–5 cm, tipped by persistent style, dehiscent, glabrescent. **Seeds** 3–5, black or brown, subglobose, 4–7 mm; hilum 2.5–3 mm with aril. x = 11.

Species 1: introduced, California; s Africa; introduced also in s South America, Pacific Islands (New Zealand), Australia.

Dipogon is native to the Cape Province, South Africa; it is naturalized in temperate regions of Australia and New Zealand. It is cultivated mainly as an ornamental in temperate and tropical areas worldwide.

SELECTED REFERENCES Freeman, G. 1918. The purple hyacinth bean. Bot. Gaz. 66: 512–523. Stirton, C. H. 1981b. The genus *Dipogon* (Leguminosae-Papilionoideae). Bothalia 13: 327–330.

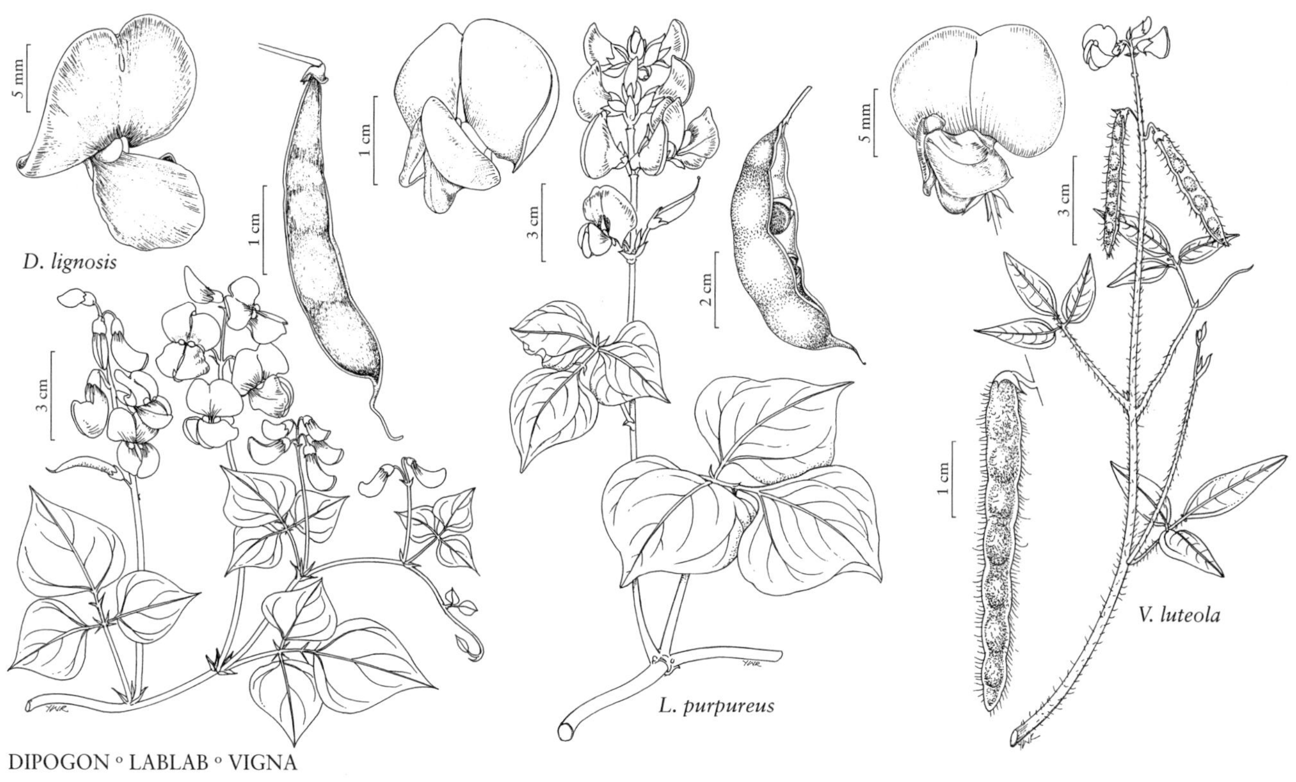

DIPOGON ◦ LABLAB ◦ VIGNA

1. **Dipogon lignosus** (Linnaeus) Verdcourt, Taxon 17: 537. 1968 • Cape sweet or Dolichos or Australian pea, Okie-bean, mile-a-minute [F] [I]

Dolichos lignosus Linnaeus, Sp. Pl. 2: 726. 1753; *Verdcourtia lignosa* (Linnaeus) R. Wilczek

Vines to 6 m. **Leaves:** stipules oblong-lanceolate, 6 × 1 mm, apex acuminate; petiole 2–7 cm, strigose, glabrescent; rachis 1–2 cm, strigose or glabrescent; stipels filiform, 2–3 mm; leaflet blades ovate to lanceolate, 20–70 × 10–45 mm, laterals smaller, base rounded, laterals often with lobed base, apex acuminate, surfaces strigose or glabrescent. **Peduncles** 7–12 cm. **Inflorescences** clustered apically; bracts caducous, obovate. **Pedicels** 5–7 mm, longer than calyx tube; bracteoles 2 mm. **Flowers:** calyx 3–5 mm, tube 2 times longer than lobes, 2 upper lobes rounded and connate nearly to apex, lower and lateral lobes triangular; corolla banner reflexed, with 1 prominent appendage on base of inner-face lamina, base auriculate, apex emarginate; wings oblong, longer than keel; keel beaked, purple tipped, apex incurved at right angle; free stamen with gibbous appendage at base, filaments alternately longer and shorter; ovary with hairs along distal margin; style sinuate-curved, stigma capitate. **Legumes** 3–5 × 0.8–1 cm. **Seeds** 4–7 × 3.5–5 mm. **2*n*** = 22.

Flowering spring–summer. Disturbed areas, forest edges; 0–100 m; introduced; Calif.; s Africa; introduced also in South America (Argentina, Chile, Uruguay), Pacific Islands (New Zealand), Australia.

Dipogon lignosus is widely cultivated in the tropics and subtropics; it is known in the flora area from San Diego County.

98. LABLAB Adanson, Fam. Pl. 2: 325. 1763 • [Arabic *lablab*, perhaps mercy, ivy, marsh, or dull rattle, probably alluding to nutritional value of beans, habit, habitat, or sound of seeds in dry pods] [I]

Alfonso Delgado-Salinas

Herbs, perennial, unarmed, base woody; taproot well developed. **Stems** climbing or suberect, young growth densely strigose, hairs not uncinate, glabrescent. **Leaves** alternate, odd-pinnate, pulvinate; stipules present, sessile, not produced below point of insertion; petiolate; leaflets 3, stipels present, blade margins entire, surfaces glabrous or strigose. **Inflorescences** 5–10[–30]-flowered, axillary, pseudoracemes, rachis with swollen nodes; bracts and bracteoles present, bracteoles subpersistent, elliptic-rounded. **Pedicels** shorter than calyx tube. **Flowers** papilionaceous; calyx campanulate, lobes 5; corolla red-purple or white, 12–15 mm, glabrous, banner with 2 prominent appendages at base, wings relatively long, enclosing keel, keel narrow, beaked; stamens 10, diadelphous; anthers basifixed and dorsifixed, alternate, dehiscing laterally, pollen tricolporate; ovary straight, nectary disc at base, style laterally flattened with brush on internal face, stigma terminal. **Fruits** legumes, sessile, dark purple, compressed, usually oblong-falcate, 5–10 cm, tipped by persistent style, dehiscent, ventral sutures verrucose, glabrescent. **Seeds** 2–5, white or reddish brown to black, oblong, 9–13 mm; with long, lateral hilum covered by conspicuous linear, white rim aril, extending more than ½ seed length. x = 11, 12.

Species 1: introduced; e Africa; introduced widely.

Lablab cultivars are grown widely throughout the tropics and some temperate regions of the world.

SELECTED REFERENCE Maass, B. L. et al. 2010. *Lablab purpureus*—A crop lost for Africa? Trop. Pl. Biol. 3: 123–135.

1. Lablab purpureus (Linnaeus) Sweet, Hort. Brit., 481. 1826 • Hyacinth or bonavist or lablab bean, purple hyacinth [F] [I]

Dolichos purpureus Linnaeus, Sp. Pl. ed. 2, 2: 1021. 1763; *D. albus* Loureiro; *D. lablab* Linnaeus; *Lablab niger* Medikus; *L. vulgaris* Savi; *Vigna aristata* Piper

Herbs climbing or bushy-erect, 1–6 m. **Leaves:** stipules reflexed in age, ovate-triangular, 4–6 × 1 mm; petiole 1–18 cm, strigose, ± glabrescent; rachis 0.7–4.5 cm; stipels linear lanceolate, 2 mm; leaflet blades ovate-triangular, 2–15 × 1.5–14 cm, base cuneate to truncate, apex acute to acuminate. **Peduncles** 2–40 cm. **Inflorescences:** bracts often deciduous, ovate-lanceolate, 4 mm. **Pedicels** 2–3.5 mm, shorter than calyx tube; bracteoles 4–6 × 1–4.5 mm, appressed to calyx. **Flowers:** calyx 3–6 mm, glabrous or strigose, tube longer than lobes, 2 upper lobes connate, lower and lateral lobes triangular or linear-oblong, 2–4 mm; corolla banner reflexed, with 2 prominent appendages on base of inner-face lamina, base auriculate, apex emarginate; wings oblong, longer than keel, auriculate; keel beak purple-tipped, incurved at right angle; vexillary stamen with gibbous appendage at base, filaments alternately long and short; ovary glabrous or pubescent, often with minute tubercular hairs. **Legumes** 5–10 × 1.5–40 cm. **Seeds** compressed, 9–13 × 6.5–9 mm. $2n$ = 22 or 24.

Flowering summer–fall. Waste areas, roadsides, railroads; 0–300 m; introduced; D.C., Fla., Ga., Md., N.J., N.Y., Ohio, Pa., Va., W.Va.; e Africa; introduced nearly worldwide.

Lablab purpureus is widely cultivated in warm temperate to tropical climates for human food and livestock fodder, green cover, and medicine, and as an ornamental (http://plants.usda.gov/plantguide/pdf/pg_lapu6.pdf). A historical record from Ontario should be treated as a waif.

99. VIGNA Savi, Nuovo Giorn. Lett. 8: 113. 1824, name conserved • Cowpea [For Domenico Vigni, 1577(?)–1647, botanist and curator of the Pisa Botanic Garden] [I]

Alfonso Delgado-Salinas

Azukia Takahashi ex Ohwi

Vines, annual or perennial, herbaceous [woody], 1–3 m; roots tuberous or fibrous. **Stems** spreading, climbing, twining, or erect, striate, glabrous or pubescent, hairs not uncinate. **Leaves** alternate, odd-pinnate; stipules present, persistent, slightly auriculate, distinctly peltate, or conspicuously retrorse; petiolate; leaflets 3, stipels present, blades 1.5–16 cm, membranous or firm, margins usually entire or shallowly deeply incised, surfaces glabrous or pubescent. **Inflorescences** 2–30-flowered, axillary, pseudoracemes, with swollen floral nodes, glandular, 2 flowers per node, clustered distally; bracts present, primary nodal bracts deciduous, entire; bracteoles minute or deciduous, shorter or longer than calyx. **Pedicels** erect, arcuate to reflexed near pod. **Flowers** papilionaceous; calyx campanulate, 2–6 mm, lobes 4, shorter to longer than tube, adaxial lobes usually ± connate; corolla greenish yellow to golden yellow, purple, or white, sometimes with reddish veins, 7–30 mm; banner symmetric or asymmetric, glabrous, often with appendages on central, inner face, slightly to strongly thickened at point where reflexed, apex emarginate; wings subequal to banner and keel; keel apically expanded, sometimes appendaged; stamens 10, diadelphous, vexillary filament thickened at base; pollen triporate; anthers dorsifixed; ovary with nectary disc at base, linear; style incurved, with distal brush, usually extended beyond stigma into conic or slender tip; stigma lateral. **Fruits** legumes, ascending, spreading, or pendulous, stipitate, usually linear to falcate, valves membranous or paper, dehiscent, resupinate by twisting of pedicel, glabrous. **Seeds** 1–25, globular to oblong, cylindric, or reniform; hilum concave or protruding; mostly with white rim aril; seedlings hypogeal or epigeal. x = 10, 11.

Species ca. 60 (5 in the flora): introduced; Asia, Africa; introduced also in Mexico, West Indies, Central America, South America.

Vigna species occur mostly in the tropics and warmer temperate regions of Asia and Africa; fewer than ten occur in the New World (D. Isely 1998; N. Tomooka et al. 2002; N. Maxted et al. 2004; A. Delgado-Salinas et al. 2011). Seven species have been cultivated in the flora area: *V. aconitifolia* (Jacquin) Maréchal (moth bean), *V. angularis*, *V. hosei*, *V. mungo* (Linnaeus) Hepper (mung bean), *V. radiata*, *V. umbellata* (Thunberg) Ohwi & H. Ohashi (rice bean), and *V. unguiculata* (R. L. Fery 2002). Only four have become locally naturalized, in addition to the widely distributed *V. luteola*.

SELECTED REFERENCE Delgado-Salinas, A. et al. 2011. *Vigna* (Leguminosae) sensu lato: The names and identities of the American segregate genera. Amer. J. Bot. 98: 1694–1715.

1. Stipules slightly auriculate or unequally lobed at base; corollas yellow, keel petals incurved or broadly curved, distally expanded or vertically incurved; legumes pendulous.
   2. Corollas 7–10 mm; legumes 2–3 cm; seeds 1–4 . . . . 1. *Vigna hosei*
   2. Corollas 15–20 mm; legumes 4–7 cm; seeds 5–12 . . . . 2. *Vigna luteola*
1. Stipules with narrower appendage at base or distinctly peltate; corollas white or purple (rarely yellowish), grayish yellow, or golden yellow, keel petals slightly twisted right, incurved through 1 circle, or apex incurved nearly ½ circle; legumes spreading or pendulous.

[3. Shifted to left margin.—Ed.]

3. Stipules with narrow appendage at base; corollas usually white or purple, rarely yellowish, 25–30 mm; bracteoles equal to calyx tubes; keel without lateral appendage; style short-beaked, lobelike appendage at stigma short; legumes 10–30 cm; seeds 18–25 . . . . 3. *Vigna unguiculata*
3. Stipules distinctly peltate; corollas grayish yellow to golden yellow, 10–15 mm; bracteoles longer than calyx tubes; keel with lateral keel-pocket or hornlike appendage supporting left wing petal; style elongate-beaked, lobelike appendage extending beyond stigma into slender tip; legumes 4–11 cm; seeds 5–15.
    4. Stipules widely ovate; corollas grayish yellow; legumes with hispid hairs, yellowish brown becoming black; seeds globose to oblong or shortly cylindric, green or yellow-brown, rim-aril not raised . . . . 4. *Vigna radiata*
    4. Stipules lanceolate; corollas golden yellow; legumes sparsely pilose, glabrescent, brown; seeds oblong to cylindric, grayish brown or red, rim-aril raised . . . . 5. *Vigna angularis*

1. Vigna hosei (Craib) Backer in C. A. Backer and D. F. van Slooten, Geill. Handb. Jav. Theeonkr., 153. 1924 • Sarawak bean [I]

Dolichos hosei Craib, Bull. Misc. Inform. Kew 1914: 76. 1914

Vines perennial. **Stems** spreading or twining, slender, often numerous and rooting at nodes, pilose or glabrate. **Leaves:** stipules lanceolate, 5 mm, base unequally lobed; petiole 3.5–8 cm; rachis 0.6–1.5 cm; stipels triangular, 1–2 mm; leaflet blades ovate to ovate-lanceolate, 1.5–9 × 1.5–5 cm, base rounded. **Peduncles** to 10 cm. **Inflorescences** flexuous, floral nodes 2–11, sparse or clustered at apex (sometimes shorter in trailing stems, with cleistogamous flowers); bracts deciduous, lanceolate, 2 mm. **Pedicels** ascending, distally curved, 1.5–3 mm; bracteoles deciduous, lanceolate, 1 mm. **Flowers:** calyx tube 2 mm, lobes triangular, dark-veined; corolla pale yellow, reddish veined, 7–10 mm; banner oblong-orbiculate, with 2 appendages on inner face; wings oblong; keel incurved, short-beaked, distally expanded, 4 mm; style incurved, extending beyond stigma into conic tip. **Legumes** pendulous, brown, linear to ± falcate, cylindric, 2–3 × 0.4 cm, beak curved, relatively short, sparsely strigose to glabrescent. **Seeds** 1–4, light brown, oblong to reniform, 5 × 4 mm; hilum short, not raised.

Flowering spring–fall. Waste or disturbed areas; 0–20 m; introduced; Fla.; Asia; introduced also widely in tropical regions.

Vigna hosei was apparently introduced in the flora area as a cover crop but is no longer cultivated; it is naturalized in southern Florida.

2. Vigna luteola (Jacquin) Bentham in C. F. P. von Martius et al., Fl. Bras. 15(1): 194. 1859 • Hairypod or wild cowpea [F] [I]

Dolichos luteolus Jacquin, Hort. Bot. Vindob. 1: 39, plate 90. 1771; *D. mexicanus* Schlechtendal; *D. repens* Linnaeus 1759, not *Vigna repens* Baker 1876; *Orobus trifoliatus* Sessé & Mociño; *Phaseolus hernandesii* Savi; *P. luteolus* (Jacquin) Gagnepain; *Vigna villosa* Savi

Vines perennial. **Stems** trailing or twining, sometimes rooting at nodes, hirsute. **Leaves:** stipules triangular, 3–5 mm, base slightly auriculate-cordate; petiole 1.5–8 cm; rachis 0.4–1 cm; stipels linear, 1.5–2.5 mm; leaflet blades ovate- or linear-lanceolate, 3–8 × 0.5–5 cm, base obtuse or rounded, apex acute or acuminate. **Peduncles** to 30 cm. **Inflorescences** often flexuous, floral nodes 10–15, mostly clustered at apex; bracts deciduous, ovate-lanceolate, 1–1.5 mm. **Pedicels** ascending, curved distally, 3–5 mm; bracteoles tardily deciduous, triangular, 1.5–2.5 mm. **Flowers:** calyx tube 4.5–6 mm, apex acute to acuminate, adaxial lobe broader, 2.5–3.5 mm; corolla yellow, 15–20 mm; banner suborbiculate, 1.5–2 × 1.5–2 mm, with 2 basal auricles; wings obliquely obovate, 15 × 1 mm; keel broadly curved, vertically incurved, 15 × 5–6 mm; style curved, extending beyond stigma into tip. **Legumes** pendulous, brown-black in age, linear, torulose, 4–7 × 0.5–0.8 cm, strigose to pilose. **Seeds** 5–12, brownish black, reniform, 4–6 × 3–4 mm; hilum white, not raised.

Flowering year-round. Moist, silty, clay, or sandy soils, on limestone rock, river and lake margins, edges of brackish marshes, pinelands, seashores; 0–200 m; introduced; Ala., Fla., Ga., La., Miss., N.J., N.C., Pa., S.C., Tex., Va.; Africa; introduced also in South America, Asia.

Vigna luteola is common and widespread around the world; it bears a complicated nomenclature (R. Pasquet 2001, 2001b).

3. Vigna unguiculata (Linnaeus) Walpers, Repert. Bot. Syst. 1: 779. 1843 • Black-eyed or blackeyed or southern or crowder or pinkeye pea, cowpea, yardlong bean [I] [W]

Dolichos unguiculatus Linnaeus, Sp. Pl. 2: 725. 1753

Vines annual. **Stems** trailing, climbing, or erect, sometimes hollow, nodes in trailing stems streaked red, glabrous. **Leaves:** stipules triangular-lanceolate, 15 mm, basal appendage short and narrow; petiole 5–14 cm, striate, canaliculate; rachis 2 cm; stipels lanceolate, 1.5–2 mm; leaflet blades ovate to lanceolate or rhombic-ovate, 4–15 × 3–8 cm, base often lobed. **Peduncles** (8–) 15–25 cm. **Inflorescences:** floral nodes 1–3, clustered distally; bracts deciduous, lanceolate or ovate, 12–15 mm. **Pedicels** straight, 0.2 cm; bracteoles deciduous, lanceolate, 5 mm. **Flowers:** calyx tube striate, 5 mm, adaxial lobe shorter, 5 mm; corolla usually white or purple, rarely yellowish, 25–30 mm; banner broadly orbiculate-oblate, with 2 parallel appendages on inner face; wings spatulate; keel slightly twisted right, beak short, without lateral appendage; style short-beaked, lobelike appendage at stigma short. **Legumes** spreading or pendulous, white to yellowish, sometimes streaked rose or dark purple, subterete, linear to slightly falcate, 10–30 × 1 cm, glabrous. **Seeds** (8–)18–25, light brown tinged with red or purple, with purple or pink eyes, creamy white with black eyes, or reddish black, reniform or subglobose, 4–12 × 0.3–0.6 mm; hilum white, not raised.

Flowering summer. Roadsides, railroads, disturbed areas; 10–100 m; introduced; Ala., Ark., Calif., Del., Fla., Ill., Ind., La., Md., Mich., Miss., Mo., N.C., Ohio, Pa., S.C., Tex. Va.; Africa; introduced also in South America, Asia.

Vigna unguiculata is a species of African origin now cultivated worldwide (N. Maxted et al. 2004).

4. Vigna radiata (Linnaeus) R. Wilczek in W. Robyns, Fl. Congo Belge 6: 386. 1954 • Mungbean, green or golden gram [I]

Phaseolus radiatus Linnaeus, Sp. Pl. 2: 725. 1753; *Azukia radiata* (Linnaeus) Ohwi

Vines annual. **Stems** green to grayish brown, trailing, climbing, or erect, ribbed, hollow in age, hispid, with brown, spreading hairs. **Leaves:** stipules widely ovate, distinctly peltate, 8–12 mm, ciliate; petiole 5–21 cm; rachis 2.5–4 cm; stipels lanceolate, 4–7 mm; leaflet blades ovate to widely ovate or lanceolate, 5–16 × 3–12 cm, base broadly cuneate or rounded, lateral ones oblique, apex acuminate, surfaces sparsely pilose. **Peduncles** to 20 cm. **Inflorescences:** floral nodes 2–12, clustered distally; bracts deciduous, ovate-triangular, 3 mm. **Pedicels** arcuate, 1–2 mm; bracteoles deciduous, striate, linear-lanceolate or oblong, 5 mm. **Flowers:** calyx tube 3–4 mm, lobes triangular, 1 mm; corolla grayish yellow, 10–12 mm; banner yellow-green outside, suboblate, 12 × 16 mm, auriculate; wings yellow, ovate; keel green tinged with red, falcate and incurved through 1 circle, with lateral keel-pocket or hornlike appendage supporting left wing petal; style incurved, elongate-beaked, lobelike appendage extending beyond stigma into slender tip. **Legumes** spreading, yellowish brown, becoming black, linear, terete, 4–9 × 0.6 cm, beak straight, short, shortly hispid, hairs pale brown. **Seeds** 8–15, greenish or yellow-brown, often mottled black or green, globular to oblong or shortly cylindric, 2.5–4 × 2.5–3 mm; hilum not raised, rim-aril not raised.

Flowering late spring–early summer. Sandy soils next to riverbanks; 50–100 m; introduced; Va.; se Asia; introduced also in Africa.

5. Vigna angularis (Willdenow) Ohwi & H. Ohashi, J. Jap. Bot. 44: 29. 1969 • Adzuki bean, self-perpetuating pea [I]

Dolichos angularis Willdenow, Sp. Pl. 3: 1051. 1802; *Azukia angularis* (Willdenow) Ohwi

Vines annual. **Stems** trailing, climbing, or erect, angular, hollow, sparsely white-pilose. **Leaves:** stipules lanceolate, distinctly peltate, 10–15 mm, lobe 0.2–0.4 cm; petiole to 15 cm; rachis to 3.5 cm; stipels lanceolate, 3–5 mm; leaflet blades ovate or rhombic-ovate, 5–10 × 5–8 cm, base cuneate or rounded, lateral ones oblique, margins entire or shallowly 3-lobed, apex broadly triangular or subrounded, surfaces sparsely pilose. **Peduncles** to 16 cm. **Inflorescences:** floral nodes 4 or 5, clustered distally; bracts deciduous, triangular, striate, 4 mm. **Pedicels** arcuate, 5–8 mm; bracteoles tardily dehiscent, narrowly lanceolate, 10–12 mm. **Flowers:** calyx tube 3 mm, lobes triangular, 1 mm; corolla golden yellow, 15 mm; banner oblate to subreniform, auriculate, apex emarginate; wings ovate, broader than keel, shortly clawed, auriculate; keel clawed, apex incurved nearly 0.5 circle, with lateral keel-pocket or hornlike appendage supporting left wing petal; style incurved, elongate-beaked, lobelike appendage extending beyond stigma into slender tip. **Legumes** pendulous, brown, straight or curved distally, terete, linear, 5–11 × 0.6–0.8 cm, valves papery, upper suture thickened, sparsely pilose, glabrescent. **Seeds**

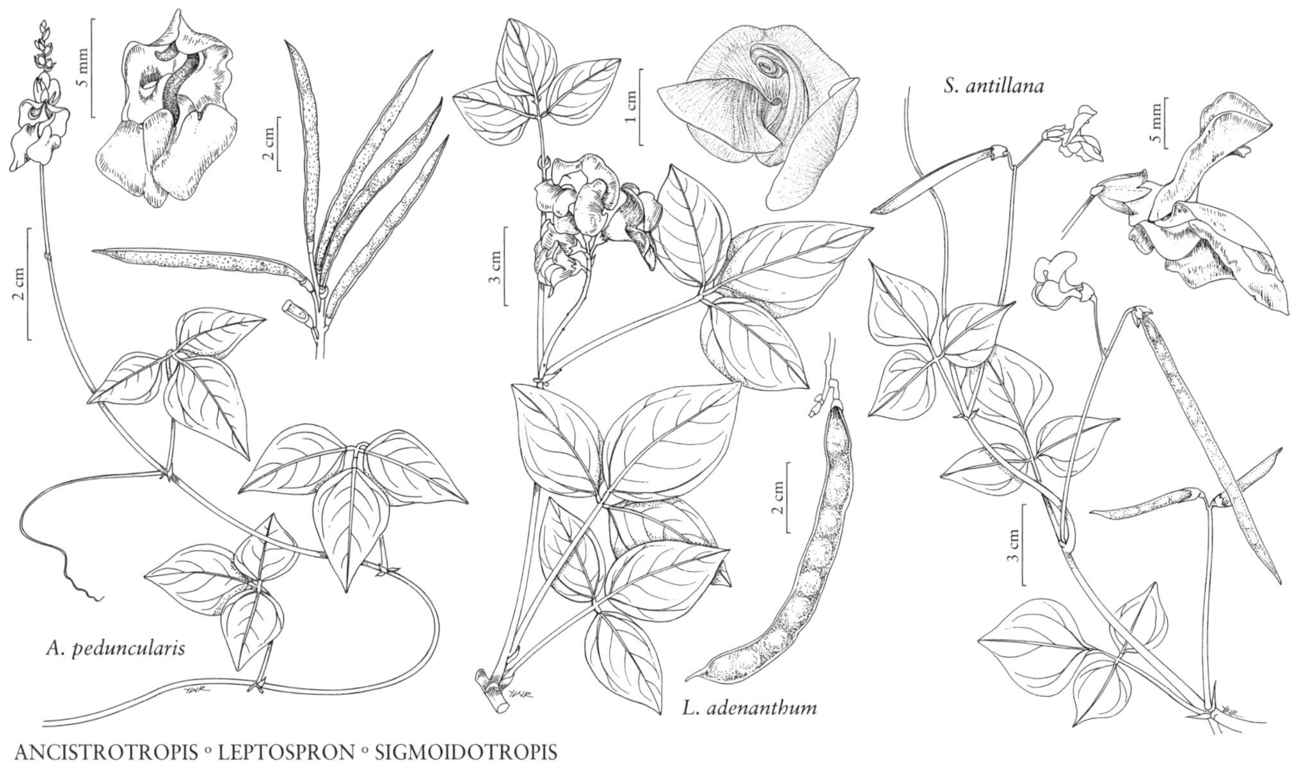

ANCISTROTROPIS ◦ LEPTOSPRON ◦ SIGMOIDOTROPIS

5–10, grayish brown or red, oblong to cylindric, 8–8.5 × 4–5 mm, ends truncate or rounded; hilum flattened, rim-aril white, raised.

Flowering summer. Fields, roadsides, stream banks; 0–50 m; introduced; La., Miss.; Asia; introduced also in South America, Africa.

Vigna angularis is cultivated widely.

100. ANCISTROTROPIS A. Delgado, Amer. J. Bot. 98: 1704. 2011 • [Greek *ancistron*, fish-hook, and *tropis*, keel of a ship, alluding to hooked distal portion of keel petals)

Alfonso Delgado-Salinas

Phaseolus Linnaeus ser. *Pedunculares* Hassler, Candollea 1: 424, 433. 1923; *Vigna* Savi sect. *Pedunculares* (Hassler) Maréchal, Mascherpa & Stainier

Vines, annual [perennial], unarmed; with thick taproot. **Stems** usually twining or trailing, rarely suberect, angled, base lignescent, strigose, hairs not uncinate, glabrescent. **Leaves** alternate, odd-pinnate, pulvinate; stipules present, persistent, sessile, not produced below point of insertion, striate; petiolate, petiole and rachis canaliculate, pubescent, stipels present; leaflets 3, blades membranous to leathery, often basally lobed, margins entire, surfaces sparsely pilose. **Inflorescences** 2–12[–30]-flowered, axillary, pseudoracemes, with 1 or 2 swollen floral nodes, glandular, flowers 2 per node; bracts present, primary nodal bracts entire; bracteoles present. **Pedicels** mostly shorter than calyx tube. **Flowers** papilionaceous; calyx campanulate to tubular, tube pleated, lobes 4 (by connation of 2 adaxial ones); petals distinct; corolla usually light purple or white-purple, rarely lavender; banner forming hood at apex; wings spatulate, conspicuously projected beyond distal bend of keel; keel beak gradually twisted into a hook with conspicuous, interlocking, marginal hairs, distalmost portion of beak folded back on itself, tip of beak not hidden by wings; stamens 10, diadelphous, vexillary stamen geniculate; anthers sub-basifixed, dehiscing laterally, pollen tricolporate; ovary with nectary disc at base, style distally thickened with short brush, extending beyond stigma, stigma laterally extrorse from torsion of style. **Fruits** legumes, sessile, mostly erect, straight to slightly curved, linear-cylindric, short-beaked distally, sutures thickened, dehiscent, pubescent. **Seeds** 9–11[–13], oblique position from long funicles, oblong; hilum lateral, aril broad-rimmed. $x = 9$.

Species ca. 5 (1 in the flora): Arizona, Mexico, West Indies, Central America, South America.

Ancistrotropis is distributed throughout the Neotropics (southern Arizona, Mexico to northern Argentina, also in West Indies), mainly in secondary and primary forests, on sandy or granitic soils.

1. Ancistrotropis peduncularis (Fawcett & Rendle) A. Delgado, Amer. J. Bot. 98: 1704. 2011 [F]

Vigna peduncularis Fawcett & Rendle, Fl. Jamaica 4: 68. 1920, based on *Phaseolus peduncularis* Kunth in A. von Humboldt et al., Nov. Gen. Sp. 6(fol.): 350; 6(qto.): 447. 1824, not (Muhlenberg) W. P. C. Barton 1818

Vines 0.2–1.8 m; often rooting at nodes. **Stems** ridged, densely spreading-pilose (hairs usually ± tubercular-based), glabrescent. **Leaves:** stipules lanceolate, 3–12 mm; petiole 1–8.5(–14) cm; rachis 0.5–1.4(–1.9) cm; stipels lanceolate; leaflet blades ovate or ovate-triangular, 1.2–10 × 1.1–6.5 cm, base rounded, truncate or subhastate, sometimes distinctly 3-lobed, apex rounded or subacute to acuminate. **Peduncles** 1–45 cm. **Inflorescences:** rachis 0.3–2 cm, with conspicuous glandular nodes; bracts deciduous. **Pedicels** erect, 2–4 mm; bracteoles deciduous, linear, 1.5 mm. **Flowers:** calyx tube 6 mm, lobes deltate, 2 mm, adaxial lobe rounded, emarginate, glabrous or pubescent; corolla 1.5 cm; banner oblong, with flaplike auricles at base, above claw; wings spatulate, right wing twisted to horizontal position; keel pale, tinged blue, twisted, beak hooked, with distalmost portion splayed open, inner margins of keel beak not fused but closed by conspicuous interlocking marginal hairs. **Legumes** 6–10 × 0.2–0.5 cm. **Seeds** dark red or brown, angular, narrowly oblong, 4 mm; hilum relatively small, subcentral.

Flowering Aug. Riparian in pine-oak forests; 1300 m; Ariz.; Mexico (Chiapas, Guerrero, Jalisco, Michoacán, Nayarit, Oaxaca, Sinaloa, Sonora, Tabasco, Veracruz); Central America; South America.

Ancistrotropis peduncularis is characterized by its hook-shaped keel and erect fruits. It has been collected only once in the flora area [*J. L. Gardner 17* (US) in 1953], in riparian forests in Walnut Wash, one mile north of Tombstone, Cochise County.

101. LEPTOSPRON (Bentham & Hooker f.) A. Delgado, Amer. J. Bot. 98: 1709. 2011 • [Greek *leptos*, slender, and *ospron*, legume, alluding to linear curved pods] [I]

Alfonso Delgado-Salinas

Phaseolus Linnaeus sect. *Leptospron* Bentham & Hooker f., Gen. Pl. 1: 538. 1865; *Vigna* Savi sect. *Leptospron* (Bentham & Hooker f.) Maréchal, Mascherpa & Stainier

Vines, perennial, herbaceous, unarmed; taproot thick. **Stems** twining or trailing, strigose or hirsute, hairs not uncinate, [or glabrous]. **Leaves** alternate, odd-pinnate, pulvinate; stipules present, not produced proximal to insertion; petiolate; leaflets 3, stipels present, blade margins entire [lobed], surfaces glabrous, puberulent, or pilose. **Inflorescences** 50-flowered, axillary, pseudoracemes, nodes swollen, glandular; bracts and bracteoles present. **Pedicels** mostly shorter than calyx tube. **Flowers** papilionaceous; calyx broadly campanulate, lobes 4, lower lobe slightly longer than tube; petals distinct; corolla usually light pink to purple, sometimes white, becoming yellowish, wings with purple pattern; wings obovate, conspicuously projected beyond distal bend of keel; keel incurved to coiled, beak very tightly coiled distally, projected downward, tip not hidden by wings, not folded back distally; stamens 10, diadelphous; anthers basifixed, pollen tricolporate; ovary glabrous or puberulent, nectary disc surrounding ovary, style with brush of hairs, stigma laterally extrorse (in anthesis). **Fruits** legumes, sessile, broadly linear to falcate, valves thickened at margins with short, stiff hairs, beaked, dehiscent, strigose or pilose or glabrate. **Seeds** [8 or]9–15, ovate to reniform, often D-shaped, testa smooth. $x = 11$.

Species 2 (1 in the flora): introduced, Florida; Mexico, West Indies, Central America, South America; tropical to warm temperate regions; introduced also in Asia, Africa.

Leptospron gentryi (Standley) A. Delgado is known from northern Mexico.

Leptospron inhabits secondary and primary forests, with or without a dry season, and also coastal vegetation or temperate forests. Dispersal has naturalized *L. adenanthum* in limited areas of the paleotropics, including Africa and Asia.

Leptospron is characterized by the very tightly coiled distal portion of the keel, similar to the keel coil in *Phaseolus*.

1. **Leptospron adenanthum** (G. Meyer) A. Delgado, Amer. J. Bot. 98: 1710. 2011 • Wild pea [F] [I]

Phaseolus adenanthus G. Meyer, Prim. Fl. Esseq., 239. 1818; *P. cuernavacanus* Rose; *P. occidentalis* Rose; *P. truxillensis* Kunth; *Vigna adenantha* (G. Meyer) Maréchal, Mascherpa & Stainier

Vines to 5 m. **Stems** hollow, striate, sparingly to densely strigose or thinly hirsute. **Leaves:** stipules triangular, 2–5 mm, margins entire; petiole 4–6 cm; rachis 0.7–1.2 cm; stipels linear to ovate, 0.5–1.3 mm; leaflet blades broadly linear, lanceolate, rhombic, or ovate-oblong, base rounded, apex usually acute, sometimes acuminate, 4–12 × 1–4 cm, surfaces glabrous or puberulent abaxially. **Inflorescences** spherical to ovoid, to 30 cm; rachis with ± 25 prominent and glandular nodes, nodes 2-flowered; primary bracts deciduous, ovate. **Pedicels** 2–5 mm; bracteoles deciduous, ovate to lanceolate-ovate, 2–4 mm, apex acute. **Flowers:** 2.5–3 cm; calyx 6–8 mm, glabrous or sparsely pubescent, tube 4 mm; lower lobe narrowly triangular, 2–3.5 mm; lateral lobes curved, triangular-falcate, 2–4 mm; upper lobe broad and emarginate; banner suborbiculate, 1.6–2.5 cm diam.; wings obliquely obovate, 2–3 × 1 cm, claws 5–6 mm; keel base broad, incurved distally into a tight coil of 2–2.5 turns, claw 6–7 mm; vexillary stamen thickened distal to base; ovary linear to slightly curved; style coiled like keel, style with a brush of hairs proximal to stigma. **Legumes** slightly pendent, 7–12 × 0.8–1 cm, strigose to short-pilose on valves, densely and minutely barbed on margins. **Seeds** reddish brown, turgid, 4–7 × 5 mm. $2n = 22$.

Flowering Jan–May. Pine forests, rocky soils, disturbed areas; 0–20 m; introduced; Fla.; Mexico; West Indies; Central America; South America; introduced also in Asia, Africa.

Leptospron adenanthum is introduced in southern peninsular Florida (R. P. Wunderlin and B. F. Hansen, http://florida.plantatlas.usf.edu/).

102. SIGMOIDOTROPIS (Piper) A. Delgado, Amer. J. Bot. 98: 1710. 2011 • [Greek *sigmoid*, sigma-shaped, and *tropis*, keel of a vessel, alluding to S-form of keel petals] [I]

Alfonso Delgado-Salinas

Phaseolus Linnaeus sect. *Sigmoidotropis* Piper, Contr. U.S. Natl. Herb. 22: 674. 1926; *Vigna* Savi subg. *Sigmoidotropis* (Piper) Verdcourt

Vines, perennial, unarmed, base woody; taproot woody. **Stems** twining or trailing, densely pilose or hirsute, hairs spreading, not uncinate, glabrous, or glabrescent. **Leaves** alternate, odd-pinnate, pulvinate; stipules present, persistent, not produced proximal to insertion; petiolate; leaflets 3, stipels present, blade margins entire, surfaces pubescent or glabrous. **Inflorescences**

2–10-flowered, axillary, pseudoracemes, rachis with glandular, swollen nodes, 1 or 2 flowers per node; bracts present; bracteoles deciduous, ovate, shorter than calyx tube. **Pedicels** mostly shorter than calyx tube. **Flowers** papilionaceous; calyx campanulate, lobes 4, ca. ¼ as long as tube; lower and lateral lobes triangular to lanceolate, equal to or 2 times longer than tube, upper lobes triangular, broad and emarginate; petals distinct; corolla light to deep purple or deep lilac; banner expanded at anthesis, usually hooded; wings obovate, conspicuously projected beyond distal bend of keel; keel beak sigmoid to coiled, distally flaplike, very tightly coiled distally, projected downward, tip not hidden by wings, not folded back distally; stamens 10, diadelphous; anthers sub-basifixed, oblong; ovary straight, nectary disc at base; style distally thickened with pollen brush distal to stigma; stigma apical to slightly introrse or laterally extrorse. **Fruits** legumes, sessile, compressed, narrowly linear or slightly curved, sometimes long-beaked at apex, dehiscent, puberulent or thinly strigose. **Seeds** 1–20, oblong to reniform, testa smooth.

Species ca. 9 (2 in the flora): introduced, Florida; Mexico, West Indies, Central America, South America; tropical to warm temperate regions.

Sigmoidotropis inhabits secondary and primary forests, with or without a dry season, as well as coastal thickets and riparian forests throughout much of the Neotropics.

Sigmoidotropis is characterized by its relatively large flowers with sigmoid (S-shaped) keels and slightly curved pods with thickened margins.

1. Stems twining or trailing; leaflet blades membranous to papery, usually glabrous; inflorescences with 2–5 nodes; flowers 2–3 cm; legumes 6–14 x 0.5 cm . . . . 1. *Sigmoidotropis antillana*
1. Stems often intricately twining; leaflet blades membranous, usually densely pale-pubescent abaxially; inflorescences with 2 or 3 nodes; flowers 3–4 cm; legumes 10–18 x 0.4–0.7 cm . . . . 2. *Sigmoidotropis speciosa*

1. Sigmoidotropis antillana (Urban) A. Delgado, Amer. J. Bot. 98: 1711. 2011 • Caribbean cowpea [F] [I]

Phaseolus antillanus Urban, Symb. Antill. 4: 309. 1905; *Vigna antillana* (Urban) Fawcett & Rendle

Vines 3–7 m. **Stems** twining or trailing, hollow, striate, hirsute, hairs sometimes retrorse. **Leaves:** stipules ovate-lanceolate, 4–8 x 4 mm; petiole 6–8 cm; rachis 2–2.5 cm; stipels persistent, awl-shaped, minute; leaflets membranous to papery, blades broadly ovate to deltate, lateral ones asymmetric, 3–9 x 2–7.5 cm, base cuneate to truncate, apex acuminate, surfaces glabrous. **Inflorescences** to 40 cm, flowers clustered at 2–5 nodes; bracts persistent, minute. **Pedicels** 1–2 mm; bracteoles 3 mm. **Flowers** light to deep purple, 2–3 cm; calyx 4–7 mm, puberulent, lower lobes triangular, 3 mm, lateral lobes lanceolate, slightly curved, upper lobe obtuse; banner oblong, 2–2.5 x 2 cm; wings obovate, 2–2.2 x 1–1.5 cm; keel beak sigmoid; vexillary stamen geniculate at base. **Legumes** narrowly linear to slightly curved, 6–14 x 0.5 cm, puberulent. **Seeds** 13–17, oblong to oval-reniform, 3.5–4 x 2–3 mm.

Flowering Nov–Mar. Coastal areas, limestone soils; 0–10 m; introduced; Fla.; West Indies (Lesser Antilles); n South America.

Sigmoidotropis antillana is known in the flora area from Miami-Dade County.

The name *Phaseolus alatus* Linnaeus was rejected in order to preserve the name *Vigna antillana* (now *Sigmoidotropis antillana*), a well-known species of the West Indies (A. Delgado-Salinas and N. J. Turland 2008).

2. Sigmoidotropis speciosa (Kunth) A. Delgado, Amer. J. Bot. 98: 1711. 2011 • Snail vine, wandering cowpea [I]

Phaseolus speciosus Kunth in A. von Humboldt et al., Nov. Gen. Sp. 6(fol.): 354; 6(qto.): 452. 1824; *Vigna speciosa* (Kunth) Verdcourt

Vines 2–5 m. **Stems** often intricately twining, usually softly pilose, rarely glabrous. **Leaves:** stipules triangular-ovate, 3–4 mm; petiole 2.5–8 cm; rachis 0.4–1(–1.7) cm; stipels thin, linear or broader, 0.5–1.5 mm; leaflets membranous, blades ovate, 4–11 x 2–6 cm, base cuneate to truncate, apex acuminate, surfaces usually densely pale-pubescent abaxially. **Inflorescences** 5–30 cm, flowers clustered at 2 or 3 nodes; primary bracts caducous. **Pedicels** 3–4 mm; bracteoles 2.5–4 mm. **Flowers** light purple to deep-lilac, 3–4 cm; calyx 8.5–10 mm, glabrous or sparsely pubescent, lower and lateral lobes triangular, 4–4.5 × 3 mm, upper lobes rounded, 7–11 mm wide; banner oblong to suborbiculate, 3–3.5 × 2.5–3 cm; wings obliquely obovate, 3.5–4 × 1.5–1.8 cm; keel beak abruptly curved and sigmoid; vexillary stamen geniculate distal to base. **Legumes** narrowly linear, 10–18 × 0.4–0.7 cm, thinly strigose. **Seeds** 1–20, reniform or oblong, 4.5–5 × 2.3–3 mm.

Flowering May–Jan. Pinelands, roadsides, vacant lots; 0–20 m; introduced; Fla.; Mexico; Central America; South America.

Sigmoidotropis speciosa is used as an ornamental; it is established in central peninsular Florida (R. P. Wunderlin and B. F. Hansen, http://florida.plantatlas.esf.edu/) and been listed as a Category II invasive species by the Florida Exotic Pest Plant Council (www.fleppc.org). It has frequently been confused with another ornamental vine, *Cochliasanthus caracalla* (Linnaeus) Trew (corkscrew flower), that has showy white-yellow or light lavender corollas with keel petals that loosely coil several turns.

103. OXYRHYNCHUS Brandegee, Univ. Calif. Publ. Bot. 4: 270. 1912 • Frijol monilla [Greek *oxy-*, sharp, and *rhynchos*, beak, alluding to shape of keel petals] I

Alfonso Delgado-Salinas

Monoplegma Piper; *Peekelia* Harms

Vines, perennial, unarmed. **Stems** trailing to climbing, strigose to pilose, glabrescent, hairs not uncinate. **Leaves** alternate, odd-pinnate; stipules present, caducous; petiolate, petiole longer than rachis, both canaliculate; leaflets 3, stipels present, often caducous, blade margins entire, surfaces glabrous or glabrate. **Inflorescences** 50–60+-flowered, axillary, pseudoracemes, floral nodes relatively conspicuous, glandular; bracts present, often caducous, bracteoles early caducous, proximal to calyx, sometimes subpeltate. **Pedicels** mostly shorter than calyx tube. **Flowers** papilionaceous; calyx campanulate, lobes 5; corolla greenish yellow to purple, glabrous; banner usually longer than wings and keel, with 2 prominent appendages on inner face; wing blades oblong, not projected beyond distal bend of keel; keel petals connate along upper margin, not forming gibbosity or hump, incurved, and beaked; stamens 10, diadelphous; anthers basifixed, pollen tricolporate; ovary oblong, nectary disc at base; style slightly curved, distally bearded; stigma terminal or subterminal. **Fruits** legumes, stipitate, terete or subcylindric, widely oblong, leathery, with rostrate, curved beak, slightly compressed between seeds, dehiscent, glabrous or puberulent; endocarp white-spongy. **Seeds** 2 or 3[–6], spherical [oblong to reniform or spherical-prismatic]; hilum linear-oblong, circumlinear, elongated ½ to nearly entire length of seed. $x = 11$.

Species 4 (1 in the flora): introduced, Texas; Mexico, West Indies (Bahamas, Cuba), Central America, n South America, Pacific Islands (New Guinea).

Oxyrhynchus is distinguished by spheroidal to oblong and rounded seeds with hila extending 50–98% of the seed length, and by subcylindric, leathery legumes. Molecular evidence established *Oxyrhynchus* as closely related to *Ramirezella* Rose (A. Delgado-Salinas et al. 2011). Species of *Oxyrhynchus* inhabit seasonally dry to wet tropical and subtropical forests and montane forests or coastal thickets. The water-dispersed floating seeds of some species may explain their irregular distribution (V. E. Rudd 1967; B. Verdcourt 1979; A. Delgado-Salinas and E. Estrada-Castillón 2010).

SELECTED REFERENCE Rudd, V. E. 1967. *Oxyrhynchus* and *Monoplegma* (Leguminosae). Phytologia 15: 289–294.

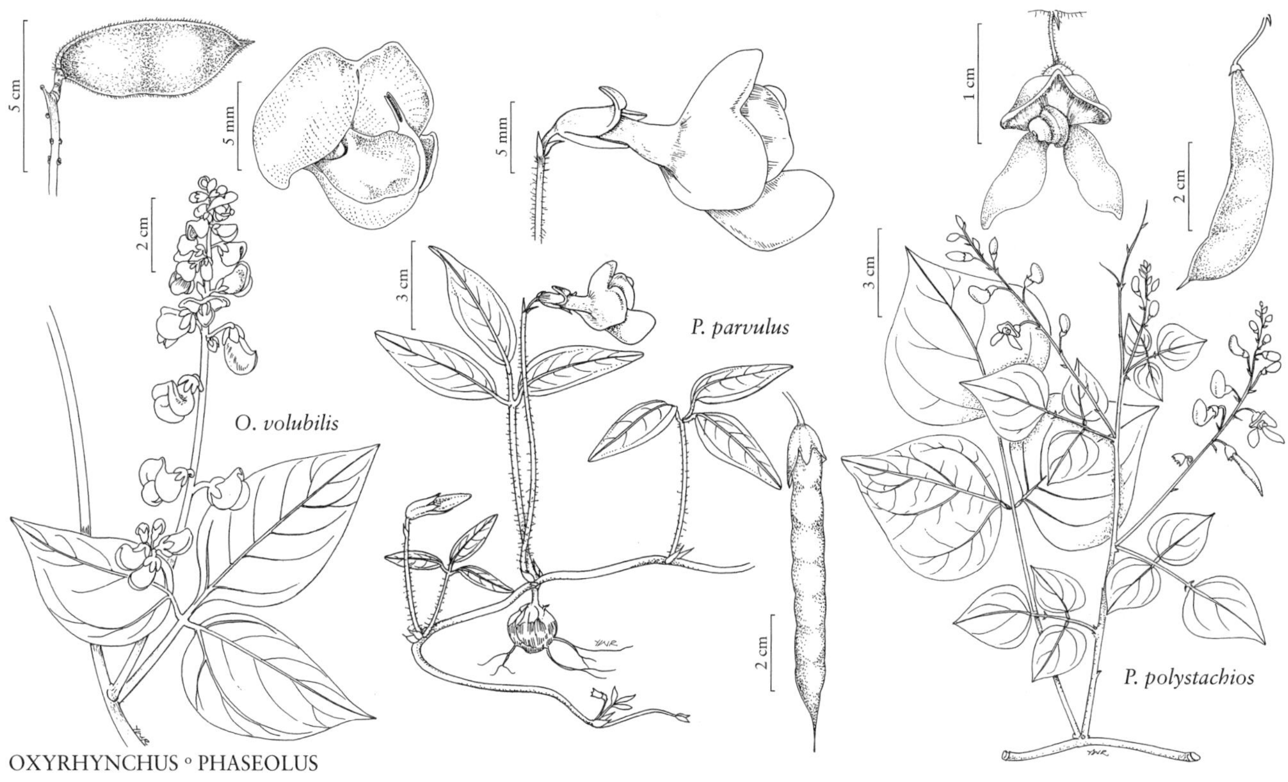

OXYRHYNCHUS ∘ PHASEOLUS

1. Oxyrhynchus volubilis Brandegee, Univ. Calif. Publ. Bot. 4: 271. 1912 [F] [I]

Dolichos insularis Britton; *Oxyrhynchus alienus* Piper; *O. insularis* (Britton) Piper

Stems to 10+ m. **Leaves:** stipules deltate, 3–4 × 1–1.5 mm; stipels striate, linear-deltate, 2–3.5 × 1 mm; leaflet blades ovate to subhastate, lateral blades obliquely ovate, 5–8 × 3–4 cm, base trinervate, apex acute to acuminate, surfaces glabrous or glabrate, hairs subadpressed. **Peduncles** 12–18 cm, covered with antrorse trichomes. **Inflorescences** 20–40 cm, rachis with 10+ floral nodes, each with 5 or 6 flowers; bracts subulate, 3 mm. **Pedicels** 3–6 mm; bracteoles ovate-elliptic, 2 mm, 3- or 4-veined. **Flowers** 1 cm; calyx purplish, 3–5 mm, lobes subequal, lateral lobes ovate, ciliate; banner greenish outside, inner face purple, 9–10 mm, length less than width, base auriculate and unguiculate, apex emarginate; wings purple, widely oblong, 8–9 mm, base auriculate, short-clawed; keel light purple, curved, 7.5–8.5 mm, base auriculate, short-clawed, apex slightly twisted to right; ovules 2 or 3. **Legumes** light brown with dark patterns, 4–6 × 2–3 cm, dehiscent first on adaxial suture, slightly twisting, valves pulverulent. **Seeds** 1 cm diam.; hilum 0.8–1.1 mm. $2n = 22$.

Flowering Sep–Nov. Shrublands; 100–500 m; introduced; Tex.; Mexico; West Indies (Bahamas, Cuba).

Oxyrhynchus volubilis was described as *O. alienus* from plants grown in Austin, Texas. The species is now cultivated as an ornamental; there appears to be little information available about it in the flora area (G. L. Nesom 2009), and it may not be naturalized there.

104. PHASEOLUS Linnaeus, Sp. Pl. 2: 723. 1753; Gen. Pl. ed. 5, 323. 1754 • Bean, frijol [Greek *phaseolos*, name for kidney bean or cowpea, and Latin *olus*, diminutive suffix, probably alluding to boat-shaped pods]

Alfonso Delgado-Salinas

Alepidocalyx Piper; *Lipusa* Alefeld; *Minkelersia* M. Martens & Galeotti

Vines, annual or perennial, unarmed; roots tuberous or elongated (non-tuberous) taproots or fibrous. **Stems** usually prostrate to climbing, rarely erect, striate, often lignescent, pubescent, covered with oblique to appressed, retrorse hairs, interspersed with finely uncinate, minutely hooked hairs. **Leaves** alternate, odd-pinnate; stipules and stipels present (terminal ones ascending, those of lateral leaflets spreading), at times covered with glandular hairs, these nectariferous; petiole present, petiole and rachis canaliculate; leaflets 3, blade margins entire, surfaces glabrous or pubescent. **Inflorescences** (1–)3–60+-flowered, terminal or axillary, usually pseudoracemes, rarely also with basal and lateral branches (compound racemes), (1 or)4–60 floral nodes, not swollen, often biflorous; primary bracts present, usually persistent, secondary bracts at base of pedicels; bracteoles minute or equal to calyx tube; bracts and bracteoles often nectariferous as stipules. **Pedicels** equal to or longer than calyx tube, arcuate or reflexed in fruit. **Flowers** papilionaceous; calyx campanulate or campanulate-tubular, lobes 5, usually shorter than tube, adaxial usually ± connate throughout; corolla pink, purple, red, violet, or white; banner glabrous abaxially, often hairy adaxially, slightly to strongly thickened at point of reflexion, often with two intramarginal thickenings; wings longer than other petals; keel beaked, apex 1.5–2 laterally and tightly coiled, coils 1.5–5.5 mm diam.; stamens 10, diadelphous, vexillary stamen dilated or with globose to bladelike appendage basally; anthers dorsifixed alternating with basifixed; pollen tricolporate to triporate, often with pseudocolpi; ovary with nectary disc at base, linear; stigma introrse, laterally or extrorsely placed because of stylar rotation, apical or extrorse. **Fruits** legumes, sessile or stipitate, usually falcate, sometimes straight, linear or oblong, short-beaked, usually elastically dehiscent, membranous, papery, or leathery, compressed or expanding over seeds, glabrous or pubescent. **Seeds** 1–20, oblong, quadrate, suborbicular, or reniform; epihilum white. x = 10, 11.

Species 70 (12 in the flora): North America, Mexico, West Indies, Central America, South America (n Argentina, Bolivia, Colombia, Ecuador, Peru, Venezuela); tropical to warm temperate areas.

Phaseolus species share an indument of uncinate hairs, inflorescences with non-swollen floral nodes, bracts that are usually persistent, pedicels that are longer than the calyx tubes, and floral keel petals that are distally coiled laterally. The pseudoracemes or compound racemes have two (or three) flowers per node (this with a primary bract), and each flower is subtended by a secondary bract and two bracteoles covering partially or completely the sides of the calyx, at the apex of each pedicel. Some *Phaseolus* species develop reduced lateral inflorescences (G. Prenner 2013). The latter are referred to as panicles by G. F. Freytag and D. G. Debouck (2002). The seedlings have hypogeal or epigeal germination; in the flora area all species have hypogeal seedlings, except *P. acutifolius* and *P. filiformis*. A phylogenetic classification of the different groups of species in *Phaseolus* has been proposed (A. Delgado-Salinas et al. 2006).

Phaseolus has five cultivated species, and at least two (*P. lunatus* Linnaeus and *P. vulgaris* Linnaeus) have numerous cultivars and are important sources of food worldwide. Four species (*P. acutifolius*, *P. coccineus* Linnaeus, *P. lunatus*, and *P. vulgaris*) are grown in the United States and have been reported to escape (D. Isely 1998).

SELECTED REFERENCES Delgado-Salinas, A., R. Bibler, and M. Lavin. 2006. Phylogeny of the genus *Phaseolus* (Leguminosae): A recent diversification in an ancient landscape. Syst. Bot. 31: 779–791. Freytag, G. F. and D. G. Debouck. 2002. Taxonomy, Distribution, and Ecology of the Genus *Phaseolus* (Leguminosae – Papilionoideae) in North America, Mexico and Central America. Fort Worth. [Sida Bot. Misc 23.]

1. Inflorescences often with basal floral branches; c, e North America (including e Texas).
    2. Leaflet blades leathery, bases obtuse or broadly rounded and lobed, apices obtuse to acute, venation reticulate; inflorescences with flowers clustered apically, rarely with basal floral branches; legumes 35–55 × 8–10 mm . . . . 10. *Phaseolus sinuatus*
    2. Leaflet blades membranous to leathery or slightly papery, bases rounded to depressed-ovate or truncate, apices usually acute to acuminate, rarely obtuse, venation not reticulate; inflorescences usually with basal floral branches; legumes (30–)45–78(–86) × 7.5–13 mm.
        3. Leaflet blades ovate to rhombic-ovate, not lobed basally; corollas 10–12 mm; legumes (30–)45–78(–86) × 7.5–13 mm . . . . .7. *Phaseolus polystachios*
        3. Leaflet blades ovate-lanceolate, distinctly 3-lobed, with rounded or quadrate lobes basally; corollas 13 mm; legumes 53–60 × 8–10 mm . . . . .11. *Phaseolus smilacifolius*
1. Inflorescences without basal floral branches; sw United States.
    4. Inflorescences with (1 or)2–6 biflorous (or usually 1-flowered in *P. parvulus*) nodes; roots fibrous, tuberous, or slender taproots.
        5. Roots fibrous or slender taproots; bracteoles linear to lanceolate or oblong-ovate to narrowly triangular, 0.6–1.8 mm; legumes linear-falcate, 23–70 × 4–9 mm; seeds 4–10.
            6. Leaflet blades ovate to widely ovate or linear to lanceolate, often weakly to conspicuously lobed on one or both sides basally, apices acute to attenuate, bases rounded or truncate to cuneate, 2.5–11.5 × 0.3–5 cm; legumes 32–70 × 5–9 mm; seeds 5–10, oblong, 3–6 × 2.5–5.5 mm, smooth to slightly rugose . . . . 1. *Phaseolus acutifolius*
            6. Leaflet blades ovate in outline, not lobed or shallowly to deeply lobed basally (lobes quadrate-obtuse to oblong-attenuate), apices obtuse to acute, bases broadly cuneate to truncate, 1–5 × 1–4.5 cm; legumes 23–35 × 4–5 mm; seeds 4–7, usually oblong to quadrate, rarely reniform, 2–4.3 × 2.3–4 mm, rugose . . . . 3. *Phaseolus filiformis*
        5. Roots tuberous; bracteoles ovate to lanceolate, oblong, or obsolete, 0.1–0.5 or 1–1.5 mm; legumes linear-falcate or linear-straight to slightly falcate, 23–45 × 3–8 mm; seeds 3 or 4, or 8–11.
            7. Taproots elongate; stems climbing or trailing, to 150 cm; leaflet blades linear, narrowly oblong to lanceolate, or narrowly trullate; calyces campanulate; corollas 12 mm; bracteoles 1–1.5 mm; legumes linear-falcate, 23–30 × 4–8 mm; seeds 3 or 4, oblong, 3.5–5 × 3–4 mm, rugose . . . . .2. *Phaseolus angustissimus*
            7. Taproots oblong or spherical; stems erect, trailing, or twining, 5–50 cm; leaflet blades usually linear to lanceolate, sometimes narrowly trullate; calyces campanulate-tubular; corollas 15–25 mm; bracteoles 0.1–0.5 mm; legumes linear-straight to slightly falcate, 35–45 × 3–4 mm; seeds 8–11, oblong or reniform, 2–3.7 × 1.7–2.6 mm, smooth . . . . .6. *Phaseolus parvulus*
    4. Inflorescences with (3–)6–25 biflorous (sometimes 3-flowered in *P. texensis*) nodes; roots tuberous or taproots (often large and thick).
        8. Leaflet blades leathery, apices usually obtuse to rounded, retuse to emarginate, strongly apiculate; stipules ovate to lanceolate, 5–10 × 1–2.5 mm; primary bracts (2–)3–6.5(–8) mm; legumes sessile, oblong, somewhat curved, valves leathery, weakly dehiscent, 30–74 × 12–17 mm . . . . 5. *Phaseolus maculatus*
        8. Leaflet blades membranous to firm, papery, or leathery, apices acute, long-acuminate, apiculate, or obtuse, sometimes apiculate; stipules oblong or triangular, lanceolate, widely ovate, or orbiculate, 1.5–7 × 0.5–4 mm; primary bracts 1–5(–10) mm; legumes sessile or stipitate, oblong- or linear-falcate, or oblong and slightly falcate, valves thin, papery, or leathery, elastically dehiscent, (10–)30–53 × 3–11(–15) mm.

[9. Shifted to left margin.—Ed.]

9. Leaflet blades leathery, not lobed, apices acute; petioles shorter than terminal leaflet (often only pulvinus); legumes stipitate, stipe to 5.5 mm . . . . 8. *Phaseolus ritensis*
9. Leaflet blades membranous to slightly papery or firm, faintly to deeply 3-lobed (lobes often dissected), apices acute, sometimes apiculate; petioles often equaling or longer than terminal leaflet; legumes sessile.
    10. Leaflet blades faintly or deeply 3-lobed, dissected . . . . 9. *Phaseolus scabrellus*
    10. Leaflet blades ovate to slightly lobed basally, not dissected.
        11. Stipules triangular to widely ovate or orbiculate, 4–7 mm; banners 4–8 mm; legumes sparsely covered with long, incumbent and hooked hairs; Arizona . . . . 4. *Phaseolus leptostachyus*
        11. Stipules lanceolate, 1.5–3 mm; banners 12 mm; legumes strigose; Texas. . . . . . 12. *Phaseolus texensis*

1. Phaseolus acutifolius A. Gray, Smithsonian Contr. Knowl. 3(5): 43. 1852 • Tepary bean

Vines annual, with narrow, fibrous roots. **Stems** weak or vigorous twiners, often trailing, to 400 cm. **Leaves:** stipules ascending, triangular to oblong, 1.5–3 × 0.5–2 mm; petiole 2–8 cm; rachis 0.5–2.5 cm; stipels linear to lanceolate, often clavate, 1.3–2 mm, 1-veined; leaflet blades linear to lanceolate or ovate to widely ovate, often weakly to conspicuously lobed on one or both sides basally, 2.5–11.5 × 0.3–5 cm, membranous to rigid, venation often prominent, base rounded or truncate to cuneate, apex acute to attenuate, surfaces abaxially sparsely to densely covered with minute, uncinate hairs, with incumbent hairs along veins and marginally, adaxially covered with sparsely incumbent and uncinate hairs. **Peduncles** 0.8–11.5 cm. **Inflorescences** to 26 cm; main axis sparsely to densely covered with uncinate hairs; rachis 2–24 cm, with 2–6 usually biflorous nodes; peduncular basal bracts linear to lanceolate, 1–1.5 × 3–5 mm; primary bracts ovate to lanceolate, 2–3 × 0.5 mm, 1–3-veined. **Pedicels** 3–7 mm, covered with minute uncinate hairs; bracteoles persistent, linear to lanceolate, 1.5–1.8 mm. **Flowers:** calyx campanulate, 3–4 mm, sparsely covered with incumbent and uncinate hairs; abaxial and lateral lobes triangular to lanceolate; adaxial lobes usually connate into apiculum; corolla pink to lavender, violet, or purple, 10 mm; banner suborbiculate, 7–8 mm, apex emarginate, rarely adaxial surface covered with straight hairs; wings obovate to oblong, 10–12 mm, base slightly constricted, apex obtuse; keel 6 mm; ovary linear, 4 mm, covered with appressed hairs. **Legumes** pendent, compressed, linear-falcate, 32–70 × 5–9 mm, elastically dehiscent, valves thin to papery, sparsely covered with appressed and uncinate hairs. **Seeds** 3–6(–10), brown to ivory, punctate and mottled with black, oblong, 3–6 × 2.5–5.5 mm, smooth to slightly rugose; hilum ovate, 0.5–1.2 mm.

Varieties 2 (2 in the flora): sw, sc United States, n Mexico.

Both varieties of *Phaseolus acutifolius* often occur in the same habitats, although var. *tenuifolius* is more often associated with open and drier areas.

Phaseolus acutifolius in the broad sense is a widespread polymorphic assemblage that shows a seemingly continuous series of variants that have developed marked leaflet differences toward the extremes of an almost continuous range. M. W. Blair et al. (2012) have recently established, with molecular evidence, that both varieties show evidence of intercrossed individuals.

1. Leaflet blades ovate to widely ovate, apex acute, base rounded; terminal leaflet blades 2.5–8.5 × 1–5 cm; legumes 36–70 × 5–9 mm; seeds 4–10, 3–6 × 3.3–5.5 mm. . . . . 1a. *Phaseolus acutifolius* var. *acutifolius*
1. Leaflet blades linear to lanceolate, apex acute to attenuate, base truncate to subtruncate; terminal leaflet blades 3.5–11.5 × 0.3–2.3 cm; legumes 32–54 × 5–6 mm; seeds 3–6, 3–4.5 × 2.5–4.5 mm . . . . 1b. *Phaseolus acutifolius* var. *tenuifolius*

1a. Phaseolus acutifolius A. Gray var. **acutifolius**

Phaseolus acutifolius var. *latifolius* G. F. Freeman; *P. pauper* Standley

Leaflet blades ovate to widely ovate, terminal ones 2.5–8.5 × 1–5 cm, base rounded, apex acute. **Legumes** 36–70 × 5–9 mm. **Seeds** 4–10, 3–6 × 3.3–5.5 mm. **2*n*** = 22.

Flowering Jun–Nov. Open pine-oak forests, mesquite thickets, grasslands, chaparral, scrub, igneous or limestone soils; 200–2000 m; Ariz., N.Mex., Tex.; Mexico (Baja California Sur, Chihuahua, Coahuila, Colima, Durango, Jalisco, Nayarit, Sinaloa, Sonora).

Variety *acutifolius* is found in central and southern Arizona, Catron, Doña Ana, Grant, and Luna counties in New Mexico, and Jeff Davis and Pecos counties in Texas.

The leaflets of the type collection of *Phaseolus acutifolius*, as well as others from specimens of western Texas, are characterized by having smaller and narrower leaflets than those from populations elsewhere.

The cultivated plants of *Phaseolus acutifolius* are classified under this variety, commonly having fruits 5–9 × 0.8–1.3 cm, from elastically to weakly dehiscent, and white, yellow-brown, tan-mottled, and blue-black seeds (R. C. Pratt and G. P. Nabhan 1988).

1b. Phaseolus acutifolius A. Gray var. **tenuifolius** A. Gray, Smithsonian Contr. Knowl. 5(6): 33. 1853

Phaseolus montanus Brandegee; *P. tenuifolius* (A. Gray) Wooton & Standley

Leaflet blades linear to lanceolate, terminal ones 3.5–11.5 × 0.3–2.3 cm, base truncate to subtruncate, apex acute to attenuate, often weakly to conspicuously lobed at base. **Legumes** 32–54 × 5–6 mm. **Seeds** 3–6, 3–4.5 × 2.5–4.5 mm. **2*n*** = 22.

Flowering Jun–Nov. Open pine-oak forests, mesquite thickets, grasslands, chaparral, scrub, igneous or limestone soils; 200–2000 m; Ariz., N.Mex., Tex.; Mexico (Baja California Sur, Chihuahua, Coahuila, Colima, Durango, Jalisco, Sinaloa, Sonora)

Variety *tenuifolius* is found in central and southeastern Arizona, Doña Ana and Hidalgo counties in New Mexico, and El Paso and Jeff Davis counties in Texas.

Phaseolus angustissimus occurs within the range of var. *tenuifolius* and might be confused with it. Plants of var. *tenuifolius* can be distinguished from *P. angustissimus* by their fibrous roots and many-seeded pods.

2. Phaseolus angustissimus A. Gray, Smithsonian Contr. Knowl. 5(6): 33. 1853 • Slimleaf or narrowleaf bean

Phaseolus angustissimus var. *latus* M. E. Jones; *P. dilatatus* Wooton & Standley

Vines perennial, often forming dense growth, with thick and elongate tuberous, woody taproots. **Stems** climbing or trailing, to 150 cm. **Leaves:** stipules spreading to reflexed, ovate to triangular, often faintly lobed basally, 2.5–4 × 1–2 mm; petiole 2–5 cm; rachis 0.8–1.7 cm; stipels narrowly triangular to lanceolate, 1–2.5 mm; leaflet blades linear, narrowly oblong to lanceolate, or narrowly trullate, often lobed basally, 2.5–6 × 0.2–3 cm, thin to subcoriaceous, base truncate to broadly cuneate, apex usually obtuse or long-attenuate, surfaces covered with minute, uncinate hairs, also with incumbent hairs along veins abaxially and marginally. **Peduncles** 3–11 cm. **Inflorescences** to 20 cm, rarely with axillary flowers at base; axis covered with uncinate hairs; rachis 2–9 cm, with 2–6 biflorous nodes; primary bracts ovate, 1–1.5 × 0.8 mm, 3–5-veined. **Pedicels** 3–5(–7) mm, hairs uncinate; bracteoles persistent, ovate to lanceolate or oblong, 1–1.5 mm, often densely covered with incumbent hairs, often at midpoint of pedicel. **Flowers:** calyx campanulate, 2.5–3.5 mm, sparsely to densely covered with uncinate hairs, veins prominent; abaxial lobes triangular to narrowly so, apex acute, 1–1.5 mm; lateral lobes triangular, apex acute, 1 × 1 mm; adaxial lobes connate, apex emarginate or cleft; corolla pink to light purple, 12 mm; banner oblong to orbiculate, 1 mm, apex slightly emarginate; wings obovate, 12 mm; keel 5.5 mm; ovary linear, 3.5 mm, sparsely covered with appressed hairs. **Legumes** pendent, compressed, linear-falcate, 23–30 × 4–8 mm, elastically dehiscent, valves thin, sparsely covered with minute, appressed hairs. **Seeds** 3 or 4, brown often mottled with black, oblong, 3.5–5 × 3–4 mm, rugose, reticulate-areolate patterns with rounded mounds; hilum ovate, 0.5 mm. **2*n*** = 22.

Flowering May–Nov. Semidesert regions, dry river or creek beds and banks, under pines, pinyon-juniper-oak forests, igneous or calcareous rocky soils; 1000–2500 m; Ariz., N.Mex., Tex.; Mexico (Sonora).

Phaseolus angustissimus is widespread in Arizona and the western half of New Mexico but is restricted to Brewster, El Paso, Presidio, and Terrell counties in Texas.

Phaseolus angustissimus is readily distinguished by its habit, linear leaflets, few floral nodes per inflorescence, and falcate pods with three or four rugosely ornamented seeds. It is most likely to be confused with *P. filiformis* by a combination of characters, but differences in root system, stipule length, ovule number, and fruit width are usually sufficient to separate the two. However, rugose seeds are also found in *P. filiformis*.

Flowers and crushed roots have been reported by the Zuñi people as a health strengthener for children (M. C. Stevenson 1915).

3. Phaseolus filiformis Bentham, Bot. Voy. Sulphur, 13. 1844 • Wright's or slender-stemmed bean

Phaseolus sanctorum M. E. Jones; *P. wrightii* A. Gray

Vines annual or short-lived perennial, frequently mat-forming, with slender taproots. **Stems** trailing or climbing, to 250 cm. **Leaves:** stipules usually ascending, ovate to broadly triangular, 1–2.5 × 0.8–2.4 mm; petiole 2–5.5 cm; rachis 0.5–2 cm; stipels linear to ovate-lanceolate, 0.5–1.5 mm; leaflet blades ovate in outline, not lobed or shallowly to deeply lobed basally, lobes quadrate-obtuse to oblong-attenuate, 1–5 × 1–4.5 cm, membranous to rigid, base broadly cuneate to truncate, apex obtuse to acute, surfaces covered with uncinate hairs, abaxially with incumbent hairs along veins. **Peduncles** often angled, 1–10 cm. **Inflorescences** 1.2–16 cm; axis covered with uncinate hairs; rachis 0.2–7.5 cm, with 2–6 biflorous nodes; primary bracts ovate to lanceolate, 1–2 × 0.5 mm, often pigmented, 3-veined. **Pedicels** 5 mm, hairs uncinate; bracteoles persistent, oblong-ovate to narrowly triangular, 0.6–1.3 mm, often covered with uncinate hairs. **Flowers:** calyx campanulate, 2–3.5 mm, sparsely to densely covered with uncinate hairs; abaxial and lateral lobes triangular; adaxial lobes connate; corolla pink, lavender, reddish to light purple, or white fading yellowish, 10 mm; banner oblong to orbiculate, 10 mm, apex emarginate, surfaces glabrous; wings obovate, 10 mm, apex acute or obtuse; keel 6 mm; ovary linear, 3 mm. **Legumes** pendent, compressed, linear-falcate, 23–35 × 4–5 mm, elastically dehiscent, valves membranous, sparsely covered with incumbent and uncinate hairs. **Seeds** 4–6(or 7), brown, usually oblong to quadrate, rarely reniform, 2–4.3 × 2.3–4 mm, rugose; hilum ovate, 0.3 mm. **2*n*** = 22.

Flowering year-round. Sandy, gypsum, limestone, or volcanic soils, juniper communities, open oak-pine forests; 0–1700 m; Ariz., Calif., N.Mex., Tex.; Mexico (Baja California, Baja California Sur, Chihuahua, Coahuila, Durango, Sonora).

Phaseolus filiformis occurs from Riverside County, California, eastward through Arizona and New Mexico to western Texas (El Paso, Jeff Davis, and Presidio counties).

Phaseolus filiformis is easily distinguished by its slender taproot or fibrous root system, conspicuous variation in leaflet lobation, small number of flowers per inflorescence, falcate fruits, and seeds with rugose surfaces. In appearance, it is often confused with *P. scabrellus*, but the latter has a thick root system and smooth seeds.

Flowers, mature seeds, and immature pods are sometimes used as food (D. R. Newton 2013).

4. **Phaseolus leptostachyus** Bentham, Comm. Legum. Gen. 72. 1837

Phaseolus anisotrichos Schlechtendal; *P. fulvus* Brandegee; *P. intonsus* Piper; *P. opacus* Piper

Vines perennial, with short tuberous roots. **Stems** often reddish pigmented, prostrate or twining, to 300 cm, slender, terete or angulate, usually sparsely to densely covered with spreading, straight hairs, often yellowish, interspersed with white, hooked hairs. **Leaves:** stipules ascending or spreading, triangular to widely ovate or orbiculate, 4–7 × 3–4 mm, acute or obtuse, sometimes auriculiform, 3-many-veined, glabrate or strigillose, ciliate; petiole 1–5(–8) cm; rachis 0.5–2 cm; stipels usually triangular to lanceolate, 1–3 × 1 mm, acute; leaflet blades narrowly to widely ovate, often with a basal lobe, 1.5–9 × 1–7 cm, membranous or thin, rarely leathery, base broadly cuneate, apex obtuse or acute to long-acuminate, surfaces usually sparsely strigose or hirtellous, often glabrate. **Peduncles** to 30 cm. **Inflorescences** 20–56 cm, axis usually covered with uncinate hairs, if straight hairs present, then mainly on peduncle; rachis 5–12 cm, with 4–40 usually biflorous nodes, often scattered along rachis; primary bracts usually lanceolate, 2.5–7(–10) × 3–4 mm, 3-many-veined, ciliate, nectariferous. **Pedicels** arcuate or reflexed and thicker in fruit, 1–3.5(–5) mm, usually shorter than calyx, hairs straight and hooked; bracteoles persistent, ovate to subulate, 0.5–1.5 mm, usually 1-veined, ciliate, sometimes along pedicels. **Flowers:** calyx campanulate, 1.5–3.5(–4.5) mm, inner surfaces of tube strigillose, outer surfaces usually hirtellous, especially on lower lobe; abaxial and lateral lobes triangular, 0.5–1.2 mm, apex acute; adaxial lobes connate, apex emarginate; corolla pink, lilac, purple, or white, 10 mm; banner obovate to orbiculate, 4–8 mm, apex emarginate, glabrous; wings obovate, auriculiform, 0.5–1.4(–1.8) mm; keel 5 mm; ovary oblong, 2.5–5 mm, covered with hooked hairs or strigillose. **Legumes** pendent, compressed, usually linear-falcate, 10–33 × 3–7 mm, elastically dehiscent, valves thin, sparsely covered with long, incumbent and hooked hairs or glabrate, sessile. **Seeds** 2–6, brown or gray mottled with black, oblong, orbicular, or reniform, 2–4.5 × 1.9–4.3 mm, smooth; hilum ovate, 0.3 mm. **2*n*** = 20.

Flowering Apr–Jan. Clearings, margins and understory of pine, pine-oak or oak forests, sandy slopes, rocky clay soils; 400–2300 m; Ariz.; Mexico; Central America (Costa Rica, El Salvador, Guatemala, Honduras).

Phaseolus leptostachyus is distinctive with its short inflorescences and numerous flowers, primary bracts that are similar in shape to the stipules, and pedicels that are shorter than calyx and strongly curved soon after anthesis. Only three collections are known from the flora area, collected in the 1930s from Cochise and Maricopa counties.

5. Phaseolus maculatus Scheele, Linnaea 21: 465. 1848
• Spotted or Metcalf bean

Phaseolus metcalfei Wooton & Standley

Vines perennial, with large, tuberous, woody taproots. **Stems** coarse, trailing or climbing, to 600 cm. **Leaves:** stipules spreading, later reflexed, ovate to lanceolate, often slightly lobed basally, 5–10 × 1–2.5 mm; petiole 1.5–6.5 cm; rachis 1.4–3.6 cm; stipels ovate to triangular, 1.3–3.5 mm, 3-veined; leaflet blades often variegated on midvein, widely ovate to very widely depressed-ovate or rhombic, laterals 3–7 × 2.5–5 cm, terminal 3–9.5 × 3–7.4 cm, leathery, base rounded to subcordate or subtruncate to cuneate, apex obtuse to rounded, rarely acute, retuse to emarginate, strongly apiculate, surfaces covered with minute uncinate hairs, margins and often abaxial surfaces, along prominent veins with incumbent hairs. **Peduncles** often with lateral inflorescences, sometimes with a floral node close to base, to 28 cm. **Inflorescences** to 50 cm; main axis sparsely to densely covered with minute uncinate hairs; rachis 5–24 cm, with 6–20 nodes, often proximal nodes subopposite, biflorous; primary bracts usually lanceolate, sometimes orbiculate, (2–)3–6.5(–8) × 0.5–1.5(–2) mm, 3–6-veined, glabrous or covered by uncinate and appressed hairs. **Pedicels** 3.5–7(–10) mm, covered with uncinate hairs, often with scattered incumbent hairs; bracteoles often persistent, lanceolate to oblanceolate, often clavate, 0.8–2 mm. **Flowers:** calyx campanulate, 4–5.5 mm, sparsely strigillose to short-strigose; abaxial lobes narrowly triangular; lateral lobes triangular; adaxial lobes connate, often partially divided; corolla reddish, violet, or bright pink to purple, 10–15 mm; banner oblong to obovate, 10 mm, apex emarginate, adaxial surface often covered with appressed hairs; wings obovate to widely obovate, 10–15 mm; keel 7 mm; ovary oblong, 4–5 mm, glabrous. **Legumes** pendent, compressed, oblong, somewhat curved, or obovate (when 1-seeded), 30–74 × 12–17 mm, sometimes with constriction in proximal ½, weakly dehiscent or sometimes elastically dehiscent, valves leathery, glabrous, sessile. **Seeds** 1–5, brown, mottled and often streaked with black, suborbicular to subquadrate, (6–)8–13 mm diam., smooth; hilum ovate to lanceolate or oblong, 1.3 mm. **2*n*** = 22.

Flowering Jun–Oct. Rocky slopes of deep canyons, valley bottoms, along streams, well-drained, sandy soils, open pine-oak or oak forests, grasslands, dry scrub; 1400–2700 m; Ariz., N.Mex., Tex.; Mexico.

Phaseolus maculatus is found throughout Arizona, except the western tier of counties, in the southwestern quarter of New Mexico, and in Brewster, Jeff Davis, Presidio, and Terrell counties in Texas.

Phaseolus maculatus is characterized by leaves with rigid margins and relatively large, passively or weakly dehiscent pods.

Phaseolus maculatus is closely related to *P. ritensis*. Both possess deep and enlarged taproots, trailing habits, leathery leaves with short petioles, and long inflorescences with few to many flowers. It has also been reported as *P. ritensis* for its useful roots, foliage (forage), and seed (G. P. Nabhan et al. 1980).

Phaseolus retusus Bentham (1839) is an illegitimate name that pertains here.

6. Phaseolus parvulus Greene, Bot. Gaz. 6: 217. 1881
• Pinos Altos Mountain bean [F]

Alepidocalyx parvulus (Greene) Piper

Vines perennial, with deep-seated, oblong or spherical tuberous taproots. **Stems** erect, trailing, or twining, 5–50 cm. **Leaves:** stipules sometimes red-purple pigmented, appressed to stem, reflexed or distally spreading, ovate to ovate-lanceolate, 1.8–6.5(–8.5) × 0.7–3(–4) mm (larger distally); petiole 1.8–3.4 cm; rachis 0.4–1 cm; stipels subulate to ovate or lanceolate, 1–2.5 mm; leaflet blades usually linear to lanceolate, sometimes narrowly trullate, sometimes terminal leaflets with 2 basal lobes each side, lateral leaflets often ± distinctly round lobed basally on 1 or both sides, laterals 2–4.7 × 0.5–1.3(–2.8) cm, terminal 2.4–5.6 × 0.3–1.2(–2.7) cm, thin, base attenuate, apex round or acute, obscurely apiculate, surfaces sparsely pubescent abaxially, scabrous adaxially. **Peduncles** 2–12 cm. **Inflorescences** 2–18 cm; axis sparsely covered with minute, uncinate hairs; rachis 0.2–0.6 cm, with 1–3 (usually 1-flowered) nodes; bracts lanceolate, 4 × 1.5 mm, 4–6-veined. **Pedicels** to 10 mm, shorter than flowers, uncinate-pubescent; bracteoles persistent, ovate or obsolete, 0.1–0.5 mm. **Flowers:** calyx campanulate-tubular, 5–8 mm, adaxial proximal portion rounded, papillate, covered with minute, uncinate hairs; abaxial lobes lanceolate; lateral lobes usually triangular, sometimes falcate; adaxial lobes connate nearly throughout; corolla violet, lavender-pink, or purple, 15–25 mm; banner obovate or spatulate, 12–16 mm, apex obtuse, emarginate; wings obovate, 15–27 mm, rounded-auriculate on distal margin at base; keel 10 mm; ovary linear, 6–7.5 mm, glabrous, marginally scabrous. **Legumes** horizontal to pendent, terete, linear-straight to slightly falcate, 35–45 × 3–4 mm, elastically dehiscent, valves leathery, glabrous. **Seeds** 8–11, usually brown to light brown or grayish green, punctate and mottled black, sometimes light green, oblong or reniform, 2–3.7 × 1.7–2.6 mm, smooth; hilum ovate-oblong, 0.4–0.5 mm. **2*n*** = 22.

Flowering Jul–Sep. *Pinus-Pseudotsuga* or pine-oak forests, wet meadows; 1500–3000 m; Ariz., N.Mex.; Mexico (Chihuahua, Durango, Jalisco, Nayarit, Sinaloa, Sonora, Zacatecas).

Phaseolus parvulus is known from Apache, Cochise, Coconino, Graham, Pima, and Santa Cruz counties in Arizona, and Catron, Grant, Hidalgo, and Sierra counties in New Mexico.

Phaseolus parvulus is a relatively small and unique wild bean characterized by its small, radishlike root, erect to trailing habit, and tubular calyx.

7. **Phaseolus polystachios** (Linnaeus) Britton, Sterns & Poggenburg, Prelim. Cat., 15. 1888 (as polystachyus) • Bean-vine, thicket or wild kidney bean, sacsac [E] [F]

Dolichos polystachios Linnaeus, Sp. Pl. 2: 726. 1753; *Phaseolus paniculatus* Michaux; *P. perennis* Walter; *P. polystachios* var. *aquilonius* Fernald

Vines perennial, with tuberous taproots. **Stems** climbing or trailing, 100–400+ cm. **Leaves:** stipules spreading or reflexed, triangular to lanceolate, 1.5–3.5 × 0.5–1.5 mm, often strigillose; petiole (2–)3–6(–9) cm; rachis (0.5–)1–2(–2.5) cm; stipels ovate to lanceolate, 1–2.5 mm; leaflet blades ovate to rhombic-ovate, (1–)3–13 × (1–)3–12 cm, membranous to leathery, venation not reticulate, base rounded to depressed-ovate, apex acute to acuminate or obtuse, surfaces abaxially sparsely to densely covered with ascending and uncinate hairs, adaxially glabrous or sparsely covered with ascending and uncinate hairs. **Peduncles** (1–)5–25 cm. **Inflorescences** usually with basal and lateral branches developed along main axis (compound raceme), 8–55 cm; axis sparsely to densely covered with uncinate and often ascending hairs; rachis (2.5–)8–27.5 cm, with 5–32 often scattered, biflorous nodes, secondary rachis often developed with 3–5 flowers; primary bracts ovate to lanceolate, 1–4 × 0.3–1.2 mm, 3-veined, glabrous or strigillose; secondary bracts usually caducous, ovate, 0.5–2.5 × 0.4 mm. **Pedicels** 4–9 mm, sparsely covered with uncinate, and often, ascending hairs; bracteoles usually persistent, ovate to oblong, 0.5–1.2 mm. **Flowers:** calyx campanulate, 3–3.5 mm, glabrous or sparsely covered with ascending hairs; abaxial and lateral lobes triangular; adaxial lobes connate; corolla usually pink to light purple, rarely white, 10–12 mm; banner usually wider than long, 5–8 mm, apex emarginate, glabrous; wings obovate, 10–12 mm; keel 6–7.5 mm; ovary linear, 5 mm; style twisted at apex. **Legumes** pendent, compressed, oblong-falcate, (30–)45–78(–86) × 7.5–13 mm, elastically dehiscent, valves papery to slightly leathery, strigillose. **Seeds** 4–6, light brown, blackish mottled, oblong to reniform, 6–13 × (4–)5–8.3 mm, smooth; hilum oblanceolate, (1.6–)2.3–3.2 mm. $2n = 22$.

Flowering Jul–Oct. Open or shaded, deciduous woodlands, stream banks, thickets, rocky, sandy, or alluvial soils; 0–900 m; Ala., Ark., Conn., Del., D.C., Fla., Ga., Ill., Ind., Iowa, Kans., Ky., La., Maine, Md., Mass., Mich., Minn., Miss., Mo., Nebr., N.H., N.J., N.Y., N.C., Ohio, Okla., Pa., R.I., S.C., Tenn., Tex., Vt., Va., W.Va.

Phaseolus polystachios is distinguished from other species of the genus by a combination of characters including its large inflorescences, with the presence of basal and lateral floral branches, floral nodes usually scattered along the axis, and banners without transverse thickenings.

8. **Phaseolus ritensis** M. E. Jones, Contr. W. Bot. 12: 14. 1908 • Santa Rita Mountain bean

Phaseolus maculatus Scheele subsp. *ritensis* (M. E. Jones) Freytag

Vines perennial, with large, tuberous taproots. **Stems** stiff-branched, usually trailing, sometimes climbing, to 300 cm. **Leaves** often unifoliolate on 1–5 nodes of new growth; stipules spreading or reflexed, triangular to lanceolate, 2–4.5 × 0.5–2 mm, strigillose; petiole reduced, shorter than terminal leaflet (often only pulvinus), 0.4–3.5 cm; rachis 0.5–2 cm; stipels oblong to ovate or triangular, 1.5–2.5 mm; leaflet blades often variegated on midvein, usually ovate to widely ovate or trullate to widely trullate, sometimes lanceolate, laterals 2.5–7(–8.6) × 1–5(–6.5) cm, terminal 3–8(–10.5) × 0.1–0.6(–1) cm, leathery, base oblique, cuneate or truncate, apex acute, strongly apiculate, surfaces glabrous or sparsely covered with incumbent and uncinate hairs along veins and margins. **Peduncles** often with lateral inflorescences, to 40 cm. **Inflorescences** to 85 cm; main axis glabrous or sparsely covered with uncinate hairs, often also with incumbent hairs; rachis to 45 cm, with 6–25 biflorous nodes or with additional flowering axes (sometimes proximal nodes subopposite); primary bracts triangular, 1–2.5(–3.5) × 0.5–1 mm, 3-veined. **Pedicels** 3–10 mm, glabrous or sparsely to densely covered with uncinate hairs; bracteoles often persistent, triangular to lanceolate, 0.5–1 mm, apex ciliate. **Flowers:** calyx campanulate, 3–4 mm, glabrous or sparsely covered with incumbent and uncinate hairs; abaxial lobes triangular; lateral lobes triangular; adaxial lobes ± connate; corolla lavender to purple or violet, 13 mm; banner obovate to oblong, 10 mm, apex emarginate, outer surface often sparsely to densely covered with appressed hairs; wings obovate to oblong, 10–13 mm; keel 6 mm; ovary linear, 4–5 mm, glabrous. **Legumes** pendent, compressed, oblong-falcate, (25–)35–53 × 6–11 mm, elastically dehiscent, valves leathery, glabrous, stipe to 5.5 mm. **Seeds** 3–6, grayish or light brown, mottled and streaked with black, oblong to transversely oblong, 4–7.5 × 4–5.7 mm; hilum ovate to lanceolate, 1.2 mm, smooth. 2*n* = 22.

Flowering Jul–Oct. Rocky volcanic slopes or ash, sandy or gravelly soils, pine-oak forests; 1300–2700 m; Ariz., N.Mex., Tex.; Mexico (Chihuahua, Durango, Guanajuato, Jalisco, Nayarit, Sinaloa, Sonora, Zacatecas).

Phaseolus ritensis is known from Apache, Cochise, Gila, Graham, Maricopa, Pima, and Santa Cruz counties in Arizona, Catron County in New Mexico, and El Paso and Jeff Davis counties in Texas.

Roots of *Phaseolus ritensis* are reportedly used as a base for fermenting, as a purgative, and as a stimulant. The foliage has been used for animal forage (G. P. Nabhan et al. 1980).

Phaseolus ritensis and *P. maculatus* are similar in appearance, and both species, in flower, have been confused. In describing *P. ritensis*, M. E. Jones sensed the similarity with *P. maculatus* (there *P. retusus*) and explained that *P. ritensis* rarely has obtuse, never retuse, leaflets tips; bracts are minute, not conspicuous and persistent as in *P. maculatus*, and that the fruit of *P. ritensis* is distinctly falcate and long-stipitate. His diagnosis specified quite neatly the differences between the species. G. P. Nabhan et al. (1980) later revealed new distinguishable features between both taxa, such as the eophylls morphology, number of leaflets on the third node, leaf color, inflorescence length, fruit length, fruit valves and their distinct degrees of dehiscence, and seed dimensions.

9. Phaseolus scabrellus Bentham ex S. Watson, Proc. Amer. Acad. Arts 17: 346. 1882

Phaseolus floribundus Piper; *P. foliaceus* Piper; *P. grayanus* Wooton & Standley; *P. palmeri* Piper; *P. pedicellatus* Bentham var. *grayanus* (Wooton & Standley) A. Delgado ex Isely; *P. polymorphus* S. Watson; *P. polymorphus* var. *albus* Freytag; *P. purpusii* Brandegee; *P. pyramidalis* Freytag; *P. shaffneri* Piper; *P. teulensis* Piper; *P. wrightii* A. Gray var. *grayanus* (Wooton & Standley) Kearney & Peebles

Vines perennial, with thick, elongate, tuberous taproots. **Stems** usually climbing, to 200 cm. **Leaves:** stipules ascending, spreading, or reflexed, oblong to triangular or lanceolate, 3–5.5 × 1–2.5(–3) mm; petiole 1–6.5(–7.3) cm; rachis 0.5–2 cm; stipels oblong-subulate, 1–1.5 mm, 1 or 2-veined; leaflet blades ovate to lanceolate, deeply 3-lobed, dissected, basal lobe rounded to quadrate, middle lobe triangular to oblong or linear-lanceolate, laterals (0.7–)2–5.5(–6.5) × (0.4–)1.3–4(–5.5) cm, terminal (1.5–)2.5–6.5(–7.5) × (0.5–)1.5–4.6(–7.5) cm, membranous to firm, base rounded to truncate, apex acute, surfaces glabrous or sparsely covered with ascending hairs, mainly along veins. **Peduncles** 1.5–18.5 cm. **Inflorescences** often also with lateral, floral branches, 5–30(–40) cm; main axis usually sparsely to densely covered with ascending (often retrorse) and uncinate hairs or glabrous; rachis usually 2.5–10 cm, with 3–14 often biflorous nodes; primary bracts ovate to lanceolate or broadly ovate, 1–5(–7) × 0.5–3.5 mm, 3–9-veined. **Pedicels** 3–10 mm, covered with only uncinate hairs or with ascending and interspersed uncinate hairs; bracteoles usually persistent, ovate to linear-lanceolate, 0.5–2 mm. **Flowers:** calyx campanulate, 2–3(–4) mm, glabrous or hirtellous to strigillose, abundantly so on abaxial lobe; abaxial and lateral lobes triangular; adaxial lobes connate; corolla usually pink or purple, rarely white, 12–15 mm; banner oblong to orbiculate, 10 mm, apex emarginate, glabrous; wings obovate, 12–16 mm; keel 5.5–9 mm; ovary linear, 4–6.5 mm, sparsely covered with appressed hairs. **Legumes** pendent, compressed, linear-falcate, 30–45(–51) × 8–10(–15) mm, elastically dehiscent, valves thin, sparsely covered with ascending hairs, sessile. **Seeds** 2–5(or 6), brown or gray, mottled with black, oblong to reniform, 4.2–7.5 × 3.5–7 mm, smooth; hilum oblong-ovate, 0.8–1.2 mm.

Flowering Jun–Oct. Open pine or pine-oak forests, chaparral, rocky limestone or igneous soils; 1600–2800 m; Ariz., N.Mex., Tex.; Mexico (Aguascalientes, Chihuahua, Coahuila, Durango, Hidalgo, Jalisco, Nuevo León, Sinaloa, San Luis Potosí, Sonora, Tamaulipas, Zacatecas).

Phaseolus scabrellus, which is mainly restricted to the Chihuahua Desert Region and adjacent mountains, is characterized by its deeply 3-lobed leaflets, basal lobes rounded to quadrate, and relatively small flowers. It is readily confused with *P. filiformis*, but the latter has fibrous roots, smaller flowers and fruits, and rugose seeds.

10. Phaseolus sinuatus Nuttall ex Torrey & A. Gray, Fl. N. Amer. 1: 279. 1838 • Sandhill or trailing wild bean [E]

Phaseolus polystachios (Linnaeus) Britton, Sterns & Poggenburg subsp. *sinuatus* (Nuttall ex Torrey & A. Gray) Freytag; *P. polystachios* var. *sinuatus* (Nuttall ex Torrey & A. Gray) Maréchal, Mascherpa & Stainier

Vines perennial, with tuberous taproots. **Stems** trailing, 100 to 400 cm. **Leaves:** stipules spreading or reflexed, triangular to lanceolate, 1.5–3.5 × 0.5–1.5 mm, often strigillose; petiole and rachis with same pubescence as stem;

petiole (2–)3–6(–9) cm; rachis (0.5–)1–2(–2.5) cm; stipels ovate, 1 mm, proximal stipels ovate to lanceolate, 1–2.5 mm; leaflet blades usually 3-lobed, sometimes deltate or broadly ovate, 2–4 × 1–3 cm, leathery, venation reticulate, base obtuse or broadly rounded, apex usually obtuse, rarely acute, surfaces abaxially sparsely to densely covered with ascending and uncinate hairs, adaxially glabrous or sparsely covered with ascending and uncinate hairs. **Peduncles** (1–)5–25 cm. **Inflorescences** rarely with basal and lateral branches, flowers clustered apically, 8–55 cm; main axis sparsely to densely covered with uncinate and often ascending hairs; rachis (2.5–)8–27.5 cm, with 5–15 often scattered, biflorous nodes, secondary rachis often developed with 3–5 flowers; primary bracts ovate to lanceolate, 1–4 × 0.3–1.2 mm, 3-veined, glabrous or strigillose. **Pedicels** 5–10 mm, sparsely covered with uncinate and often with ascending hairs; bracteoles usually persistent, ovate to oblong, 0.5–1.2 mm. **Flowers:** calyx campanulate, 2.5–3 mm, glabrous or sparsely covered with ascending hairs; lateral and abaxial lobes orbiculate; adaxial lobes connate; corolla deep rose or rosy pink, 10–12 mm; banner ovate, 9–11 mm, usually wider than long, apex emarginate; wings obovate, 10 mm; keel strongly incurved, 10 mm; ovary lanceolate-falcate, 5–6 mm. **Legumes** pendent, compressed, falcate, 35–55 × 8–10 mm, elastically dehiscent, valves leathery, glabrous, short-stipitate. **Seeds** 4–6, dark red-brown to blackish, reniform, 7 × 5.5 mm, smooth; hilum lanceolate, 1.5 mm, epihilum white.

Flowering May–Nov. Pine-scrub vegetation, loamy, sandy soils; 0–100 m; Ala., Fla., Ga., Miss., N.C., S.C.

Phaseolus sinuatus is widespread in Florida, but it is restricted to the coastal plain in the rest of its range.

D. Isely (1998) noticed that in addition to the trailing habit and its distinctive deltate, subcoriaceous leaflets, *Phaseolus sinuatus* has brownish floral buds, which is an unusual trait in the genus.

11. Phaseolus smilacifolius Pollard, Bot. Gaz. 21: 233. 1896 [E]

Phaseolus polystachios (Linnaeus) Britton, Sterns & Poggenburg subsp. *smilacifolius* (Pollard) Freytag

Vines perennial, with tuberous taproots. **Stems** climbing or trailing, to 300 cm. **Leaves:** stipules spreading, ovate to triangular, 2 × 1 mm; petiole 3.5–10 cm; rachis 1.5–4 cm; stipels lanceolate, 1.2 mm; leaflet blades ovate-lanceolate, distinctly 3-lobed, with rounded or quadrate lobes basally, 4–8 × 5 cm, membranous to slightly papery, venation not reticulate, base truncate, apex acute, surfaces glabrous. **Peduncles** 4–11 cm. **Inflorescences** with basal and lateral branches, 5–20 cm; main axis pubescent; rachis 7–8 cm, flowers loosely spaced on elongated axis, with to 7 biflorous nodes; bracts lanceolate, 1.3–1.5 × 1 mm, 3-veined. **Pedicels** 5–15 mm, hairs straight or curved; bracteoles persistent, ovate-elliptic or oblong, 0.8 mm. **Flowers:** calyx campanulate, 3.2 mm, strigillose; lobes obtuse; corolla pink to purplish, 13 mm; banner broadly ovate, 9 mm, apex emarginate; wings obovate, 12–13 mm; keel 0.8 mm; ovary lanceolate, 5 mm. **Legumes** pendent, compressed, lanceolate-falcate, 53–60 × 8–10 mm, dehiscent, valves leathery, glabrous. **Seeds** 5 or 6, light brown, mottled black, ovoid, 4 × 3.5 mm, smooth; hilum lanceolate, 1 mm.

Flowering Aug–Sep. Wet or mesic forests, coastal hydric hammocks, limestone soils; 0–50 m; Fla.

Phaseolus smilacifolius is known from Alachua, Columbia, Levy, and Suwannee counties.

G. F. Freytag and D. G. Debouck (2002) listed specimens from Texas under this species; these later were used to describe *Phaseolus texensis* (A. Delgado-Salinas and W. R. Carr 2007).

Phaseolus smilacifolius has been proposed as a hybrid between *P. polystachios* and *P. sinuatus*; however, J. R. Abbott and W. S. Judd (2000) reported that plants in Waccasassa Bay State Preserve are distinctive and should be considered a separate species.

12. Phaseolus texensis A. Delgado & W. R. Carr, Lundellia 10: 13, figs. 2, 3. 2007 • Texas bean [C] [E]

Vines perennial, with tuberous taproots. **Stems** trailing or climbing, to 700 cm. **Leaves:** stipules ascending to reflexed, lanceolate, 1.5–3 × 0.8–1.2 mm; petiole 1–5 cm; rachis 0.7–1.7 cm; stipels subulate-obovate, 1–2.5 mm; leaflet blades: laterals ovate, sometimes lobed basally, terminal ovate to broadly ovate, sometimes lobed basally, laterals 1.5–7 × 2.2–4.8 cm, terminal 2–8.5 × 2–7 cm, membranous to slightly papery, base rounded to subtruncate, apex acute, apiculate, surfaces sparsely covered with uncinate hairs intermixed with ascending-curved hairs. **Peduncles** 5–10 cm. **Inflorescences** often with minute secondary axes or stalks developed on floral nodes, 6–22 cm; main axis usually covered with uncinate hairs; rachis to 12 cm, with 5–13 floral nodes, each 2- or 3-flowered; primary bracts triangular, 1–2 × 0.8 mm, 3-veined. **Pedicels** 4–9 mm, sparsely covered with uncinate hairs; bracteoles persistent, ovate, 0.5 mm. **Flowers:** calyx campanulate, 2.5–3.5 mm, covered with minute uncinate and straight hairs on lobe margins; abaxial and lateral lobes triangular; adaxial lobe connate; corolla pink fading dark pink, 12–15 mm;

banner oblong to orbiculate, 12 mm, apex emarginate, glabrous; wings obovate, 12–15 mm; keel 6.5–9 mm; ovary linear, 6 mm, sericeous. **Legumes** pendent, compressed, oblong, slightly falcate, 35–52 × 8 mm, elastically dehiscent, valves papery, strigose, sessile. **Seeds** 4–7, brown mottled black, oblong, 5 × 4.5 mm, smooth; hilum oblong, 1 mm.

Flowering Sep–Nov. Mixed woodlands, limestone cliffs and outcrops, along creeks; of conservation concern; 200–600 m; Tex.

Phaseolus texensis is similar to *P. scabrellus*, but it differs strikingly in leaf form, quantity of hairs, length of inflorescences, bracts and bracteoles, and seed number. The leaflets in *P. scabrellus* are mostly deeply 3-lobed, while terminal leaflets in *P. texensis* are broadly ovate to slightly 3-lobed, and not as dissected as in the former. Indument in *P. scabrellus* is more profuse than in *P. texensis*, especially distinctive by the presence of more ascending hairs on petioles, peduncles, and pedicels. Bracts and, especially, bracteoles are slightly smaller in *P. texensis* (1–2 mm and 0.5 mm respectively) than in *P. scabrellus* [1–5(–7) and 0.5–2 mm respectively]. Ovaries in *P. texensis* have five to seven ovules, whereas ovaries in *P. scabrellus* have mostly four or five, rarely six ovules. The species is restricted to the Edwards Plateau in central Texas.

105. STROPHOSTYLES Elliott, Sketch Bot. S. Carolina 2: 229. 1823, name conserved • Fuzzy bean [Greek *strophos*, twisted, and *stylis*, column, alluding to style spirally twisted]

Alfonso Delgado-Salinas

Matt Lavin

Erin Thais Riley

Phasellus Medikus, name rejected; *Phaseolus* sect. *Strophostyles* (Elliott) de Candolle

Vines, annual or perennial, unarmed, to 2 m. **Stems** slender, flexible, trailing or climbing, often branching at proximal nodes, not woody, sometimes lignescent at base, sparsely to densely short-pilose. **Leaves** alternate, odd-pinnate, pulvinate; stipules present, persistent, sessile, divergent from stem, striate, triangular-ovate, not produced proximal to point of insertion; long-petiolate, petiole and rachis canaliculate, pubescent; leaflets 3, stipels persistent, striate, often curved, linear, blades 1.3–5.6(–7.2) cm, membranous to papery, margins entire or lobed, sometimes basally lobed, surfaces sericeous or strigose. **Peduncles** angular. **Inflorescences** 1–12(–22)-flowered, axillary, pseudoracemes, rachis much contracted, with 1–6(–11)-flowering nodes, nodes often swollen, glandular, each bearing at most 2 flowers; primary bracts early deciduous or absent; secondary bracts subtending pedicels, persistent, ovate to lanceolate; bracteoles persistent, rigid and striate, lanceolate, equal to or longer than calyx tube. **Pedicels** mostly shorter than calyx tube, thickened in fruit. **Flowers** papilionaceous; calyx campanulate, 1.3–7 mm, lobes 4 (due to connation of 2 adaxial lobes into 1 acute-attenuate lobe), abaxial lobe more narrowly triangular and often longest, lateral lobes triangular, adaxial lobes connate into acute lobe; corolla pink or pinkish, banner often with yellowish maculae, keel pinkish, tip (beak) dark purple, 3.6–15 mm; wings oblong, not projected beyond distal bend of keel; keel petals connate along upper margin, incurved, with a prominent gibbosity along upper margin proximal to beak; stamens 10, diadelphous; anthers sub-basifixed, uniform; pollen tricolporate; ovary sessile, arched, sparsely to densely strigose, at base surrounded by a nectariferous sheath; style incurved like the keel, often becoming twisted, jointed at the first (proximal) curve, distinctly incrassate and flattened, distal portion introrsely bearded; stigma terminal and introrse. **Fruits** legumes, sessile, held horizontally or somewhat drooping, linear or slightly curved, cylindric to subcylindric, dehiscent with twisting valves, sericeous, strigose, glabrate, or glabrous. **Seeds** 4–10, spherical or oblong, subquadrate or reniform, ends truncate, usually covered with a cellular layer; hilum oblanceolate, elongated ½ length of seed, rim-aril and hilar tongue much reduced, lens distinct and divided; seedlings with epigeal germination. *x* = 11.

Species 3 (3 in the flora): North America, n Mexico.

Strophostyles flowers fade to pale brownish yellow when dry; the keel is proximally broad, with a prominent gibbosity along the upper margin proximal to the beak, usually with a longitudinal fold where it is adherent to the wing, gradually narrowing above this; the tubular apical portion curves to one side of the flower.

Systematics and phylogenetic relationships of *Strophostyles* have been studied (E. T. Riley-Hulting et al. 2004). Additional clarification on the nomenclature of *Strophostyles* have recently been published (A. Delgado-Salinas and M. Lavin 2004). *Strophostyles* species have been reported to serve as food and to have medicinal properties (D. E. Moerman 1998).

SELECTED REFERENCE Riley-Hulting, E. T., A. Delgado-Salinas, and M. Lavin. 2004. Phylogenetic systematics of *Strophostyles* (Fabaceae): A North American temperate genus within a Neotropical diversification. Syst. Bot. 29: 627–653.

1. Keel petals: beak mostly concealed by wings; peduncles slender, herbaceous, 1.2–11(–12.3) cm in fruit; leaf blades and fruits sericeous; banners 3.6–7(–8.3) mm; legumes 1.2–4.7 cm; leaflet blades lanceolate, margins usually entire, never deeply lobed . . . . 1. *Strophostyles leiosperma*
1. Keel petals: beak protruding well above wings; peduncles stout, lignescent, (2.4–)5–30 cm in fruit; leaf blades and fruits sparsely strigose to glabrate or glabrous; banners 6.7–15 mm; legumes 3–7(–9.6) cm; leaflet blades lanceolate to narrowly lanceolate or pandurate, margins entire or lobed.
    2. Keel petals with slender, curved beaks; bracteoles 1.5–4.2 mm, equal to or longer than calyx tube; legumes cylindric; leaflet blade margins lobed or entire, terminal leaflet blades 1.8–7.2 × 0.9–4.6 cm . . . . 2. *Strophostyles helvola*
    2. Keel petals with stout, erect, slightly curved beaks; bracteoles 0.8–2.4 mm, shorter than calyx tube; legumes subcylindric; leaflet blade margins usually entire or shallowly lobed, rarely deeply lobed, terminal leaflet blades (1.5–)2–4(–7) × 0.2–2.2(–3) cm . . . . 3. *Strophostyles umbellata*

1. Strophostyles leiosperma (Torrey & A. Gray) Piper, Contr. U.S. Natl. Herb. 22: 668. 1926 • Slickseed fuzzy bean [W]

Phaseolus leiospermus Torrey & A. Gray, Fl. N. Amer. 1: 280. 1838; *Strophostyles pauciflora* S. Watson; *S. pauciflora* var. *canescens* R. S. Cocks

Vines usually annual, rarely short-lived perennial, with relatively long, slender taproot. **Stems** terete, herbaceous at base, not from subterranean, branched caudex, proximal stems 1 mm diam. **Leaves:** leaflet blades lanceolate, margins usually entire, rarely shallowly lobed, sinus 0–1 mm, lateral leaflets 1.5–5.6 × 0.2–2.1 cm, terminal leaflet 1.7–5.4 × 0.2–2.3 cm, surfaces sericeous. **Peduncles** slender, herbaceous, 1.2–11(–12.3) cm, 0.2–0.7 mm diam. **Inflorescences** with 1 or 2(–4) flower-bearing nodes. **Flowers:** bracteoles 0.8–2.3 mm, ± equal to calyx tube; calyx tube 0.8–2.4 mm, lobes 0.5–1.5 mm; banner light pink, 3.6–7(–8.3) mm; wings light pink, 3.5–6.5 mm; keel 3.5–6 mm, beak slightly curved, to 1 mm diam., mostly concealed by wings. **Legumes** subcylindric, laterally compressed, 1.2–4.7 × 0.2–0.4 (–0.5) cm, usually sericeous. **Seeds** 4–9, distinctly mottled, reniform to oblong, without cellular or waxy covering.

Flowering Jul–Sep. Sandy prairies, stream banks, roadsides, open understories; 0–1500 m; Ont.; Ala., Ark., Colo., Fla., Ill., Iowa, Kans., Ky., La., Minn., Miss., Mo., Nebr., N.Mex., N.Dak., Okla., Pa., S.Dak., Tex., Wis.; Mexico (Chihuahua).

Strophostyles leiosperma is characterized by its narrower and sericeous leaflets and fruits and relatively small flowers with a keel beak only slightly laterally curved and largely enveloped by the wing petals. *Phaseolus pauciflorus* Bentham (1837), not Sessé & Mociño ex G. Don (1832), pertains here.

2. Strophostyles helvola (Linnaeus) Elliott, Sketch Bot. S. Carolina 2: 230. 1823 • Annual woolly bean, trailing wild or trailing fuzzy bean, strophostyle ocracé [E] [W]

Phaseolus helvolus Linnaeus, Sp. Pl. 2: 724. 1753 (as helvulus), name and orthography conserved; *Cajanus helvolus* (Linnaeus) Sprengel; *Dolichos helvolus* (Linnaeus) Nuttall; *Glycine angulosa* Muhlenberg ex Willdenow; *G. helvola* (Linnaeus) Elliott; *G. peduncularis* Muhlenberg; *G. peduncularis* var. *parabolica* Muhlenberg ex W. P. C Barton; *P. angulosus* Ortega; *P. diversifolius* Persoon; *P. farinosus* Linnaeus; *Strophostyles angulosa* (Muhlenberg ex Willdenow) Elliott; *S. angulosa* var. *missouriensis* S. Watson; *S. helvola* var. *missouriensis* (S. Watson) Britton; *S. missouriensis* (S. Watson) Small; *S. peduncularis* Muhlenberg ex Elliott

Vines perennial, with thick taproot. **Stems** angular, sometimes lignescent at base, from subterranean, branched caudex. **Leaves:** leaflet blades usually ovate, rarely orbiculate to lanceolate or panduriform, margins deeply to shallowly lobed or entire, sinus 0–18.2 mm, lateral leaflets 1.3–6.3 × 0.6–4.3 cm, terminal leaflet 1.8–7.2 × 0.9–4.6 cm, surfaces strigose. **Peduncles** stout, lignescent, (2.4–)5–21.5 cm, 0.8–1.3 mm diam. **Inflorescences** with (1 or)2–5 flower-bearing nodes. **Flowers:** bracteoles 1.5–4.2 mm, equal to or longer than calyx tube; calyx tube 1.3–3.6 mm, lobes 1–2.5 mm; banner pinkish, 6.7–13.3 mm; wings light pink, 7–9 mm; keel 8–13 mm, beak slender, distinctly curved, 1 mm diam., projected away from face of banner, protruding well above wings. **Legumes** cylindric, laterally compressed, 3–9.6 × (0.3–)0.4–0.8 cm, glabrous or sparsely strigose. **Seeds** 5–10, faintly mottled, with cellular or waxy covering. $2n = 22$.

Flowering Jul–Oct. Fields, grasslands, roadsides, open woodlands, sandy soils, dunes, beaches; 0–1500 m; Ont., Que.; Ala., Ark., Conn., Del., D.C., Fla., Ga., Ill., Ind., Iowa, Kans., Ky., La., Md., Mass., Mich., Minn., Miss., Mo., Nebr., N.J., N.Mex., N.Y., Okla., Pa., R.I., S.C., S.Dak., Tenn., Tex., Va., W.Va., Wis.

Strophostyles helvola has flowers with a prominently curved, slender keel beak that projects upward from the keel lamina and outward away from the face of the banner petal and cylindrical fruits.

Phaseolus peduncularis (Muhlenberg) W. P. C. Barton, *P. trilobus* Michaux ex Richard, and *P. vexillatus* Walter are illegitimate names that pertain here.

3. Strophostyles umbellata (Muhlenberg ex Willdenow) Britton in N. L. Britton and A. Brown, Ill. Fl. N. U.S. 2: 339. 1897 • Pink fuzzy or perennial woolly or perennial sand bean [E] [F]

Glycine umbellata Muhlenberg ex Willdenow, Sp. Pl. 3: 1058. 1802; *Phaseolus umbellatus* (Muhlenberg ex Willdenow) Britton; *Strophostyles umbellata* var. *paludigena* Fernald

Vines perennial, with slender taproot. **Stems** terete, often lignescent at base, from subterranean, branched caudex, sometimes with adventitious roots. **Leaves:** leaflet blades usually ovate-lanceolate, sometimes narrowly lanceolate, margins entire or shallowly, rarely deeply, lobed, sinus 0–1(–6) mm, lateral leaflets 1.5–4.2 × 0.3–2.7 cm, terminal leaflet (1.5–)2–4(–7) × 0.2–2.2(–3) cm, surfaces strigose. **Peduncles** stout, lignescent, (4.4–)6–30 cm, 0.8–1.3 mm diam. **Inflorescences** with (1 or)2–6(–11) flower-bearing nodes. **Flowers:** bracteoles 0.8–2.4 mm, shorter than calyx tube; calyx tube (1.4–)2–4 mm, lobes 1–2.5(–3) mm; banner pink, 7.3–15 mm; wings pinkish, 7–12 mm; keel 8–13 mm, beak prominent, erect, slightly curved, 1.5–2 mm diam., closely positioned to face of banner petal, protruding well above wings. **Legumes** subcylindric, laterally compressed, 3–7 × 0.2–0.6 cm, glabrate or sparsely strigose. **Seeds** 5–10, sometimes faintly mottled, with cellular or waxy covering. $2n = 22$.

Flowering Jul–Sep. Fields, meadows, rarely in woodlands; 0–1500 m; Ala., Ark., Conn., Del., D.C., Fla., Ga., Ill., Ind., Iowa, Kans., Ky., La., Md., Mass., Mich., Miss., Mo., N.J., N.Mex., N.Y., Okla., Pa., R.I., S.C., S.Dak., Tenn., Tex., Va., W.Va., Wis.

Strophostyles umbellata is highly variable in leaflet shape, from narrowly lanceolate like those of *S. leiosperma* to ovate-lanceolate like those of *S. helvola*. It is best distinguished by its prominent keel beak, which has a thick base, a curved tip, and is held close to the banner face.

106. MACROPTILIUM (Bentham) Urban, Symb. Antill. 9: 457. 1928 • [Greek *makros*, large, and *ptilon*, wing, alluding to wing petals being larger than banner petal]

Leticia Torres-Colín

Alfonso Delgado-Salinas

Phaseolus Linnaeus sect. *Macroptilium* Bentham, Comm. Legum. Gen., 76. 1837

Herbs or vines, biennial or perennial, unarmed; roots turnip-shaped or elongate. **Stems** twining, erect, semierect, or prostrate, slender, sometimes hollow, sparsely to densely pubescent. **Leaves** alternate, usually odd-pinnate, rarely unifoliolate; stipules present, persistent, not prolonged proximally, veined; petiolate; leaflets 3, stipels persistent, often reflexed, blade margins entire or 2-lobed, surfaces pubescent or glabrescent. **Inflorescences** 6–12-flowered, axillary, pseudoracemes, cleistogamous flowers present in some species, with modified inflorescences, tufts of bracts present at base of peduncle, persistent or caducous, nodes swollen, glandular; node bracts present, caducous or inconspicuous, bracteoles present, usually caducous. **Pedicels** mostly shorter than calyx tube. **Flowers** papilionaceous; calyx tubular or campanulate, lobes 5, lobes shorter to longer than tube, distinct or adaxial lobes partly connate; petals connate; corolla salmon-orange, red, or purple-black; banner orbiculate, obovate, or oblong, emarginate; wings ovate or oblong to obovate, conspicuously projected beyond distal bend of keel one directed upward to adopt function of banner; keel incurved, beak hooked, tip of beak hidden by wings; stamens 10, diadelphous; anthers sub-basifixed; ovary with nectary disc at base, style apically recurved and thickened, distal portion introrsely bearded, stigma terminal; ovules 4–24. **Fruits** legumes, patent or pendent, substipitate, valves plane or twisting, linear or oblong-falcate, dehiscent, non-septate, pilose, strigose, or hirsute. **Seeds** 2–20, oblong or reniform; hilum not centric, oblong or ovate. $x = 11$.

Species 18 (4 in the flora): s United States, Mexico, West Indies, Central America, South America.

Flowers of *Macroptilium* species often become purple when dry; in some species, the banner is mostly pale green, with two basal auricles, wings are larger than banner and long-stipitate, brightly colored, and glabrous or pubescent; keel petals are distally connate and hooklike and basally adnate to the staminal tube. Vexillary stamens are distinct and often dilated at base. The ovary is subsessile, pubescent, and surrounded at the base by a cylindric, nectariferous disc; the style has an introrse beard and is apically recurved and thickened, with a terminal stigma.

The greatest diversity in *Macroptilium* is found in South America (about 16 species; S. M. Espert et al. 2007); some species have been introduced for fodder and naturalized in the tropics and subtropics nearly worldwide.

Molecular evidence establishes the monophylly of *Macroptilium* among the other New World genera of Phaseolinae (A. Delgado-Salinas et al. 2011). A diagnostic feature is the flower architecture: one wing petal is directed upward to adopt the function of the banner petal, which becomes a supporting structure of the wing petal and encloses the distally-hooked keel characteristic of all of the species.

SELECTED REFERENCE Espert, S. M. et al. 2007. Phylogeny of *Macroptilium* (Leguminosae): Morphological, biochemical and molecular evidence. Cladistics 23: 119–129.

1. Stems twining or erect to semierect; taproots elongate; extrafloral nectaries conspicuous at inflorescence nodes; tufts of bracts at base of peduncle persistent; flowers 1.7–3 cm, corollas red or purple-black; legumes linear, patent, 7–10.5 cm, valves twisting at dehiscence; seeds 12–20.
   2. Stems twining, solid; leaflets papery, lateral blades 2-lobed, surfaces canescent abaxially, strigose adaxially; corollas purple-black; seeds 12 or 13; Arizona, California, Florida, Mississippi, New Mexico, Texas . . . . 1. *Macroptilium atropurpureum*
   2. Stems erect or semierect, hollow; leaflets membranous, lateral blades not lobed, surfaces strigulose abaxially, glabrescent adaxially; corollas red; seeds 15–20; Florida, Georgia, Louisiana, South Carolina . . . . 3. *Macroptilium lathyroides*
1. Stems prostrate; roots turnip-shaped; extrafloral nectaries inconspicuous at inflorescences nodes; tufts of bracts at base of peduncle caducous; chasmogamous flowers 0.9–1 cm, corollas salmon-orange or red; legumes oblong-falcate, pendent, 1–2.5 cm, valves not twisting at dehiscence; seeds 2–5.
   3. Leaflet blades orbiculate, ovate to broadly ovate, or obovate, lateral blades sometimes 2-lobed; corollas salmon-orange; ovules 6; Arizona, New Mexico, Texas. . . 2. *Macroptilium gibbosifolium*
   3. Leaflet blades linear, entire; corollas red; ovules 4; Arizona . . . . 4. *Macroptilium supinum*

1. **Macroptilium atropurpureum** (de Candolle) Urban, Symb. Antill. 9: 457. 1928 • Siratro or purple bean, conchito

Phaseolus atropurpureus de Candolle in A. P. de Candolle and A. L. P. P. de Candolle, Prodr. 2: 395. 1825 (as atro-purpureus); *P. atropurpureus* var. *canescens* (M. Martens & Galeotti) Hassler; *P. atropurpureus* var. *pseuderythroloma* Hassler; *P. atropurpureus* var. *sericeus* A. Gray; *P. canescens* M. Martens & Galeotti; *P. dysophyllus* Bentham; *P. schiedeanus* Schlechtendal

Vines, perennial; root elongate. **Stems** twining, solid, sericeous. **Leaves:** stipules retrorse, lanceolate or ovate, 5–6 × 1.8–2 mm; petiole 3.5–8 cm, canescent; rachis 5–8 mm; stipels linear, 1.2–2.5 mm; leaflets papery, blades elliptic or ovate, base cuneate or obtuse, apex acute, surfaces often canescent abaxially, strigose adaxially; lateral blades 3.3–4 × 2.7–3.3 cm, 2-lobed, terminal blades often hastate, 4.5–4.7 × 3–4.3 cm. **Inflorescences** 26–36 cm, axes pilose; tufts of bracts at base of peduncle persistent, 5.5 mm, lanceolate, canescent; extrafloral nectaries conspicuous at nodes; bracts and bracteoles lanceolate or subulate. **Pedicels** 1–2 mm. **Flowers** 1.7–3 cm; calyx campanulate, 6.2–8 mm, canescent, calyx lobes shorter than tube; corolla purple-black; banner oblong, 13–17 × 9–10.4 mm; wings obovate, 13–24 × 8–14.3 mm; keel 9–16 mm; ovary nectary disc distally oblique; ovules 13. **Legumes** patent, linear, 7–10 × 0.3–0.4 cm, valves twisting at dehiscence. **Seeds** 12 or 13, oblong, 3.5–5.2 × 2–3.2 mm. $2n = 22$.

Flowering Mar–Sep. Sandy soils; 10–1200 m; Ariz., Calif., Fla., Miss., N.Mex., Tex.; Mexico; West Indies; Central America; South America (n Argentina); introduced in tropical areas nearly worldwide.

2. **Macroptilium gibbosifolium** (Ortega) A. Delgado, Syst. Bot. 6: 295. 1981 [F]

Phaseolus gibbosifolius Ortega, Nov. Pl. Descr. Dec., 25. 1797; *Macroptilium heterophyllum* (Humboldt & Bonpland ex Willdenow) Maréchal & Baudet; *M. heterophyllum* var. *rotundifolium* (A. Gray) Maréchal, Mascherpa & Stainier; *P. bilobatus* Engelmann; *P. heterophyllus* Humboldt & Bonpland ex Willdenow; *P. heterophyllus* var. *rotundifolius* (A. Gray) Piper; *P. macropoides* A. Gray; *P. macropus* Bentham; *P. rotundifolius* A. Gray; *P. seleri* Harms

Herbs, perennial; root turnip-shaped, small. **Stems** prostrate, solid, strigulose or hirsute. **Leaves:** stipules spreading, widely deltate or ovate, 4.5–8 × 2–2.7 mm; petiole 1.7–6 cm, strigose or hirsute; rachis 5–9 mm; stipels subulate, 1–5.5 mm; leaflets papery, blades orbiculate, ovate to broadly ovate or obovate, base attenuate or cuneate, apex acute or obtuse, surfaces strigose abaxially, hirtellous adaxially; lateral blades 2–4.3 × 1.6–2.9 cm, sometimes 2-lobed, terminal blades 2.3–4.7 × 1.6–2.8 cm. **Inflorescences** 14–25 cm (cleistogamous inflorescence over soil, 1.5–2.2 mm, flowers 3.5 mm, corolla whitish), axes adpressed-pilose; tufts of bracts at base of peduncle mostly caducous; extrafloral nectaries inconspicuous at nodes; bracts and bracteoles subulate or lanceolate. **Pedicels** 0.7–1 mm. **Flowers** 1 cm; calyx campanulate, 3.5–4.5 mm, hirtellous, calyx lobes as long as tube or longer; corolla salmon-orange; banner orbiculate, 5.5–7.5 × 4.5–6.5 mm; wings oblong-ovate, 5.1–10 × 3.3–6.6 mm; keel 4–8 mm; ovary nectary disc distally even; ovules 6. **Legumes** pendent, oblong-falcate, 1.6–2.5 × 2.7–3 cm, valves not twisting at dehiscence. **Seeds** 4 or 5, oblong, 2.9–3 × 2–2.2 mm.

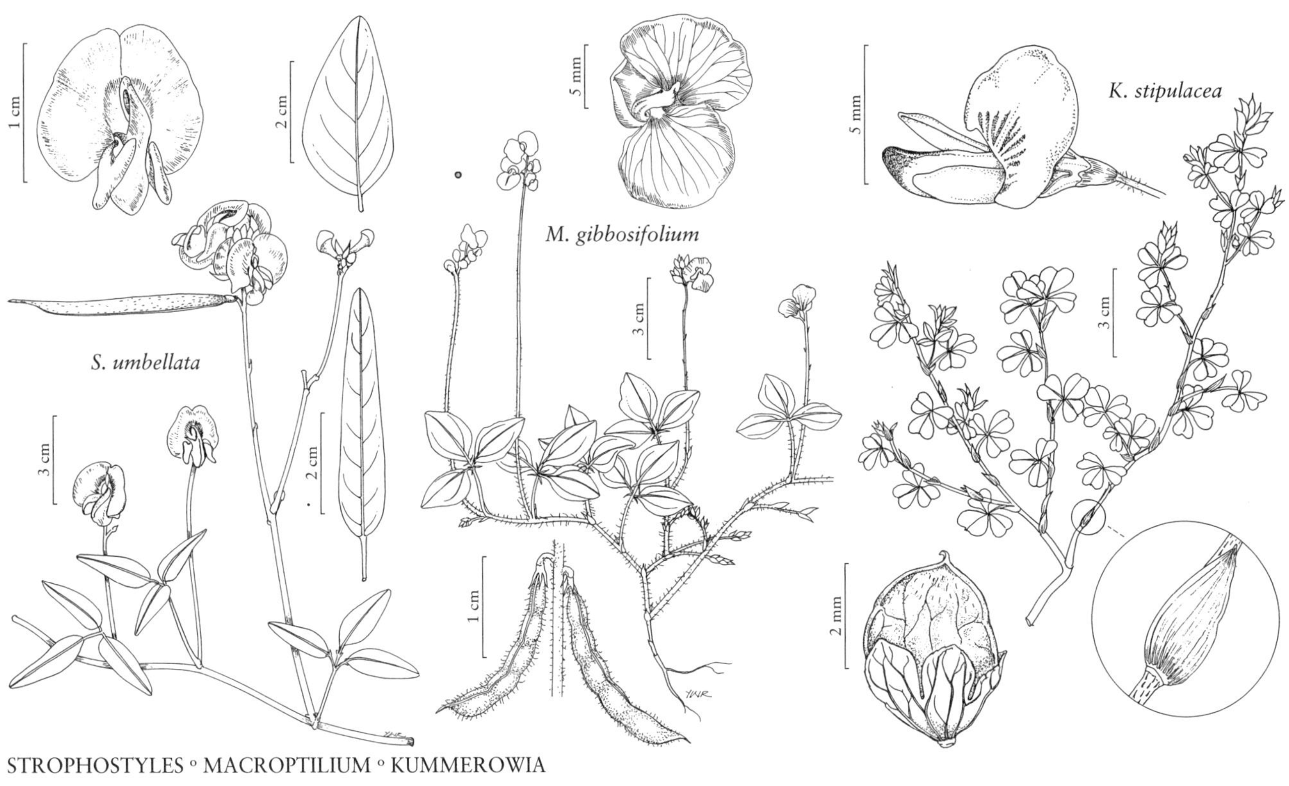

STROPHOSTYLES ∘ MACROPTILIUM ∘ KUMMEROWIA

Flowering Jul–Sep. Rocky summits, oak forests, savanna-grasslands; 1300–2500 m; Ariz., N.Mex., Tex.; Mexico; Central America.

Phaseolus micranthus M. Martens & Galeotti and *P. parviflorus* Schlechtendal are illegitimate names that pertain here.

3. **Macroptilium lathyroides** (Linnaeus) Urban, Symb. Antill. 9: 457. 1928 • Pasey or wild bean, one-leaf clover [I]

Phaseolus lathyroides Linnaeus, Sp. Pl. ed. 2, 2: 1018. 1763; *Macroptilium lathyroides* var. *semierectum* (Linnaeus) Urban; *P. crotalarioides* Martius ex Bentham; *P. hastifolius* Martius ex Bentham; *P. maritimus* Bentham; *P. psoraleoides* Wight & Arnott; *P. semierectus* Linnaeus var. *angustifolius* Bentham; *P. semierectus* var. *nanus* Bentham

Herbs, biennial; root elongate. **Stems** erect or semierect, with hollow pith, glabrescent. **Leaves:** stipules retrorse, lanceolate, 42–60 × 8–15 mm; petiole 1.8–4.5 cm, glabrescent; rachis 5–11 mm; stipels linear, 1–1.8 mm; leaflets membranous, blades ovate, elliptic, or oblong, base attenuate, apex acute, surfaces strigulose abaxially, glabrescent adaxially; lateral blades 2–4.5 × 0.6–2 cm, terminal blades 2–5.5 × 0.6–4 cm. **Inflorescences** 19–46 cm, axes glabrous; tufts of bracts at base of peduncle persistent, 3.3–6.3(–7.5) mm, triangular, puberulent; extrafloral nectaries conspicuous at nodes; bracts and bracteoles subulate. **Pedicels** 0.8–1.9 mm. **Flowers** 2–2.6 cm; calyx tubular, 3–7 mm, strigose or glabrescent, calyx lobes shorter than tube; corolla red; banner oblong, 9.5–15 × 8–9 mm; wings oblong, 11.5–26 × 6.5(–12) mm; keel 9–16 mm; ovary nectary disc distally oblique; ovules 24. **Legumes** patent, linear, 9.5–10.5 × 0.2–0.3 cm. **Seeds** 15–20, oblong, 2.5–4.4 × 2.5 mm, valves twisting at dehiscence. $2n$ = 22.

Flowering May–Nov. Disturbed sites, flat pinelands, oak forests, grassy sandy fields; 0–20 m; introduced; Fla., Ga., La., S.C.; Mexico; West Indies; Central America; South America; introduced also in Asia, Africa, Australia.

Macroptilium lathyroides is relatively common throughout central and southern peninsular Florida; other occurrences in the flora area are mainly in the Coastal Plain. A report of *M. lathyroides* as a nursery weed in Texas (J. Aplaca 2012) has not been confirmed.

Lotus maritimus Vellozo is an illegitimate name that pertains here.

4. **Macroptilium supinum** (Wiggins & Rollins) A. Delgado & L. Torres-Colín, Anales Inst. Biol. Univ. Nac. Autón. México, Bot. 66: 189. 1996

Phaseolus supinus Wiggins & Rollins, Contr. Dudley Herb. 3: 270, plate 60. 1943

Herbs, perennial; root turnip-shaped. **Stems** prostrate, solid, hirsute. **Leaves:** stipules spreading, ovate-lanceolate, 2.3–6.2 × 1.5–2 mm; petiole 2–5 cm, hirsute; rachis 5–7 mm; stipels subulate or linear, 1–2.5 mm; leaflets leathery, blades linear, base rounded or cuneate, margins entire, apex acute, surfaces densely hispid abaxially, glabrescent adaxially; lateral blades 3.8–4.5 × 0.9–1.1 cm, terminal blades 2.5–4.2 × 0.5–0.8 cm. **Inflorescences** 11–15 cm, (cleistogamous inflorescence above soil, 3.9–6.3 mm, flowers 6 mm, corolla whitish), axes glabrous; tufts of bracts at base of peduncle mostly caducous; extrafloral nectaries inconspicuous at nodes; bracts and bracteoles subulate. **Pedicels** 0.6 mm. **Flowers** 0.9 cm; calyx campanulate, 2–2.3 mm, hirsute or glabrescent, calyx lobes as long as the tube or longer; corolla red; banner obovate, 5.3 × 5 mm; wings oblong-ovate, 8.1–8.9 × 3.2–5.4 mm; keel 6.2 mm; ovary nectary disc distally even; ovules 4. **Legumes** pendent, oblong-falcate, 1 × 0.2–0.3 cm, valves not twisting at dehiscence. **Seeds** 2 or 3 (or 4), reniform, 1.7–2.3 × 1.2–3.5 mm.

Flowering Sep–Nov. Slopes, grasslands; 300–900 m; Ariz.; Mexico (Nayarit, Sonora).

In the flora area, *Macroptilium supinum* is found only in Pima and Santa Cruz counties (A. Delgado-Salinas and L. Torres-Colín 1995).

107. KUMMEROWIA Schindler, Repert. Spec. Nov. Regni Veg. 10: 403. 1912 • [For Heinrich Johannes Gotthilf Kummerow, 1860–1929, German professor in Poznań, now in Poland] [I]

Hiroyoshi Ohashi

Lespedeza Michaux subg. *Microlespedeza* Maximowicz, Trudy Imp. S.-Peterburgsk Bot. Sada 2: 346, 382. 1873

Herbs, annual, unarmed. **Stems** prostrate, ascending, or erect, usually much-branched, pubescent. **Leaves** alternate, odd-pinnate; stipules present, persistent, amplexicaul, papery or membranous, striate, broadly ovate-elliptic; sessile or petiolate, petiole to 5 mm; leaflets 3, stipels absent, blade margins entire, apex mucronate, lateral veins parallel, unbranched, extending to margins, surfaces glabrous except abaxial midrib and margins. **Inflorescences** 1–4-flowered, axillary, reduced pseudoracemes, simple or singly branched, subtended by prophyll; prophyll similar to bract, 1 or 2, each persistent at base of axis, proximal one at base of peduncle, second proximal one at base of branch; bracts present, persistent, 4 at base of calyx, proximal 2 lateral, distal 2 opposite, larger than proximal bracts, shorter than calyx. **Flowers** chasmogamous and cleistogamous; chasmogamous flowers papilionaceous, 1 or 2; calyx persistent, campanulate, broadly so in fruit, strongly leafy veined, lobes 5, lobes broad, subequal to tube, adaxial 2 partly or mostly connate; corolla long-exserted from calyx, banner pink-purple, wings white, distinctly shorter than keel, keel purple apically; stamens 10, diadelphous; anthers dorsifixed; disc present inside staminal tube; ovary sessile, style glabrous; cleistogamous flowers indistinct, often absent, rudimental flower-bud, enclosed in calyx, 0–4. **Fruits** legumes, sessile, ± flattened, elliptic or broadly ovate to ± globose, style apex early deciduous, indehiscent, reticulate, pubescent; chasmogamous legumes 1 or 2; cleistogamous legumes 0–2 at base, usually slightly smaller than chasmogamous. **Seed** 1, brown, compressed, orbicular or broadly ovoid; hilum eccentric. x = 10, 11.

Species 2 (2 in the flora): introduced; e Asia; introduced also in Pacific Islands (Hawaii), Australia.

Kummerowia is most closely related to *Lespedeza* (T. Nemoto et al. 2010; Han J. E. et al. 2010; Xu B. et al. 2012) and is distinguished by its annual habit and unique inflorescence structure. A reduced pseudoraceme is the common basic structure of the inflorescence in subtribe Lespedezinae of tribe Desmodieae and has shown evolutionary change among the genera *Kummerowia*, *Lespedeza*, and *Campylotropis* Bunge (T. Nemoto and H. Ohashi 1990, 1993, 1996). The flowers of *Kummerowia* bear four bracts at the base of the calyx; that of *Lespedeza*, as well as other genera of Desmodieae, have only one pair of bracts, called bracteoles. The extra two bracts of *Kummerowia* correspond to a bract at the base of the pedicel and a primary bract subtending two or more pedicels (= pseudoraceme) of other genera of Desmodieae. The pedicels are inferred to be reduced in *Kummerowia*; the seemingly single or pair of flowers in the genus is interpreted as a reduced pseudoraceme.

Species of *Kummerowia* are widely planted in the southern United States for forage and soil improvement and are established ubiquitously (D. Isely 1990).

Microlespedeza (Maximowicz) Makino, which pertains here, is an illegitimate and superfluous name.

1. Stems with antrorse hairs; leaflets dimorphic, proximal blades obovate, distals narrowly obovate, apex retuse or emarginate; inflorescences with 1 chasmogamous flower; calyx glabrous; legumes elliptic, less than ½ covered by persistent calyx, apex rounded . . . 1. *Kummerowia stipulacea*
1. Stems with retrorse hairs; leaflets monomorphic, blades narrowly oblong-obovate or narrowly elliptic, apex acute to obtuse; inflorescences with (1 or)2 chasmogamous flowers; calyx lobe margins densely ciliate; legumes broadly obovate to ± globose, ⅔+ covered by persistent calyx, apex acute . . . 2. *Kummerowia striata*

1. Kummerowia stipulacea (Maximowicz) Makino, Bot. Mag. (Tokyo) 28: 107. 1914 • Korean lespedeza or clover [F] [I] [W]

Lespedeza stipulacea Maximowicz, Mém. Acad. Imp. Sci. St.-Pétersbourg Divers Savans 9: 85. 1859

Stems 10–50 cm, hairs antrorse. **Leaves:** stipules 3–5 mm, acute to acuminate; leaflets dimorphic, proximal blades obovate, distals narrowly obovate, abaxial surface sparsely pubescent on midrib and margins, hairs appressed or ascending, white, apex retuse or emarginate; terminal leaflet blade 6–13 × 3–9 mm. **Peduncles** to 0.5 mm in cleistogamous flowers, 1–1.5 mm in chasmogamous; glabrous or sparsely puberulent. **Inflorescences:** chasmogamous flower 1, cleistogamous flower 0 or 1; prophylls 1 or 2, blades ovate, proximal one 0.5 mm, second proximal one 1 mm. **Bracts:** proximal bracts minute, subulate; second proximal blade elliptic, 0.8 mm, apex acute; distal blades broadly ovate, 1.6–1.8 mm, 3-veined. **Chasmogamous flowers** 5–6 mm; calyx 1.5–2 mm, glabrous. **Cleistogamous flowers** often absent, 0.5 mm. **Legumes** elliptic, 2.5–3.5 × 1.5–2.5 mm, sparsely appressed-puberulent, less than ½ covered by persistent calyx; apex rounded. **Seeds** 1.5–1.8 × 1.2 mm. $2n$ = 20, 22.

Flowering Jul–Sep. Pastures, open woodlands and borders, old fields, roadsides, urban waste areas, lawns; 30–500 m; introduced; Ala., Ark., Del., D.C., Ga., Ill., Ind., Iowa, Kans., Ky., La., Md., Mich., Miss., Mo., Nebr., N.J., N.Y., N.C., Ohio, Okla., Pa., S.C., Tenn., Tex., Va., W.Va.; Asia; introduced also in Australia.

Kummerowia stipulacea was introduced into the flora area in 1919 (D. Isely 1948) as a forage plant; some improved strains are sold. It has a slightly more northerly distribution than *K. striata*.

2. Kummerowia striata (Thunberg) Schindler, Repert. Spec. Nov. Regni Veg. 10: 403. 1912 • Common or Japanese lespedeza, Japanese clover [I] [W]

Hedysarum striatum Thunberg in J. A. Murray, Syst. Veg. ed. 14, 675. 1784; *Lespedeza striata* (Thunberg) Hooker & Arnott

Stems (7–)20–50 cm, hairs retrorse. **Leaves:** stipules 5–7 mm, acuminate; leaflets uniform, blades narrowly oblong-obovate or narrowly elliptic, abaxial surface pubescent on midrib, margins ciliate, apex acute to obtuse; terminal leaflet 4–23 × 2–8 mm. **Peduncles** 0.5–1 mm in cleistogamous flowers, 4–5 mm in chasmogamous; densely puberulent, hairs ascending. **Inflorescences:** chasmogamous flowers (1 or)2, cleistogamous flowers 2; prophylls 2, blades ovate, proximal one 0.3 mm, second proximal one 1 mm. **Bracts:** proximal bracts minute, subulate; second proximal blade distinct, elliptic, 0.8 mm; distal blades broadly ovate, 1.5 mm, 5+-veined. **Chasmogamous flowers** 5–6 mm; calyx 3.2–3.5 mm, appressed-pilose or glabrous, lobe margins densely ciliate. **Cleistogamous flowers** 2.5–3 mm, petals rudimentary, 1 mm, stamens 1 mm. **Legumes** broadly obovoid to ± globose, 3.5 × 3–3.5 mm, densely appressed-puberulent, ⅔+ covered by persistent calyx; apex acute. **Seeds** 2.5–3 × 2 mm. $2n = 22$.

Flowering Jul–Sep. Pastures, old fields, roadsides, diverse barren or eroding ruderal sites, urban waste areas, lawns; 10–400 m; introduced; Ala., Ark., Conn., Del., D.C., Fla., Ga., Ill., Ind., Iowa, Kans., Ky., La., Md., Miss., Mo., N.J., N.Y., N.C., Ohio, Okla., Pa., S.C., Tenn., Tex., Vt., Va., W.Va.; Asia; introduced also in Pacific Islands (Hawaii), Australia.

Kummerowia striata was introduced in the flora area in the nineteenth century and was widely naturalized in the southeastern United States by the 1860s (D. Isely 1948).

108. LESPEDEZA Michaux, Fl. Bor.-Amer. 2: 70, plates 39, 40. 1803 • Bush-clover [For Vicente Manuel de Céspedes y Velasco, d. 1794, Spanish governor of eastern Florida 1784–1790, sponsor of André Michaux]

Hiroyoshi Ohashi

Herbs, perennial, or shrubs, unarmed, without uncinate hairs; rootstock woody. **Stems** erect, ascending, procumbent, or trailing, often woody near base in herbs, usually branched, pubescent or glabrescent. **Leaves** alternate, trifoliolate, often larger on medial stems than those subtending inflorescences; stipules present, usually persistent (caducous in *L. texana*), ciliate, striate-veined, apex acuminate; petiolate proximally, sessile or subsessile distally; stipels absent; leaflets 3, blade margins entire, ciliate, main lateral veins anastomosing before reaching margin, surfaces glabrous or pubescent; lateral leaflets pulvinate, sessile or subsessile, blade often ± oblique; terminal leaflet usually petiolulate (sometimes sessile in *L. repens*), usually larger than laterals. **Inflorescences** (1 or)2–40-flowered, axillary or appearing terminal due to reduction of subtending leaves, pseudoracemes, consisting of clusters of 2–4 flowers, rarely capitate, sometimes appearing paniclelike when subtending leaves reduced, cleistogamous flowers often in proximal fascicles, bracteolate; bracts present, 1, subtending each flower cluster; bracteoles 2, subtending each flower. **Flowers** papilionaceous, chasmogamous or cleistogamous, chasmogamous pedicellate or subsessile, cleistogamous enclosed in calyx with reduced corolla; calyx campanulate, lobes 4 or 5, often longer than tube, adaxial 2 distinct or proximally ± connate (and thus calyx 4-lobed), apex 2-toothed; corolla pink to purple, lavender, magenta, reddish purple, or white to pale yellow; banner broadly obovate to orbiculate, proximally clawed or cuneate, with inflexed auricles, darker purple marks (nectar guides) at throat of adaxial surface of lamina; wings and keel long-clawed, lamina elliptic-oblong, proximally rounded; stamens 10, diadelphous; anthers dorsifixed (uniform); disc present around base of ovary; ovary minutely stipitate; style adaxially incurved, slightly exserted from stamens; stigma minute, terminal. **Fruits** loments, usually subsessile, sometimes stipitate (sessile in *L. procumbens*), unilocular, strongly compressed laterally, indehiscent, papery, usually appressed-pubescent, sericeous, or villous; loments from chasmogamous flowers usually subsessile, sometimes stipitate, usually elliptic-ovate or suborbicular to rounded, style straight; loments from cleistogamous flowers sessile, usually crowded at base of peduncle, obovate to suborbicular, slightly smaller than chasmogamous, style curved and relatively short. **Seed** 1, asymmetrical, ellipsoid or oblong, rim-arillate, chasmogamous seeds slightly longer or similar to cleistogamous. $x = 9, 10, 11$.

Species 47 (16 in the flora): North America, n Mexico, Asia; introduced in s Africa, Pacific Islands (Hawaii), Australia.

Lespedeza species are distributed in Asia mainly from China to Japan, with a few extending to India to Afghanistan, and to New Guinea.

Lespedeza is monophyletic and most closely related to *Campylotropis* Bunge and *Kummerowia* (Han J. E. et al. 2010; T. Nemoto et al. 2010; Xu B. et al. 2012). The genus is divided into subg. *Lespedeza*, native to North America, and subg. *Macrolespedeza* (Maximowicz) H. Ohashi, confined to Asia (H. Ohashi and Nemoto 2014).

North American *Lespedeza* is divided into sect. *Lespedeza* and sect. *Lespedezariae* (as Lespedezaria) Torrey & A. Gray, which are supported by cpDNA analyses (T. Nemoto et al. 2010). The North America species were mostly well defined by A. F. Clewell (1966) and D. Isely (1998). Thirty putative hybrids are recognized.

Six Asiatic species are recorded as naturalized in North America (D. Isely 1998); *Lespedeza virgata* (Thunberg) de Candolle, reported from Florida and North Carolina (L. C. Anderson 1988; A. F. Clewell and W. H. Stickell 1990), is excluded because the identifications of vouchers are not confirmed.

SELECTED REFERENCES Clewell, A. F. 1966. Native North American species of *Lespedeza* (Leguminosae). Rhodora 68: 359–405. Clewell, A. F. 1966b. Identification of the lespedezas of North America. II. Selected bibliography of *Lespedeza*. Bull. Tall Timbers Res. Sta. Clewell, A. F. 1966c. Natural history, cytology, and isolating mechanisms of the native American lespedezas. Bull. Tall Timbers Res. Sta. Han, J. E. et al. 2010. Phylogenetic analysis of eastern Asian and eastern North American disjunct *Lespedeza*. Bot. J. Linn. Soc. 164: 221–235. Nemoto, T. et al. 2010. Phylogeny of *Lespedeza* (Leguminosae) based on chloroplast *trn*L-*trn*F sequences. J. Jap. Bot. 85: 213–229. Ohashi, H. and T. Nemoto. 2014. A new system of *Lespedeza* (Leguminosae tribe Desmodieae). J. Jap. Bot. 89: 1–11. Xu, B. et al. 2012. Analysis of DNA sequences of six chloroplast and nuclear genes suggests incongruence, introgression, and incomplete lineage sorting in the evolution of *Lespedeza* (Fabaceae). Molec. Phylogen. Evol. 62: 346–358.

1. Shrubs or herbs; stems 50–300 cm, erect, ascending, or pendent; flowers chasmogamous, (8–)10–15(–16) mm; corollas usually pink-purple, magenta, or reddish purple with darker marks at throat, rarely white.
   2. Racemes shorter than subtending leaves; lateral calyx lobes spine-tipped; keel petals shorter than wings; leaflet blade apices retuse to obtuse . . . . 5. *Lespedeza cyrtobotrya*
   2. Racemes longer than subtending leaves; lateral calyx lobes not spine-tipped; keel petals longer than wings; leaflet blade apices usually obtuse to acute, sometimes retuse.
      3. Shrubs; flowers 8–13 mm; lateral calyx lobes shorter than or equal to tube, apex obtuse or acute; wings slightly shorter than keel petals; loments broadly elliptic to suborbicular, stipe to 0.5 mm; leaves often of 2 sizes, those on medial stems much larger than distal ones subtending racemes . . . . .2. *Lespedeza bicolor*
      3. Herbs or shrubs; flowers 12–16 mm; lateral calyx lobes longer than tube, apex acute to shortly acuminate; wings distinctly shorter than keel petals; loments elliptic, stipe 1–2 mm; leaves gradually smaller distally. . . . . 14. *Lespedeza thunbergii*
1. Herbs; stems 10–200 cm, procumbent, trailing, sprawling, erect, or ascending; flowers cleistogamous and chasmogamous (cleistogamous rare in *L. leptostachya*), 5–10(–12) mm, corollas white to yellow, sometimes with purplish or bluish marks at throat, or pink to lavender or purple.
   4. Corollas white to pale yellow or cream; calyx lobes usually 5 (except 4 and deeply lobed in *L. cuneata*, adaxial lobe pair proximally connate most or part of their length), nearly equaling or exceeding loments; bracteoles longer than calyx tube (except *L. cuneata* with shorter bracteoles); racemes 1–4-flowered or 10–40-flowered.
      5. Terminal leaflet blades ovate-elliptic, obovate, or rounded, lengths 1.3–1.8 times widths. . . . . 8. *Lespedeza hirta*
      5. Terminal leaflet blades usually linear, narrowly elliptic-oblong, or narrowly obovate, rarely elliptic-oblong or narrowly obdeltate, lengths 2–8 times widths.

6. Petioles shorter than rachis; racemes shorter than to 1.5 times length of subtending leaves; calyces 8–12 mm . . . . 3. *Lespedeza capitata*
6. Petioles equaling or longer than rachis; racemes shorter than to 1–4 times length of subtending leaves; calyces 4–7 mm.
    7. Leaflet adaxial surface appressed-pubescent; racemes loosely flowered; corollas 5–6 mm . . . . 9. *Lespedeza leptostachya*
    7. Leaflet adaxial surface glabrous, appressed-puberulent, or glabrescent; racemes closely flowered; corollas 5.5–8 mm.
        8. Leaflet abaxial surface appressed-pubescent; terminal blade narrowly elliptic, length 2–3 times width . . . . 6. *Lespedeza daurica*
        8. Leaflet abaxial surface densely sericeous or strigose; terminal blade narrowly oblong, narrowly obovate, or narrowly obdeltate, length 3–8 times width.
            9. Leaflet blades usually narrowly oblong, rarely elliptic-oblong; flowers 5.5–7 mm; bracteoles longer than calyx tube; loments included in calyx. . . . . 1. *Lespedeza angustifolia*
            9. Leaflet blades narrowly obovate or narrowly obdeltate; flowers 6.5–8 mm; bracteoles shorter than calyx tube; loments distinctly exserted from calyx. . . . . 4. *Lespedeza cuneata*

[4. Shifted to left margin.—Ed.]

4. Corollas usually pink to purple, pink-lavender, or violet, rarely whitish; calyx lobes 4 (adaxial lobe pair proximally connate), to ½ as long as loments; bracteoles shorter than calyx tube; racemes 2–15-flowered.
    10. Stems erect or strongly ascending, initially simple or wandlike, generally branched distally; racemes shorter than or nearly equal to subtending leaves, distal flowers crowded or clustered.
        11. Leaflet adaxial surface glabrous, sometimes appressed-puberulent on midrib . . . . 15. *Lespedeza violacea*
        11. Leaflet adaxial surface densely to uniformly appressed-pubescent, sometimes glabrescent (but not glabrous).
            12. Leaflet blades elliptic to elliptic-oblong, terminal blade length 1.5–2.5(–3) times width, base obtuse . . . . 12. *Lespedeza stuevei*
            12. Leaflet blades narrowly elliptic-oblong to linear, terminal blade length 3–7 times width, base obtuse or cuneate . . . . 16. *Lespedeza virginica*
    10. Stems procumbent to weakly ascending, trailing, or sprawling, often branched most of length; racemes longer than subtending leaves, flowers not clustered at stem apices.
        13. Stems and peduncles sericeous or glabrescent, pedicels appressed-puberulent.
            14. Keel petals usually longer than wings; leaflet blades apiculate; stems ascending or sprawling . . . . 7. *Lespedeza frutescens*
            14. Keel petals nearly equal to wings; leaflet blades scarcely or minutely apiculate; stems procumbent or trailing . . . . 11. *Lespedeza repens*
        13. Stems, peduncles, and pedicels with some pubescence patent-pilose.
            15. Leaflet blades apiculate; pedicels of chasmogamous flowers 0.5–2 mm; chasmogamous loments sessile, elliptic, 4.5–5.5 mm . . . . 10. *Lespedeza procumbens*
            15. Leaflet blades scarcely apiculate; pedicels of chasmogamous flowers 3–5 mm; chasmogamous loments stipitate (stipe 1 mm), rounded, 5–7 mm . . . . 13. *Lespedeza texana*

1. Lespedeza angustifolia (Pursh) Elliott, Sketch Bot. S. Carolina 2: 206. 1822 • Narrow-leaved bush-clover [E]

Lespedeza capitata Michaux var. *angustifolia* Pursh, Fl. Amer. Sept. 2: 480. 1813; *L. angustifolia* var. *brevifolia* Britton

Herbs, woody at base. **Stems** erect or ascending, 50–100 (–150) cm, branched throughout or only distally, appressed- or ascending-pubescent or glabrescent. **Leaves:** stipules subulate, 2–4 mm; petiole 1–3 mm, equaling or longer than rachis; leaflet blades usually narrowly oblong, rarely elliptic-oblong, with swollen, whitish reticulate veins adaxially, apex apiculate, surfaces densely sericeous abaxially, glabrous adaxially; laterals without oblique base; terminal blade 20–45 × 2–7 mm, length 4–8 times width. **Peduncles** longer (1–2 times) than subtending leaves. **Racemes** 10–20+-flowered, densely flowered, flowers chasmogamous and cleistogamous, racemes shorter than to 1–4 times length of subtending leaves. **Pedicels** 1–2 mm; bracteoles longer than calyx tube. **Flowers:** chasmogamous 5.5–7 mm; calyx 5.5–7 mm, densely pubescent, tube 1.5–2 mm; lobes 5, lateral narrowly deltate, 4–5 mm, apices spinelike; corolla white to cream; wings 5.5–6.5 mm; keel 5–5.3 mm. **Loments:** chasmogamous included in calyx, rounded, 4–5 mm, cleistogamous similar to chasmogamous, densely strigose; stipe subsessile.

Flowering late summer–fall. Open, moist woodlands and borders, pine flatlands, mixed or deciduous woodlands, savannas, swales, boggy areas, sandy oak-wire grass ridges, railroads, roadsides; 0–300 m; Ala., Conn., Del., Fla., Ga., Md., Mass., Miss., N.J., N.Y., N.C., Pa., R.I., S.C., Tenn., Va.

Lespedeza angustifolia is primarily a species of the Atlantic Coastal Plain with scattered occurrences inland.

Lespedeza angustifolia forms natural hybrids with *L. capitata*, *L. hirta*, *L. repens*, *L. stuevei*, and *L. virginica*. Hybrids with *L. hirta* are common (A. F. Clewell 1966) and have been described as varieties of *L. hirta* (var. *appressipilis* S. F. Blake, var. *intercursa* Fernald, and var. *oblongifolia* Britton).

2. Lespedeza bicolor Turczaninow, Bull. Soc. Imp. Naturalistes Moscou 13: 69. 1840 • Bicolored lespedeza [I]

Shrubs. Stems erect or ascending, clustered, young branches terete, 60–200 cm, branched distally, densely pubescent or glabrescent. **Leaves** often 2 sizes, distal ones subtending racemes much smaller; stipules subulate, 3–7 mm; petiole 20–40 mm, longer than rachis; leaflet blades elliptic to broadly elliptic or ovate, apex retuse to obtuse or acute, apiculate, surfaces uniformly sericeous abaxially, somewhat sparsely sericeous, at least along midrib, or glabrescent adaxially; terminal blade 20–60 × 10–35 mm, length 1.5–2 times width. **Peduncles** longer than subtending leaves. **Racemes** 5–15-flowered, axillary or compound and appearing terminal, flowers chasmogamous only. **Pedicels** 0.8–3 mm; bracteoles shorter than calyx tube. **Flowers** 8–13 mm; calyx 3–5 mm, tube 1.5–2.4 mm; lobes 4, subequal or abaxial slightly longer, lateral ovate to narrowly ovate, 1.2–2.5 mm, adaxial connate proximally, apices obtuse or acute, not spine-tipped; corolla usually pink-purple or magenta, rarely white, banner with darker marks at throat on adaxial surface; wings 7.3–9.5 mm; keel 8.6–9.8 mm. **Loments:** body exserted from calyx, broadly elliptic to suborbicular, 5–7 × 4–6 mm, slightly to densely white-appressed-pilose, sometimes glabrescent; stipe to 0.5 mm. $2n = 22$.

Flowering late summer–early fall. Woodlands and borders, mountain slopes, pine flatwoods, savannas, creek banks, thickets, old fields, roadsides, waste areas; 0–900 m; introduced; Ont.; Ala., Ark., Conn., Del., Fla., Ga., Ill., Ind., Iowa, Kans., Ky., La., Md., Mass., Mich., Miss., Mo., N.J., N.Y., N.C., Ohio, Okla., Pa., S.C., Tenn., Tex., Va., W.Va.; Asia (China, Japan, Korea, Russian Far East, Siberia).

Lespedeza bicolor is planted as an ornamental, for wildlife food, and for soil improvements; while some naturalization occurs, it is seldom found far from plantings. In the flora area, differences between *L. bicolor* and *L. thunbergii* are not always apparent, perhaps due to introgression in cultivated strains (A. F. Clewell 1966b).

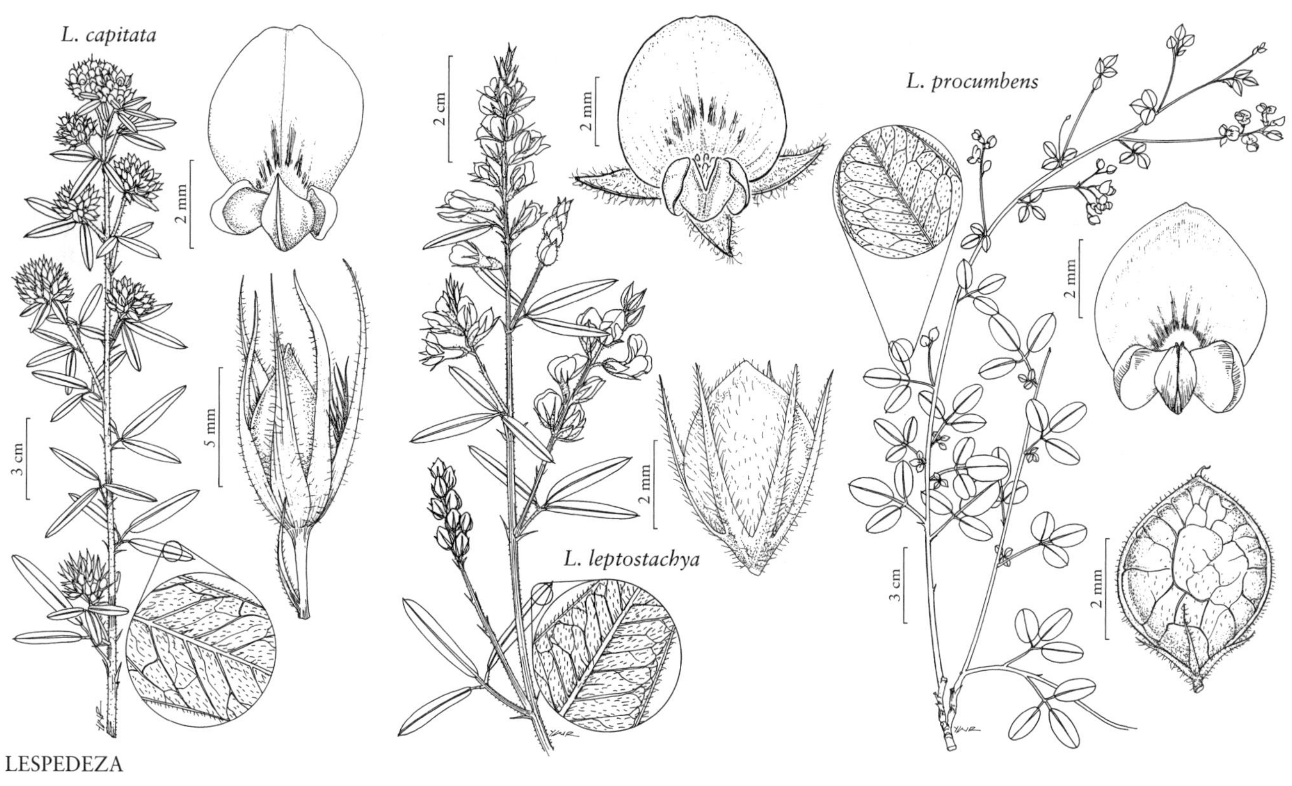

LESPEDEZA

3. **Lespedeza capitata** Michaux, Fl. Bor.-Amer. 2: 71. 1803 • Round-headed bush-clover [E] [F]

Lespedeza bicknellii House; *L. capitata* var. *sericea* Hooker; *L. capitata* var. *stenophylla* Bissell & Fernald; *L. capitata* var. *velutina* Fernald; *L. capitata* var. *vulgaris* Torrey & A. Gray

Herbs, woody at base. **Stems** erect or ascending, clustered, 50–150 cm, simple or branched distally, villous. **Leaves:** stipules subulate to narrowly triangular, to 6 mm; petiole 1–3 mm, shorter than rachis; leaflet blades usually narrowly elliptic-oblong, rarely linear, with raised, whitish reticulate veins adaxially, apex apiculate, surfaces densely whitish gray- or silvery-sericeous abaxially, densely appressed-sericeous or glabrescent adaxially; laterals slightly smaller; terminal blade 20–40 × 2–14 mm, length 2–5(–8) times width. **Peduncles** shorter to longer (to 1.5 times) than subtending leaves. **Racemes** capitate, 15+-flowered, flowers closely clustered distally, congested, flowers chasmogamous and cleistogamous, racemes shorter than to 1.5 length of subtending leaves. **Pedicels** 1–3 mm; bracteoles longer than calyx tube. **Flowers:** chasmogamous 8–12 mm; calyx 8–12 mm, longer than corolla, tube 2 mm; lobes 5, lateral narrowly ovate, 7–8 mm, apices spinelike; corolla yellow-white or cream and often purple-marked; wings 6.5–7 mm; keel 6 mm. **Loments:** chasmogamous included in calyx, oblong, 4–7 × 3–4 mm, cleistogamous similar to chasmogamous, sericeous; stipe subsessile. $2n = 20$.

Flowering spring–fall. Open woodlands, borders, clearings, ruderal sites, fields, prairies, moist pine flatland savannas, flood plains, swamps, pocosins; 0–900 m; N.B., Ont.; Ala., Ark., Conn., Del., D.C., Fla., Ga., Ill., Ind., Iowa, Kans., Ky., La., Maine, Md., Mass., Mich., Minn., Miss., Mo., Nebr., N.H., N.J., N.Y., N.C., Ohio, Okla., Pa., R.I., S.C., S.Dak., Tenn., Tex., Vt., Va., W.Va., Wis.

Lespedeza capitata forms natural hybrids with *L. angustifolia*, *L. frutescens*, *L. leptostachya*, *L. repens*, *L. stuevei*, *L. violacea*, and *L. virginica* with more commonly observed hybrids receiving species epithets before their origins were understood. Hybrids with *L. frutescens* have been called *L.* ×*manniana* Mackenzie & Bush [= *L. nuttallii* var. *manniana* (Mackenzie & Bush) Gleason], with *L. hirta* as *L.* ×*longifolia* de Candolle [= *L. hirta* var. *longifolia* (de Candolle) Fernald], and *L. hirta* var. *dissimulans* Fernald, and with *L. virginica* as *L.* ×*simulata* Mackenzie & Bush.

4. Lespedeza cuneata (Dumont de Courset) G. Don, Gen. Hist. 2: 307. 1832 • Sericea, sericea lespedeza [I] [W]

Anthyllis cuneata Dumont de Courset, Bot. Cult. ed. 2, 6: 100. 1811

Herbs. Stems erect or ascending, clustered, 80–200 cm, copiously branched distally, striate, densely ascending or appressed white-pubescent on ridges. **Leaves:** stipules subulate, 4–8 mm; petiole 5–10 mm, longer than rachis; leaflet blades narrowly obovate or narrowly obdeltate, apex obtuse to rounded, truncate, or retuse, apiculate, surfaces densely white-appressed-strigose abaxially, sparsely appressed-puberulent or glabrescent adaxially, scarcely reticulate-veined between principle lateral veins abaxially; terminal blade 7–32 × 2–8 mm, length 3–5 times width. **Peduncles** shorter than subtending leaves, scarcely pedunculate. **Racemes** 2–4-flowered, closely flowered, flowers chasmogamous and cleistogamous, chasmogamous with 2–4 flowers, cleistogamous usually with (1 or)2 flowers at base of peduncle, racemes shorter than to 1–4 times length of subtending leaves. **Pedicels** 1.5–2 mm; bracteoles shorter than calyx tube. **Flowers:** chasmogamous 6.5–8 mm; calyx 3–4.5 mm, tube 1 mm; lobes 4, lateral triangular, 2–3.5 mm, deeply 4-lobed, adaxial pair proximally connate most or part of their length; corolla white to pale yellow and pale purplish striate, or with blotch at throat adaxially, wing and keel petals white; wings 6–7 mm; keel 6–7.5 mm; cleistogamous flowers 2 mm, calyx lobes usually 1-veined, rarely with 1 distinct midrib and 2 inconspicuous lateral veins. **Loments**: sparsely appressed-pubescent or glabrescent; stipe 0.5 mm; chasmogamous, deciduous, distinctly exserted from calyx, elliptic-oblong or broadly elliptic, 3.5–5 × 2–3 mm, cleistogamous suborbicular, 3 × 2 mm. **2*n*** = 20.

Flowering late spring–fall. Pastures, open pine or deciduous woodlands, clearings, borders, lowland or moist areas, roadsides, old fields, urban waste areas; 0–1000 m; introduced; Ont.; Ala., Ark., Conn., Del., D.C., Fla., Ga., Ill., Ind., Iowa, Kans., Ky., La., Md., Mass., Mich., Minn., Miss., Mo., Nebr., N.J., N.Y., N.C., Ohio, Okla., Pa., S.C., Tenn., Tex., Va., W.Va., Wis.; Asia (Afghanistan, China, Himalayas, India, Indo-China, Japan, Korea, Malesia, Myanmar, Taiwan); introduced also in Africa (Republic of South Africa), Pacific Islands (Hawaii), Australia.

Lespedeza cuneata is widely planted for forage, erosion control, soil improvement, wildlife food, and strip mine regrowth (W. J. Guernsey 1970). The species tolerates sterile soils and is drought resistant; it is one of the characteristic plants of the rural, southeastern United States landscape (D. Isely 1998).

Lespedeza sericea Miquel is an illegitimate name that pertains here.

5. Lespedeza cyrtobotrya Miquel, Ann. Mus. Bot. Lugduno-Batavi 3: 48. 1867 • Leafy lespedeza [I]

Shrubs. Stems erect or ascending, clustered, young branches terete, 70–200 cm, branched distally, densely appressed- or patent-pubescent. **Leaves** usually 2 sizes, axillary ones subtending racemes much smaller; stipules subulate, 2–4 mm; petiole 30–40 mm, longer than rachis; leaflet blades usually elliptic to broadly elliptic or obovate, sometimes suborbiculate, apex retuse to obtuse, apiculate, surfaces appressed-pubescent abaxially, glabrous or sparsely puberulent along midrib adaxially; terminal blade 20–50 × 10–30 mm, length 1–2 times width. **Peduncles** usually shorter than subtending leaves. **Racemes** 5–15-flowered, flowers chasmogamous only. **Pedicels** 0.8–3 mm; bracteoles shorter than calyx tube. **Flowers** 10–15 mm; calyx 4.5–6 mm, tube 2.5 mm; lobes 4, subequal or abaxial slightly longer, lateral narrowly triangular-ovate, 2.3–3.5 mm, adaxial connate proximally, apices long-acuminate and spine-tipped; corolla reddish purple; wings 8–10.5 mm; keel 7.5–9.5 mm. **Loments**: body exserted from calyx, broadly elliptic to suborbicular, 6–7 × 3.5–4.5 mm, densely white-appressed-pilose, sometimes glabrescent; stipe subsessile. **2*n*** = 22.

Flowering late summer–early fall. Disturbed areas; 0–100 m; introduced; Conn., Mass., Va.; Asia (n China, Japan, Korea, Russian Far East).

Lespedeza cyrtobotrya has been planted for wildlife food (V. E. Davidson 1940) and rarely spreads from cultivation.

6. Lespedeza daurica (Laxmann) Schindler, Repert. Spec. Nov. Regni Veg. 22: 274. 1926 • Dahurian lespedeza [I]

Trifolium dauricum Laxmann, Novi Comment. Acad. Sci. Imp. Petrop. 15: 560, plate 30, fig. 5. 1771

Herbs. Stems ascending, clustered, 30–100 cm, simple or branched at base, pubescent. **Leaves:** stipules subulate, 3–4 mm; petiole 5–10 mm, longer than rachis; leaflet blades narrowly elliptic, apex obtuse to rounded or retuse, apiculate, surfaces appressed-pubescent abaxially, glabrous or sparsely pubescent along midrib adaxially, conspicuously reticulate-veined between principle lateral veins abaxially; terminal blade 8–30 × 4–16 mm, length 2–3 times width. **Peduncles** shorter than or equal to subtending leaves, subsessile or shortly pedunculate, densely pubescent. **Racemes** 4–13-flowered, densely flowered, flowers chasmogamous and cleistogamous, cleistogamous flowers clustered in leaf axils, racemes shorter than to 1–4 times length of subtending leaves. **Pedicels** 1–2 mm; bracteoles longer than calyx tube. **Flowers:** chasmogamous 7–8 mm; calyx 4.5–7 mm, tube 1–1.2 mm; lobes 5, lateral narrowly ovate, 4–6 mm, apices acuminate; corolla white or yellowish white; wings 6–6.5 mm; keel 7–7.3 mm; cleistogamous: calyx 3–4 mm, tube 0.5 mm, lobes narrowly deltate. **Loments:** body included in calyx, obovate, chasmogamous 3.5–5 × 2.5–3 mm, cleistogamous 3–3.7 × 2–2.5 mm; stipe subsessile.

Flowering summer. Roadsides, woodland borders; 0–300 m; introduced; Del., Ill., Iowa; Asia (China, Korea, Mongolia, Russia).

Lespedeza daurica has been cultivated in the United States for soil improvement (A. J. Pieters et al. 1950). In the flora area, only a handful of specimens have been collected from widely scattered localities outside of cultivation.

7. Lespedeza frutescens (Linnaeus) Hornemann, Hort. Bot. Hafn. 2: 699. 1815 • Violet bush-clover, shrubby lespedeza [E]

Hedysarum frutescens Linnaeus, Sp. Pl. 2: 748. 1753; *Lespedeza prairea* (Mackenzie & Bush) Britton; *L. violacea* (Linnaeus) Persoon var. *divergens* (Muhlenberg ex Willdenow) G. Don; *L. violacea* var. *prairea* Mackenzie & Bush

Herbs. Stems ascending or sprawling, clustered, 10–50 cm, branched much of length, sericeous or glabrescent. **Leaves** usually 2 sizes, axillary ones subtending racemes much smaller; stipules subulate, 2.5–6 mm; petiole (5–)10–15(–20) mm, longer than rachis; leaflet blades elliptic to narrowly elliptic, apex obtuse or retuse, apiculate, surfaces sericeous abaxially, glabrous adaxially; laterals similar to terminal, without oblique base; terminal blade 10–30 (–40) × 8–22 mm (6–10 mm in axillary leaves), length 1.4–2.5 times width. **Peduncles** usually much longer than subtending leaves, sericeous. **Racemes** slender, 4–7-flowered, flowers not clustered at apex, flowers chasmogamous and cleistogamous. **Pedicels** 0.5–3 mm, appressed-puberulent; bracteoles shorter than calyx tube. **Flowers:** chasmogamous 6.5–9 mm; calyx 4–6 mm, appressed-puberulent, tube 1–1.2 mm; lobes 4, lateral narrowly triangular, 2.5–3 mm, adaxial connate proximally, apices acuminate; corolla purple; wings 5.5–6.5 mm; keel 6–8 mm. **Loments:** chasmogamous as long as calyx, ovate to rounded, 5–7 mm, cleistogamous exserted from calyx, calyx 1/5 loment length, rounded, 4–5 mm; stipe subsessile. $2n = 20$.

Flowering late summer–fall. Open deciduous, dry upland woodlands, prairie fragments, alluvial woodlands, ruderal areas, limestone or sandy soils; 0–900 m; Ont.; Ala., Ark., Conn., Del., D.C., Fla., Ga., Ill., Ind., Iowa, Kans., Ky., La., Maine, Md., Mass., Mich., Miss., Mo., Nebr., N.H., N.J., N.Y., N.C., Ohio, Okla., Pa., R.I., S.C., Tenn., Tex., Vt., Va., W.Va.

The name *Lespedeza violacea* was widely applied to *L. frutescens* in the past; however, the type specimen of the basionym (*Hedysarum violaceum*) represents the species previously called *L. intermedia*. The result is that the name *L. violacea* replaces what was called *L. intermedia*, and *L. frutescens* must be taken up for this species (J. L. Reveal and F. R. Barrie 1991).

Lespedeza frutescens forms natural hybrids with *L. capitata*, *L. hirta*, *L. procumbens*, *L. repens*, *L. stuevei*, *L. violacea*, and *L. virginica*. Hybrids with *L. violacea* are common (A. F. Clewell 1966) and have been called *L.* ×*acuticarpa* Mackenzie & Bush.

8. Lespedeza hirta (Linnaeus) Hornemann, Hort. Bot. Hafn. 2: 699. 1815 • Hairy bush-clover or lespedeza [E]

Hedysarum hirtum Linnaeus, Sp. Pl. 2: 748. 1753

Herbs. Stems erect or ascending, 80–200 cm, branched distally, short appressed-pubescent, pilose, or villous. **Leaves:** stipules subulate to narrowly triangular, 3–6 mm; petiole 10–15 (–20) mm, longer than rachis; leaflet blades ovate-elliptic, obovate, or rounded, apex obtuse or retuse, minutely apiculate, surfaces green, cinereous, or silvery abaxially, sparsely to densely sericeous abaxially, glabrous, sericeous, pilose, or silvery with fine, dense, appressed-silky hairs adaxially; terminal blade 10–40(–50) × (7–)10–30 mm, length 1.3–1.8 times width. **Peduncles** longer than subtending leaves. **Racemes** 10–40-flowered, axillary from distal leaves or clustered in compound inflorescences, flowers compact to lax, axis and pedicels visible, flowers chasmogamous and cleistogamous. **Pedicels** 1–2 mm; bracteoles longer than calyx tube. **Flowers:** chasmogamous 7–10 mm; calyx 7–10 mm, pubescent, tube 1–2 mm; lobes 5, lateral narrowly triangular, 7–8 mm, apices spinelike; corolla cream-white or creamy with pink or purple at throat; wings 6–7 mm; keel 5–6 mm. **Loments:** chasmogamous slightly included in calyx, ovate-oblong, 6–8 × 4–5 mm, cleistogamous slightly included in calyx, oblong, 6 × 4 mm; stipe subsessile.

Subspecies 2 (2 in the flora): North America.

Lespedeza hirta forms natural hybrids with *L. angustifolia*, *L. capitata*, *L. frutescens*, *L. procumbens*, *L. repens*, *L. stuevei*, *L. violacea*, and *L. virginica*. Hybrids with *L. violacea* have been called *L.* ×*nuttallii* Darlington, and offspring from Indiana plants of *L.* ×*nuttallii* show morphologies that range from one parental species to the other. Other purple-petaled species may hybridize with *L. hirta* to produce offspring similar to the morphology of *L.* ×*nuttallii* (D. Isely 1998).

1. Leaflet adaxial surface glabrous, strigose, or pilose; stems villous or pilose . . . . 8a. *Lespedeza hirta* subsp. *hirta*
1. Leaflet adaxial surface silvery with fine, dense, appressed-silky hairs; stems appressed-pubescent or densely short-pilose . . . . 8b. *Lespedeza hirta* subsp. *curtissii*

8a. Lespedeza hirta (Linnaeus) Hornemann subsp. **hirta** [E]

Lespedeza hirta var. *calycina* Schindler; *L. hirta* var. *sparsiflora* Torrey & A. Gray

Stems villous or pilose. **Leaflet blade** surfaces glabrous, strigose, or pilose adaxially. **2*n*** = 20.

Flowering summer–fall. Open, dry uplands, rocky woodlands, openings, often on sandy soils; 0–1000 m; Ont.; Ala., Ark., Conn., Del., D.C., Fla., Ga., Ill., Ind., Kans., Ky., La., Maine, Md., Mass., Mich., Miss., Mo., N.H., N.J., N.Y., N.C., Ohio, Okla., Pa., R.I., S.C., Tenn., Tex., Vt., Va., W.Va.

Subspecies *hirta* ranges from New England, southern Ontario, southern Michigan, and eastern Oklahoma, to central Florida and eastern Texas; it is rare on the sandy soils of the Atlantic Coastal Plain (A. F. Clewell 1964).

8b. Lespedeza hirta (Linnaeus) Hornemann subsp. **curtissii** Clewell, Brittonia 16: 75. 1964 [E]

Lespedeza hirta var. *curtissii* (Clewell) Isely

Stems appressed-pubescent or densely short-pilose. **Leaflets blade** surfaces silvery with fine, dense, appressed-silky hairs adaxially. **2*n*** = 20.

Flowering fall. Pine flatwoods, savanna openings and margins, oak woods, palmetto scrub, old fields, mesic or dry sites; 0–100 m; Ala., Fla., Ga., La., N.C., S.C., Va.

Subspecies *curtissii* is known from the Atlantic and Gulf Coast coastal plains (A. F. Clewell 1964b).

9. Lespedeza leptostachya Engelmann ex A. Gray, Proc. Amer. Acad. Arts 12: 57. 1876 • Prairie bush-clover [E] [F]

Herbs. Stems erect, slender, 70–100 cm, mostly simple, with axillary, exserted inflorescences distally, pubescent. **Leaves:** stipules subulate to narrowly triangular, to 5 mm; petiole 6–10 mm, longer than rachis; leaflet blades linear to narrowly oblong, apex rounded or obtuse, apiculate, surfaces densely sericeous abaxially, uniformly appressed-pubescent adaxially; terminal blade 20–40 × 2–7 mm, length 2.5–7 times width. **Peduncles** equal to or much longer than subtending leaves. **Racemes** 8–15-flowered, flowers lax on axis, flowers chasmogamous, cleistogamous rare, racemes shorter than to 1–4 times length of subtending leaves. **Pedicels** to 1 mm; bracteoles longer than calyx tube. **Flowers:** chasmogamous 5–6 mm; calyx 4.5–6 mm, longer than corolla and loments, tube 1 mm; lobes 5, lateral narrowly triangular to subulate, 4–5 mm, setaceous, villous, apices spinelike; corolla whitish yellow or lavender-tinged; wings 4.5–5.2 mm; keel 4–4.5 mm. **Loments:** chasmogamous included in calyx, rounded, 4–6 mm, cleistogamous similar to chasmogamous; stipe subsessile.

Flowering late summer–fall. Upland prairie remnants; 100–500 m; Ill., Iowa, Minn., Wis.

Hybridization of *Lespedeza leptostachya* with *L. capitata* has been documented (J. B. Fant et al. 2010). *Lespedeza leptostachya* is in the Center for Plant Conservation's National Collection of Endangered Plants.

10. Lespedeza procumbens Michaux, Fl. Bor.-Amer. 2: 70, plate 39. 1803 • Downy trailing bush-clover [E] [F]

Herbs, mat-forming. **Stems** procumbent and spreading, to 100 cm, branched much of length, villosulous and patent-pilose. **Leaves:** stipules subulate to narrowly triangular, 2–5 mm; petiole 5–15 mm, longer than rachis; leaflet blades elliptic to broadly elliptic, apex obtuse or emarginate, apiculate, surfaces uniformly to densely pubescent or pilose abaxially, sparsely to uniformly pubescent adaxially; terminal blade 10–35 × 12–18 mm, length 1.2–2 times width. **Peduncles** longer than subtending leaves, patent-pilose. **Racemes** 4–14-flowered, flowers not clustered at apex, flowers chasmogamous and cleistogamous, cleistogamous flowers subsessile and clustered in leaf axils, or borne distally on axis. **Pedicels** 0.5–2 mm, patent-pilose; bracteoles shorter than calyx tube. **Flowers:** chasmogamous 6.2–6.8 mm; calyx 3.5–4 mm, tube 1–1.5 mm; lobes 4, lateral narrowly triangular, 2–2.5 mm, adaxial connate proximally; corolla pink to pink-purple; wings 6.1–6.5 mm; keel 6 mm. **Loments:** elliptic, sparsely appressed-puberulent or glabrescent; stipe 0 mm; chasmogamous exserted ½+ from calyx, 4.5–5.5 mm, cleistogamous included in calyx. **2*n*** = 20.

Flowering summer–early fall. Open uplands, dry woodlands, borders, clearings, glades, old fields, rail- and roadsides, ruderal sites; 0–1000 m; Ont.; Ala., Ark., Conn., Del., D.C., Fla., Ga., Ill., Ind., Kans., Ky., La., Md., Mass., Mich., Miss., Mo., N.H., N.J., N.Y., N.C., Ohio, Okla., Pa., R.I., S.C., Tenn., Tex., Va., W.Va., Wis.

Lespedeza procumbens forms natural hybrids with *L. angustifolia*, *L. frutescens*, *L. hirta*, *L. repens*, *L. stuevei*, and *L. virginica*. Hybrids with *L. virginica* have been named *L.* ×*brittonii* E. P. Bicknell and *L. procumbens* var. *elliptica* S. F. Blake.

11. Lespedeza repens (Linnaeus) W. P. C. Barton, Comp. Fl. Philadelph. 2: 77. 1818 • Smooth trailing bush-clover [E]

Hedysarum repens Linnaeus, Sp. Pl. 2: 749. 1753

Herbs, mat-forming. **Stems** procumbent or trailing, initially ascending, becoming decumbent with continued growth, clustered, slender, to 100 cm, branched much of length, sericeous or glabrescent. **Leaves:** stipules subulate, 2–3(–4) mm; petiole 7–10(–15) mm, equaling or longer than rachis; leaflet blades usually narrowly elliptic to elliptic, rarely obovate, apex obtuse, scarcely or minutely apiculate, surfaces sericeous abaxially, sparsely sericeous or glabrescent adaxially; laterals similar to terminal; terminal blade petiolulate or sessile, 10–20(–25) × 5–10 mm, length 1.5–2.5(–3) times width. **Peduncles** longer than subtending leaves, filiform, usually sericeous, sometimes glabrescent. **Racemes** 2–6(–10)-flowered, erect, flowers not clustered at apex, flowers chasmogamous and cleistogamous. **Pedicels** 0.5–4 mm, appressed-puberulent; bracteoles shorter than calyx tube. **Flowers:** chasmogamous 6–8 mm; calyx 3–4 mm, appressed-puberulent, tube 1 mm; lobes 4, lateral narrowly deltate, 2–2.5 mm, adaxial connate proximally; corolla usually pink-lavender to violet, rarely whitish; wings 7–7.5 mm; keel 6.8–7.3 mm. **Loments:** chasmogamous exserted from calyx, calyx ½ loment length, rounded to elliptic, 4–7 × 3–4 mm, cleistogamous rare, exserted from calyx, calyx ¼–⅓ loment length; stipe 1.5 mm. **2*n*** = 20.

Flowering spring–fall. Upland open woodlands, borders, openings, thickets, barren or eroded areas, roadsides; 0–1000 m; Ala., Ark., Conn., Del., D.C., Fla., Ga., Ill., Ind., Iowa, Kans., Ky., La., Md., Miss., Mo., N.J., N.Y., N.C., Ohio, Okla., Pa., S.C., Tenn., Tex., Va., W.Va., Wis.

Lespedeza repens forms natural hybrids with *L. angustifolia*, *L. frutescens*, and *L. stuevei.*

12. Lespedeza stuevei Nuttall, Gen. N. Amer. Pl. 2: 107. 1818 (as stüvei) • Tall bush-clover [E] [F]

Herbs. Stems ascending or erect, clustered, slender, 70–150 cm, simple or branched apically, villosulous or strigose. **Leaves:** stipules subulate to narrowly triangular, 3–5 mm; petiole 7–10 mm, longer than rachis; leaflet blades elliptic to elliptic-oblong, base obtuse, apex obtuse to retuse, apiculate, surfaces appressed-pubescent or subappressed-pilose abaxially, lateral veins often conspicuous abaxially, sparsely appressed-pubescent adaxially; laterals similar to terminal; terminal blade 10–40 × 5–12 mm, length 1.5–2.5(–3) times width. **Peduncles** shorter than or equal to subtending leaves. **Racemes** 5–15-flowered, flowers clustered distally, shortly glomerate, flowers chasmogamous and cleistogamous. **Pedicels** 0.5–2 mm; bracteoles shorter than calyx tube. **Flowers:** chasmogamous 5–6 mm; calyx 3–4 mm, sericeous or villous, tube 1 mm; lobes 4, lateral narrowly triangular, 2–2.5 mm, adaxial connate proximally, apices acuminate; corolla purple; wings 5.7–6.2 mm; keel 5–5.3 mm. **Loments:** chasmogamous exserted from calyx, calyx ⅖ loment length, ovate, 4–6 mm, cleistogamous exserted from calyx, ovate, 4–5 mm, sericeous or villous; stipe 0.2 mm. **2*n*** = 20.

Flowering summer–fall. Open, dry, often sterile, rocky woodlands, openings, glades, old fields, roadsides, river bottoms, moist pine savannas, on sandy soils; 0–900 m; Ala., Ark., Conn., Del., D.C., Fla., Ga., Ill., Ind., Kans., Ky., La., Md., Mass., Miss., Mo., N.J., N.Y., N.C., Okla., Pa., R.I., S.C., Tenn., Tex., Vt., Va., W.Va.

Lespedeza stuevei forms natural hybrids with *L. angustifolia*, *L. frutescens*, *L. hirta*, and *L. virginica*. Hybrids with *L. virginica* have been called *L.* ×*neglecta* (Britton) Mackenzie & Bush and *L. stuevei* var. *angustifolia* Britton.

13. Lespedeza texana Britton ex Small, Fl. S.E. U.S., 641, 1332. 1903 • Texas bush-clover or lespedeza

Herbs. Stems erect becoming trailing, 50–150 cm, branched much of length, appressed-pubescent and patent-pilose. **Leaves:** stipules caducous, subulate, 3–8 mm; petiole 10–16 mm, longer than rachis; leaflet blades elliptic or obovate, apex obtuse, scarcely apiculate, surfaces abaxially grayish or pale green, appressed-puberulent or pilose, especially along midrib and margin abaxially, sparsely puberulent or glabrescent adaxially; terminal blade (10–)15–25(–30) × 6–10 mm, length 1.7–2.2 times width. **Peduncles** much longer than subtending leaves, patent-pilose. **Racemes** 3–8-flowered, flowers not clustered at apex, flowers chasmogamous and cleistogamous. **Pedicels** 3–5 mm, patent-pilose; bracteoles shorter than calyx tube. **Flowers:** chasmogamous 5.5–8.5 mm; calyx 2–4 mm, tube 1–1.5 mm; lobes 4, lateral narrowly triangular, 1.2–1.5 mm, adaxial connate proximally; corolla purple; wings 5–6 mm; keel 6–6.5 mm. **Loments:** body exserted from calyx, rounded, chasmogamous 5–7 mm, cleistogamous 4–6.5 mm; stipe 1 mm. **2*n*** = 20.

Flowering summer–fall. Limestone hills, open fields; 200–1600 m; Tex.; Mexico (Coahuila).

Lespedeza texana is known only from Texas, especially the Edwards Plateau, except for a disjunct population in northern Mexico. Stems are procumbent or trailing, or sometimes erect or ascending near the base, to 15 cm, arching for about the next 10 cm, and trailing the rest of their lengths (A. F. Clewell 1966).

14. Lespedeza thunbergii (de Candolle) Nakai, Bull. Forest Exp. Sta., Chosen 6: 15. 1927 • Thunberg's lespedeza, pink or purple bush-clover [I] [W]

Desmodium thunbergii de Candolle in A. P. de Candolle and A. L. P. P. de Candolle, Prodr. 2: 337. 1825; *Lespedeza formosa* (Vogel) Koehne; *L. japonica* L. H. Bailey

Herbs or shrubs. Stems ascending or pendent, clustered, 50–300 cm, branched throughout, young branches densely covered with appressed to spreading whitish to yellowish hairs. **Leaves** gradually smaller distally; stipules subulate to narrowly deltate, 4–8 mm; petiole 10–50 mm, longer than rachis; leaflet blades narrowly elliptic to elliptic, ovate, or oblong, apex acute or obtuse, apiculate, surfaces densely appressed-pubescent abaxially, glabrous or sparsely to densely puberulent or pubescent adaxially; terminal blade 20–90 × 10–50 mm, length 1.5–2.2 times width. **Peduncles** longer than subtending leaves. **Racemes** 5–20-flowered, single or compound and appearing terminal and paniculate, flowers chasmogamous only. **Pedicels** 1.5–5 mm; bracteoles shorter than calyx tube. **Flowers** 12–16 mm; calyx 3.5–6 mm, tube 1.6–1.9 mm; lobes 4, lateral narrowly ovate-triangular, 2.2–3.6 mm, apices acute to shortly acuminate, not spine-tipped; corolla usually reddish purple, rarely white, banner with darker marks at throat on adaxial surface; wings 8.5–10.5 mm; keel 10.5–15 mm. **Loments:** body exserted from calyx, elliptic, 5–14 × 4–6 mm, slightly to densely white appressed-pilose, sometimes glabrescent; stipe 1–2 mm. **2*n*** = 22.

Flowering late summer–early fall. Woodland borders, roadsides; 0–500 m; introduced; Ont.; Ala., Ark., Conn., Fla., Ga., Ill., Ind., Kans., Ky., La., Md., Mass., Mich., Mo., N.J., N.Y., N.C., Ohio, Pa., S.C., Va., Wis.; Asia (China, e India, Japan, Korea, Taiwan).

Lespedeza thunbergii is polymorphic in habit of natural and cultivated forms, type and density of indument on stems and leaves, size and shape of leaflets, and size of flowers in East Asia (H. Ohashi et al. 2009). It is most notably distinguished by relatively large flowers with long, acuminate or acute calyx lobes and relatively large, elliptic loments. In the flora area, it has been planted for wildlife food and has naturalized more extensively than other shrubby *Lespedeza* species.

15. Lespedeza violacea (Linnaeus) Persoon, Syn. Pl. 2: 318. 1807 • Wandlike bush-clover [E]

Hedysarum violaceum Linnaeus, Sp. Pl. 2: 749. 1753; *Lespedeza intermedia* (S. Watson) Britton

Herbs. Stems erect or ascending, 40–150 cm, wandlike or branched apically, strigose or puberulent. **Leaves:** stipules subulate to narrowly triangular, 2–4 mm; petiole 7–20 mm, longer than rachis; leaflet blades obovate to elliptic-oblong, apex obtuse or retuse, apiculate, surfaces strigose abaxially, often glabrous, sometimes sparsely appressed-puberulent only on midrib adaxially; laterals not oblique at base; terminal blade 10–40 × 5–15 mm, length 1.5–3 times width. **Peduncles** shorter than or equal to subtending leaves. **Racemes** 4–10-flowered, crowded distally, flowers chasmogamous and cleistogamous. **Pedicels** 2–3 mm; bracteoles shorter than calyx tube. **Flowers:** chasmogamous 6–7 mm; calyx 3–4.5 mm, appressed-puberulent, tube 1–1.5 mm; lobes 4, lateral narrowly triangular, 2–3 mm, adaxial connate proximally; corolla pink-lavender to purple; wings 6–7 mm; keel 5–6 mm. **Loments:** body exserted from calyx, calyx ½ loment length, chasmogamous ovate to rounded, 5–7 mm, cleistogamous rounded, 4–6 mm, appressed-puberulent; stipe 1.5 mm. **2*n*** = 20.

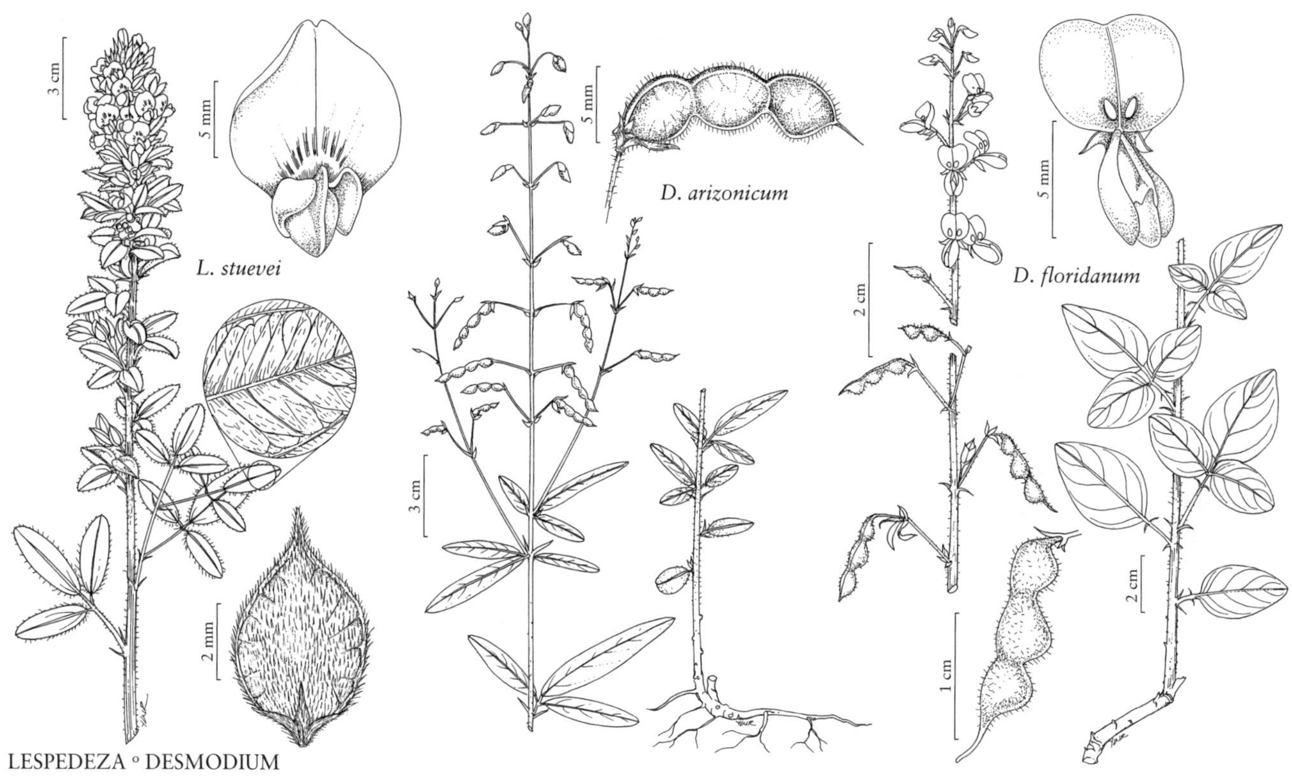

LESPEDEZA ◦ DESMODIUM

Flowering summer–fall. Open, upland rocky, deciduous woodlands, mixed or dry pine woods, mesic bottoms, old fields, roadsides, often on acidic, sandy soils; 0–1000 m; Ont.; Ala., Ark., Conn., Del., D.C., Ga., Ill., Ind., Iowa, Kans., Ky., La., Md., Mass., Mich., Minn., Miss., Mo., Nebr., N.H., N.J., N.Y., N.C., Ohio, Okla., Pa., R.I., S.C., Tenn., Tex., Vt., Va., W.Va., Wis.

The name *Lespedeza intermedia* has traditionally been used for plants here called *L. violacea* (J. L. Reveal and F. R. Barrie 1991). The species that previously was called *L. violacea* is now *L. frutescens*.

Lespedeza violacea forms natural hybrids with *L. capitata*, *L. frutescens*, *L. hirta*, *L. procumbens*, *L. repens*, *L. stuevei*, and *L. virginica*.

16. Lespedeza virginica (Linnaeus) Britton, Trans. New York Acad. Sci. 12: 64. 1893 • Slender bush-clover

Medicago virginica Linnaeus, Sp. Pl. 2: 778. 1753; *Lespedeza reticulata* (Muhlenberg ex Willdenow) Persoon

Herbs. Stems ascending or erect, clustered, 30–160 cm, initially wandlike, branched apically, villosulous or appressed-pubescent. **Leaves:** stipules subulate to narrowly triangular, to 6 mm; petiole 7–12 mm, longer than rachis; leaflet blades narrowly elliptic-oblong to linear, base obtuse or cuneate, apex apiculate, surfaces appressed-pubescent abaxially, usually sparsely appressed-pubescent, sometimes glabrescent (but not glabrous), adaxially; laterals similar to terminal; terminal blade 10–35 × 3–5 mm, length 3–7 times width. **Peduncles** shorter than or equal to subtending leaves. **Racemes** 4–14-flowered, crowded distally, flowers chasmogamous and cleistogamous. **Pedicels** 0.5–2 mm; bracteoles shorter than calyx tube. **Flowers:** chasmogamous 5–7 mm; calyx 3–4.5 mm, tube 1 mm; lobes 4, lateral narrowly triangular, 1–1.5 mm, adaxial connate proximally; corolla pink to purple; wings 5–6 mm; keel 4.5–5 mm. **Loments:** chasmogamous exserted from calyx, suborbicular, 4–7 mm, cleistogamous exserted from calyx, calyx 1/5–2/5 loment length, similar to chasmogamous, 3.5–5 mm; stipe 1 mm. $2n = 20$.

Flowering late summer–fall. Dry upland woodlands, clearings and borders, ruderal sites, old fields, eroded ridges, roadsides, pine barrens, moist savannas, prairie fragments; 0–1000 m; Ont.; Ala., Ark., Conn., Del., D.C., Fla., Ga., Ill., Ind., Iowa, Kans., Ky., La., Md., Mass., Mich., Minn., Miss., Mo., N.H., N.J., N.Y., N.C., Ohio, Okla., Pa., R.I., S.C., Tenn., Tex., Va., W.Va., Wis.; Mexico (Nuevo León).

Lespedeza virginica forms natural hybrids with *L. angustifolia*, *L. capitata*, *L. frutescens*, *L. hirta*, *L. procumbens* (*L.* ×*brittonii* E. P. Bicknell), *L. repens*, *L. stuevei* (*L.* ×*neglecta* Mackenzie & Bush), and *L. violacea*.

109. DESMODIUM Desvaux, J. Bot. Agric. 1: 122, plate 5, fig. 15. 1813, name conserved • Tick trefoil [Greek *desmos*, bond, and *-idium*, diminutive, alluding to moniliform loments]

Hiroyoshi Ohashi

Meibomia Heister ex Fabricius, name rejected

Herbs, usually perennial, sometimes annual, subshrubs, or shrubs, unarmed. **Stems** erect to diffusely spreading or decumbent to prostrate, pubescent, glabrous, or glabrescent. **Leaves** alternate (rarely mostly clustered near base of stem), trifoliolate or unifoliolate; stipules present, persistent or caducous, striate, ciliate, sometimes amplexicaul or subamplexicaul; petiolate; stipels usually present; leaflets 1 or 3, blade margins usually entire, main lateral veins arcuate along margin, rarely reaching margin, surfaces usually pubescent, sometimes glabrous, abaxially paler, sometimes glaucous; terminal leaflet petiolulate, larger than laterals, lateral leaflets 1-stipellate, blades usually oblique. **Inflorescences** 10–50+-flowered, axillary or terminal, usually pseudoracemes, usually 2–5 flowers per node, unbranched when axillary, branched and paniclelike (compound pseudoracemes) when terminal; bracts present, primary bracts 1, subtending flower pairs, sometimes collectively conspicuous before flowering, secondary bracts usually 2, subtending each flower, sometimes absent; bracteoles absent. **Pedicels** usually uncinate-puberulent, sometimes glutinous-pubescent. **Flowers** papilionaceous; calyx campanulate, lobes 5, usually appearing 4-lobed, adaxial pair connate except apically, with 2 minute teeth, lateral lobes equal to or slightly longer than tube, abaxial lobe longer than tube and other lobes, or sometimes as long as lateral lobes; corolla usually pink to purple, blue-purple, or purple, sometimes lavender to greenish blue, ochroleucous, or white, banner clawed or tapering proximally, blade usually broadly obovate, often with a pair of dark spots (false nectar guides) at base; wings and keel petals clawed; stamens 10, usually monadelphous, sometimes diadelphous; anthers dorsifixed. **Fruits** loments, usually stipitate, rarely sessile, compressed, straight or ± incurved, sometimes twisted or contorted, oblong, narrowly oblong, or linear, splitting between indehiscent segments, usually conspicuously uncinate-pubescent throughout, rarely sutures glabrous; segments (articles) (1 or)2–10, lateral faces reticulate (rugose in *D. scorpiurus*); sutures constricted at joints, abaxial incised deeper than adaxial or both equally incised, connections between segments (isthmi) adaxial or central. **Seeds** 1 per segment, usually brown, yellowish brown, or tan, asymmetric, usually oblong, 4-sided, or reniform, rim-arillate. x = [10] 11.

Species ca. 120 (36, including 1 hybrid, in the flora): c, e North America, Mexico, West Indies, Central America, South America; introduced in Asia, Africa, Indian Ocean Islands, Pacific Islands, Australia; mainly in seasonally dry to wet tropical to temperate regions.

Desmodium, as traditionally circumscribed, had its greatest diversity in southeastern Asia at infrageneric level and Mexico to northern South America at specific level (H. Ohashi 2005). More recent data (K. Ohashi et al. 2018) showed that *Desmodium* is polyphyletic. The traditional North American *Desmodium* (B. G. Schubert 1950; D. Isely 1990, 1998) was divided into two genera: *Desmodium* in the narrow sense adopted here and *Hylodesmum*, the previous *Desmodium* ser. *Americana* B. G. Schubert (H. Ohashi and R. R. Mill 2000). North American species of *Desmodium* are geographically separated into two groups: those of the central and eastern United States, and those of the Southwest (trans-Pecos Texas to Arizona), which mostly represent the northern peripheries of Mexican species (Isely 1990, 1998); they are otherwise absent west of the Rocky Mountains.

Most of the North American species of *Desmodium* are well established as natural species except for three species complexes that D. Isely (1990, 1998) designated as species groups due to the frequency of intermediate morphology among the traditional species. Each species complex, *D. ciliare* Group, *D. paniculatum* Group, and *D. procumbens* Group, is here regarded as a single species: *D. marilandicum*, *D. paniculatum*, and *D. procumbens*, respectively.

Few natural hybrids in *Desmodium* are known. Only *D.* ×*humifusum* is demonstrated to have a hybrid origin in nature in North America (J. A. Raveill 2002). Forms intermediate between different species have been presumed to be natural hybrids (D. Isely 1990, 1998). B. G. Schubert (1970) stated that hybridization is rare, and the morphological characters are relatively stable; her concepts are followed here except as previously noted.

Mature loments are helpful in identifying *Desmodium* species; they consist of multiple segments that break into one-seeded units or articles at maturity. The shape of the segments and location of the connections between segments (isthmi) vary widely among species. Fruits typically have uncinate (hooked) hairs, facilitating dispersal via animal fur and human clothing.

SELECTED REFERENCES Ohashi, K. et al. 2018. Phylogenetic analyses for a new classification of the *Desmodium* group of Leguminosae tribe Desmodieae. J. Jap. Bot. 93: 165–189. Schubert, B. G. 1940. *Desmodium*: Preliminary studies-I. Contr. Gray Herb. 129: 3–31. Schubert, B. G. 1950. *Desmodium*: Preliminary studies III. Rhodora 52: 135–155.

1. Inflorescences fascicles, terminal (appearing axillary); leaflet blades broadly obovate or cuneate-obovate, terminal blade 5–10 mm; stems prostrate . . . . 33. *Desmodium triflorum*
1. Inflorescences racemes or panicles, terminal or axillary; leaflet blades usually ovate, elliptic, or oblong, terminal blade (9–)10–120(–150) mm; stems erect, ascending, decumbent, or prostrate.
    2. Leaves unifoliolate.
        3. Leaflet blades linear, 2–5 mm wide, length 10+ times width; loments: stipe to 1 mm, sutures equally crenate, moderately uncinate-puberulent, segments 3–6, each (2–)3–3.5 mm, connections central . . . . 9. *Desmodium gramineum*
        3. Leaflet blades ovate to narrowly ovate, 10–30 mm wide, length (2–)2.5–5 times width; loments: stipe 1.5–2.5 mm, sutures crenate abaxially, sinuate adaxially, glabrous, segments 3–5, each 2.5–6 mm, connections adaxial . . . . 23. *Desmodium psilophyllum*
    2. Leaves usually trifoliolate, rarely unifoliolate proximally and/or distally.
        4. Stems decumbent, decumbent-assurgent, procumbent, climbing, or prostrate (sometimes vinelike, rarely erect in *D. procumbens*).
            5. Stipules persistent, amplexicaul or subamplexicaul.
                6. Loment sutures equally shallow-undulate abaxially and adaxially, segments narrowly oblong or narrowly elliptic, 1.5 mm wide, faces rugose; stipules amplexicaul, 2–3.5 mm, base auriculate . . . . 28. *Desmodium scorpiurus*
                6. Loment sutures deeply crenate abaxially, crenate adaxially, segments subglobose or subrhombic to elliptic, 4–8 mm wide, faces reticulate; stipules subamplexicaul, 5–12 mm, base obliquely cordate.
                    7. Terminal leaflet blades ovate, length 1.2–2 times width; corollas white or ochroleucous, 7–8 mm; loments glabrous, sutures uncinate-pubescent . . . . 19. *Desmodium ochroleucum*
                    7. Terminal leaflet blades elliptic, orbiculate, or broadly ovate, length 0.8–1.2 times width; corollas pink, fading blue-purple, 9–11 mm; loments uncinate-puberulent throughout . . . . 26. *Desmodium rotundifolium*
            5. Stipules caducous or persistent, not amplexicaul.
                8. Leaves trifoliolate, often unifoliolate proximally and/or distally; leaflets polymorphic between proximal and/or distal ones and median ones . . . . 21. *Desmodium procumbens* (in part)
                8. Leaves trifoliolate, rarely unifoliolate proximally; leaflets monomorphic.
                    9. Terminal leaflet blades ovate-elliptic to narrowly so, 8–10 mm wide . . . . 2. *Desmodium batocaulon*
                    9. Terminal leaflet blades ovate, elliptic, broadly ovate to rhombic, suborbiculate, or orbiculate, 10–60 mm wide.

10. Stems angular (3-sided); loment segments 5–9; primary bracts densely imbricate before anthesis, narrowly ovate, 7–10 mm . . . . 12. *Desmodium intortum*
10. Stems terete; loment segments 2–6; primary bracts not imbricate, ovate, 1–6.5 mm.
    11. Terminal leaflet blades ovate or rhombic-ovate, 30–70 mm, length 1.4–2 times width; loment segments obtusely angled abaxially. . . . . 36. *Desmodium ×humifusum*
    11. Terminal leaflet blades orbiculate to broadly ovate or broadly rhombic-ovate, 15–45 mm, length 1–1.7 times width; loment segments symmetrically rounded abaxially.
        12. Leaflets: adaxial surface appressed bulbous-pilose; inflorescence rachis densely patent uncinate-pubescent and usually bulbous-pilose; primary bracts 4.5–6.5 mm; calyces 5–6 mm; corollas 7–8 mm . . . . 8. *Desmodium grahamii*
        12. Leaflets: adaxial surface glabrous; inflorescence rachis uncinate-puberulent; primary bracts 1–2 mm; calyces 2 mm; corollas 3.5–5 mm . . . . 15. *Desmodium lineatum*

[4. Shifted to left margin.—Ed.]

4. Stems usually erect or ascending, rarely procumbent or sprawling.
    13. Stipules persistent or partly persistent, amplexicaul or subamplexicaul.
        14. Loments: connections adaxial, sutures dentate or crenate abaxially, sinuate adaxially . . . . 4. *Desmodium canescens*
        14. Loments: connections central, sutures equally or subequally crenate, or deeply crenate abaxially, shallowly dentate adaxially.
            15. Loments sparsely pubescent, at least on sutures . . . . 22. *Desmodium psilocarpum*
            15. Loments densely uncinate-pubescent, at least on sutures.
                16. Loment segments glabrous except uncinate-puberulent on sutures; leaflet blades densely villosulous abaxially . . . . 14. *Desmodium lindheimeri*
                16. Loment segments uncinate-puberulent throughout; leaflet blades subappressed-villous or uncinate-puberulent and strigose abaxially, or uncinate-puberulent only on veins.
                    17. Leaflets uncinate-puberulent on veins; calyces 4–5 mm; loments: segment margins not twisted, not rolled, connections ½–⅘ as broad as segments . . . . 10. *Desmodium illinoense*
                    17. Leaflets uncinate-puberulent and strigose or subappressed-villous; calyces 1.5–3 mm; loments twisted conspicuously when young, margins alternately involute and revolute, connections ¼ as broad as segments . . . . 32. *Desmodium tortuosum*
    13. Stipules persistent or caducous, not amplexicaul.
        18. Inflorescence rachis and/or stems pilose or villous and uncinate-pubescent, sometimes glabrescent.
            19. Terminal leaflet blades 5–7 mm wide, linear, length 8–10 times width . . . . 31. *Desmodium tenuifolium*
            19. Terminal leaflet blades 15–90 mm wide, elliptic, narrowly to broadly ovate, or broadly rhombic, length 1–4 times width.
                20. Loments: adaxial sutures straight or slightly sinuate, connections ½–⅔ as broad as segments; herbs stoloniferous or rhizomatous . . . . 11. *Desmodium incanum*
                20. Loments: adaxial sutures usually sinuate, sometimes repand, connections ¼–½ as broad as segments; herbs not stoloniferous.
                    21. Corollas 8–11 mm; primary bracts 6–7 mm; loment stipe 2(–3) mm; leaflet blades slightly or evidently strigulose abaxially, sparsely puberulent, almost glabrescent adaxially . . . . 3. *Desmodium canadense*
                    21. Corollas 6–8 mm; primary bracts 2–4 mm; loment stipe 3–6 mm; leaflet blades spreading-villous or velvety abaxially, uncinate-puberulent on veins adaxially.

22. Corollas 6–7 mm; leaflet blades ovate to narrowly ovate, bases usually rounded; loment segments 2–4, rounded abaxially . . . . 18. *Desmodium nuttallii*
22. Corollas 7–8 mm; leaflet blades broadly ovate or broadly rhombic, bases acute to cuneate or truncate; loment segments (3 or)4 or 5, symmetrically angled abaxially . . . . 35. *Desmodium viridiflorum*

[18. Shifted to left margin.—Ed.]

18. Inflorescence rachis and stems uncinate-pubescent, sometimes also sparsely pilose, glutinous, or glutinous-villous.
23. Stems conspicuously angled; leaflet blades usually with pale-blotched along midrib . . . . .34. *Desmodium tweedyi*
23. Stems usually striate, not conspicuously angled (angled in *D. metcalfei*); leaflet blades without pale blotching along midrib.
24. Stipules usually caducous, sometimes moderately persistent.
25. Loments: distal segment much larger than proximal segments . . . . . 27. *Desmodium scopulorum*
25. Loments: distal segment size similar to proximal segments.
26. Loment segments angled abaxially.
27. Leaflets thick, ± leathery, adaxial surface glabrous or sparsely puberulent; pedicels 10–20 mm in fruit . . . . 13. *Desmodium laevigatum*
27. Leaflets usually thin, rarely ± thick, papery, adaxial surface sparsely appressed-puberulent and pilose; pedicels to 12(–20) mm in fruit . . . . 20. *Desmodium paniculatum*
26. Loment segments rounded abaxially.
28. Terminal leaflet blades narrowly oblong-elliptic to linear, 4–10 mm wide . . . . 1. *Desmodium arizonicum*
28. Terminal leaflet blades mostly ovate or elliptic-ovate, 6–33 mm wide.
29. Corollas 4–6 mm; loment segments 1–4 . . . . 16. *Desmodium marilandicum*
29. Corollas 8–12 mm; loment segments (2 or)3–8.
30. Leaflet blades narrowly elliptic-oblong, apex obtuse, lateral veins reaching margin, margins flat; loments villosulous or pubescent and uncinate-puberulent, connections central . . . . 5. *Desmodium cinerascens*
30. Leaflet blades narrowly ovate-oblong, apex acute, lateral veins looped within margin, margins revolute; loments uncinate-pubescent, connections slightly adaxial . . . . .17. *Desmodium metcalfei*
24. Stipules persistent or moderately so.
31. Loment connections central, sutures ± equally crenate.
32. Loment margins involute, segments usually angled abaxially, sometimes rounded . . . . 21. *Desmodium procumbens* (in part)
32. Loment margins flat (sometimes slightly involute in *D. rosei*), segments rounded abaxially.
33. Terminal leaflet blades 8–10 mm wide, usually oblong-ovate to narrowly so, sometimes broadly elliptic to oblong, length 1–3.5 times width; corollas 4–5 mm; herbs perennial, with woody rootstock. . . . . 24. *Desmodium retinens*
33. Terminal leaflet blades 2–5 mm wide, linear to narrowly oblong, length 7+ times width; corollas 3–3.5 mm; herbs annual, with slender taproot . . . . .25. *Desmodium rosei*
31. Loment connections adaxial, sutures crenate or dentate abaxially, sinuate or straight adaxially (dentate in *D. cuspidatum*).
34. Terminal leaflet blades linear to narrowly oblong or narrowly elliptic, length 4–10 times width.
35. Petioles 1–5 mm; pedicels 2–5 mm; corollas 5 mm . . . . 29. *Desmodium sessilifolium*
35. Petioles 6.5–18 mm; pedicels 5–13 mm; corollas 4 mm. . . . . . . 30. *Desmodium strictum*
34. Terminal leaflet blades ovate, broadly ovate, or rhombic, length 1.3–3 times width.

[36. Shifted to left margin.—Ed.]

36. Leaves trifoliolate proximally, leaflet blade apex sharply acuminate to shortly cuspidate; loment segments (7–)9–11 mm; corollas 8–12 mm; calyces glabrate, margins sparsely ciliate; stems usually glabrous, sometimes sparsely uncinate-puberulent or pilose .... 6. *Desmodium cuspidatum*

36. Leaves unifoliolate proximally, leaflet blade apex acute or obtuse; loment segments 4–8 mm; corollas 5–7 mm; calyces puberulent to pubescent; stems usually densely uncinate-puberulent to -pubescent and villous .... 7. *Desmodium floridanum*

1. **Desmodium arizonicum** S. Watson, Proc. Amer. Acad. Arts 20: 363. 1885 [F]

Meibomia arizonica (S. Watson) Vail

Herbs, perennial. **Stems** erect or ascending, usually striate, sparsely branched, 20–80 cm, pubescent. **Leaves** trifoliolate; stipules caducous, narrowly ovate, 6–8 mm; petiole 1–5 mm; leaflet blades narrowly oblong-elliptic to linear, apex acute, surfaces villosulous; terminal blade 40–60 × 4–10 mm, length 3.5–10 times width. **Inflorescences** usually unbranched; rachis uncinate-puberulent; primary bracts caducous, broadly ovate, 4.5–5.5 mm. **Pedicels** 8–15 mm. **Flowers:** calyx 3 mm, uncinate-puberulent, lobes pubescent, tube 1.2 mm; abaxial lobes 2 mm, lateral lobes 1.5 mm; corolla blue-purple, 5–6 mm. **Loments:** sutures undulate abaxially, crenate adaxially; connections adaxial, ⅓ as broad as segments; segments (2 or)3–5, semiorbiculate, 4–5(–6) × 4 mm, rounded abaxially, convex adaxially, uncinate-puberulent; stipe 1–2 mm. 2*n* = 22.

Flowering summer–fall. Oak-juniper or pine woodlands, canyons, roadsides; 1700–2500 m; Ariz., N.Mex.; Mexico (Baja California, Chihuahua, Sinaloa, Sonora, Tamaulipas).

In the flora area, *Desmodium arizonicum* is known from southeastern Arizona and adjacent New Mexico.

2. **Desmodium batocaulon** A. Gray, Smithsonian Contr. Knowl. 5(6): 47. 1853

Meibomia batocaulos (A. Gray) Kuntze

Herbs, perennial. **Stems** decumbent or decumbent-assurgent, branched, 30–120 cm, densely uncinate-pubescent. **Leaves** trifoliolate; stipules caducous, narrowly ovate, 5+ mm; petiole 20–30 mm; leaflet blades ovate-elliptic to narrowly so, apex acute to obtuse, surfaces densely appressed-pubescent abaxially, sparsely so adaxially; terminal blade (20–)35–60 × 8–10(–15) mm, length 2.5–4 times width. **Inflorescences** axillary and terminal, branched or unbranched; rachis patent uncinate-puberulent to pubescent; primary bracts closely imbricate before anthesis, caducous, ovate, 5 mm. **Pedicels** 5–10 mm. **Flowers:** calyx 3–4 mm, sparsely pubescent, tube 1 mm; abaxial lobes 3 mm, lateral lobes 2 mm; corolla pink or purple to blue, 7–9 mm. **Loments:** sutures undulate abaxially, sinuate adaxially; connections adaxial, ¼–⅓ as broad as segments; segments 4–7, semiorbiculate, 3–5 × 3–3.5 mm, rounded abaxially, slightly convex adaxially, glabrous or sparsely uncinate-puberulent throughout; stipe 1–2 mm.

Flowering late summer–fall. Dry, rocky woodlands, pine or oak-juniper woodlands, canyons, roadsides; 1200–2100 m; Ariz., N.Mex.; Mexico (Baja California, Baja California Sur, Chihuahua, Guerrero, Sonora, Tamaulipas, Zacatecas).

In the flora area, *Desmodium batocaulon* is known from southeastern Arizona and southwestern New Mexico.

3. **Desmodium canadense** (Linnaeus) de Candolle in A. P. de Candolle and A. L. P. P. de Candolle, Prodr. 2: 328. 1825 [E] [W]

Hedysarum canadense Linnaeus, Sp. Pl. 2: 748. 1753; *Meibomia canadensis* (Linnaeus) Kuntze

Herbs, perennial. **Stems** erect, 50–100 cm, sparsely to densely pilose or villous, usually patent uncinate-puberulent and -pubescent, sometimes glabrescent. **Leaves** trifoliolate; stipules ± persistent, subulate to narrowly ovate, 4.5–9.5 mm; petiole 10–60 mm; leaflet blades often pale green abaxially, ovate to narrowly ovate, apex acute, surfaces slightly or visibly strigulose abaxially, sparsely puberulent or nearly glabrescent adaxially; terminal blade 40–110 × 15–30 mm, length 2.5–3.5 times width. **Inflorescences** terminal and branched, or unbranched from distal axils; rachis villous and uncinate-pubescent, sometimes appearing glabrescent; primary bracts caducous, narrowly ovate, 6–7 mm. **Pedicels** 4–8 mm. **Flowers:** calyx 3.5–5 mm, densely uncinate-puberulent and sparsely pilose, tube 1–1.5 mm; abaxial lobes 3–3.5 mm, lateral lobes 2 mm; corolla usually blue-violet, rarely white, 8–11 mm. **Loments:**

sutures crenate abaxially, repand or sinuate adaxially; connections adaxial, ½ as broad as segments; segments 3–5, semiorbiculate, 4–8 × 4–5 mm, rounded abaxially, convex adaxially, densely uncinate-puberulent; stipe 2(–3) mm. **2*n*** = 22.

Flowering summer. Prairie relics, woodland borders and openings, roadsides; 0–900 m; Man., N.B., N.S., Ont., Que.; Conn., Del., Ill., Ind., Iowa, Kans., Maine, Md., Mass., Mich., Minn., Mo., N.H., N.J., N.Y., N.Dak., Ohio, Okla., Pa., R.I., S.Dak., Tex., Vt., Va., W.Va., Wis.

In Texas, *Desmodium canadense* is known only from Wheeler County.

4. Desmodium canescens (Linnaeus) Poiret in F. Cuvier, Dict. Sci. Nat. ed. 2, 13: 110. 1819 E

Hedysarum canescens Linnaeus, Sp. Pl. 2: 748. 1753; *Meibomia canescens* (Linnaeus) Kuntze

Herbs, perennial. **Stems** erect or ascending, branched, 50–200 cm, conspicuously or sparsely villous and uncinate-pubescent. **Leaves** trifoliolate; stipules mostly persistent, usually reflexed, broadly or narrowly ovate, 5–13 mm, base oblique, often auriculate, subamplexicaul; petiole 30–60 mm; leaflet blades ovate, thick, papery, apex acute to gradually acuminate, surfaces densely uncinate-puberulent abaxially, uncinate-puberulent and pubescent on veins adaxially; terminal blade 50–130 × 30–100 mm, length 1.5–2 times width. **Inflorescences** paniclelike, branched; rachis densely patent bulbous-villous and uncinate-puberulent; primary bracts caducous, narrowly ovate, 4–6 mm. **Pedicels** persistent, 8–13 mm. **Flowers:** calyx 3–5 mm, sparsely or densely puberulent, tube 1 mm; abaxial lobes to 3 mm, lateral lobes 1 mm; corolla usually purple to pinkish, rarely white, 9–13 mm. **Loments:** sutures dentate or crenate abaxially, sinuate adaxially; connections adaxial, ⅓–½ as broad as segments; segments 4–6, broadly elliptic, 6.5–13 × 4–7 mm, obtusely angled abaxially becoming round, convex adaxially, uncinate-puberulent and villous, hairs particularly dense on sutures and between segments; stipe 2.5–6 mm. **2*n*** = 22.

Flowering summer. Open, dry woodlands, cutover areas, thickets, roadsides; 0–900 m; Ont.; Ala., Ark., Conn., Del., D.C., Fla., Ga., Ill., Ind., Iowa, Kans., Ky., La., Md., Mass., Mich., Miss., Mo., Nebr., N.J., N.Y., N.C., Ohio, Okla., Pa., R.I., S.C., Tenn., Tex., Va., W.Va., Wis.

In Texas, *Desmodium canescens* is known from the eastern third of the state. In Florida, it occurs only in the panhandle region.

5. Desmodium cinerascens A. Gray, Smithsonian Contr. Knowl. 5(6): 48. 1853

Meibomia cinerascens (A. Gray) Kuntze

Herbs, perennial; base woody. **Stems** ascending to erect or sprawling, usually striate, branched, 60–150 cm, sparsely to densely appressed-pilose and sparsely uncinate-pubescent. **Leaves** trifoliolate; stipules caducous, narrowly ovate-deltate, 3–4 mm; petioles 20–40 mm proximally, 8–20 mm distally; leaflet blades narrowly elliptic-oblong, apex obtuse, lateral veins prominent, reaching margin, margin flat, surfaces subappressed-villous abaxially, glabrescent adaxially; terminal blade 25–70 × 15–25 mm, length 2–3 times width. **Inflorescences** branched or unbranched and elongate when terminal, or unbranched from distal axils; rachis closely appressed-pubescent and patent uncinate-puberulent; primary bracts caducous, narrowly ovate, 3–5 mm. **Pedicels** 8–10 mm. **Flowers:** calyx 4 mm, densely uncinate-puberulent, tube 2 mm; abaxial lobes 2 mm, lateral lobes 1 mm; corolla purple, 8–11 mm. **Loments:** sutures crenate; connections central, ⅓ as broad as segments; segments 3–8, semiorbiculate, 5–7 × 4–5 mm, rounded abaxially, convex adaxially, villosulous or pubescent and uncinate-puberulent throughout; stipe 2–5 mm.

Flowering late summer–fall. Open, dry slopes, with oak or pine, canyons, washes, roadsides; 1200–1800 m; Ariz.; Mexico (Chihuahua, Durango, Nayarit, Sinaloa, Sonora).

Desmodium cinerascens is known in the flora area from the south-central and southeastern areas of Arizona.

6. Desmodium cuspidatum (Muhlenberg ex Willdenow) de Candolle ex G. Don in J. C. Loudon, Hort. Brit., 309. 1830 E

Hedysarum cuspidatum Muhlenberg ex Willdenow, Sp. Pl. 3: 1198. 1802; *Desmodium bracteosum* (Michaux) de Candolle; *D. cuspidatum* var. *longifolium* (Torrey & A. Gray) B. G. Schubert; *D. grandiflorum* de Candolle; *Meibomia grandiflora* (de Candolle) Kuntze; *M. longifolia* (Torrey & A. Gray) Vail

Herbs, perennial. **Stems** erect or ascending, usually striate, 50–150 cm, usually glabrous, sometimes sparsely uncinate-pubescent or pilose. **Leaves** trifoliolate; stipules usually persistent, narrowly ovate or subulate, 10–20 mm; petiole 40–70 mm; leaflet blades ovate to broadly ovate, apex sharply acuminate to shortly cuspidate, surfaces glabrous (except veins spreading-villosulous); terminal blade 50–120 × 30–70 mm, length 1.5–3 times width. **Inflorescences** branched; rachis densely uncinate-pubescent to rarely glabrescent; primary bracts conspicuously covering apex of inflorescences, narrowly ovate, 8–14 mm. **Pedicels** 4–8 mm, densely patent uncinate-puberulent and sparsely pilose. **Flowers:** calyx 3–4 mm, glabrate, margins sparsely ciliate, lobes pilose, tube 1.5–2 mm; abaxial lobes 3–4 mm, lateral lobes 2–3 mm; corolla purple, 8–12 mm. **Loments:** sutures dentate abaxially, sinuate adaxially; connections adaxial, ½ as broad as segments; segments (1–)4–7, obliquely narrow-rhombic or suborbiculate, (7–)9–11 × 4–5 mm, angled abaxially, slightly convex adaxially, sparsely uncinate-puberulent, sutures densely uncinate-puberulent; stipe 1–2.5 mm.

Flowering summer–fall. Rich, moist woodlands, thickets, openings, dry, rocky woodlands, ruderal areas; 0–1000 m; Ont.; Ala., Ark., Conn., Del., D.C., Fla., Ga., Ill., Ind., Iowa, Kans., Ky., La., Md., Mass., Mich., Minn., Miss., Mo., Nebr., N.H., N.J., N.Y., N.C., Ohio, Okla., Pa., R.I., S.C., Tenn., Tex., Vt., Va., W.Va., Wis.

In Texas, *Desmodium cuspidatum* is known only from Bowie County, at the northeastern corner of the state.

7. **Desmodium floridanum** Chapman, Fl. South. U.S., 102. 1860 [E] [F]

Meibomia floridana (Chapman) Kuntze

Herbs, perennial. **Stems** ascending to erect, usually striate, usually unbranched, 40–100 cm, usually densely uncinate-puberulent to -pubescent and villous. **Leaves** trifoliolate, with 1 unifoliolate proximally, sometimes mostly clustered near base; stipules persistent, some conspicuously reflexed, narrowly ovate, 4–10 mm; petiole 15–35 mm; leaflet blades rhombic or ovate, ± leathery, apex acute or obtuse, surfaces sparsely to densely spreading-villous abaxially, often glaucous, conspicuously reticulate-veined, lateral veins conspicuous, arcuate along margin, sparsely uncinate-puberulent adaxially, more densely so on thick veins; terminal blade (30–)60–120 × 20–70 mm, length 1.3–2.5 times width. **Inflorescences** panicles, often relatively large, usually branched; rachis densely uncinate-pubescent and long-pilose; primary bracts caducous, narrowly ovate, 2.5–3 mm. **Pedicels** 3–8 mm. **Flowers:** calyx 2.5–3 mm, puberulent to pubescent, tube 1–1.5 mm; abaxial lobes 1–1.5 mm, lateral lobes 1 mm; corolla purple, 5–7 mm. **Loments:** sutures deeply crenate abaxially, sinuate adaxially; connections adaxial, ⅕–¼ as broad as segments; segments 2–5, obtusely rhombic or semiorbiculate, 4–8 × 4–5 mm, obtusely angled abaxially, convex adaxially, uncinate-pubescent throughout; stipe 1–4 mm.

Flowering spring–fall. Pine or pine-turkey-oak woodlands, pine-palmetto flatwoods, old fields, urban waste areas; 0–300 m; Ala., Fla., Ga., S.C.

Desmodium floridanum is known from throughout Florida, southern Alabama, Georgia, and southern South Carolina.

8. **Desmodium grahamii** A. Gray, Smithsonian Contr. Knowl. 5(6): 48. 1853 (as grahami)

Meibomia grahamii (A. Gray) Kuntze

Herbs, perennial, sometimes mat-forming; rhizomatous. **Stems** prostrate, decumbent, or trailing, branched from base, 25–70 cm, uncinate-puberulent to -pubescent. **Leaves** usually trifoliolate, rarely unifoliolate proximally; stipules persistent, reflexed, narrowly deltate, 3–5.5 mm; petiole 12–20 mm; leaflet blades pale green abaxially, broadly ovate to suborbiculate, apex obtuse, surfaces clearly reticulate-veined abaxially, prominently reticulate-veined adaxially, loosely strigulose or glabrescent abaxially, appressed, bulbous-pilose adaxially; terminal blade 20–45 × 15–25 mm, length 1.2–1.7 times width. **Inflorescences** terminal and unbranched; rachis densely patent uncinate-pubescent and often bulbous-pilose; primary bracts ovate, 4.5–6.5 mm. **Pedicels** 10–15 mm. **Flowers:** calyx 5–6 mm, pubescent, tube 1 mm; abaxial lobes 4–5 mm, lateral lobes 3–4 mm; corolla pink, lilac to purple, or greenish white, 7–8 mm. **Loments:** sutures crenate abaxially, strongly crenate adaxially; connections adaxial, ⅓ as broad as segments; segments (2 or)3–6, elliptic to suborbiculate, 4.5–8 × 3–5 mm, symmetrically rounded abaxially, convex adaxially, densely uncinate-pubescent throughout; stipe 3–3.5 mm. $2n = 22$.

Flowering late summer–fall. Pine, juniper, oak woodlands, grasslands, canyons, sandy alluvia along streams, moist areas, roadsides; 1600–2400 m; Ariz., N.Mex., Tex.; Mexico (Baja California, Baja California Sur, Chihuahua, Coahuila, México, Puebla, Sonora, Tamaulipas).

In the flora area, *Desmodium grahamii* is known from the trans-Pecos region of Texas; it is also found in the southern half of Arizona, and southwestern New Mexico.

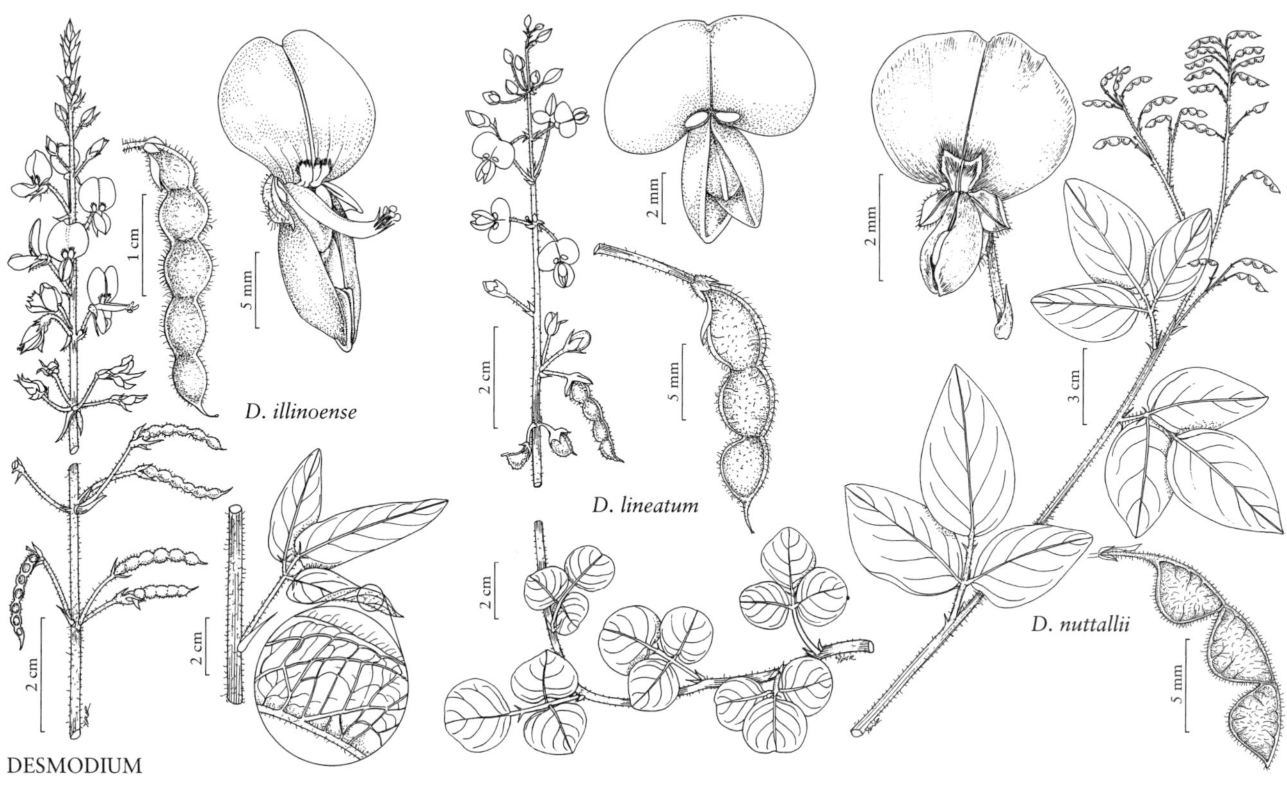

9. Desmodium gramineum A. Gray, Smithsonian Contr. Knowl. 5(6): 46. 1853

Desmodium angustifolium (Kunth) de Candolle var. *gramineum* (A. Gray) B. G. Schubert; *Meibomia graminea* (A. Gray) Kuntze

Herbs, perennial. **Stems** stiffly erect or ascending, branched at base and appearing clustered, 40–80 cm, glabrescent or sparsely uncinate-puberulent. **Leaves** unifoliolate; stipules caducous, narrowly ovate, 3–9 mm; petiole 10–30 mm; leaflet blades linear, (40–)70–130 × 2–5 mm, length 10+ times width, apex acute or acuminate, surfaces uncinate-puberulent and sparsely strigose on veins abaxially, uncinate-puberulent adaxially. **Inflorescences** branched or unbranched; rachis sparsely uncinate-puberulent; primary bracts ovate, 2–3 mm. **Pedicels** 10–20 mm, uncinate-puberulent or glabrescent. **Flowers:** calyx 2 mm, puberulent and uncinate-puberulent, tube 0.8 mm; abaxial lobes 1.2 mm, lateral lobes 1 mm; corolla ephemeral, purple, 3 mm. **Loments:** margins slightly involute, sutures equally crenate; connections central, ¼ as broad as segments; segments 3–6, broadly elliptic, (2–)3–3.5 × 2.5–3 mm, convex or rounded abaxially and adaxially, sparsely uncinate-puberulent, sutures moderately uncinate-puberulent; stipe to 1 mm.

Flowering late summer–fall. Dry woodlands, grasslands, open hillsides; 1100–1500 m; Ariz.; Mexico (Chihuahua, Colima, Jalisco, Michoacán, Oaxaca, Sinaloa, Sonora, Tamaulipas).

In Arizona, *Desmodium gramineum* is known from Cochise, Pima, Pinal, and Santa Cruz counties.

10. Desmodium illinoense A. Gray, Proc. Amer. Acad. Arts 8: 289. 1870 [E] [F]

Meibomia illinoensis (A. Gray) Kuntze

Herbs, perennial. **Stems** ascending to erect, branched or unbranched, 50–100 cm, medially uncinate-pubescent, sometimes also ± pilose. **Leaves** trifoliolate; stipules persistent, ovate, 8–15 mm, base amplexicaul, pilose-ciliate; petiole 30–50 mm; leaflet blades narrowly ovate to ovate, thick, papery, apex acute to rounded, surfaces conspicuously reticulate-veined abaxially, uncinate-puberulent on veins abaxially, sparsely spreading-villous or glabrous adaxially; terminal blade 35–80 × 30–70 mm, length 1.5–3 times width. **Inflorescences** usually unbranched; rachis patent-pilose and uncinate-puberulent; primary bracts narrowly ovate, 4–5 mm. **Pedicels** 7–15(–23) mm. **Flowers:** calyx 4–5 mm, uncinate-puberulent and pilose, tube 2–3 mm; abaxial lobes 2.5 mm, lateral lobes 2 mm; corolla purplish, 6–8 mm. **Loments:** sutures equally crenate; connections central, ½–⅘ as broad as segments; segments 4–7, elliptic or suborbiculate, 4–7 × 3.5–5 mm, symmetrically convex abaxially and adaxially, densely uncinate-puberulent and villous; stipe 2–4 mm.

Flowering summer(–fall). Prairie relics, thickets, roadsides; 100–500 m; Ark., Ill., Ind., Iowa, Kans., Mich., Minn., Mo., Nebr., Ohio, Okla., S.Dak., Tex., Wis.

Desmodium illinoense is considered extirpated from Ontario, where it was collected once in 1888 near London.

11. Desmodium incanum (Swartz) de Candolle in A. P. de Candolle and A. L. P. P. de Candolle, Prodr. 2: 332. 1825, name conserved [I] [W]

Hedysarum incanum Swartz, Prodr., 107. 1788, name conserved; *Aeschynomene incana* (Swartz) G. Meyer; *Desmodium ancistrocarpum* (Ledebour) de Candolle; *D. canum* (J. F. Gmelin) Schinz & Thellung; *D. frutescens* Schindler; *D. frutescens* var. *amplyophyllum* (Urban) Schindler; *D. malacophyllum* (Link) de Candolle; *D. mauritianum* (Willdenow) de Candolle; *D. supinum* de Candolle var. *amblyophyllum* Urban; *H. ancistrocarpum* Ledebour; *H. malacophyllum* Link; *H. mauritianum* Willdenow; *H. racemosum* Aublet; *Meibomia adscendens* (Swartz) de Candolle var. *incana* (Swartz) Kuntze; *M. incana* (Swartz) Vail; *M. malacophylla* (Link) Kuntze; *M. supina* (de Candolle) Britton

Herbs, subshrubs, or shrubs, perennial; stoloniferous or rhizomatous. **Stems** erect or ascending, to 300 cm, pubescent or glabrescent. **Leaves** trifoliolate; stipules usually persistent, narrowly ovate-deltate, 5–10 mm; petiole usually 15–20 mm; leaflet blades elliptic to ovate, apex obtuse or acute, surfaces finely spreading-villosulous to substrigose abaxially, uncinate-puberulent or glabrescent adaxially; terminal blade 20–90 × 15–45 mm, length 1.5–4 times width. **Inflorescences** unbranched; rachis densely patent uncinate-pubescent; primary bracts caducous, narrowly ovate, 6–7 mm. **Pedicels** persistent with calyx-remnant at top after loments drop, 5–9 mm. **Flowers:** calyx 2–3.5 mm, uncinate-puberulent, lobes pilose, tube 1 mm; abaxial lobes 1.5–2.5 mm, lateral lobes 1–2 mm; corolla purple, 5–8 mm. **Loments:** sutures symmetrically crenate abaxially, straight or slightly sinuate adaxially; connections central, ½–⅔ as broad as segments; segments 4–8, semiobovate, 3.5–5 × 2.5–3 mm, broadly rounded abaxially, straight or barely convex adaxially, uncinate-puberulent; stipe 1.5–2 mm. 2*n* = 22.

Flowering spring–fall. Pine-palmetto flatwoods, woodland borders, lawns, ruderal sites, disturbed or waste areas; 0–50 m; introduced; Ala., Fla., Ga., Tex.; Mexico (Chiapas, Jalisco, Oaxaca, Quintana Roo, Tamaulipas, Veracruz); West Indies; Central America; South America; introduced also in Asia (Taiwan), Africa, Indian Ocean Islands (Mauritius, Reunion), Pacific Islands, Australia.

Desmodium incanum may be distinguished by its long-persistent stipules usually fused and nearly surrounding the stem, at least when young, and by its pedicels which are usually borne singly and are each subtended by one primary bract and two (lateral) secondary bracts (B. G. Schubert 1980).

Desmodium incanum was long known as *D. canum* Schinz & Thellung (= *Meibomia cana* S. F. Blake) based on the illegitimate *Hedysarum canum* J. F. Gmelin, a superfluous name for *H. racemosum* Aublet. The complex nomenclatural history was elaborated by D. H. Nicolson (1978) and L. C. P. Lima et al. (2012, 2014). *Hedysarum canescens* Miller (1768) is a later homonym of *H. canescens* Linnaeus (1753), thus illegitimate, and pertains here. *Hedysarum canum* J. F. Gmelin is a superfluous name for *H. racemosum* Aublet; *Meibomia cana* S. F. Blake was intended as a new combination based on that name.

12. Desmodium intortum (Miller) Urban, Symb. Antill. 8: 292. 1920

Hedysarum intortum Miller, Gard. Dict. ed. 8., Hedysarum no. 11. 1768; *Desmodium sonorae* A. Gray; *D. uncinatum* (Jacquin) de Candolle; *Meibomia intorta* (Miller) S. F. Blake

Herbs, perennial. **Stems** prostrate or climbing, branched, angular (3-sided), 40–200 cm, uncinate-pubescent and villous. **Leaves** trifoliolate; stipules usually persistent, sometimes caducous, ovate-deltate, 5.5–12 mm; petiole 4–8 cm; leaflet blades ovate, elliptic to broadly ovate, or rhombic, apex acute to acuminate, surfaces more densely sericeous abaxially, sparsely to densely sericeous adaxially; terminal blade 35–100 × 24–60 mm, length 2.5–3 times width. **Inflorescences** branched or unbranched; rachis patent-villous and uncinate-pubescent to puberulent; primary bracts densely imbricate before anthesis, caducous, narrowly ovate, 7–10 mm. **Pedicels** 4–8 mm. **Flowers:** calyx 3–5 mm, sparsely puberulent throughout, lobes often villous, tube 1 mm; abaxial lobes 4–5.5 mm, lateral lobes 2.5–4 mm; corolla purple, fading blue-green, 7–9 mm. **Loments:** sutures crenate or somewhat angled abaxially, sinuate adaxially; connections adaxial, ½ as broad as segments; segments 5–9, semiorbiculate, 3–4 × 2–2.5 mm, obliquely rounded abaxially, slightly angled adaxially, uncinate-pubescent; stipe 1–2 mm. $2n = 22$.

Flowering late summer–fall. Open, grassy areas, roadsides; 1000–1700 m; Ariz.; Mexico (Chiapas, Colima, Guerrero, Michoacán, Sonora, Veracruz); Central America; introduced in Pacific Islands (Hawaii), Australia.

In the flora area, *Desmodium intortum* is known only from Cochise County.

13. Desmodium laevigatum (Nuttall) de Candolle in A. P. de Candolle and A. L. P. P. de Candolle, Prodr. 2: 329. 1825 [E]

Hedysarum laevigatum Nuttall, Gen. N. Amer. Pl. 2: 109. 1818; *Meibomia laevigata* (Nuttall) Kuntze

Herbs, perennial; base woody, from thick rootstock, sometimes with somewhat tuberous roots. **Stems** ascending to erect, usually striate, 30–100 (–150) cm, glabrous or uncinate-puberulent. **Leaves** trifoliolate; stipules caducous, narrowly ovate to ovate, 2–4 mm; petiole 20–60 mm; leaflet blades ovate, thick, ± leathery, apex obtuse or somewhat acute, surfaces pale to glaucous, glabrous or sparsely puberulent and/or strigose abaxially, glabrous or sparsely puberulent adaxially; terminal blade 35–90 × 20–45 mm, length 1.5–2.5 times width. **Inflorescences** branched or unbranched; rachis densely uncinate-puberulent; primary bracts ovate, 3–3.5 mm. **Pedicels** 5–10 mm, 10–20 mm in fruit, uncinate-puberulent. **Flowers:** calyx 3–4 mm, puberulent, tube 1.5 mm; abaxial lobes 2 mm, lateral lobes 1.5 mm; corolla lavender to purple, 8–10 mm. **Loments:** sutures deeply dentate abaxially, sinuate adaxially; connections adaxial, ¼ as broad as segments; segments (2 or)3–5, deltate to oblique-rhombic, 5–8 × 3.5–4 mm, obtusely angled abaxially, convex or straight adaxially, uncinate-puberulent; stipe 5–6.5 mm. $2n = 22$.

Flowering late summer–fall. Deciduous or mixed, open, upland or bottom woodlands and borders, abandoned fields, roadsides; 0–900 m; Ala., Ark., Del., D.C., Fla., Ga., Ill., Ind., Ky., La., Md., Miss., Mo., N.J., N.Y., N.C., Ohio, Okla., Pa., S.C., Tenn., Tex., Va., W.Va.

In Texas, *Desmodium laevigatum* is known from the eastern third of the state.

14. Desmodium lindheimeri Vail, Bull. Torrey Bot. Club 18: 120. 1891

Meibomia lindheimeri (Vail) Vail

Herbs, perennial. **Stems** erect, branched, angled and grooved, 40–60 cm, uncinate-puberulent and -pubescent, also sparsely pilose. **Leaves** trifoliolate; stipules ± persistent, reflexed, broadly or obliquely ovate, 7–8 mm, base subamplexicaul; petiole 10–50 mm; leaflet blades usually ovate, rhombic to broadly ovate, or semiorbiculate, rarely narrowly ovate, base truncate or broadly obtuse, apex acute, surfaces densely villosulous abaxially, uncinate-puberulent and pilose adaxially; terminal blade 50–100 × 40–75 mm, length usually less than 2 times width. **Inflorescences** usually unbranched; rachis densely patent uncinate-pubescent; primary bracts broadly ovate, 4.5–7 mm. **Pedicels** 5 mm. **Flowers:** calyx 2–2.5 mm, uncinate-puberulent, tube 1 mm; abaxial lobes 1–1.5 mm, lateral lobes 0.7 mm; corolla blue-green, 6–7 mm. **Loments:** margins ± involute and contorted, sutures deeply crenate abaxially, shallowly dentate adaxially; connections central, ⅕ as broad as segments; segments (1–)3–5, subrhombic to semiovate, 7–15 × 5–8 mm, rounded abaxially, obtusely angled adaxially, glabrous, sutures densely uncinate-pubescent; stipe 2–3.5 mm.

Flowering summer–fall. Rocky ravines, oak-juniper woodlands; 200–300 m; Tex.; Mexico (Chiapas, Coahuila, Durango, Nuevo León, San Luis Potosí, Tamaulipas).

Desmodium lindheimeri resembles *D. canescens* and its relatives, especially *D. ochroleucum*, in having relatively large loments. It is common in its narrow range in the Edwards Plateau (Comal County) and is widespread in Mexico (M. Enquist 1995).

15. Desmodium lineatum de Candolle in A. P. de Candolle and A. L. P. P. de Candolle, Prodr. 2: 330. 1825 [E] [F]

Hedysarum lineatum Michaux, Fl. Bor.-Amer. 2: 72. 1803, not Linnaeus 1759; *Meibomia arenicola* Vail var. *polymorpha* (Vail) Vail; *M. lineata* (de Candolle) Kuntze; *M. lineata* var. *polymorpha* Vail; *M. polymorpha* (Vail) Small

Herbs, perennial, often mat-forming. **Stems** prostrate, lineate, to 100 cm, uncinate-puberulent and -pubescent, also sparsely to moderately pilose. **Leaves** trifoliolate; stipules mostly persistent, inconspicuous, narrowly ovate, 2–5 mm; petiole 5–21 mm; leaflet blades orbiculate or broadly rhombic-ovate, apex rounded, surfaces glabrous or inconspicuously spreading-villous abaxially, glabrous adaxially; terminal blade 15–30 × 10–30 mm, length 1–1.2 times width. **Inflorescences** densely flowered, ascending, usually terminal and branched, axillary and unbranched; rachis uncinate-puberulent; primary bracts caducous, ovate, 1–2 mm. **Pedicels** 6–12 mm. **Flowers:** calyx 2 mm, puberulent and ± pilose, tube 1 mm; abaxial lobes 1.5 mm, lateral lobes 1 mm; corolla usually purple, rarely white, 3.5–5 mm. **Loments:** sutures deeply crenate abaxially, sinuate adaxially; connections adaxial, 1/3 as broad as segments; segments 2–4, ovate-orbiculate or obovate, 3.5–6 × 2.5–4 mm, symmetrically rounded abaxially, convex adaxially, uncinate-pubescent and pilose throughout; stipe 1–2.5 mm.

Flowering late summer–fall(–spring). Open woodlands, savannas, sandhills, pastures, abandoned fields; 0–200 m; Ala., Del., D.C., Fla., Ga., La., Md., Miss., N.C., S.C., Tex., Va., W.Va.

Desmodium arenicola (Vail) F. J. Hermann and *Meibomia arenicola* Vail are illegitimate names that pertain here.

In Texas, *Desmodium lineatum* is known from fewer than ten counties adjacent to Louisiana.

16. Desmodium marilandicum (Linnaeus) de Candolle in A. P. de Candolle and A. L. P. P. de Candolle, Prodr. 2: 328. 1825 (as marylandicum)

Hedysarum marilandicum Linnaeus, Sp. Pl. 2: 748. 1753; *Meibomia marilandica* (Linnaeus) Kuntze

Herbs, perennial. **Stems** ascending to erect, usually striate, branched or unbranched, 30–150 cm, glabrous or sparsely to densely uncinate-puberulent, sometimes also patent long-pilose. **Leaves** trifoliolate; stipules caducous or moderately persistent, subulate to narrowly ovate, 2–5 mm; petiole 1–30 mm; leaflet blades narrowly ovate, elliptic, elliptic-ovate, ovate-rhombic, or suborbiculate, apex obtuse or acute, mucronulate, surfaces sparsely to densely uncinate-puberulent and appressed-villous abaxially, uncinate-puberulent or glabrescent adaxially; terminal blade 9–75 × 6–33 mm, length 1.5–4(–5) times width. **Inflorescences** terminal and branched, axillary and unbranched; rachis uncinate-puberulent; primary bracts ovate, 1.5–3 mm. **Pedicels** 3–19 mm, uncinate-puberulent. **Flowers:** calyx 1.5–2.5 mm, pubescent (not uncinate-puberulent), tube 1 mm; abaxial lobes 1.2–1.5 mm, lateral lobes 1 mm; corolla usually lavender to red-violet or pink-purple, rarely white, 4–6 mm. **Loments:** sutures crenate abaxially, sinuate adaxially; connections adaxial, 1/4–1/2 as broad as segments; segments 1–4, broadly elliptic, 3.5–5.5 × 2.5–4 mm, rounded abaxially, convex adaxially, uncinate-puberulent throughout; stipe 1–2 mm. $2n = 22$.

Varieties 3 (3 in the flora): e, sc United States, West Indies.

Desmodium ciliare, *D. lancifolium*, and *D. marilandicum* have generally been recognized as closely related but distinct species in floras of the United States. They commonly have two or three articulate, small loments. D. Isely (1990, 1998) grouped them as the *D. ciliare* Group and regarded forms intermediate between them as putative hybrids: *D. ciliare* × *D. marilandicum* and *D. ciliare* × *D. lancifolium*. They have been separated by differences in the leaflets and pubescence, but the differences are not always clear. They are treated here as one species with three varieties.

1. Terminal leaflet blades elliptic-ovate to narrowly ovate, 50–75 × 20–33 mm, apex acute to obtuse .... 16c. *Desmodium marilandicum* var. *lancifolium*
1. Terminal leaflet blades elliptic, ovate, ovate-rhombic, or suborbiculate, 9–40 × 6–17 mm, apex obtuse.
    2. Petioles 12–30 mm, sparsely uncinate-puberulent; stems with a few, scattered hairs; pedicels (6–)8–19 mm .... 16a. *Desmodium marilandicum* var. *marilandicum*
    2. Petioles 1–15 mm; stems and petioles uncinate-puberulent and patent long-pilose; pedicels 3–8 mm. . .16b. *Desmodium marilandicum* var. *ciliare*

16a. Desmodium marilandicum (Linnaeus) de Candolle var. **marilandicum** [E]

Stems with a few, scattered hairs. **Leaves:** petiole 12–30 mm, sparsely uncinate-puberulent; terminal leaflet blade ovate, ovate-rhombic, or suborbiculate, 15–25(–40) × 10–17 mm, apex obtuse. **Pedicels** (6–)8–19 mm.

Flowering summer–fall. Dry, open or regrowth woodland and borders, old fields, roadsides; 0–1000 m; Ala., Ark., Conn., Del., D.C., Fla., Ga., Ill., Ind., Kans., Ky., La., Md., Mass., Mich., Miss., Mo., N.H., N.J., N.Y., N.C., Ohio, Okla., Pa., R.I., S.C., Tenn., Tex., Va., W.Va.

Variety *marilandicum* was last documented in Ontario in 1903 and is now considered extirpated.

16b. Desmodium marilandicum (Linnaeus) de Candolle var. **ciliare** (Muhlenberg ex Willdenow) H. Ohashi, J. Jap. Bot. 88: 169. 2013

Hedysarum ciliare Muhlenberg ex Willdenow, Sp. Pl. 3: 1196. 1802; *Desmodium ciliare* (Muhlenberg ex Willdenow) de Candolle; *D. rhombifolium* (Elliott) de Candolle; *Meibomia ciliaris* (Muhlenberg ex Willdenow) S. F. Blake; *M. rhombifolia* (Elliott) Vail

Stems uncinate-puberulent and patent long-pilose. **Leaves:** petiole 1–15 mm, uncinate-puberulent and patent long-pilose; terminal leaflet blade elliptic, ovate, or ovate-rhombic, 9–40 × 6–17 mm, apex obtuse. **Pedicels** 3–8 mm.

Flowering summer–fall. Dry, open woodlands or savannas, clearings, abandoned fields, roadsides; 0–900 m; Ala., Ark., Conn., Del., D.C., Fla., Ga., Ill., Ind., Kans., Ky., La., Md., Mass., Mich., Miss., Mo., N.J., N.Y., N.C., Ohio, Okla., Pa., R.I., S.C., Tenn., Tex., Va., W.Va.; West Indies (Cuba, Hispaniola).

Variety *ciliare* was last documented in Ontario in 1891, and is now considered extirpated there.

16c. Desmodium marilandicum (Linnaeus) de Candolle var. **lancifolium** (Fernald & B. G. Schubert) H. Ohashi, J. Jap. Bot. 88: 169. 2013 [E]

Desmodium ciliare (Muhlenberg ex Willdenow) de Candolle var. *lancifolium* Fernald & B. G. Schubert, Rhodora 40: 437, plate 523. 1938; *D. obtusum* (Muhlenberg ex Willdenow) de Candolle; *D. rigidum* (Elliott) de Candolle; *Hedysarum obtusum* Muhlenberg ex Willdenow; *H. rigidum* Elliott; *Meibomia obtusa* (Muhlenberg ex Willdenow) Vail; *M. rigida* (Elliott) Kuntze

Stems sparsely to densely uncinate-puberulent. **Leaves:** petiole 2–20 mm, sparsely to densely uncinate-puberulent; terminal leaflet blade elliptic-ovate to narrowly ovate, 50–75 × 20–33 mm, apex acute to obtuse. **Pedicels** 4–10 mm.

Flowering late summer–fall. Open, often sterile, woodlands, along streams, roadsides; 0–900 m; Ala., Ark., Conn., Del., D.C., Fla., Ga., Ill., Ind., Kans., Ky., La., Md., Mass., Mich., Miss., Mo., N.H., N.J., N.Y., N.C., Ohio, Okla., Pa., R.I., S.C., Tenn., Tex., Va., W.Va.

Variety *lancifolium* is presumed extirpated from Colorado.

17. Desmodium metcalfei (Rose & Painter) Kearney & Peebles, J. Wash. Acad. Sci. 29: 485. 1939

Meibomia metcalfei Rose & J. H. Painter, Bot. Gaz. 40: 144. 1905 (as metcalfii)

Herbs, perennial. **Stems** erect or ascending, usually striate, angled, 30–90 cm, densely uncinate-puberulent. **Leaves** trifoliolate; stipules caducous, linear-lanceolate, 1–4 mm; petiole 3–13 mm; leaflet blades somewhat paler abaxially, narrowly ovate-oblong, lateral slightly smaller than terminal, apex acute, lateral veins looped within margin, margins revolute, surfaces strigulose; terminal blade 30–80 × 6–20 mm, length 3–5 times width. **Inflorescences** branched or unbranched; rachis densely uncinate-puberulent; primary bracts caducous, broadly deltate, 6 mm. **Pedicels** 7–10 mm. **Flowers:** calyx 4 mm, glabrous, tube 1.5–2 mm; abaxial lobes 2 mm, lateral lobes 1.5–2 mm; corolla purple, 10–12 mm. **Loments:** sutures ± deeply crenate abaxially, crenate adaxially; connections slightly adaxial, ½ as broad as segments, sometimes contorted (twisted); segments 2–5, elliptic, 5–6 × 3 mm, rounded abaxially, slightly rounded adaxially, uncinate-pubescent throughout; stipe 1–2 mm.

Flowering summer–fall. Rocky slopes, canyons, ditches; 1400–2000 m; Ariz., N.Mex.; Mexico (Sinaloa).

In the flora area, *Desmodium metcalfei* is known from Coconino and Yavapai counties in central Arizona, and from southwestern New Mexico.

18. Desmodium nuttallii (Schindler) B. G. Schubert, Rhodora 52: 142. 1950 [E] [F]

Meibomia nuttallii Schindler, Repert. Spec. Nov. Regni Veg. 23: 354. 1927

Herbs or subshrubs, perennial. **Stems** ascending to erect, 30–100 cm, medially villous, uncinate-puberulent and -pubescent, scarcely pilose. **Leaves** trifoliolate; stipules persistent, narrowly ovate or ovate, 3–6.5 mm; petiole 5–30 mm; leaflet blades ovate to narrowly ovate, base usually rounded, apex obtuse or acute, surfaces closely spreading-villous (often velvety) abaxially, slightly uncinate-puberulent on veins adaxially; terminal blade 50–100 × 30–56 mm, length 1.5–2(–2.2) times width. **Inflorescences** terminal and branched; rachis patent uncinate-puberulent and pilose; primary bracts ovate, 2–4 mm, usually villous. **Pedicels** 4–10 mm. **Flowers:** calyx 2–3 mm, puberulent and sparsely pilose, tube

1 mm; abaxial lobes 1.5–2 mm, lateral lobes 1 mm; corolla purple or pink, 6–7 mm. **Loments:** sutures deeply crenate abaxially, sinuate adaxially; connections adaxial, ¼–⅓ as broad as segments; segments 2–4, semiorbiculate, 4–7 × 3–4.5 mm, rounded abaxially, convex adaxially, often somewhat angled when young, uncinate-pubescent throughout; stipe 3–4 mm.

Flowering summer–fall. Open woodlands and borders, savannas, fields, roadsides; 0–900 m; Ala., Ark., Del., Fla., Ga., Ill., Ind., Ky., La., Md., Miss., Mo., N.J., N.Y., N.C., Ohio, Okla., Pa., S.C., Tenn., Tex., Va., W.Va.

19. Desmodium ochroleucum M. A. Curtis ex Canby, Proc. Acad. Nat. Sci. Philadelphia 16: 17. 1864 [C] [E]

Meibomia ochroleuca (M. A. Curtis ex Canby) Kuntze

Herbs, perennial. **Stems** decumbent or prostrate, 50–100 cm, patent-villous and uncinate-puberulent. **Leaves** usually trifoliolate, rarely unifoliolate; stipules persistent, reflexed in age, deltate or ovate, 5–12 mm, base obliquely cordate, subamplexicaul; petiole 10–35 mm; leaflet blades ovate, ± leathery, apex obtuse or sometimes acute, surfaces prominently reticulate-veined adaxially, uncinate-puberulent on veins or glabrescent abaxially, uncinate-puberulent adaxially; terminal blade 30–75 × 22–53 mm, length 1.2–2 times width. **Inflorescences** ascending to erect, axillary distally and unbranched, sometimes also terminal and branched; rachis pilose and uncinate-puberulent; primary bracts caducous, broadly ovate, 5–6 mm. **Pedicels** 10–20 mm. **Flowers:** calyx 3–4 mm, pilose and uncinate-puberulent, tube 1 mm; abaxial lobes 3 mm, lateral lobes 1.2–1.5 mm, to 2.5 mm in fruit; corolla white or ochroleucous, 7–8 mm. **Loments:** sutures deeply crenate abaxially, crenate adaxially, contorted by irregular folding of margins near or at connection between segments; connections adaxial, ⅕–¼ as broad as segments; segments 3–5, suborbiculate to subrhombic, 7–10 × 5–8 mm, symmetrically rounded abaxially, convex adaxially, glabrous, sutures uncinate-pubescent; stipe 0 mm (or indistinctly stipitate by narrowing proximal segment).

Flowering summer–fall. Open woodland, roadsides; of conservation concern; 30–500 m; Ala., Del., D.C., Fla., Ga., Md., Miss., Mo., N.J., N.C., Tenn., Va.

The range of *Desmodium ochroleucum* is highly fragmented, and only about a dozen populations are known. Fire suppression may have been responsible for closing the canopy in forests in which *D. ochroleucum* is usually found (R. W. Tyndall and P. L. Groller 2006).

20. Desmodium paniculatum (Linnaeus) de Candolle in A. P. de Candolle and A. L. P. P. de Candolle, Prodr. 2: 329. 1825 [E]

Hedysarum paniculatum Linnaeus, Sp. Pl. 2: 749. 1753; *Meibomia paniculata* (Linnaeus) Kuntze

Herbs, perennial; base woody, rootstock thick. **Stems** erect or ascending, usually striate, 30–100(–150) cm, glabrous or sparsely to densely uncinate-puberulent or conspicuously pilose or glabrescent. **Leaves** trifoliolate; stipules caducous, subulate to narrowly ovate-deltate, 2–6 mm; petiole (10–)20–50 mm; leaflet blades polymorphic, linear, narrowly ovate, narrowly ovate-oblong, ovate, broadly ovate to subrounded, or rhombic, usually thin, rarely thick, papery, apex acute to obtuse, surfaces closely to subdensely appressed pilose, inconspicuously reticulate-veined abaxially, sparsely appressed-puberulent and pilose adaxially; terminal blade 20–100 × 8–65 mm, length 1–8 times width. **Inflorescences** terminal panicles and axillary racemes, branched, very diffuse; rachis moderately to densely uncinate-puberulent to -pubescent; primary bracts narrowly ovate, 1–3.5 mm. **Pedicels** (3–)6–12(–20) mm. **Flowers:** calyx 2–3 mm, pubescent, tube 1–1.5 mm; abaxial lobes 2 mm, lateral lobes 1 mm; corolla lilac to purple, 6–9 mm. **Loments:** sutures deeply crenate or dentate abaxially, sinuate adaxially; connections adaxial, ⅕–⅓ as broad as segments; segments (2 or)3–5, deltate to rhombic, (4–)5–10 × 3–5 mm, angled abaxially (sometimes obtusely), convex adaxially, uncinate-puberulent to -pubescent; stipe 1–7 mm. $2n = 22$.

Varieties 2 (2 in the flora): North America; introduced in e Asia (Japan).

Desmodium paniculatum is allied with *D. fernaldii*, *D. glabellum*, and *D. perplexum*, and the four are called the *D. paniculatum* Group, which is characterized by having straight loments with 3–5 angled segments. These species have been studied intensively by B. G. Schubert (1950, 1950b) and D. Isely (1953, 1983b, 1990, 1998). According to Isely (1990, 1998), *D. paniculatum* intergrades with both *D. perplexum* and *D. glabellum*, resulting in a continuum of variation among the members of the *D. paniculatum* Group that suggests introgression, including: *D. paniculatum* × *D. perplexum*; *D. paniculatum* × *D. glabellum*; and *D. glabellum* × *D. perplexum*. They are treated here as varieties of a single polymorphic species. The varieties are distinguished by somewhat continuous or overlapping characters.

1. Leaflet blade surfaces slightly strigose to conspicuously subappressed-villous, sometimes uncinate-pubescent abaxially; stems and petioles glabrescent to conspicuously pilose or uncinate-pubescent . . . . 20a. *Desmodium paniculatum* var. *paniculatum*
1. Leaflet blade surfaces uncinate-puberulent on veins, sparsely strigulose abaxially; stems and petioles glabrous or uncinate-pubescent . . . . 20b. *Desmodium paniculatum* var. *fernaldii*

20a. Desmodium paniculatum (Linnaeus) de Candolle var. **paniculatum** E

Desmodium dichromum Shinners; *D. dillenii* Darlington; *D. glabellum* (Michaux) de Candolle; *D. paniculatum* var. *angustifolium* Torrey & A. Gray; *D. paniculatum* var. *dillenii* (Darlington) Isely; *D. paniculatum* var. *epetiolatum* B. G. Schubert; *D. perplexum* B. G. Schubert; *D. pubens* (Torrey & A. Gray) M. J. Young; *Hedysarum glabellum* Michaux; *Meibomia chapmanii* Small; *M. dillenii* (Darlington) Kuntze; *M. glabella* (Michaux) Kuntze; *M. pubens* (Torrey & A. Gray) Rydberg

Stems and petioles glabrescent to conspicuously pilose or uncinate-pubescent. **Leaflets:** blade surfaces slightly strigose to conspicuously subappressed-villous, sometimes uncinate-pubescent abaxially.

Flowering summer–fall. Woodlands and margins, low, moist alluvial sites, dry slopes, uplands, clearings, fields, thickets, roadsides; 0–1000 m; Ont., Que.; Ala., Ark., Conn., Del., D.C., Fla., Ga., Ill., Ind., Iowa, Kans., Ky., La., Maine, Md., Mass., Mich., Miss., Mo., Nebr., N.H., N.J., N.Y., N.C., Ohio, Okla., Pa., R.I., S.C., Tenn., Tex., Vt., Va., W.Va., Wis.; introduced in e Asia (Japan).

20b. Desmodium paniculatum (Linnaeus) de Candolle var. **fernaldii** (B. G. Schubert) H. Ohashi, J. Jap. Bot. 88: 171. 2013 E

Desmodium fernaldii B. G. Schubert, Rhodora 52: 147. 1950

Stems and petioles glabrous or uncinate-pubescent. **Leaflets:** blade surfaces uncinate-puberulent on veins, sparsely strigulose abaxially.

Flowering late summer–fall. Open woodland, pine savannas, abandoned fields, roadsides, sandy soils; 0–600 m; Ala., Del., Fla., Ga., La., Md., Miss., N.C., S.C., Tex., Va.

Variety *fernaldii* occurs primarily on the Atlantic Coastal Plain with only scattered occurrences along the Gulf Coast.

21. Desmodium procumbens (Miller) Hitchcock, Rep. (Annual) Missouri Bot. Gard. 4: 76. 1893 F

Hedysarum procumbens Miller, Gard. Dict. ed. 8, Hedysarum no. 10. 1768; *Meibomia procumbens* (Miller) Britton

Herbs, annual or perennial, often diminutive. **Stems** erect or procumbent, usually striate, usually unbranched, sometimes branched, 10–40(–150) cm, uncinate-puberulent and sparsely pubescent or glabrescent. **Leaves** trifoliolate, usually unifoliolate proximally and/or distally; stipules persistent, patent or deflexed, subulate to narrowly ovate-deltate, 1–7 mm; petiole 10–35 mm; leaflet blades polymorphic between proximal and/or distal ones and median ones in a single individual, linear, narrowly to broadly ovate, rhombic or transversely ovate, lateral leaflets nearly as large as terminal, apex acute to acuminate or obtuse, surfaces uncinate-puberulent and villous; terminal blade 25–50 × 6–10 mm, length 0.8–10 times width; unifoliolate blades transversely elliptic or depressed ovate, 10 × 15–20 mm, or ovate or oblong to broadly ovate, 2–4 × 2–3 mm. **Inflorescences** branched or unbranched; rachis densely patent uncinate-puberulent; primary bracts caducous or persistent, narrowly ovate, 1.5–5.5 mm. **Pedicels** 6–23 mm. **Flowers:** calyx 2–3 mm, scabrous, often glandular, tube 1 mm; abaxial lobes 1.5–2 mm, lateral lobes 1.3–1.5 mm; corolla ephemeral, pinkish or rose-violet, fading yellow-green or blue-green, 2.5–3.5 mm. **Loments:** margins involute, sutures subequally crenate, contorted or appearing spirally twisted when young; connections central, 1/4–1/5 as broad as segments; segments (1 or)2–5, rhombic, 2–4 × 2–3 mm, angled abaxially, sometimes rounded, obtusely angled adaxially, uncinate-puberulent throughout; stipe 0.3–3.5 mm.

Varieties 5 (2 in the flora): United States, Mexico, West Indies, Central America, n South America; introduced in Asia, Africa.

Desmodium procumbens was characterized by B. G. Schubert (1940, 1980) and R. McVaugh (1987) as an erect or procumbent annual species. It was grouped by D. Isely (1998) with *D. neomexicanum* A. Gray and *D. rosei* B. G. Schubert in the *D. procumbens* Group. *Desmodium neomexicanum* is united with *D. procumbens* in having twisted loments and is here recognized at the rank of variety.

1. Loments distinctly spirally twisted when young, stipes 1.5–3.5 mm; primary bracts 1.5–2.5 mm; leaves unifoliolate and trifoliolate . . . . 21a. *Desmodium procumbens* var. *procumbens*
1. Loments slightly spirally twisted, stipes 0.3–2 mm; primary bracts 2.5–5.5 mm; leaves mostly trifoliolate . . . . 21b. *Desmodium procumbens* var. *neomexicanum*

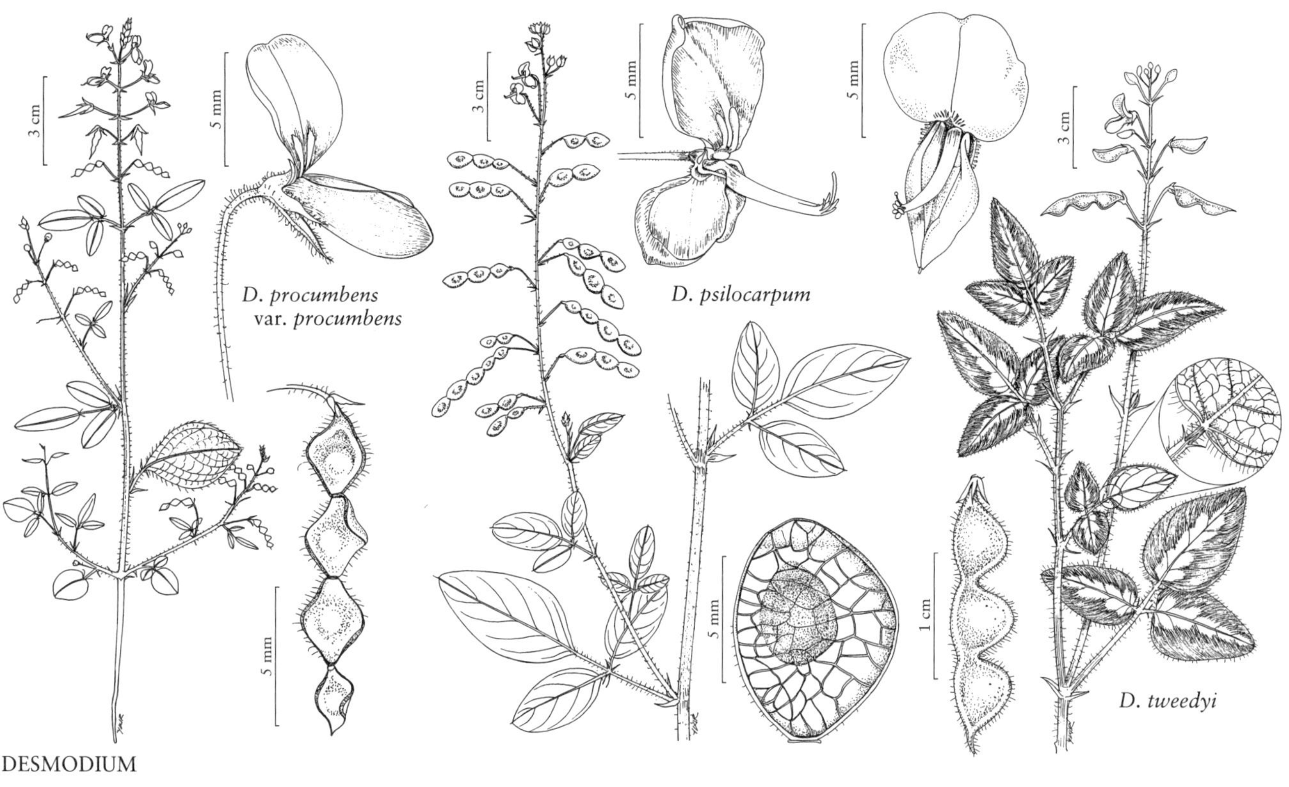

DESMODIUM

21a. Desmodium procumbens (Miller) Hitchcock var. **procumbens** [F]

Desmodium exiguum A. Gray; *D. procumbens* var. *exiguum* (A. Gray) B. G. Schubert; *D. spirale* var. *exiguum* (A. Gray) B. L. Robinson & Greenman; *Meibomia exigua* (A. Gray) Kuntze

Herbs perennial. **Stems** uncinate-puberulent and sparsely pubescent. **Leaves** unifoliolate and trifoliolate; leaflet blades: apex acute or acuminate, surfaces uncinate-puberulent and villous. **Primary bracts** caducous or partly persistent, 1.5–2.5 mm. **Loments** distinctly spirally twisted when young; segments 2–3 (–4); stipe 1.5–3.5 mm. **2*n*** = 22.

Flowering late summer–fall. Open grasslands, pine-oak woodlands, mesas, canyons; 1000–2000 m; Ariz., N.Mex.; Mexico (Chihuahua, Guerrero, Jalisco, Michoacán, Sinaloa, Sonora); West Indies; Central America; n South America; introduced in Asia, Africa.

21b. Desmodium procumbens (Miller) Hitchcock var. **neomexicanum** (A. Gray) H. Ohashi, J. Jap. Bot. 88: 174. 2013

Desmodium neomexicanum A. Gray, Smithsonian Contr. Knowl. 3(5): 53. 1852 (as neo-mexicanum)

Herbs annual. **Stems** sparsely uncinate-pubescent or glabrescent. **Leaves** mostly trifoliolate; leaflet blades: apex obtuse, surfaces uncinate-puberulent. **Primary bracts** usually persistent, 2.5–5.5 mm. **Loments** slightly spirally twisted; segments (1 or)2–5; stipe 0.3–2 mm. **2*n*** = 22.

Flowering late summer–fall. Mountain slopes, mesas, streamsides, grasslands, pinyon-juniper woodlands; 1100–2100 m; Ariz., N.Mex., Tex.; Mexico (Baja California, Chihuahua, Coahuila, Durango, Guanajuato, México, Sinaloa, Sonora, Zacatecas); Central America; n South America; introduced in Asia.

In Texas, var. *neomexicanum* is known from the trans-Pecos region.

22. Desmodium psilocarpum A. Gray, Smithsonian Contr. Knowl. 5(6): 48. 1853 [F]

Meibomia psilocarpa (A. Gray) Kuntze

Herbs or shrubs, perennial. **Stems** erect or ascending, branched, 40–100 cm, slightly uncinate-pubescent and pilose or glabrescent. **Leaves** trifoliolate; stipules mostly persistent, broadly ovate, 4–10 mm, base subamplexicaul; petiole 30–40 mm; leaflet blades broadly ovate-elliptic or ovate to narrowly ovate, apex acute, surfaces uncinate-puberulent; terminal blade 20–70(–100) × 10–20(–50) mm, length 1.8–2 times width. **Inflorescences** branched or unbranched; rachis bulbous-villous and uncinate-puberulent; primary bracts caducous, subulate, 1 mm. **Pedicels** 10–20 mm, patent uncinate-pubescent. **Flowers:** calyx 1.5–2 mm, pilose and uncinate-puberulent, tube 0.8 mm; abaxial lobes 1 mm, lateral lobes 0.8–1 mm; corolla pink-purple, fading greenish, 4–5 mm. **Loments:** sutures subequally deeply crenate; connections central, 1/8–1/7 as broad as segments; segments 3–6, rounded, 6–10 × 5–7 mm, rounded, sparsely pubescent, at least on sutures; stipe 1(–2) mm.

Flowering late summer–fall. Woodland, grasslands, canyon slopes, streamsides; 1000–2000 m; Ariz., N.Mex.; Mexico (Chihuahua, Nuevo León, Sonora, Tamaulipas).

Desmodium psilocarpum is known in the flora area from southern Arizona and adjacent southwestern New Mexico.

23. Desmodium psilophyllum Schlechtendal, Linnaea 12: 310. 1838

Meibomia psilophylla (Schlechtendal) Kuntze

Herbs, perennial. **Stems** ascending to erect, branched, 30–80 cm, inconspicuously uncinate-puberulent or glabrescent. **Leaves** unifoliolate; stipules ± persistent, narrowly ovate-deltate, 3–3.5 mm; petiole 6–11 mm; leaflet blades ovate to narrowly ovate, 30–80 × 10–30 mm, length (2–)2.5–5 times width, apex acute or obtuse, with paler patches along midrib adaxially, surfaces uncinate-puberulent and villous. **Inflorescences** often numerous, slender and flexuous, branched or unbranched; rachis densely uncinate-puberulent and villous; primary bracts narrowly ovate, 1–2 mm. **Pedicels** 4–10 mm. **Flowers:** calyx 2.5–3 mm, puberulent and sparsely pilose, tube 1 mm; abaxial lobes 2–3 mm, lateral lobes 2 mm, adaxial connate nearly to apex; corolla pink to purple, 4–5 mm. **Loments:** margins slightly involute when young, sutures crenate abaxially, sinuate adaxially; connections adaxial, 1/5 as broad as segments; segments 3–5, elliptic to obovate, 2.5–6 × 3–3.5 mm, rounded abaxially, convex adaxially, sparsely uncinate-puberulent, sutures glabrous; stipe 1.5–2.5 mm. 2*n* = 22.

Flowering summer–fall. Mountain woodlands, creek beds, terraces; 1000–2200 m; Ariz., Tex.; Mexico (Baja California Sur, Chiapas, Chihuahua, Coahuila, Durango, Hidalgo, Puebla, San Luis Potosí, Sinaloa, Sonora, Zacatecas).

Desmodium psilophyllum is known in the flora area from southern Arizona to western and central Texas at the edge of Edwards Plateau; it is not known from New Mexico.

24. Desmodium retinens Schlechtendal, Linnaea 12: 311. 1838

Desmodium wislizeni Engelmann ex A. Gray; *Meibomia retinens* (Schlechtendal) Kuntze

Herbs, perennial, diffuse; base woody, rootstock woody. **Stems** erect, ascending, or procumbent, usually striate, 30–60(–100) cm, sparsely to densely pilose and uncinate-pubescent. **Leaves** trifoliolate, sometimes unifoliolate proximally; stipules persistent, recurved, subulate, 2–3 mm; petiole 7–25 mm; leaflet blades usually oblong-ovate to narrowly so, sometimes broadly elliptic to oblong, apex obtuse or acute, surfaces sparsely uncinate-puberulent; terminal blade 10–30(–35) × 8–10 mm, length 1–3.5 times width. **Inflorescences** usually unbranched, sometimes branched; rachis patent uncinate-puberulent; primary bracts narrowly ovate, 2.5–3 mm. **Pedicels** 8–15 mm. **Flowers:** calyx 1.5–2.5 mm, pubescent, tube 1 mm; abaxial lobes 1.5 mm, lateral lobes 1 mm; corolla pink-purple, 4–5 mm. **Loments:** sutures subequally crenate; connections central, 1/5–1/4 as broad as segments; segments 2–7, rounded or broadly elliptic, 2.5–3 × 2.5 mm, abaxially and adaxially rounded, glabrous or slightly puberulent; stipe 1–2 mm.

Flowering late summer–fall. Wooded or grassy rocky slopes, oak or oak-pine forests; 1400–2100 m; Ariz.; Mexico; Central America (Guatemala).

Desmodium retinens is known in the flora area from Cochise, Graham, Pima, and Santa Cruz counties.

25. Desmodium rosei B. G. Schubert, Contr. Gray Herb. 129: 22, plate 1, fig. A. 1940

Herbs, annual; with slender taproot. **Stems** erect, usually striate, 10–50 cm, obscurely uncinate-puberulent or glabrescent. **Leaves** trifoliolate; stipules persistent, patent, subulate or narrowly deltate (from broad base), 2–3 mm; petiole 10–35 mm; leaflet blades linear to narrowly oblong, apex obtuse, surfaces sparsely uncinate-puberulent; terminal blade 20–70 × 2–5 mm, length 7+ times width. **Inflorescences** usually unbranched; rachis sparsely patent uncinate-puberulent; primary bracts usually persistent, subulate, patent, 1.5–4 mm. **Pedicels** 15–20(–25) mm. **Flowers:** calyx 1 mm, sparsely puberulent, tube 0.8–1 mm; abaxial lobes 1 mm, lateral lobes 1 mm; corolla pink or pink-purple, 3–3.5 mm. **Loments:** margins sometimes slightly involute, sutures equally crenate; connections central, 1/5 as broad as segments; segments 2–4, rounded, 3–3.5 × 3 mm, rounded abaxially and adaxially, inconspicuously reticulate, glabrous; stipe 1–1.5 mm.

Flowering late summer–fall. Dry, open woodlands, with yucca, desert shrubs, grasslands, pinyon-juniper woodlands, on ledges; 1000–2400 m; Ariz., N.Mex.; Mexico (Chihuahua, Sonora, Zacatecas).

Desmodium rosei is known in the flora area from southeastern Arizona and southwestern New Mexico.

26. Desmodium rotundifolium de Candolle in A. P. de Candolle and A. L. P. P. de Candolle, Prodr. 2: 330. 1825 [E]

Hedysarum rotundifolium Michaux, Fl. Bor.-Amer. 2: 72. 1803, not Vahl 1791; *Desmodium rotundifolium* var. *glabratum* A. Gray; *Meibomia rotundifolia* (de Candolle) Kuntze

Herbs, perennial. **Stems** prostrate, (50–)100–200(–300) cm, villous and uncinate-puberulent. **Leaves** trifoliolate; stipules mostly persistent, reflexed, broadly ovate, 5–12 mm, base obliquely cordate, subamplexicaul; petiole 2–4.6 mm; leaflet blades transversely elliptic, orbiculate, or broadly ovate, apex emarginate, retuse, rounded, or obtuse, surfaces densely spreading-villous abaxially, appressed-villous adaxially; terminal blade 20–60 × 25–55 mm, length 0.8–1.2 times width. **Inflorescences** terminal or axillary and erect, usually unbranched, rarely branched; rachis shortly hirsute or sparsely uncinate-puberulent; primary bracts broadly ovate, 5–6 mm. **Pedicels** (5–)10–15 mm. **Flowers:** calyx (4–)5–6 mm, uncinate-puberulent and sparsely pilose, tube 1.5 mm; abaxial lobes 3–5 mm, lateral lobes 3.5–4.5 mm; corolla pink, fading blue-purple, 9–11 mm. **Loments:** sutures deeply crenate abaxially, crenate adaxially; connections adaxial, 1/6–1/4 as broad as segments; segments 3–6(or 7), subrhombic to elliptic, 4.5–7.5 × 4–5 mm, reticulate, obtusely angled abaxially, convex adaxially, uncinate-puberulent throughout; stipe 3–6 mm. $2n = 22$.

Flowering summer–fall. Open woodlands, bottoms of steep uplands, borders, recently cleared areas, ruderal sites; 0–1000 m; Ont.; Ala., Ark., Conn., Del., D.C., Fla., Ga., Ill., Ind., Kans., Ky., La., Md., Mass., Mich., Miss., Mo., N.H., N.J., N.Y., N.C., Ohio, Okla., Pa., R.I., S.C., Tenn., Tex., Vt., Va., W.Va.

Desmodium rotundifolium, with relatively small leaflets, resembles 15. *D. lineatum*, which has loments with 2–4 segments and uncinate stem hairs (D. Isely 1998).

27. Desmodium scopulorum S. Watson, Proc. Amer. Acad. Arts 24: 47. 1889

Desmodium wigginsii B. G. Schubert; *Meibomia scopulorum* (S. Watson) Rose & Standley

Herbs, annual. **Stems** erect or ascending, usually striate, branched, 10–80 cm, pubescent. **Leaves** trifoliolate; stipules caducous, narrowly deltate to subulate, 3–4 mm; petiole 10–40 mm; leaflet blades narrowly ovate to ovate, apex acute to acuminate, surfaces densely uncinate-puberulent and pilose abaxially, uncinate-puberulent and pilose adaxially; terminal blade 20–100 × 7–25 mm, length 4–8 or 2–3 times width. **Inflorescences** branched or unbranched; rachis uncinate-puberulent; primary bracts narrowly ovate, 1.4–2.6 mm. **Pedicels** 5–15 mm. **Flowers:** calyx 1–1.5 mm, puberulent, tube 0.5 mm; abaxial lobes 1–1.5 mm, lateral lobes longer than tube; corolla pink, drying greenish yellow, 3–4 mm. **Loments:** sutures subequally incised, spirally arranged between young segments when young; connections adaxial, 1/8 as broad as segments; segments 2–4, proximal segments subrhombic, 4–6 × 2.5–3.5 mm, irregularly involute, uncinate-pubescent, distal segment semiorbiculate or broadly deltate, much larger than proximal segments, not contorted, 7–10 × 4–5 mm, glabrous, sutures uncinate-puberulent; stipe 1 mm.

Flowering fall. Open grassy slopes, oak-pine woodlands; 800–1800 m; Ariz.; Mexico (Baja California Sur, Sinaloa, Sonora).

In the flora area, *Desmodium scopulorum* is known from Pima and Santa Cruz counties.

28. Desmodium scorpiurus (Swartz) Poiret in F. Cuvier, Dict. Sci. Nat. ed. 2, 13: 110. 1819 [I]

Hedysarum scorpiurus Swartz, Prodr., 107. 1788; *Meibomia scorpiurus* (Swartz) Kuntze

Herbs, perennial. **Stems** slender, procumbent or decumbent, 20–100 cm, densely patent uncinate-puberulent and/or inconspicuously pilose. **Leaves** trifoliolate; stipules persistent, obliquely ovate, 2–3.5 mm, base auriculate, amplexicaul; petiole 10–20 mm; leaflet blades usually ovate to shortly elliptic, rarely narrowly elliptic, apex obtuse, surfaces appressed-pubescent; terminal blade usually 10–35(–50) × 7–30 mm, length (1.5–)2–3 times width. **Inflorescences** lax-flowered, terminal and axillary, usually unbranched; rachis densely spreading-pubescent; primary bracts caducous, narrowly ovate, 1.5–2 mm. **Pedicels** 3–10 mm. **Flowers:** calyx 1.5–2.5 mm, pilose, tube 1 mm; abaxial lobes 1.5 mm, lateral lobes 0.7–1 mm; corolla lavender-pink or reddish purple, banner with yellow spots, 4–5 mm. **Loments** turgid, straight or curved, linear; sutures equally shallow-undulate; connections central, ⅔–¾ as broad as segments; segments 5–10, narrowly oblong or narrowly elliptic, 4–5 × 1.5 mm, rugose, not reticulate, symmetrically convex abaxially and adaxially, densely uncinate-pubescent throughout; stipe 1 mm.

Flowering year-round. Waste places, lawns; 0–10 m; introduced; Fla.; Mexico (Durango, Guerrero, Guanajuato, Jalisco, Michoacán, Oaxaca, Sonora, Veracruz); West Indies; Central America; South America; introduced also in Asia, Africa, Pacific Islands, Australia.

29. Desmodium sessilifolium Torrey & A. Gray, Fl. N. Amer. 1: 363. 1840 [E] [W]

Meibomia sessilifolia (Torrey & A. Gray) Kuntze

Herbs, perennial; base woody, rootstock thick, woody. **Stems** ascending to erect, usually striate, mostly unbranched, 50–100 (–150) cm, medially uncinate-puberulent and uncinate-pubescent. **Leaves** trifoliolate; stipules moderately persistent, narrowly ovate, 4–9.5 mm, apex often awn-tipped; petiole 1–5 mm; leaflet blades narrowly elliptic to linear, apex obtuse or acute, surfaces prominently reticulate-veined abaxially, uncinate-puberulent and subappressed pubescent abaxially, glabrate or sparsely pubescent adaxially; terminal blade (30–)40–85 × 5–15 mm, length 4–10 times width. **Inflorescences** terminal and branched; rachis terete to subangulate, densely uncinate-puberulent and sparsely pilose; primary bracts ovate, 2.5–3 mm. **Pedicels** 2–5 mm. **Flowers:** calyx 2.5–3 mm, puberulent, tube 1.5 mm; abaxial lobes ovate, 1.5 mm, lateral lobes ovate, 1 mm; corolla pale lavender to reddish purple, 5 mm. **Loments:** sutures deeply crenate abaxially, sinuate adaxially; connections adaxial, ⅓ as broad as segments; segments (1 or)2(–4), semiorbiculate, 4.5–6 × 3–4.5 mm, symmetrically rounded abaxially, nearly straight or convex adaxially, densely uncinate-puberulent throughout; stipe 1–3 mm. $2n = 22$.

Flowering summer–fall. Open, dry upland woods, abandoned fields, roadsides; 0–500 m; Ala., Ark., Conn., Fla., Ga., Ill., Ind., Iowa, Kans., Ky., La., Md., Mass., Mich., Miss., Mo., Nebr., N.J., N.C., Ohio, Okla., Pa., R.I., S.C., Tenn., Tex., Va.

Desmodium sessilifolium is considered extirpated from Ontario.

30. Desmodium strictum (Pursh) de Candolle in A. P. de Candolle and A. L. P. P. de Candolle, Prodr. 2: 329. 1825 [E]

Hedysarum strictum Pursh, Fl. Amer. Sept. 2: 483. 1813; *Meibomia stricta* (Pursh) Kuntze

Herbs, perennial. **Stems** ascending or erect, usually striate, unbranched to inflorescence, 50–100 cm, uncinate-puberulent. **Leaves** trifoliolate; stipules mostly persistent, linear to narrowly ovate-deltate, 2–5 mm; petiole 6.5–18 mm; leaflet blades linear to narrowly oblong, usually folded and appearing narrower, leathery, apex obtuse to acute, surfaces reticulate-veined adaxially, glabrous or sparsely puberulent abaxially, glabrous adaxially; terminal blade 35–60(–80) × 4–7 mm, length 8–10 times width. **Inflorescences** branched or unbranched; rachis densely uncinate-puberulent to pubescent; primary bracts narrowly lanceolate-triangular, 1.4–2 mm. **Pedicels** 5–13 mm. **Flowers:** calyx 2.5–3.5 mm, uncinate-puberulent to pubescent on lobes, tube 1 mm; abaxial lobes 2–2.5 mm, lateral lobes 1.5–2 mm; corolla pink or purple, 4 mm. **Loments:** sutures deeply crenate abaxially, with narrow connection between segments, nearly straight adaxially, slightly sinuate at isthmus; connections adaxial, ⅕ as broad as segments; segments 1 or 2(or 3), semiorbiculate, 4.5–6 × 3–4 mm, symmetrically rounded abaxially, incipiently or plainly concave adaxially, densely uncinate-puberulent, more densely on sutures; stipe 1.5 mm. $2n = 22$.

Flowering late summer–fall. Dry woodland, barren sandhills, ruderal areas; 0–500 m; Ala., Del., D.C., Fla., Ga., La., Md., Miss., Mo., N.J., N.C., Okla., S.C., Tex., Va.

Desmodium strictum is mostly restricted to dry, sandy soils along the Atlantic and Gulf coasts. Because of the close similarities between *D. strictum* and *D. tenuifolium*, mature fruits are necessary to distinguish the two species.

31. Desmodium tenuifolium Torrey & A. Gray, Fl. N. Amer. 1: 363. 1840 [E]

Meibomia tenuifolia (Torrey & A. Gray) Kuntze

Herbs, perennial. **Stems** ascending or erect, 50–100 cm, inconspicuously uncinate-puberulent. **Leaves** trifoliolate; stipules caducous, narrowly deltate, 3 mm, glabrous; petiole 5–20 mm; leaflet blades linear, leathery, usually folded and appearing narrower, apex acute or obtuse, surfaces reticulate-veined adaxially, glabrous or sparsely puberulent abaxially, glabrous adaxially; terminal blade 30–60(–80) × 5–7 mm, length 8–10 times width. **Inflorescences** branched or unbranched; rachis uncinate-pubescent and villous; primary bracts ovate, 2.5 mm. **Pedicels** 5–10 mm. **Flowers:** calyx 1.5–2 mm, uncinate-puberulent, tube 0.8–1 mm; abaxial lobes 1 mm, lateral lobes 0.7–0.8 mm; corolla pink, 4–5 mm. **Loments:** sutures crenate abaxially, sinuate adaxially; connections adaxial, ⅓–½ as broad as segments; segments (1 or)2 or 3, semiorbiculate, 3.5–5 × 3 mm, symmetrically rounded abaxially, convex adaxially, densely uncinate-puberulent throughout; stipe 0.5–3 mm.

Flowering late summer. Moist pine savannas, grass-sedge marshes, pocosins, borders, alluvial woodlands, ditches, moist ruderal areas; 0–100 m; Ala., Fla., Ga., La., Md., Miss., N.C., S.C., Va.

32. Desmodium tortuosum (Swartz) de Candolle in A. P. de Candolle and A. L. P. P. de Candolle, Prodr. 2: 332. 1825 [I] [W]

Hedysarum tortuosum Swartz, Prodr., 107. 1788; *Meibomia purpurea* (Miller) Vail; *M. tortuosa* (Swartz) Kuntze

Herbs, perennial. **Stems** erect, 50–200 cm, medially uncinate-pubescent and patent-villous. **Leaves** trifoliolate; stipules persistent, often patent or reflexed, obliquely ovate and apex acuminate or narrowly ovate and apex aristate, 3–12.5 mm, base amplexicaul; petiole 8–50 mm; leaflet blades narrowly ovate to ovate, elliptic, or rhombic, apex obtuse or acute, surfaces obscurely prominently reticulate-veined abaxially, uncinate-puberulent and strigose or subappressed-villous; terminal blade (20–)40–150 × 10–50 mm, length 2–3 times width. **Inflorescences** branched or unbranched; rachis villous (often with bulbous hairs) and uncinate-puberulent, or only uncinate-puberulent; primary bracts caducous, narrowly ovate, 4 mm. **Pedicels** 10–15 mm. **Flowers:** calyx 1.5–3 mm, uncinate-puberulent, tube to 1 mm; abaxial lobes 2 mm, lateral lobes 1 mm; corolla lavender, 4–6 mm. **Loments:** margins alternately involute and revolute, sutures equally crenate, twisted conspicuously when young; connections central, ¼ as broad as segments; segments (3 or)4–7, orbiculate, broadly elliptic, or rhombic, 3–4.5 × 3–3.5 mm, rounded abaxially and adaxially, densely uncinate-pubescent; stipe 0.5–1 mm. 2*n* = 22.

Flowering summer–fall (year-round). Open, disturbed sites, ruderal areas, pinelands, savannas; 0–300 m; introduced; Ala., Ark., Fla., Ga., La., Miss., N.C., S.C., Tex.; Mexico (Chiapas, Colima, Guerrero, Jalisco, Nayarit, Oaxaca, Sinaloa, Sonora); West Indies; Central America; South America; introduced also in Asia, Africa, Indian Ocean Islands, Pacific Islands, Australia.

Desmodium tortuosum is most easily distinguished from its relatives by the thick leaflets with prominent reticulate venation, the large persistent stipules, and the long, stiff, ascending to spreading pedicels (B. G. Schubert 1980).

33. Desmodium triflorum (Linnaeus) de Candolle in A. P. de Candolle and A. L. P. P. de Candolle, Prodr. 2: 334. 1825 [I] [W]

Hedysarum triflorum Linnaeus, Sp. Pl. 2: 749. 1753; *Grona triflora* (Linnaeus) H. Ohashi & K. Ohashi; *Meibomia triflora* (Linnaeus) Kuntze; *Sagotia triflora* (Linnaeus) Duchassaing & Walpers

Herbs, annual or perennial, often mat-forming; stoloniferous. **Stems** prostrate, densely branched, 20–80 cm, ascending-pilose or strigose. **Leaves** trifoliolate; stipules persistent, narrowly ovate, 3–5 mm; petiole 3–7.5 mm; leaflet blades broadly obovate or cuneate-obovate, often folding downwards, apex emarginate, surfaces usually sparsely uncinate-puberulent or subappressed-pilose along midrib abaxially, rarely entire surface, glabrous adaxially; terminal blade 5–10 × 3–11 mm, length 0.8–1.2 times width. **Inflorescences** terminal fascicles opposite distal leaf, appearing axillary, unbranched; rachis pubescent; primary bracts narrowly ovate, 4 mm. **Pedicels** 8–12 mm. **Flowers:** calyx 2.5–3 mm, appressed-pubescent, tube 1.2 mm; abaxial lobes 1.5–1.7 mm, lateral lobes 1.5–1.7 mm, adaxial lobes deeply 2-toothed; corolla pale pink to purplish, 4–5 mm, keel distinctly longer than wings. **Loments:** sutures weakly crenate abaxially, with broad connection between segments, barely sinuate adaxially; connections $^2/_3$–$^4/_5$ as broad as segments; segments 3–5, nearly square, 2.5–3.5 × 2.5–3 mm, symmetrically convex abaxially, slightly concave adaxially, inconspicuously uncinate-pubescent or glabrescent; stipe 0 mm. **2*n*** = 22.

Flowering year-round. Ruderal areas, lawns, disturbed open woodlands; 0–50 m; introduced; Fla., La.; Mexico (Jalisco, Sinaloa); West Indies; Central America; South America; Asia; Africa; introduced also in Indian Ocean Islands, Pacific Islands, Australia.

Inflorescences of *Desmodium triflorum* are produced opposite the leaf at the distal end of stem and are usually described as axillary. The branching system of *D. triflorum* is a monopodial sympodium and the inflorescences are terminal (H. Ohashi and T. Nemoto 1986). Evolution of inflorescences in *Desmodium* is inferred from comparative morphology and anatomy with *Campylotropis*, *Kummerowia*, and *Lespedeza* (Nemoto and Ohashi 1990, 1993, 1996).

Based on molecular and morphological data, H. Ohashi and K. Ohashi (2018) transferred *Desmodium triflorum* and the other species formerly in *Desmodium* sects. *Nicolsonia* (de Candolle) Bentham and *Sagotia* (Duchassaing & Walpers) Bentham to the genus *Grona* Loureiro.

34. Desmodium tweedyi Britton, Trans. New York Acad. Sci. 9: 183. 1890 [E] [F]

Meibomia tweedyi (Britton) Vail

Herbs, perennial. **Stems** ascending or erect, usually striate, angled, 30–100 cm, densely uncinate-puberulent to -pubescent and sparsely glutinous-pilose. **Leaves** trifoliolate; stipules persistent, ovate, 7.5–14.5 mm; petiole 40–90 mm; leaflet blades narrowly ovate to ovate or broadly ovate, thick, leathery, apex acute, usually pale-blotched along midrib adaxially, surfaces uncinate-puberulent to -pubescent and villous; terminal blade 40–120 × 20–66 mm, length 2 times width. **Inflorescences** branched or unbranched; rachis densely uncinate-puberulent to -pubescent and glutinous-villous; primary bracts ovate to broadly ovate, 7–10 mm. **Pedicels** 8–25 mm, patent uncinate-pubescent and pilose. **Flowers:** calyx 3–5 mm, puberulent and pubescent, ± glutinous, tube 1.2–1.5 mm; abaxial lobes 2.5–4 mm, lateral lobes 1.5 mm; corolla white, 7–8 mm. **Loments:** sutures nearly equally crenate; connections adaxial, $^1/_4$ as broad as segments; segments (2 or)3–5(or 6), subrhombic, 6–8 × 4 mm, obtusely angled abaxially, somewhat angled adaxially, densely uncinate-pubescent throughout; stipe 2–4 mm.

Flowering early summer. Woodlands near creeks, usually calcareous soils; 200–800 m; Okla., Tex.

Desmodium tweedyi is known from the Edwards Plateau area and north-central Texas northward to central Oklahoma.

35. Desmodium viridiflorum (Linnaeus) de Candolle in A. P. de Candolle and A. L. P. P. de Candolle, Prodr. 2: 329. 1825 [E]

Hedysarum viridiflorum Linnaeus, Sp. Pl. 2: 748. 1753; *Meibomia viridiflora* (Linnaeus) Kuntze

Herbs or subshrubs, perennial. **Stems** erect, mostly unbranched, 30–300 cm, densely (sparsely in age) villosulous, also densely uncinate-puberulent and -pubescent. **Leaves** trifoliolate; stipules caducous, narrowly ovate to ovate, 3–7 mm; petiole 15–40 mm; leaflet blades broadly ovate or broadly rhombic, base acute to cuneate or truncate, apex acute to acuminate, surfaces densely velvety or villous, especially on veins abaxially, uncinate-puberulent and obscurely strigose on veins adaxially; terminal blade 50–120(–150) × 35–90 mm, length 1–1.5(–2) times width. **Inflorescences** branched or unbranched; rachis uncinate-pubescent and sparsely villous; primary bracts narrowly deltate, 3 mm, pilose. **Pedicels** 3–9 mm. **Flowers:** calyx 2–3 mm, spreading-pilose, tube 2 mm; abaxial lobes 2.5–4.5 mm, lateral lobes 2–4 mm; corolla purple to pink or pallid lavender, 7–8 mm. **Loments:** sutures subdentate abaxially, sinuate adaxially; connections adaxial, $^1/_3$–$^1/_2$ as broad as segments; segments (3 or)4 or 5, rhombic, 5–8(–9) × 3–3.5 mm, symmetrically angled abaxially, straight or convex adaxially, moderately to densely uncinate-puberulent throughout; stipe 3–6 mm. **2*n*** = 22.

Flowering summer–fall. Open, often cutover woodlands and borders, old fields, roadsides; 0–900 m; Ala., Ark., Del., D.C., Fla., Ga., Ill., Ind., Ky., La., Md., Miss., Mo., N.C., Ohio, Okla., Pa., S.C., Tenn., Tex., Va., W.Va.

In Illinois, *Desmodium viridiflorum* is known only from Alexander County.

36. Desmodium ×humifusum (Muhlenberg ex Bigelow) L. C. Beck, Bot. North. Middle States, 86. 1833 (as species) C E

Hedysaum humifusum Muhlenberg ex Bigelow, Fl. Boston ed. 2, 274. 1824; *Meibomia humifusa* (Muhlenberg ex Bigelow) Kuntze

Herbs, perennial. **Stems** prostrate, 100–200(–300) cm, sparsely to densely patent-pubescent and uncinate-puberulent. **Leaves** trifoliolate; stipules often caducous, sometimes persistent, ovate or narrowly ovate, 4.5–8 mm; petiole 28–50 mm; leaflet blades ovate or rhombic-ovate, lateral veins inconspicuous, arcuate along margin, apex acute or obtuse, surfaces sparsely strigose; terminal blade 30–70 × 20–50 mm, length 1.4–2 times width. **Inflorescences** lax-flowered, ascending, terminal and branched, also axillary and unbranched; rachis uncinate-puberulent; primary bracts caducous, ovate, 3–4 mm. **Pedicels** 7–9 mm. **Flowers:** calyx 2.5–3.5 mm, uncinate-puberulent, tube 1 mm; abaxial lobes 2 mm, lateral lobes 1.5 mm; corolla purple, 8–9.5 mm. **Loments:** sutures obtusely dentate abaxially, sinuate adaxially; connections adaxial, 1/4–1/3 as broad as segments; segments 3 or 4, deltate-rhombic, 6–8 × 4–5 mm, obtusely angled abaxially, straight or slightly convex adaxially, uncinate-pubescent; stipe 2 mm.

Flowering summer–fall. Woodland openings and edges, powerline cuts, near exposed limestone; of conservation concern; 0–300 m; Conn., Del., Ind., Md., Mass., Mo., N.J., N.Y., Pa.

Desmodium ×*humifusum* had been recognized as a species, but J. A. Raveill (2002) confirmed a hybrid origin from *D. paniculatum* and *D. rotundifolium* by allozyme electrophoresis. *Desmodium* ×*humifusum* is likely to occur more widely than reported. It is in the Center for Plant Conservation's National Collection of Endangered Plants as *D. humifusum*.

110. HYLODESMUM H. Ohashi & R. R. Mill, Edinburgh J. Bot. 57: 173. 2000 • [Greek *hyle*, woodland, and genus *Desmodium*, alluding to habitat and resemblance]

Hiroyoshi Ohashi

Podocarpium (Bentham) Yen C. Yang & P. H. Huang, Bull. Bot. Lab. N. E. Forest. Inst., Harbin 4: 4. 1979, based on *Desmodium* Desvaux sect. *Podocarpium* Bentham in F. A. W. Miquel, Pl. Jungh., 226. 1852, not *Podocarpium* A. Braun ex Stizenberger (1851); *Desmodium* ser. *Americana* B. G. Schubert

Herbs, perennial, unarmed; roots ± woody, often partly subtuberous or tuberous. **Stems** ascending to erect or spreading, terete, usually pubescent, rarely glabrous. **Leaves** whorled or alternate, usually odd-pinnate, rarely unifoliolate; stipules present, usually scarious, rarely thinly papery, striate, glabrate or hairy; petiolate; leaflets usually 3, rarely 1 [5 or 7], stipels present or absent, sometimes partly or wholly, filiform, usually reduced, scarious, blade margins entire, rarely undulate, ciliate, surfaces pubescent. **Inflorescences** 2–26-flowered, terminal, sometimes also axillary, sometimes a fertile shoot separately arising from basal part of vegetative stem, pseudoracemes, sometimes in panicles, lax-flowered, branched or unbranched; bracts caducous, primary ones subtending flower cluster with secondary bracts each subtending 1 pedicel. **Pedicels** densely uncinate-puberulent or glabrous. **Flowers** papilionaceous; calyx broadly campanulate, lobes 5, usually appearing 4-lobed, adaxial pair connate except apically, with 2 minute teeth, lobes shorter than tube; corolla pink, pink-purple, or white [orange, red], banner clawed or tapering proximally, blade usually broadly obovate, often with pair of spots (false nectar guides) at base; wing and keel petals clawed, keel usually connate along abaxial margin of blade (distinct in *H. pauciflorum*); stamens 10, monadelphous; anthers dorsifixed; ovary stipitate. **Fruits** loments, distinctly stipitate, stipe exserted from calyx, greater than 5 mm, glabrous or puberulent, compressed, very deeply incised abaxially, straight or shallowly undulate adaxially, 1–4-jointed, lateral faces densely uncinate-puberulent;

segments obliquely depressed or very shallowly obovate or obtriangular; sutures glabrate, abaxial suture very deeply incised, adaxial distinctly thickened, connections between segments (isthmi) less than 1/5 as broad as pod. **Seeds** 2–5, flat, obliquely depressed-obovate, broadest 2/3 distance towards anterior end, without rim-aril around hilum; cotyledons of seedlings hypogeous, remaining underground being enclosed in loment-segment, rarely epigeous. $x = 11$.

Species ca. 11 (3 in the flora): North America, n Mexico, Asia, n Africa.

Plants of *Hylodesmum* and *Desmodium* are alike in having three-foliolate leaves and uncinate-puberulent loments that are easily separable into 1-seeded segments; *Hylodesmum* differs from *Desmodium* in having calyx lobes shorter than the tubes, monadelphous stamens, long-stipitate loments with abaxial sutures incised to the adaxial sutures, shallowly obtriangular segments, and seeds without a rim-aril around the hilum.

Phylogenetic relationships between the three North American species were illustrated in the phylogenetic trees in K. Ohashi et al. (2018b) and discussed by Li H. C. et al. (2019).

SELECTED REFERENCES Isely, D. 1951. *Desmodium*: Section *Podocarpium* Benth. Brittonia 7: 185–224. Kajita, T. and H. Ohashi. 1994. Chloroplast DNA variation in *Desmodium* subgenus *Podocarpium* (Leguminosae): Infrageneric phylogeny and infraspecific variations. J. Pl. Res. 107: 349–354. Li, H. C. et al. 2019. Molecular phylogeny of the genus *Hylodesmum* (Fabaceae). Phytotaxa 403: 221–229. Ohashi, H. and R. R. Mill. 2000. *Hylodesmum*, a new name for *Podocarpium* (Leguminosae). Edinburgh J. Bot. 57: 171–188.

1. Inflorescences usually terminal, sometimes axillary; corollas white; keel petals distinct (reproductive organs exposed); loment stipe uncinate-puberulent; stipels sometimes present . . . . 3. *Hylodesmum pauciflorum*
1. Inflorescences terminal or on peduncles from bases of plants; corollas usually pink or pink-purple, rarely white; keel petals connate along abaxial margin (enclosing reproductive organs); loment stipe glabrous or glabrate; stipels usually absent, rarely present.
   2. Inflorescences terminal; pedicels 3–8 mm, stout; terminal leaflet blades broadly ovate, apex abruptly acuminate; stipules often persistent; loment stipe 4–10 mm . . . 1. *Hylodesmum glutinosum*
   2. Inflorescences on peduncles arising from bases of plants; pedicels 10–25 mm, slender; terminal leaflet blades rhombic, elliptic, obovate, or orbiculate, apex acute or short-acuminate; stipules deciduous; loment stipe (5–)10–22 mm . . . . 2. *Hylodesmum nudiflorum*

1. Hylodesmum glutinosum (Muhlenberg ex Willdenow) H. Ohashi & R. R. Mill, Edinburgh J. Bot. 57: 177. 2000

Hedysarum glutinosum Muhlenberg ex Willdenow, Sp. Pl. 3: 1198. 1802; *Desmodium acuminatum* (Michaux) de Candolle; *D. glutinosum* (Muhlenberg ex Willdenow) Alph. Wood; *H. acuminatum* Michaux; *Meibomia acuminata* (Michaux) S. F. Blake; *M. grandiflora* (de Candolle) Kuntze var. *chandonnetii* Lunell

Stems monomorphic; erect, unbranched, 30–80 cm, sparsely to densely patent- to ascending-pilose. **Leaves** usually 3-foliolate, rarely unifoliolate, 6–8 usually whorled medially on stem, often with 1 or 2 alternate leaves proximally, sometimes scattered and alternate; stipules often persistent, subulate to narrowly ovate, 8–12 mm; petiole 6–14.5 cm; leaflets estipellate, surfaces densely pubescent abaxially, sparsely appressed-pubescent adaxially; lateral blades oblique, smaller than terminal; terminal blade broadly ovate, 5–13 × 5–14 cm, apex abruptly acuminate. **Inflorescences** terminal, unbranched or branched; rachis densely uncinate-puberulent and villous; primary bract subulate to narrowly ovate, 5–9 mm. **Pedicels** stout, 3–8 mm, uncinate-puberulent. **Flowers:** calyx 3–3.5 mm, white-puberulent, hairs scattered, long, stiff; corolla usually pink-purple, rarely white, 5–7 mm, keel connate along abaxial margin (enclosing reproductive organs). **Loments** 1–4-articulate; segments asymmetrically depressed-obovate, 7.5–11 × 4–7 mm; stipe 4–10 mm, glabrous or glabrate. $2n = 22$.

Flowering summer. Rich woodlands, north-facing slopes, open dry woods and margins; 0–800 m; N.B., N.S., Ont., Que.; Ala., Ark., Conn., Del., D.C., Fla., Ga., Ill., Ind., Iowa, Kans., Ky., La., Maine, Md., Mass., Mich., Minn., Miss., Mo., Nebr., N.H., N.J., N.Y., N.C., N.Dak., Ohio, Okla., Pa., R.I., S.C., S.Dak., Tenn., Tex., Vt., Va., W.Va., Wis.; Mexico (Nuevo León, Puebla, San Luis Potosí).

Desmodium grandiflorum de Candolle, a synonym of *D. cuspidatum*, has been widely misapplied to this species.

2. Hylodesmum nudiflorum (Linnaeus) H. Ohashi & R. R. Mill, Edinburgh J. Bot. 57: 180. 2000 [E]

Hedysarum nudiflorum Linnaeus, Sp. P1. 2: 749. 1753; *Desmodium nudiflorum* (Linnaeus) de Candolle; *Meibomia nudiflora* (Linnaeus) Kuntze

Stems dimorphic; leafy stems ascending to erect, unbranched, 10–50 cm, glabrous or sparsely pilose; leafless or nearly leafless stems essentially peduncles arising from base of plant, erect, divergent, or spreading, to 70 cm. **Leaves** 3-foliolate, 4–7 usually whorled, sometimes scattered on stem; stipules deciduous and rarely observed, linear, 2–2.5 mm; petiole 4.5–12.5 cm; leaflets usually estipellate, rarely partly stipellate, blades with sparsely pilose veins on both surfaces, sometimes glabrate adaxially; lateral blades oblique, nearly as large as terminal; terminal blade rhombic, elliptic, obovate, or orbiculate, 4.5–12 × 3–8 cm, apex acute or short-acuminate. **Inflorescences** on peduncle arising from base of plant, branched; rachis white-pilose and uncinate-puberulent; primary bract narrowly ovate to subulate, 5 mm. **Pedicels** slender, 10–25 mm, glabrous. **Flowers:** calyx 1.5–2.5 mm, white-puberulent, hairs scattered, long, stiff; corolla usually pink, rarely white, 6–9 mm, keel connate along abaxial margin (enclosing reproductive organs). **Loments** 1–4-articulate; segments asymmetrically depressed-obtriangular, 7–12 × 4–5 mm; stipe (5–)10–22 mm, glabrous or glabrate.

Flowering spring–summer(–fall). Deciduous woodlands and borders, ravines, slopes, dry open woods; 50–150 m; Ont., Que.; Ala., Ark., Conn., Del., D.C., Fla., Ga., Ill., Ind., Iowa, Kans., Ky., La., Maine, Md., Mass., Mich., Minn., Miss., Mo., N.H., N.J., N.Y., N.C., Ohio, Okla., Pa., R.I., S.C., Tenn., Tex., Vt., Va., W.Va., Wis.

Flower-bearing stems of *Hylodesmum nudiflorum* are usually leafless; occasionally one leaf will be present or, very rarely, multiple leaves. Rare plants with a whorl of leaves on flower-bearing stems most often occur after the vegetative stem has been extensively damaged; they superficially resemble *H. glutinosum* but retain the remainder of the vegetative and reproductive differences.

3. Hylodesmum pauciflorum (Nuttall) H. Ohashi & R. R. Mill, Edinburgh J. Bot. 57: 181. 2000 [E] [F]

Hedysarum pauciflorum Nuttall, Gen. N. Amer. Pl. 2: 109. 1818; *Desmodium pauciflorum* (Nuttall) de Candolle; *Meibomia pauciflora* (Nuttall) Kuntze

Stems monomorphic; ascending or spreading, branched or unbranched, 20–60 cm, uncinate-puberulent and sparsely pilose. **Leaves** 3-foliolate, usually 4–6 and alternate; stipules caducous, subulate to narrowly ovate, 1.5–5 mm, apex acute; petiole 5.5–6.5 cm; leaflets often estipellate, sometimes stipellate, surfaces appressed-pubescent; lateral blade oblique, slightly smaller than terminal; terminal blade broadly obovate to rhombic, 3–9 × 4–6.5 cm, apex acute or short-acuminate. **Inflorescences** usually terminal, mostly unbranched, sometimes axillary from distal leaf axils and relatively short; rachis white-pilose and densely uncinate-puberulent; primary bract linear to narrowly ovate, 1–4 mm. **Pedicels** stout, 2–7 mm, uncinate-puberulent. **Flowers:** calyx 1.5–1.8 mm, white-puberulent, hairs rather abundant, long, stiff; corolla white, 4.5–6.5 mm, keel distinct, not connate along abaxial margin (exposing reproductive organs). **Loments** 1 or 2(or 3)-articulate; segments asymmetrically obtriangular, 9–14 × 6–8 mm; stipe 5–9 mm, uncinate-puberulent. $2n = 22$.

Flowering summer–fall. Rich, moist woodlands, bottomlands or slopes, drier uplands; 10–300 m; Ala., Ark., Del., D.C., Fla., Ga., Ill., Ind., Kans., Ky., La., Md., Miss., Mo., N.J., N.Y., N.C., Ohio, Okla., S.C., Tenn., Tex., Va., W.Va.

Hylodesmum pauciflorum can be locally abundant in mesic woods with rich soil, although it is less common than the other two members of the genus in the flora area. The stems are initially upright and are weak; they are often bent by wind and rain as the season progresses. The absence of fusion of the keel petals is unusual for the tribe; apparently, the pollination biology of *H. pauciflorum* has never been examined.

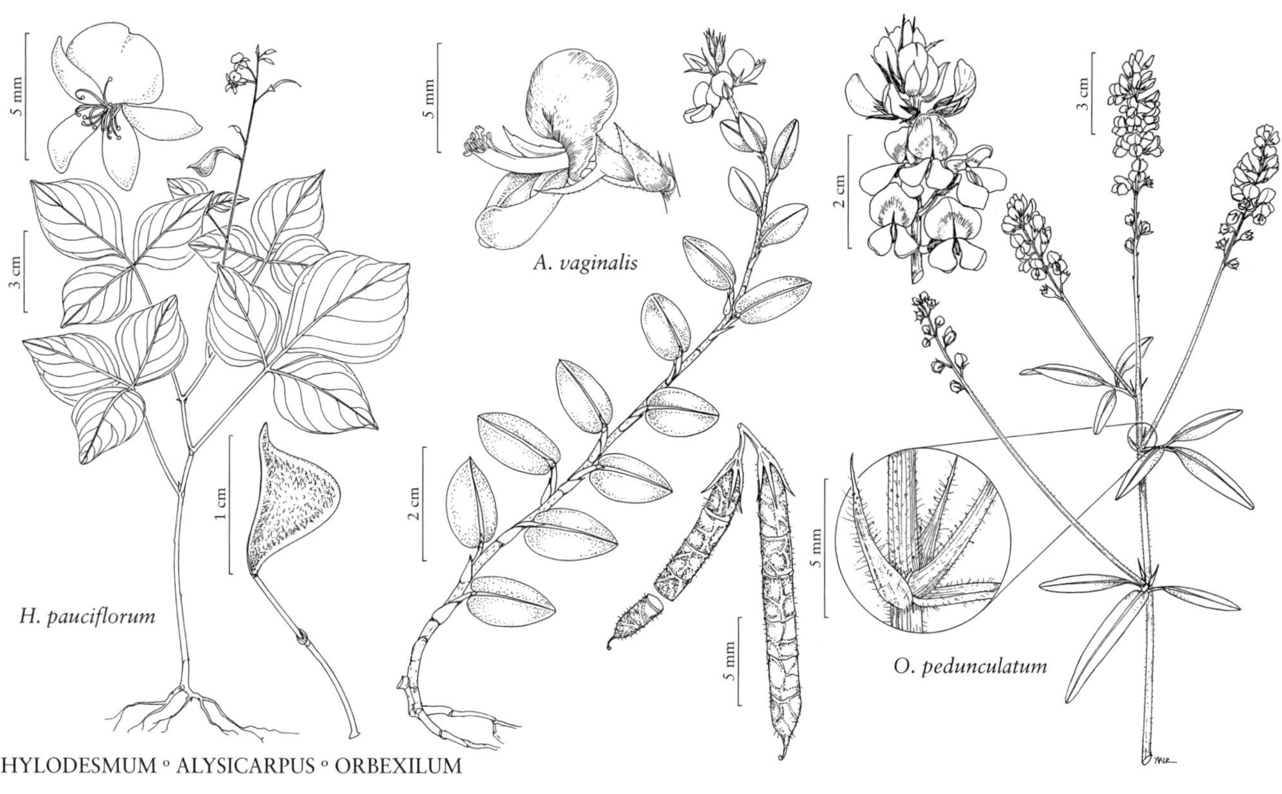

HYLODESMUM ◦ ALYSICARPUS ◦ ORBEXILUM

111. ALYSICARPUS Necker ex Desvaux, J. Bot. Agric. 1: 120, plate 4, fig. 8. 1813, name conserved • [Greek *halysis*, chain, and *karpos*, fruit, alluding to appearance of loments] I

Hiroyoshi Ohashi

Herbs, annual or perennial, unarmed. **Stems** erect to prostrate or sprawling, usually uncinulate-pubescent. **Leaves** alternate, usually unifoliolate, rarely odd-pinnate; stipules present, persistent, striate, narrowly ovate, acuminate; petiolate, petiole channeled, minutely winged; leaflet(s) usually 1, rarely 3, stipels 2, minute, blade margins entire, surfaces usually pubescent, at least abaxial. **Inflorescences** 6–30+-flowered, usually leaf-opposed or terminal, sometimes axillary, usually racemes, sometimes panicles; bracts present often conspicuous, striate, secondary bracts present; bracteoles absent. **Flowers** papilionaceous; calyx campanulate, sepals connate only near base, lobes 5, striate, subequal, adaxial 2 often connate nearly to apex; corolla red to reddish blue, reddish violet, orange, orange-buff, pink, pinkish lavender, or white; stamens 10, diadelphous; anthers basifixed; ovary sessile or shortly stipitate, style incurved at apex, glabrous, stigma terminal, slightly capitate. **Fruits** loments, sessile, distal segment often abortive and stipelike, turgid or laterally compressed, straight or constricted, ovoid or oblong to linear, indehiscent, reticulate, sometimes also rugose, glabrescent or uncinate-puberulent; segments 2–8. **Seeds** 2–8, oblong or 4-sided; scarcely rim-arillate. x = (7), 8, [11].

Species ca. 30 (3 in the flora): introduced; Asia, Africa; introduced also in Mexico, West Indies, Central America, South America, Pacific Islands, Australia.

Alysicarpus glumaceus (Vahl) de Candolle was collected in 1958 as a waif on chrome ore piles in Maryland by C. F. Reed (*41715*, MO).

1. Loments constricted between segments, enclosed in calyx, lateral surfaces reticulate and cross-rugose, distinctly sculpted; calyx lobes imbricate at base . . . . 1. *Alysicarpus rugosus*
1. Loments straight, not constricted between segments, distinctly exserted from calyx, lateral surfaces reticulate, obscurely sculpted; calyx lobes valvate at base.
    2. Loments ridged, without internal cross partition between segments, sometimes with partitions distally; inflorescences laxly flowered; infructescences lax, internodes longer than ½ loment length; plants annual; stems much branched, erect or ascending . . . . 2. *Alysicarpus ovalifolius*
    2. Loments furrowed, with internal cross partition between segments; inflorescences densely flowered; infructescences much crowded, internodes much shorter than loments; plants perennial; stems diffuse, ascending or sprawling . . . . 3. *Alysicarpus vaginalis*

1. **Alysicarpus rugosus** (Willdenow) de Candolle in A. P. de Candolle and A. L. P. P. de Candolle, Prodr. 2: 353. 1825 • Red moneywort I

Hedysarum rugosum Willdenow, Sp. Pl. 3: 1172. 1802

Herbs annual or perennial. **Stems** prostrate, ascending, or erect, diffuse, 30–100(–200) cm, pubescent, hairs sparsely uncinate. **Leaves** usually unifoliolate, rarely 3-foliolate; stipules 5–30 mm; petiole 2–17 mm; leaflet blades oblong, obovate, or narrowly ovate to linear, 2–4.5(–6.5) × 0.2–2 cm, base obtuse or rounded, apex rounded, retuse, acute, or acuminate, abaxial surface sparsely subappressed-villous, slightly reticulate. **Inflorescences** 6–30+-flowered, axillary, terminal, or leaf-opposed, racemes, usually 2–8 cm. **Pedicels** 2–5 mm. **Flowers:** calyx 5–7 mm, tube 1–1.5 mm, lobes imbricate at base, lanceolate, 5–8 mm, acute or acuminate; corolla white or red-blue, 6–7 mm. **Infructescences** dense to lax, internodes shorter than or equal to loment length, sometimes lax proximally (5–10 mm), dense distally (to 1 mm). **Loments** subterete or laterally compressed, ovoid to shortly oblong, 4–12 × 2.5–3 mm, shorter or longer than calyx, scarcely exserted from calyx, margins constricted between segments, glabrescent; segments 1–4, globose or transversely elliptic, 1–2 × 2–2.5 mm, lateral surfaces distinctly reticulate and cross-rugose; septa with internal cross partition between segments. **Seeds** compressed, olive, oblong, rhombic, or 4-sided, 1.5–2.5 × 1.2–1.8 mm, 0.8–1.2 mm thick. $2n = 16$.

Flowering Jul–Nov. Waste areas, fallow fields; 0–10 m; introduced; Fla.; Asia; Africa.

Alysicarpus rugosus is known from Miami-Dade County. It has been cultivated experimentally for forage or plowed under to improve soil quality, and rarely escapes cultivation.

2. **Alysicarpus ovalifolius** (Schumacher) J. Léonard, Bull. Jard. Bot. État Bruxelles 24: 88. 1954 • Alyce clover I

Hedysarum ovalifolium Schumacher, Beskr. Guin. Pl., 359. 1827

Herbs annual. **Stems** erect or ascending, usually much branched, sometimes woody at base, 20–100 cm, puberulent or pubescent, glabrescent. **Leaves** unifoliolate; stipules 5–20 mm; petiole 2–8 mm; leaflet blades: proximals usually orbiculate, elliptic, or oblong, distals often lanceolate, 1–10 × 0.6–3 cm, base subcordate, apex acute to emarginate and mucronulate, abaxial surface finely puberulent, with some hairs on veins. **Inflorescences** 6–20-flowered, terminal or leaf-opposed, usually racemes, sometimes panicles, usually 5–15 cm. **Pedicels** 1–2 mm. **Flowers:** calyx 5–6 mm, tube 1.5–2 mm, lobes valvate at base, narrowly triangular, 3–4 mm, acuminate; corolla orange-buff to reddish violet or pink, 5–6 mm. **Infructescences** lax, internodes longer than ½ loment length. **Loments** subterete, oblong or linear, 10–25 × 2 mm, much longer than calyx, margins straight, not constricted between segments, uncinulate-puberulent; segments (2–)4–6(–8), broadly oblong or quadrate, 2.5–4 mm, lateral surfaces coarsely reticulate, obscurely sculpted, ridged between segments, puberulent; septa without internal cross partitions, except sometimes present at distal joints. **Seeds** brown, oblong, 2 × 1 mm. $2n = 16$.

Flowering Sep–Nov. Open pinelands and margins, roadsides, urban waste areas, lawns; 0–300 m; introduced; Ala., Fla., Ga., La., Miss., N.C., Tex.; Asia; Africa; introduced also in Mexico, Australia.

Alysicarpus ovalifolius is planted for forage and has become naturalized.

Alysicarpus ovalifolius has been regarded as distinct, dubious, or conspecific with *A. vaginalis*. B. Verdcourt (1971, 2000) accepted *A. ovalifolius* with some doubts. D. Isely (1998) treated *A. ovalifolius* as conspecific with

A. vaginalis but recorded that most material from the United States trends towards the *A. ovalifolius* type. Y. Endo and H. Ohashi (1990) treated them as separate species based on distinctions in the loments; both are recognized in India (D. S. Pokle 2000, 2017). F. Adema (2003) noted a continuous variation from septate loments to non-septate ones among Malesian material of the *A. vaginalis-ovalifolius* complex and merged the two as *A. vaginalis*. A. Gholami et al. (2017) and K. Ohashi et al. (2018) suggested that *A. ovalifolius* is distinct from *A. vaginalis* based on results of the molecular phylogenetic analyses. Possible hybrids between *A. ovalifolius* and *A. vaginalis* were suggested by Verdcourt (1971, 2000).

3. **Alysicarpus vaginalis** (Linnaeus) de Candolle in A. P. de Candolle and A. L. P. P. de Candolle, Prodr. 2: 353. 1825 F I W

Hedysarum vaginale Linnaeus, Sp. Pl. 2: 746. 1753

Herbs perennial. **Stems** ascending or sprawling, diffuse, 20–50 cm, pubescent [puberulent]. **Leaves** unifoliolate; stipules 7–20 mm; petiole 1–2 mm; leaflet blades: proximals usually orbiculate, broadly ovate, elliptic, or oblong, distals lanceolate or narrowly lanceolate, 0.5–5 × 0.3–2.5 cm, base subcordate, apex acute to emarginate and mucronulate, abaxial surface inconspicuously uncinulate-pubescent. **Inflorescences** densely 6–20-flowered, usually terminal, racemes, 2–5 (–7) cm. **Pedicels** 1–2 mm. **Flowers:** calyx 5–6 mm, tube 1.5–2 mm, lobes valvate at base (separated by sinuses), narrowly triangular, 3–4 mm, acuminate; corolla orange or lavender-pinkish, 5–6 mm (slightly longer than calyx). **Infructescences** dense (much crowded), internodes much shorter than loment length. **Loments** subterete, oblong or linear, 10–20 × 2–3 mm, much longer than calyx, margins straight, not constricted between segments, uncinulate-puberulent; segments 3–7(or 8), broadly oblong or quadrate, 2–3 mm, lateral surfaces reticulate, obscurely sculpted; septa furrowed between segments with internal cross partitions inside. **Seeds** brown or yellowish brown, oblong, 1.5–2.5 × 1–1.2 mm. $2n$ = (14) 16.

Flowering year-round. Roadsides, disturbed ground, open woods, pinelands; 0–20 m; introduced; Ala., Fla.; Asia; Africa; introduced also in West Indies, Central America, South America, Pacific Islands, Australia.

Alysicarpus vaginalis is occasionally planted for forage in the Gulf Coast states and has been documented as escaped only in southern Alabama and southern Florida.

112. ORBEXILUM Rafinesque, Atlantic J. 1: 145. 1832 • Snakeroot or leather-root [Latin *orbis*, circular, and *exilum*, spreading or vexillum, alluding to shape of banner in *O. latifolium*, the type species]

Billie L. Turner†

Rhytidomene Rydberg

Herbs, perennial, unarmed; with lignescent rhizome, tuber, or fusiform taproot. **Stems** erect to ascending, usually gland-dotted, pubescent or glabrous. **Leaves** alternate, unifoliolate, palmate, or odd-pinnate; stipules present, persistent or caducous; petiolate; stipels absent; leaflets 1–7, blade margins entire, surfaces glandular-punctate or eglandular, pubescent or glabrous. **Inflorescences** pedunculate, 5–50-flowered, terminal, spicate; bracts present; bracteoles absent. **Flowers** papilionaceous; calyx tubular-campanulate, lobes 5, lobes 2–3 times tube length; corolla violet, purple, or purplish blue, banner, wings, and keel well developed, keel connate apically; stamens 10, diadelphous or proximally monadelphous; anthers in 2 series, proximal dorsifixed, distal basifixed, introrse. **Fruits** loments, dark brown to black, subsessile, asymmetric or curved, flattened, round-obovate to obovate, 0.4–1.2 cm, indehiscent, thickly leathery, rugose or papillose, glandular-punctate or eglandular, glabrous. **Seeds** 1, reniform, obovate, depressed-obovate, or round-obovate. x = 11.

Species 11 (8 in the flora): c, se United States, Mexico.

As treated by J. W. Grimes (1990), *Orbexilum* comprises closely related species confined to North America, this largely confirmed by DNA data (A. N. Egan and K. A. Crandall 2008). B. L. Turner (2008b) proposed three additional species known from Mexico [*O. chiapasanum* B. L. Turner, *O. melanocarpum* (Bentham) Rydberg, and *O. oliganthum* (Brandegee) B. L. Turner], bringing to 11 the number of species recognized for the genus.

SELECTED REFERENCE Turner, B. L. 2008b. Revision of the genus *Orbexilum* (Fabaceae: Psoraleeae). Lundellia 11: 1–7.

1. Leaves unifoliolate . . . . 1. *Orbexilum virgatum*
1. Leaves 3–7-foliolate (sometimes unifoliolate in *O. simplex*).
    2. Leaves mostly palmately (3–)5–7-foliolate . . . . 2. *Orbexilum lupinellus*
    2. Leaves pinnately 3-foliolate (sometimes unifoliolate or palmately 5–7-foliolate in *O. simplex*).
        3. Leaflet blades: base cordate . . . . 3. *Orbexilum macrophyllum*
        3. Leaflet blades: base not cordate.
            4. Herbs eglandular; stipules narrowly oblong, 10–13 mm . . . . 4. *Orbexilum stipulatum*
            4. Herbs ± glandular-punctate, at least adaxial leaflet surfaces; stipules long-triangular, lanceolate, or linear, 3–10 mm.
                5. Legumes papillose or warty . . . . 5. *Orbexilum onobrychis*
                5. Legumes rugose.
                    6. Flowers 8–10 mm . . . . 8. *Orbexilum simplex*
                    6. Flowers 4–7 mm.
                        7. Bracts, calyces, and legumes markedly glandular-punctate; bracts ovate, 5–8 × 2–4 mm; Atlantic Coastal Plain . . . . 6. *Orbexilum psoralioides*
                        7. Bracts, calyces, and legumes eglandular; bracts lanceolate to narrowly ovate, 5–8 × 1–2.5 mm; sc United States . . . . 7. *Orbexilum pedunculatum*

1. Orbexilum virgatum (Nuttall) Rydberg in N. L. Britton et al., N. Amer. Fl. 24: 6. 1919 [C] [E]

Psoralea virgata Nuttall, Gen. N. Amer. Pl. 2: 104. 1818; *Lotodes virgatum* (Nuttall) Kuntze

Herbs to 5 dm; with ovoid or globose tuber. **Stems** appressed-pubescent. **Leaves** unifoliolate; stipules long-triangular or linear, 3–8 mm; petiole 1–35 mm; leaflet blades elliptic to narrowly lanceolate, 20–90 × 3–12 mm, surfaces glandular-punctate, sparsely pubescent. **Peduncles** 2–13 cm. **Inflorescences** ovoid to long-ellipsoid, 1–4 cm. **Flowers** 5–7 mm; calyx 3–5 mm, glandular, appressed-pubescent; corolla purple, banner obtrullate. **Legumes** 4 × 4 mm, glandular, rugose. **Seeds** obovate, 2 mm.

Flowering May–Jun. Along swamps and roadways in flat pine-barrens; of conservation concern; 0–50 m; Fla., Ga.

Orbexilum virgatum is known only from northeastern Florida and southeastern Georgia.

2. Orbexilum lupinellus (Michaux) Isely, Sida 11: 432. 1986 (as lupinellum) [E]

Psoralea lupinellus Michaux, Fl. Bor.-Amer. 2: 58. 1803; *Lotodes lupinellus* (Michaux) Kuntze; *Rhytidomene lupinellus* (Michaux) Rydberg

Herbs to 7.5 dm; with ligneous taproot or slender rhizome. **Stems** glabrous. **Leaves** mostly palmately (3–)5–7-foliolate; stipules linear or linear-lanceolate, 2–5 mm; petiole 10–40 mm; leaflet blades linear, 20–70 × 0.5–3.5 mm, surfaces glandular-punctate, glabrous or glabrate. **Peduncles** 3–10 cm. **Inflorescences** ellipsoid, 1–6 cm. **Flowers** 5–7 mm; calyx 2–3 mm, glandular-punctate, glabrous or sparsely pubescent; corolla purplish blue, banner rounded. **Legumes** 9–11 × 5–6 mm, glandular-punctate, rugose. **Seeds** reniform, 5–7 mm.

Flowering May–Aug. Pine-oak forests, sandy soils; 0–100 m; Fla., Ga., N.C., S.C.

Orbexilum lupinellus has been treated as the sole member of *Rhytidomene*; J. W. Grimes (1990) and D. Isely (1998) included it in *Orbexilum*.

3. Orbexilum macrophyllum (Rowlee ex Small) Rydberg in N. L. Britton et al., N. Amer. Fl. 24: 5. 1919 E

Psoralea macrophylla Rowlee ex Small, Fl. S.E. U.S., 623, 1332. 1903

Herbs to 10 dm. **Stems** pubescent, hairs fine, retrorse. **Leaves** pinnately 3-foliolate; stipules linear, 9–10 mm; petiole 30–90 mm; leaflet blades broadly ovate, 60–70 × 5.2–6.3 mm, base cordate, surfaces glandular-punctate, sparsely pubescent. **Peduncles** 11–15 cm. **Inflorescences** columnar, 10+ cm. **Flowers** 9 mm; calyx 7–8 mm, eglandular, villous; corolla color unknown, banner ovate. **Legumes** unknown. **Seeds** unknown.

Flowering Jun. Woods; 500–1000 m; N.C.

Orbexilum macrophyllum is known only from the type specimen collected at Tryon Mountain. Repeated searches have been unfruitful, and it is presumed to be extinct (D. Isely 1990).

4. Orbexilum stipulatum (Torrey & A. Gray) Rydberg in N. L. Britton et al., N. Amer. Fl. 24: 6. 1919 E

Psoralea stipulata Torrey & A. Gray, Fl. N. Amer. 1: 688. 1840; *Lotodes stipulatum* (Torrey & A. Gray) Kuntze

Herbs to 10 dm, eglandular. **Stems** striate, sparsely pubescent or glabrous. **Leaves** pinnately 3-foliolate; stipules narrowly oblong, 10–13 mm; petiole 10–35 mm; leaflet blades elliptic to oblanceolate, 37–55 × 15–30 mm, surfaces eglandular, glabrate. **Peduncles** 4–10 cm. **Inflorescences** ovoid, 1–2 cm. **Flowers** 10–11 mm; calyx 6–8 mm, eglandular, sparsely pubescent; corolla color unknown, banner elliptic. **Legumes** unknown. **Seeds** unknown.

Flowering Jun. Flood-scoured riverbank bedrock, gravel bars, limestone barrens and glades; 100–150 m; Ky.

Orbexilum stipulatum is known only by collections from Rock Island, a locality just below the falls of the Ohio River where it descends into the state of Kentucky. First collected by C. W. Short in 1841, it was last collected in 1881 and now is presumably extinct (C. A. McCormick 2007). J. W. Grimes (1990) placed it in *Orbexilum*, but placement is uncertain since fruits are unknown (P. A. Rydberg 1928).

5. Orbexilum onobrychis (Nuttall) Rydberg in N. L. Britton et al., N. Amer. Fl. 24: 5. 1919 E

Psoralea onobrychis Nuttall, Gen. N. Amer. Pl. 2: 104. 1818; *Lotodes onobrychis* (Nuttall) Kuntze; *Orbexilum latifolium* (Torrey) Rafinesque; *P. latifolia* Torrey

Herbs to 10 dm; with ligneous rhizome. **Stems** pubescent, glabrescent. **Leaves** pinnately 3-foliolate; stipules lanceolate to linear, 4–9 mm; petiole 20–90 mm; leaflet blades lanceolate to elliptic-lanceolate, 40–120 × 15–50 mm, surfaces adaxially sparsely glandular-punctate, sparsely pubescent. **Peduncles** 5–15 cm. **Inflorescences** cylindric, 3–20 cm. **Flowers** 5–6.5 mm; calyx 2–3 mm, eglandular or sparsely glandular-punctate, puberulent; corolla violet to purple, banner rounded. **Legumes** 8–12 × 5–5.5 mm, eglandular, papillose or warty. **Seeds** reniform, 4–6 mm.

Flowering May–Jun. Plains, along roadsides, dry, open woods, fallow pastures; 200–500 m; Ill., Ind., Iowa, Ky., Mo., N.C., Ohio, Tenn., Va.

Orbexilum onobrychis is apparently extirpated from South Carolina.

6. Orbexilum psoralioides (Walter) Vincent, Phytoneuron 2014-36: 2. 2014 E

Trifolium psoralioides Walter, Fl. Carol., 184. 1788; *Lotodes psoralioides* (Walter) Kuntze; *Melilotus psoralioides* (Walter) Nuttall; *Orbexilum gracile* (Torrey & A. Gray) Rydberg; *O. pedunculatum* (Miller) Rydberg var. *gracile* (Torrey & A. Gray) J. W. Grimes; *O. pedunculatum* var. *psoralioides* (Walter) Isely; *Psoralea melilotoides* Michaux var. *gracilis* Torrey & A. Gray; *P. psoralioides* (Walter) Cory; *P. psoralioides* var. *gracilis* (Torrey & A. Gray) F. L. Freeman

Herbs 3–8 dm; with ligneous, often tuberous, taproot or slender rhizome. **Stems** sparsely strigose or glabrous. **Leaves** pinnately 3-foliolate; stipules lanceolate to linear, 3–7 mm; petiole 2–30 mm; leaflet blades lanceolate to elliptic, 20–70 × 6–12 mm, surfaces glandular-punctate, glabrous or sparsely pubescent. **Peduncles** 3–12 cm. **Inflorescences** columnar, 1–8 cm; bracts ovate, 5–8 × 2–4 mm, glandular-punctate. **Flowers** 4–7 mm; calyx 2–5 mm, glandular-punctate, hirsute; corolla violet to purple, banner ovate. **Legumes** 4–6 × 3–4 mm, glandular-punctate, rugose. **Seeds** round-obovate, 3–3.5 mm. $2n = 22$.

Flowering May–Jun. Along railroads and roadways, sandy pine-flats; 0–200 m; Fla., Ga., N.C., S.C., Va.

Nomenclature of this species is complex, since it has been applied in many ways by various authors (M. A. Vincent 2014). Nomenclatural stability has been introduced by neotypification of *Trifolium psoralioides* with a specimen from the coastal plain area, and tying the name to plants with glandular-punctate bracts, calyces, and fruits. B. L. Turner (2008b) confused application of the two epithets *gracile* and *pedunculatum*, essentially reversing the glandularity of bracts, calyces, and fruits.

Psoralea melilotoides Michaux, which pertains here, is a superfluous name since *Trifolium psoralioides* Walter was cited as a synonym. *Orbexilum gracile* (Torrey & A. Gray) B. L. Turner, which also pertains here, is invalid; it is an isonym of the combination by Rydberg.

7. **Orbexilum pedunculatum** (Miller) Rydberg in N. L. Britton et al., N. Amer. Fl. 24: 7. 1919 [E] [F]

Hedysarum pedunculatum Miller, Gard. Dict. ed. 8, Hedysarum no. 17. 1768; *Desmodium pedunculatum* (Miller) de Candolle; *Orbexilum pedunculatum* var. *eglandulosum* (Elliott) Isely; *Psoralea eglandulosa* Elliott; *P. psoralioides* (Walter) Cory var. *eglandulosa* (Elliott) F. L. Freeman

Herbs 6–8 dm; with ligneous, often tuberous, taproot or slender rhizome. **Stems** densely strigose to glabrate. **Leaves** pinnately 3-foliolate; stipules lanceolate to linear, 6–10 mm; petiole 3–65 mm; leaflet blades lanceolate to elliptic, 20–70 × 6–22 mm, surfaces eglandular or sparsely glandular-punctate, strigose. **Peduncles** 4–16 cm. **Inflorescences** columnar, 2–13 cm; bracts lanceolate to narrowly ovate, 5–8 × 1–2.5 mm, eglandular. **Flowers** 5–7 mm; calyx 4–7 mm, eglandular, strigose; corolla violet to purple, banner ovate. **Legumes** 3–5 × 3–4 mm, eglandular, rugose. **Seeds** round-obovate, 3–3.5 mm. $2n = 22$.

Flowering May–Jul. Open woods, grasslands; 200–500 m; Ala., Ark., Fla., Ga., Ill., Ind., Ky., La., Miss., Mo., Nebr., N.C., Ohio, Okla., S.C., Tenn., Tex.

Orbexilum pedunculatum is allopatric with its closest relative, *O. psoralioides*, and the two taxa show little evidence of intergradation in regions of near contact (R. L. Wilbur 1963b; J. W. Grimes 1990; D. Isely 1990).

The combination *Psoralea pedunculata* (Miller) Vail (1894), which pertains here, is a later homonym of *P. pedunculata* Ker Gawler (1817) [= *Otholobium sericeum* (Poiret) C. H. Stirton (C. H. Stirton 1986)].

8. **Orbexilum simplex** (Nuttall ex Torrey & A. Gray) Rydberg in N. L. Britton et al., N. Amer. Fl. 24: 6. 1919 [E]

Psoralea simplex Nuttall ex Torrey & A. Gray, Fl. N. Amer. 1: 303. 1838; *Lotodes simplex* (Nuttall ex Torrey & A. Gray) Kuntze; *P. palustris* Bush

Herbs to 7.5 dm; with fusiform taproot. **Stems** appressed-pubescent, glabrescent. **Leaves** usually pinnately 3-foliolate, sometimes unifoliolate or palmately 5–7-foliolate; stipules long-triangular to linear, 4–6 mm; petiole usually 5–70 mm; leaflet blades elliptic to elliptic-lanceolate, 40–80 × 6–15 mm, surfaces ± glandular-punctate, sparsely pubescent. **Peduncles** 3–10 cm. **Inflorescences** columnar, 2–6 cm. **Flowers** 8–10 mm; calyx 5–7 mm, glandular-punctate, sparsely pubescent; corolla purple, banner oblanceolate. **Legumes** 4–6 × 3–5 mm, glandular-punctate, rugose. **Seeds** depressed-obovate, 3–4 mm.

Flowering May–Jun. Sandy soils, marshy areas; 0–400 m; Ala., Ark., La., Miss., Okla., Tex.

A collection by Buckley labeled as from Carlyle, Illinois, at GH may be mislabeled; *Orbexilum simplex* is not known to occur so far north (J. W. Grimes 1990).

113. HOITA Rydberg in N. L. Britton et al., N. Amer. Fl. 24: 7. 1919 • Leather-root [Native American name for fiber-yielding *H. macrostachya*, the type species]

Martin F. Wojciechowski

Herbs, perennial, unarmed; stoloniferous, with woody caudex or root. **Stems** erect or prostrate, often fistulose, usually pubescent and glandular-punctate; cataphylls often present on proximalmost nodes. **Leaves** alternate, odd-pinnate; stipules present; petiolate; leaflets 3, blade margins entire, surfaces pubescent, glandular. **Inflorescences** 3–75+-flowered, axillary, pseudoracemes; bracts soon or tardily deciduous. **Flowers** papilionaceous; calyx tubular-campanulate, lobes 5, not enlarging in fruit, becoming papery, lobes longer than tube; corolla purple, or greenish tinged violet or purple, banner biauriculate, wings auriculate, keel always shorter than other petals, connate on apical margins, glabrous; stamens 10, monadelphous early, vexillary stamen becoming distinct; anthers in 2 series, proximal dorsifixed, distal basifixed; ovule 1. **Fruits** legumes, included in calyx, longer than tube, stipitate, compressed, ovate to obovate indehiscent, eglandular, pubescent, with secondary, internal wall of sclereids. **Seeds** 1, reniform to ellipsoid. $x = 11$.

Species 3 (3 in the flora): California, nw Mexico.

Species of *Hoita* are known from streamsides to moist banks and humid wooded slopes of coastal mountains and foothills of the Sierra Nevada.

J. W. Grimes (1990) recognized only three species in *Hoita*, reducing four of the 11 species recognized by Rydberg to synonymy under *H. macrostachya*, transferring one to *Otholobium* C. H. Stirton, and three to *Rupertia*. *Hoita* in the sense of Grimes is distinguished from other genera of Psoraleeae by the presence of the extra, internal wall in the fruit, and it is the only genus of the tribe in which the calyx does not enlarge or change shape through flowering and fruiting. Separation of *Hoita* from other Psoraleeae is further validated by a molecular phylogenetic study of the tribe (A. N. Egan and K. A. Crandall 2008).

1. Stems prostrate . . . . 1. *Hoita orbicularis*
1. Stems erect.
   2. Stipules falcately lanceolate to caudate-elliptic, 7–16 mm, erect to reflexed. . . . . 2. *Hoita strobilina*
   2. Stipules triangular to linear-triangular, 1.5–5 mm, erect . . . . 3. *Hoita macrostachya*

1. Hoita orbicularis (Lindley) Rydberg in N. L. Britton et al., N. Amer. Fl. 24: 11. 1919 • Roundleaf leather-root

Psoralea orbicularis Lindley, Edwards's Bot. Reg. 23: plate 1971. 1837

Stems prostrate, to 6.5 cm; root deep, woody; proximalmost nodes with cataphylls. **Leaves:** stipules erect, long-triangular to linear, 4.5–10 mm, sparsely glandular, margins with scattered hairs; petiole 1.2–7.5 cm; leaflet blades orbiculate or obovate to oblate, 32–105 × 28–120 mm, base widely attenuate, apex rounded to broadly acute, surfaces brown-glandular, usually pubescent, sometimes glabrate. **Peduncles** 15–95 cm. **Inflorescences** ovoid to long-ellipsoid, nodes (3–)10–35, flowers 1(–3) per node; rachis 11–250 mm. **Flowers:** calyx 14–19 mm, peltate-glandular, densely dark hispid-villose; corolla dark purple, banner 10–16 × 6.5–11 mm; stamens 9.5–15 mm. **Legumes** 6–9 × 3.5–5 mm, distal ⅔ strigose, especially on abaxial suture. **Seeds** reddish brown, reniform, 4–5 × 3–3.5 mm.

Flowering Apr–Aug. Meadows, streamsides, moist hillsides; 0–1800 m; Calif.; Mexico (Baja California).

Hoita orbicularis is known from Shasta County to northern Baja California, Mexico.

2. Hoita strobilina (Hooker & Arnott) Rydberg in N. L. Britton et al., N. Amer. Fl. 24: 11. 1919 • Loma prieta [C] [E]

Psoralea strobilina Hooker & Arnott, Bot. Beechey Voy., 332, plate 80. 1838

Stems erect, to 100 cm; caudex woody; proximalmost nodes without leaves or cataphylls. **Leaves:** stipules erect to reflexed, falcately lanceolate to caudate-elliptic, 7–16 mm, glandular, pubescent; petiole 6–13.5 cm; leaflet blades usually orbiculate or oblate, rarely ovate or lanceolate, 45–80 × 32–75 mm, base cordate or rounded, apex acute, surfaces pale and eglandular abaxially, dark brown to black-glandular and strigose adaxially. **Peduncles** 4.5–6.5 cm. **Inflorescences** long-ellipsoid, nodes 5–12, flowers 2 or 3 per node; rachis 33–60 mm. **Flowers:** calyx 13–17 mm, dark brown- to black-glandular, hirsute to villose; corolla purple, banner base greenish, 12–13 × 7.5–9 mm; stamens 8.5–10.5 mm. **Legumes** 9.5–10.5 × 5.5–6 mm, short-hairy. **Seeds** dark red-brown, reniform-ellipsoid, 6–7 × 4–5 mm.

Flowering Jun–Aug. Woody slopes, usually on serpentine soils; of conservation concern; 100–900 m; Calif.

Hoita strobilina is known from Alameda, San Mateo, Santa Clara, and Santa Cruz counties.

3. Hoita macrostachya (de Candolle) Rydberg in N. L. Britton et al., N. Amer. Fl. 24: 9. 1919 • Large leather-root [F]

Psoralea macrostachya de Candolle in A. P. de Candolle and A. L. P. P. de Candolle, Prodr. 2: 220. 1825; *Hoita longiloba* Rydberg; *H. villosa* Rydberg; *P. douglasii* Greene

Stems erect, to 150 cm; caudex woody; proximalmost nodes with caducous leaves, without cataphylls. **Leaves:** stipules erect, triangular to linear-triangular, 1.5–5 mm, sparsely glandular, densely pubescent; petiole 0.7–6.2 cm; leaflet blades lanceolate, 25–97 × 14–51 mm, base broadly attenuate, apex acute, surfaces less densely glandular and strigose abaxially, densely glandular and sparingly puberulent to glabrate adaxially. **Peduncles** 4.8–15 cm. **Inflorescences** ellipsoid, nodes 6–30, flowers 2 or 3 per node; rachis 20–152 mm. **Flowers:** calyx 4.5–9 mm, usually eglandular, sometimes lobes glandular, strigose to villose or puberulent; corolla greenish, tinged violet or purple, banner 5.5–10 × 6–8 mm; stamens 5.5–8 mm. **Legumes** 6–8 × 4–5 mm, sparsely strigose. **Seeds** reddish brown, reniform-ellipsoid, 5–7 × 3.4–4.5 mm. **2*n*** = 20.

Flowering May–Aug. Streamsides, moist places, open, disturbed areas; 50–2300 m; Calif.; Mexico (Baja California).

Hoita macrostachya is known from the Coast Ranges and western foothills of the Sierra Nevada to northern Baja California.

114. RUPERTIA J. W. Grimes, Mem. New York Bot. Gard. 61: 52, fig. 6. 1990 • California tea, scurfpea [For Rupert Charles Barneby, 1911–2000, American legume taxonomist]

Martin F. Wojciechowski

Herbs, perennial, unarmed; from diffuse, woody, branched root system, sometimes stoloniferous. **Stems** erect, ± glandular, glabrate; unbranched or sparsely branched; proximal nodes often with cataphylls. **Leaves** alternate, odd-pinnate; stipules present, deciduous or persistent, reflexed, distinct; petiolate; leaflets 3, very rarely 4, petiolulate, blade margins entire, surfaces glabrous or pubescent. **Inflorescences:** 2 or 3 flowers per node (3–20 nodes), axillary, pseudoracemes; bracts present, deciduous. **Pedicels** present. **Flowers** papilionaceous; calyx tubular-campanulate (in bud), gibbous to campanulate (in fruit, concealing fruit), lobes 5, lobes equal to or less than tube; corolla cream or yellow, sometimes with purple blotch on wing blades and keel petals; banner bi-auriculate, wings auriculate, keel always shorter, apical margins connate; stamens 10, monadelphous early with vexillary stamen becoming distinct; anthers in 2 series, proximal ones dorsifixed, distal basifixed, introrse; receptacle tumid, style reflexed. **Fruits** legumes, sessile, elliptic or compressed-obovate, indehiscent, sometimes secondarily dehiscent by transverse rupture, apiculate or with beak ventrally displaced at maturity, eglandular or sparsely glandular, pubescent. **Seeds** 1, round to reniform, smooth.

Species 3 (3 in the flora): w North America, nw Mexico.

Segregated by Grimes from *Hoita* in the sense of P. A. Rydberg (1919–1920) for the absence of a secondary internal wall in the fruit, *Rupertia* is distinguished from other genera of Psoraleeae by a combination of characters, including an accrescent calyx, cream to light yellow petals, deciduous bracts, and a tumid receptacle. Delimitation of *Rupertia* from *Hoita* is further validated by a molecular phylogenetic study of Psoraleeae (A. N. Egan and K. A. Crandall 2008).

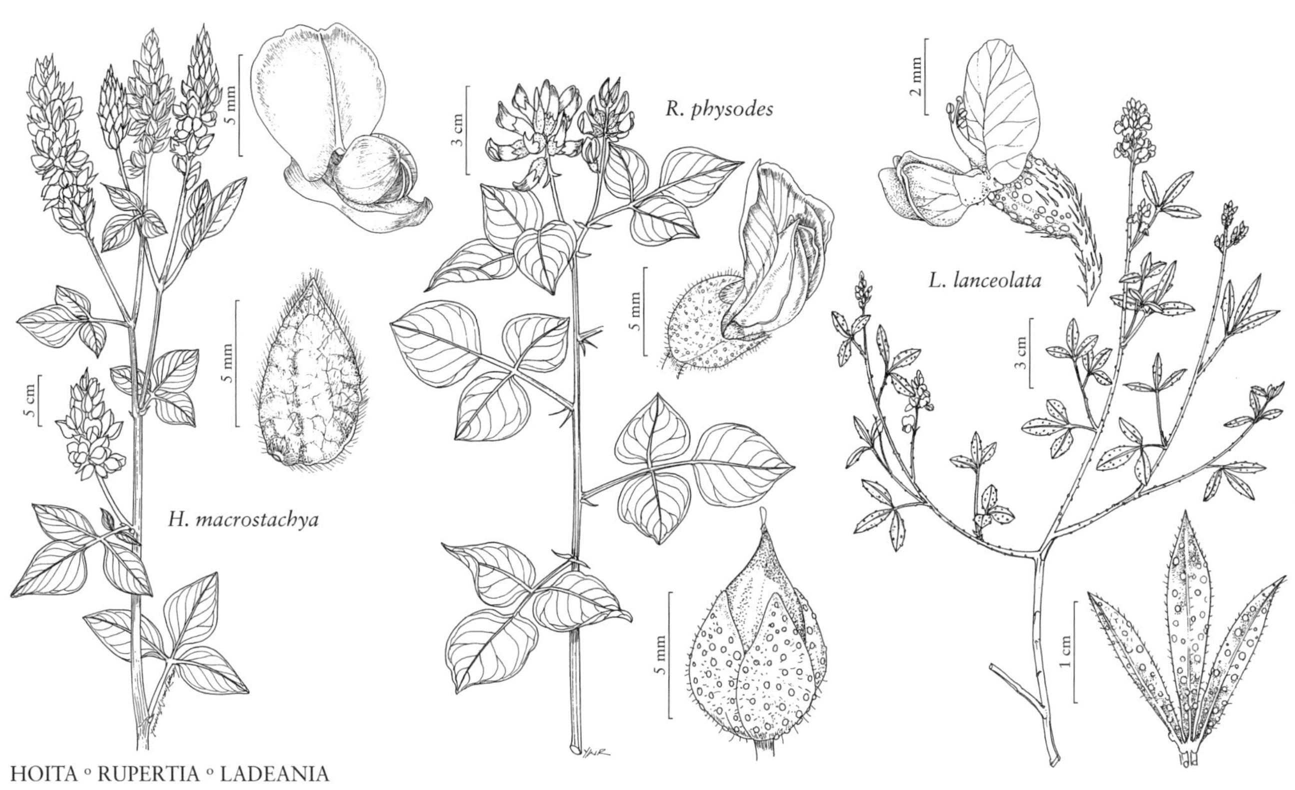

HOITA ◦ RUPERTIA ◦ LADEANIA

1. Stipules 13–15 mm, widely elliptic to obtriangular; floral bracts 9–13 mm .... 1. *Rupertia hallii*
1. Stipules 4–10 mm, linear-oblanceolate, linear-spatulate, triangular, or narrowly elliptic; floral bracts 3–7 mm.
    2. Calyx in flower 6–8 mm; corolla banner 10–13.5 mm; legumes 4–7 mm, apiculate .... 2. *Rupertia physodes*
    2. Calyx in flower 9–10 mm; corolla banner 14–15 mm; legumes 9–13 mm, beaked (beak broadly attached) .... 3. *Rupertia rigida*

1. Rupertia hallii (Rydberg) J. W. Grimes, Mem. New York Bot. Gard. 61: 56. 1990 • Hall's California tea [E]

Hoita hallii Rydberg in N. L. Britton et al., N. Amer. Fl. 24: 10. 1919; *Psoralea hallii* (Rydberg) Jepson

Herbs, root system poorly known. **Stems** to 100 cm, unbranched, glandular, minutely pubescent basally, mostly glabrate distally; cataphylls only at distal nodes, to 7 mm. **Leaves:** stipules persistent or tardily deciduous, green, widely elliptic to obtriangular, 13–15 × 3–5 mm, glandular, sparsely puberulent; petiole 1–3 cm, canaliculate, base swollen and different color and texture, glandular, glabrate; rachis 2–2.8 cm; petiolules brown (darker than rachis), 1.5–3 mm, very sparsely pubescent (more so on adaxial surface); leaflet blades darker adaxially, lanceolate to widely ovate, 4–9 × 1.4–4.2 cm, base broadly attenuate, apex acute, surfaces glandular and glabrous. **Peduncles** 1–8 cm, sometimes darker, less glandular than petiole. **Inflorescences** with 5–20 nodes, 3 flowers per node, short-ellipsoid; rachis 1.5–6 cm, longer or shorter than peduncle, not elongated in fruit, internodes to 4 mm; bracts late deciduous, caudate-flabelliform, 9–13 × 5–8 mm, glandular, puberulent. **Pedicels** 2 mm. **Flowers** 14–15 mm; calyx persistent, slightly gibbous-campanulate in fruit, becoming stramineous, veins prominent, glandular, darker brown in fruit, villosulous to glabrate, tube stramineous, 5–6 mm, lobes green; corolla cream or yellow; filaments 9–10 mm; anthers elliptic; pistil 8.5–10 mm; ovary sparsely pubescent apically. **Legumes** elliptic, 7–10 mm, beak broadly attached, 1–3 mm, glandular, glands golden, minute, fading in age, sparsely pubescent. **Seeds** red-brown, 6–7 × 4 mm.

Flowering Jun–Aug. Clearings in woodlands; 900–2300 m; Calif.

Rupertia hallii is known only from Butte and Tehama counties. Legumes are rarely produced and poorly known.

2. Rupertia physodes (Douglas) J. W. Grimes, Mem. New York Bot. Gard. 61: 53. 1990 • Forest scurfpea [E] [F]

Psoralea physodes Douglas in W. J. Hooker, Fl. Bor.-Amer. 1: 136. 1831; *Hoita physodes* (Douglas) Rydberg

Herbs sometimes stoloniferous; caudex compact to diffuse. **Stems** to 50 cm, sparsely branched, eglandular or sparsely glandular, puberulent to pubescent, hairs black and/or white; proximal 1–5 nodes usually naked and with cataphylls, light to dark brown, 3–7 mm, glabrous, margins sometimes ciliate. **Leaves:** stipules persistent or tardily deciduous, yellow-green to green, narrowly elliptic to linear-oblanceolate, 4–10 × 1–3 mm; petiole 1.1–6.5 cm, ribbed, base slightly constricted, jointed to stem, different color and texture, glandular, sparsely to moderately pubescent; rachis 0.9–2.1 cm, rarely longer than petiole; petiolules brown, 1–3 mm, densely pubescent (more so than petiole); leaflet blades usually lanceolate or triangular, rarely widely elliptic or widely ovate, 2–7 × 1.5–5 cm, base broadly attenuate to cordate, apex acute, surfaces sparsely faint, golden-glandular and sparsely pubescent. **Peduncles** 1.5–10.5 cm. **Inflorescences** with 4–15 nodes, 2 or 3 flowers per node, ovoid to ellipsoid; rachis 0.6–4.5 cm, slightly elongated in fruit, internodes 1–3 mm (in flower) or 3–5 mm (in fruit); bracts early to tardily deciduous, elliptic or lanceolate to oblanceolate-caudate, 3–7 × 1–3.5 mm, obscurely glandular, abaxially pubescent, adaxially glabrous. **Pedicels** 1.5–2.5 mm. **Flowers** 11–14 mm; calyx deciduous, broadly campanulate, elongated in fruit, 6–8 mm, glandular and strigose, hairs usually black, sometimes black and white, tube 4.5–5 mm, lobes pubescent inside; corolla yellow or cream with purple blotch on apex of keel petals, banner 10–13.5 mm; filaments 9–10 mm; anthers ovate; pistil 8.5–9.5 mm; ovary and style base pubescent. **Legumes** golden-red, compressed-obovate, 4–7 × 3–5 mm, not beaked, apiculate, faintly reticulate, eglandular, sparsely pubescent, hairs red-brown. **Seeds** dark red-brown, 5–6.5 × 3–4 mm.

Flowering Apr–Sep. Forested slopes and canyon bottoms to dry, open clearings in forests and roadsides; 0–1700 m; B.C.; Calif., Idaho, Oreg., Wash.

Rupertia physodes is known from Vancouver Island, British Columbia, around Puget Sound, Washington, and south along the coastal ranges of Washington and Oregon to San Diego County, California; disjunct inland populations occur in the counties of Amador, San Bernardino, Shasta, and Tehama (California), Latah (Idaho), and Umatilla (Oregon).

3. Rupertia rigida (Parish) J. W. Grimes, Mem. New York Bot. Gard. 61: 54. 1990 • Parish's psoralea

Psoralea rigida Parish, Bull. Torrey Bot. Club 19: 91. 1892; *Hoita rigida* (Parish) Rydberg

Herbs not stoloniferous; caudex and root woody. **Stems** to 75 cm, sparsely branched, glandular, puberulent to pubescent or, sometimes, glabrate; proximal 1–9 nodes usually naked and with cataphylls, light brown, 5–7 mm, striate, puberulent. **Leaves:** stipules tardily deciduous, light to dark brown, triangular or lanceolate to linear-spatulate, 4–10 × 0.5–2 mm, venation few; petiole 1–4.6 cm, ribbed, base slightly to moderately swollen and different color and texture, sometimes slightly winged, glandular, minutely puberulent; rachis 1.2–2.2 cm; petiolules brown, 2–3.5 mm, sparsely glandular, brown-puberulent; leaflet blades usually lanceolate, rarely rhombic to obovate, 3.5–6.5 × 2–3.7 cm, base attenuate, apex rounded to acute, surfaces abaxially less glandular and sparsely puberulent and with prominent veins, adaxially glandular and glabrous. **Peduncles** 5–9.5 cm. **Inflorescences** with 5–20 nodes, 2 or 3 flowers per node, ovoid; rachis 1.5–4 cm, internodes 1.5–3 mm; bracts usually late deciduous, caudate-lanceolate to oblanceolate, 3–7 × 1–2.5 mm, abaxially glandular, sparsely pubescent, hairs black. **Pedicels** 1.5–2 mm, at a node often subtended by very reduced, secondary bracts. **Flowers** 13–15 mm; calyx persistent (in fruit), broadly campanulate (in fruit), 9–10 mm, glandular and strigose, hairs white and/or black, tube stramineous-brown, 6 mm, lobes triangular, 2–3 mm; corolla cream to light yellow, banner 14–15 mm; filaments 10.5–12 mm; anthers elliptic; pistil 10–11.5 mm; ovary sericeous, style base subsericeous. **Legumes** elliptic, 9–13 × 5–6 mm, beak broadly attached, triangular, to 3 mm, glandular, pubescent, hairs red-brown, short. **Seeds** red-brown, 6.5–7 × 3.5–4 mm.

Flowering May–Jun. Grasslands, open woodlands; 500–2300 m; Calif.; Mexico (Baja California).

Rupertia rigida is known from the San Bernardino Mountains and Peninsular Ranges of Los Angeles, Riverside, and San Diego counties, south to the Sierra de Juárez and Sierra de San Pedro Mártir of Baja California.

115. LADEANIA A. N. Egan & Reveal, Novon 19: 311, fig. 1. 2009 • Scurfpea [For LaDean Egan, b. 1949, mother of, and collector for, botanist Ashley Noel Egan, b. 1977] [E]

Ashley N. Egan

Herbs, perennial, or subshrubs, unarmed; roots deep and woody or rhizomatous. **Stems** erect or spreading, green, smooth or lightly striate, sometimes distinctly ribbed apically, branched, basally often with thin, tan to brown cataphylls, glandular, glabrate, or sericeous to densely pubescent throughout or basally, sometimes glabrate. **Leaves** alternate, usually palmately compound, rarely pseudopalmate, often deciduous by anthesis except basally; stipules present, caducous or tardily deciduous, usually adnate to petiole, rarely connate behind petiole, often modified to form cataphylls at base of stem, linear-lanceolate; petiolate, petiole not jointed to stem; leaflets (1 or)3 or 5, persistent or caducous, sometimes absent at maturity, blade margins entire, surfaces strigose, glabrate, or sparsely pubescent. **Inflorescences** 1–3(or 4)-flowered per node, indeterminate pseudoracemes, with 3–22 nodes; bracts caducous, lanceolate to rhombic. **Flowers** papilionaceous; calyx campanulate, lobes 5, lobes pallid green or green throughout, triangular, usually less than ½ length of calyx tube, mostly equal in length, abaxial lobe sometimes slightly longer, flaring back and tearing along a lateral sinus in fruit, glandular, pubescent or glabrate to sericeous; corolla violet to blue, purple, white, or bicolored; stamens 10, diadelphous, distinct portion of filaments filiform; anthers basifixed. **Fruits** legumes, deciduous above receptacle, sessile, subglobose, indehiscent, pilose, strigose, or glabrate. **Seed** 1, brown, somewhat compressed, round to elliptic, smooth. $x = 11$.

Species 2 (2 in the flora): North America.

Recent treatments of *Psoralidium* Rydberg have recognized three species: the narrow endemic, *P. junceum*, and two widespread species, *P. tenuiflorum* and *P. lanceolatum* (J. W. Grimes 1990; D. Isely 1998). A phylogenetic analysis of *Psoralidium* and other genera of tribe Psoraleeae based on eight DNA regions found the type of the genus, *P. tenuiflorum*, to be nested within *Pediomelum* Rydberg (A. N. Egan and K. A. Crandall 2008), resulting in the transfer of *P. tenuiflorum* to *Pediomelum* as *P. tenuiflorum* (Pursh) A. N. Egan. Because the type of *Psoralidium* was moved to *Pediomelum*, the new genus *Ladeania* was created to accommodate the remaining two species, with the type designated as *L. lanceolata*.

1. Mature stems rushlike, leafless or with few basal leaves when flowering; peduncles 15–40+ cm; calyces 2.5–4 mm; legumes eglandular . . . . 1. *Ladeania juncea*
1. Mature stems not rushlike, leaves persistent through flowering; peduncles 0.7–12 cm; calyces 1.5–2.5 mm; legumes glandular . . . . 2. *Ladeania lanceolata*

1. Ladeania juncea (Eastwood) A. N. Egan & Reveal, Novon 19: 312. 2009 • Rush lemonweed, rush scurfpea [E]

Psoralea juncea Eastwood, Proc. Calif. Acad. Sci., ser. 2, 6: 286, plate 44. 1896; *Psoralidium junceum* (Eastwood) Rydberg

Herbs or subshrubs. Stems much-branched proximally, sparsely so distally, mature ones appearing rushlike. **Leaves** palmate, present on young plants; petiole 1–7 cm; leaflets (1 or)3(or 5), blades oblanceolate to elliptic, 35 × 2.5–9 mm, base cuneate-attenuate, apex acuminate, surfaces strigose. **Peduncles** 15–40+ cm. **Inflorescences:** rachis 5–22 cm, internodes 0.5–1 cm, elongating in fruit. **Flowers:** calyx 2.5–4 mm; corolla deep purple, 4–6.5 mm. **Legumes** eglandular, densely pilose.

Flowering spring–summer. Open sand dunes, semi-stabilized sands, rocky slopes; 1000–1800 m; Ariz., Utah.

Although *Ladeania juncea* is locally abundant, the geographic distribution is narrowly restricted mainly to Garfield, Kane, and San Juan counties in Utah, and northern Coconino County, Arizona, along the Colorado, Paria, and San Juan rivers, where it is often dominant in the community. It is apparently disjunct and rare in Grand and Wayne counties, Utah. Phytochemical studies have discovered antimutagenic (S. R. Menon et al. 1999; G. Turchi et al. 2009) and antibacterial (A. Schmitt et al. 1991) properties stemming from the compound plicatin B.

2. Ladeania lanceolata (Pursh) A. N. Egan & Reveal, Novon 19: 312. 2009 • Lemon or lanceleaf scurfpea E F

Psoralea lanceolata Pursh, Fl. Amer. Sept. 2: 475. 1813; *Lotodes elliptica* (Pursh) Kuntze; *P. elliptica* Pursh; *P. micrantha* A. Gray; *P. scabra* Nuttall; *P. stenophylla* Rydberg; *P. stenostachys* Rydberg; *Psoralidium lanceolatum* (Pursh) Rydberg

Herbs. Stems branched throughout, not rushlike. **Leaves** usually palmate, rarely pseudopalmate, persistent through flowering; petiole (0.5–)0.9–2.9 cm; leaflets 3(or 5), blades obovate or oblanceolate to linear, 17–35(–40) × 2–13(–16) mm, base attenuate, apex retuse to acuminate, surfaces glabrate to sparsely pubescent. **Peduncles** 0.7–12 cm. **Inflorescences:** rachis 0.5–14 cm, internodes to 1.5 cm, elongating or not in fruit. **Flowers:** calyx 1.5–2.5 mm; corolla blue to purple, white, or bicolored, 5–7 mm. **Legumes** conspicuously glandular, sparsely strigose to glabrate. $2n = 22$.

Flowering early spring–late summer. Aeolian sand dunes, sandsage and sand prairies; 20–1800 m; Alta., Sask.; Ariz., Calif., Colo., Idaho, Iowa, Kans., Mont., Nebr., Nev., N.Mex., N.Dak., Okla., Oreg., S.Dak., Tex., Utah, Wash., Wyo.

Ladeania lanceolata is variable in morphology, which has resulted in the recognition of three to five taxa (P. A. Rydberg 1919; S. L. Welsh et al. 2015). The length of inflorescences, vestiture of pods, and shape of leaflets vary along geographic trendlines throughout its range and seem to grade from one trend to another.

The names *Psoralea lanceolata* Pursh (1813) and *P. elliptica* Pursh (1813) have equal priority. However, J. Torrey and A. Gray (1838–1843) placed *P. elliptica* in synonymy under *P. lanceolata*, establishing priority of the latter name.

116. PEDIOMELUM Rydberg in N. L. Britton et al., N. Amer. Fl. 24: 17. 1919 • Indian breadroot, scurfpea [Greek *pedion*, plain, and *milon*, apple, alluding to pomme de prairie, French name for *Pediomelum esculentum*, the type species]

Ashley N. Egan

James L. Reveal†

Psoralea Linnaeus subg. *Pediomelum* (Rydberg) Ockendon

Herbs, perennial, unarmed; roots deep, apically swollen, woody, rarely fibrous with scattered tubers. **Stems** erect to ascending, decumbent, prostrate, or absent, glabrous or pubescent. **Leaves** clustered or alternate, usually palmate, pseudopalmate, or pinnately 3-foliolate (rarely phylloidal in *P. rhombifolium*), glandular or eglandular; stipules present; petiolate or sessile; stipels absent; leaflets (1–)3–7(or 8), blade margins entire, surfaces glabrous or pubescent. **Inflorescences** 3–51-flowered, axillary, pseudoracemes; bracts present. **Flowers** papilionaceous; calyx campanulate, usually enlarging through fruiting, rarely not enlarging, but flaring backwards and tearing along a lateral sinus (*P. tenuiflorum*), lobes 5, abaxial often enlarged; corolla usually purple, blue, violet, or lavender, sometimes white, yellow or ochroleucous, rarely brick red or salmon-pink; stamens 10, diadelphous; anthers dorsifixed; style arched to sharply reflexed. **Fruits** legumes, persistent on receptacle (except deciduous in *P. tenuiflorum*), sessile or short-stipitate, compressed, straight or curved, oblong, ellipsoid to lanceoloid, ovoid, obovoid, or globose, beaked, glabrous or pubescent, dehiscence circumscissile. **Seed** 1, globose to ellipsoid, oblong, or reniform, usually smooth; hilum usually not surrounded by raised, white ridge. $x = 11$.

Species 25 (25 in the flora): North America, n Mexico.

Pediomelum has been classically recognized as *Psoralea* Linnaeus, a genus now circumscribed for psoraleoid species primarily of Africa. P. A. Rydberg (1919–1920) segregated *Pediomelum* from *Psoralea* based on the transverse dehiscence of the pod and a gibbous calyx, characters also supported as diagnostic of *Pediomelum* by J. W. Grimes (1990), along with a persistent fruit base following dehiscence. Molecular phylogenetic studies have also confirmed the natural grouping that is *Pediomelum* (A. N. Egan and K. A. Crandall 2008). *Psoralidium* was dissolved, with remaining species placed in *Ladeania*.

J. W. Grimes (1990) divided *Pediomelum* into three subgenera: subg. *Leucocraspedon* J. W. Grimes to accommodate two prostrate species with salmon, brick red, or yellowish flowers and a white ridge surrounding the hilum of the seed; subg. *Pediomelum* to accommodate those species that are usually caulescent and have a persistent inflorescence; and subg. *Disarticulatum* J. W. Grimes whose members are largely acaulescent and whose inflorescence becomes disjointed with age at the base of the peduncle. Molecular phylogenetic studies strongly support subg. *Leucocraspedon*, and somewhat follow membership of the other two subgenera, but not completely. Associations surrounding *P. aromaticum* and *P. esculentum*, in particular, are problematic (A. N. Egan and K. A. Crandall 2008, 2008b).

Endemism is high in *Pediomelum* with most species having restricted geographical ranges. This, coupled with habitat degradation from grazing and urbanization, has resulted in a number of *Pediomelum* species being listed as rare, threatened, or endangered (K. S. Walter and H. J. Gillett 1998). The rapid and recent evolutionary diversification of *Pediomelum* may have contributed to the level of endemism within the group (A. N. Egan and K. A. Crandall 2008b) and has made species delimitation within the genus difficult. Considerable differences of opinion exist as to what criteria should be used for species delimitation and how many species exist within the genus, particularly for those in the southwestern United States.

Several species of *Pediomelum* are of historical economic importance. *Pediomelum esculentum* was once an important starch source for Native American tribes of the Great Plains, as recorded on the historic Lewis and Clark Expedition (Mer. Lewis and W. Clark 2003).

SELECTED REFERENCE Ockendon, D. J. 1965. A taxonomic study of *Psoralea* subgenus *Pediomelum* (Leguminosae). SouthW. Naturalist 10: 81–124.

1. Stems usually prostrate, rarely decumbent, leaves dispersed uniformly along stems; corollas usually brick red to salmon-pink, or with whitish green or yellow base and salmon-pink apex, or yellow throughout, rarely white; hilum surrounded by raised, white ridge.
   2. Leaves usually pinnately 3-foliolate, rarely reduced to phyllodes; corollas usually brick red to salmon-pink, rarely white . . . . 1. *Pediomelum rhombifolium*
   2. Leaves mostly pseudopalmately 5-foliolate, sometimes proximalmost leaves pinnately 3-foliolate; corollas whitish green to yellow with salmon-pink apex, or yellow throughout . . . . 2. *Pediomelum palmeri*
1. Stems erect or absent and leaves clustered or dispersed along stems, if decumbent lateral stems present, then leaves and inflorescences clustered at base of plant or tips of lateral stems; corollas usually blue, violet, lavender, or purple, sometimes ochroleucous, rarely white, cream, or yellowish; hilum not surrounded by raised, white ridge.
   3. Herbs acaulescent or subacaulescent (sometimes with clustered leaves), or shortly caulescent (main stem to 13 cm), sometimes with decumbent branches from basal nodes, and subtended by cataphylls.
      4. Leaves usually 3-foliolate, rarely 5-foliolate, adaxial surface with veins conspicuously hairier than remaining surface.
         5. Leaves palmate; flowers 8–12.5 mm; s Utah . . . . 3. *Pediomelum pariense*
         5. Leaves pinnate; flowers 12–20 mm; w Texas . . . . 4. *Pediomelum humile*
      4. Leaves usually 5–7-foliolate, rarely 1–3-foliolate (rarely 8-foliolate in *P. megalanthum*), adaxial surface veins not conspicuously hairier than remaining surface.

6. Adaxial calyx lobes 1–2 mm; Alabama, Georgia, Tennessee. . . . . 5. *Pediomelum subacaule*
6. Adaxial calyx lobes 2+ mm; c, w North America.
    7. Herbs eglandular or sparsely glandular with obscure pale, sunken glands on one or both leaflet surfaces or rarely on calyx tube.
        8. Stipules and bracts glabrate to sparsely pubescent with semi-erect hairs; inflorescences persistent (not disjointing at base of peduncle in fruit); calyx strongly gibbous-campanulate in fruit; seeds brown. . . . . 6. *Pediomelum esculentum* (in part)
        8. Stipules and bracts appressed-pubescent; inflorescences disjointing in age at base of peduncle; calyx weakly gibbous-campanulate in fruit; seeds red-brown or gray . . . . 7. *Pediomelum hypogaeum*
    7. Herbs mostly glandular throughout with obvious blond to dark brown glands.
        9. Calyx tubes 5–8(–10) mm.
            10. Leaflet blade surfaces adaxially glabrous or sparsely strigose only along base of veins . . . . 8. *Pediomelum epipsilum*
            10. Leaflet blade surfaces adaxially pubescent . . . . 9. *Pediomelum megalanthum*
        9. Calyx tubes 2–5 mm.
            11. Some leaves pseudopalmate; abaxial calyx lobe broadly oblanceolate, 3.5–4.5 mm wide; seeds rugose.
                12. Leaflet blades oblanceolate or orbiculate to elliptic, apex rounded or retuse; flowers 9–13 mm; calyx lobes 4–5 mm . . . . 10. *Pediomelum castoreum*
                12. Leaflet blades lanceolate, rhombic, or slightly oblanceolate, apex acute, mucronate; flowers 14–18 mm; calyx lobes 7–12 mm . . . . .11. *Pediomelum pentaphyllum*
            11. All leaves palmate; abaxial calyx lobe linear-lanceolate to oblanceolate or elliptic, 1.5–3.5 mm wide; seeds smooth.
                13. Herbs often with decumbent lateral stems; peduncles appressed-spreading pubescent; calyx tube 2–3 mm; California. . . . . .12. *Pediomelum californicum*
                13. Herbs rarely with decumbent lateral stems; peduncles pilose, hairs spreading, retrorse or antrorse; calyx tube 2.5–5 mm; nw Arizona, se Nevada, sw Utah.
                    14. Peduncles (2–)4–8(–10) cm; calyx tube 2.5–4 mm; nw Arizona, se Nevada, sw Utah . . . . 13. *Pediomelum mephiticum*
                    14. Peduncles (0.5–)1–5.5(–6) cm; calyx tube (3.5–)4–5 mm; Mohave and Yavapai counties, Arizona . . . . 14. *Pediomelum verdiense*

[3. Shifted to left margin—Ed.]

3. Herbs caulescent, leaves dispersed along stems, branches subtended by leaves.
    15. Petioles, when present, usually shorter than petiolules.
        16. Inflorescences loose (much of rachis exposed); petiolules 5–9 mm . . . . 15. *Pediomelum canescens*
        16. Inflorescences crowded (rachis usually concealed); petiolules 1.8–3 mm. . . . . .16. *Pediomelum piedmontanum*
    15. Petioles longer than petiolules.
        17. Herbs eglandular throughout . . . . 6. *Pediomelum esculentum* (in part)
        17. Herbs glandular (or only on adaxial leaflet surfaces in *P. digitatum*).
            18. Stems decumbent to erect-ascending or suberect.
                19. Inflorescences umbellate or subcapitate, rarely reduced to a single flower; flowers (7–)8–11(–12) mm; desert communities of Arizona, Colorado, and Utah. . . . . 17. *Pediomelum aromaticum*
                19. Inflorescences ellipsoid to elongate, flowers numerous; flowers 12–22 mm; grasslands, meadows, and woodland communities of midwestern United States . . . . .18. *Pediomelum cuspidatum* (in part)
            18. Stems strongly erect.

[20. Shifted to left margin.—Ed.]

20. Flowers 5–6 mm; calyx tube 1–1.5 mm . . . . 19. *Pediomelum tenuiflorum*
20. Flowers 7–26 mm; calyx tube 2–8 mm.
    21. Flowers 7–11 mm; calyx tube 2–4 mm.
        22. Herbs mostly silvery-sericeous; pedicels 0.5–1 mm; corollas deep blue . . . . 20. *Pediomelum argophyllum*
        22. Herbs strigose, glabrate, or appressed-canescent, but not silvery; pedicels 1–10 mm; corollas purple to violet, blue-violet, blue-lavender, white, or white suffused with purple.
            23. Herbs eglandular except on adaxial leaflet surfaces; pedicels 1–3 mm . . . . 21. *Pediomelum digitatum*
            23. Herbs glandular throughout; pedicels 3.5–10 mm . . . . 22. *Pediomelum linearifolium*
    21. Flowers 12–26 mm, calyx tube 4–8 mm.
        24. Stems decumbent to erect-ascending; legumes with beak 1.5–2 mm . . . . 18. *Pediomelum cuspidatum* (in part)
        24. Stems erect; legumes with beak 2–6 mm.
            25. Herbs 5–45 cm; calyx tube 6–8 mm . . . . 23. *Pediomelum latestipulatum*
            25. Herbs to 150 cm; calyx tube 4–5 mm.
                26. Inflorescences globose-ovoid (compact), with rachis 0.5–0.7 cm; bracts orbiculate, 6–13 mm wide; pedicels 3.5–5 mm . . . . 24. *Pediomelum reverchonii*
                26. Inflorescences oblong to elliptic, with rachis 1.5–7 cm; bracts mostly oblanceolate to obovate, 1.5–4 mm wide; pedicels 1.5–2 mm . . . 25. *Pediomelum cyphocalyx*

1. Pediomelum rhombifolium (Torrey & A. Gray) Rydberg in N. L. Britton et al., N. Amer. Fl. 24: 23. 1919 • Gulf Indian breadroot [F]

Psoralea rhombifolia Torrey & A. Gray, Fl. N. Amer. 1: 303. 1838; *Pediomelum coryi* Tharp & F. A. Barkley

Herbs caulescent, to 100 cm, pubescent and glandular on adaxial leaflet surfaces, rarely calyx lobes, stipules, or bracts eglandular. **Stems** usually prostrate, rarely decumbent, often branched from base, rarely distally, leaves dispersed uniformly along stems; pseudoscapes to 10 cm (when present); cataphylls to 15 mm. **Leaves** usually pinnately 3-foliolate, rarely reduced to phyllodes; stipules persistent, lanceolate to linear-lanceolate, 3–6.5 × 1–2 mm, glabrate except along margin; petiole swollen or not, not jointed, ribbed, not canaliculate, 9–90 mm, pubescent; petiolules 1–1.5 mm; leaflet blades lanceolate to rhombic or orbiculate (sometimes dimorphically so), 0.9–5 × 0.6–3 cm, base attenuate, apex broadly acute to rounded, surfaces abaxially glandular and pubescent to glabrate, adaxially pubescent or glabrous. **Peduncles** 0.8–8.5 (–10) cm, longer than subtending petiole, appressed-spreading pubescent to glabrate. **Inflorescences** persistent, subcapitate, globose to ovoid; rachis 0.3–1 cm, nodes 1–6, 3 flowers per node, internodes to 5 mm; bracts persistent, lanceolate to spatulate, 1–3 × 0.5–1.5 mm, pubescent abaxially. **Pedicels** 1–2 mm. **Flowers** (5–)7.5–11 mm; calyx gibbous-campanulate in fruit, 4.5–6.5 mm abaxially, 4.5–6 mm adaxially, eglandular, strigose; tube 2.5–3.5 mm; lobes lanceolate, abaxial 2.5–3 × 1–1.5 mm, adaxial 1.5–2 × 1–1.5 mm; corolla usually brick red to salmon-pink, rarely white, banner oblanceolate or rhombic, emarginate, 7.5–10 × 4–5 mm with claw 2.5 mm, wings 7–10 × 2–2.5 mm with claw 2.5–3 mm, keel 5–7.5 × 2–2.5 mm with claw 2.5–3 mm; filaments 6–7 mm; anthers elliptic, 0.5 mm; ovary glabrous, except pubescent apically, style hairy. **Legumes** globose, 4.5–5 × 3–4 mm, eglandular, pubescent distally, abruptly narrowing to a beak 6–8 mm, exserted beyond calyx. **Seed** gray-green to brown, often mottled black, lenticular, 4 × 3–3.5 mm; hilum surrounded by raised, white ridge. $2n = 22$.

Flowering summer. Grasslands, woodland communities; 0–1000 m; Ark., La., Okla., Tex.; Mexico.

Pediomelum rhombifolium is widespread in Texas, with isolated collections in Mexico. It is morphologically variable, particularly in leaflet shape and size, and petiole and peduncle lengths and ratio thereof. Along with *P. palmeri*, *P. rhombifolium* is distinct from its congeners in its creeping, prostrate habit. The salmon or brick red corollas are unique within the genus.

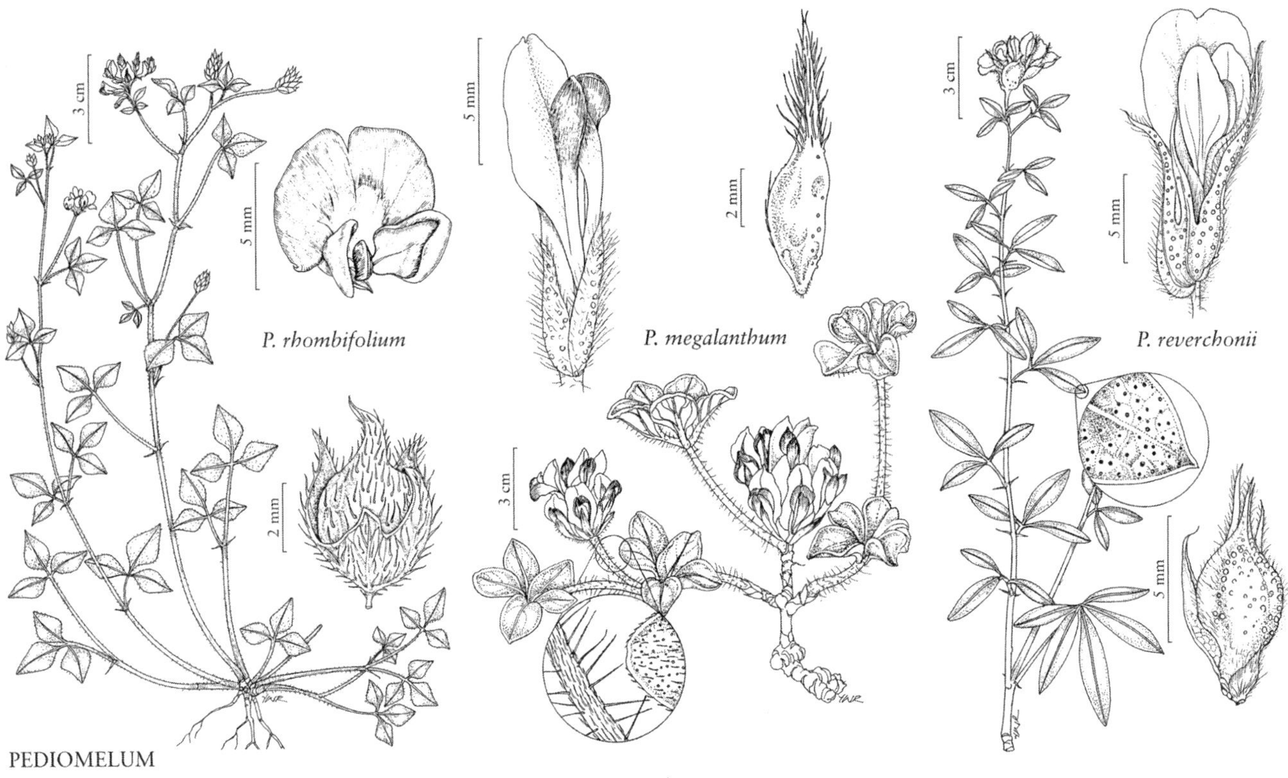

2. **Pediomelum palmeri** (Ockendon) J. W. Grimes ex Gandhi, Harvard Pap. Bot. 20: 213. 2015

Psoralea palmeri Ockendon, SouthW. Naturalist 11: 412. 1966

Herbs caulescent, to 60 cm, pubescent and glandular on adaxial leaflet surfaces, rarely on calyx lobes, stipules, or bracts. **Stems** usually prostrate, rarely decumbent, often branched from base, sometimes branched distally, leaves dispersed uniformly along stems; pseudoscapes to 30 cm (when present); cataphylls blond to brown, to 15 mm, veined. **Leaves** mostly pseudopalmately 5-foliolate, sometimes proximalmost leaves pinnately 3-foliolate; stipules persistent, lanceolate to linear-lanceolate, 2–5.5 × 1–2 mm, appressed-spreading pubescent; petiole swollen proximally, not jointed, slightly canaliculate, 6–75 mm; petiolules 1 mm, terminal petiolule often to 10 mm; leaflet blades elliptic to lanceolate or orbiculate (sometimes dimorphically so), 0.7–3.1 × 0.3–1.3 cm, base cuneate, apex broadly acute to acuminate, surfaces abaxially eglandular and glabrate to pubescent along veins, adaxially obscurely glandular and glabrate to pubescent with pubescent margins. **Peduncles** 0.5–10.5 cm, usually longer than subtending petiole, sparsely strigose. **Inflorescences** persistent, subcapitate to ovoid; rachis 0.4–1.8 cm, nodes 1–5, 3 flowers per node, internodes to 5 mm; bracts persistent, lanceolate to spatulate, 1–3 × 0.5–2 mm, margins pubescent. **Pedicels** 0.5–2 mm. **Flowers** 6–9 mm; calyx gibbous-campanulate in fruit, 4.5–6 mm abaxially, 4.5–5.5 mm adaxially, strigose, lobes rarely glandular; tube stramineous, 2–4 mm; abaxial lobe lanceolate or elliptic to slightly oblanceolate, 3.5–4 × 2 mm, adaxial lobes lanceolate, 2–3 × 1 mm; corolla with whitish green to yellow base and salmon-pink apex, or yellow throughout, banner oblanceolate-obovate, 5–9 × 2–2.5 mm with claw 1.5–2.5 mm, wings 6–8 × 1.5–2.5 mm with claw 2–4 mm, keel 5–7 × 2–2.5 mm with claw 2–3.5 mm; filaments 4.5–6.5 mm; anthers elliptic, 0.3 mm; ovary sparsely pubescent apically, style sparsely pubescent. **Legumes** globose-ellipsoid, 4.5–5.5 × 4–5 mm, eglandular, sparsely strigose on distal ½, abruptly narrowing to a beak 5.5–10 mm, exserted well beyond calyx. **Seed** light brown or gray-brown, lenticular, 4.5 × 3–4 mm, shiny; hilum surrounded by raised, white ridge.

Flowering spring–summer. Open areas in grasslands and pine forest communities; 1000–2000 m; Ariz.; Mexico (Chihuahua, Coahuila, Durango, Guanajuato, Jalisco, San Luis Potosí, Sonora).

Pediomelum palmeri is found in a variety of habitats; it is known from a few collections in Santa Cruz County and is widespread in Mexico.

Pediomelum palmeri has a rather difficult nomenclatural history. *Psoralea pentaphylla* Linnaeus was misapplied to this taxon by P. A. Rydberg (1919–1920). D. J. Ockendon (1965) discovered the misapplication and, in a footnote, renamed the species *Psoralea palmeri* Ockendon but without a Latin description, then required for valid naming of a new species. J. W. Grimes (1990) transferred *Psoralea palmeri* to *Pediomelum*, with the name then purported to be *Pediomelum palmeri* (Ockendon) Grimes, but again without a valid Latin description. J. T. Kartesz and K. N. Gandhi (1992b) recognized the error and presented a Latin description with the name *P. ockendonii* Gandhi & Kartesz but overlooked the correction made by Ockendon (1966) wherein he provided a Latin description, rendering their name as superfluous. Gandhi (2015) validated *P. palmeri* Grimes.

3. **Pediomelum pariense** (S. L. Welsh & N. D. Atwood) J. W. Grimes, Brittonia 38: 185. 1986 • Paria Plateau Indian breadroot E

Psoralea pariensis S. L. Welsh & N. D. Atwood, Great Basin Naturalist 35: 353. 1976

Herbs acaulescent or subacaulescent, 2–9 cm, mostly glandular and strigose throughout. **Stems** short-erect, rarely branched (when branched then branches subtended by cataphylls), leaves clustered; pseudoscapes to 2.5 cm; cataphylls 6–11 mm, glabrous. **Leaves** palmately 3(–5)-foliolate; stipules persistent, obovate to oval, 4–10 × 2.5–6 mm, glabrous or sparsely pubescent; petiole not enlarged but jointed basally, slightly canaliculate, 13–70 mm; petiolules 0.5–1 mm; leaflet blades obovate, 0.9–2.5 × 0.7–2.2 cm, base cuneate or attenuate, apex rounded or emarginate, surfaces abaxially gray-green and evenly strigose, adaxially yellow-green and strongly white-strigose along veins. **Peduncles** 2–4.5 cm, shorter than subtending petiole, pubescent. **Inflorescences** disjointing in age at peduncle base, globose; rachis 0.5–8.5 cm, elongating through fruiting, nodes (1 or)2–6, 3 flowers per node, internodes 1–3 mm; bracts tardily deciduous or persistent, oblanceolate to elliptic, 4–8 × 3–4 mm, apex abruptly acuminate, short-pubescent. **Pedicels** 2–5 mm. **Flowers** 8–12.5 mm; calyx broadly gibbous-campanulate in fruit, 10–11.5 mm abaxially, 8–8.5 mm adaxially, eglandular or sparsely glandular, pubescent; tube 3.3–4.5 mm; lobes lanceolate or oblanceolate, abaxial 4–6.5 × 2–3.5 mm, adaxial 3–5 × 1–1.5 mm; corolla ochroleucous, wings and keel suffused purple or purple, banner broadly orbiculate to obovate, (8.5–)10–14 × 5.5–7.5 mm with claw 2.5–3 mm, wings 9–11 × 2.5–3 mm with claw 3.5–4 mm, keel 8–8.5 × 2.5–3 mm with claw 3–4 mm; filaments 7–8 mm; anthers broadly elliptic, 0.4 mm; ovary pubescent apically, style pubescent basally. **Legumes** ellipsoid, 6–7 × 4–4.5 mm, eglandular, strigose, beak 3–4 mm, not exserted beyond calyx. **Seed** gray-green to brown, obovoid, 4.5–5 × 2.5–3 mm, shiny.

Flowering spring–summer. Barren outcrops in open pine-juniper woodlands; 1700–2500 m; Utah.

Pediomelum pariense is known from Garfield, Kane, and Washington counties. It much prefers open, barren rocky soils, particularly limestone and is considered rare, with fewer than 20 populations known. A few known populations inhabiting the high-elevation escarpment ridges of Bryce Canyon National Park are assured protection, but the bulk of populations exist on the lower steps of the Grand Staircase-Escalante area, areas that may become targets for mining and oil developments. In 2005 and 2006, considerable effort was spent to seek out new populations but without success.

4. **Pediomelum humile** Rydberg in N. L. Britton et al., N. Amer. Fl. 24: 24. 1919 • Rydberg's scurfpea C

Psoralea rydbergii Cory

Herbs acaulescent, to 20 cm, mostly glandular and pubescent throughout. **Stems** absent, leaves clustered; pseudoscapes 5–7 cm (when present); cataphylls 7–9 mm, striate, clustered apically. **Leaves** pinnately 3-foliolate; stipules persistent, lanceolate to oblanceolate-oblong, 5–7(–12) × 2.5–3 mm, stramineous, eglandular, glabrous; petiole swollen proximally or not, not jointed, (30–)50–120 mm; petiolules 2 mm; leaflet blades orbiculate to obovate-trullate, lateral 2 usually asymmetrical, 1.5–2.5(–3.2) × 1–2.4 cm, base broadly cuneate or truncate, apex broadly acute, surfaces abaxially white-pubescent, adaxially white-hirsute along veins and margins. **Peduncles** 2–10 cm, shorter than subtending petiole, glabrous proximally, pubescent distally. **Inflorescences** disjointing in age at peduncle base, ovate to elliptic; rachis 1.4–1.6 cm, crowded, nodes 4–7, 3 flowers per node; bracts persistent, caudate-lanceolate, 5–8 × 2–3.5 mm, pubescent throughout or only at apex. **Pedicels** 1–3 mm. **Flowers** 12–20 mm; calyx gibbous-campanulate in fruit, 10–15(–17) mm, pubescent throughout or teeth only; tube 5–7 mm; lobes linear or linear-lanceolate, abaxial 8–8.5 × 1–1.5 mm, adaxial 6–7.5 × 0.5–1 mm; corolla white and blue-purple, banner white to pale purple, oblanceolate, 15–17 × 6–7 mm with claw 4.5–5.5 mm, wings blue-purple, 12–14 × 2.5–3 mm with claw 5.5–6.5 mm, keel dark purple, 14–16 × 2.5–3 mm with claw 8.5 mm; filaments 16 mm; anthers elliptic, 0.7 mm; ovary glabrous, style glabrous. **Legumes** oblong-ellipsoid, 5–7 × 3.5–4 mm, eglandular, pubescent apically, beak 4–5 mm, about as long as calyx. **Seed** black, ellipsoid-reniform, 3.5–6 × 2.5–4 mm.

Flowering spring. Shallow, rocky clay or limestone soils, shortgrass prairies, shrublands; of conservation concern; 700–2000 m; Tex.; Mexico (Coahuila).

Pediomelum humile, historically known from along the Rio Grande in Texas (Val Verde County) and Mexico, is very rare and on the verge of extinction. Several known populations have been destroyed by urban development in the recent past. The few populations in existence today are located near Del Rio and are all in danger of extirpation due to human influences. *Pediomelum humile* is in the Center for Plant Conservation's National Collection of Endangered Plants.

Psoralea humilis (Rydberg) J. F. Macbride 1922, an illegitimate name (not Miller 1768), pertains here.

5. Pediomelum subacaule (Torrey & A. Gray) Rydberg in N. L. Britton et al., N. Amer. Fl. 24: 20. 1919 • White-rim scurfpea [E]

Psoralea subacaulis Torrey & A. Gray, Fl. N. Amer. 1: 302. 1838; *Lotodes subacaulis* (Torrey & A. Gray) Kuntze

Herbs acaulescent or subacaulescent, to 20 cm, eglandular except leaves or rarely stipules and bracts, pubescent. **Stems** absent, leaves clustered; pseudoscapes erect, 3–10 cm, usually 1, sometimes to 6, rarely branched proximally; cataphylls 10–20 mm (when present). **Leaves** palmately 5–7-foliolate; stipules often fragmented on plant, partly connate, ovate, 11–24 × 11–16 mm, scarious, usually eglandular, sparsely pubescent; petiole jointed basally, 40–150(–190) mm, shorter than peduncle, hirsute-villous; petiolules 1–2.5 mm; leaflet blades oblanceolate to elliptic, 1.5–4.5(–6) × 0.5–1.3(–1.8) cm, base cuneate, apex acuminate to obtuse, surfaces glandular, abaxially pubescent, adaxially sparsely so, usually along margins. **Peduncles** 4–14 cm (8–19 cm in fruit), longer than subtending petiole, setose. **Inflorescences** disjointing in age at peduncle base, long-ovoid; rachis 2.5–9.5 cm, elongating through fruiting, nodes 4–11(–15), 3 flowers per node, internodes 1–5 mm, elongating to 25 mm in fruit; bracts persistent, orbiculate to lanceolate, 7–14 × 2–7 mm, margins pubescent, apex sometimes caudate or emarginate, becoming papery and veined in age. **Pedicels** 1–2 mm. **Flowers** 10–15(–22) mm; calyx weakly gibbous-campanulate in fruit, 6–10 mm abaxially, 5–8 mm adaxially, glabrate and eglandular on gibbous portion, sparsely setose and glandular distally; tube stramineous, 4.5–6 mm; lobes triangular, abaxial 2–4 × 2 mm, adaxial 1–2 × 1 mm; corolla dark blue to purple, banner oblanceolate to oval, 13–23 × 4–5 mm with claw 5–6 mm, wings 12–18 × 2–3 mm with claw 5–7 mm, keel 10–15 × 2–3 mm with claw 2–3 mm; filaments 10–12 mm; anthers obovate, 0.3 mm; ovary pubescent apically, style pubescent basally. **Legumes** globose to ovoid, 6–7 × 4–5 mm, eglandular, sparsely pubescent apically, beak triangular, 4–6 mm, exserted beyond calyx. **Seed** gray-brown to red-brown, obovoid-reniform, 5–6 × 3–4 mm. $2n = 22$.

Flowering spring. Calcareous soils, cedar glades; 200–1500 m; Ala., Ga., Tenn.

Pediomelum subacaule is known from Colbert and Franklin counties in Alabama, Catoosa County in Georgia, and Davidson, Maury, Rutherford, and Wilson counties in Tennessee.

Pediomelum subacaule is quite distinct and disjunct from its fellow members of subg. *Disarticulatum*, this evidenced by its large, partly connate stipules and short, broad calyx lobes, and by being the only species in the subgenus east of the Mississippi River. *Pediomelum subacaule* is restricted to limestone soil in open cedar glades. Although *P. subacaule* is well established in the protected cedar glades of Tennessee, its historical range is shrinking due to habitat loss. Several historical sites that were, or still are, active limestone quarries have no remaining evidence of *P. subacaule*, particularly in Alabama and Georgia.

6. Pediomelum esculentum (Pursh) Rydberg in N. L. Britton et al., N. Amer. Fl. 24: 20. 1919 • Prairie turnip or potato, Indian breadroot [E]

Psoralea esculenta Pursh, Fl. Amer. Sept. 2: 475, plate 22. 1813

Herbs usually caulescent, rarely subacaulescent to acaulescent, to 50 cm, eglandular and pubescent throughout. **Stems** erect, usually unbranched, sometimes branched basally, leaves dispersed along stem and arising nearly perpendicular to it; pseudoscapes 0.5–2 cm; cataphylls 0.5–15 mm, striate. **Leaves** palmately (3–)5-foliolate; stipules persistent, broadly lanceolate proximally to linear-lanceolate distally, 10–20 × 2–8 mm, stramineous basally, eglandular, glabrate to sparsely pubescent, hairs semi-erect; petiole not jointed basally, (2–)30–100(–150) mm; petiolules 1.5–4 mm; leaflet blades elliptic to oblanceolate, 2–4(–6) × 0.7–2.3 cm, base attenuate to cuneate, apex broadly acute to rounded or retuse, surfaces abaxially pubescent, adaxially glabrate except on midvein. **Peduncles** (0.5–)5–12(–15) cm, shorter than subtending petiole, pilose. **Inflorescences** persistent (not disjointing at base of peduncle in fruit), elliptic to oblong; rachis 1.6–7 cm, elongating slightly in fruit, nodes (6–)8–15, (2 or)3 flowers per node; bracts persistent, oblanceolate to elliptic, 5–15 × (0.5–)4–9 mm, glabrate to sparsely pubescent, hairs semi-erect. **Pedicels** 1–3 mm. **Flowers** 12–20 mm; calyx strongly gibbous-campanulate in fruit, 13–16 mm abaxially, 12–14 mm adaxially, eglandular, pubescent; tube 5–6 mm; lobes linear or linear-lanceolate to elliptic, abaxial 7.5–10 × 2–2.5 mm, adaxial 4–7 × 1–1.5 mm; corolla violet to blue-purple, banner sometimes paler, oblanceolate, 17–18 × 6 mm with claw 7–8 mm, wings 15–16.5 × 3–3.5 mm with claw 6–6.5 mm, keel 12–12.5 × 3 mm with claw 6–6.5 mm; filaments 11–14 mm; anthers elliptic, 0.5 mm; ovary pubescent apically, style glabrous apically. **Legumes** oblong, 4–6 × 2.5–3.5 mm, eglandular, pubescent, beak 9–13(–16) mm, exserted beyond calyx. **Seed** brown, reniform, 4 × 3 mm, somewhat rugose. **2*n*** = 22.

Flowering late spring–summer. Prairies, grasslands, open pine woodlands; 500–2000 m; Alta., Man., Sask.; Ark., Colo., Ill., Iowa, Kans., Minn., Mo., Mont., Nebr., N.Mex., N.Dak., Okla., S.Dak., Tex., Wis., Wyo.

Pediomelum esculentum was once one of the main sources of starch for Native American tribes of the Great Plains, eaten fresh, boiled, dried, or ground into flour and used as a thickening agent. Use of the root for food and barter was documented by Lewis and Clark on their historic expedition across the United States (Mer. Lewis and W. Clark 2003).

Pediomelum esculentum ranges in morphology from strongly caulescent to acaulescent with no apparent geographical structuring in this most widespread species. J. W. Grimes (1990) placed this species in subg. *Pediomelum* due to its persistent inflorescences. Molecular phylogenetic and network analyses suggest a split affinity for *P. esculentum* between both subgenera, suggesting that this may be an intermediate form and bridge between his subgenera or the groupings suggested by D. J. Ockendon (1965) based on habit—groupings somewhat supported by molecular phylogenies (A. N. Egan and K. A. Crandall 2008, 2008b).

7. Pediomelum hypogaeum (Nuttall) Rydberg in N. L. Britton et al., N. Amer. Fl. 24: 21. 1919 [E]

Psoralea hypogaea Nuttall in J. Torrey and A. Gray, Fl. N. Amer. 1: 302. 1838

Herbs usually acaulescent, rarely subacaulescent, to 25 cm, pubescent throughout and eglandular or sparsely glandular with pale, sunken obscure glands on leaflets and/or calyx tubes only. **Stems** short-erect, with decumbent laterals, decumbent stems 0–6 cm, overtopped by leaves, leaves clustered; pseudoscapes usually 1, unbranched, rarely 2, 0.5–9.5 cm; cataphylls 5–20 mm. **Leaves** palmately (3–)5-foliolate; stipules persistent, linear-lanceolate to elliptic, 4–19 × 2–6 mm, appressed-pubescent; petiole not obviously jointed basally, (20–)30–210 mm; petiolules 1–3 mm; leaflet blades elliptic to lanceolate, oblanceolate, or rhombic, 1–7.5 × 0.3–4 cm, base cuneate, apex acuminate, surfaces glabrate to sparsely pubescent. **Peduncles** 1–14 cm, shorter than subtending petiole, subappressed-pubescent. **Inflorescences** disjointing in age at peduncle base, ovate to oblong; rachis 0.5–6 cm, elongating slightly in fruit, nodes 3–15, 3 flowers per node, internodes crowded in flower, elongating to 25 mm in fruit; bracts mostly persistent or very tardily deciduous, linear to oblanceolate or rhombic, 3–11 × 1.5–4.5 mm, appressed-pubescent. **Pedicels** 1–5 mm. **Flowers** 11–18 mm; calyx weakly gibbous-campanulate in fruit, 9–15 mm abaxially, 6–14 mm adaxially, usually eglandular, very rarely glandular on tube, pubescent; tube 2.5–6 mm; lobes subulate or linear-lanceolate to lanceolate, abaxial 6–10 × 1.5–3(–4) mm, adaxial 4.5–9 × 1–1.5 mm; corolla lavender to purple, banner paler, sometimes also marginally white, elliptic to obovate, 11–18 × 4–7 mm with claw 2–5 mm, wings 11–16 × 2–3 mm with claw 3.5–6 mm, keel 6–12 × 2–3 mm with claw 2.5–7 mm; filaments 6–11 mm; anthers round to elliptic, 0.3–0.5 mm; ovary glabrous or pubescent apically, style pubescent basally. **Legumes** ellipsoid-lanceoloid to oblong, 5–6.5 × 3–5 mm, eglandular, glabrous or slightly pubescent, beak 7–19 mm, exserted beyond calyx. **Seed** red-brown or gray, globose-reniform, 4–5 × 2.5–3.5 mm, smooth to somewhat rugose. **2*n*** = 22.

Varieties 3 (3 in the flora): w, c United States.

J. W. Grimes (1990) recognized three varieties under *Pediomelum hypogaeum*. Many specimens exist with intermediate traits that obscure strong delineations between taxa.

1. Peduncles 1–3.5 cm, less than ½ as long as subtending petiole . . . . 7a. *Pediomelum hypogaeum* var. *hypogaeum*
1. Peduncles (1.7–)4–14 cm, more than ½ as long as subtending petiole.
    2. Peduncles appressed-pubescent; leaflet blades lanceolate to elliptic . . . . 7b. *Pediomelum hypogaeum* var. *scaposum*
    2. Peduncles hirsute-villous; leaflet blades oblanceolate to rhombic . . . . 7c. *Pediomelum hypogaeum* var. *subulatum*

7a. Pediomelum hypogaeum (Nuttall) Rydberg var. hypogaeum [E]

Leaves: petiole 40–120 mm, usually 2 times longer than subtended peduncle; leaflet blades elliptic to oblanceolate. **Peduncles** 1–3.5 cm, less than ½ as long as subtending petiole, appressed-pubescent. **Seed** usually red-brown, rarely gray.

Flowering spring–early summer. Sandy soils, grasslands, open woodlands; 0–1700 m; Colo., Kans., Mont., Nebr., N.Mex., Okla., Tex., Wyo.

Variety *hypogaeum* is known from Cascade and Rosebud counties in Montana southward through mostly eastern counties in Wyoming, far western Nebraska (Deuel and Sioux counties), eastern Colorado, western Kansas and Oklahoma, to central new Mexico and central Texas. It is uncommon within its range but more prevalent in the southern states of its distribution.

7b. Pediomelum hypogaeum (Nuttall) Rydberg var. **scaposum** (A. Gray) Mahler, Sida 12: 250. 1987 E

Psoralea hypogaea Nuttall var. *scaposa* A. Gray, Boston J. Nat. Hist. 6: 173. 1850; *Pediomelum scaposum* (A. Gray) Rydberg; *Psoralea hypogaea* subsp. *scaposa* (A. Gray) Ockendon; *P. scaposa* (A. Gray) J. F. Macbride

Leaves: petiole (20–)35–70 mm, barely longer to shorter than peduncle; leaflet blades lanceolate to elliptic. **Peduncles** (1.7–)4–9 cm, usually longer than, sometimes equal to, petiole, appressed-pubescent. **Seed** usually gray, rarely red-brown.

Flowering spring–early summer. Primarily on limestone, sometimes sandy soils, rocky hills, grasslands; 200–700 m; Tex.

Variety *scaposum* is found along the eastern edge of the Edwards Plateau and northwards into the Cross Timbers and Blackland Prairie ecoregions.

7c. Pediomelum hypogaeum (Nuttall) Rydberg var. **subulatum** (Bush) J. W. Grimes, Mem. New York Bot. Gard. 61: 76. 1990 E

Psoralea subulata Bush, Rep. (Annual) Missouri Bot. Gard. 17: 120. 1906; *Pediomelum subulatum* (Bush) Rydberg

Leaves: petiole 30–210 mm, usually ½ as long as or equal to subtended peduncle; leaflet blades oblanceolate to rhombic. **Peduncles** 2–14 cm, equal to or more than ½ as long as subtending petiole, hirsute-villous. **Seed** red-brown.

Flowering spring–early summer. Dry, sandy soils, open woodlands, grasslands; 0–400 m; Ark., Okla., Tex.

Variety *subulatum* is found in Miller and Nevada counties in Arkansas, Marshall County in Oklahoma, and in Texas in Gulf and blackland prairies vegetation and post-oak savanna woodlands, as well a few collections from Piney Woods in Hardin County.

8. Pediomelum epipsilum (Barneby) S. L. Welsh, Great Basin Naturalist 46: 257. 1986 • Kane breadroot E

Psoralea epipsila Barneby, Leafl. W. Bot. 3: 193. 1943; *Pediomelum megalanthum* (Wooton & Standley) Rydberg var. *epipsilum* (Barneby) J. W. Grimes

Herbs clump-forming, acaulescent or subcaulescent, 3–16 (–22) cm, mostly glandular (with obvious blond to dark brown glands) and pubescent throughout. **Stems** short-erect, unbranched or branched, with 2–5 internodes, sometimes with decumbent lateral stems to 22 cm, strigose to ascending-hairy, leaves appearing clustered basally or on tips of some lateral stems, or dispersed along more elongated stems; pseudoscapes to 4.5 cm; cataphylls to 15 mm. **Leaves** palmately 5(–8)-foliolate; stipules persistent, lanceolate to slightly elliptic, 5–11 × 2.5–4.5 mm, pubescent; petiole jointed basally, 50–80 (–100) mm; petiolules 0.5–2 mm; leaflet blades obovate to oblanceolate or ± rhombic, 1.5–2.5(–4) × 1.2–2.5 cm, base cuneate or attenuate, apex broadly acute to rounded, surfaces bicolor, abaxially glandular, cinereous, adaxially bright green, glabrous or sparsely strigose only along base of veins. **Peduncles** 1.4–5 cm, shorter than subtending petiole, pubescent with erect-ascending hairs. **Inflorescences** disjointing in age at peduncle base, subglobose to elongate; rachis 1.4–4 cm, elongating in fruit, nodes 4–9, (1–)3(or 4) flowers per node, internodes relatively short or to 10 mm; bracts persistent to tardily deciduous, ovate to broadly lanceolate, 13–18(–22) × 6–10 mm, apex caudate, pubescent. **Pedicels** 2–4 mm. **Flowers** 14–19 mm; calyx gibbous-campanulate in fruit, (10–)11–16(–18) mm abaxially, (9–)10–15 (–16) mm adaxially, tube glandular, pubescent; tube 5–6(–8) mm; lobes linear-lanceolate to elliptic, abaxial 6.5–10 × 2–3 mm, adaxial 6–9 × 1–1.5 mm, glandular or eglandular; corolla purple, banner sometimes paler, oblanceolate, 14–19 × 5–7 mm with claw 6–9 mm, wings 9–18 × 2–3 mm with claw 6–9 mm, keel (10–)12–16 × 2–3 mm with claw 7–9 mm; filaments 11–16 mm; anthers elliptic, 0.3 mm; ovary pubescent or only apically, style pubescent basally. **Legumes** ovoid, 6–9 × 4–4.5 mm, eglandular, pubescent, beak 5–8 mm, ± equal to calyx. **Seed** brown, reniform, 4–5 × 3 mm, shiny.

Flowering late spring–summer. Rocky to clay soils, pine or juniper woodlands, desert shrub communities; 1600–1700 m; Ariz., Utah.

Pediomelum epipsilum is known from Coconino and Mohave counties in Arizona and Kane County in Utah. It has been variously treated at specific and varietal rank, but bract and leaflet morphology, as well as phylogenetic data (A. N. Egan and K. A. Crandall 2008, 2008b), support recognition of the taxon at the rank of species.

9. Pediomelum megalanthum (Wooton & Standley) Rydberg in N. L. Britton et al., N. Amer. Fl. 24: 22. 1919 • Breadroot E F

Psoralea megalantha Wooton & Standley, Contr. U.S. Natl. Herb. 16: 140. 1913; *Pediomelum megalanthum* var. *retrorsum* (Rydberg) J. W. Grimes; *P. retrorsum* Rydberg; *Psoralea mephitica* S. Watson var. *retrorsa* (Rydberg) Kearney & Peebles; *P. retrorsa* (Rydberg) Tidestrom

Herbs mostly acaulescent, 4–25 cm, glandular (with obvious blond to dark brown glands) and pubescent. **Stems** erect to decumbent, short and hidden by stipules, sometimes with decumbent lateral stems with dense cluster of leaves and inflorescences distally, unbranched, leaves clustered; pseudoscapes to 0.5 cm; cataphylls to 15 mm, conspicuously veined. **Leaves** palmately 5(–8)-foliolate; stipules persistent, lanceolate to elliptic, 5–14 × 2.5–5 mm, pubescent; petiole jointed to leaf spur, 4–13(–15) mm, glabrate to sparsely pubescent; petiolule 0.5–2 mm; leaflet blades broadly ovate, orbiculate, oblanceolate, or ± rhombic, 1–4 × 0.6–4 cm, base cuneate or attenuate, apex rounded to broadly acute, surfaces gray-green to yellow-green, sometimes bicolor, glandular, appressed-pubescent. **Peduncles** 2.5–7.5(–10) cm, shorter than subtending petiole, pubescent, with relatively long, erect to reflexed hairs or with hairs of 2 types: short, appressed to incurved-ascending hairs and long, spreading-erect to reflexed, straight to curly hairs. **Inflorescences** disjointing in age at peduncle base, subglobose to elongate; rachis 0.5–7 cm, elongating in fruit, nodes 2–10, (1–)3(or 4) flowers per node, internodes relatively short or to 9 mm; bracts tardily deciduous, oblanceolate, lanceolate, or elliptic, (6–)8–13(–18) × 2.5–10 mm, eglandular to sparsely glandular, strigose abaxially. **Pedicels** 1.5–6(–8) mm. **Flowers** (13–)15–20(–22) mm; calyx gibbous-campanulate in fruit, (14–)16–19 mm abaxially, (13–)15–17 mm adaxially, eglandular or minutely glandular, setose or with appressed hairs; tube 6–8(–10) mm; lobes lanceolate to oblanceolate or elliptic, abaxial 7–10 × 2.5–3 mm, adaxial 6–8 × 1–2 mm; corolla whitish blue to purple, banner lighter than or similar to wings and keel, obovate-lanceolate, 16–22 × 6–9 mm with claw 6–7 mm, wings 13–20 × 2–3 mm with claw 8–10 mm, keel 14–16 × 2–3 mm with claw 8–9 mm, blade with darker blotch distal to middle; filaments 13–17 mm; anthers elliptic, 0.3 mm; ovary pubescent throughout or on distal ½, style pubescent at base. **Legumes** oval-ellipsoid, 6–9 × 4–5 mm, eglandular, erect- to appressed-pubescent distally, beak attenuate, (3–)5–8 mm, included within calyx. **Seed** brown, reniform-elliptic, 4–5 × 3–4 mm, shiny.

Flowering spring–late summer. Decaying sandstone and clay soils on rock outcrops, desert shrub and pinyon-juniper communities; 500–2000 m; Ariz., Colo., Nev., N.Mex., Utah.

Pediomelum megalanthum and its varieties have variably been recognized at specific or varietal levels. J. W. Grimes (1990) and D. Isely (1998) included *P. epipsilum* as a variety under *P. megalanthum* along with var. *retrorsum* and var. *megalanthum*, while others have recognized these at the specific level (S. L. Welsh et al. 1993), based largely on the directionality and type of peduncle vestiture. A recent morphometric analysis showed no clear break between vars. *megalanthum* and *retrorsum* (A. N. Egan 2015). Intrapopulational variation in peduncle vestiture and hair type has also been observed (Max Licher and John Anderson, pers. comm.). Therefore, these are here recognized as a single species.

10. Pediomelum castoreum (S. Watson) Rydberg in N. L. Britton et al., N. Amer. Fl. 24: 22. 1919 • Beaver Indian breadroot E

Psoralea castorea S. Watson, Amer. Naturalist 12: 601. 1878

Herbs acaulescent or subacaulescent, to 16 cm, glandular (with obvious blond to dark brown glands) on leaflets, less so on bracts and stipules, mostly silver-strigose throughout. **Stems** short-erect, sometimes with proximal, decumbent lateral stems to 25 cm, unbranched or sparsely branched, leaves appearing clustered at base or alternate along short stem, with clusters of leaves or inflorescences distally; pseudoscapes to 10(–14) cm; cataphylls 5–20 mm, glabrous or strigose. **Leaves** usually palmately, rarely pseudopalmately, (3–)5 or 6-foliolate; stipules persistent, triangular or lanceolate to narrowly oblong, 5–13.5 × 2–5 mm, pubescent; petiole slightly enlarged and jointed basally, slightly canaliculate, (30–)65–150 mm; petiolules 1.5–2.5 mm; leaflet blades oblanceolate or orbiculate to elliptic, (1.5–)2–4.5 × (1.5–)2.3–4 cm, base attenuate, apex broadly acute to rounded or retuse, surfaces abaxially gray-green and pubescent, adaxially yellow-green and sparsely pubescent along veins to pubescent, not white-veined. **Peduncles** (1.5–)2.4–7 cm, shorter than subtending petiole, appressed-spreading pubescent. **Inflorescences** disjointing in age at peduncle base, ellipsoid to ovoid; rachis 1.5–1.6 cm, elongating to 2–5.5 cm in fruit, nodes 3–11, 2 or 3 flowers per node; bracts tardily deciduous or persistent, narrowly elliptic or spatulate to oval, 3.5–8 × 3–7 mm, pubescent. **Pedicels** 0–2 mm. **Flowers** 9–13 mm; calyx gibbous-campanulate in fruit, 10–12 mm abaxially (elongating to 20 mm in fruit),

9–10.5 mm to adaxial lobe (elongating to 14 mm in fruit), usually eglandular, strigose to setose; tube 3–4 mm; abaxial lobe broadly oblanceolate, 4–5 × 4–4.5 mm, often with 3 prominent veins, adaxial lobes linear, 4–5 × 1–1.5 mm; corolla ochroleucous with purple tinge to purple, banner usually elliptic, 9–13 × 3.5–5 mm with claw 2–4 mm, wings 10–13 × 2 mm with claw 4–4.5 mm, keel 6.5–8 × 2 mm with claw 3–4 mm; filaments 6–7.5 mm; anthers elliptic, 0.4 mm; ovary pubescent apically, style glabrous, sometimes pubescent basally. **Legumes** ellipsoid to ovoid, 6–8 × 5–6 mm, eglandular, strigose, beak 8–11(–15) mm, equal to or longer than calyx. **Seed** gray-green to dark brown, narrowly reniform, 5.5–6 × 3.5–4 mm, rugose, dull.

Flowering spring. Sand or sandy soils, open desert scrub communities; 400–1000 m; Ariz., Calif., Nev.

Pediomelum castoreum is known from Mohave County in Arizona, San Bernardino County in California, and Clark and Lincoln counties in Nevada.

11. Pediomelum pentaphyllum (Linnaeus) Rydberg in N. L. Britton et al., N. Amer. Fl. 24: 23. 1919 • Chihuahua scurfpea [C]

Psoralea pentaphylla Linnaeus, Sp. Pl. 2: 764. 1753

Herbs subacaulescent, to 30 cm, mostly glandular (with obvious blond to dark brown glands) and appressed-spreading pubescent throughout. **Stems** mostly very short-erect, sparsely branched, with leaves clustered at base, rarely with decumbent lateral stems 0–15 cm, with leaves and inflorescences in terminal clusters; pseudoscapes 0–4 cm; cataphylls 7–15 mm (when present), apically emarginate. **Leaves** palmately or pseudopalmately 5(or 6)-foliolate, sometimes with 2 leaflets distal to others; stipules persistent, lanceolate to linear, 9–15 × 5 mm, strigose-tomentose; petiole jointed basally, 60–150 mm, strigose-tomentose; petiolules 1.5–2 mm; leaflet blades lanceolate, rhombic, or slightly oblanceolate, 2–5.5 × (1.5–)2–3.2 cm, base cuneate, margins undulate, apex acute, mucronate, surfaces glandular and pubescent. **Peduncles** (3–)4–9.5 cm, equal to or shorter than subtending petiole, appressed-pubescent. **Inflorescences** disjointing in age at peduncle base, globose to long-ovoid; rachis 2–4.5 cm, nodes 6–9, 3 flowers per node; bracts persistent to tardily deciduous, lanceolate to elliptic, often ensiform, 5–7 × 2–3 mm, membranous in age, strigose. **Pedicels** 2–3 mm. **Flowers** 14–18 mm; calyx gibbous-campanulate in fruit, 14–16 mm abaxially, 11–12 mm adaxially, glandular, strigose; tube 4–5 mm; abaxial lobe broadly oblanceolate, 10–12 × 3.5–4 mm, adaxial lobes linear-lanceolate, 7–8 × 1–1.5 mm; corolla white to purple, banner white to lavender, paler than other petals, lanceolate to elliptic, 15–17 × 6–7 mm with claw 4–5 mm, wings 15–16 × 3–3.5 mm with claw 6 mm, keel 9–12 × 3 mm with claw 6–7 mm; filaments 8.5–10.5 mm; anthers round-elliptic, 0.3 mm; ovary pubescent apically, style pubescent basally. **Legumes** ellipsoid-oblanceoloid, 7–8 × 4–5 mm, eglandular, pubescent, beak broad, flat, 10–15 mm, barely exserted beyond calyx. **Seed** gray-green to brown, oblong-reniform, 5–6 × 3–4 mm, rugose.

Flowering spring–early summer. Desert grasslands; of conservation concern; 1500–2000 m; Ariz., N.Mex., Tex.; Mexico (Chihuahua).

A history of the confusing nomenclature of *Pediomelum pentaphyllum* was given by P. Tonne (2000). The name was misapplied by P. A. Rydberg (1919–1920); the plant that Rydberg described as *P. pentaphyllum* was actually *P. palmeri*; the plant denoted here as *P. pentaphyllum* was called *P. trinervatum* Rydberg. J. W. Grimes (1990), before completion of his monograph, erroneously annotated several *P. pentaphyllum* specimens as *P. trinervatum*.

Pediomelum pentaphyllum is rare, with only a few confirmed populations in Arizona (Cochise and Graham counties) and New Mexico (Hidalgo County); it was also collected in Texas (Presidio County), and Chihuahua, Mexico (P. Tonne 2000), but may be extirpated in those states.

Pediomelum pentaphyllum is said to have been used by Native Americans and indigenous Mexicans as a fever reducer, the use of which may have contributed historically to its spread through cultivation. It is uncertain as to why *P. pentaphyllum* has declined, but causes may include over-collecting, grazing, and herbicide application (WildEarth Guardians, https://pdf.wildearthguardians.org/site/DocServer/petition_scurfpea.pdf?docID=624&AddInterest=1103).

12. Pediomelum californicum (S. Watson) Rydberg in N. L. Britton et al., N. Amer. Fl. 24: 21. 1919 • California Indian breadroot

Psoralea californica S. Watson, Proc. Amer. Acad. Arts 12: 251. 1877; *P. monticola* Greene

Herbs subacaulescent to shortly caulescent, to 26 cm, mostly glandular (with obvious blond to dark brown glands) and pubescent throughout. **Stems** short-erect, branched sparsely proximally and often with decumbent lateral branches, to 26 cm at maturity, these with terminal cluster of leaves and inflorescences, very rarely branched again, leaves dispersed along short main stem or appearing clustered at base; pseudoscapes to 4 cm; cataphylls 0.5–7 mm, glabrous. **Leaves** palmately 5–7-foliolate;

stipules tardily deciduous or persistent, lanceolate to slightly falcate, 7–10 × 2.5–3 mm, stramineous, appressed-spreading pubescent; petiole slightly enlarged and jointed basally, (20–)40–100(–110) mm, sparsely glandular abaxially, appressed-spreading pubescent; petiolules 1.5–2.5 mm; leaflet blades obovate to slightly rhombic, 1.3–3 × 1–1.7 cm, base attenuate, apex broadly acute to rounded or retuse, surfaces glandular and appressed-pubescent. **Peduncles** (1.5–) 2.5–6.5 cm, shorter than subtending petiole, appressed-spreading pubescent. **Inflorescences** disjointing in age at peduncle base, globose to slightly elongate; rachis 0.7–2.5 cm, fairly crowded, nodes (2–)4–10, (1 or)2 or 3 flowers per node, internodes to 9 mm; bracts tardily deciduous or persistent, oblanceolate to elliptic, 6.5–8 × 2–4 mm, appressed-spreading pubescent. **Pedicels** 3–5 (–7) mm. **Flowers** 8–12 mm; calyx gibbous-campanulate in fruit, 9.5–10.5 mm abaxially, 8.5–10 mm adaxially, glandular, white-villous; tube 2–3 mm; abaxial lobe elliptic to oblanceolate, 6.5–8.5 × 1.5–2 mm, adaxial lobe linear to linear-lanceolate, 6.5–7.5 × 1–1.5 mm; corolla blue to violet, banner usually white or lighter than other petals, oblanceolate, 10–11 × 6 mm with claw 2.5–3 mm, wings 9.5–10.5 × 2–2.5 mm with claw 2.5–3.5 mm, keel 7–8 × 2–3 mm with claw 3–4 mm; filaments 6.5–7 mm; anthers elliptic, 0.3 mm; ovary pubescent apically, style pubescent basally. **Legumes** ellipsoid to ovoid, 4–9 × 3.5–5 mm, eglandular, short-pubescent, beak linear, 1–4 mm, not exserted beyond calyx. **Seed** red-brown to brown, black-mottled, narrowly reniform, 5–5.5 × 3–3.5 mm. $2n = 22$.

Flowering late spring–summer. Rocky soils, chaparral, pine, juniper, or oak woodland openings; 500–2500 m; Calif.; Mexico (Baja California).

Pediomelum californicum is morphologically similar to *P. mephiticum,* and some have chosen to combine them into a single species (A. M. Vail 1894), suggesting that *P. californicum* is simply a disjunct *P. mephiticum.* Others have relied on the distinct geographic separation and difference in caulescent versus acaulescent habit as distinguishing characters (J. W. Grimes 1990; S. L. Welsh et al. 1993).

Pediomelum californicum is found from Tehama County southward to San Diego County and northern Mexico.

13. **Pediomelum mephiticum** (S. Watson) Rydberg in N. L. Britton et al., N. Amer. Fl. 24: 22. 1919 • Skunktop [E]

Psoralea mephitica S. Watson, Proc. Amer. Acad. Arts 14: 291. 1879

Herbs acaulescent or subacaulescent, 4–16 cm, mostly glandular (with obvious blond to dark brown glands) and pubescent throughout. **Stems** erect, unbranched, retrorsely hairy, leaves clustered; pseudoscapes mainly subterranean, to 4 cm; cataphylls 0–5 mm, glabrous or pubescent. **Leaves** palmately 5(or 6)-foliolate; stipules usually persistent, sometimes tardily deciduous, lanceolate to elliptic, (4–)7–11 × 2.5–8 mm, glabrate to pubescent; petiole jointed basally, (30–)50–120 mm, retrorse-hairy; petiolules 2–3 mm; leaflet blades abaxially gray-green, adaxially green to yellow-green, cuneate-obovate to orbiculate, (1.5–)2–4 × (0.8–)1.5–3.5 cm, base cuneate, apex broadly acute to rounded or retuse, surfaces glandular and pubescent. **Peduncles** (2–)4–8(–10) cm, equal to or shorter than subtending petiole, pilose, hairs spreading or spreading-retrorse. **Inflorescences** disjointing in age at peduncle base, globose to elongate, 1.5–5(–8) cm; rachis 1.5–2.5 cm, nodes 4–6(–10), (2 or)3 flowers per node, internodes to 8 mm; bracts tardily deciduous or persistent, ovate to elliptic, 5–12 × 3–7 mm, long-pubescent. **Pedicels** 2–4(–6) mm. **Flowers** 10–13 mm; calyx gibbous-campanulate in fruit, 10–12.5 mm abaxially, 10–12 mm adaxially, glandular, pubescent; tube 2.5–4 mm; lobes linear or linear-lanceolate to elliptic, abaxial 7–9 × 2–3 mm, adaxial 4–8 × 1–1.5 mm; corolla mostly purple, banner white to ochroleucous, elliptic to oblanceolate, 9–12 × 6 mm with claw 2–4 mm, wings 10–12 × 2–2.5 mm with claw 4–4.5 mm, keel 8–9 × 2–3 mm with claw 3.5–4.5 mm; filaments 7–8.5 mm; anthers elliptic, 0.3 mm; ovary glabrous or pubescent apically, style glabrous or pubescent proximally. **Legumes** globose to ovoid, 5–7 × 3.5–5 mm, eglandular, pubescent on adaxial ½, beak 1–4 mm, not exserted beyond calyx. **Seed** red-brown to dark brown or gray-green and black-mottled, ellipsoid to reniform, 4–5 × 3 mm.

Flowering spring–summer. Rocky or sandy soils, pine, juniper, or oak woodlands; 700–2000 m; Ariz., Nev., Utah.

The type locality of *Pediomelum mephiticum* is stated as Beaver City, Utah, which is largely agreed to be erroneous. The type locality is more likely Beaver Dam, Arizona (J. W. Grimes 1990). *Pediomelum mephiticum* is known from Mohave County in Arizona, Clark and Lincoln counties in Nevada, and Washington County in Utah.

14. Pediomelum verdiense S. L. Welsh, Licher & N. D. Atwood, W. N. Amer. Naturalist 70: 12, fig. 3. 2010 (as verdiensis) • Verde breadroot [E]

Pediomelum pauperitense S. L. Welsh, Licher & N. D. Atwood

Herbs acaulescent to short-caulescent, 4.5–13(–15) cm, mostly glandular (with obvious blond to dark brown glands) and pubescent throughout. **Stems** erect, rarely with decumbent laterals, unbranched or with few branches near base, spreading white hairy, leaves appearing clustered or dispersed along short stems; pseudoscapes to 6 cm (when present); cataphylls 0–15 mm, glabrous or pubescent. **Leaves** palmately (3–)5(or 6)-foliolate; stipules tardily deciduous or persistent, lanceolate to elliptic, 4–16 × 2–8 mm, scarious, strigose to glabrate; petiole jointed basally, 10–100(–115) mm, hairs appressed-ascending; petiolules 1.5–3 mm; leaflet blades abaxially gray-green, adaxially green to yellow-green, cuneate-obovate, (0.8–)1.2–3 × 0.7–1.8(–2.2) cm, base cuneate, apex broadly acute to rounded or retuse, surfaces glandular and pubescent, with more hairs abaxially and also along veins adaxially. **Peduncles** (0.5–)1–5.5(–6) cm, shorter than subtending petiole, pilose, spreading or spreading-ascending white-hairy, sometimes with longer spreading hairs. **Inflorescences** disjointing in age at peduncle base, cymose; rachis 1–3 cm, nodes (1 or)2–4(–6), (2 or)3 flowers per node; bracts tardily deciduous or persistent, elliptic, 3.5–8.5(–10) × 2–6 mm, strigose. **Pedicels** 2.5–4.5(–6) mm. **Flowers** (8–)10–13.5(–15) mm; calyx gibbous-campanulate in fruit, (7–)9–11.5 mm abaxially, (7–)9–11 mm adaxially, glandular, with blond glands obscured by indument, pubescent; tube (3.5–)4–5 mm; lobes lanceolate to oblong or elliptic, abaxial (4–)5–9 × (1.5–)2–3.5 mm, adaxial 4–7(–8) × 1–2.5 mm; corolla white to purple, banner white, cream, purple, or suffused with pale purple, wings and keel dark purple, wings sometimes lighter, banner broadly elliptic to ± oblanceolate, (7–)9–12(–14) × 6–8 mm with claw 2–5 mm, wings 10–13 × 2–3 mm with claw 4–5 mm, keel 8–10 × 2–3.5 mm with claw 3–5 mm; filaments 7–8.5 mm; anthers elliptic, 0.3 mm; ovary glabrous or apically pubescent, style glabrous or pubescent proximally. **Legumes** round to ovoid, 5–7 × 3.5–5 mm, eglandular, pubescent, beak 1–4 mm, not exserted beyond calyx. **Seed** olive to gray-brown, with or without purple mottling, oval to reniform, 3.5–5 × 2.5–3 mm, shiny.

Flowering spring–summer. Limestone soils, desert scrub and pinyon-juniper communities; 1000–1700 m; Ariz.

Pediomelum verdiense and *P. pauperitense* were described as separate taxa by S. L. Welsh and M. H. Licher (2010), with *P. verdiense* endemic to the silty, white limestone soil of the Verde Formation, Yavapai County, and *P. pauperitense* endemic to the pink limestone soil of Poverty Mountain, Mohave County. *Pediomelum pauperitense* was described as having smaller flowers, pedicels, bracts, and seeds. Morphometric analysis showed extensive overlap in all quantitative characters between *P. pauperitense* and *P. verdiense* (A. N. Egan 2015). Beyond range and substrate differences, *P. pauperitense* is said to differ from *P. verdiense* by having banner and wings suffused with purple, more upright leaves with leaflets held above the inflorescences, and less silvery vestiture—traits that some would argue merit recognition of *P. pauperitense* at least at varietal status. Both peduncle and petiole length overlap between the taxa, and live specimens of both taxa exhibit inflorescences held below the leaves, and vestiture density varies greatly, even within a population. Banner color may be a character difference, but further research into soil substrate specificity and impacts of soil pH on flower color is needed. *Pediomelum pauperitense* may represent a hybrid between *P. mephiticum* and *P. verdiense*, as several characters overlap or are intermediate between the two. Molecular phylogenetic work would help to clarify the relationships of *P. verdiense* with morphologically similar congeners, including *P. californicum* and *P. mephiticum*.

15. Pediomelum canescens (Michaux) Rydberg in N. L. Britton et al., N. Amer. Fl. 24: 18. 1919 • Buckroot [E]

Psoralea canescens Michaux, Fl. Bor.-Amer. 2: 57. 1803

Herbs caulescent, to 100 cm, mostly glandular throughout and strigose or canescent. **Stems** usually 1, rarely 2, erect, unbranched proximally to much branched distally, leaves dispersed along distal branches; pseudoscapes 0; cataphylls 6–11 mm (when present), glabrous. **Leaves** palmately 1 or 3-foliolate; stipules absent; petiole not swollen or jointed basally, slightly canaliculate, (0 or)2–6(–10) mm, usually shorter than petiolule, rarely to 1 mm longer, strigose; petiolules often adnate to leaf spur, 5–9 mm; leaflet blades broadly elliptic to obovate or oblanceolate to orbiculate, 3–5 × 2–3.2 cm, base attenuate, apex acute to rounded, surfaces abaxially densely canescent, adaxially glabrous or glabrate. **Peduncles** 2.7–8.2 cm, longer than subtending petiole, canescent. **Inflorescences** persistent, loose, much of rachis exposed, ovoid-ellipsoid or shortly elongate; rachis loose, 1.5–5.5 cm, elongating in fruit, nodes (2 or)3–6, 3 flowers per node; bracts persistent or tardily deciduous, lanceolate to broadly elliptic, 7–12 × 4–5 mm, appressed-pubescent to canescent. **Pedicels** 4–5 mm. **Flowers** 11–16 mm; calyx broadly campanulate in fruit, 8–12 mm abaxially, 7–9 mm adaxially, glandular, strigulose to canescent; tube 3–5 mm; lobes triangular or narrowly elliptic, abaxial 4.5–6 × 2.5 mm, adaxial 2–3.5 × 1.5–2 mm; corolla blue to blue-purple, sometimes fading yellowish green, banner oblanceolate, 11–15 × 6–8 mm with claw 3–5 mm, wings 10–13 × 2.5–3 mm with claw 4–5 mm, keel 7.5–9 × 2–2.5 mm with claw 4–5 mm; filaments 9–9.5 mm; anthers broadly elliptic, 0.5 mm; ovary glabrous or pubescent, style pubescent on proximal ½. **Legumes** ellipsoid, 5–6 × 4–5 mm, densely glandular, pubescent, beak 4–6 mm, equal to or slightly shorter than calyx. **Seed** gray-green to red-brown, reniform, 4–5 × 3–4 mm.

Flowering summer. Sandy soils, open woodlands, pine barrens; 0–200 m; Ala., Fla., Ga., N.C., S.C., Va.

Pediomelum canescens is found only in the Atlantic Coastal Plain in Florida and southern portions of Alabama and Georgia, with isolated populations known from the Carolinas and Sussex County, Virginia. It is well distinguished within the genus by the petioles being shorter than petiolules, particularly in middle and distal leaves.

16. **Pediomelum piedmontanum** J. R. Allison, M. W. Morris & A. N. Egan, Sida 22: 229, figs. 1, 2. 2006 • Dixie Mountain breadroot [C] [E]

Herbs caulescent, 50–80(–100) cm, mostly glandular throughout and strigose. **Stems** usually 1, rarely 2, erect, unbranched proximally to much branched distally, leaves dispersed along distal branches; pseudoscapes 0; cataphylls 6–10 mm. **Leaves** palmately 3(–5)-foliolate; stipules persistent, mostly linear-lanceolate, 7–12 × 6.5–9 mm, sparsely strigose; petiole, when present, not swollen or jointed basally, slightly canaliculate, (0 or)2–2.5(–4) mm, usually shorter than petiolules, sparsely strigose; petiolules often adnate to leaf spur, 1.8–3 mm; leaflet blades narrowly to broadly elliptic, (1–)1.2–5(–5.5) × (0.4–)0.6–2.7 cm, base cuneate, apex rounded to shallowly retuse and often mucronate, surfaces sparsely strigose. **Peduncles** 0.6–2.8(–3.4) cm, longer than subtending petiole, appressed-spreading pubescent. **Inflorescences** persistent, crowded, rachis usually concealed, usually elliptic to oblong, rarely ovate; rachis (1–)2–5(–5.5) cm, nodes (4–)6–13(–15), (1–)3(or 4) flowers per node; bracts persistent, broadly ovate to suborbiculate, 8–11.5 × (7–)9–10 mm, glabrous. **Pedicels** 1–3 mm. **Flowers** 12.5–14 mm; calyx strongly gibbous-campanulate in fruit, 12–16 mm abaxially, (10–)12–13 mm adaxially, glandular, pilose; tube 4–5 mm; lobes linear-lanceolate, abaxial (6–)7–11 (–11.5) × 1.5–3 mm, adaxial 4–8 × 1–1.5 mm; corolla violet to lavender or cream to yellowish and tinged with violet, banner broadly oblanceolate to obovate, (8.5–)10–14 × 5.5–7 mm with claw (3.5–)4.5–7 mm, wings (7–)8–12 × 2–2.5 mm with claw (3–)4–6 mm, keel (5–)6–10 × 2–2.5(–3) mm with claw (3–)4–5 mm; filaments 9.5–11 mm; anthers broadly elliptic, 0.5(–0.8) mm; ovary glabrous, style glabrous, sometimes strigulose basally. **Legumes** broadly ellipsoid to nearly obovoid, 6–7 × 4–4.5 mm, glabrous, dark brown-glandular on distal ½, beak (5–)6–8 mm, exserted beyond calyx. **Seed** gray-brown, reniform, 3.5–5 × 2.5–3.5(–4) mm.

Flowering summer. Rocky, open areas, adjacent open woodlands; of conservation concern; 0–100 m; Ga., S.C.

Pediomelum piedmontanum is known from only three populations, one in Georgia and two in South Carolina, with an estimated 1000 individuals in existence. Populations are newly threatened by the recent invasion of *Megacopta cribraria* (the Kudzu Bug), seen inhabiting plants in South Carolina, as well as continued herbivory and damage by moths, which make this species of special conservation concern.

17. **Pediomelum aromaticum** (Payson) W. A. Weber, Phytologia 53: 188. 1983 [E]

Psoralea aromatica Payson, Bot. Gaz. 60: 379. 1915; *Pediomelum aromaticum* var. *ambiguum* S. L. Welsh; *P. aromaticum* var. *barnebyi* S. L. Welsh; *P. aromaticum* var. *tuhyi* S. L. Welsh

Herbs caulescent, to 25 cm, mostly glandular and strigose throughout; spreading by rhizomes, often forming patches. **Stems** suberect to decumbent, branched, leaves dispersed along stems; pseudoscapes 0–12 cm; cataphylls 0–7 mm, prominently veined. **Leaves** palmately (3–)5–7-foliolate; stipules persistent, triangular, 2–8(–9) × 1–5 mm, glandular and strigose abaxially; petiole jointed to stem, 12–80 mm, strigose; petiolules 1–3 mm; leaflet blades oblanceolate, ovate, or rhombic, (0.6–)1.2–2.6 × (0.3–)1–2 cm, base cuneate, apex rounded to retuse, usually apiculate, surfaces glandular, abaxially uniformly strigose, adaxially strigose to glabrate or with hairs concentrated along veins. **Peduncles** 0.2–1.3 cm, shorter than subtending petiole, strigose. **Inflorescences** persistent, umbellate or subcapitate, rarely reduced to a single flower; rachis 0–0.8 cm, nodes 1–7, 3 flowers per node, internodes 1–2(–4) mm; bracts tardily deciduous or persistent, lanceolate to narrowly elliptic, sometimes short-cupulate, 2–7 × 1–3 mm, glandular and strigose abaxially. **Pedicels** 1–2.5(–4) mm. **Flowers** (7–)8–11 (–12) mm; calyx gibbous-campanulate in fruit, 5.5–10 mm abaxially, 4.5–8 mm adaxially, glandular, pubescent; tube 3–4 mm; abaxial lobe elliptic to oblanceolate, 2.5–7 × 1.5–2 mm, adaxial lobes triangular, 2–4(–5) × 1 mm; corolla blue-purple, banner white or paler than other petals, oblanceolate, 9–11 × 4–5.5 mm with claw 2.5–3 mm, wings 9–11 × 2–3 mm with claw 3.5–4 mm, keel 7–8 × 2 mm with claw 3–4 mm; filaments 6–6.5 mm; anthers ovate, 0.3 mm; ovary glabrous, style pubescent basally. **Legumes** globose to ovoid, 5–6 × 4 mm, glandular and short-strigose distally, beak broad, slightly arcuate, 5–6 mm, exserted beyond calyx. **Seed** gray-green to red-brown, oblong-reniform, 4.5–5 × 3.5–4 mm, shiny.

Flowering spring–summer. Rocky clay or sandstone soils, barren or open places in pinyon-juniper woodlands; 1000–2000 m; Ariz., Colo., Utah.

Pediomelum aromaticum is known from Mohave County in Arizona, Montrose County in Colorado, and southern Utah.

In the past, varieties were recognized based on the number of flowers per node, flower and peduncle length, and stem robustness. These varieties are largely confined to distinct geographical populations or areas. Variety *ambiguum* was described from Little Valley in Grand County as having long peduncles (5–28 mm) and an often bidentate abaxial calyx tooth. Variety *barnebyi* was described from populations from the Canaan Mountain region in Washington county and adjacent Arizona, an area at the westernmost edge of the *P. aromaticum* distribution. These plants are more robust than others, have more flowers per inflorescence, and have longer peduncles, but plants from across the range show similar robustness with number of flowers per inflorescence varying widely. Variety *tuhyi* was described as differing from var. *aromaticum* in having flowers smaller than 9 mm, coupled with decumbent stems. J. W. Grimes (1990) pointed out that mature flowers on several collections, including the holotype, are longer than 9 mm, and not all plants are decumbent.

18. Pediomelum cuspidatum (Pursh) Rydberg in N. L. Britton et al., N. Amer. Fl. 24: 19. 1919 • Largebract Indian breadroot [E]

Psoralea cuspidata Pursh, Fl. Amer. Sept. 2: 741. 1813

Herbs caulescent, to 100+ cm, mostly glandular throughout, strigose becoming glabrate. **Stems** 1+, decumbent to erect-ascending, much branched, leaves dispersed along stems; pseudoscapes rarely branched, 0–14 cm; cataphylls 0–13 mm. **Leaves** palmately 3–5-foliolate; stipules persistent, erect to reflexed, linear-lanceolate to lanceolate, 6–15 × 1–5 mm, glandular, pubescent; petiole enlarged but not jointed basally, often canaliculate, 5–40 mm, sparsely strigose; petiolules 1.5–3.5 mm; leaflet blades oblanceolate to elliptic, oblong, or obovate, 2–4.8 × 0.5–2 cm, base cuneate, apex acute to obtuse or apiculate, surfaces abaxially pubescent, adaxially glabrous. **Peduncles** 0.6–15 cm, longer than subtending petiole, strigose. **Inflorescences** persistent, ellipsoid to elongate; rachis 1.5–8.5 cm, nodes (2–)6–17, 3 flowers per node, internodes to 13 mm; bracts persistent, erect to reflexed, lanceolate, 4–17 × 1–6 mm, glandular, pubescent. **Pedicels** 2–3 mm. **Flowers** 12–22 mm; calyx strongly gibbous-campanulate in fruit, 9–15 mm abaxially, 8–12 mm adaxially, glandular, pubescent; tube 4–5.5 mm; abaxial lobe lanceolate to elliptic, 8–19 × 2–3.5 mm, adaxial lobes lanceolate, 4–7 × 1–1.5 mm; corolla blue, purple, or violet, banner broadly oblanceolate to obovate, 13–21 × 7–8 mm with claw 4–6 mm, wings 12–18.5 × 3–4 mm with claw 4–7.5 mm, keel 9–13 × 4–7 mm with claw 2.5–3 mm; filaments 8–12 mm; anthers elliptic, 0.5–0.6 mm; ovary glabrous or pubescent and glandular on distal ¼–⅓, style pubescent basally. **Legumes** ovoid to obovate, 6–8 × 4–4.5 mm, glandular, pubescent distally, beak 1.5–2 mm, shorter than calyx. **Seed** reddish brown, reniform to globose, 3.5–4 × 4.5–5 mm.

Flowering spring–summer. Grasslands, meadows, woodlands; 50–1500 m; Colo., Kans., Mont., Nebr., Okla., S.Dak., Tex.

Pediomelum cuspidatum is one of the larger species in the genus, in spite of its procumbent habit with erect-ascending, copious lateral branches. Horizontal stems are often bicolored, purple adaxially and light green abaxially. It is variable, particularly in plant height, flower length, and inflorescence length.

19. Pediomelum tenuiflorum (Pursh) A. N. Egan, Novon 19: 311. 2009 • Slimflower scurfpea

Psoralea tenuiflora Pursh, Fl. Amer. Sept. 2: 475. 1813; *Psoralidium tenuiflorum* (Pursh) Rydberg

Herbs caulescent, to 130 cm, glandular, glabrate to pubescent. **Stems** erect, much branched distally, leaves dispersed along stems; pseudoscapes 0; cataphylls 4–12 mm, papery, glabrous. **Leaves** palmately (1 or)3–5-foliolate, rarely with unifoliolate leaf subtending peduncles; stipules persistent to tardily deciduous, linear-lanceolate, (2–)4–5 × 1 mm, glandular, strigose; petiole rarely from swollen pulvinus, 1.5–17(–22) mm; petiolules 1–2.5 mm; leaflet blades elliptic to narrowly oblanceolate, (1–)1.4–3(–4.1) × 0.4–0.8(–1.5) cm, base rounded to attenuate, apex rounded to retuse, often apiculate, surfaces glandular, abaxially strigose, adaxially glabrous. **Peduncles**

2–9.5 cm, longer than subtending petiole, strigose. **Inflorescences** persistent, long-ovoid to elongate; rachis 1.5–6 cm, elongating through fruiting, nodes 3–12, 1–3 flowers per node, internodes 1–35 mm; bracts persistent, trullate to lanceolate, 1.5–3(–5) × 0.5–2 mm, glandular, glabrate to strigose. **Pedicels** 1.5–3 mm. **Flowers** 5–6 mm; calyx not or only slightly elongating in fruit and not changing shape or becoming gibbous, 2–4 mm, glandular, strigose to glabrate; tube 1–1.5 mm; lobes triangular, abaxial 1.5–2 × 1 mm, adaxial 0.5–1 × 0.5–1 mm; corolla usually dark blue to purple, rarely white, banner usually paler, elliptic to obovate, 4.5–6 × 4.5–6 mm with claw 1–2 mm, wings 6 × 1.5–2.5 mm with claw 1.5–3 mm, keel 3.5–4.5 × 1.5–2 mm with claw 1.5–2 mm; filaments 3.5–4 mm; anthers elliptic, 0.3 mm; ovary glabrous or pubescent apically, style glabrous. **Legumes** deciduous with calyx and pedicel, ellipsoid, 7–8 × 3–4 mm, glandular, glabrous, beak broad, 1–2.5 mm, well exserted beyond calyx. **Seed** brown, reniform, 5–6 × 3–4 mm, shiny.

Flowering spring–summer. Grasslands, desert scrub, woodlands; 200–2300 m; Ariz., Colo., Ill., Ind., Iowa, Kans., Minn., Mo., Mont., Nebr., Nev., N.Mex., Okla., S.Dak., Tex., Utah, Wis., Wyo.; Mexico (Chihuahua, Sonora).

Pediomelum tenuiflorum is widespread with morphological gradations across its distribution, especially in leaf and inflorescence size and shape and calyx pubescence. P. A. Rydberg (1919–1920) recognized as many as four separate species based on these differences, which seem to be environmentally influenced. The calyx morphology of *P. tenuiflorum* resembles that of *Ladeania lanceolata* in that it does not enlarge through fruiting, but differs by the fruit being persistent on the receptacle and falling with the calyx.

20. Pediomelum argophyllum (Pursh) J. W. Grimes, Mem. New York Bot. Gard. 61: 69. 1990 • Silverleaf Indian breadroot [E]

Psoralea argophylla Pursh, Fl. Amer. Sept. 2: 475. 1813

Herbs caulescent, to 100 cm, mostly glandular throughout, silvery-sericeous. **Stems** ± erect, branched distally, branches subtended by leaves, leaves dispersed along stems, more so distally; pseudoscapes to 10 cm (when present); cataphylls 9–20 mm, glabrous or pubescent apically. **Leaves** palmately 3–6-foliolate; stipules tardily deciduous proximally, persistent distally, linear, 8–18 × 2–4 mm, rarely glandular, glabrous; petiole not swollen or jointed basally, slightly canaliculate, 2–55 mm, strigose; petiolules 1–4 mm; leaflet blades oblanceolate to narrowly elliptic or orbiculate, 1.1–4.5 × 0.6–2.2 cm, base attenuate, apex acute, acuminate to apiculate, surfaces abaxially sparsely to densely sericeous, rarely eglandular, adaxially glabrous or less sericeous. **Peduncles** 3–9 cm, longer than subtending petiole, densely white-strigose. **Inflorescences** persistent, oblong, elongate; rachis 0–6 cm, exposed, nodes (1 or)2–4(–8), (1–)3 flowers per node, internodes 3–7(–17) mm; bracts persistent, linear to lanceolate or elliptic, 3–9 × 1.5–4 mm, sericeous. **Pedicels** 0.5–1 mm. **Flowers** 7–11 mm; calyx elongating and becoming broadly and shallowly campanulate in fruit but not gibbous, 6–8 mm abaxially, 4–6 mm adaxially, glandular (glands often hidden by hairs), sericeous (sometimes sparsely so); tube 2–3 mm; lobes linear-lanceolate to lanceolate, abaxial 4.5–5 × 2–2.5 mm, adaxial 1.5 × 1 mm; corolla deep blue, banner oblanceolate to obovate or orbiculate, 6–7.5 × 3.5–5 mm with claw 1.5–2 mm, wings 6–7 × 1.5–2.5 mm with claw 2–2.5 mm, keel 5–6 × 1.5–2 mm with claw 2–3 mm; filaments 4.5–5 mm; anthers elliptic, 0.4 mm; ovary glabrous proximally, canescent on distal ⅔, style canescent basally. **Legumes** narrowly oblong, 5–6 × 3–4.5 mm, obscurely glandular, tomentose, beak 3–5 mm, equal to or slightly longer than calyx. **Seed** red-brown, round-reniform, 4–5 × 3–4 mm, dull. 2*n* = 22.

Flowering summer. Grasslands; 200–1500 m; Alta., Man., Sask.; Colo., Ill., Iowa, Kans., Minn., Mo., Mont., Nebr., N.Y., N.Dak., Okla., S.Dak., Tex., Wis., Wyo.

Pediomelum argophyllum is unique in the genus in its gray, silvery pubescence, earning it the common name silverleaf Indian breadroot. It has one of the widest distributions of its congeners, ranging from Canada to Texas, but seems more prevalent in the northern states. It has been used by native cultures for food or medicine for at least 2500 years (D. F. Dexter et al. 2014).

21. Pediomelum digitatum (Nuttall ex Torrey & A. Gray) Isely, Sida 11: 430. 1986 • Palmleaf Indian breadroot [E]

Psoralea digitata Nuttall ex Torrey & A. Gray, Fl. N. Amer. 1: 300. 1838; *Pediomelum digitatum* var. *parvifolium* (Shinners) Gandhi & L. E. Brown; *Psoralea digitata* var. *parvifolia* Shinners; *Psoralidium digitatum* (Nuttall ex Torrey & A. Gray) Rydberg

Herbs caulescent, 30–90 cm, sparsely glandular on adaxial leaf surfaces, mostly eglandular elsewhere, appressed-canescent. **Stems** erect, several branched distally, leaves dispersed along stems; pseudoscapes to 6 cm (when present); cataphylls 7–14 mm, glabrous or pubescent, at least abaxially. **Leaves** palmately (3–)5(–7)-foliolate; stipules persistent, linear becoming arcuate-recurved, 4–11 × 2–3 mm, eglandular or sparsely glandular, sparsely pubescent; petiole sometimes swollen but not jointed basally, slightly canaliculate, 10–35 mm; petiolules 1.5–3 mm;

leaflet blades linear-lanceolate to oblanceolate, 0.9–5.5 × 0.2–0.8 cm, base cuneate, apex acuminate to apiculate, surfaces abaxially eglandular and appressed-pubescent, adaxially glandular and glabrate, or at least pubescent, along midvein. **Peduncles** 6.5–22 cm, much longer than subtending petiole, strigose. **Inflorescences** persistent, elongate, lax; rachis 2–6.5 cm, nodes (1 or)2–8, 3 flowers per node, internodes to 32 mm; bracts persistent, spatulate, obovate, or orbiculate, 2–10 × 1–5 mm, appressed-pubescent abaxially, glabrous adaxially. **Pedicels** 1–3 mm. **Flowers** 9.5–10.5 mm; calyx broadly and shallowly campanulate in fruit but not gibbous, 6–8 mm abaxially, 5–6 mm adaxially, eglandular to sparsely glandular, with light blond glands, appressed-pubescent, sometimes sparsely so; tube 2–3 mm; lobes deltate to lanceolate, abaxial 4–5 × 1–1.5 mm, adaxial 1.5 × 1 mm; corolla purple, violet, or blue-lavender, banner oblanceolate, 9.5–10 × 5–6 mm with claw 2–3 mm, wings 9–10 × 3 mm with claw 3–4 mm, keel 6.5–7 × 2–3 mm with claw 3 mm; filaments 6–6.5 mm; anthers ovoid, 0.4 mm; ovary glabrous, pubescent apically, style pubescent basally. **Legumes** obovoid to globose, 5–6 × 3.5–4 mm, glandular, sparsely strigose, at least distally, beak triangular, 1.5–4 mm, shorter than calyx lobes. **Seed** gray-green to red-brown, globose-reniform, 5 × 3–4 mm.

Flowering summer. Grasslands, shrub communities; 50–1500 m; Ark., Colo., Kans., La., Nebr., N.Mex., Okla., S.Dak., Tex., Wyo.

Pediomelum digitatum is similar to *P. linearifolium* in habit, size, and distribution but differs in having more leaflets and pedicels 1–3 mm; pedicels in *P. linearifolium* can be 3–4 times as long. Furthermore, *P. digitatum* is eglandular or very sparsely glandular abaxially on leaflet blades whereas *P. linearifolium* is profusely glandular on both leaflet blade surfaces. Variety *parvifolium* refers to plants in Texas with narrow leaflets; J. W. Grimes (1990) and D. Isely (1998) stated that variation in leaflet size is found throughout the range, and thus var. *parvifolium* is not recognized herein as distinct.

22. Pediomelum linearifolium (Torrey & A. Gray) J. W. Grimes, Mem. New York Bot. Gard. 61: 72. 1990 • Narrowleaf Indian breadroot [E]

Psoralea linearifolia Torrey & A. Gray, Fl. N. Amer. 1: 300. 1838; *Psoralidium linearifolium* (Torrey & A. Gray) Rydberg

Herbs caulescent, to 175 cm, glandular and sparsely strigose or glabrate. **Stems** erect, several branched distally, leaves dispersed along stems; pseudoscapes 0; cataphylls often deciduous, sometime persistent, 5–12 mm. **Leaves** palmately 3(or 4)-foliolate, or unifoliolate when subtending inflorescences; stipules tardily deciduous or persistent, linear-lanceolate to elliptic or rhombic, 3–10(–12) × 0.5–1.5 mm, glabrous or sparsely strigose; petiole not swollen or jointed basally, terete to slightly canaliculate, 3–11 mm; petiolules 0.5–3 mm; leaflet blades linear or narrowly to broadly elliptic, 2–6 × 0.3–0.6 cm, base attenuate, apex acuminate to apiculate, surfaces black-glandular, abaxially pubescent, adaxially glabrous. **Peduncles** 0.8–10.5 cm, much longer than subtending petiole, appressed-pubescent. **Inflorescences** persistent, elongate, lax; rachis 1.2–9.5 cm, nodes 3–7, (1–)3 flowers per node, internodes to 22 mm; bracts persistent, lanceolate to orbiculate, 1.5–3.5 × 1–1.5 mm, apex often apiculate, glandular and glabrous or abaxially pubescent. **Pedicels** 3.5–10 mm. **Flowers** 8–11 mm; calyx slightly enlarging in fruit becoming broadly and shallowly campanulate but not gibbous, 4.5–6 mm abaxially, 4–5.5 mm adaxially, glandular, appressed-pubescent, sometimes sparsely so; tube 2.5–4 mm; lobes triangular, abaxial 2–4 × 1.5–2.5 mm, adaxial 1.5–3.5 × 1–2 mm; corolla usually blue-violet to violet-purple, sometimes white, banner usually lighter in throat, oblanceolate to narrowly elliptic, 8–11.5 × 5–7 mm with claw 2–2.5 mm, wings 8–11.5 × 2–3 mm with claw 2–4 mm, keel 6–7 × 2–2.5 mm with claw 3–3.5 mm; filaments 6–6.5 mm; anthers elliptic, 0.5 mm; ovary glabrous, sometimes minutely pubescent apically, style glabrous or minutely pubescent basally. **Legumes** broadly ellipsoid to globose, 8–10.5 × 8.5–10.5 mm, glandular, glabrous, beak 3–3.5 mm, exserted beyond calyx. **Seed** olive green to light brown, globose-reniform, 4–6 × 3–4 mm.

Flowering summer. Grasslands, shrub and open woodland communities; 100–1500 m; Ark., Colo., Kans., Nebr., N.Mex., Okla., S.Dak., Tex.

Pediomelum linearifolium is easily distinguished from its congeners by the tall, gangly habit (more than 1 m) and lax inflorescences that nod (as opposed to tight heads in *P. reverchonii*, another species that achieves a tall habit), and by being glandular throughout (as opposed to *P. digitatum*, which has eglandular calyces).

23. Pediomelum latestipulatum (Shinners) Mahler, Sida 12: 250. 1987 [E]

Psoralea latestipulata Shinners, Field & Lab. 19: 22. 1951

Herbs caulescent, 5–45 cm, mostly glandular throughout and pubescent. **Stems** 1, erect, usually unbranched, rarely branched, leaves dispersed along stem from middle; pseudoscapes absent or to 8 cm; cataphylls 5–12 mm, sometimes sparsely pubescent. **Leaves** palmately 5–7-foliolate; stipules persistent, narrowly lanceolate to suborbiculate, 8–15 × 2.5–7 mm, glandular, sparsely pubescent; petiole not swollen or jointed basally, not canaliculate, 27–100 mm, strigose; petiolules 1.5–2.5 mm; leaflet blades oblanceolate to elliptic, 2–4.4 × 0.5–1.4 cm, base cuneate, apex acute to obtuse, surfaces glandular, abaxially pubescent, especially along veins and margins, adaxially glabrous. **Peduncles** 1.3–4.8 cm, shorter than or slightly longer than subtending petiole, pubescent. **Inflorescences** persistent, ovoid to ellipsoid; rachis 0.6–4.2 cm, nodes 4–12, 2 or 3 flowers per node, internodes to 7 mm; bracts persistent, elliptic to spatulate, or ovate, or oblanceolate to orbiculate, 6–11 × 2–8 mm, glandular, glabrous or sparsely pubescent. **Pedicels** 2–3 mm. **Flowers** 18–26 mm; calyx strongly gibbous-campanulate in fruit, 12–19 mm abaxially, 10–15 mm adaxially, glandular and sparsely pubescent distally; tube 6–8 mm; lobes linear-lanceolate, abaxial 4.5–7.5 × 1.5–2 mm, adaxial 3–6 × 1–1.5 mm; corolla blue to purple, banner broadly oblanceolate to obovate, 16–25 × 6–9 mm with claw 7–10 mm, wings 15–20 × 2.5–4 mm with claw 6–9 mm, keel 12–16 × 3–3.5 mm with claw 6–9 mm; filaments 11–16 mm; anthers elliptic, 0.7–0.8 mm; ovary glabrous, style glabrous. **Legumes** ovoid, 5–6.5 × 4–4.5 mm, glandular, glabrous, beak 5.5–6 mm, slightly shorter to slightly longer than calyx. **Seed** dark green to olive green, reniform, 4 × 5 mm.

Varieties 2 (2 in the flora): Texas.

1. Stems with erect to spreading hairs . . . . 23a. *Pediomelum latestipulatum* var. *latestipulatum*
1. Stems with appressed hairs . . . . 23b. *Pediomelum latestipulatum* var. *appressum*

23a. Pediomelum latestipulatum (Shinners) Mahler var. **latestipulatum** • Texas Plains Indian breadroot [E]

Stems 5–15(–30) cm, hairs erect to spreading. **Leaves:** stipules 10–14 × 4–7 mm; petiole 27–65 mm; leaflet blades 2–4.4 × 0.6–1.2 cm. **Peduncles** 1.3–4.8 cm. **Inflorescences:** bracts elliptic to spatulate or ovate, 8–11 × 3.5–4.5 mm. **Flowers** 16–24 mm. **Legumes:** beak slightly shorter than calyx.

Flowering summer. Grasslands, open woodlands; 100–500 m; Tex.

Variety *latestipulatum* is known from Brown, Callahan, Coleman, Eastland, Fisher, McCulloch, McLennan, Mills, Mitchell, Nolan, Palo Pinto, Parker, Stephens, Tarrant, Taylor, Tom Green, Wichita, Wise, and Wood counties.

23b. Pediomelum latestipulatum (Shinners) Mahler var. **appressum** (Ockendon) Gandhi & L. E. Brown, Sida 13: 373. 1989 (as appressa) • Edwards Plateau Indian breadroot [E]

Psoralea latestipulata Shinners var. *appressa* Ockendon, SouthW. Naturalist 10: 100. 1965

Stems 5–45 cm, hairs appressed. **Leaves:** stipules 8–15 × 2.5–7 mm; petiole 45–100 mm; leaflet blades 2.9–4.2 × 0.5–1.4 cm. **Peduncles** 2.4–4.8 cm. **Inflorescences:** bracts oblanceolate to orbiculate, 6–11 × 2–8 mm. **Flowers** 19–26 mm. **Legumes:** beak equal or slightly longer than calyx. $2n = 22$.

Flowering spring–summer. Oak-dominated hills, ridges, and outcrops; 400–700 m; Tex.

Variety *appressum* is known from Bexar, Blanco, Caldwell, Gillespie, Gonzales, Hays, Kerr, Pecos, Travis, and Williamson counties.

24. Pediomelum reverchonii (S. Watson) Rydberg in N. L. Britton et al., N. Amer. Fl. 24: 19. 1919 (as reverchoni) • Rock Indian breadroot [E] [F]

Psoralea reverchonii S. Watson, Proc. Amer. Acad. Arts 21: 447. 1886 (as reverchoni)

Herbs caulescent, to 150 cm, mostly glandular throughout and pubescent. **Stems** 1, erect, much branched distally, leaves dispersed along stem, more so apically; pseudoscapes 0; cataphylls 5–15 mm. **Leaves** palmately 3–5-foliolate; stipules tardily deciduous, linear to linear-lanceolate, 7–12 × 1–4 mm, sparsely strigose; petiole sometimes swollen but not jointed basally, 2–40 mm; petiolules 1.5–2 mm; leaflet blades narrowly elliptic, 1.3–4.5 × 0.3–1.4 cm, base obtuse to slightly cuneate, apex apiculate, surfaces abaxially tomentose, adaxially glabrous. **Peduncles** 1.4–2 cm, usually longer than subtending petiole, appressed-pubescent. **Inflorescences** persistent, globose-ovoid, compact; rachis 0.5–0.7 cm, crowded, nodes 2, (1–)3 flowers per node; bracts persistent, orbiculate, 7–14(–20) × 6–13 mm, apex cuspidate to caudate, short-pubescent. **Pedicels** 3.5–5 mm. **Flowers** 14–20 mm; calyx strongly gibbous-campanulate in fruit, 11–19 mm abaxially, 10–12 mm adaxially, glandular, pubescent; tube 4–5 mm; lobes linear-lanceolate, abaxial 10.5–12 × 2–3.5 mm, adaxial 2.5–3 × 0.8–1 mm; corolla lavender, banner oblanceolate, 13–16 × 6–7 mm with claw 4–5 mm, wings 12–14 × 2.5–3 mm with claw 4–5 mm, keel 8–10 × 2.5–3 mm with claw 3.5–6 mm; filaments 8–10 mm; anthers elliptic, 0.3–0.4 mm; ovary glabrous, pubescent on distal 1/6, style pubescent basally. **Legumes** ellipsoid, 7–8 × 4.5–5 mm, densely glandular, sparsely pubescent apically, beak 3–4 mm, subequal to calyx. **Seed** red-brown, oblong-reniform, 4 × 6 mm.

Flowering summer. Open rocky fields, prairies; 200–500 m; Okla., Tex.

Pediomelum reverchonii is recognized by its large, persistent bracts and slender, branching habit. It is restricted to south-central Oklahoma and north-central Texas.

25. **Pediomelum cyphocalyx** (A. Gray) Rydberg in N. L. Britton et al., N. Amer. Fl. 24: 19. 1919 • Turniproot [E]

Psoralea cyphocalyx A. Gray, Boston J. Nat. Hist. 6: 172. 1850

Herbs caulescent, to 100 cm, mostly glandular throughout, strigose, sometimes becoming glabrate. **Stems** 1, erect, slender, usually unbranched, rarely branched, leaves sparsely dispersed along stem, proximal ones often caducous; pseudoscapes to 6 cm (when present); cataphylls absent or 5–15 mm. **Leaves** palmately 3–5-foliolate, sparse; stipules tardily deciduous, linear-lanceolate to lanceolate, 6–15 × 0.5–2 mm, glandular, glabrate to densely pubescent, at least basally; petiole sometimes swollen but not jointed basally, slightly canaliculate, 7–60 mm, strigose; petiolules 2–3 mm; leaflet blades narrowly oblanceolate to elliptic, 3.5–9.5 × 1.3–8 cm, base cuneate, apex obtuse-acuminate, surfaces abaxially glandular and glabrous or pubescent, adaxially glabrous. **Peduncles** 2.5–7.5 cm, longer than subtending petiole, strigose. **Inflorescences** persistent, oblong to elliptic; rachis 1.5–7 cm, nodes 3–15, 2 or 3 flowers per node, internodes elongating to 15 mm in fruit; bracts persistent or tardily deciduous, mostly oblanceolate to obovate, 4–9 × 1.5–4 mm, glabrate to pubescent. **Pedicels** 1.5–2 mm. **Flowers** 12–18 mm; calyx strongly gibbous-campanulate in fruit, 7.5–12 mm abaxially, 6–10 mm adaxially, glandular, pubescent; tube 4–4.5 mm; abaxial lobe lanceolate to elliptic, 3.5–7.5 × 1.5–3 mm, adaxial lobes linear-lanceolate, 2.5–3 × 1 mm; corolla pale blue to lavender, banner narrowly oblanceolate, 12–15.5 × 6–7 mm with claw 4–5 mm, wings 11–14 × 2–3 mm with claw 5–6 mm, keel 8–11 × 2.5–3 mm with claw 2.5–3 mm; filaments 9–11 mm; anthers elliptic, 0.5–0.6 mm; ovary glabrous or pubescent on distal 1/4, style pubescent basally. **Legumes** globose-ovoid, 5–6 × 3.5–5 mm, glandular, pubescent apically, beak 2–4 mm, shorter than calyx. **Seed** brown, reniform to globose, 3–3.5 × 4–4.5 mm. $2n = 22$.

Flowering spring–summer. Shallow, limestone soils, hillsides, rock outcrops, open woodlands; 200–500 m; Tex.

Pediomelum cyphocalyx is infrequently found in a narrow range along the southern to southeastern edge of the Edwards Plateau in Texas. It is distinguished from its congeners in the area by its narrow leaflets and slender, erect habit.

117. ASPALTHIUM Medikus, Vorles. Churpfälz. Phys.-Öcon. Ges. 2: 380. 1787 • [Greek *asphaltion*, kind of trefoil with smell of tar, probably alluding to *Psoralea bituminosa*] [I]

Martin F. Wojciechowski

Herbs, perennial, sometimes suffrutescent, rarely shrubs, unarmed. **Stems** erect to spreading, sparsely to densely pubescent, gland-dotted. **Leaves** alternate, odd-pinnate; stipules present; petiolate; leaflets 3, stipels absent, blade margins entire [denticulate], surfaces glabrous or pubescent, gland-dotted. **Inflorescences** 7–15-flowered, axillary, racemes [pseudoracemes], dense, headlike; bracts present. **Flowers** papilionaceous; calyx campanulate, lobes 5, unequal; corolla usually blue-violet, sometimes bicolored [white]; stamens 10, diadelphous [monadelphous]; anthers dorsifixed; style glabrous; stigma penicillate. **Fruits** legumes, substipitate, compressed, straight, ovoid, with well-defined swordlike beak, indehiscent, pubescent to hirsute. **Seed** 1, oblong to reniform. $x = 10$.

Species 5 (1 in the flora): introduced, California; Europe (Mediterranean region), w Asia (Israel), Atlantic Islands (Macaronesia).

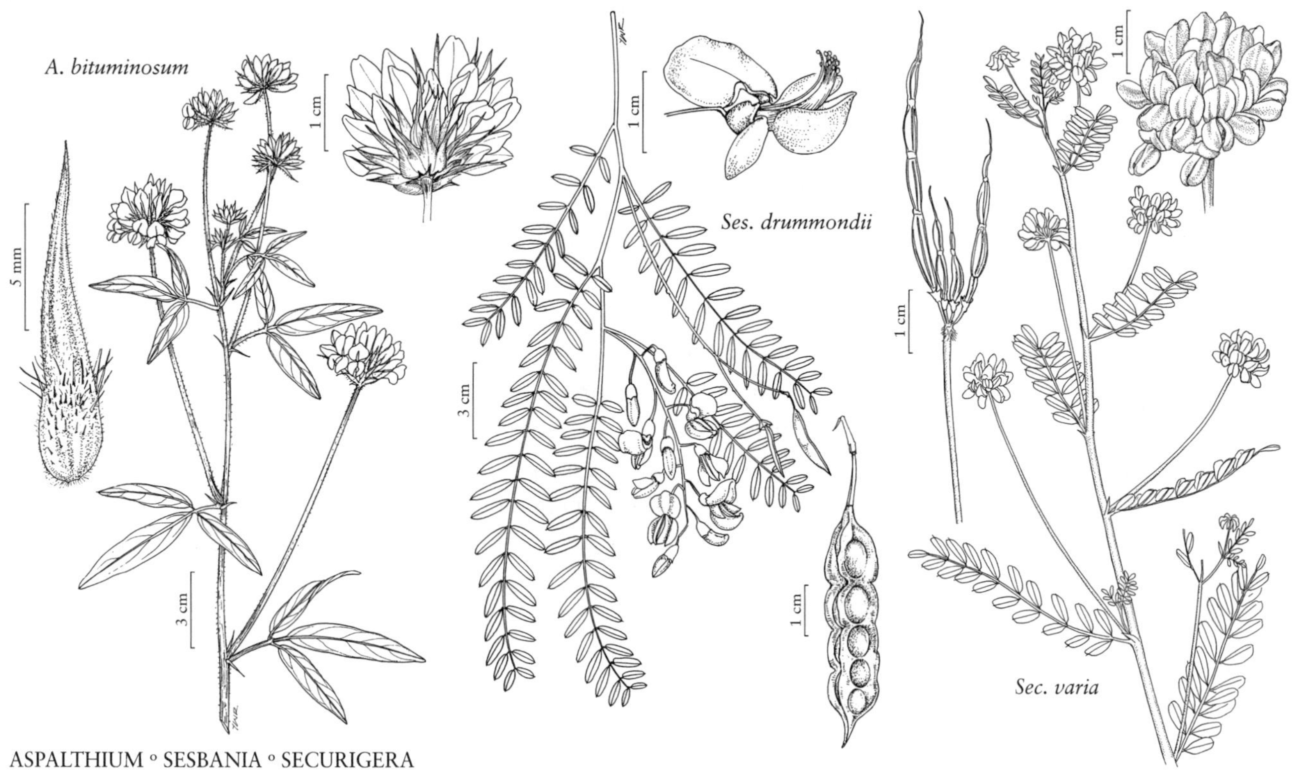

ASPALTHIUM ◦ SESBANIA ◦ SECURIGERA

Aspalthium is sometimes cultivated as a forage crop in Europe (C. H. Stirton 1981), under the generic name *Bituminaria* Heister ex Fabricius, which is an illegitimate name. Of the four additional species in the genus, two are sometimes also cultivated for forage. A key to species in the genus (but treated as *Bituminaria*) is given by P. Minissale et al. (2013).

1. **Aspalthium bituminosum** (Linnaeus) Fourreau, Ann. Soc. Linn. Lyon, n. s., 16: 365. 1868 (as Asphaltium) • Arabian pea [F] [I]

Psoralea bituminosa Linnaeus, Sp. Pl. 2: 763. 1753; *Bituminaria bituminosa* (Linnaeus) C. H. Stirton

Stems 1–2 m. **Leaves:** stipules persistent, distinct, narrow or setaceous; leaflet blades linear-lanceolate to ovate, 10–60 × 3–30 mm. **Peduncles** 5–20 cm, usually longer than leaves, often densely black-strigose. **Racemes:** bracts 3(–5) each node, partially connate, often densely black-strigose. **Pedicels** 1–2 mm. **Flowers:** calyx 9–15 mm; corolla 12–20 mm; ovary pubescent. **Legumes** 4–5 mm, beak to 15 mm; pericarp adnate to seed.

Flowering Apr–May (Sep–Oct). Open, disturbed sites, slopes, chaparral, oak woodland; 50–1100 m; introduced; Calif.; s Europe.

Aspalthium bituminosum is known from Los Angeles County. It has been reported for Florida (P. A. Rydberg 1919–1920; J. K. Small 1933), but specimen documentation has not been found.

118. SESBANIA Adanson, Fam. Pl. 2: 327, 604. 1763 (as Sesban), name and orthography conserved • Riverhemp [Arabic *saisabaan* or Persian *sisabaan*, vernacular name for *Sesbania sesban* (Linnaeus) Merrill, the type species]

Frank T. Farruggia

Agati Adanson, name rejected; *Daubentonia* de Candolle; *Daubentoniopsis* Rydberg; *Glottidium* Desvaux; *Monoplectra* Rafinesque

Herbs, annual [perennial], shrubs, subshrubs, or trees, usually unarmed, rarely armed as prickles on stems. **Stems** ascending, young growth pubescent or glabrous, hairs simple, long, close-pressed to spreading, pith solid, spongy, or partitioned. **Leaves** alternate, even-pinnate; stipules present, caducous, narrowly triangular; rachis canaliculate; petiolate, petiole base with stipitate, multicellular glands; stipels usually present, often persistent, glandular; leaflets 10–96+, opposite, folding closed at night, blade margins entire, surfaces glabrous or pubescent. **Inflorescences** 1–18+-flowered, axillary, racemes or panicles, spreading; bracts and bracteoles present, early deciduous. **Flowers** papilionaceous; calyx zygomorphic or actinomorphic, campanulate, undulate-truncate, rim of tube glabrous or hairy, stalked glands sometimes present between lobes, lobes 5 (except sometimes 0 in *S. grandiflora*), ¼–⅓ as long as tube; corolla white, pale yellow to orange or red, with or without purple spots on outer surface of banner, glabrous; banner usually with a pair of thickened calluses along claw, rarely calluses absent or reduced; stamens 10, diadelphous; anthers dorsifixed; pistil glabrous or style with spreading hairs; stigma capitate or slightly elongate, at same position as anthers. **Fruits** legumes, stipitate, bladdery-inflated or long-slender, terete, elliptic, or 4-angled, with or without wings, indehiscent or dehiscent, glabrous, with spongy mesocarp. **Seeds** 1–40(–51), reniform, reniform-orbicular, globose, or columnar; hilum recessed. x = 6, 7, 12.

Species ca. 70 (7 in the flora): North America, Mexico, West Indies, Central America, South America, Asia, Africa, Pacific Islands, Australia; tropical and subtropical regions nearly worldwide.

Darwinia Rafinesque 1817 (not Rudge 1815) and *Emerus* Kuntze 1891 (not Miller 1754) are illegitimate names that pertain here.

Introduced species of *Sesbania* are commonly found in agricultural areas within tropical to temperate regions throughout the world.

Sesbania is distinctive among legumes and combines morphologies that are atypical among papilionoids. The most unusual morphology of *Sesbania* is the even- or odd-pinnate leaf in which the strictly opposite leaflets fold forward during night-time (nyctinasty), similar to the mimosoid clade of Caesalpinioideae (for example, the sensitive *Mimosa*). Root nodules of *Sesbania* are variable (produced on roots and laterally on stems) and differ from other legume groups, which generally have uniform nodule morphology (for example, dalbergioids, M. Lavin et al. 2001). Finally, *Sesbania* fruits are distinctive from other legume groups. They have a well-developed, often spongy, mesocarp having four different variations: tardily dehiscent, linear, and many-seeded (for example, sect. *Sesbania*); tardily dehiscent, bladdery-inflated, and 2-seeded [sect. *Glottidium* (Desvaux) Lavin]; indehiscent, 4-winged, and several-seeded [sect. *Daubentonia* (de Candolle) Bentham & Hooker f.]; and indehiscent, torulose, and several-seeded [Mexican sect. *Daubentoniopsis* (Rydberg) Lavin]. These divergent fruit morphologies were used traditionally to separate the genus into these four sections, in addition to two others from Africa and the South Pacific.

Species of *Sesbania* are widely cultivated for multiple agronomic and ecological uses, especially for soil improvement as a green manure (D. O. Evans 1990). *Sesbania* is used also for shade, as windbreaks, cover crops, ornamentals, fish poisons (isoflavones), fiber sources, construction materials, and food for humans and livestock and for heavy-metal bioremediation (J. B. Gillett 1963; R. Barlow et al. 2000; R. H. Qureshi et al. 2002; Yang B. et al. 2003). However, several species are considered agricultural pests and, in the case of *S. punicea*, may become noxious weeds in natural wetland and riparian areas.

Unlike the related Loteae and Robinieae, most *Sesbania* species occupy either riparian or wetland habitats. Many *Sesbania* are well adapted to fluctuations in soil moisture and are tolerant of both drought and waterlogged conditions, forming floating roots and producing a surrounding layer of spongy aerenchyma to protect stems, roots, and root nodules.

Specimens collected from chrome-ore piles in Maryland and Virginia in the late 1950s by C. F. Reed (1964) were identified as *Sesbania exaltata*. These collections are actually immature *S. bispinosa* (Jacquin) W. Wight, which has not been collected in the flora area since. *Sesbania bispinosa* most closely resembles *S. herbacea* and *S. sericea* from which it can easily be distinguished by floral characters. The keel apex of *S. bispinosa* is reduced and the rectangular blade has a long, downward curved tooth, the banner claw calluses are winglike ridges with rounded apices, and both the peduncle and the leaf rachis are armed with prickles, and the leaflet blades are glabrous abaxially.

SELECTED REFERENCE Farruggia, F. T. 2009. Phylogenetic and Monographic Studies of the Pantropical Genus Sesbania. Ph.D. dissertation. Arizona State University.

1. Legumes narrow-elongate or flattened; seeds (3–)12–40(–51); keel blades with basal tooth; banners with calluses as ridges or winglike along claw; seeds columnar or reniform-orbicular [sect. *Sesbania*].
    2. Trees; flowers (5.1–)6.3–7(–7.9) cm; corollas white or red-crimson; banners without purple-maroon spots on outer surface, calluses as shallow ridges along claw; calyx zygomorphic, lobes 0 or 5 and rounded or obsolete; legumes rectangular in cross section, (35.1–)38.7–43.8(–49.7) cm; seeds reniform-orbicular . . . . 5. *Sesbania grandiflora*
    2. Herbs; flowers (0.7–)0.8–1.5(–1.9) cm; corollas yellow-orange; banners often with purple-maroon spots on outer surface, calluses as ridges or winglike along claw; calyx actinomorphic, lobes 5, deltate- or subulate-acuminate; legumes ± terete to elliptic in cross section, (1.7–)8.3–19.4(–23.5) cm; seeds columnar.
        3. Leaflet blades golden tan-sericeous abaxially; keel apex truncate, curved toward calyx, yellow-orange throughout; seeds without mottling . . . . 6. *Sesbania sericea*
        3. Leaflet blades glabrous abaxially; keel apex rounded-acute, curved toward banner, yellow with purple or maroon at apex; seeds often with purple-black mottling . . . . 7. *Sesbania herbacea*
1. Legumes flattened-inflated or 4-angled (sometimes winged); seeds 1–7(–10); keel blades without basal tooth; banners with calluses absent or as small ridges or teeth at claw base; seeds reniform, reniform-orbicular, or globose.
    4. Herbs, often woody at base; legumes flattened-inflated, flat to elliptic in cross section; seeds 1 or 2(or 3); peduncles (3.7–)6.4–7.4(–12.2) cm; wings with basal tooth; banner yellow-orange with bright yellow spot at base, wings and keel darker [sect. *Glottidium*] . . . . 1. *Sesbania vesicaria*
    4. Trees, shrubs, or subshrubs, woody; legumes 4-angled (sometimes with wings), square in cross section; seeds (1–)3–7(–10); peduncles (0.6–)0.9–2.4(–4.1) cm; wings without basal tooth; banner pale yellow, yellow, or orange-grenadine-red, sometimes with darker venation, wings and keel ± same color throughout [sect. *Daubentonia*].
        5. Legumes indehiscent, angles not winged; corollas yellow, banner venation sometimes darker; stems with close-pressed hairs (in age) . . . . 2. *Sesbania virgata*
        5. Legumes indehiscent or tardily dehiscent, angles winged; corollas yellow or orange-grenadine-red, banner venation not darker; stems glabrous (in age).

[6. Shifted to left margin.—Ed.]

6. Corollas orange-grenadine-red; legumes with pronounced, spreading wings, slightly torulose or not, stipes (0.8–)1.1–1.2(–1.6) cm . . . . 3. *Sesbania punicea*
6. Corollas pale yellow; legumes with pronounced torulose wings, stipes (1.1–)1.6(–2) cm . . . . 4. *Sesbania drummondii*

1. Sesbania vesicaria (Jacquin) Elliott, Sketch Bot. S. Carolina 2: 222. 1823 • Bagpod, bladderpod [E] [W]

Robinia vesicaria Jacquin, Collectanea 1: 105. 1787; Icon. Pl. Rar. 1: plate 148. 1787; *Aeschynomene platycarpa* Michaux; *Colutea floribunda* Poiret; *Dalbergia polyphylla* Poiret; *Emerus vesicarius* (Jacquin) Kuntze; *Glottidium floridanum* var. *atrorubrum* Nash; *G. vesicarium* (Jacquin) R. M. Harper; *G. vesicarium* var. *atrorubrum* (Nash) Small; *G. vesicarium* var. *sericeum* R. S. Cocks; *Phaca floridana* Willdenow; *Sesbania platycarpa* (Michaux) Persoon; *S. vesicaria* var. *atrorubra* (Nash) S. C. Brooks

Herbs, often woody at base, to 2.5 m. **Stems** persistent late into following year, glabrous in age; pith spongy. **Leaves** 8–30+ cm; stipules 0.9–1.1 cm, with inconspicuous inner fold ⅔ its length, inner fold and base often with stipitate, multicellular glands or glabrous; pulvinus as long as petiole; rachis ± glabrous, without stipitate glands, obscure gland sometimes present at petiolule base; stipels absent; leaflets 16–50+, blades elliptic-ovate to oblong, base acute, apex rounded-obtuse, surfaces usually glabrous. **Peduncles** (3.7–)6.4–7.4(–12.2) cm. **Inflorescences** 1–6+-flowered, racemes. **Flowers** (8–)8.4–9(–9.7) cm; calyx ± zygomorphic, ± persistent in fruit, lobes 5, short-acuminate, rim of tube glabrous, stalked glands sometimes present between lobes; corolla yellow-orange, banner base with bright yellow spot, wings and keel usually darker; banner ovate, base truncate, apex emarginate, calluses absent or as relatively small teeth at claw base, thickened, knoblike at base of blade/top of claw; wings with basal tooth; keel apex ± darker, acute, curved upward to slightly inward, without basal tooth; stamens incurved within keel; style recurved; ovules 1–3. **Legumes** tan-brown, often with horizontal mottling in age, flattened-inflated, flat to elliptic in cross section, straight, (4.5–)6.1–6.7(–8.2) × (1.1–)1.2–1.3(–1.6) cm, beak gradually tapered, flattened, (0.4–)0.5–0.6(–0.7) cm, tardily dehiscent; stipe (0.8–)1.1–1.2(–1.5) cm. **Seeds** 1 or 2(or 3), gray-brown to reddish, without mottling, reniform, not easily released, enveloped in indehiscent, papery endocarp. **2*n*** = 12.

Flowering early summer–early fall. Wet areas, riparian, wetlands, coastal, agricultural fields, disturbed sites; 0–500 m; Ala., Ark., Fla., Ga., La., Miss., Mo., N.C., Okla., S.C., Tex.

Sesbania disperma Pursh is an illegitimate name and *Glottidium floridanum* (Willdenow) de Candolle is a superfluous name; both pertain here.

2. Sesbania virgata (Cavanilles) Poiret in J. Lamarck et al., Encycl. 7: 129. 1806 (as Sesban) • Wand riverhemp [I]

Aeschynomene virgata Cavanilles, Icon. 3: 47, plate 293. 1795/1796; *Agati virgata* (Cavanilles) Desvaux; *Coursetia virgata* (Cavanilles) de Candolle; *Emerus marginatus* (Bentham) Lindman; *Sesbania marginata* Bentham; *S. tetragona* Pampanini

Shrubs or trees, to 4 m. **Stems** glabrous or pilose, hairs persistent, close-pressed, golden or clear in age, developing leaves and young stems with same pubescence of simple hairs; pith solid or spongy. **Leaves** 13–25+ cm; stipules 0.3–0.4 cm, with conspicuous inner fold throughout, hairs dense, close-pressed, inner fold and base with stipitate, multicellular glands; pulvinus slightly more than ½ as long as petiole; rachis ± sericeous, without stipitate glands, obscure gland(s) present at petiolule base; stipels reduced in size between successive leaflets, long-filamentous glandular; leaflets 28–36+, blades elliptic-ovate to oblong, base acute, apex obtuse to acute, surfaces silky sericeous abaxially, usually glabrous adaxially. **Peduncles** (0.6–)1.7–2.1(–4.1) cm. **Inflorescences** 5–15+-flowered, racemes. **Flowers** (0.7–)0.9–1(–1.3) cm; calyx ± zygomorphic, lobes 5, short-acuminate, rim of tube villose, stalked glands between abaxial lobes absent in fruit; corolla yellow, banner venation sometimes darker; banner ovate, base cordate-truncate, apex emarginate, becoming strongly reflexed and contorted, calluses as relatively small, acute teeth at claw base, thickened, knoblike at base of blade/top of claw; wings without basal tooth; keel ± same color throughout, apex acute, curved strongly inward, without basal tooth; stamens incurved within keel; style recurved; ovules 4–6. **Legumes** red- to gray-brown, without horizontal mottling in age, 4-angled, square in cross section, straight or slightly falcate, (0.8–)4.4–5.5(–6.5) × (0.7–)0.8(–0.9) cm, thick, woody, seed chambers apparent in young fruits becoming obscure at maturity, margins of young fruits with shallow thin ridges resembling early wings of *S. punicea* or *S. drummondii*, ridges becoming thickened and rounded at maturity, beak short-pyramidal, (0.2–) 0.4–0.7(–1.3) cm, indehiscent; stipe (0.4–)0.5–0.6 (–0.9) cm. **Seeds** (1–)4 or 5(or 6), reddish brown to gray, without mottling, reniform-orbicular. **2*n*** = 12.

Flowering early summer–early fall. Wet areas, riparian, wetlands, coastal, disturbed sites; 0–20 m; introduced; Fla., Miss.; South America; introduced also in se Mexico (Veracruz), West Indies, Central America.

Sesbania virgata is native to northern Argentina and southern Paraguay and has been introduced to numerous port cities in the Americas. In the flora area, it is known from the Pensacola, Florida, region and from several populations along the coastline southeastward to Hillsborough and Pinellas counties and westward to Harrison County, Mississippi. The most distinguishing characteristic of the species is the quadrangular pod.

Sesbania affinis De Wildeman (1904) is a later homonym (not Schrader ex de Candolle 1825) that pertains here.

3. **Sesbania punicea** (Cavanilles) Bentham in C. F. P. von Martius et al., Fl. Bras. 15(1): 43. 1859 • Rattlebox, scarlet sesban [I] [W]

Piscidia punicea Cavanilles, Icon. 4: 8, plate 316. 1797; *Aeschynomene miniata* Ortega; *Daubentonia punicea* (Cavanilles) de Candolle; *Sesbania tripetii* (Poiteau) Mouillefert

Shrubs or trees, to 4 m. **Stems** glabrous in age; pith spongy, soon becoming obsolete. **Leaves** 4.5–30+ cm; stipules 0.4–0.5 cm, with inconspicuous inner fold ⅔ its length, inner fold and base often with stipitate, multicellular glands and long, simple hairs; pulvinus less than ½ as long as petiole; rachis ± appressed-pilose, with or without stipitate glands in canal, stipitate gland present at petiolule base; stipels narrow, gland tipped; leaflets 14–40, blades elliptic to oblong-obovate, base acute-obtuse, apex truncate to obtuse, surfaces glabrous or sparsely pubescent abaxially, usually glabrous adaxially. **Peduncles** (1.1–)2.1–2.4(–3.3) cm. **Inflorescences** 5–15+-flowered, racemes. **Flowers** (1.8–)2–2.2(–2.5) cm; calyx ± zygomorphic, usually absent at fruit maturity, lobes 5, short and broad, sinuses shallow, rim of tube glabrous, stalked glands absent; corolla orange-grenadine-red; banner ovate, base truncate, apex emarginate, calluses as relatively small, acute teeth at claw base; wings without basal tooth; keel ± same color throughout, apex rounded-obtuse, curved upward, without basal tooth; stamens curved upward within keel; style curved upward with stamens; ovules 6 or 7(–10). **Legumes** red-brown, with or without horizontal mottling, 4-angled, square in cross section, ± straight, with pronounced, spreading wings, torulose or not, (5.2–)8.8–9.5(–10.7) × (0.7–)0.8(–9) cm, seed compartments slightly pronounced externally in age, beak long-pyramidal to triangular, (0.5–)0.9–1(–1.4) cm, tardily dehiscent; stipe (0.8–)1.1–1.2(–1.6) cm. **Seeds** (1–)6 or 7(–10), red-brown to gray, without mottling, globose to reniform-orbicular. **2*n*** = 12.

Flowering early summer–fall. Wet areas, riparian, wetlands, coastal, disturbed sites; 0–500 m; introduced; Ala., Ark., Calif., Fla., Ga., La., Miss., N.C., S.C., Tex., Va.; South America; introduced also in e Mexico, West Indies, Central America, Africa (South Africa).

Sesbania punicea is used as an ornamental and is commonly sold under the name Scarlet Sesban. This native of central South America can survive short freezes and has escaped and become a noxious weed in some wetland locations.

4. **Sesbania drummondii** (Rydberg) Cory, Rhodora 38: 406. 1936 • Poisonbean [F] [W]

Daubentonia drummondii Rydberg, Amer. J. Bot. 10: 498. 1923

Shrubs or subshrubs, to 3 m. **Stems** glabrous in age; pith spongy. **Leaves** 12–19 cm; stipules 0.2–0.4 cm, with inconspicuous inner fold throughout, inner fold and base with stipitate, multicellular glands or glabrous; pulvinus less than ½ as long as petiole; rachis ± glabrous, without stipitate glands in canal; stipels narrow obscure glands; leaflets 16–50+, blades elliptic-ovate to oblong, base acute, apex obtuse, surfaces glaucous, usually glabrous abaxially, sometimes with diffuse, close-pressed hairs. **Peduncles** (0.9–)1.7–1.8(–3) cm. **Inflorescences** 1–12-flowered, racemes. **Flowers** (0.9–)1.3–1.5(–1.7) cm; calyx ± zygomorphic, deciduous before fruits mature, lobes 5, short-deltate, rim of tube with spreading hairs, stalked glands usually present between abaxial lobes; corolla pale yellow; banner ovate, base truncate-obcordate, apex emarginate, calluses as relatively small ridges at claw base, forming a pocket, thickened, knoblike at top of claw; wings without basal tooth; keel ± same color throughout, apex rounded-obtuse, curved upward to slightly outward in apical tooth, without basal tooth; stamens curved upward; style curved upward with stamens; ovules 4–9. **Legumes** light tan to reddish brown, 4-angled, with pronounced torulose wings, square in cross section, straight, (3.2–)5.7–6.2(–9.3) × 0.8(–0.9) mm, seed chambers clearly visible externally, beak short- to long-pyramidal, (0.4–)0.7–0.8(–1.3) cm, indehiscent or tardily dehiscent; stipe (1.1–)1.6(–2) cm.

Seeds (1–)3 or 4(–9), dark reddish brown, without mottling, reniform-orbicular. **2*n*** = 12.

Flowering summer–fall. Wet areas, riparian on sandy soils, coastal sites, disturbed sites; 0–600 m; Ala., Ark., Fla., Ga., La., Miss., S.C., Tex.; Mexico (Tamaulipas).

Sesbania drummondii is often mistaken for the Mexican species *S. cavanillesii* S. Watson (= *Sesbania longifolia* de Candolle). It is distinguished by rounded versus acute leaf apices and winged versus not winged legumes. In bloom, the yellow-orange corollas make *S. drummondii* clearly distinct from *S. punicea*; in fruit, identification is simplified by the acuminate versus pyramidal beak and wavy versus straight-edged wings.

Daubentonia texana Pierce is a superfluous name that pertains here.

5. Sesbania grandiflora (Linnaeus) Poiret in J. Lamarck et al., Encycl. 7: 127. 1806 (as Sesban grandiflorus) [I]

Robinia grandiflora Linnaeus, Sp. Pl. 2: 722. 1753; *Aeschynomene grandiflora* (Linnaeus) Linnaeus; *Agati grandiflora* (Linnaeus) Desvaux; *Coronilla grandiflora* (Linnaeus) Willdenow; *Dolichos arboreus* Forsskål; *Emerus grandiflorus* (Linnaeus) Kuntze; *Resupinaria grandiflora* (Linnaeus) Rafinesque; *Sesbania coccinea* (Linnaeus f.) Poiret

Trees, to 6 m. **Stems** with close-pressed hairs; pith not observed. **Leaves** 8–43+ cm; stipules 0.8–0.9 cm, with conspicuous inner fold throughout, inner fold often with velutinous, stipitate glands, glands absent at base; pulvinus at least ½ as long as petiole; rachis glabrescent or glabrous, with stipitate glands at base of leaflets in canal (not between leaflet pairs); stipels long, narrow, glandular; leaflets 10–20–50+, blades ligulate to elliptic-oblong, base obtuse to acute, apex emarginate to truncate, surfaces usually glabrous, sometimes with close-pressed, golden hairs. **Peduncles** (1.2–)1.9–2.3(–3.1) cm. **Inflorescences** 1–12+-flowered, racemes or panicles. **Flowers** (5.1–)6.3–7(–7.9) cm; calyx zygomorphic, ± bilabiate, lobes 0 or 5, rounded or obsolete, rim often with sinuous hairs from inner surface, with short, straight, close-pressed hairs on outer surface near teeth, stalked glands absent from rim, absent in fruit; corolla white or red-crimson; banner oblong, base truncate to cordate, apex emarginate, calluses as shallow ridges along claw; wings without basal tooth; keel ± same color throughout or claw white and blade pink or scarlet, apex acute-rounded, curved upward to slightly inward, with basal tooth; stamens curved upward within keel; style curved upward with keel; ovules 27–48. **Legumes** brown-tan, without mottling, flattened parallel to sutures, rectangular in cross section, straight to falcate, (35.1–)38.7–43.8(–49.7) × (0.5–)0.7–0.8(–0.9) cm, beak gradually tapered, flattened, (0.6–)1–1.7(–2) cm, tardily dehiscent; stipe (4.3–)4.4–4.5(–4.6) cm. **Seeds** (27–)35–40(–46), yellow-green or brown to reddish, without mottling, reniform-orbicular. **2*n*** = 12.

Flowering summer–fall. Wet areas, riparian and wetland sandy soils, disturbed sites; 0–20 m; introduced; Fla.; s Mexico; West Indies; Central America; South America; se Asia; Africa; Pacific Islands; Australia.

Sesbania grandiflora has relatively large, showy flowers and is grown throughout the tropics as an ornamental. Its original range is difficult to ascertain due to its widespread horticultural use; other *Sesbania* species endemic to the South Pacific have similar morphology, and molecular evidence suggests shared ancestry (F. T. Farruggia 2009).

In the flora area, *Sesbania grandiflora* is known from the Florida Keys.

6. Sesbania sericea (Willdenow) Link, Enum. Hort. Berol. Alt. 2: 244. 1822 • Silky sesban [I]

Coronilla sericea Willdenow, Enum. Pl., 773. 1809; *Agati sericea* (Willdenow) Hitchcock; *Emerus pubescens* (de Candolle) Schumacher & Thonning; *Sesbania laevigata* Afr. Fernandes & E. P. Nunes; *S. pubescens* de Candolle

Herbs, [trees or shrubs], to 6 m. **Stems** sometimes with prickles, sericeous, hairs persistent, golden tan; pith spongy. **Leaves** 10.5–22.3 cm; stipules 0.6 cm, golden tan-sericeous, with conspicuous inner fold ¾ its length, base of fold unlike other *Sesbania* with additional shorter fold that parallels long one, inner fold without stipitate, multicellular glands, glands often present at base; pulvinus more than ½ as long as petiole; rachis sericeous, with stipitate glands in canal; stipels long, narrow, ± glandular; leaflets 34–96+, blades elliptic-ovate to broadly linear, base obtuse to acute, apex truncate to rounded obtuse, surfaces sericeous, hairs dense, golden tan abaxially, usually glabrous adaxially. **Peduncles** (0.2–)0.5–0.6(–1.5) cm. **Inflorescences** 1–18+-flowered, racemes. **Flowers** (0.7–)0.8–0.9(–1.9) cm; calyx actinomorphic, lobes 5, deltate-acuminate, rim of tube with net of long hairs, stalked glands present at base of sinus, absent in fruit; corolla yellow-orange, banner sometimes with purple-maroon spots on outer surface; banner ovate, base broadly tapered, apex emarginate, calluses as ridges along claw, callus apices truncate; wings without basal tooth; keel same color throughout, similar to wings, apex ± truncate, curved upward to inward towards calyx, with basal tooth; stamens curved inward within keel; style recurved towards banner; ovules 18–32. **Legumes** reddish brown, with horizontal mottling, narrow-elongate, terete to elliptic in cross section, straight to falcate, (1.7–)10–12.7(–18.8) × (0.2–)0.3(–0.4) cm, beak connate, narrowly tapered, 0.2(–0.4) cm, tardily elastic dehiscent; stipe (0.1–)0.2(–0.3) cm. **Seeds** (3–)19–24(–32), greenish gray to brownish red, without mottling, columnar. $2n$ = 12, 24.

Flowering early summer–fall. Wet areas, riparian, wetlands, coastal, disturbed sites; 0–200 m; introduced; Fla., Tex.; Asia (Sri Lanka); introduced also in Mexico, West Indies, Central America, South America, Africa.

Sesbania sericea is sometimes mistaken for *S. herbacea* but is more limited in its distribution, found only in Florida and Texas, while *S. herbacea* is widespread in the flora area. Identification is straightforward when relying upon the dense tomentum of appressed hairs found on the underside of the leaves, as no other North American species of *Sesbania* shares this attribute.

7. **Sesbania herbacea** (Miller) McVaugh in R. McVaugh and W. R. Anderson, Fl. Novo-Galiciana 5: 695. 1987 • Bigpod sesbania, Colorado riverhemp [W]

Emerus herbacea Miller, Gard. Dict. ed. 8., Emerus no. 3. 1768; *Aeschynomene emerus* Aublet; *Coronilla occidentalis* Willdenow; *Darwinia exaltata* Rafinesque; *Emerus sesban* (Linnaeus) Kuntze var. *occidentalis* (Willdenow) Kuntze; *Sesbania cassioides* G. Don; *S. emerus* (Aublet) Urban; *S. exaltata* (Rafinesque) Rydberg; *S. microcarpa* Muhlenberg ex Rafinesque var. *picta* S. Watson; *S. occidentalis* (Willdenow) Poiret; *S. sonorae* Rydberg

Herbs, often woody at base, to 4.5 m. **Stems** sometimes with prickles along stem and leaf rachis, glabrous in age; pith spongy becoming septate. **Leaves** 10–30+ cm; stipules 1–1.1 mm, with inner fold throughout, inner fold and base with stipitate, multicellular glands; pulvinus at least ½ as long as petiole; rachis glabrous, with stipitate glands in canal at base of each leaflet pair; stipels narrow, ± glandular; leaflets 20–80+, blades rectangular to oblong, base obtuse, apex truncate to obtuse, surfaces usually glabrous. **Peduncles** (0.2–)1.6–1.9(–4.2) cm. **Inflorescences** 1–18+-flowered, racemes. **Flowers** (1–)1.4–1.5(–1.9) cm; calyx actinomorphic, lobes 5, subulate–acuminate, rim of tube glabrous or with short hairs inside, stalked glands absent; corolla yellow-orange, banner with purple-maroon spots on outer surface; banner ovate to obovate, base truncate, apex obtuse-retuse, calluses as shallow ridges or winglike along claw, callus apices truncate to rounded with lobes less than 2 mm; wings with basal tooth (short, blunt); keel yellow, apex purple or maroon, rounded-acute, curved upward to inward towards banner, with basal tooth; stamens strongly curved inward within keel; style recurved towards banner; ovules (12–)29–36(–51). **Legumes** brown, with maroon-red mottling, narrow-elongate, terete to elliptic in cross section, straight to falcate, (8.3–)16.9–19.4(–23.5) × 0.3(–0.4) cm, beak connate, narrowly tapered, (0.3–)0.6–0.8(–1.1) cm, tardily elastic dehiscent; stipe (0.2–)0.5(–0.7) mm. **Seeds** (12–)29–36(–51), green-brown to reddish, often with purple-black mottling, columnar.

Flowering early summer–fall. Wet areas, riparian, wetlands, coastal, disturbed sites; 0–900 m; Ala., Ariz., Calif., Fla., Ga., Ill., Kans., Ky., La., Md., Mass., Miss., Mo., N.J., N.Y., N.C., Okla., Pa., S.C., Tenn., Tex., Va.; Mexico (Baja California, Colima, Nayarit, Oaxaca, Sinaloa, Sonora); West Indies; Central America; South America.

The range of *Sesbania herbacea* is expanding in North America and South America. It has been collected once in Ontario, as a waif.

Sesbania macrocarpa Muhlenberg ex Rafinesque is a superfluous illegitimate name that pertains here.

119. SECURIGERA de Candolle in J. Lamarck and A. P. de Candolle, Fl. Franç. ed. 3, 4: 609. 1805, name conserved • [Latin *securis*, axe, and *-ger*, bearing, alluding to shape of fruit beak found in *Securigera securidaca*, the type species] [I]

Peter W. Ball

Herbs, perennial [**annual**], unarmed. **Stems** spreading, furrowed or ridged, pubescent or glabrate. **Leaves** alternate, odd-pinnate; stipules present, free, membranous [herbaceous], dark-tipped; petiolate; leaflets 11–25, blade margins entire, surfaces glabrous. **Inflorescences** pedunculate, 6–25-flowered, axillary, umbels [heads]; bracts absent; bracteoles present. **Flowers** papilionaceous; calyx weakly zygomorphic, campanulate, lobes 5; corolla white, pink, purple, or bicolored [yellow], keel acute; stamens 10, diadelphous; anthers basifixed. **Fruits** loments, stipitate, not or only slightly constricted between seeds, angled in cross-section [cylindric], indehiscent or tardily dehiscent, with weak longitudinal, anastomosing veins, glabrous. **Seeds** 2–12, oblong, smooth; hilum lateral. $x = 6$.

Species 12 (1 in the flora): introduced; Europe, w Asia (Mediterranean region); temperate areas.

The circumscription of *Securigera* followed here is that proposed by P. Lassen (1989), who transferred more than half of the species of *Coronilla* to *Securigera* and *Hippocrepis* based on characters other than those of the fruits. The molecular phylogenetic studies by G. J. Allan and J. M. Porter (2000) do not contradict the rearrangement by Lassen, but a sufficient diversity of species of *Coronilla* and *Securigera* were not examined to support it firmly.

Three other species of *Securigera* have been reported from North America, each from a single locality; they appear not to have become naturalized. *Securigera securidaca* (Linnaeus) Degen & Dörfler, reported from South Carolina, is annual, with a yellow corolla and indehiscent or tardily dehiscent fruit; *S. globosa* (Lamarck) Lassen (*Coronilla globosa* Lamarck), reported from New York, is very similar to *S. varia,* but heads are 15–40-flowered and fruit segments are 9–10 mm; *S. cretica* (Linnaeus) Lassen (*C. cretica* Linnaeus), reported from Maryland, is annual, heads are 3–9-flowered, and corollas are white or pink, 4–7 mm.

1. **Securigera varia** (Linnaeus) Lassen, Svensk Bot. Tidskr. 83: 86. 1989 • Crown-vetch, coronille bigarrée [F] [I] [W]

Coronilla varia Linnaeus, Sp. Pl. 2: 743. 1753

Stems 20–120 cm. **Leaves** 5–16 × 2–4 cm; stipules linear to oblong, 1–6 mm; leaflet blades oblong or elliptic, 6–25 × 2.5–12 mm, margins narrowly scarious, brownish or purplish resinous-punctate adaxially, apex mucronate. **Peduncles** 4–14 cm. **Inflorescences** 2–3.5 cm. **Pedicels** 2–5 mm; bracteoles distinct, linear, 1–2 mm, dark-tipped. **Flowers:** calyx 2.2–4 mm, lobes 0.7–1 mm; corolla (8–)10–15 mm. **Loments** 20–60(–80) × 1.5–2.2 mm; segments 2–10(–12), oblong, 4–6 mm, 4-angled in cross-section. **Seeds** 3.5–4 × 1–1.5 mm. $2n = 24$.

Flowering late spring–summer. Fields, roadsides, pine or pine-oak woodlands, waste places; 10–2400 m; introduced; Alta., B.C., Man., N.B., Nfld. and Labr. (Nfld.), N.S., Ont., P.E.I., Que., Sask.; Ala., Ariz., Ark., Calif., Colo., Conn., Del., D.C., Fla., Ga., Idaho, Ill., Ind., Iowa, Kans., Ky., La., Maine, Md., Mass., Mich., Minn., Miss., Mo., Mont., Nebr., Nev., N.H., N.J., N.Mex., N.Y., N.C., Ohio, Okla., Oreg., Pa., R.I., S.C., S.Dak., Tenn., Tex., Utah, Vt., Va., Wash., W.Va., Wis., Wyo; c, s Europe; sw Asia; introduced also in ne Mexico, South America, Pacific Islands (New Zealand), se Australia.

Securigera varia has been cultivated for fodder; in recent years, it has been extensively planted on banks and roadsides to control erosion, from where it frequently spreads to fields and waste places. In some midwestern states, it has spread into upland prairies, glades, and watersheds; because of this it is considered an invasive exotic (G. Yatskievych, pers. comm.).

120. CORONILLA Linnaeus, Sp. Pl. 2: 742. 1753; Gen. Pl. ed. 5, 330. 1754, name conserved • Crown-vetch [Latin *corona*, crown, and *–illa*, diminutive, alluding to appearance of inflorescence] [I]

Peter W. Ball

Shrubs [herbs], unarmed. **Stems** ascending to erect, glabrous. **Leaves** alternate, odd-pinnate [unifoliolate]; stipules present; petiolate; leaflets [1–](3–)5–7[–13], blade margins entire, surfaces glabrous. **Inflorescences** 7–12-flowered, axillary, heads or umbels; bracts absent; bracteoles present. **Flowers** papilionaceous; calyx campanulate, lobes 5; corolla yellow; stamens 10, diadelphous; anthers basifixed. **Fruits** loments, stipitate, cylindrical, not or weakly constricted between seeds, linear, indehiscent, glabrous. **Seeds** 1–10, oblong; hilum lateral. $x = [5], 6$.

Species 9 (1 in the flora): introduced, California; s Europe (Mediterranean region), n Africa.

The results obtained by G. J. Allan and J. M. Porter (2000) indicate that *Coronilla*, as circumscribed by P. Lassen (1989), may be polyphyletic. See under 119. *Securigera* for discussion of the circumscription of *Coronilla*.

Coronilla scorpioides has been reported from Massachusetts and Ohio, probably introduced with pasture seed imported from southern Europe or farther north; the records are old, and the species does not appear to have persisted. A report from Connecticut was based on a misidentified specimen.

1. **Coronilla valentina** Linnaeus, Sp. Pl. 2: 742. 1753, name conserved • Yellow crown-vetch F I

Subspecies 2 (1 in the flora): introduced, California; s Europe, nw Africa.

1a. **Coronilla valentina** Linnaeus subsp. **glauca** (Linnaeus) Battandier in J. A. Battandier et al., Fl. Algérie 1(1): 285. 1889 F I

Coronilla glaca Linnaeus, Cent. Pl. I, 23. 1755

Shrubs 20–110 cm. **Stems** terete. **Leaves** 2–4 × 1.5–2 cm, glaucous; stipules deciduous, distinct, linear, 2–6 mm, membranous; leaflet blades obovate, 5–15 × 3–10 mm, base cuneate, apex emarginate, mucronate. **Peduncles** 2–7 cm. **Inflorescences** 2.5–3 cm diam.; bracteoles connate, forming cup at base of pedicel, 1 mm. **Pedicels** 3–5 mm. **Flowers:** calyx weakly zygomorphic, 2–3.5 mm, lobes 0.3–1 mm; corolla 7–12 × 5–8 mm, keel acute. **Loments** brown, 10–30(–50) × 2.3–3 mm, longitudinally veined, veins anastomosing; segments 1–4(–10), 6.5–7 mm. **Seeds** brown, 3.5 × 1.5 mm. $2n = 12$.

Flowering spring. Sides of roads and trails, shaded oak canyons; 10–300 m; introduced; Calif.; s Europe; nw Africa.

Subspecies *glauca* is apparently spreading from cultivation into disturbed native vegetation in Los Angeles County; it was first collected in 1988. Subspecies *valentina* has leaves with 7–13 leaflets [versus (3–)5–7 in subsp. *glauca*] and herbaceous stipules, 5–10 mm.

121. ANTHYLLIS Linnaeus, Sp. Pl. 2: 719. 1753; Gen. Pl. ed. 5, 321. 1754 • Kidney vetch, woundwort [Greek *anthos*, flower, and *ioylos*, down, alluding to downy calyx] I

Zoya V. Akulova-Barlow

Herbs [shrubs], biennial or perennial [annual], unarmed. **Stems** erect, ascending, or decumbent, sericeous or hirsute. **Leaves** alternate, odd-pinnate; stipules present [absent]; petiolate; leaflets (1–)9–15, blade margins entire, surfaces short-sericeous abaxially, glabrous adaxially. **Inflorescences** 5–25+-flowered, terminal [axillary], headlike racemes or umbels; bracts present [absent]; prophylls present or absent. **Flowers** papilionaceous; calyx tubular [campanulate], lobes 5, often accrescent, pubescent; corolla yellow or reddish; stamens 10, monadelphous, [diadelphous or adaxial distinct to ½ its length, or at first all connate into a closed tube, distally becoming partly or entirely distinct]; anthers dorsifixed. **Fruits** legumes, stipitate [sessile], straight, falcate, or arcuate, constricted between seeds or not, flattened-ovoid [short-linear], winged or not, indehiscent or tardily dehiscent, glabrous. **Seeds** 1 or 2, globose to ovoid. $x = 6$.

Species ca. 25 (1 in the flora): introduced; Europe, w Asia, n Africa.

The term prophyll is used here to include small bractlike structures on the peduncles in genera of the Loteae that are distinct from the bases of flowers and not bracts themselves, which sit adjacent to the calyces (Z. V. Akulova et al. 2000; D. D. Sokoloff et al. 2007).

CORONILLA ◦ ANTHYLLIS ◦ ORNITHOPUS

In Europe, *Anthyllis* is cultivated for animal forage and is also used in cosmetics for skin care; it is an ancient remedy for skin eruptions, slow-healing wounds, and cuts and bruises. In traditional medicine, it is used as an astringent, laxative, antitussive, and antitoxin. Several species are cultivated as ornamentals. Some species have root nodules of the *Phaseolus* type.

SELECTED REFERENCE Puidet, E. et al. 2005. Morphological variation in eight taxa of *Anthyllis vulneraria* s. lato (Fabaceae). Ann. Bot. Fennici 42: 293–304.

1. Anthyllis vulneraria Linnaeus, Sp. Pl. 2: 719. 1753 • Vulnéraire [F] [I]

Herbs with slender taproots. **Stems** 1–12, simple or branched from distal leaf axils, 5–60 cm. **Leaves** uniformly distributed along stem or absent in distal ⅓; stipules caducous, dark, linear, relatively small, proximal pair of leaflets sometimes bent toward stem, forming false stipules; basal leaves 2–8 cm, reduced to terminal leaflet or with a much larger terminal leaflet and 2–8 reduced lateral leaflets; cauline leaves 2–7, leaflet blades ovate to elliptic or oblong to linear-lanceolate, ± equal, apex acute, sometimes apiculate. **Peduncles** 5–16 cm. **Racemes** 2–5, hemispheric or globose, 2–3 cm; bracts palmately lobed, divided ½ their lengths, lobes acute or obtuse; prophyll 3-lobed, at midpoint or apex of peduncle; bracteoles dark, relatively small. **Flowers** sessile, 10–15 mm; calyx 7–10 × 3–4 mm, contracted apically, mouth oblique, lobes unequal, adaxial 2 ± coherent, off-white or gray, apex sometimes purple; corolla 12–15 mm, blades long-clawed; banner ovate, base truncate or auriculate; wings ovate, obtuse; keel obtuse or apiculate, shorter than wings, incurved, inflated laterally, often adnate to base of staminal tube; filaments thickened distally, enclosed in corolla; anthers uniform; ovary usually stalked, rarely subsessile; style glabrous; stigma terminal. **Legumes** brown, 3–4 mm, included in calyx, surfaces reticulate. **Seeds** brown or bicolored, 2.4–3.2 × 1.6–2 mm, 0.8–1.2 mm thick, smooth or tubercled, sometimes with slight lateral indentation; hilum ventral, whitish with darker border, round. $2n = 12$ (Europe).

Flowering Jun–Jul. Waste places, ballast, disturbed ground, dry calcareous open gravel and adjacent grassy areas, chalk cliffs, hayfields, roadsides; 0–200 m; introduced; Man., N.B., Nfld. and Labr. (Nfld.), Ont.; Ill., Mich., Wis.; Europe; w Asia; introduced also in Pacific Islands (New Zealand), Australia.

Reports of *Anthyllis vulneraria* from British Columbia (C. Rothfels 2004; J. T. Kartesz and C. A. Meacham 1999) could not be substantiated. Historical records exist for the species in the following provinces and states: Canada: Alberta, Quebec; United States: California, Connecticut, Idaho, Iowa, Kentucky, New Hampshire, New Jersey, New York, North Dakota, Ohio, Oregon, Pennsylvania, and Vermont.

Anthyllis vulneraria is a very polymorphic species, including about 35 subspecies that are sometimes treated as species, and intermediate forms and hybrids occur. Rarely, it was used historically in North America as a forage crop. In North America, three subspecies have been identified from herbarium records. Subspecies *maritima* (Schweigger) Corbierei has been found in Manitoba, New Brunswick, Newfoundland, and Ontario; it can be recognized by its sericeous stem, concolorous calyx with two straight upper lobes, and yellow corolla. Subspecies *vulneraria* (historically more widespread in the flora area) is distinguished by its bicolored calyx with a dark red apex and coherent two upper lobes. One sample from New York (1880) was identified as subsp. *rubriflora* (de Candolle) Arcangeli; it is distinguished by its calyx with a purple apex, red corolla, and hirsute stem.

122. ORNITHOPUS Linnaeus, Sp. Pl. 2: 743. 1753; Gen. Pl. ed. 5, 331. 1754 • Bird's-foot, serradela [Greek *ornithos*, bird, and *pous*, foot, alluding to similarity of infructescence to a bird's foot] [I]

Peter W. Ball

Herbs, annual, unarmed. **Stems** erect to procumbent or decumbent, terete, pubescent. **Leaves** alternate, odd-pinnate; stipules present, distinct, dark-tipped, membranous; petiolate; leaflets 15–37, blade margins entire, surfaces pubescent. **Inflorescences** pedunculate, 2–8-flowered, axillary, umbellate heads; bracts present or absent, pinnate or unifoliolate and leaflike; bracteoles 1–8, 0.5 mm, dark-tipped, membranous. **Flowers** papilionaceous; calyx ± actinomorphic, tubular or campanulate, lobes 5; corolla white, pink, or yellow [purple], keel obtuse, inconspicuous; stamens 10, diadelphous; anthers basifixed; styles glabrous; stigmas terminal. **Fruits** loments, stipitate, laterally compressed [terete], linear or curved, constricted between seeds or not, laterally dehiscent into indehiscent segments, segments oblong or elliptic oblong, reticulate-veined, pubescent. **Seeds** 3–9, compressed-orbicular to ellipsoid-orbicular, smooth; hilum lateral. $x = 7$.

Species 6 (3 in the flora): introduced; Europe, w Asia, s, n Africa; introduced also in Australia.

Ornithopus pinnatus (Miller) Druce has 5–15 leaflets, heads without leaflike bracts, yellow corollas, and terete fruits with densely reticulate-rugose segments. It was collected along a roadside in Santa Cruz County, California, where it was growing with *O. sativus* and other introduced species that are known to have persisted for ten years or more. The site has since been developed for housing; it is not known whether plants have survived in this or a neighboring area.

1. Corollas 3–5 mm, white or pink, sometimes with darker lines; loments 1.5–2 mm wide, segments 2–2.5 mm . . . . 2. *Ornithopus perpusillus*
1. Corollas 5–9 mm, white, pink, or yellow; loments 2–3 mm wide, segments 2.8–4 mm.
    2. Corollas white or pink; bracteoles shorter than flowers. . . . . 1. *Ornithopus sativus*
    2. Corollas yellow; bracteoles equaling or longer than flowers . . . . 3. *Ornithopus compressus*

1. Ornithopus sativus Brotero, Fl. Lusit. 2: 160. 1805 F I

Subspecies 2 (1 in the flora): introduced; Europe (Mediterranean region), sw Asia, s, n Africa.

1a. Ornithopus sativus Brotero subsp. **sativus** F I

Ornithopus roseus Dufour

Stems 20–70 cm. **Leaves** 30–70 × 10–20 mm; stipules linear, 1–2 mm; leaflets (9–)19–37, blades elliptical or ovate, leaflets of larger leaves 3.5–6 × 1.5–2.5 mm. **Peduncles** 1–3 cm in flower, 3–7 cm in fruit. **Heads** 2–5-flowered, 10 mm diam.; bract shorter than flowers, 5–9-foliolate. **Pedicels** 0–1 mm. **Flowers:** calyx 3.5–5 mm, lobes 1.5–2.5 mm, less than or equaling tube length; corolla white or pink, 6–9 mm. **Loments** compressed, constricted between seeds, 12–25 × 2–2.7 mm; segments 3–7, elliptic-oblong, 2.8–3.5 mm; beaks straight, sometimes hooked at tip, 2–5 mm. **Seeds** 1.5–2 × 1 mm.

Flowering late spring–early summer. Roadsides, fields, waste places; 10–100 m; introduced; Calif., Md., Mass., N.Y.; s Europe (Mediterranean region); sw Asia; n Africa.

Subspecies *sativus* was previously cultivated for fodder in the flora area.

North American members of the species are subsp. *sativus*, which has fruits 12–25 mm, straight, without narrow cylindrical constrictions between seeds, and beaks 2–5 mm and straight, while subsp. *isthmocarpus* (Cosson) Dostál has fruits 20–40 mm, curved, long narrow cylindrical segments between seeds, and beaks 10+ mm and curved. Subspecies *isthmocarpus* has been reported from California, but the specimens seen are subsp. *sativus*.

2. Ornithopus perpusillus Linnaeus, Sp. Pl. 2: 743. 1753 I

Stems 5–30 cm. **Leaves** 10–40 × 5–10 mm; stipules deltate, 1 mm; leaflets 15–27, blades ovate, elliptic, or oblong, leaflets of larger leaves 3–6 × 1–3 mm. **Peduncles** 1–3 cm in flower, 2–5 cm in fruit. **Heads** 3–8-flowered, 5 mm diam.; bract equaling or longer than flowers, 5–9-foliolate. **Pedicels** 0–1 mm. **Flowers:** calyx 2–2.5 mm, lobes 0.4–0.7 mm, 1/4–1/3 tube length; corolla white or pink, sometimes with darker lines, 3–5 mm. **Loments** compressed, constricted between seeds, 10–18(–25) × 1.5–2 mm; segments 4–9, elliptic-oblong, 2–2.5 mm; beaks straight, often hooked at tip, 1–3 mm. **Seeds** 1 × 1 mm. **2*n*** = 14.

Flowering late spring–summer. Disturbed ground, roadsides, waste places; 10–50 m; introduced; B.C.; Oreg., Pa.; Europe; temperate w Asia.

3. Ornithopus compressus Linnaeus, Sp. Pl. 2: 744. 1753 • Yellow serradela I

Stems 10–50 cm. **Leaves** 30–60 × 10–15 mm; stipules linear, 1 mm; leaflets 15–37, blades elliptical to oblong-lanceolate, leaflets of larger leaves 5–9 × 2–3 mm. **Peduncles** 1.5–2 cm in flower, 4–6 cm in fruit. **Heads** 3–8-flowered, 7–10 mm diam.; bract equaling or longer than flowers, 7–9-foliolate. **Pedicels** 0–1 mm. **Flowers:** calyx 3.5–4.3 mm, lobes 1.2–1.8 mm, more than 1/2 tube length; corolla yellow, 5–8 mm. **Loments** weakly compressed, not or slightly constricted between seeds, 20–50 × 2–3 mm; segments 5–8, oblong, 3.5–4 mm; beaks ± curved, 3–7 mm. **Seeds** 2 × 1.5 mm. **2*n*** = 14.

Flowering late spring–early summer. Disturbed open areas, waste places; 10–30 m; introduced; Oreg.; Europe; w Asia; introduced also in Australia.

123. ACMISPON Rafinesque, Atlantic J. 1: 144. 1832 • [Greek *acme*, point or apex, and *spao*, to draw or stretch, alluding to hooked-tipped pods]

Luc Brouillet

Acmispon sect. *Anisolotus* (Bernhardi) D. D. Sokoloff; *Acmispon* sect. *Simpeteria* (Ottley) Lassen; *Anisolotus* Bernhardi; *Lotus* Linnaeus sect. *Simpeteria* Ottley; *Ottleya* D. D. Sokoloff; *Syrmatium* Vogel

Herbs, annual or perennial, shrubs or subshrubs, unarmed. **Stems** procumbent or decumbent to ascending or erect, glabrous or pubescent. **Leaves** alternate, odd- or even-pinnate, palmate, or subpalmate; stipules usually present, glandlike, ovate, or conic, sometimes absent; sessile, subsessile, or petiolate; leaflets (2 or)3–10(–12), blade margins usually entire (sometimes denticulate in *A. americanus*, *A. denticulatus*), surfaces usually pubescent, rarely glabrous. **Inflorescences** solitary flowers or 2–12(–20)-flowered umbels, axillary; bracts present, usually subtending umbel or distal on pedicel, or absent. **Flowers** papilionaceous; calyx symmetric, bell-shaped or short-cylindric, lobes 5; corolla yellow to orange-yellow, cream, greenish white, white, pink, salmon, or pinkish red, sometimes marked with red, turning pink, orange, red, or brown, banner equaling or shorter than wings, wings symmetric or asymmetric, one wing ± above and one under keel; stamens 10, diadelphous; anthers basifixed, longitudinal; style with or without collar; stigma terminal. **Fruits** legumes, persistent or deciduous at base of pedicel with persistent calyx, included to ± strongly exserted from calyx, sessile, straight or ± curved to arched at apex, deflexed or not, usually linear to oblong or ovoid, rarely lanceoloid, abruptly short-beaked or tapered into an incurved beak exserted from calyx and appearing hooked, dehiscent or indehiscent, glabrous, glabrate, or ± strigillose to villous or silky. **Seeds** 1–10(–30), mottled or not, oblong, obovoid, ovoid, elliptic, lenticular, globose, subglobose, reniform, or cylindric. $x = 6, 7$.

Species 34 (28 in the flora): North America, nw Mexico, South America (Chile).

Six species of *Acmispon* are found only in Mexico [*A. flexuosus* (Greene) Brouillet, *A. niveus* (S. Watson) Brouillet, *A. nudatus* (Greene) Brouillet, *A. oroboides* (Kunth) Brouillet, *A. watsonii* (Vasey & Rose) Brouillet] or in Chile [*A. subpinnatus* (Lagasca) D. D. Sokoloff].

Throughout the twentieth century, *Acmispon* was usually included within *Lotus* (D. Isely 1981, 1993). Recent phylogenetic work, both morphologic (A. M. Arambarri 2000) and molecular (G. J. Allan and J. M. Porter 2000; Allan et al. 2003; D. D. Sokoloff et al. 2007), has shown that *Acmispon* is distinct from the Eurasian *Lotus* and the North American *Hosackia*. Notable differences among the three genera include the leafy or scarious, caducous stipules in *Hosackia* (where leaves are odd-pinnate) versus glandlike in *Lotus* (leaves with a pair of basal leaflets in stipular position with three palmate terminal leaflets) and *Acmispon* (leaves odd- or even-pinnate, palmate, or subpalmate).

In *Acmispon* and *Hosackia*, the banner sometimes is implicate, remaining folded longitudinally and enclosing the rest of the petals; if the banner is implicate-ascending, it remains folded but is partially raised above the other petals.

1. Shrubs or subshrubs (sometimes perennial herbs in *A. procumbens*), usually bushy or erect to procumbent, rarely mat-forming, prostrate, or cespitose.
    2. Leaves usually subpalmate (sometimes only distally), sometimes pinnate, leaflets 3 (except *A. glaber* sometimes to 7); inflorescences 1–3(–7)-flowered.

3. Herbs perennial, sometimes subshrubs, gray-canescent or strigose; stems leafy; wings longer than keel; seeds 2 or 3+ . . . . 20. *Acmispon procumbens* (in part)
3. Subshrubs, green, strigose, strigillose, or glabrous; stems remotely leafy; wings shorter than or equaling keel; seeds 1 or 2.
4. Leaf rachises 2–8(–10) mm; leaflet blades elliptic to lanceolate, apex acute; inflorescences (1 or)2–7-flowered; flowers 7–12 mm; petal claws slightly longer than calyx tube; legumes greenish to reddish brown, linear-oblong, curved to ± straight, 10–15 mm, smooth . . . . .21. *Acmispon glaber* (in part)
4. Leaf rachises absent; leaflet blades elliptic, apex obtuse; inflorescences 1 (or 2)-flowered; flowers 4–5 mm; petal claws shorter than calyx tube; legumes tawny, oblong, curved, (5–)6–9 mm, finely veined . . . . 24. *Acmispon haydonii*
2. Leaves pinnate (usually irregularly) or subpalmate, leaflets 3–6; inflorescences (1 or)2–12-flowered.
5. Plants green or gray; stems erect or decumbent, woody; leaflet blades sparsely to densely strigose (and wings ± equaling keel); California Channel Islands . . . 22. *Acmispon dendroideus*
5. Plants green, greenish, or brownish; stems usually procumbent to ± ascending, sometimes erect to spreading (wiry or stout), herbaceous, sometimes ± woody; leaflet blades strigillose or strigose (and wings longer than keel in *A. rigidus*), to glabrate or glabrous; mainland w United States, nw Mexico.
6. Leaflet blades strigose; peduncles much longer than leaves, 20–60(–130) mm; legumes dehiscent, straight, short-beaked; seeds 18–30 . . . . 3. *Acmispon rigidus*
6. Leaflet blades strigillose to glabrate or glabrous; peduncles shorter than leaves, 0–10 mm, or if longer, to 25 mm; legumes indehiscent, usually curved, sometimes straight, beaked to long-beaked; seeds 1 or 2.
7. Plants often bushy, sometimes mat-forming, robust, 5–20 dm; stems usually erect to spreading, sometimes procumbent, herbaceous, slender, remotely leafy; inflorescences in axil of distal leaves, spaced or congested, peduncles 0–2 mm; legumes curved to ± straight .21. *Acmispon glaber* (in part)
7. Plants usually mat-forming, cespitose, or prostrate, sometimes bushy or wiry, 0.8–8 dm; stems procumbent to ascending, wiry, thick or stout, leafy; inflorescence peduncles 1–25 mm; legumes arched.
8. Stems greenish; flowers 8–10 mm; petal claws shorter than calyx tube, wings slightly longer than keel; legumes mostly included. . . . . . .23. *Acmispon cytisoides*
8. Stems brownish; flowers 6–8 mm; petal claws longer than calyx tube, wings shorter than keel (and other petals); legumes ± exserted . . . 25. *Acmispon junceus*
1. Herbs annual or perennial (rarely subshrubs), mat-forming, cespitose, or prostrate.
9. Herbs annual, cespitose, sometimes mat-forming or solitary; taprooted.
10. Inflorescences 2–8-flowered; legumes indehiscent, strongly exserted from calyx, arched, turgid, constricted between seeds; seeds 2, mottled.
11. Stems remotely leafy; inflorescences 3–8-flowered, peduncles 8–30 mm; flowers 5–7 mm, claws longer than calyx tube, wings equaling or longer than keel; legumes glabrous . . . . 18. *Acmispon prostratus*
11. Stems leafy; inflorescences 2–5-flowered, peduncles 1–2(–5) mm; flowers 3–4 (–5) mm, claws shorter than calyx tube, wings shorter than keel; legumes strigillose . . . . .19. *Acmispon micranthus*
10. Inflorescences 1 or 2(–5)-flowered; legumes dehiscent, exserted from calyx (except mostly included in *A. rubriflorus*), usually straight or ± curved, compressed, not or slightly constricted between seeds; seeds 2–10, not or faintly or ± mottled (often black-mottled in *A. americanus*).
12. Leaves tomentose or tomentulose to glabrate; wings equaling or longer than keel, styles puberulent or glabrous.
13. Herbs usually mat-forming, sometimes cespitose, strigillose, hirsute, canescent-tomentose, or scantily pubescent; wings longer than keel. . . 1. *Acmispon strigosus*
13. Herbs not mat-forming (rounded, straggly), glabrate; wings equaling keel . . . . 2. *Acmispon intricatus*

12. Leaves glabrous, sparsely appressed-hairy, hirsute, or villous to pubescent, strigillose, or strigose; wings ± equaling or shorter than keel; styles glabrous.
    14. Plants usually glabrous or strigillose, sometimes glabrate to ± pilose; inflorescences 1–5-flowered; peduncles (0–)3–25 mm, bracts usually 1–3-foliolate, rarely absent; legumes straight or ± curved; seeds 3–9.
        15. Plants ± fleshy; stems procumbent to ascending; leaves pinnate, leaflets (3–)5–7; inflorescences 1–5-flowered, pedunculate; corollas bright yellow or orange-yellow; legumes leathery . . . . 11. *Acmispon maritimus*
        15. Plants not fleshy; stems erect to procumbent; leaves pinnate or palmate, leaflets (1–)3–5; inflorescences 1 or 2-flowered, subsessile or pedunculate; corollas pink or salmon, or whitish or cream; legumes thinly leathery.
            16. Leaflet blades obovate to oblong or elliptic, apex obtuse, surfaces strigose; flowers (2.5–)4–6 mm, calyx tube sparsely strigillose, corollas pink or salmon, claws longer than calyx tube; legumes hook-beaked; seeds not mottled . . . . 12. *Acmispon parviflorus*
            16. Leaflet blades obovate, ovate, or elliptic to lanceolate, apex acute, surfaces sparsely appressed-hairy; flowers (4–)5–9 mm, calyx tube pilose, corollas whitish or cream, claws shorter than calyx tube; legume apex abruptly downward angled and curved; seeds often black-mottled . . . . 13. *Acmispon americanus*
    14. Plants usually hirsute, villous, or pubescent, sometimes glabrate or glabrous; inflorescences 1 or 2-flowered; peduncles 0–2 mm, bracts absent; legumes straight; seeds 2–4(–7).
        17. Stems decumbent to ascending or erect; leaflet blades hirsute or villous; calyx lobes subulate; corollas cream-white to pale yellow and banner purple-tinged, or bright pinkish red.
            18. Leaves petiolate, rachises 5–12 mm, leaflet blades elliptic to obovate; legumes exserted, 8–20 mm, leathery, strigose or glabrous . . . . 14. *Acmispon denticulatus*
            18. Leaves subsessile, rachises 4–6 mm, leaflet blades lanceolate; legumes mostly included, 8–9 mm, papery, villous . . . . 17. *Acmispon rubriflorus*
        17. Stems procumbent to low-ascending; leaflet blades villous or pubescent; calyx lobes lanceolate; corollas yellow, or pale yellow and reddish-tipped.
            19. Plants not fleshy; leaves petiolate; wings shorter than keel; legumes thinly leathery, pubescent (to glabrate), ± septate . . . . . . 15. *Acmispon wrangelianus*
            19. Plants ± fleshy; leaves subsessile or sessile; wings ± equaling keel; legumes stiffly papery, villous, not septate. . . . . 16. *Acmispon brachycarpus*

[9. Shifted to left margin.—Ed.]

9. Herbs perennial (rarely subshrubs), usually mat-forming, sometimes bushy, from woody caudices, rhizomatous caudices, or woody-taprooted.
    20. Flowers 4–12 mm; styles curved, geniculate 90°, or incurved; legumes indehiscent, strongly arched or curved, sometimes ± straight, apex tapering, short- or long-beaked, beak sometimes curved; leaves subpalmate, sometimes irregularly pinnate.
        21. Leaves subpalmate, leaflets usually 3, blades canescent to strigose; stems gray-canescent or strigose; calyx tube ± densely strigose; petal claws longer than calyx tube, wings longer than keel; seeds 2 or 3+. . . . . 20. *Acmispon procumbens* (in part)
        21. Leaves irregularly pinnate or subpalmate, leaflets 3–6(or 7), blades pilose, villous, or densely sericeous; stems tomentose to canescent, strigose, or ± villous (young) to glabrate (mature); calyx tube villous or sparsely or densely villosulous; petal claws shorter than or equaling calyx tube; seeds 1 or 2(or 3).
            22. Leaflet blades sparsely to densely pilose; flowers 4–6(–7) mm, calyx lobes setaceous; legumes 3–5 mm, villous . . . . 26. *Acmispon tomentosus*
            22. Leaflet blades villous or densely sericeous; flowers 4.5–12 mm, calyx lobes subulate; legumes 6–10 mm, strigillose or glabrate to silky.

23 Stems ± villous to glabrate; leaflet blades villous; calyx tube sparsely villosulous; corollas: wings longer than keel; legumes exserted, ovoid-ellipsoid, strigillose . . . . .27. *Acmispon decumbens*

23. Stems tomentose to canescent or strigose; leaflet blades densely sericeous; calyx tube densely villous; corollas: wings ± equaling keel; legumes included to moderately(–strongly) exserted, lanceoloid, glabrate to silky. . . 28. *Acmispon argophyllus*

[20. Shifted to left margin.—Ed.]

20. Flowers 5–25 mm; styles straight or slightly curved, sometimes basally curved; legumes dehiscent, usually straight, ± curved, or curved distally, apex short-beaked; leaves palmate or pinnate, or subpalmate to irregularly pinnate.

24. Stems stiff; leaves palmate and leaflets villous to strigose.

25. Leaves sessile; inflorescences (1 or)2–5(or 6)-flowered, peduncles longer than leaves, (10–)20–50(–80) mm, bracts 1–3-foliolate; banners recurved ca. 45° . . .6. *Acmispon utahensis*

25. Leaves short-petiolate proximally, subsessile or sessile distally; inflorescences 1 or 2-flowered, peduncles usually longer, sometimes shorter, than leaves, 0–30 mm, bracts absent or (when pedunculate) unifoliolate; banners implicate-ascending . . . . 7. *Acmispon wrightii*

24. Stems herbaceous; leaves pinnate to subpalmate (distal) and leaflets gray-puberulent, villous, tomentose, strigose, strigillose, or puberulent, or if palmate, then leaflets sericeous to canescent.

26. Leaves pinnate, leaflets 7–9(–12); corollas greenish white, white, or yellow, fading rose or reddish . . . . 10. *Acmispon grandiflorus*

26. Leaves pinnate or subpalmate, leaflets 3–5(–7)[–13]; corollas usually yellow or cream to orange-yellow.

27. Petal claws ± equaling calyx tube; flowers 5–16(–20) mm; legumes straight or ± curved, slightly constricted between seeds.

28. Plants silvery or gray, sericeous to canescent; rachises 1–4 mm; legumes turgid. . . . . .4. *Acmispon argyraeus*

28. Plants green, ± strigose to puberulent; rachises (1.5–)5–10 mm; legumes compressed . . . . 5. *Acmispon plebeius*

27. Petal claws shorter than calyx tube; flowers (10–)12–22 mm; legumes straight, not constricted between seeds.

29. Plants greenish, densely hirsute; leaf blades villous to tomentose; inflorescences 1–3(–5)-flowered; calyx tubes densely villous; banners obliquely ascending. . . . . 8. *Acmispon neomexicanus*

29. Plants silvery, tomentose; leaf blades gray-puberulent; inflorescences (1 or)2–7-flowered; calyx tubes puberulent; banners ascending 45–90° . . . . .9. *Acmispon mearnsii*

1. Acmispon strigosus (Nuttall) Brouillet, J. Bot. Res. Inst. Texas 2: 392. 2008

Hosackia strigosa Nuttall in J. Torrey and A. Gray, Fl. N. Amer. 1: 326. 1838; *Anisolotus strigosus* (Nuttall) A. Heller; *Lotus strigosus* (Nuttall) Greene; *Ottleya strigosa* (Nuttall) D. D. Sokoloff

Herbs, annual, usually mat-forming, sometimes cespitose (ascending and bushy), green to grayish, 0.3–5 dm, not or ± fleshy, strigillose, hirsute, canescent-tomentose, or scantily pubescent; taprooted. **Stems** 1–20+, procumbent or decumbent to ascending, branched basally, herbaceous, slender, leafy. **Leaves** irregularly pinnate; stipules glandlike; subsessile; rachis 3–20 mm, flattened; leaflets 4–10, blades unequal, obovate to oblanceolate to linear-oblong or oblong, apex acute to obtuse or truncate, surfaces ± densely tomentose to glabrate. **Peduncles** ascending or reflexed, upturned, 3–25 mm, shorter to longer than leaves (often elongated in fruit); bract absent or 1–3-foliolate, usually subtending umbel. **Inflorescences** 1–3-flowered. **Flowers** (5–)6–10(–12) mm; calyx 3–5.5 mm, tube ± sparsely strigillose or glabrous, lobes subulate; corolla yellow (sometimes banner orangish abaxially), turning orange or reddish, claws ± equaling calyx tube, banner implicate-ascending or remaining closely implicate, wings longer than keel; style corneously thickened, marked by color, straight, puberulent or glabrous. **Legumes** persistent, exserted, erect or divergent, brown, straight to ± curved distally, compressed, not or slightly constricted, incompletely septate, linear-oblong, 10–35 × 2–3 mm, thinly leathery, apex initially short-beaked, dehiscent, smooth, margins smooth, thin, glabrous or ± strigose. **Seeds** 5–10, greenish to brown, ± mottled, ovoid to cuboid or globose, rugulose or granular.

Varieties 3 (3 in the flora): sw United States, n Mexico.

D. Isely (1981) discussed the variation in *Acmispon strigosus* (as *Lotus*), distinguishing three varieties, two rather distinct but with intergrading phases, and one apparently more transitional, although distinct enough to be recognized. These varieties were only noted for California in recent treatments (for example, L. Brouillet 2012, following D. Isely 1993). Nonetheless, the typical (for example, excluding intergrading phases) varieties represent recognizable morphologies that also have geographic distinction. Specimens representing intergradation seem to occur throughout the range of overlap of these varieties, sometimes rendering determination difficult.

1. Herbs evidently hirsute, especially at apex, greenish. . . . . 1b. *Acmispon strigosus* var. *hirtellus*
1. Herbs usually strigillose or canescent-tomentose to scantly pubescent, rarely strigillose, green or cinereous.
   2. Stems ascending or decumbent, not markedly succulent, usually appearing green, sometimes cinereous; leaflet blades linear-oblong, apices acute to obtuse; corolla opening; California . . . . 1a. *Acmispon strigosus* var. *strigosus*
   2. Stems prostrate, succulent, cinereous (–greenish); leaflet blades oblong, apices obtuse or truncate; corolla not opening; Arizona, California, Nevada . . . . 1c. *Acmispon strigosus* var. *tomentellus*

1a. Acmispon strigosus (Nuttall) Brouillet var. **strigosus**

Anisolotus nudiflorus (Nuttall) A. Heller; *A. rubellus* (Nuttall) A. Heller; *Hosackia nudiflora* Nuttall; *H. rubella* Nuttall; *Lotus nudiflorus* (Nuttall) Greene; *L. rubellus* (Nuttall) Greene; *L. strigosus* (Nuttall) Greene var. *nudiflorus* (Nuttall) Jepson

Herbs green in appearance, sometimes cinereous, not markedly succulent, strigillose, hairs appressed. **Stems** ascending or decumbent. **Leaflet blades** linear-oblong, apex acute to obtuse. **Peduncles** (0.5–)1 cm, usually elongated in fruit to 2+ cm, shorter to longer than leaves. **Corollas** opening. **Legumes** (10–)15–35 × 2–3 mm. **Seeds** greenish to brown, cuboid (rounded-oblong in cross section), less than 1 mm, irregularly rugulose. **2*n*** = 14.

Flowering late winter–spring(–fall). Usually open, dry, sandy or gravelly soils, foothills, desert slopes, coast ranges, coastal scrub, chaparral, roadsides, disturbed areas, conspicuous after fires; 0–1500(–2500) m; Calif.; Mexico (Baja California, Sonora).

Variety *strigosus* is widespread from central California south, mainly west of the deserts. D. Isely (1981) recognized phases within vars. *strigosus* and *tomentellus*, which could correspond to intermediate forms between them.

1b. Acmispon strigosus (Nuttall) Brouillet var. **hirtellus** (Greene) D. W. Taylor, Fl. Yosemite Sierra, 147, 373. 2010

Lotus hirtellus Greene, Pittonia 2: 142. 1890; *Anisolotus hirtellus* (Greene) A. Heller; *Hosackia hirtella* (Greene) Brand; *H. strigosa* Nuttall var. *hirtella* (Greene) H. M. Hall; *L. strigosus* (Nuttall) Greene var. *hirtellus* (Greene) Ottley

Herbs greenish, ± succulent, evidently hirsute, hairs not appressed, especially at apex. **Stems** ascending or decumbent. **Leaflet blades** obovate to linear-oblong, apex obtuse. **Peduncles** (0.5–)1 cm, generally elongating in fruit to 2+ cm, shorter to longer than leaves. **Corollas** opening. **Legumes** 20–30 × 2–3 mm. **Seeds** pale greenish or buff, cuboid (rounded-oblong in cross section), usually granular, rarely rugulose. **2*n*** = 14.

Flowering (late winter–)spring. Coastal ranges, washes, deserts, palm springs, ponderosa pine forests; (100–)500–2000 m; Calif.; Mexico (Baja California).

Variety *hirtellus* is present in the Coast Ranges and the Mojave and Sonoran deserts.

1c. Acmispon strigosus (Nuttall) Brouillet var. **tomentellus** (Greene) Brouillet, Phytoneuron 2020-29: 1. 2020

Lotus tomentellus Greene, Pittonia 2: 140. 1890; *Hosackia tomentella* (Greene) Brand; *L. strigosus* (Nuttall) Greene var. *tomentellus* (Greene) Isely

Herbs cinereous (to greenish), succulent, canescent-tomentose to scantly pubescent or sometimes strigillose, hairs appressed. **Stems** prostrate. **Leaflet blades** oblong, apex obtuse or truncate. **Peduncles** less than 0.5(–1) cm, little (or sometimes) elongating in fruit, mostly shorter than leaves. **Corollas** not opening. **Legumes** usually curved toward apex, 10–25(–30) × 2 mm. **Seeds** pale buff or light green, ± mottled purplish brown, globose to cuboid, 1 mm, finely granular.

Flowering late winter–spring. Desert slopes and washes, usually with creosote bush, rocky desert foothills, canyons, roadsides, sandy or gravelly soils; 0–1500 (–2400) m; Ariz., Calif., Nev.; Mexico (Baja California, Chihuahua, Sonora).

Variety *tomentellus* is the main morphotype encountered in the Mojave and Sonoran deserts and the only form present in Arizona and Nevada. Some Arizona individuals occasionally exhibit pubescence features characteristic of var. *strigosus* (phase 2 of D. Isely 1981).

2. Acmispon intricatus (Eastwood) Brouillet, J. Bot. Res. Inst. Texas 2: 390. 2008 [C] [E]

Lotus intricatus Eastwood, Leafl. W. Bot. 3: 159. 1942; *Ottleya intricata* (Eastwood) D. D. Sokoloff

Herbs, annual, rounded, straggly (like tumbleweed), green to grayish, 2–3 dm, not fleshy, glabrate; taprooted. **Stems** 1–20+, ascending, branched basally, herbaceous, leafy. **Leaves** pinnate; stipules glandlike; subsessile; rachis 3–8 mm, flattened; leaflets 5–7, blades oblong, apex obtuse, surfaces tomentulose. **Peduncles** ascending, filiform, 10–20 mm, longer than leaves; bract absent. **Inflorescences** 1-flowered. **Flowers** 4–5 mm; calyx 2.5–3 mm, tube pubescence not observed, lobes subulate, shorter than tube; corolla yellow turning red, claws ± equaling calyx tube, banner cuneate to short-clawed, wings equal to keel; style thickening and shape not observed, puberulent becoming glabrate. **Legumes** persistent, exserted, erect, brown, curved distally, compressed, oblong, leathery, dehiscent, smooth, margins smooth, strigillose. **Seeds** olive green to dark brown, ± mottled, oblong, sculpture not observed.

Flowering spring. Desert scrub; of conservation concern; 600–800 m; Nev.

Acmispon intricatus is known only from the type locality in the Valley of Fire in Clark County; it has not been recollected. D. Isely (1981) acknowledged that *A. intricatus* could be a phenotypic variant of *A. strigosus* var. *tomentellus*, but he stated that they differ in growth habit.

3. Acmispon rigidus (Bentham) Brouillet, J. Bot. Res. Inst. Texas 2: 392. 2008 • Shrubby deervetch, desert deerweed, desert rock pea, broom or hairy lotus

Hosackia rigida Bentham, Pl. Hartw., 305. 1849; *Anisolotus argensis* (Coville) A. Heller; *A. rigidus* (Bentham) Rydberg; *Lotus argensis* Coville; *L. rigidus* (Bentham) Greene; *Ottleya rigida* (Bentham) D. D. Sokoloff

Subshrubs, bushy, green, (2–)3–9(–15) dm, not fleshy, sparsely strigose to glabrate; from woody caudices. **Stems** 1–30+, ascending, branched (distal branches ± flexuous and herbaceous), stiff (± woody), remotely leafy. **Leaves** irregularly pinnate or palmate; stipules evanescent, glandlike, ovoid-deltoid; short-petiolate or sessile; rachis 0–5 mm, not flattened; leaflets 3–5, blades obovate to oblanceolate, apex obtuse to emarginate, surfaces strigose. **Peduncles** ascending to erect, slender, often flexuous, 20–60(–130) mm, much longer than leaves; bract absent or unifoliolate, subtending umbel. **Inflorescences** 1–4(or 5)-flowered. **Flowers** 12–20 (–24) mm; calyx 6.5–10 mm, tube ± densely strigillose, lobes subulate, abaxial pair sometimes connate behind banner; corolla yellow, sometimes ± suffused with red or orange, banner often red-backed, claws ± equaling calyx tube, banner remaining implicate, ± ascending to 45°, wings longer than keel; style corneously thickened and laterally grooved proximally, straight, glabrous. **Legumes** persistent, exserted, erect or divergent, yellow-brown to reddish, straight, turgid, not constricted, not septate, linear-oblong to oblong, 20–40(–45) × 3–5 mm, leathery, apex short-beaked, dehiscent, smooth, margins smooth, keeled, usually glabrate, rarely sparsely strigillose. **Seeds** 18–30, light brown, ± mottled, subglobose, finely granulose or papillose. $2n = 14$.

Flowering late winter–spring. Washes, rocky hillsides, talus and cliff-ledges of desert canyons, shrubby grasslands, scrub, oak chaparral, pinyon woodlands, Joshua tree woodlands, roadsides, on granite, limestone, or lava; 10–1400(–1600) m; Ariz., Calif., Nev., Utah; Mexico (Baja California, Sonora).

Acmispon rigidus occurs in the Californian Transverse Ranges to the Mojave and Sonoran deserts, into central Arizona, southern Nevada, and Washington County, Utah. It is reported to hybridize with *A. plebeius*, *A. argyraeus* (variety not specified), *A. mearnsii* var. *mearnsii*, *A. neomexicanus* (also reported by D. Isely 1981), *A. utahensis*, *A. wrightii* (also reported by Isely), and possibly with *A. grandiflorus* var. *grandiflorus* (as var. *mutabilis* Ottley) (A. M. Ottley 1944).

4. Acmispon argyraeus (Greene) Brouillet, J. Bot. Res. Inst. Texas 2: 389. 2008 (as argyreus)

Hosackia argyraea Greene, Bull. Calif. Acad. Sci. 1: 184. 1885; *Anisolotus argyraeus* (Greene) A. Heller; *Lotus argyraeus* (Greene) Greene; *Ottleya argyraea* (Greene) D. D. Sokoloff

Herbs, perennial, mat-forming, silvery or gray, 1–3 dm, not fleshy, sericeous to canescent; from woody caudices. **Stems** 1–20+, procumbent or decumbent to diffusely ascending, branched, herbaceous, slender, leafy. **Leaves** palmate or irregularly subpinnate; stipules glandlike; subsessile to short-petiolate; rachis 1–4 mm, ± flattened; leaflets 3–5, blades obovate to oblanceolate, apex usually obtuse, sometimes acute, surfaces sericeous to canescent. **Peduncles** ascending or spreading, (2–)10–20 mm, shorter to longer than leaves; bract absent (reduced to stipules) or unifoliolate, distal. **Inflorescences** 1–3(–5)-flowered. **Flowers** 5–12 mm; calyx 4–7 mm, tube villous, lobes subulate; corolla yellow, turning orange-red, claws ± equaling calyx tube, banner ascending to 45°, wings unequal, longer than keel; style slightly curved or straight, glabrous or finely puberulent. **Legumes** persistent, exserted, divergent, brown, straight or curved at tip, turgid, slightly constricted, imperfectly septate, linear-oblong to oblong, (10–)18–25 × 1.5–2 mm, leathery, apex short-beaked, dehiscent, smooth, margins smooth, strigillose to glabrate. **Seeds** 2–5+, olive brown, mottled, roundish-oblong to angled, smooth, 2-veined.

Varieties 3 (3 in the flora): California, nw Mexico.

Acmispon argyraeus (variety not specified) is reported to hybridize with *A. rigidus* (A. M. Ottley 1944).

1. Banner panduriform; pistils arched more than 90°, ovary-style junction defined by a line; leaflet blades oblanceolate to obovate, usually folded; legumes curved at tip . . . . 4b. *Acmispon argyraeus* var. *multicaulis*
1. Banner not panduriform; pistils arched less than 90°, ovary-style junction with a jog (style base broader than apex of ovary) or confluent; leaflet blades obovate, not folded; legumes usually straight.
   2. Herbs usually prostrate; stems branched, silvery-canescent; ovary-style junction with a jog; flowers 5–10 mm . . . . 4a. *Acmispon argyraeus* var. *argyraeus*
   2. Herbs low-spreading or low-ascending; stems diffusely branched, green or canescent; ovary-style junction confluent; flowers (8–)10–12 mm . . . . 4c. *Acmispon argyraeus* var. *notitius*

4a. Acmispon argyraeus (Greene) Brouillet var. **argyraeus**

Herbs usually prostrate. **Stems** prostrate, silvery-canescent, branched. **Leaflet blades** obovate, length 2 times width, not folded. **Flowers** 5–10 mm; calyx lobes 2 mm; banner not panduriform; pistils arched less than 90°, ovary-style junction with a jog (style base broader than apex of ovary), ovules 11–14. **Legumes** usually straight, 15–20 mm.

Flowering late spring–summer. Dry, open granitic slopes, pine woodlands, desert scrub; 1100–2700 m; Calif.; Mexico (Baja California).

Variety *argyraeus* is known from the San Bernardino, San Jacinto, and Santa Rosa mountains of southern California.

4b. Acmispon argyraeus (Greene) Brouillet var. **multicaulis** (Ottley) Brouillet, J. Bot. Res. Inst. Texas 2: 389. 2008 (as argyreus) [C] [E]

Lotus wrightii (A. Gray) Greene var. *multicaulis* Ottley, Univ. Calif. Publ. Bot. 10: 211, plate 70, figs. 7–13. 1923; *Hosackia wrightii* A. Gray subsp. *multicaulis* (Ottley) Abrams; *L. argyraeus* (Greene) Greene subsp. *multicaulis* (Ottley) Munz; *L. argyraeus* var. *multicaulis* (Ottley) Isely

Herbs decumbent to low-ascending. **Stems** decumbent to ascending, glabrous or sparsely hairy, diffusely branched. **Leaflet blades** oblanceolate to obovate, length 3–4 times width, usually folded. **Flowers** (8–)10–12 mm; calyx lobes 2.5–3 mm; banner panduriform; pistils arched more than 90°, ovary-style junction defined by a line, ovules 9–11. **Legumes** curved at tip, 20–25 mm.

Flowering late spring–early summer. Dry slopes, flats, pinyon-juniper woodlands; of conservation concern; 1200–1500 m; Calif.

Variety *multicaulis* is known only from the New York Mountains in the Mojave Desert, where it is uncommon.

4c. Acmispon argyraeus (Greene) Brouillet var. **notitius** (Isely) Brouillet, J. Bot. Res. Inst. Texas 2: 389. 2008 (as argyreus) [C] [E]

Lotus argyraeus (Greene) Greene var. *notitius* Isely, Brittonia 30: 466. 1978

Herbs low-spreading or low-ascending. **Stems** decumbent to ascending, green or canescent, diffusely branched. **Leaflet blades** obovate (distal leaves), length 2 times width, not folded. **Flowers** (8–)10–12 mm; calyx lobes 2–3 mm; banner not panduriform; pistils arched less than 90°, ovary-style junction confluent, ovules 11 or 12. **Legumes** straight, 10–25 mm.

Flowering late spring–early summer. Pinyon-juniper woodlands to upper sagebrush scrub, canyon slopes; of conservation concern; 1200–2000 m; Calif.

Variety *notitius* is known from the Cottonwood and Providence mountains in the Mojave Desert, where it is uncommon.

5. Acmispon plebeius (Brandegee) Brouillet, Phytoneuron 2020-29: 2. 2020

Hosackia plebeia Brandegee, Proc. Calif. Acad. Sci., ser. 2, 2: 144. 1889; *Anisolotus longebracteatus* (Rydberg) Rydberg; *A. nummularius* (M. E. Jones) Wooton & Standley; *H. rigida* Bentham var. *nummularia* M. E. Jones; *Lotus longebracteatus* Rydberg; *L. nummularius* (M. E. Jones) Tidestrom; *L. oroboides* (Kunth) Ottley var. *nanus* Isely; *L. oroboides* var. *nummularius* (M. E. Jones) Isely; *L. oroboides* var. *plebeius* (Brandegee) Ottley; *L. oroboides* var. *ramulosus* (M. E. Jones) Ottley; *L. plebeius* (Brandegee) Barneby; *L. ramulosus* M. E. Jones; *Ottleya plebeia* (Brandegee) D. D. Sokoloff & Gandhi

Herbs, perennial, mat-forming or cespitose, diffuse, green, 0.5–4.5 dm, not fleshy, ± strigose to puberulent; from woody caudices. **Stems** 1–10+, decumbent to ascending, branched, herbaceous, sometimes slender, leafy, base with or without persistent leaves. **Leaves** irregularly pinnate to subpalmate with a terminal trefoil, often dimorphic (proximal with smaller, rounder leaflets); stipules glandlike; subsessile to short-petiolate; rachis (1.5–)5–10 mm, flattened; leaflets (3 or)4 or 5(–7)[–13], blades obovate (widely obovate) to linear-oblanceolate [elliptic], apex emarginate or obtuse to acute, surfaces strigose to villous. **Peduncles** ascending, 10–70(–90) mm, longer than leaves; bract absent or 1–3[–5]-foliolate, subtending umbel. **Inflorescences** 1–3(or 4)-flowered. **Flowers** 10–16(–20) mm; calyx 5–8.5[–10] mm, tube villous, lobes lanceolate to subulate; corolla yellow, turning orange or red [banner red, keel and wings white], claws ± equaling calyx tube, banner ascending to 45°, wings longer than keel; style straight, glabrous. **Legumes** persistent, exserted, erect to spreading, green or purplish brown [ashy], straight or ± curved, compressed, slightly constricted, imperfectly septate, linear-oblong, 17–35 × 2–3 mm, leathery, apex short-beaked, dehiscent, smooth, margins keeled, strigillose [glabrate]. **Seeds** 10–18, dark brown, ± mottled, oblong, dull, ± compressed, smooth. $2n = 14$.

Flowering spring or fall. Sandy or gravelly, often dry, sometimes moist soils, on rock, flats, creekbeds, talus or colluvial slopes, rocky hillsides, ridges, canyons, grasslands, savannas, montane or desert scrub, cypress or juniper-pinyon or oak woodlands, oak-Douglas-fir-pine, ponderosa pine or pine-oak forests, washes, roadsides; 1000–2700 m; Ariz., Nev., N.Mex., Tex., Utah; Mexico (Baja California, Baja California Sur, Chihuahua, Durango, Hidalgo, Jalisco, Puebla).

Acmispon plebeius occurs in the plateaus of southern Utah and into Lincoln County, Nevada, as well as in the plateaus and ranges of Arizona and New Mexico. It is reported to hybridize with *A. neomexicanus* and *A. rigidus* (A. M. Ottley 1944; D. Isely 1981), as well as *A. wrightii* (Isely).

Lotus nummulus Dayton is an illegitimate, superfluous name that pertains here.

6. Acmispon utahensis (Ottley) Brouillet, J. Bot. Res. Inst. Texas 2: 392. 2008 • Utah deervetch or lotus [E]

Lotus utahensis Ottley, Brittonia 5: 108. 1944; *Ottleya utahensis* (Ottley) D. D. Sokoloff

Herbs, perennial, cespitose, greenish or grayish (base), 1–5 dm, not fleshy, puberulent to sparsely strigose or glabrate; rhizomatous caudex from a taproot. **Stems** 1–10+, decumbent to ascending or erect, branched sparsely, stiff, leafy, base without persistent leaves. **Leaves** palmate, homomorphic; stipules ovate; sessile; rachis absent; leaflets (2–)4–6, blades linear-oblanceolate to oblanceolate, apex acute to obtuse, surfaces villous to strigose. **Peduncles** ascending to deflexed, curved to erect, (10–)20–50(–80) mm, longer than leaves; bract 1–3-foliolate, subtending umbel. **Inflorescences** (1 or)2–5(or 6)-flowered. **Flowers** 8–15 mm; calyx 5–7.5 mm, tube villous, lobes subulate; corolla yellow with red-backed banner, often suffused with red, turning orange, claws shorter than calyx tube, banner recurved ca. 45°, pandurate, wings longer than keel (nearly equaling banner); style straight, glabrous. **Legumes** persistent, exserted, spreading or deflexed, reddish to grayish brown, ± straight, turgid, not constricted, incompletely septate, linear-oblong, (14–)25–35 × 1.5–3.5 mm, leathery, apex short-beaked, dehiscent, smooth, lustrous, margins keeled, strigillose or glabrous. **Seeds** (1–)3–6, olive green to dark brown, mottled, oblong, smooth.

Flowering spring(–summer). Open places, dry, stony or sandy soils, sagebrush, desert scrub, pinyon-juniper woodlands, chaparral, oak woodlands, yellow pine or spruce-aspen forests, riparian communities; (1500–) 1700–2900 m; Ariz., Nev., Utah.

Acmispon utahensis is nearly restricted to Utah, barely penetrating into Arizona and Nevada. It is encountered on the plateaus of the intermountain region. It is reported to hybridize with *A. rigidus* and *A. wrightii* (A. M. Ottley 1944).

7. **Acmispon wrightii** (A. Gray) Brouillet, J. Bot. Res. Inst. Texas 2: 392. 2008 • Scrub deervetch or lotus [E] [F]

Hosackia wrightii A. Gray, Smithsonian Contr. Knowl. 5(6): 42. 1853; *Anisolotus wrightii* (A. Gray) Rydberg; *Lotus wrightii* (A. Gray) Greene; *Ottleya wrightii* (A. Gray) D. D. Sokoloff

Herbs, perennial, cespitose, erect or sprawling, greenish or grayish, 2–4(–8) dm, not fleshy, usually strigose to hirsute, rarely canescent; from woody caudices. **Stems** 1–20+, procumbent to ascending, branched proximally, stiff, leafy, base without persistent leaves. **Leaves** palmate, often ± dimorphic (proximal with broader leaflets, distal with filiform ones), sometimes subtending axillary clusters of filiform leaflets; stipules ovate; proximal short-petiolate, medial and distal subsessile or sessile; rachis absent; leaflets 3–6, blades obovate (proximal) or oblanceolate to linear (distal), apex usually acute, sometimes obtuse, surfaces ± densely villous to strigose. **Peduncles** ascending to deflexed, 0–30 mm, usually longer, sometimes shorter, than leaves; bract absent or (when pedunculate) unifoliolate, distal. **Inflorescences** 1 or 2-flowered. **Flowers** 10–15(–18) mm; calyx 5–7.5 mm, tube villous to strigose, lobes subulate to setaceous; corolla yellow with back of banner red, turning reddish, claws shorter than calyx tube, banner implicate-ascending, wings longer than keel; style straight, glabrous. **Legumes** persistent, exserted, divergent or declined, reddish or grayish brown, straight, turgid, slightly constricted, incompletely septate, linear-oblong, (17–)20–35 × 1.5–3(–3.5) mm, leathery, apex short-beaked, dehiscent, smooth, margins smooth, thickened, sparsely strigose to glabrate. **Seeds** 4–7, greenish to dark reddish brown, ± mottled, oblong, smooth. $2n = 14$.

Flowering late spring–summer. Canyon slopes, mesas, washes, ± dry hillsides, sandy-loam, sandy, or gravelly soils, sometimes saline, pine-oak-Douglas-fir, pine or aspen forests, oak-pinyon-*Cercocarpus* or pinyon-juniper woodlands, juniper-oak grasslands, desert grasslands or scrub, riparian woodlands, roadsides; (1500–) 1700–3200 m; Ariz., Colo., Nev., N.Mex., Utah.

Acmispon wrightii is reported to hybridize with *A. mearnsii* var. *mearnsii*, *A. rigidus*, and *A. utahensis* (A. M. Ottley 1944; D. Isely 1981), as well as *A. plebeius* (Isely).

8. **Acmispon neomexicanus** (Greene) Brouillet, Phytoneuron 2020-29: 2. 2020

Lotus neomexicanus Greene, Pittonia 2: 144. 1890 (as neo-mexicanus); *Acmispon greenei* (Ottley) Brouillet; *Anisolotus mollis* A. Heller; *A. neomexicanus* (Greene) A. Heller; *Hosackia greenei* (Ottley) Wiggins; *H. neomexicana* (Greene) Brand; *Lotus greenei* Ottley; *Ottleya mollis* (A. Heller) D. D. Sokoloff & Gandhi

Herbs, perennial, mat-forming, greenish, 0.5–3 dm, not fleshy, densely hirsute; from woody caudices. **Stems** 1–20+, procumbent or decumbent, branched, herbaceous, leafy, proximally covered by small, persistent leaves. **Leaves** pinnate to subpalmate (distal); stipules conic; proximal short-petiolate or sessile, distal subsessile to short-petiolate; rachis 0–4 mm, sometimes flattened; leaflets (3 or)4 or 5(or 6), blades obovate to oblanceolate (proximal ± orbiculate), apex acute to rounded, surfaces villous to tomentose. **Peduncles** ascending or reflexed, upturned, (5–)20–50 mm, longer than leaves; bract absent (reduced to gland) or 1(–3)-foliolate, distal. **Inflorescences** 1–3(–5)-flowered. **Flowers** (10–)13–22 mm; calyx 4.3–7 mm, tube densely villous, lobes subulate; corolla cream to orange-yellow, rose-tinted, claws shorter than calyx tube, banner obliquely ascending, wings longer than banner and keel, auriculate, spurred; style ± straight, glabrous. **Legumes** persistent, exserted, erect, reddish brown, straight, turgid, not constricted, imperfectly septate, linear-oblong, 15–30 × (2–)2.5–3 mm, ± leathery, apex short-beaked, dehiscent, smooth, margins smooth, strigillose. **Seeds** 5–8, olive green to brown, ± mottled, oblong, smooth. $2n = 14$.

Flowering (late winter–)spring. Washes, canyons, stream banks, sandy or clayey soils, dry, gravelly and rocky slopes, riparian woodlands, desert or mesquite grasslands, desert slope scrub, grassy mountain foothills, chaparral, pinyon-oak-juniper woodlands, oak savannas; 1200–2600 m; Ariz., N.Mex.; Mexico (Chihuahua, Durango, Sonora).

Acmispon neomexicanus occurs in southeastern Arizona and adjacent southwestern New Mexico. It is reported to hybridize with *A. plebeius* and *A. rigidus* (A. M. Ottley 1944; D. Isely 1981). *Anisolotus greenei* Wooton & Standley and *Ottleya greenei* (Wooton & Standley) D. D. Sokoloff are superfluous illegitimate names; *Hosackia mollis* Greene (1885, not Nuttall 1838), and *Lotus mollis* Greene (1890, not Balfour f. 1882) are illegitimate names that pertain here.

9. Acmispon mearnsii (Britton) Brouillet, J. Bot. Res. Inst. Texas 2: 391. 2008 • Mearns's deervetch [E]

Hosackia mearnsii Britton, Trans. New York Acad. Sci. 8: 65. 1889; *Anisolotus mearnsii* (Britton) A. Heller; *Lotus mearnsii* (Britton) Britton ex Greene; *Ottleya mearnsii* (Britton) D. D. Sokoloff

Herbs, perennial, mat-forming, silvery, 2–6 dm, not fleshy, tomentose; from woody caudices. **Stems** 1–20+, procumbent or the central ascending, branched, herbaceous, leafy. **Leaves** pinnate to subpalmate; stipules glandlike; short-petiolate; rachis 2–5 mm, flattened; leaflets 3–5, blades obovate to oblanceolate or broadly obovate to obcordate, apex usually obtuse to acute, sometimes mucronulate, or retuse to cordate, surfaces gray-puberulent. **Peduncles** curved to erect, 25–75(–95) mm, longer than leaves; bract absent or 1(–3)-foliolate, distal. **Inflorescences** (1 or)2–7-flowered. **Flowers** 12–20 mm; calyx 3.5–5 mm, tube puberulent, lobes narrow lanceolate; corolla yellow to cream, often suffused with red, claws shorter than calyx tube, banner ascending 45–90°, wings ± equaling to longer than keel; style nearly straight, glabrous. **Legumes** subpersistent, exserted, erect to ascending, tawny to brown, straight, turgid, not constricted, ± septate, oblong, 15–35(–40) × 3–7 mm, leathery, apex short-beaked, dehiscent, smooth, margins smooth, thickened, strigillose. **Seeds** 3–6, brown, ± mottled, oblong, ± rugose to smooth.

Varieties 2 (2 in the flora): Arizona.

1. Leaflet blades obovate to oblanceolate, apices obtuse to acute, sometimes mucronulate; peduncles 30–60(–80) mm; flowers 12–16 mm; legumes 15–25(–30) × 3–4 mm . . . . 9a. *Acmispon mearnsii* var. *mearnsii*
1. Leaflet blades broadly obovate to obcordate, apices obtuse or retuse to cordate; peduncles 25–75(–95) mm; flowers 14–20 mm; legumes 25–35(–40) × 4–7 mm . . . . 9b. *Acmispon mearnsii* var. *equisolensis*

9a. Acmispon mearnsii (Britton) Brouillet var. **mearnsii** [E]

Leaflet blades obovate to oblanceolate, apex obtuse to acute, sometimes mucronulate. **Peduncles** 30–60(–80) mm. **Flowers** 12–16 mm. **Legumes** 15–25(–30) × 3–4 mm.

Flowering spring–summer. Dry limestone mesas, ridges, slopes, washes, sandy or tuffaceous soils, scrub, dry, rocky grasslands, open Ponderosa pine or oak-pinyon-juniper woodlands; 900–2300 m; Ariz.

Variety *mearnsii* is present in northern Arizona in Coconino, Navajo, and Yavapai counties. It possibly hybridizes with *Acmispon rigidus* and *A. wrightii* (A. M. Ottley 1944; D. Isely 1981).

9b. Acmispon mearnsii (Britton) Brouillet var. **equisolensis** (J. L. Anderson) Brouillet, J. Bot. Res. Inst. Texas 2: 391. 2008 [C] [E]

Lotus mearnsii (Britton) Britton ex Greene var. *equisolensis* J. L. Anderson, Madroño 43: 261. 1996

Leaflet blades broadly obovate to obcordate, apex obtuse or retuse to cordate. **Peduncles** 25–75(–95) mm. **Flowers** 14–20 mm. **Legumes** 25–35(–40) × 4–7 mm.

Flowering late winter–spring. Desert scrub on calcareous or white lacustrine outcrops; of conservation concern; 600–700 m; Ariz.

Variety *equisolensis* is known only from Maricopa County, in the Lower Verde River basin.

10. Acmispon grandiflorus (Bentham) Brouillet, J. Bot. Res. Inst. Texas 2: 390. 2008

Hosackia grandiflora Bentham, Trans. Linn. Soc. London 17: 366. 1836; *Anisolotus grandiflorus* (Bentham) A. Heller; *Lotus grandiflorus* (Bentham) Greene; *Ottleya grandiflora* (Bentham) D. D. Sokoloff

Herbs, perennial, cespitose, sometimes robust, grayish or green, 1–4(–15) dm, not fleshy, ± densely puberulent or strigillose; rhizomatous, woody based. **Stems** 1–5+, decumbent to erect, branched, herbaceous, often striate, leafy. **Leaves** irregularly pinnate; stipules glandlike, conic; petiolate or sessile; rachis 2–3.5(–5.5) mm, not flattened; leaflets 7–9(–12), blades usually elliptic to obovate, sometimes ovate, apex acute to obtuse, surfaces sparsely to densely puberulent or villosulous to strigillose. **Peduncles** ascending or spreading, 10–80 mm, longer than leaves; bract 1(–3)-foliolate, distal. **Inflorescences** 3–9(–11)-flowered. **Flowers** 12–25 mm; calyx (4.5–)5.5–10 mm, tube villosulous, lobes subulate; corolla greenish white, white or yellow, fading to rose or reddish, claws shorter than calyx tube, banner ascending 45–90°, wings longer than banner and keel; style nearly straight or basally curved, glabrous. **Legumes** persistent, exserted, brown, linear-oblong, straight, turgid, sometimes slightly constricted, incompletely septate, 25–42(–70) × 2–3 mm, leathery, apex short hook-beaked, dehiscent, smooth, margins smooth, thickened, glabrate. **Seeds** 5–9, olive to reddish brown, mottled, broadly ovoid, smooth.

Varieties 2 (2 in the flora): California, nw Mexico.

1. Herbs densely puberulent or villosulous, usually grayish; ovules 22–30 . . . . 10a. *Acmispon grandiflorus* var. *grandiflorus*
1. Herbs strigillose or puberulent, green; ovules ca. 45 . . . . 10b. *Acmispon grandiflorus* var. *macranthus*

10a. Acmispon grandiflorus (Bentham) Brouillet var. **grandiflorus**

Anisolotus leucophaeus (Greene) A. Heller; *Hosackia anthylloides* (A. Gray) Millspaugh; *H. confinis* (Greene) Brand; *H. grandiflora* Bentham var. *anthylloides* A. Gray; *H. guadalupensis* (Greene) Brand; *H. leucophaea* (Greene) Abrams; *H. occulta* Greene; *Lotus confinis* Greene; *L. grandiflorus* (Bentham) Greene var. *mutabilis* Ottley; *L. guadalupensis* Greene; *L. leucophaeus* Greene

Herbs densely puberulent or villosulous, usually grayish. **Ovules** 22–30.

Flowering (late winter–)spring(–early summer). Dry, open disturbed sites, rocky slopes, gravelly soils, serpentine, chaparral, pine or pine-juniper woodlands, canyon washes, burnt forests; (0–)100–2500 m; Calif.; Mexico (Baja California).

Variety *grandiflorus* occurs from northwestern to southwestern California along the coast and is also present in the Sierra Nevada. A form with larger leaves named *Lotus grandiflorus* var. *mutabilis*, not recognized by D. Isely (1981, 1993), that is present notably in the Channel Islands and adjacent coastal areas of California, deserves taxonomic investigation. Variety *grandiflorus* (as *L. grandiflorus* var. *mutabilis*) is reported to hybridize with *A. argyraeus* and possibly *A. rigidus* (A. M. Ottley 1944).

10b. Acmispon grandiflorus (Bentham) Brouillet var. **macranthus** (Greene) Brouillet, J. Bot. Res. Inst. Texas 2: 390. 2008 [E]

Hosackia macrantha Greene, Bull. Calif. Acad. Sci. 1: 81. 1885; *Anisolotus macranthus* (Greene) A. Heller; *Lotus grandiflorus* (Bentham) Greene var. *macranthus* (Greene) Isely

Herbs strigillose or puberulent, green. **Ovules** ca. 45.

Flowering spring. Ponderosa pine, oak-pine, or semi-open mixed conifer forests, chaparral, clayey, sandy, gravelly, or cobbly volcanic soils, wet or moist, gravelly stream bottoms and banks, gravelly roadsides; 300–1800 m; Calif.

Variety *macranthus* is known from the northern and central Sierra Nevada and the Cascade Range. *Lotus macranthus* (Greene) Greene 1890 (not Lowe 1838) is an illegitimate name that pertains here.

11. Acmispon maritimus (Nuttall) D. D. Sokoloff, Ann. Bot. Fenn. 37: 129. 2000

Hosackia maritima Nuttall in J. Torrey and A. Gray, Fl. N. Amer. 1: 326. 1838; *Anisolotus maritimus* (Nuttall) A. Heller; *Lotus salsuginosus* Greene

Herbs, annual, cespitose, green, 0.5–3.5(–5) dm, ± fleshy, glabrous or strigillose; taprooted. **Stems** 1–20, procumbent to ascending, branched basally, herbaceous, leafy. **Leaves** irregularly pinnate; stipules glandlike; sessile or subsessile to short-petiolate; rachis 8–20(–35) mm, flattened; leaflets (3–)5–7, blades unequal, obovate to ± orbiculate, apex obtuse, surfaces glabrous or ± strigillose. **Peduncles** erect then spreading or declined, 3–15 mm, shorter to longer than leaves, sometimes branched, slender; bract absent or 1–3-foliolate, subtending umbel. **Inflorescences** 1–5-flowered. **Flowers** 2.5–8(–11) mm; calyx 1.2–4.5 mm, tube strigose to villous, lobes lanceolate; corolla bright yellow or orange-yellow, claws shorter than to equaling calyx tube, banner implicate-ascending, wings symmetric, equaling or shorter than keel; style curved, glabrous. **Legumes** persistent, exserted, ascending or spreading, tawny to brown, straight or curved, ± compressed, scarcely or distinctly constricted, not septate, narrowly oblong, 10–30 × 3–4 mm, leathery, apex short hook-beaked, dehiscent, margins smooth, thin, glabrous or sparsely strigillose. **Seeds** 5–9, brown to dark olive green, not mottled, oblong-ovoid, smooth.

Varieties 2 (2 in the flora): w United States, nw Mexico.

1. Flowers 6–8(–11) mm; calyces 4–4.5 mm, lobes 1.5–2.2(–2.5) mm; legumes (15–)20–30 mm, scarcely constricted between seeds . . . . 11a. *Acmispon maritimus* var. *maritimus*
1. Flowers 2.5–4 mm; calyces 1.2–2 mm, lobes 0.2–1 mm; legumes 10–15 mm, distinctly constricted between seeds . . . . 11b. *Acmispon maritimus* var. *brevivexillus*

11a. Acmispon maritimus (Nuttall) D. D. Sokoloff var. **maritimus**

Flowers 6–8(–11) mm; calyx 4–4.5 mm, lobes 1.5–2.2(–2.5) mm; keel equaling other petals; ovules ca. 9. **Legumes** scarcely constricted between seeds, (15–)20–30 mm. **2*n*** = 14.

Flowering (late winter–) spring. Coastal sage scrub, chaparral, desert scrub, oak woodlands, sea bluffs, washes, canyons, dry exposed slopes and ridges, talus, grassy areas, sandy stream beds, floodplains, riparian forests, vernal pools, gravelly, sandy, or clayey soils, burnt areas, disturbed areas, roadsides, trailsides; 0–1300 m; Calif.; Mexico (Baja California).

Variety *maritimus* is known from central and southwestern California and the Sonoran Desert.

11b. Acmispon maritimus (Nuttall) D. D. Sokoloff var. **brevivexillus** (Ottley) Brouillet, J. Bot. Res. Inst. Texas 2: 391. 2008

Lotus salsuginosus Greene var. *brevivexillus* Ottley, Univ. Calif. Publ. Bot. 10: 217. 1923, based on *L. humillis* Greene, Pittonia 2: 140. 1890; *Hosackia humilis* (Greene) Abrams; *L. salsuginosus* subsp. *brevivexillus* (Ottley) Munz

Flowers 2.5–4 mm; calyx 1.2–2 mm, lobes 0.2–1 mm; keel longer than other petals; ovules ca. 5. **Legumes** distinctly constricted between seeds, 10–15 mm. **2*n*** = 14.

Flowering late winter–early spring. Deserts, desert mountains, washes, riparian forests, rocky hillsides, outcrops, canyons, desert scrub, sandy, clayey, gravelly or rocky, granitic or basaltic soils, roadsides; (-10–) 0–1900 m; Ariz., Calif., Nev.; Mexico (Baja California, Sonora).

Variety *brevivexillus* is known from the Mojave and Sonoran deserts.

12. Acmispon parviflorus (Bentham) D. D. Sokoloff, Ann. Bot. Fenn. 37: 129. 2000 [E]

Hosackia parviflora Bentham, Edwards's Bot. Reg. 15: sub plate 1257. 1829; *Anisolotus parviflorus* (Bentham) A. Heller; *H. microphylla* Nuttall; *Lotus micranthus* Bentham

Herbs, annual, cespitose, green, 0.3–4.8 dm, not fleshy, glabrous or sparsely strigillose; taprooted. **Stems** 1–10, erect to procumbent, branched or unbranched, herbaceous, leafy. **Leaves** irregularly pinnate to palmate; stipules glandlike; subsessile to short-petiolate; rachis 2–8 mm, sometimes flattened; leaflets 3–5, blades obovate to oblong or elliptic, apex obtuse, surfaces strigose. **Peduncles** ascending, filiform, (0 or)1–26(–55) mm, shorter to longer than leaves; bract (1–)3-foliolate, distal. **Inflorescences** 1-flowered. **Flowers** (2.5–)4–6 mm; calyx 1–2.5 mm, tube sparsely strigillose, lobes subulate; corolla pink or salmon, quickly fading, with yellowish wings and keel, claws longer than calyx tube, banner implicate, wings ± equaling to slightly longer than keel; style curved, glabrous. **Legumes** persistent, exserted, erect or spreading, brown or tawny, curved or straight, compressed, constricted, not septate, narrowly oblong, 15–27 × 2–2.5 mm, thinly leathery, apex short hook-beaked, dehiscent, smooth, margins smooth, thin, wavy, glabrous or sparsely strigillose. **Seeds** 3–9, brown, not mottled, subglobose to shortly oblong, smooth. **2*n*** = 14.

Flowering spring(–early summer). Coastal bluffs, clearings in oak-pine or fir woodlands, open grassy areas, burnt chaparral, cut-overs, riverbars, banks, thickets, open disturbed areas, roadsides; 0–1400 m; B.C.; Calif., Oreg., Wash.

Acmispon parviflorus occurs in California from the Peninsular Ranges, the South Coast, and the Channel Islands northward to the northwest, the Sacramento Valley, and the northern and central Sierra Nevada, through coastal western Oregon and Washington from the Cascade Range westward, into southwestern British Columbia.

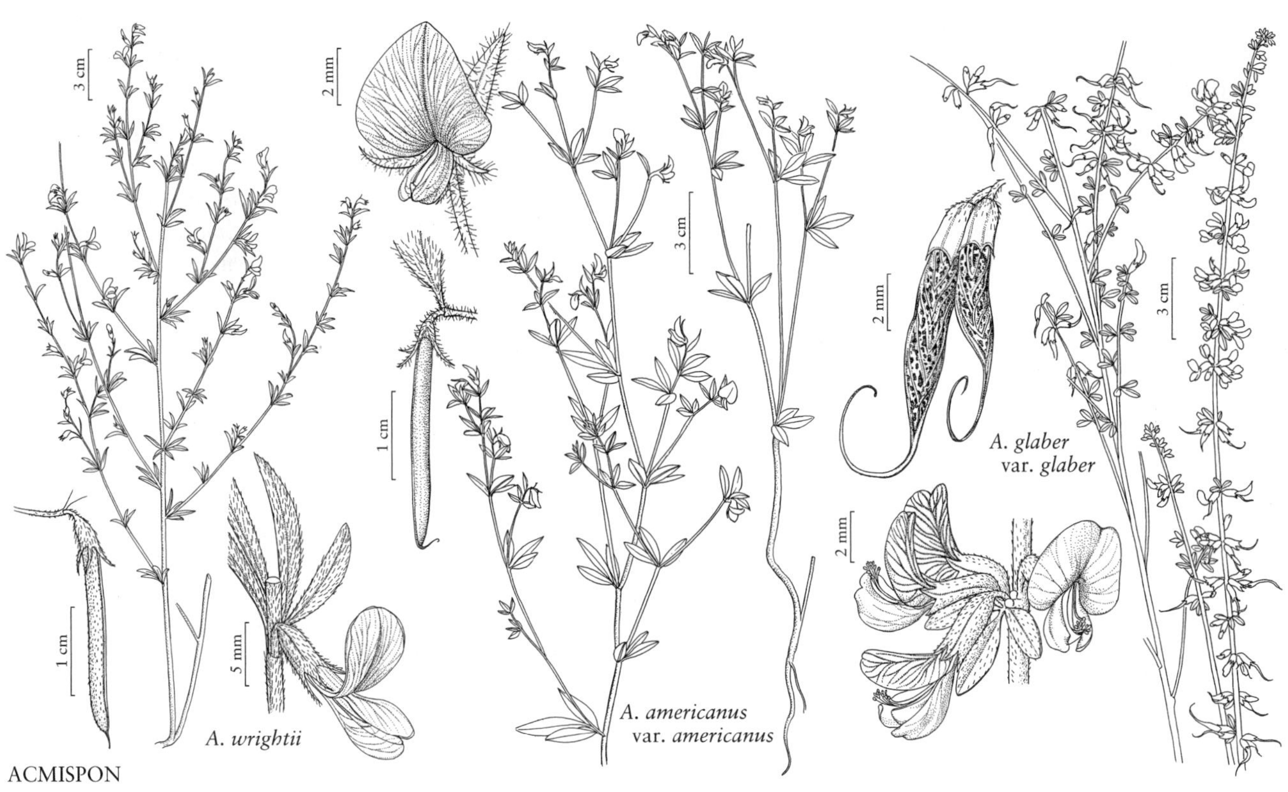

13. Acmispon americanus (Nuttall) Rydberg, Bull. Torrey Bot. Club 40: 45. 1913 • Spanish clover, prairie deervetch or trefoil, American deervetch [F]

Trigonella americana Nuttall, Gen. N. Amer. Pl. 2: 120. 1818, based on *Lotus sericeus* Pursh, Fl. Amer. Sept. 2: 489. 1813, not Moench 1802; *Hosackia americana* (Nuttall) Piper

Herbs, annual, solitary or cespitose, green, 0.5–6(–12) dm, not fleshy, glabrate to ± pilose; taprooted. **Stems** 1–10+, erect to procumbent, branched proximally, herbaceous, leafy. **Leaves** pinnate; stipules glandlike; subsessile to short-petiolate; rachis 0.5–3(–4) mm, not flattened; leaflets (1–)3(–5), blades obovate, ovate, or elliptic to lanceolate, margins denticulate or entire, apex acute, surfaces sparsely appressed-hairy. **Peduncles** in distal axils, ascending, 3–25 mm, longer than leaves; bract unifoliolate, distal. **Inflorescences** 1(or 2)-flowered. **Flowers** (4–)5–9 mm; calyx (2.5–)3–6.5 mm, tube pilose, lobes linear-lanceolate, accrescent; corolla whitish or cream, turning pink or salmon, banner rose-striate, keel tip yellow, claws shorter than calyx tube, banner implicate-ascending to erect, wings ± equaling keel; style abruptly angled upward 45°, glabrous. **Legumes** persistent, exserted, spreading or pendent, brown, straight or ± curved, compressed, slightly constricted, not septate, linear-oblong to narrowly oblong, (15–)20–30(–40) × (1.5–)2–2.5 mm, thinly leathery, apex abruptly downward angled and curved, dehiscent, smooth, margins smooth, thickened, glabrous. **Seeds** (3–)5–8, olive to light brown, often black-mottled, oblong, smooth.

Varieties 2 (2 in the flora): North America, nw Mexico.

1. Herbs usually conspicuously pilose, sometimes glabrate; leaflet blades: length 3–3.5 times width .... 13a. *Acmispon americanus* var. *americanus*
1. Herbs glabrate; leaflet blades: length 4–5 times width .... 13b. *Acmispon americanus* var. *helleri*

13a. Acmispon americanus (Nuttall) Rydberg var. **americanus** [F] [W]

Acmispon aestivalis A. Heller; *A. elatus* (Nuttall) Rydberg; *A. floribundus* (Nuttall) A. Heller; *A. glabratus* A. Heller; *A. gracilis* A. Heller; *A. mollis* (Nuttall) A. Heller; *A. pilosus* (Nuttall) A. Heller; *A. sparsiflorus* A. Heller; *Hosackia americana* (Nuttall) Piper var. *glabra* (Nuttall) G. S. Torrey; *H. americana* var. *pilosa* (Nuttall) Piper; *H. elata* Nuttall; *H. elata* var. *glabra* Nuttall; *H. floribunda* Nuttall; *H. mollis* Nuttall; *H. pilosa* Nuttall; *H. unifoliolata* Hooker; *Lotus americanus* (Nuttall) Bischoff var. *glaber* (Nuttall) Ewan ex

Jepson; *L. americanus* var. *minutiflorus* Ottley; *L. purshianus* Clements & E. G. Clements; *L. purshianus* var. *glaber* (Nuttall) Munz; *L. unifoliatus* (Hooker) Bentham

Herbs usually conspicuously pilose, sometimes glabrate. **Leaflet blades:** length 3–3.5 times width. **2*n*** = 14.

Flowering late spring–fall. Prairies, rocky hillsides, dunes, sandy stream valleys, coastal chaparral or grasslands, open, wooded hillsides, roadsides, disturbed areas; 0–2400 m; B.C., Man., Sask.; Ariz., Ark., Calif., Idaho, Ill., Ind., Iowa, Kans., La., Minn., Mo., Mont., Nebr., Nev., N.Mex., N.Dak., Okla., Oreg., S.Dak., Tex., Wash., Wyo.; Mexico (Baja California).

Variety *americanus* is widespread in the United States from the west coast nearly to the Appalachian Mountains, and in southwestern Canada. *Acmispon sericeus* Rafinesque (1832), *Hosackia purshiana* Bentham (1829), and *H. sericea* Branner & Coville (1891), superfluous for *Trigonella americana* Nuttall (1818), and *Lotus americanus* (Nuttall) Bishoff (1839, not Vellozo 1829) are illegitimate names that pertain here.

13b. Acmispon americanus (Nuttall) Rydberg var. **helleri** (Britton) Brouillet, J. Bot. Res. Inst. Texas 2: 388. 2008 [E]

Lotus helleri Britton, Bull. Torrey Bot. Club 17: 312. 1890; *Acmispon helleri* (Britton) A. Heller; *Hosackia helleri* (Britton) Brand; *L. purshianus* Clements & E. G. Clements var. *helleri* (Britton) Isely; *L. unifoliatus* (Hooker) Bentham var. *helleri* (Britton) Kartesz & Gandhi

Herbs glabrate. **Leaflet blades:** length 4–5 times width. **2*n*** = 14.

Flowering late summer–early fall. Woodlands, river bottoms, pastures, old fields, ditches, roadsides; 100–200 m; Ga., N.C., S.C., Va.

Variety *helleri* is the only *Acmispon* present east of the Appalachian Mountains. Although sometimes recognized at the species level (for example, B. A. Sorrie 2015), differences with var. *americanus* appear insufficient to warrant species status. The report by P. Lesica (2012) of this variety in Colorado is probably based on specimens of var. *americanus*.

14. Acmispon denticulatus (Drew) D. D. Sokoloff, Ann. Bot. Fenn. 37: 130. 2000 • Riverbar lotus, Mohave trefoil [E]

Hosackia denticulata Drew, Bull. Torrey Bot. Club 16: 151. 1889; *Anisolotus denticulatus* (Drew) A. Heller; *Lotus denticulatus* (Drew) Greene

Herbs, annual, cespitose, often glaucous, 0.3–4 dm, not fleshy, glabrous or hirsute; taprooted. **Stems** 1(–5), decumbent to erect, apically or basally coarse-branched, herbaceous, leafy. **Leaves** subpinnate, pinnate, or palmate; stipules glandlike or absent; petiolate; rachis 5–12 mm, flattened; leaflets 2–4, often 1 or 2 on one side and 2 terminal, blades elliptic to obovate (lateral sometimes asymmetric), margins denticulate or entire, apex acute to obtuse, surfaces hirsute. **Peduncles** ± sessile; bract absent. **Inflorescences** 1 or 2-flowered. **Flowers** 5–8 mm; calyx 3–5 mm, tube hirsute or glabrous, lobes subulate, ± denticulate; corolla cream-white to pale yellow, banner purple-tinged, keel tip yellowish, claws shorter to slightly longer than calyx tube, banner ascending, wings ± equaling keel, with deep, triangular auricle; style curved, glabrous. **Legumes** persistent, solitary or paired, exserted, erect or spreading, tawny, straight, compressed, slightly constricted, not septate, widely oblong, 8–20 × 3 mm, leathery, apex abruptly downward angled and curved, dehiscent, smooth, margins often undulate-verrucose, strigose or glabrous. **Seeds** (2 or)3(or 4), gray, faintly mottled, asymmetrically ± angular-obovoid, flattened, smooth. **2*n*** = 12.

Flowering spring–summer. Grassy slopes, meadows, prairies, clearings, gravel bars, stream banks, vernal pools, pastures, grainfields, usually sandy soils, sometimes alkali, clay, or serpentine soils, roadsides; 0–1900 m; B.C.; Calif., Idaho, Oreg., Utah, Wash.

Acmispon denticulatus occurs in California from the San Francisco Bay area, Sacramento Valley, and northern Sierra Nevada Foothills to the northwest, Cascade Range and Modoc Plateau, into adjacent southern Oregon (Siskiyou and Klamath regions), northward on both sides of the Cascade Range into southern British Columbia, with eastern outliers in southwestern Utah (Washington County), and in south-central Idaho (Lincoln County).

15. Acmispon wrangelianus (Fisher & C. A. Meyer) D. D. Sokoloff, Taxon 48: 58. 1999 [E]

Lotus wrangelianus Fisher & C. A. Meyer, Index Seminum (St. Petersburg) 2: 41. 1836; *Anisolotus wrangeliana* (Fischer & C. A. Meyer) Bernhardi; *Hosackia wrangeliana* (Fischer & C. A. Meyer) Torrey & A. Gray; *L. subpinnatus* Lagasca var. *wrangelianus* (Fisher & C. A. Meyer) Jepson

Herbs, annual, cespitose, grayish green, 0.5–3 dm, ± not fleshy, sparsely villous to glabrate; taprooted. **Stems** 1–20+, usually procumbent (when small, unbranched, erect or ascending), diffusely branched proximally, herbaceous, leafy. **Leaves** irregularly pinnate; stipules glandlike or absent; petiolate; rachis 5–15 mm, flattened; leaflets (3 or)4(or 5), usually 2 on one side and 2 terminal, blades elliptic to obovate (lateral sometimes asymmetric), apex usually obtuse, sometimes acute, surfaces sparsely long-ciliate, pubescent. **Peduncles** ascending, 0–2 mm, shorter than leaves; bract absent. **Inflorescences** 1-flowered. **Flowers** 5–9 mm; calyx 2.5–5 mm, tube pubescent to villous, lobes lanceolate; corolla yellow, turning red, claws shorter than calyx tube, banner implicate-ascending, with irregular or inrolled margins, wings shorter than keel; style ± curved, glabrous. **Legumes** persistent, exserted, erect or spreading, tawny to brown, straight, compressed, slightly constricted, ± septate, oblong, 10–18 × 2.2–3 mm, thinly leathery, apex abruptly downward angled and curved, dehiscent, smooth, margins smooth, thin, pubescent (to glabrate). **Seeds** 3–7, olive green to brown, not mottled, asymmetric-reniform, smooth. $2n = 12$.

Flowering (late winter–)spring(–early summer). Coastal bluffs, hills, open or rocky slopes, chaparral, coastal scrub, oak woodlands or savannas, grasslands, stream banks, vernal ponds, gravelly, sandy, or clayey soils, bare areas, burnt or disturbed areas, roadsides; 0–1200(–2200) m; Calif., Oreg.

Acmispon wrangelianus is widespread in California, except in the Mojave Desert, barely entering Oregon in Jackson County; it is possibly introduced in the Modoc Plateau and Sonoran Desert. It was found in 1911 on ballast in Multnomah County, Oregon, but does not appear to have become established there.

16. Acmispon brachycarpus (Bentham) D. D. Sokoloff, Ann. Bot. Fenn. 37: 130. 2000 • Colchita

Hosackia brachycarpa Bentham, Pl. Hartw., 306. 1849; *Anisolotus brachycarpus* (Bentham) Rydberg; *A. trispermus* (Greene) Wooton & Standley; *H. trisperma* (Greene) Brand; *Lotus humistratus* Greene; *L. trispermus* Greene

Herbs, annual, mat-forming, cinereous or greenish, 0.5–4 dm, ± fleshy, villous to pubescent; taprooted. **Stems** 1–20+, procumbent to low-ascending, branched, herbaceous, leafy. **Leaves** pinnate or palmate; stipules glandlike, sometimes absent; subsessile or sessile; rachis 4–10 mm, flattened; leaflets (3 or)4(or 5), usually 2 on one side and 2 terminal, blades elliptic to obovate (–oblanceolate), apex usually obtuse, sometimes acute, surfaces villous to pubescent. **Peduncles** ± sessile; bract absent. **Inflorescences** 1-flowered. **Flowers** 5–9 mm; calyx 3–6 mm, accrescent, tube villous, lobes lanceolate; corolla pale yellow, reddish-tipped, turning red, claws shorter than calyx tube, banner horizontal to ascending to 90°, wings ± equaling keel; style curved, glabrous. **Legumes** persistent, exserted, erect, brown or tawny, straight, compressed, slightly constricted, not septate, oblong, 6–12(–14) × 3–4 mm, stiffly papery, apex obtuse, dehiscent, smooth, margins smooth, thin, villous. **Seeds** (2 or)3(–5), tan to dark brown or blackish, faintly mottled, lenticular-elliptic (asymmetric), smooth. $2n = 12$.

Flowering late winter–spring. Rocky, open, disturbed areas, ridges, sand bars, desert flats or washes, stream beds and banks, sandy, gravelly, or clayey soils, serpentine, grasslands, oak-pine woodlands, chaparral, desert scrub, roadsides, agricultural fields; 0–1900(–2000) m; Ariz., Calif., Idaho, Nev., N.Mex., Oreg., Utah; Mexico (Sonora).

Acmispon brachycarpus occurs throughout California into southwestern Oregon (one old collection further north in the Willamette Valley), east through the Mojave Desert into Arizona and southwestern Nevada, and into southwestern New Mexico. *Lotus brachycarpus* Bentham & Hooker f. ex S. Watson (1878) is an invalid name that pertains here.

17. Acmispon rubriflorus (Sharsmith) D. D. Sokoloff, Ann. Bot. Fenn. 37: 130. 2000 • Red-flowered deervetch or trefoil [C] [E]

Lotus rubriflorus Sharsmith, Madroño 6: 56, fig. 1. 1941

Herbs, annual, cespitose, greenish, 0.4–0.9 dm, not fleshy, villous; taprooted. **Stems** 1–5+, decumbent to ascending, branched basally, herbaceous, leafy. **Leaves** irregularly pinnate or palmate; stipules glandlike, barely visible; subsessile; rachis 4–6 mm, flattened; leaflets 4, 2 on one side and 2 terminal, blades lanceolate, sometimes asymmetric apex acute, surfaces villous. **Peduncles** ± sessile; bract absent. **Inflorescences** 1-flowered. **Flowers** 5–8 mm; calyx 1.5–5 mm, tube villous, lobes subulate, acuminate; corolla bright pinkish red, claws shorter than calyx tube, banner implicate-ascending, wings ± equaling keel; style curved or geniculate, glabrous. **Legumes** persistent, mostly included, erect, stramineous, straight, compressed, slightly constricted, not septate, broadly oblong, 8–9 × 2.5 mm, papery, apex obtuse, dehiscent, smooth, margins smooth, keeled, villous. **Seeds** 2–4, olive green to brownish, ± mottled, ± lenticular, semilustrous, smooth to rugose.

Flowering spring. Open, oak woodlands, grasslands; of conservation concern; 100–500 m; Calif.

Acmispon rubriflorus is known only from Colusa, Stanislaus, and Tehama counties.

18. Acmispon prostratus (Torrey & A. Gray) Brouillet, J. Bot. Res. Inst. Texas 2: 392. 2008 • Nuttall's deervetch or lotus [C]

Hosackia prostrata Torrey & A. Gray, Fl. N. Amer. 1: 325. 1838 (as prostratus); *Lotus nuttallianus* Greene; *Syrmatium prostratum* (Torrey & A. Gray) Greene

Herbs, usually annual, sometimes ± perennial, cespitose, prostrate, greenish gray (young growth cinereous), 1–10 dm, not fleshy, strigose to glabrate; taprooted. **Stems** 1–10+, procumbent or diffuse, branched basally, herbaceous, slender, remotely leafy. **Leaves** irregularly pinnate or palmate; stipules glandlike; subsessile; rachis 3–9 mm, flattened; leaflets 4, 2 on one side and 2 terminal, blades obovate to oblanceolate, apex acute to obtuse, surfaces appressed-hairy. **Peduncles** ascending, slender, 8–30 mm, longer than leaves; bract absent or 1(–3)-foliolate, usually distal. **Inflorescences** 3–8-flowered. **Flowers** 5–7 mm; calyx 2–3 mm, tube strigose, lobes triangular, shorter than tube; corolla yellow, often red on banner and wing tips, reddening, claws longer than calyx tube, banner implicate-ascending to 45°, wings equaling or longer than keel; style curved, glabrous. **Legumes** persistent, strongly exserted, widely spreading or reflexed, greenish to tawny, arched, turgid, constricted, not septate, linear-oblong, 8–15 × 1 mm, leathery, apex tapering, shortly hook-beaked, indehiscent, smooth, margins often sinuate, glabrous. **Seeds** 2, greenish brown, mottled, elongate-oblong, smooth.

Flowering (late winter–)spring(–summer). Sandy and gravelly areas near coast, beaches, dunes, coastal scrub, urban, weedy areas; of conservation concern; 0–30 m; Calif.; Mexico (Baja California).

Acmispon prostratus is known in the flora area only from the southern South Coast in San Diego County.

19. Acmispon micranthus (Torrey & A. Gray) Brouillet, J. Bot. Res. Inst. Texas 2: 391. 2008

Hosackia micrantha Torrey & A. Gray, Fl. N. Amer. 1: 324. 1838 (as micranthus); *Lotus hamatus* Greene; *Syrmatium micranthum* (Torrey & A. Gray) Greene

Herbs annual, cespitose, prostrate, green, 1–8 dm, not fleshy, glabrous or ± villosulous; taprooted. **Stems** 1–10+, procumbent to ascending, unbranched, herbaceous, leafy. **Leaves** irregularly pinnate or palmate; stipules glandlike or absent; short-petiolate to subsessile; rachis 4–8 mm, sometimes flattened; leaflets 4–6, often 2 on one side and 2 terminal, blades obovate to elliptic, apex acute to obtuse, surfaces ± villous. **Peduncles** ascending, 1–2 (–5) mm, shorter than leaves; bract absent. **Inflorescences** 2–5-flowered. **Flowers** 3–4(–5) mm; calyx 1–1.5 (–2.5) mm, tube strigillose to villosulous, lobes subulate; corolla yellowish, claws shorter than calyx tube, banner implicate-ascending, wings shorter than keel; style abruptly incurved 90°, strigillose. **Legumes** persistent, strongly exserted, widely spreading or reflexed, tawny, arched, turgid, constricted, not septate, linear, 10–15 × 1–2 mm, leathery, apex tapering, long hook-beaked, indehiscent, veined, margins keeled, smooth, strigillose (also on beak). **Seeds** 2, olive green, mottled, ± curved, cylindric, smooth. $2n = 14$.

Flowering (late winter–)spring(–early summer). Coastal scrub, mesas, desert canyons, washes, disturbed areas, dry, gravelly plains and hillsides, prairies, roadsides; 0–600 m; Calif.; Mexico (Baja California).

Acmispon micranthus occurs in the southern South Coast Ranges, the South Coast, the Channel Islands, and the Peninsular Ranges.

20. Acmispon procumbens (Greene) Brouillet, J. Bot. Res. Inst. Texas 2: 392. 2008 [E]

Hosackia procumbens Greene, Bull. Calif. Acad. Sci. 1: 82. 1885; *Lotus procumbens* (Greene) Greene; *Syrmatium procumbens* (Greene) Greene

Herbs, perennial, sometimes subshrubs, sometimes bushy, gray, 1–10 dm, not fleshy, gray-canescent or strigose; from woody caudices. **Stems** 1–10+, procumbent to ascending, much branched, stiff, sometimes ± woody, leafy. **Leaves** subpalmate; stipules glandlike; subsessile to short-petiolate; rachis 1–4 mm, flattened; leaflets usually 3, blades obovate to oblanceolate, apex usually acute, sometimes obtuse to emarginate, surfaces canescent to strigose. **Peduncles** ascending, 0–3 mm, shorter than leaves; bract absent. **Inflorescences** 1–3(–5)-flowered. **Flowers** 6–12 mm; calyx 2–6 mm, tube ± densely strigose, lobes triangular or subulate; corolla yellow or with red, claws scarcely to much longer than calyx tube, banner implicate-ascending, wings longer than banner and keel; style curved, glabrous. **Legumes** persistent, exserted, reflexed, green to pale reddish brown, straight to ± curved (initially), turgid, not or slightly constricted, not septate, linear-oblong, 10–16 × 1.5–2 mm, leathery, apex tapering, short-beaked, indehiscent, transverse-ridged, margins slightly keeled, smooth, glabrate to ± densely strigillose. **Seeds** 2 or 3+, dull yellowish brown, not mottled, elongate-oblong, smooth.

Varieties 2 (2 in the flora): California.

1. Stems procumbent to ascending; inflorescences 1–3(–5)-flowered; flowers 6–8 mm; calyces 2–3 mm, lobes shorter than calyx tube, triangular; petal claws well exserted . . . . 20a. *Acmispon procumbens* var. *procumbens*
1. Stems ascending; inflorescences 1 or 2(or 3)-flowered; flowers (7–)9–12 mm; calyces 4–6 mm, lobes ± equaling calyx tube, subulate; petal claws scarcely exserted . . . . 20b. *Acmispon procumbens* var. *jepsonii*

20a. Acmispon procumbens (Greene) Brouillet var. **procumbens** [E]

Hosackia sericea Bentham; *Lotus leucophyllus* Greene; *Syrmatium leucophyllum* (Greene) Brand; *S. sericeum* (Bentham) Greene

Stems procumbent to ascending. **Inflorescences** 1–3(–5)-flowered. **Flowers** 6–8 mm; calyx 2–3 mm, lobes shorter than calyx tube, triangular; petal claws well exserted.

Flowering spring. Chaparral, creosote bush scrub, desert slopes, sandy flats and slopes, roadsides; 30–2300 m; Calif.

Variety *procumbens* is known from the Sacramento Valley, the Peninsular and Transverse ranges, and the Mojave Desert.

20b. Acmispon procumbens (Greene) Brouillet var. **jepsonii** (Ottley) Brouillet, J. Bot. Res. Inst. Texas 2: 392. 2008 [C] [E]

Lotus leucophyllus Greene var. *jepsonii* Ottley, Univ. Calif. Publ. Bot. 10: 227. 1923; *Hosackia sericea* Bentham subsp. *jepsonii* (Ottley) Abrams; *L. procumbens* (Greene) Greene var. *jepsonii* (Ottley) Ottley

Stems ascending. **Inflorescences** 1 or 2(or 3)-flowered. **Flowers** (7–)9–12 mm; calyx 4–6 mm, lobes ± equaling calyx tube, subulate; petal claws scarcely exserted.

Flowering spring. Open slopes and ridges, on sand, sometimes with Jeffrey pine; of conservation concern; 1800–2400 m; Calif.

Variety *jepsonii* is local and rare in the southern Sierra Nevada, in Kern and Tulare counties.

21. Acmispon glaber (Vogel) Brouillet, J. Bot. Res. Inst. Texas 2: 389. 2008 (as glabrus) • California broom [F]

Syrmatium glabrum Vogel, Linnaea 10: 591. 1836; *Anisolotus glaber* (Vogel) M. Armstrong & Thornber; *Hosackia glabra* (Vogel) Torrey

Subshrubs, often bushy, sometimes mat-forming, robust, green, 5–20 dm, not fleshy, glabrous or finely strigose; from woody caudices. **Stems** 1–30+, usually erect to spreading, rarely procumbent, branched basally, herbaceous, slender, striate, sometimes ± woody, remotely leafy, usually deciduous mid-season, foliage developing after rain. **Leaves** ± pinnate (distally 3-foliolate); stipules glandlike; subsessile to petiolate; rachis 2–8(–10) mm, not flattened; leaflets 3–6(or 7), blades elliptic to lanceolate, apex acute, surfaces strigillose to glabrate. **Peduncles** ascending, 0–2 mm, shorter than leaves; bract absent. **Inflorescences** (1 or)2–7-flowered, in axil of distal leaves, spaced or congested. **Flowers** 7–12 mm; calyx 2.5–5 mm, tube usually glabrous, sometimes sparsely strigillose, lobes short-subulate; corolla yellow, turning orange or red, claws slightly longer than calyx tube, banner implicate-ascending to 90°, wings shorter than or equaling keel; style curved, glabrous. **Legumes** persistent, much exserted, divergent or pendent, greenish to reddish brown, curved to ± straight, turgid, slightly constricted, not septate, linear-oblong, 10–15 × 1–2 mm, leathery, apex long-beaked, indehiscent, smooth, margins thickened, smooth, strigillose or glabrate. **Seeds** (1 or)2, olive to brown, not mottled, elongate-oblong, smooth.

Varieties 2 (2 in the flora): California, nw Mexico.

D. Isely (1981) reported a potential hybrid between *Acmispon glaber* (variety not specified) and *A. argophyllus* (variety not specified). *Lotus glaber* (Vogel) Greene 1890 (not Miller 1768) is an illegitimate name that pertains here.

1. Flowers 7–12 mm; keel ± equaling wings . . . . 21a. *Acmispon glaber* var. *glaber*
1. Flowers 8–9(–10) mm; keel usually longer than wings . . . . .21b. *Acmispon glaber* var. *brevialatus*

21a. Acmispon glaber (Vogel) Brouillet var. **glaber** [F]

Hosackia scoparia Torrey & A. Gray; *H. scoparia* var. *diffusa* A. Gray; *Lotus diffusus* (A. Gray) A. Heller; *L. scoparius* (Torrey & A. Gray) Ottley

Flowers 7–12 mm; keel ± equaling wings. **2*n*** = 14.

Flowering (late winter–) spring(–fall, year-round). Chaparral, gravelly hillsides, grasslands, sand dunes, pine forests, sandy or gravelly soils, on rock, roadsides, ruderal, disturbed sites, conspicuous after fire; 0–2500 m; Calif.; Mexico (Baja California).

In California, var. *glaber* is present in the North Coast and North Coast Ranges to the San Francisco Bay area, the foothills of the northern Sierra Nevada, the South Coast, and the Western Transverse and Peninsular ranges. It is sporadic inland, where it is possibly introduced. A generally erect shrub, it may become trailing in the shade or mat-forming on beaches. Confusion may occur between coastal forms and plants of *Acmispon cytisoides* and *A. junceus*. D. Isely (1981) reported possible hybrids with *A. cytisoides* (as *Lotus benthamii*), *A. junceus* (*A. glaber* as *L. scoparius* var. *perplexans* Hoover), and *A. decumbens*.

Hosackia crassifolia Torrey & A. Gray 1838 (not Bentham 1836) is an illegitimate name that pertains here.

21b. Acmispon glaber (Vogel) Brouillet var. **brevialatus** (Ottley) Brouillet, J. Bot. Res. Inst. Texas 2: 390. 2008 (as glabrus)

Lotus scoparius (Torrey & A. Gray) Ottley var. *brevialatus* Ottley, Univ. Calif. Publ. Bot. 10: 229, plate 77, figs. 10–16. 1923; *Hosackia glabra* (Vogel) Torrey subsp. *brevialata* (Ottley) Abrams; *L. scoparius* subsp. *brevialatus* (Ottley) Munz

Flowers 8–9(–10) mm; keel usually longer than wings. **2*n*** = 14.

Flowering late winter–spring(–fall). Desert slopes, flats, washes; 0–1400 m; Calif.; Mexico (Baja California, Baja California Sur).

In California, var. *brevialatus* is present in the South Coast, the Peninsular and Transverse ranges, and the Sonoran Desert. A single specimen (*Vasey*, in 1881, NMC) has been reported from Arizona; location details are lacking, and it is difficult to confirm the presence of the taxon there.

22. Acmispon dendroideus (Greene) Brouillet, J. Bot. Res. Inst. Texas 2: 389. 2008 [E]

Syrmatium dendroideum Greene, Bull. Calif. Acad. Sci. 2: 146. 1886; *Hosackia dendroidea* (Greene) Abrams; *Lotus dendroideus* (Greene) Greene; *L. scoparius* (Torrey & A. Gray) Ottley var. *dendroideus* (Greene) Ottley

Shrubs or subshrubs, erect or procumbent, low to robust, green or gray, 5–20 dm, not fleshy, sparsely to densely strigose; from woody caudices. **Stems** 1–10+, erect or decumbent, branched, woody, leafy. **Leaves** irregularly pinnate; stipules glandlike; short-petiolate to petiolate; rachis 3–10 mm, not flattened; leaflets 3–5, blades narrowly obovate to elliptic or oblong, apex acute to obtuse, surfaces sparsely to densely strigose. **Peduncles** ascending, 2–10 mm, shorter than leaves; bract absent or unifoliolate, subtending umbel. **Inflorescences** (3–)7–12-flowered. **Flowers** 8–12 mm; calyx 4–6 mm, tube sparsely strigose to glabrate, lobes short-subulate to deltate;

corolla yellow, claws ± longer than calyx tube, banner implicate-ascending to 90°, wings ± equaling keel; style abruptly incurved 90°, glabrous. **Legumes** persistent, exserted, divergent to declined, brown, straight or curved, turgid, slightly constricted, not septate, linear-oblong, 10–50 × 1–2 mm, leathery, apex tapering, long-beaked, indehiscent, ± veined, margins thickened, smooth, glabrate or sparsely strigose. **Seeds** 1–4(–6), brown (paler veined), not mottled, cylindric, smooth.

Varieties 3 (3 in the flora): California.

In a phylogeographic study of *Acmispon dendroideus*, L. E. Wallace et al. (2017) showed that var. *traskiae* is sister to vars. *dendroideus* and *veatchii*. *Acmispon dendroideus* has been reported from Baja California, Mexico, but the material is inadequate for confident determination.

1. Subshrubs (shrubs); stems decumbent; leaflets 3, blades densely strigose, almost silky, usually gray . . . . 22c. *Acmispon dendroideus* var. *veatchii*
1. Shrubs; stems erect; leaflets 3–5, blades sparsely strigose, greenish.
   2. Umbel bract absent; ovules 1–3; legumes 10–15 mm . . . . 22a. *Acmispon dendroideus* var. *dendroideus*
   2. Umbel bract unifoliolate; ovules 4–6; legumes (20–)30–50 mm . . . . 22b. *Acmispon dendroideus* var. *traskiae*

22a. Acmispon dendroideus (Greene) Brouillet var. **dendroideus** • Island broom [E]

Shrubs, greenish, sparsely strigose. **Stems** erect, woody. **Leaflets** 3–5, blades greenish, surfaces sparsely strigose. **Umbels:** bract absent. **Ovules** 1–3. **Legumes** 10–15 mm. **2*n*** = 14.

Flowering (late winter–)spring(–early fall). Open, dry sites near ocean, bluffs, sandy flats, inland in canyons, brushy and rocky slopes, ridges, dry washes, gravel; 0–400 m; Calif.

Variety *dendroideus* is known from the following Channel Islands: Anacapa, Santa Barbara, Santa Catalina (common), Santa Cruz (common), and Santa Rosa.

22b. Acmispon dendroideus (Greene) Brouillet var. **traskiae** (Eastwood ex Abrams) Brouillet, J. Bot. Res. Inst. Texas 2: 389. 2008 • Trask's Island lotus [C] [E]

Syrmatium traskiae Eastwood ex Abrams, Fl. Los Angeles ed. 3, 201. 1917; *Lotus dendroideus* (Greene) Greene var. *traskiae* (Eastwood ex Abrams) Isely; *L. scoparius* (Torrey & A. Gray) Ottley subsp. *traskiae* (Eastwood ex Abrams) P. H. Raven; *L. scoparius* var. *traskiae* (Eastwood ex Abrams) Ottley

Shrubs, greenish, sparsely strigose. **Stems** erect, woody. **Leaflets** 3–5, blades greenish, surfaces sparsely strigose. **Umbels:** bract unifoliolate. **Ovules** 4–6. **Legumes** (20–)30–50 mm. **2*n*** = 14.

Flowering (late winter–)spring(–early fall). Open, dry sites near ocean, bluffs, sandy flats, inland in canyons, brushy and rocky slopes, ridges, washes; of conservation concern; 0–400 m; Calif.

Variety *traskiae* is known only from San Clemente Island; the report from Todos Santos Island (Baja California) (*Wiggins 11979*, RSA) requires confirmation.

Variety *traskiae*, as *Lotus dendroideus* subsp. *traskiae*, is in the Center for Plant Conservation's National Collection of Endangered Plants.

22c. Acmispon dendroideus (Greene) Brouillet var. **veatchii** (Greene) Brouillet, J. Bot. Res. Inst. Texas 2: 389. 2009 • San Miguel Island deerweed [E]

Hosackia veatchii Greene, Bull. Calif. Acad. Sci. 1: 83. 1885; *Lotus dendroideus* (Greene) Greene var. *veatchii* (Greene) Isely; *L. scoparius* (Torrey & A. Gray) Ottley var. *veatchii* (Greene) Ottley; *L. veatchii* (Greene) Greene; *Syrmatium patens* Greene; *S. veatchii* (Greene) Greene

Subshrubs (shrubs), gray, densely strigose to almost silky. **Stems** decumbent, ± woody. **Leaflets** 3, blades usually gray, surfaces densely strigose, almost silky. **Umbels:** bract unifoliolate. **Ovules** 4–6. **Legumes** (20–) 30–50 mm.

Flowering (late winter–)spring(–early fall). Open, dry sites near ocean, bluffs, sandy flats, inland in canyons, brushy and rocky slopes, ridges, washes; 0–400 m; Calif.

Variety *veatchii* is known only from San Miguel Island, where it is uncommon. Reports of this variety from Baja California remain to be confirmed with better material.

23. Acmispon cytisoides (Bentham) Brouillet, J. Bot. Res. Inst. Texas 2: 389. 2008 E

Hosackia cytisoides Bentham, Trans. Linn. Soc. London 17: 366. 1837; *H. cytisoides* var. *rubescens* Torrey & A. Gray; *Lotus benthamii* Greene; *Syrmatium cytisoides* (Bentham) Greene

Subshrubs, mat-forming or cespitose, diffusely ascending, low, greenish, 1–8 dm, 50–130 dm diam., not fleshy, glabrous or strigose (young foliage); from woody caudices. **Stems** 1–20+, procumbent to ± ascending, branched, flexuous-wiry or thick, ± woody, leafy. **Leaves** irregularly pinnate to subpalmate, distal mostly 3-foliolate; stipules glandlike; subsessile to short-petiolate; rachis 1–8 mm, ± flattened; leaflets 3–5, blades obovate to elliptic, apex obtuse, surfaces glabrous or glabrate. **Peduncles** ascending, (1–)2–12(–25) mm, longer than leaves; bract absent or 1- or 2-foliolate, usually subtending umbel. **Inflorescences** 3–10-flowered. **Flowers** 8–10 mm; calyx 3.5–6 mm, tube sparsely strigillose to glabrate, lobes subulate; corolla white to pinkish (banner) or yellow (wings cream), banner often red-striate or red-backed, keel reddish or purplish, claws shorter than calyx tube, banner reflexed to 90°, wings slightly longer than keel; style upcurved, sparsely strigillose. **Legumes** persistent, mostly included, divergent or ascending, brown, arched, turgid, not or slightly constricted, not septate, linear-oblong, 7–10 × 1–2 mm, leathery, apex tapering to exserted, slender, curved or straight beak, indehiscent, smooth, margins thickened, smooth, glabrate, beak strigillose. **Seeds** 1 or 2, olive brown, mottled, subcylindric, smooth.

Flowering spring (early fall). Coastal dunes, slopes, and bluffs, cliffs, coastal scrub, chaparral, Monterrey pine forests, exposed slopes, ridges, landslides, gulches, stream banks, sandy or clayey soils, eroded granite, shale, sometimes serpentine outcrops, burnt chaparral, disturbed areas, roadsides; 0–1000 m; Calif.

Acmispon cytisoides occurs in the Central Coast, San Francisco Bay Area, and Outer South Coast Ranges. D. Isely (1981) reported possible hybrids with *A. glaber* var. *glaber* (as *Lotus scoparius* var. *perplexans* Hoover).

24. Acmispon haydonii (Orcutt) Brouillet, J. Bot. Res. Inst. Texas 2: 390. 2008 • Haydon's deervetch or lotus

Hosackia haydonii Orcutt, W. Amer. Sci. 6: 63. 1889 (as haydoni); *Lotus haydonii* (Orcutt) Greene; *Syrmatium haydonii* (Orcutt) Brand

Subshrubs, bushy, tangled, low, green, 1–20 dm, not fleshy, strigillose; from woody caudices. **Stems** 1–20+, procumbent to ascending, branched, ± woody, wiry, remotely leafy, deciduous. **Leaves** subpalmate; stipules glandlike or absent; subsessile; rachis absent; leaflets 3, blades elliptic, apex obtuse, surfaces ± strigillose. **Peduncles** 0–3 mm, shorter than leaves; bract absent (reduced to stipule), distal. **Inflorescences** 1(or 2)-flowered. **Flowers** 4–5 mm; calyx 2.5–3 mm, tube ± strigillose, lobes subulate; corolla usually yellow, sometimes ± pinkish or orangish, claws shorter than calyx tube, banner implicate-ascending, wings slightly shorter than to ± equaling keel; style upcurved, glabrous. **Legumes** persistent, exserted, ascending to deflexed, tawny, curved, turgid, not or slightly constricted, not septate, oblong, (5–)6–9 × 1–1.5 mm, leathery, apex beaked, indehiscent, finely veined, margins smooth, sparsely strigillose to glabrate. **Seeds** 1 or 2, greenish brown, not mottled, straight or ± curved, narrowly cylindric, smooth. $2n = 14$.

Flowering late winter–spring. Dry rocky slopes, cliffs, mountain washes, creosote bush scrub to pinyon-juniper woodlands; (100–)400–1300 m; Calif.; Mexico (Baja California).

Acmispon haydonii grows along the western edge of the Sonoran Desert.

25. Acmispon junceus (Bentham) Brouillet, J. Bot. Res. Inst. Texas 2: 391. 2008 • Rush deervetch or trefoil E

Hosackia juncea Bentham, Trans. Linn. Soc. London 17: 366. 1836; *Lotus junceus* (Bentham) Greene; *Syrmatium junceum* (Bentham) Greene

Subshrubs (often flowering 1st year, appearing annual), bushy or wiry and prostrate, sometimes robust, brownish, 0.8–4 dm, not fleshy, strigillose to glabrate; from woody caudices. **Stems** 1–20+, prostrate to ascending, branched, ± woody, wiry or stout, often remotely leafy. **Leaves**

irregularly subpalmate; stipules glandlike; sessile or subsessile to short-petiolate; rachis 0–9 mm, sometimes flattened; leaflets 3–5, blades obovate to oblanceolate, apex obtuse to acute, or mucronulate, surfaces ± strigillose. **Peduncles** ascending, slender, sometimes secondarily branched, 1–25 mm, usually shorter, sometimes longer, than leaves; bract absent or (when pedunculate) unifoliolate, distal. **Inflorescences** (1 or)2–8-flowered. **Flowers** 6–8 mm; calyx 3–5 mm, tube strigillose, lobes triangular to deltate; corolla yellow, tinged red, fading orange, claws longer than calyx tube, banner implicate-ascending, wings shorter than keel (and other petals); style gradually or abruptly upcurved, glabrous. **Legumes** persistent, moderately to well exserted, ascending to divergent, tawny to brown, strongly arched, curved to 90°, sometimes nearly straight, turgid, not constricted, not septate, linear-oblong, 6–8 × 1–2 mm, leathery, apex beak recurved 80–360° or irregularly contorted, nearly as long as body, indehiscent, transversely ridged, margins keeled, rugose, strigillose or glabrous. **Seeds** 1 or 2, olive to reddish brown, mottled, elongate, curved, smooth.

Varieties 2 (2 in the flora): California.

1. Stems usually stout, prostrate to ascending; peduncles 1–5 mm; legumes moderately exserted .... 25a. *Acmispon junceus* var. *junceus*
1. Stems often wiry, usually prostrate; peduncles (3–)8–25 mm; legumes well exserted. .... 25b. *Acmispon junceus* var. *biolettii*

25a. Acmispon junceus (Bentham) Brouillet var. **junceus** E

Stems usually stout, prostrate to ascending. **Peduncles** 1–5 mm. **Legumes** moderately exserted.

Flowering spring. Chaparral, rocky, open slopes, sometimes on serpentine, bluffs, sand dunes; 0–500 m; Calif.

Variety *junceus* occurs in the Central Coast and Outer South Coast Ranges. D. Isely (1981) reported hybrids with *Acmispon glaber* var. *glaber* [as *Lotus scoparius* (Torrey & A. Gray) Ottley var. *perplexans* Hoover].

25b. Acmispon junceus (Bentham) Brouillet var. **biolettii** (Greene) Brouillet, J. Bot. Res. Inst. Texas 2: 391. 2008 E

Lotus biolettii Greene, Pittonia 2: 222. 1892; *Hosackia biolettii* (Greene) Rattan; *L. junceus* (Bentham) Greene var. *biolettii* (Greene) Ottley; *Syrmatium biolettii* (Greene) Brand

Stems often wiry, usually prostrate. **Peduncles** (3–)8–25 mm. **Legumes** well exserted. $2n = 14$.

Flowering spring. Coastal sands, ridges, slopes, talus, gravelly soils, chaparral, pine forests, disturbed areas, common after fire; 0–500 m; Calif.

Variety *biolettii* occurs from the North Coast and Outer North Coast Ranges to the Central Coast and Outer South Coast Ranges.

26. Acmispon tomentosus (Hooker & Arnott) Govaerts, Skvortsovia 4(3): 76. 2018

Hosackia tomentosa Hooker & Arnott, Bot. Beechey Voy. 137. 1841

Herbs, perennial (often flowering first year, appearing annual), mat-forming, low, green, 3–10 dm, not fleshy, usually distally villous (young), sparsely hirsute to glabrate (mature); from woody caudices, taprooted. **Stems** 1–10+, procumbent, much branched, wiry or ± woody, leafy. **Leaves** irregularly subpalmate; stipules glandlike; subessile to petiolate; rachis 2–10 mm, sometimes flattened; leaflets 4–6, blades ovate to obovate, apex ± obtuse to acute, surfaces sparsely to densely pilose. **Peduncles** ascending, 1–5 mm, shorter than leaves; bract unifoliolate, distal. **Inflorescences** 3–8-flowered. **Flowers** 4–6(–7) mm; calyx 2–4 mm, tube usually villous, lobes setaceous; corolla yellow to reddish, dark-tipped, claws shorter than or equaling calyx tube, banner implicate-ascending, wings equaling to longer than keel (and other petals); style geniculate 90° or incurved, glabrous. **Legumes** deciduous with calyx, exserted, ascending to divergent, tawny, straight to strongly arched, turgid, not constricted, not septate, linear-oblong, 3–5 × 1–2 mm, leathery, apex abruptly tapering to long, curved beak, indehiscent, smooth, margins indistinctly keeled, smooth, villous. **Seeds** 1 or 2, olive green to brownish green, not mottled, straight to curved, narrowly ellipsoid, smooth.

Varieties 2 (2 in the flora): California, nw Mexico.

1. Stems usually villous distally; flowers 5–6 (–7) mm; ovaries usually ± densely strigose . . . . 26a. *Acmispon tomentosus* var. *tomentosus*
1. Stems glabrate or villous distally; flowers 4–5 mm; ovaries usually sparsely strigose . . . . 26b. *Acmispon tomentosus* var. *glabriusculus*

26a. Acmispon tomentosus (Hooker & Arnott) Govaerts var. **tomentosus** [E]

Acmispon heermannii (Durand & Hilgard) Brouillet var. *orbicularis* (A. Gray) Brouillet; *H. heermannii* Durand & Hilgard var. *orbicularis* A. Gray; *Lotus eriophorus* Greene; *L. heermannii* (Durand & Hilgard) Greene var. *eriophorus* (Greene) Ottley; *L. heermannii* var. *orbicularis* (A. Gray) Isely; *Syrmatium eriophorum* (Greene) A. Heller; *S. tomentosum* (Hooker & Arnott) Vogel

Stems usually villous distally. **Flowers** 5–6(–7) mm; ovary usually ± densely strigose. $2n$ = 14.

Flowering (late winter–)spring(–early summer). Sand flats, dunes, chaparral, pine woodlands, railroad embankments, sand or gravel; 0–300 m; Calif.

Variety *tomentosus* is present in the North Coast, Outer North Coast Ranges, the Central Coast, and the Outer South Coast Ranges. *Lotus tomentosus* (Hooker & Arnott) Greene (1890, not Desrousseaux 1792) is an illegitimate name that pertains here.

26b. Acmispon tomentosus (Hooker & Arnott) Govaerts var. **glabriusculus** (Hooker & Arnott) Govaerts, Skvortsovia 4(3): 76. 2018

Hosackia decumbens Bentham var. *glabriuscula* Hooker & Arnott, Bot. Beechey Voy. 137. 1832; *H. heermannii* Durand & Hilgard; *H. tomentosa* Hooker & Arnott subsp. *glabriuscula* (Hooker & Arnott) Abrams; *Lotus eriophorus* Greene var. *heermannii* (Durand & Hilgard) Ottley; *L. heermannii* (Durand & Hilgard) Greene; *Syrmatium heermannii* (Durand & Hilgard) Greene

Stems glabrate or villous distally. **Flowers** 4–5 mm; ovary usually sparsely strigose.

Flowering summer(–fall). Flats, washes, riverbanks, canyons, chaparral, oak chaparral, dry, sandy soils, railroad embankments; 0–2000 m; Calif.; Mexico (Baja California)

Variety *glabriusculus* is present in the South Coast, the San Bernardino Mountains, the Peninsular Ranges, and the Sonoran Desert.

Acmispon heermannii (Durand & Hilgard) Brouillet is a superfluous name that pertains here.

27. Acmispon decumbens (Bentham) Govaerts, Skvortsovia 4(3): 76. 2018 • Pine deervetch or lotus [F]

Hosackia decumbens Bentham, Bot. Reg. 12: sub plate 1257. 1829; *Anisolotus decumbens* (Bentham) M. Armstrong & Thornber; *Syrmatium decumbens* (Bentham) Greene

Herbs, perennial (seldom flowering first year), mat-forming or cespitose, diffuse, low, greenish gray (young growth cinereous), 0.5–1 dm (3–12 dm wide), not fleshy, ±villous to glabrate, hairs curved; woody-taprooted. **Stems** 1–20+, procumbent, branched, wiry, slender, leafy. **Leaves** irregularly pinnate to subpalmate; stipules glandlike; subsessile to petiolate; rachis (1–)2–10(–15) mm, not or ± flattened; leaflets 3–5, blades obovate to elliptic, apex acute to obtuse, surfaces villous, hairs curved. **Peduncles** ascending, 3–15(–30 proximally) mm, shorter than leaves; bract 1–3-foliolate, subtending umbel. **Inflorescences** (1–)3–12-flowered. **Flowers** 4.5–8(–10) mm; calyx (3.5–)4–7 mm, tube sparsely villosulous, lobes subulate, subequal; corolla yellow, reddening, usually drying dark, claws shorter than calyx tube, banner implicate-ascending, wings longer than keel; style curved, glabrous. **Legumes** deciduous with calyx, exserted, declined or deflexed, tawny, strongly arched, turgid, not constricted, not septate, ovoid-ellipsoid, 6–10 × 1.8–2.2 mm, leathery, apex long, tapering to curved, slender beak, indehiscent, veined, margins keeled, rugose, strigillose. **Seeds** 1 or 2 (or 3), brown, not mottled, narrowly oblong-reniform, smooth.

Varieties 2 (2 in the flora): w North America, nw Mexico.

D. Isely (1981) reported potential hybrids of *Acmispon decumbens* (variety not specified) with *A. argophyllus* var. *argophyllus* and *A. glaber* var. *glaber*.

1. Leaf rachises (3–)5–10(–15) mm; inflorescences (3–)5–12-flowered; flowers 4.5–8(–10) mm; calyces (3.5–)4–7 mm, lobes 0.5–1.5(–3) mm . . . . 27a. *Acmispon decumbens* var. *decumbens*
1. Leaf rachises (1–)2–5 mm; inflorescences (1–)3–5(–8)-flowered; flowers 4.5–8(–9) mm; calyces 6–7 mm, lobes 0.5–1.5(–2) mm. . . . . 27b. *Acmispon decumbens* var. *davidsonii*

27a. Acmispon decumbens (Bentham) Govaerts var. **decumbens** [F]

Acmispon nevadensis (S. Watson) Brouillet; *Hosackia decumbens* Bentham var. *nevadensis* S. Watson; *H. nevadensis* (S. Watson) Parish; *Lotus douglasii* Greene; *L. douglasii* var. *congestus* Ottley; *L. douglasii* var. *nevadensis* (S. Watson) Ottley; *L. leonis* Eastwood; *L. nevadensis* (S. Watson) Greene; *L. nevadensis* var. *congestus* (Ottley) Ottley; *L. nevadensis* var. *douglasii* (Greene) Ottley; *Syrmatium nevadense* (S. Watson) Greene

Leaves: rachis (3–)5–10(–15) mm. **Inflorescences** (3–)5–12-flowered. **Flowers** 4.5–8(–10) mm; calyx (3.5–)4–7 mm, lobes 0.5–1.5(–3) mm; corolla not blocky, banner 4.5–7(–10) mm, upcurved 30–90°, sometimes drying orange-yellow. **Legumes** usually 1.8–2 mm wide. $2n = 14$.

Flowering spring–summer. Open coniferous forests (oak, yellow pine, lodgepole, fir), open, bracken meadows, grassy slopes, prairies, sagebrush, dry, sandy and gravelly slopes and benches, stream banks, sandy shores, roadsides, serpentine, sandy soils, lava beds; 200–2100 m; B.C.; Calif., Idaho, Nev., Oreg., Wash.; Mexico (Baja California).

Variety *douglasii* was distinguished from var. *decumbens* only by flower size, a characteristic that appears to vary clinally. This led D. Isely (1993) to merge the two taxa. *Acmispon nevadensis* (S. Watson) Brouillet, based on *Hosackia decumbens* var. *nevadensis*, is a superfluous name, and *Lotus incanus* Douglas ex Hooker is an invalid name; both pertain here.

27b. Acmispon decumbens (Bentham) Govaerts var. **davidsonii** (Greene) Govaerts, Skvortsovia 4(3): 76. 2018 [E]

Lotus davidsonii Greene, Erythea 1: 207. 1893, based on *L. sulphureus* Greene, Pittonia 2: 293. 1892, not Boissier 1842; *Acmispon nevadensis* (S. Watson) Brouillet var. *davidsonii* (Greene) Brouillet; *L. argophyllus* (A. Gray) Greene var. *davidsonii* (Greene) Jepson; *L. nevadensis* (S. Watson) Greene var. *davidsonii* (Greene) Isely; *Syrmatium davidsonii* (Greene) A. Heller

Leaves: rachis (1–)2–5 mm. **Inflorescences** (1–)3–5(–8)-flowered. **Flowers** 4.5–8(–9) mm; calyx 6–7 mm, lobes 0.5–1.5(–2) mm; corolla appearing blocky, banner 4.5–6.5 mm, abruptly upcurved ± 90°, usually drying dark. **Legumes** usually 2–2.2 mm wide.

Flowering late spring–summer. Pine forests, oak groves, open rocky slopes of Douglas-fir-oak forests, open dry slopes and flats, summits, wet places; 1200–2800 m; Calif.

Variety *davidsonii* is known from the Transverse and northeastern Peninsular ranges. A. M. Ottley (1923) considered var. *davidsonii* as intermediate between *Lotus douglasii* var. *nevadensis* (*Acmispon decumbens* var. *decumbens*) and *L. argophyllus* var. *decorus* (*A. argophyllus* var. *argophyllus*). Intermediates with var. *decumbens* may occur. *Hosackia sulphurea* Abrams (1944) and *Syrmatium sulphureum* Brand (1898) are illegitimate names (superfluous for *Lotus davidsonii* 1893) that pertain here.

28. Acmispon argophyllus (A. Gray) Brouillet, J. Bot. Res. Inst. Texas 2: 388. 2008 • California deervetch or trefoil

Hosackia argophylla A. Gray, Pl. Nov. Thurb., 316. 1854; *Lotus argophyllus* (A. Gray) Greene; *Syrmatium argophyllum* (A. Gray) Greene

Herbs, perennial, or subshrubs, cespitose and ± prostrate, or shrubby and spreading to ascending, low or robust, silvery or gray, 1–6(–10+) dm, not fleshy, tomentose to canescent or strigose; from woody caudices. **Stems** 1–20+, prostrate or decumbent to ascending, branched, herbaceous, slender, or ± woody, leafy, sometimes congested at tips. **Leaves** irregularly pinnate to subpalmate; stipules glandlike; short-petiolate; rachis 2–10 mm, ± flattened; leaflets (3 or)4 or 5(–7), blades obovate to elliptic-lanceolate or ovate, apex acute, surfaces densely sericeous. **Peduncles** ascending, 0–6(–40) mm, shorter to longer than leaves; bract absent or unifoliolate, subtending umbel. **Inflorescences** 3–20-flowered, capitate. **Flowers** 6–12 mm; calyx 5–7 mm, tube densely villous, lobes subulate, shorter than or equal to tube; corolla yellow to orange, turning red or brown, claws shorter than calyx tube, banner implicate-ascending, wings ± equaling keel; style curved, glabrous. **Legumes** persistent, included to moderately (–strongly) exserted, ascending to divergent, reddish brown, arched, turgid, not constricted, not septate, lanceoloid, 6–10 × 1–2 mm, leathery, apex short-beaked, tapering, curved or geniculate, indehiscent, smooth, margins keeled smooth, glabrate to silky. **Seeds** 1 (or 2), tawny, mottled, curved-oblong, elongate, smooth.

Varieties 6 (5 in the flora): California, nw Mexico.

D. Isely (1981) reported a potential hybrid between *Acmispon argophyllus* (variety not specified) and *A. glaber* (variety not specified). Variety *ornithopus* (Greene) Brouillet is endemic to Guadalupe Island (Baja

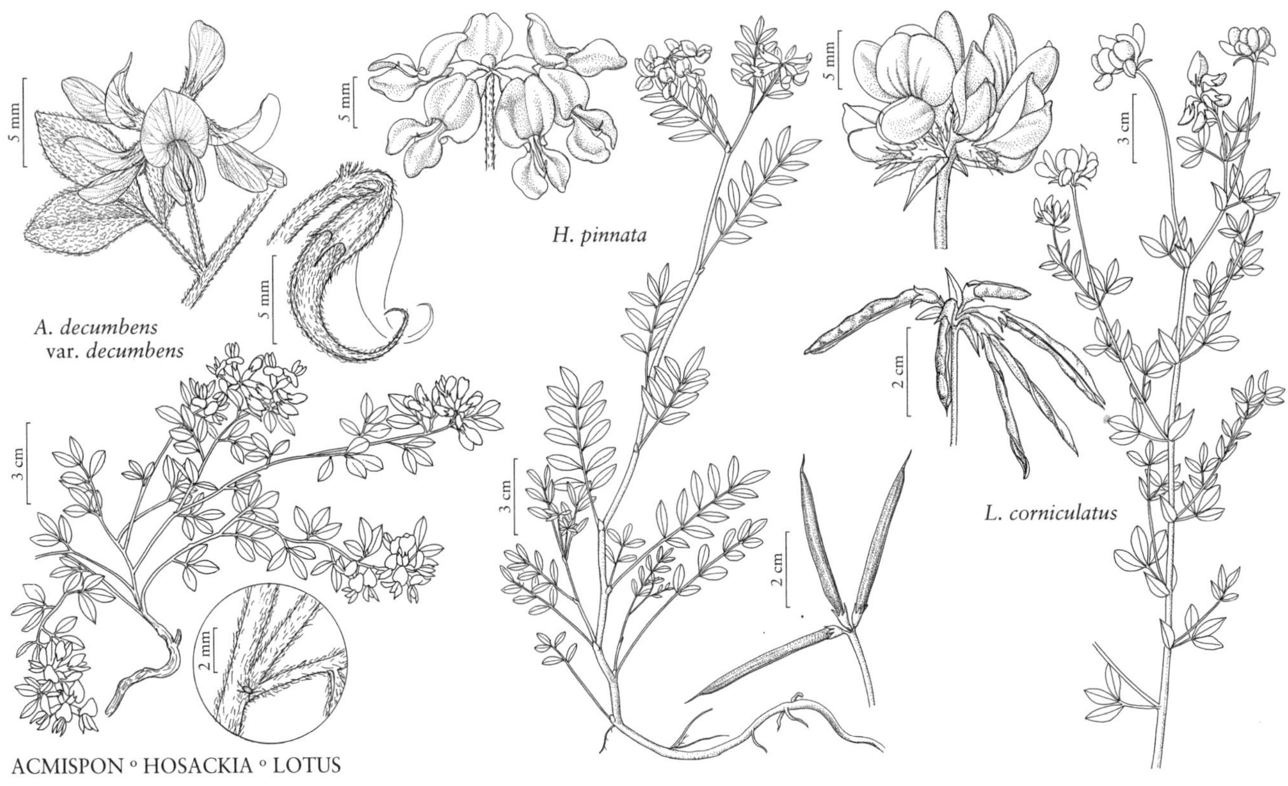

ACMISPON ◦ HOSACKIA ◦ LOTUS

California, Mexico). In a phylogeographic study of *A. agrophylus*, L. E. Wallace et al. (2017) showed that the insular endemic varieties are distinct, although var. *argenteus* is paraphyletic to var. *adsurgens*, with var. *niveus* of Santa Cruz sister to all remaining varieties in the species, including the continental ones.

1. Herbs, perennial; stems prostrate or decumbent-ascending; mainland California.
   2. Umbels 3–7-flowered, not congested, peduncles 1–6+ mm; calyces 5–6 mm, lobes 1.5–2(–3.5) mm; banner claw shorter than blade; s Sierra Nevada, s California ranges .... 28a. *Acmispon argophyllus* var. *argophyllus*
   2. Umbels 10–15-flowered, congested at branch tips, peduncles 0–2 mm; calyces 6–7 mm, lobes 2–3(–5) mm; banner claw scarcely shorter than blade; n Sierra Nevada................. 28d. *Acmispon argophyllus* var. *fremontii*
1. Subshrubs (mostly); stems ascending to erect, sometimes prostrate; Channel Islands.
   3. Umbels 12–20-flowered, peduncles 5–40 mm .... 28c. *Acmispon argophyllus* var. *argenteus*
   3. Umbels 6–13-flowered, peduncles 1–5 mm.
      4. Stems ascending to erect, densely leafy; umbels 10–13-flowered; San Clemente Island.......................... ...... 28b. *Acmispon argophyllus* var. *adsurgens*
      4. Stems ascending to bushy and spreading, not densely leafy; umbels 6–10-flowered; Anacapa and Santa Cruz islands................. 28e. *Acmispon argophyllus* var. *niveus*

28a. Acmispon argophyllus (A. Gray) Brouillet var. **argophyllus**

Hosackia argentea Kellogg; *H. argophylla* A. Gray var. *decora* I. M. Johnston; *Lotus argophyllus* (A. Gray) Greene subsp. *decorus* (I. M. Johnston) Munz; *L. argophyllus* var. *decorus* (I. M. Johnston) Ottley

Herbs, silky-canescent to silvery-strigose. **Stems** prostrate or decumbent-ascending, not densely leafy. **Peduncles** 1–6+ mm. **Umbels** 3–7-flowered, not congested. **Flowers** 6–10 mm; calyx 5–6 mm, lobes 1.5–2(–3.5) mm; banner claw shorter than blade. $2n$ = 14.

Flowering (late winter–)spring–early summer. Dry slopes in chaparral to pinyon-juniper woodlands, canyons; 0–1600(–2300) m; Calif.; Mexico (Baja California).

Variety *argophyllus* is present in the southern Sierra Nevada, the South Coast Ranges, the South Coast, the San Gabriel and San Bernardino mountains, and the Peninsular Ranges; it is also common in the lower Sonoran Desert chaparral. D. Isely (1981) considered var. *argophyllus* a variable taxon, intergrading with other varieties and species where they co-occur. Isely reported a potential hybrid with *Acmispon decumbens* (as *A. nevadensis*).

28b. Acmispon argophyllus (A. Gray) Brouillet var. **adsurgens** (Dunkle) Brouillet, J. Bot. Res. Inst. Texas 2: 388. 2008 • San Clemente Island bird's-foot trefoil [C] [E]

Lotus argophyllus (A. Gray) Greene var. *adsurgens* Dunkle, Bull. S. Calif. Acad. Sci. 39: 197. 1941; *L. argophyllus* subsp. *adsurgens* (Dunkle) P. H. Raven

Subshrubs, silvery-canescent. **Stems** ascending to erect, densely leafy. **Peduncles** 1–5 mm. **Umbels** 10–13-flowered, congested at branch tips. **Flowers** 6–7(–10) mm; calyx 6–7 mm, lobes 2–3(–4) mm; banner claw scarcely shorter than blade.

Flowering spring–early summer. Hot, dry rocky slopes, bluffs; of conservation concern; 0–300 m; Calif.

Variety *adsurgens* is known only from San Clemente Island. D. Isely (1981) considered it a variant on the same theme as var. *niveus* and did not segregate it, but later he (Isely 1993) stated that it was related to var. *niveus*.

Variety *adsurgens*, as *Lotus argophyllus* var. *adsurgens*, is in the Center for Plant Conservation's National Collection of Endangered Plants.

28c. Acmispon argophyllus (A. Gray) Brouillet var. **argenteus** (Dunkle) Brouillet, J. Bot. Res. Inst. Texas 2: 388. 2008 [E]

Lotus argophyllus (A. Gray) Greene var. *argenteus* Dunkle, Bull. S. Calif. Acad. Sci. 39: 197. 1941; *Hosackia ornithopus* Greene subsp. *venusta* (Eastwood) Abrams; *H. venusta* Eastwood; *L. argophyllus* var. *hancockii* Dunkle; *L. venustus* (Eastwood) A. Heller; *Syrmatium venustum* (Eastwood) Davidson & Moxley

Subshrubs, cinereous-canescent. **Stems** prostrate or ascending, not densely leafy. **Peduncles** 5–40 mm. **Umbels** 12–20-flowered, not congested. **Flowers** 8–10–12 mm; calyx 5–7 mm, lobes 1.5–2.5 mm; banner claw scarcely shorter than blade. **2*n*** = 14.

Flowering (late winter–)spring. Chaparral, bluffs; 0–400 m; Calif.

Variety *argenteus* is present in all Channel Islands except Santa Cruz Island. It resembles var. *argophyllus*. It has often been named var. or subsp. *ornithopus*, but this is a taxon of Guadalupe Island and islets along the northwest coast of Baja California that differs by its clusters of well-exserted pods, some containing three seeds, while var. *argenteus* has shorter pods with one or two seeds. Using nuclear ribosomal DNA evidence, A. Liston et al. (1990) showed that var. *argenteus* (as *Lotus argophyllus* subsp. *ornithopus)* hybridizes with *Acmispon dendroideus* var. *traskiae* (as *L. scoparius* subsp. *traskiae*) on San Clemente Island.

28d. Acmispon argophyllus (A. Gray) Brouillet var. **fremontii** (A. Gray) Brouillet, J. Bot. Res. Inst. Texas 2: 389. 2008 [E]

Hosackia argophylla A. Gray var. *fremontii* A. Gray, Proc. Acad. Nat. Sci. Philadelphia 15: 347. 1864 (as fremonti); *H. fremontii* (A. Gray) Abrams; *Lotus argophyllus* (A. Gray) Greene var. *fremontii* (A. Gray) Ottley; *L. fremontii* (A. Gray) A. Heller; *Syrmatium fremontii* (A. Gray) A. Heller

Herbs, strigose. **Stems** prostrate or decumbent-ascending, not densely leafy. **Peduncles** 0–2 mm. **Umbels** 10–15-flowered, congested at branch tips. **Flowers** 7–10 (–12) mm; calyx 6–7 mm, lobes 2–3(–5) mm; banner claw scarcely shorter than blade. **2*n*** = 14.

Flowering spring. Openings along rivers, outcrops, canyon slopes, shale, along trails; 600–1200 m; Calif.

Variety *fremontii* is known from the northern Sierra Nevada.

28e. Acmispon argophyllus (A. Gray) Brouillet var. **niveus** (Greene) Brouillet, Aliso 28: 63. 2010 • Santa Cruz Island deervetch or bird's-foot trefoil [E]

Syrmatium niveum Greene, Bull. Calif. Acad. Sci. 2: 148. 1886; *Lotus argophyllus* (A. Gray) Greene subsp. *niveus* (Greene) Munz; *L. argophyllus* var. *niveus* (Greene) Ottley; *L. niveus* (Greene) Greene

Subshrubs, ± spreading, silvery-tomentose. **Stems** ascending to bushy or spreading, not densely leafy. **Peduncles** 1–5 mm. **Umbels** 6–10-flowered, congested at branch tips. **Flowers** 6–7(–10) mm; calyx 5–7 mm, lobes 2–3(–5) mm, banner claw scarcely shorter than blade.

Flowering spring–early summer. Rocky slopes, bluffs, dry riverbeds; 0–300 m; Calif.

Variety *niveus* is known from Santa Cruz Island and nearby Anacapa Island. D. Isely (1981) proposed that it is possibly derived from var. *fremontii* of the mainland. Isely placed *Hosackia nivea* S. Watson [*Acmispon niveus* (S. Watson) Brouillet; syn. *Ottleya nivea* (S. Watson) D. D. Sokoloff] in synonymy of this taxon, but this is erroneous as this taxon is distinct and found only in Baja California, Mexico.

124. HOSACKIA Douglas ex Bentham, Edwards's Bot. Reg. 15: plate 1257. 1829 • [For David Hosack, 1769–1835, New York physician, botanist, and mineralogist]

Luc Brouillet

Herbs, perennial, unarmed. **Stems** erect, ascending, decumbent, or procumbent, glabrous or glabrate to pubescent, puberulent, villous, or canescent to silky. **Leaves** alternate, odd-pinnate; stipules present, caducous, leafy or scarious; petiolate; leaflets 3–19, regularly arranged, blade margins entire, surfaces glabrous or pubescent. **Inflorescences** 1–20-flowered, axillary, umbels or solitary flowers; bract usually present (absent in *H. alamosana*), medial or subtending umbel. **Flowers** papilionaceous; calyx actinomorphic to slightly zygomorphic, cylindric to obconic-cylindric, lobes 5; corolla yellow, cream, white, pink, purple, red, or lurid, keel equaling or longer than symmetrically positioned wings; stamens 10, diadelphous; anthers basifixed, relatively small, dehiscing longitudinally; style glabrous, without collar; stigma terminal. **Fruits** legumes, exserted from calyx, straight, not deflexed, linear to oblong, subterete to quadrate, abruptly short-beaked, dehiscent, usually glabrous, sometimes ± hairy or glabrate. **Seeds** (2–)4–20 (or 21), mottled, oblong, ovoid, obovoid, or reniform. $x = 7$.

Species 14 (9 in the flora): w North America, Mexico, Central America (Guatemala).

Five species of *Hosackia* are found in Mexico and not in the flora area: *H. confinis* (Greene) Brand, *H. guadalupensis* (Greene) Brand, *H. hintoniorum* (B. L. Turner) D. D. Sokoloff, *H. mexicana* Bentham, and *H. repens* G. Don, which occurs also in Guatemala.

Throughout the twentieth century, *Hosackia* usually was included within *Lotus* (D. Isely 1981, 1993). Phylogenetic work, both morphologic (A. M. Arambarri 2000) and molecular (G. J. Allan and J. M. Porter 2000; Allan et al. 2003; D. D. Sokoloff et al. 2007), has shown that *Hosackia* is distinct from the Eurasian *Lotus* and the North American *Acmispon*. Morphologic features that distinguish *Hosackia* include the well-developed stipules versus glandlike or reduced in *Acmispon*, and 3–15-pinnate leaves (proximal leaflet pairs not in stipular position as in *Lotus*) with regularly arranged leaflets versus irregularly or ± palmately arranged in *Acmispon*. *Hosackia* is distinctive in Loteae also by frequently being found in more or less wet habitats.

For definitions of "implicate" and "implicate-ascending" (in reference to the banner petal), see the discussion under 123. *Acmispon*.

1. Herbs mat-forming, 5–40 cm, taprooted, sometimes with woody caudex; stems usually decumbent, sometimes ascending or procumbent; leaves: rachis 0.5–1.5 cm, leaflets 3–5 (–7), blade surfaces glabrous; umbels 1–3(or 4)-flowered; petal claws ± equaling calyx tube; legumes ascending to erect.
   2. Flowers (7–)8–10 mm, banner yellow, wings and keel whitish yellow, calyx lobes triangular to triangular-subulate, 0.5–1 mm; legumes narrowly oblong, compressed, leathery; seeds (2–)4–7, oblong; stipules inconspicuous, scarious . . . . 8. *Hosackia yollabolliensis*
   2. Flowers 5–7(–9) mm, banner yellow, wings and keel white or cream, becoming reddish tinged, calyx lobes lanceolate, 0.5–2 mm; legumes linear-oblong, turgid, thinly leathery; seeds (8–)10–13(–15), reniform, flattened; stipules 1.5–3.5 mm, membranous . . . 9. *Hosackia alamosana*
1. Herbs not mat-forming, 10–150 cm, usually rhizomatous, stoloniferous, or root-spreading, sometimes with caudex; stems usually erect to ascending, sometimes decumbent; leaves: rachis 1–12 cm, leaflets (3 or)5–15(–19), blade surfaces glabrous or hairy; umbels (1–)3–20-flowered; petal claws usually longer, sometimes ± equaling to slightly longer, than calyx tube; legumes ± ascending to ± inclined.

[3. Shifted to left margin.—Ed.]

3. Corolla banner yellow; stems decumbent to ascending; peduncles equaling or longer than subtending leaf, bract absent or subtending umbel; seeds (6–)8–20(or 21).
    4. Leaflet blades appressed-hairy to hirsute or glabrous; calyx green, hairy; petal claws ± equaling to slightly longer than calyx tube, banner implicate-ascending; legumes leathery, not septate . . . . 7. *Hosackia oblongifolia*
    4. Leaflet blades glabrous; calyx reddish, glabrous; petal claws longer than calyx tube, banner reflexed to 180°; legumes thinly leathery, incompletely septate.
        5. Stems ± fleshy or not; corolla: wings white or cream, keel yellow, wings longer than keel; legumes linear-oblong; peduncle bract 1(or 3)-foliolate or absent; leaf rachis 2–7 cm, leaflet blades (7–)10–25 mm . . . . 5. *Hosackia pinnata*
        5. Stems fleshy, base often spongy; corolla: wings and keel pale to dark pink, sometimes whitish, keel pink- to purple-tipped, wings equaling or longer than keel; legumes oblong; peduncle bract 1 or 3(–7)-foliolate; leaf rachis 1–4 cm, leaflet blades 6–20 mm . . . . 6. *Hosackia gracilis*
3. Corolla banner red, purple, pink, rose, or white, or greenish or whitish becoming marked with red or purple; stems usually erect or ascending, sometimes decumbent (*H. rosea*); peduncles usually shorter than subtending leaf (equaling or longer in *H. rosea*), bract absent or medial, sometimes subtending umbel (*H. incana*); seeds 3–12.
    6. Herbs densely silvery- to golden-villous or -canescent; corolla banner red, wings and keel white, keel apex obtuse; leaflets (5–)7–11(–15) . . . . 1. *Hosackia incana*
    6. Herbs villous and legume ± hairy, or sparsely strigulose, puberulent, or glabrate, sometimes glabrous (*H. stipularis*); corolla purple, pink, or white, wings sometimes white, or greenish or whitish becoming marked with red or purple, keel apex acute; leaflets (7–)9–15(–19).
        7. Stipules widely ovate to lanceolate, base auriculate or subauriculate; leaf rachis 2–8 cm; calyx ± hairy, sometimes glandular; corolla banner and keel purple or pink, wings white; legumes thinly leathery. . . . . 2. *Hosackia stipularis*
        7. Stipules triangular or ovate to lanceolate, base not auriculate or subauriculate; leaf rachis 6–12 cm; calyx glabrous; corolla banner, keel, and wings white to pinkish or rose, or initially greenish or whitish with red or lurid patches, strips, or tips; legumes leathery.
            8. Umbels 6–10(–12)-flowered; corollas symmetric, white to pinkish or rose, becoming red- or pink-striate or tipped, wings longer than keel; legumes oblong, (15–)30–40 mm, not septate; peduncles little elongating in fruit; stems ± fleshy or not . . . . 3. *Hosackia rosea*
            8. Umbels 8–20-flowered; corollas asymmetric, greenish or whitish becoming marked with red or purple, wings ± equaling keel; legumes linear, (10–)35–70 mm, incompletely septate; peduncles elongating in fruit; stems fleshy. . . . . 4. *Hosackia crassifolia*

1. Hosackia incana Torrey in War Department [U.S.], Pacif. Railr. Rep. 4(5): 79, plate 4. 1857 • Woolly bird's-foot trefoil [E]

Lotus incanus (Torrey) Greene

Herbs robust, 10–25(–30) cm, densely silvery- to golden-villous or -canescent, sometimes glandular; long-rhizomatous. **Stems** 1–5+, erect to ascending, unbranched or branched, not fleshy. **Leaves:** stipules deltate to lanceolate-ovate, 4–8 mm, scarious, base subauriculate; petiolate; rachis often curved, 3–7 cm; leaflets (5–)7–11(–15), petiolulate, blades elliptic to obovate, 7–16 mm, apex obtuse to acute, surfaces villous to canescent. **Peduncles** ascending, 0.5–4(–4.5) cm, shorter than subtending leaf, little elongating in fruit, villous to canescent; bract medial to subtending umbel, 3(–5)-foliolate. **Umbels** 3–8(–10)-flowered. **Flowers** 12–15 mm; calyx purplish, 5.5–7.5 mm, hairy, tube cylindric, 4.5–6 mm, lobes linear-subulate, ½ length of tube, 1–2 mm, densely ciliate; corolla banner red, wings and keel white, wings longer than keel, claw longer than calyx tube, banner implicate-ascending, keel apex obtuse. **Legumes** ± ascending to ± inclined, reddish to dark brown, oblong, turgid, 15–35(–40) × 2.5–3(–7) mm, leathery, incompletely septate, glabrous. **Seeds** 3–6+, olive to reddish brown, ovoid, 3 mm.

Flowering late spring–early summer. Dry slopes, open pine forests, open mixed conifer forests; 800–1700 m; Calif.

Hosackia incana is known from the western side of the Sierra Nevada, from Tehama to Tulare counties.

Lotus neoincanus Munz is an illegitimate name pertaining to *Hosackia incana*.

2. Hosackia stipularis Bentham, Trans. Linn. Soc. London 17: 365. 1836 E

Lotus stipularis (Bentham) Greene

Herbs ± robust, 15–50(–100) cm, usually villous and legume hairy, sometimes glabrous, sometimes glandular-viscid; rhizomatous. **Stems** 1–10+, erect to ascending, unbranched or branched, wiry or fleshy. **Leaves:** stipules widely ovate to lanceolate, (4–)6–9 mm, usually scarious, sometimes leafy, base auriculate or subauriculate; petiolate; rachis straight, 2–8 cm; leaflets 9–15(–19), petiolulate to subsessile, blades ovate to obovate, 5–20 mm, apex obtuse to ± acute, surfaces glabrous or hairy, sometimes finely punctate. **Peduncles** ascending, then spreading, 1–7 cm, shorter than subtending leaf, little elongating in fruit, ± densely hairy, sometimes glandular; bract medial, (1–)3(–7)-foliolate. **Umbels** 4–9(or 10)-flowered. **Flowers** 10–12 mm; calyx green, purplish, or pink, 5–6.5 mm, ± hairy, sometimes glandular, tube cylindric or obconic-cylindric, 4–5 mm, lobes subulate or short-triangular, 1–1.5(–2) mm, ciliolate or eciliate; corolla banner and keel purple or pink with pink-veined white tips, wings white, longer than keel, claw ± equaling or slightly longer than calyx tube, banner implicate-ascending, keel apex acute. **Legumes** ± inclined, olive brown to reddish brown, broadly oblong, turgid, 20–25 × (2–)3–4 mm, thinly leathery, incompletely septate, ± hairy to glabrate. **Seeds** 5–7, reddish brown, oblong, to 3 mm.

Varieties 2 (2 in the flora): California.

1. Stems fleshy or wiry; stipules narrow to wide, base sometimes subauriculate . . . . 2a. *Hosackia stipularis* var. *stipularis*
1. Stems wiry; stipules wide, base auriculate . . . . 2b. *Hosackia stipularis* var. *ottleyi*

2a. Hosackia stipularis Bentham var. **stipularis** • Balsam bird's-foot trefoil, stipulate lotus E

Hosackia balsamifera Kellogg; *H. macrophylla* Kellogg; *H. stipularis* subsp. *balsamifera* (Kellogg) Abrams; *Lotus balsamiferus* (Kellogg) Greene; *L. purpurascens* Eastwood

Stems fleshy or wiry. **Leaves:** stipules narrow to wide, base sometimes subauriculate. $2n = 14$.

Flowering spring–early summer. Thickets, chaparral, logged areas; 200–1500 m; Calif.

Variety *stipularis* is found mainly in the Coast Ranges and their foothills, and also in the foothills of the Sierra Nevada. A specimen (*H. M. Pollard s.n.*, June 24, 1952; TEX 274109) extends the range southward along the coast to Ventura County.

2b. Hosackia stipularis Bentham var. **ottleyi** (Isely) Brouillet, J. Bot. Res. Inst. Texas 2: 388. 2008 • Ottley's bird's-foot trefoil E

Lotus stipularis (Bentham) Greene var. *ottleyi* Isely, Brittonia 30: 468. 1978

Stems wiry. **Leaves:** stipules wide, base auriculate.

Flowering spring. Open pine forests, streambeds, ditches, serpentine soils, montane areas; 300–1700 m; Calif.

Variety *ottleyi* is found in the Klamath Ranges, the Cascade Range, the Sierra Nevada, and their foothills from northern California to Tulare County.

3. Hosackia rosea Eastwood, Proc. Calif. Acad. Sci., ser. 2, 6: 424, plate 55. 1896 • Thicket trefoil E

Lotus aboriginus Jepson; *L. crassifolius* (Bentham) Greene var. *subglaber* (Ottley) C. L. Hitchcock; *L. stipularis* (Bentham) Greene var. *subglaber* Ottley

Herbs usually robust, 10–70 cm, puberulent to glabrate; root-spreading. **Stems** 1–10+, erect to decumbent, unbranched, sometimes branched, ± fleshy or not. **Leaves:** stipules triangular to lanceolate, 2–6 mm, scarious; petiolate; rachis ± straight, 6–12 cm; leaflets 9–15, petiolulate, blades elliptic or oblong to obovate, (5–)10–30 mm, apex obtuse to rounded, surfaces sparsely short-appressed hairy to glabrate or glabrous, or long-hairy to densely villous when glandular, pale green abaxially.

Peduncles ascending, 3.5–6.5 cm, equaling or longer than subtending leaf, little elongating in fruit, strigillose to glabrate; bract medial or absent, 1–5-foliolate. **Umbels** 6–10(–12)-flowered. **Flowers** symmetric, 10–15 mm; calyx usually green, sometimes purple or purplish, 3–6 mm, glabrous, tube cylindric, 1.5–4.5 mm, lobes triangular to triangular-subulate, 0.5–2 mm, ciliolate; corolla white to pinkish or rose, becoming red- or pink-striate or tipped, wings longer than keel, claw longer than calyx tube, banner implicate-ascending, keel apex acute. **Legumes** ± ascending to ± inclined, reddish brown, oblong, ± turgid, (15–)30–40 × 3–4 mm, leathery, not septate, glabrous. **Seeds** 4–10, olive to reddish brown, ovoid, 3.5 mm.

Flowering late spring(–early summer). Banks, streamsides, burns, logged areas, coastal regions; 0–1200 m; Calif., Oreg., Wash.

Hosackia rosea is found in the coastal ranges of Washington (northern limit from Grays Harbor to Kitsap counties) and Oregon, through the North Coast Ranges into the South Coast Ranges in Santa Barbara County in California, and east along the Cascade Range of Oregon.

4. Hosackia crassifolia Bentham, Trans. Linn. Soc. London 17: 365. 1836 • Big deervetch, broad-leaved or buck lotus

Herbs 70–150 cm, villous or sparsely strigulose to glabrate; root-spreading. **Stems** (1–)5–20+, ascending to erect, fleshy, stout, hollow. **Leaves:** stipules triangular or ovate to lanceolate, (2–)5–8 mm, membranous becoming scarious, often becoming inconspicuous; short-petiolate to petiolate; rachis often curved, 6–12 cm; leaflets (7–)9–15(–19), petiolulate, blades widely ovate to widely elliptic or widely obovate, (10–)20–30 mm, apex obtuse to emarginate, surfaces sparsely strigillose to glabrate. **Peduncles** ascending, 3–8 cm, usually shorter than, rarely equaling, subtending leaf, elongating in fruit, glabrate or glabrous; bract medial or absent, leaflets (1 or)3 or 5-foliolate. **Umbels** 8–20-flowered. **Flowers** asymmetric, 12–16(–18) mm; calyx green marked with purplish or pinkish, or purplish to pinkish, 4.5–8 mm, glabrous, tube cylindric, 4–6 mm, lobes deltate, 0.5–2 mm, sparsely ciliolate or eciliate; corolla greenish or whitish becoming marked with red or purple, wings ± equaling keel, claw ± longer than calyx tube, banner implicate-ascending to 45°, keel apex acute. **Legumes** ± ascending to inclined, reddish to brown, linear, turgid, (10–)35–70 × 3–5 mm, leathery, incompletely septate, glabrous. **Seeds** 7–12, olive or reddish to dark brown, obovoid, 3–4 mm. $2n = 14$.

Varieties 2 (2 in the flora): w United States, nw Mexico.

Lotus crassifolius (Bentham) Greene [not Persoon] is an illegitimate name that pertains to *Hosackia crassifolia*.

1. Herbs glabrate or sparsely strigulose; ovules 17–35 . . . . 4a. *Hosackia crassifolia* var. *crassifolia*
1. Herbs villous; ovules 14–21 . . . . 4b. *Hosackia crassifolia* var. *otayensis*

4a. Hosackia crassifolia Bentham var. **crassifolia**

Hosackia platycarpa Nuttall; *H. stolonifera* Lindley

Herbs glabrate or sparsely strigulose. **Ovules** 17–35. $2n = 14$.

Flowering spring(–early summer). Chaparral, pine or mixed woodlands, margins of woods, gravelly slopes, roadsides, disturbed sites, mountainous regions, serpentine soils; 600–2600 m; Calif., Nev., Oreg., Wash.; Mexico (Baja California).

Variety *crassifolia* reaches its northern limit in Grays Harbor County, western Washington. The main distribution area is in the Cascade Range and coastal ranges of Oregon, southward into the Sierra Nevada and along the California Coast Ranges to the San Bernardino Mountains and Peninsular Ranges, and into Baja California, Mexico.

4b. Hosackia crassifolia Bentham var. **otayensis** (Moran ex Isely) Brouillet, J. Bot. Res. Inst. Texas 2: 388. 2008 • Otay Mountain deervetch or hosackia [C] [E]

Lotus crassifolius (Bentham) Greene var. *otayensis* Moran ex Isely, Brittonia 30: 466. 1978

Herbs villous. **Ovules** 14–21.

Flowering spring. Chaparral, disturbed areas; of conservation concern; 300–1000 m; Calif.

Variety *otayensis* is known from Otay Mountain, San Diego County, and the Santa Lucia Mountains, San Luis Obispo County. Its legumes are shorter, the calyx lobes narrower, and the keel broader and abruptly incurved when compared to var. *crassifolia*.

5. **Hosackia pinnata** (Hooker) Abrams in L. Abrams and R. S. Ferris, Ill. Fl. Pacific States 2: 541. 1944 • Meadow or bog bird's-foot trefoil, pinnate-leaved or pinnate lotus [E] [F]

Lotus pinnatus Hooker, Bot. Mag. 56: plate 2913. 1829

Herbs usually robust, 15–50 cm, glabrous; rhizomatous, rhizomes spongy-thickened, whitish, rooting at nodes. **Stems** 1–5, usually ascending, sometimes decumbent, unbranched or branched, ± fleshy or not. **Leaves:** stipules ovate, 2–5 mm, scarious; petiolate; rachis straight, 2–7 cm; leaflets 5–9(–11), petiolulate, blades usually elliptic to obovate, rarely oblanceolate, (7–)10–25 mm, apex emarginate or rounded to obtuse or acute, surfaces glabrous. **Peduncles** ascending, (1–)5–10 cm, longer than subtending leaf, elongating in fruit, glabrous; bract subtending umbel or absent, 1(–3)-foliolate. **Umbels** 4–10-flowered. **Flowers** 10–15 mm; calyx reddish, 5.5–7.5 mm, glabrous, tube obconic-cylindric, 4–5 mm, lobes abaxial 3 subulate to lanceolate, adaxial 2 triangular, 1–2 mm, usually eciliate, sometimes sparsely ciliate; corolla banner and keel yellow, wings white or cream, wings longer than keel, claw longer than calyx tube, banner reflexed to 180°, keel apex subacute. **Legumes** ± ascending to ± inclined, ± reddish to dark brown, linear-oblong, turgid, 30–50(–85) × 1.5–2.5 mm, thinly leathery, incompletely septate, glabrous. **Seeds** 8–20, olive to reddish or dark brown, oblong, 1.5 mm. $2n = 14$.

Flowering spring–early summer. Wet to moist, open areas, springy meadows, bogs, wetlands, springs, streambeds, stream banks, seepages, in water, ditches; 30–2500 m; B.C.; Calif., Idaho, Oreg., Wash.

Hosackia pinnata reaches its northern limit near Nanaimo, southeastern Vancouver Island, British Columbia (M. Donovan 2006). It ranges southward along the inner foothills of the coastal ranges (avoiding areas of high precipitation) and in the Cascade Range, to the Coast Ranges of California (to Santa Barbara County) and along the Sierra Nevada. *Hosackia pinnata* is sometimes disjunct inland to eastern Washington and northwestern Idaho and, rarely, in central Oregon.

Hosackia bicolor Douglas ex Bentham and *Lotus bicolor* Frye & Rigg are both superfluous, illegitimate names that pertain to *H. pinnata*.

6. **Hosackia gracilis** Bentham, Trans. Linn. Soc. London 17: 365. 1836 • Harlequin lotus [E]

Anisolotus formosissimus (Greene) M. Armstrong & Thornber; *Lotus formosissimus* Greene

Herbs usually low, 10–40 cm, glabrous; stoloniferous or rhizomatous. **Stems** 1–20+, often decumbent, sometimes ascending, unbranched, fleshy, base often spongy. **Leaves:** stipules lanceolate-ovate to ovate or deltate, 2–8 mm, ± scarious, fragile; petiolate to long-petiolate; rachis ± straight, 1–4 cm; leaflets (3–)5–7, petiolulate, blades elliptic to obovate, 6–20 mm, apex obtuse to emarginate, surfaces glabrous. **Peduncles** ascending to spreading, 2.3–9 cm, equaling or longer than subtending leaf, elongating in fruit, glabrous; bract subtending umbel, 1–3(–7)-foliolate. **Umbels** (2 or)3–9-flowered. **Flowers** 10–16 mm; calyx reddish, 4.5–6 mm, glabrous, tube cylindric, 2.5–4 mm, lobes subulate to narrowly triangular, 2–2.5 mm, eciliate; corolla banner yellow, wings and keel pale to dark pink, sometimes whitish, wings fading white, keel pink- to purple-tipped, wings ± equaling or longer than keel, claw longer than calyx tube, banner reflexed to 180°, keel apex acute to subacute. **Legumes** ± ascending to ± inclined, brown, oblong, turgid, 20–30 × 2–3 mm, thinly leathery, incompletely septate, glabrous. **Seeds** (8–)10–14(–16), olive brown to brown, oblong, 1–1.5 mm. $2n = 14$.

Flowering spring(–early summer). Water or springy areas, shores, coastal meadows, wet meadows or woodlands, sphagnum bogs, pastures, roadside ditches, coastal areas; 0–200(–700) m; B.C.; Calif., Oreg., Wash.

Hosackia gracilis reaches its northern limit in southeastern Vancouver Island and adjacent Gulf islands near Victoria, British Columbia (G. W. Douglas and M. Ryan 2006). Southward it follows the coast of Washington (Grays Harbor County), Oregon (with an inland incursion to Lane County), and California (to San Luis Obispo County), with disjunct populations inland in the foothills of the Sierra Nevada.

7. Hosackia oblongifolia Bentham, Pl. Hartw., 305. 1849

Lotus oblongifolius (Bentham) Greene

Herbs robust or low, 10–60 cm, glabrous or ± hairy; with slender caudex. **Stems** 1–30+, decumbent to ascending, unbranched, not fleshy. **Leaves:** stipules ovate to lanceolate, 2.5–5 mm, scarious, fragile; short- to (proximally) long-petiolate; rachis often curved, 1–2.5(–3) cm; leaflets 3–11, petiolulate, blades usually elliptic to obovate, sometimes lanceolate, 10–25 mm, apex usually acute, sometimes obtuse (often proximally), surfaces appressed-hairy to hirsute or glabrous. **Peduncles** ascending, (1–)5–10(–12) cm, longer than subtending leaf, elongating in fruit, ± appressed-hairy; bract subtending umbel or absent, 1–3-foliolate. **Umbels** 1–6-flowered. **Flowers** 8–13 mm; calyx green, 3.5–6.5 mm, hairy, tube cylindric, 2.5–3.5 mm, lobes subulate, 1–3 mm, ciliolate; corolla whitish yellow or banner yellow, ± red-veined or reddish, and wings and keel white, keel apex yellow, wings ± equaling keel, claw ± equaling to slightly longer than calyx tube, banner implicate-ascending, keel apex subacute. **Legumes** ± ascending to ± inclined, brown, oblong, turgid, 25–50 × 1.5–2 mm, leathery, not septate, glabrous. **Seeds** (6–)8–15(–21), olive to reddish brown, oblong, 1.5–2 mm. **2*n*** = 14.

Varieties 2 (2 in the flora): w United States, n Mexico.

1. Leaflets 7–11, blade surfaces hairy or glabrous; flowers 9–13 mm; ovules 9–15(–21) . . . . 7a. *Hosackia oblongifolia* var. *oblongifolia*
1. Leaflets 3–7, blade surfaces glabrous; flowers 8–9 mm; ovules 5–8. . . 7b. *Hosackia oblongifolia* var. *cuprea*

7a. Hosackia oblongifolia Bentham var. **oblongifolia** • Streambank bird's-foot trefoil, narrow-leaved or streambank lotus

Hosackia lathyroides Durand & Hilgard; *H. oblongifolia* var. *angustifolia* S. Watson; *H. stolonifera* Lindley var. *pubescens* Torrey; *H. torreyi* A. Gray; *H. torreyi* var. *nevadensis* A. Gray; *Lotus lathyroides* (Durand & Hilgard) Greene; *L. oblongifolius* (Bentham) Greene var. *nevadensis* (A. Gray) Munz; *L. oblongifolius* var. *torreyi* (A. Gray) Ottley; *L. torreyi* (A. Gray) Greene; *L. torreyi* var. *seorsus* J. F. Macbride

Leaflets 7–11, blade surfaces hairy or glabrous. **Flowers** 9–13 mm; ovules 9–15(–21). **2*n*** = 14.

Flowering summer. Open, moist forests, river bottoms, marshy meadows; (10–)90–2600 m; Ariz., Calif., Nev., Oreg.; Mexico (Baja California, Chihuahua, Durango, Sonora).

The report of var. *oblongifolia* for Arizona in T. H. Kearney and R. H. Peebles (1951) was neglected by D. Isely (1981); this record is confirmed by collections from Apache, Cochise (Huachuca Mountains), and Maricopa (Superstition Mountains) counties. In Oregon, var. *oblongifolia* is encountered mostly south of Lane County in the Cascade Range and, in the coastal ranges, south of Douglas and Coos counties. It is found throughout much of California except in the Central Valley, the Sonoran Desert, and the Modoc Plateau. In Nevada, it is restricted to the Sierra Nevada.

7b. Hosackia oblongifolia Bentham var. **cuprea** (Greene) Brouillet, J. Bot. Res. Inst. Texas 2: 388. 2008 • Copper-flowered bird's-foot trefoil [C] [E]

Lotus cupreus Greene, Leafl. Bot. Observ. Crit. 1: 74. 1904; *Hosackia cuprea* (Greene) Smiley; *L. oblongifolius* (Bentham) Greene var. *cupreus* (Greene) Ottley

Leaflets 3–7, blade surfaces glabrous. **Flowers** 8–9 mm; ovules 5–8.

Flowering summer. Meadows, open pine woodlands; of conservation concern; 600–2700 m; Calif.

Variety *cuprea* is known from Calaveras, Inyo, Kern, and Tulare counties, in the (mainly southern) Sierra Nevada; it may represent an elevational ecotype (D. Isely 1981).

8. Hosackia yollabolliensis (Munz) D. D. Sokoloff, Kew Bull. 55: 1010. 2000 • Yolla Bolly Mountains bird's-foot trefoil [E]

Lotus yollabolliensis Munz, Aliso 3: 117, fig. 6. 1955

Herbs mat-forming, 5–15 cm, glabrate; taprooted and with caudex. **Stems** 1–30+, usually decumbent, sometimes ascending, branched, slender, not fleshy. **Leaves:** stipules ovate, inconspicuous, scarious; petiolate; rachis straight, 0.7–1.5 cm; leaflets 3–5(–7), petiolulate, blades obovate to oblanceolate, 3–10 mm, apex usually acute, sometimes obtuse, surfaces glabrous. **Peduncles** ascending or spreading, 2–3 cm, longer than subtending leaf, elongating in fruit; bract subtending umbel, 1–3-foliolate. **Umbels** 1–3-flowered. **Flowers** (7–)8–10 mm; calyx color unknown, 5–6.5 mm, glabrous, tube obconic-cylindric, (1.5–)2–3 mm, lobes triangular to triangular-subulate, 0.5–1 mm, ± ciliolate; corolla banner yellow, wings and keel whitish yellow, wings ± equaling keel, claw ± equaling calyx tube, banner erect, keel apex not known. **Legumes** erect, brown, narrowly oblong, laterally compressed, 18–25 × 1.5–2 mm, leathery, not septate, glabrous. **Seeds** (2–)4–7, olive- to red-brown, oblong, 2–2.5 mm.

Flowering summer. Open rocky, dry slopes, ridges, and summits, snowbeds and moist areas below, openings in red fir forests, moist gravelly or sandy areas, rocky loamy soils; 1600–2200 m; Calif.

Hosackia yollabolliensis is uncommon in the Yolla Bolly Mountains and South Fork Mountain of the North Coast Ranges in Humboldt and Trinity counties.

9. Hosackia alamosana Rose, Contr. U.S. Natl. Herb. 1: 96. 1891 • Sonoran bird's-foot trefoil

Lotus alamosanus Rose

Herbs mat-forming, 5–40 cm, glabrate; taprooted. **Stems** 1–20+, procumbent, unbranched or little branched, slender, not fleshy. **Leaves:** stipules ovate to lanceolate, 1.5–3.5 mm, membranous, base ± subauriculate; petiolate; rachis straight, 0.5–1.5 cm; leaflets 3–5, petiolulate, blades obovate, 4–11 mm, apex obtuse to rounded, surfaces glabrous. **Peduncles** ascending to erect, 1.5–7(–10) cm, longer than subtending leaf, elongating in fruit, strigulose; bract absent. **Umbels** 1 or 2(–4)-flowered. **Flowers** 5–7(–9)[–15] mm; calyx purplish, (3–)3.2–4(–4.4) mm, glabrous or glabrate, tube cylindric, 1.6–2 mm, lobes lanceolate, 0.5–2 mm, eciliate or sparsely ciliolate; corolla banner yellow, wings and keel white or cream, becoming reddish tinged, wings ± equaling keel, claw ± equaling calyx tube, banner implicate-ascending, keel apex obtuse. **Legumes** ascending to erect, olive brown to brown, linear-oblong, turgid, 20–30 × 1–1.5 mm, thinly leathery, not septate, glabrate or glabrous. **Seeds** (8–)10–13(–15), olive green to olive brown, reniform, flattened, 1.5 mm.

Flowering spring [winter]. Moist soils, streamsides (riparian and aquatic), oak and pine-oak-madroño woodlands, gallery forests in canyons; 1100–2500 m; Ariz.; Mexico (Chihuahua, Durango, Sinaloa, Sonora).

Hosackia alamosana is known in the flora area from Santa Cruz County. It is of conservation concern in the flora area but is globally secure.

Lotus alamosanus was validly published by Rose as an alternative name for *Hosackia alamosana*.

125. LOTUS Linnaeus, Sp. Pl. 2: 773. 1753; Gen. Pl. ed. 5, 338. 1754 • Trefoil, lotier [Latin *lotus*, or Greek *lotos*, ancient name perhaps alluding to usefulness of a plant, applied to this taxon] [I]

Luc Brouillet

Herbs, annual or perennial, rarely suffrutescent, unarmed. **Stems** prostrate or decumbent to ascending or erect, glabrous or pubescent. **Leaves** alternate, odd-pinnate; stipules present, glandlike; petiolate; leaflets 5, proximal pair stipular in position, distal 3 ± palmate, blade margins entire, surfaces glabrous or pubescent. **Inflorescences** 1–15-flowered, axillary, umbels or solitary flowers; bracts present, 1–3-foliolate. **Flowers** papilionaceous; calyx symmetric, bell-shaped or short-cylindric, lobes 5; corolla yellow, usually marked with red, (4–)5–13(–18) mm, keel equaling or longer than symmetrically positioned wings; stamens 10, diadelphous; anthers dorsifixed; ovary sessile or ± stipitate; stigma without collar. **Fruits** legumes, persistent, exserted from calyx, sessile, straight, body not deflexed, linear to narrowly oblong or cylindric, subterete to quadrate, beak slender, dehiscent, leathery, glabrous. **Seeds** (5–)10–35, mottled or not, globose to oblong or round-oblong. $x = 6$.

Species ca. 125 (6 in the flora): introduced; Eurasia, Africa, Atlantic Islands (Azores), Pacific Islands (New Caledonia, Vanuatu), Australia; introduced also nearly worldwide.

Morphological and molecular analyses (G. J. Allan et al. 2003; G. V. Degtjareva et al. 2008) have shown that the Eurasian members of *Lotus* are distinct from the North American *Acmispon* and *Hosackia*. Therefore, *Lotus* is here defined in its strict sense. *Lotus* species have been introduced to North America as forage crops and for roadbank stabilization.

SELECTED REFERENCES Degtjareva, G. V. et al. 2008. New data on nrITS phylogeny of *Lotus* (Leguminosae, Loteae). Wulfenia 15: 35–49. Kramina, T. E. 2006. A contribution to the taxonomic revision of the *Lotus angustissimus*-complex (Leguminosae, Loteae). Wulfenia 13: 57–92. Zandstra, I. I. and W. F. Grant. 1968. The biosystematics of the genus *Lotus* (Leguminosae) in Canada. I. Cytotaxonomy. Canad. J. Bot. 46: 557–583.

1. Herbs annual, hirsute.
   2. Calyx tubes villous; legumes 12–30 × 1–2 mm . . . . 1. *Lotus angustissimus*
   2. Calyx tubes hirsute; legumes 7–10 × 0.7–1.2 mm . . . . 6. *Lotus subbiflorus*
1. Herbs annual or perennial, glabrous, glabrate, or sparsely pilose to strigose.
   3. Inflorescences 1(or 2)[–4]-flowered . . . . 5. *Lotus krylovii*
   3. Inflorescences (1–)3–15-flowered.
      4. Inflorescences (4–)5–15-flowered; calyx lobes spreading or recurved in bud; herbs with conspicuous rhizome; stems hollow, glabrate to sparsely pilose . . . . 4. *Lotus uliginosus*
      4. Inflorescences (1–)3–8(–10)-flowered; calyx lobes not recurved in bud; herbs taprooted (except rarely rhizomatous in *L. corniculatus*); stems solid, glabrous, glabrate, or sparsely pilose to strigose.
         5. Leaflet blade lengths 1.6–3(–4) times widths; flowers 10–17 mm . . . . 2. *Lotus corniculatus*
         5. Leaflet blade lengths (2.5–)3–5 times widths; flowers 7–10 mm . . . . 3. *Lotus tenuis*

1. Lotus angustissimus Linnaeus, Sp. Pl. 2: 774. 1753 • Slender trefoil [I]

Herbs annual, (2–)5–50 cm, hirsute; taprooted. **Stems** prostrate, solid, not succulent. **Leaves** 7–21 mm; rachis 2–3.5 (–4.5) mm; leaflet blades elliptic to narrowly obovate, 8–12 (–16) × 2–6 mm, length 1.7–4 times width, apex usually acute, sometimes obtuse. **Peduncles** decumbent to ascending, 0.5–2 cm. **Inflorescences** 1–3-flowered; bracts 1–3-foliolate. **Flowers** 5–12 mm; calyx 4–7 mm, lobes not recurved in bud, narrowly lanceolate, 4 mm, longer than tube, tube villous; petals yellow, turning pink, (4–)5–8 mm, wings shorter than keel. **Legumes** reddish brown, linear, 12–30 × 1–2 mm, septate. **Seeds** 18–30, light olive to light brown, not mottled, globose, 0.6 mm, smooth. **2*n*** = 12, 24 (Europe).

Flowering summer. Disturbed grasslands, roadsides; 0–400 m; introduced; Calif.; Europe; n Africa; introduced also in South America, w Asia, Australia.

2. Lotus corniculatus Linnaeus, Sp. Pl. 2: 775. 1753 (as corniculata) • Bird's-foot trefoil, lotier corniculé [F] [I] [W]

Herbs annual or perennial, 5–70 cm, glabrous or sparsely pilose to strigose; usually taprooted, rarely rhizomatous. **Stems** ascending or prostrate, solid, not succulent. **Leaves** 5–30 mm; rachis (1–)2–10 mm; leaflet blades sometimes asymmetric, obovate to oblanceolate, oblong, or ovate, 4–22 × 2–11 mm, length 1.6–3(–4) times width, apex obtuse and mucronate or acuminate. **Peduncles** decumbent to erect, 1.5–12 cm. **Inflorescences** (1–)3–8(–10)-flowered; bracts (1–)3-foliolate. **Flowers** 10–17 mm; calyx 5–7.5 mm, lobes not recurved in bud, usually triangular, rarely ovate, (1.5–)2.5–4.5 mm, shorter to slightly longer than tube, tube villous; petals bright yellow, marked with red, turning orange, 8–14 mm, wings shorter to longer than keel. **Legumes** brown, narrowly oblong, 15–35 × 2–3 mm, not septate. **Seeds** 5–30, yellowish or light to dark brown, mottled or sometimes not, globose to round-oblong, 1–1.7 mm, smooth. **2*n*** = 24.

Flowering summer. Open, often wet disturbed, ruderal sites, lawns, fields, roadsides; 0–1800 m; introduced; St. Pierre and Miquelon; Alta., B.C., Man., N.B., Nfld. and Labr., N.S., Ont., P.E.I., Que., Sask., Yukon; Ala., Ariz., Ark., Calif., Colo., Conn., Del., D.C., Ga., Idaho, Ill., Ind., Iowa, Kans., Ky., Maine, Md., Mass., Mich., Minn., Mo., Mont., Nebr., Nev., N.H., N.J., N.Mex., N.Y., N.C., N.Dak., Ohio, Okla., Oreg., Pa., S.Dak., Tenn., Tex., Utah, Vt., Va., Wash., W.Va., Wis., Wyo.; Eurasia; n Africa; introduced also in Mexico, Central America, South America, Atlantic Islands (Iceland), Australia.

Lotus corniculatus has been widely introduced both as a forage crop and for roadside stabilization throughout North America. M. D. Ross and W. T. Jones (1985) presented evidence that *L. corniculatus* is an allotetraploid derived from the hybrid between either *L. tenuis* or *L. alpinus* (Seringe) Schleicher ex Ramond, as the pistillate parent, and *L. uliginosus*. This would explain the close morphological similarity with *L. tenuis*.

3. Lotus tenuis Waldstein & Kitaibel ex Willdenow, Enum. Pl., 797. 1809 • Narrow-leaved trefoil, lotier à feuilles ténues [I] [W]

Lotus corniculatus Linnaeus var. *tenuifolius* Linnaeus; *L. corniculatus* subsp. *tenuis* (Waldstein & Kitaibel ex Willdenow) Briquet

Herbs perennial, 2.5–90 cm, glabrous or glabrate, rarely sparsely strigose at nodes; taprooted. **Stems** ascending or prostrate, solid, not succulent. **Leaves** 9–23 mm; rachis 2–6 mm; leaflet blades oblanceolate or lanceolate-obovate to linear, 5–25 × 1–4(–5) mm, length (2.5–) 3–5 times width, apex acute or apiculate. **Peduncles** ascending to erect, (1–)2–12 cm. **Inflorescences** (1–)3–5(–7)-flowered; bracts 1–3-foliolate. **Flowers** 7–10 mm; calyx 4–6 mm, lobes not recurved in bud, triangular, 1.5–3 mm, ± equaling or shorter than tube, tube glabrous; petals yellow, sometimes marked with red, turning orange, 8–12 mm, wings slightly longer than keel. **Legumes** brown, narrowly cylindric, (10–)15–30 × 2–2.5 mm, not septate. **Seeds** 15–30, yellowish, light to dark brown, or tan, lightly mottled or not, globose to oblong, 1–1.8 mm, smooth to rugose. $2n$ = 12.

Flowering summer. Open disturbed, ruderal sites, usually on heavy, poorly drained soils, sometimes saline; 0–1000 m; introduced; B.C., Ont.; Ariz., Calif., Colo., Idaho, Ind., Kans., La., Md., Mont., Nebr., Nev., N.Y., N.C., Oreg., Pa., R.I., Utah, Va., Wash., W.Va.; Europe; introduced also in Mexico, South America, Asia.

The name *Lotus glaber* Miller, recently used in the literature for this taxon, is a rejected name.

4. Lotus uliginosus Schkuhr, Bot. Handb. 2: 412, plate 211 [upper right center]. 1796 • Big or large trefoil, lotier des marais [I]

Herbs perennial, suffrutescent, 10–120 cm, glabrate to sparsely pilose; rhizomatous. **Stems** erect or ascending, hollow, succulent. **Leaves** 10–34 mm; rachis 3–10 mm; leaflet blades ovate-elliptic to elliptic, 8–25 × 3–15 mm, length 1.4–2.4 times width, apex obtuse, often mucronate. **Peduncles** ascending to declined, 0.7–10 (–15) cm. **Inflorescences** (4 or)5–15-flowered; bracts (1–)3-foliolate. **Flowers** 10–14(–20) mm; calyx 4.5–8 mm, lobes spreading or recurved in bud, triangular, (1.5–)2.2–3.5 mm, shorter, ± equaling to slightly longer than tube, tube glabrate to pilose; petals yellow, often mottled with red, darkening, 8–13(–18) mm, wings equaling keel. **Legumes** brown, cylindric, (10–)15–35 × 1.5–2.5 mm, not septate. **Seeds** 15–35, yellowish, olive green, or yellowish brown, not or sometimes mottled, globose to round-oblong, 0.8–1.4 mm, smooth. $2n$ = 12.

Flowering late spring–summer. Wet fields, roadsides, ditches, coastal saline flats; 0–500 m; introduced; B.C., Man., N.B., N.S., Ont., Que.; Calif., Fla., Idaho, Ill., Oreg., Wash.; Europe; w Asia; n Africa; introduced also in South America, e Asia, elsewhere in Africa, Pacific Islands (Hawaii, New Zealand), Australia.

The name *Lotus pedunculatus* Cavanilles has been misapplied to specimens of *L. uliginosus* in North America.

5. Lotus krylovii Schischkin & Sergievskaja, Sist. Zametki Mater. Gerb. Tomsk. 1932(7–8): 5. 1932 • Krylov's bird's-foot trefoil [I]

Lotus corniculatus Linnaeus var. *versicolor* Bongard & C. A. Meyer

Herbs perennial [annual], 10–45 cm, glabrous (except glabrate on leaves and calyx); taprooted. **Stems** erect or decumbent, solid, not succulent. **Leaves** 8–16 mm; rachis 1.5–5 mm; leaflet blades: basal 2 obliquely ovate, terminal 3 obovate to obovate-elliptic or obovate-lanceolate, 5–15 × 1–4 mm, length 3.2–5 times width, apex rounded to ± acute. **Peduncles** ascending, 1–4.5(–6) cm. **Inflorescences** 1(or 2[–4])-flowered; bracts 1–3-foliolate. **Flowers** 7–9.2[–10] mm; calyx 4–6 mm, lobes erect in bud, triangular to deltate-acuminate, (1.5–)2–2.8[–3.5] mm, ± equaling tube, tube glabrate; petals light yellow, ± pink-tinged abaxially, turning pinkish or red, 6.6–8.5 mm, wings equaling keel. **Legumes** brown, cylindric, 15–25[–35] × 2–3 mm, not septate. **Seeds** 6–10[–30], brown, finely mottled, globose, 0.8–1.4 mm, smooth. $2n$ = 12.

Flowering summer. Alkaline meadows, saline lake shores, dry hillsides; 500–600 m; introduced; B.C.; e Europe (Russia, Ukraine); c, w Asia.

Lotus krylovii is known in the flora area only from the the Okanagan Valley of British Columbia, near White Lake. I. I. Zandstra and W. F. Grant (1968) reported it in their study of *Lotus* in Canada, and it is still extant there.

S. I. Ali (1977) synonymized this species with an expanded *Lotus corniculatus* var. *tenuifolius* Linnaeus (synonym of *L. tenuis*), but the taxa are distinct in morphology, distribution, and ecology.

6. Lotus subbiflorus Lagasca, Varied. Ci. 2(4): 213. 1805 • Hairy bird's-foot trefoil [I]

Lotus hispidus Desfontaines ex de Candolle; *L. suaevolens* Persoon

Herbs annual, 7–25[–100] cm, hirsute; taprooted. **Stems** erect to decumbent, solid, not succulent. **Leaves** 8–15[–25] mm; rachis 2–4 mm; leaflet blades: basal 2 ovate, terminal 3 obovate to oblong or lanceolate, 5–10[–20] × 1–5.5[–8] mm, length 2–4 times width, apex acute to obtuse, often mucronate. **Peduncles** ascending to declined, 0.7–3[–15] cm. **Inflorescences** (1 or)2–4(–6)-flowered; bracts 3-foliolate. **Flowers** 5.5–7[–10] mm; calyx 3.3–4.7 mm, lobes not recurved in bud, linear, 2.5–3.2 mm, longer than tube, tube hirsute; petals yellow, turning reddish, 5–6.7[–10] mm, wings shorter than angled and beaked keel. **Legumes** brown, cylindric, 7–10 × 0.7–1.2 mm, not or partially septate. **Seeds** 8–10, brown to greenish brown, ± mottled, globose to round-oblong, 1 mm, smooth. $2n$ = 12, 24 (Europe).

Flowering summer. Moist roadside ditches; 40–200 m; introduced; Oreg.; w Europe; n Africa (Algeria); Atlantic Islands (Azores); introduced also in South America (Argentina), Pacific Islands (Hawaii, New Zealand), Australia.

Lotus subbiflorus is easily distinguished by its very hirsute foliage and its sharply angled, beaked keel that is longer than the wings.

The introduced *Lotus subbiflorus* was collected first in 2009 at four locations in Curry County. The taxon is introduced elsewhere in the world, reported under the names *L. hispidus*, *L. subbiflorus*, or *L. suaevolens* (R. P. Randall 2002); when plotted worldwide, reports of *L. hispidus* and *L. subbiflorus* have similar overall distributions. Thus, it seems that in areas outside the native range, only a single entity is present that should be called *L. subbiflorus*.

The name *Lotus hispidus* Desfontaines (1804) was considered an invalid name by T. E. Kramina (2006). Kramina, however, appears to have been unaware of the subsequent validation of the name by de Candolle: *L. hispidus* Desfontaines ex de Candolle in J. Lamarck and A. P. de Candolle, Fl. Franç. ed. 3, 4: 556. 17 Sep 1805. The exact publication date of the name *L. subbiflorus* by Lagasca, however, is not known, but it may have been late in 1805 because Varied. Ci. 2(4) has 6 numbers (19–24) that were issued in 1805, and the name was published in number 22. Without an exact date for that publication, it is not possible to decide which name has priority, and currently the name *L. subbiflorus* is adopted for the species.

Index to Subfamilies, Tribes, and Genera, Volume 11, Parts 1 and 2

The list below gives the part number and page on which each taxon is treated.